BIBLIOGRAPHY OF
FOSSIL VERTEBRATES
1969-1972

THE GEOLOGICAL SOCIETY OF AMERICA, INC.

Memoir 141

BIBLIOGRAPHY OF
FOSSIL VERTEBRATES
1969-1972

J. T. Gregory, J. A. Bacskai,
B. Brajnikov, and K. Munthe

Museum of Paleontology
University of California
Berkeley

1973

Published by

THE GEOLOGICAL SOCIETY OF AMERICA, INC.

3300 Penrose Place

Boulder, Colorado 80301

Printed in the United States of America
by Edwards Brothers, Inc., Ann Arbor, Michigan 48104.
Type composed at the Museum of Paleontology,
University of California, Berkeley, California 94720.

The printing of this volume has been made possible

through the bequest of Richard Alexander Fullerton Penrose, Jr.,

and the generous support of all contributors

to the publication program.

To Charles Lewis Camp,

Scientist, Historian, Bibliographer

CONTENTS

PREFACE

The present volume of the Bibliography of Fossil Vertebrates is the last in a series begun in 1928 by C. L. Camp and V. L. Vanderhoof. Previous volumes have been published by The Geological Society of America as its Special Papers 27 and 42, and Memoirs 37, 57, 84, 92, 117, and 134. Attempts during the past five years to arrange for financing the compilation of further volumes have been fruitless.

Like the "Bibliography and Catalogue of the Fossil Vertebrata of North America" by O. P. Hay which preceded them, the primary objective of these bibliographies has been to provide rapid access to citations to all publications dealing with any taxon of fossil vertebrates that appeared during the years included in each volume. Dr. Camp extended the geographic scope from North America to the entire world, and added an extensive index to subject matter other than biological systematics.

The author catalogue contains citations to publications on fossil vertebrates which appeared during the years 1969 through 1972 and were received in Berkeley before the end of January 1973. Articles published before 1969 which had been omitted from earlier volumes are also cited. We regret that some works published in 1972 were received too late for inclusion.

The Subject Index of the present volume has been extensively revised. Its columnar format and triple hierarchy of headings are adapted from the "Bibliography and Index of Geology", compiled by the American Geological Institute and published by the Geological Society of America. This change was part of an unsuccessful attempt to collaborate with the A.G.I. in production of the vertebrate bibliography. We hope the new format will facilitate locating desired references. Several headings of the Subject Index were changed to conform to those used in "Bibliography and Index of Geology". We have attempted to cross-reference terms used in subject indices of the previous volumes. New categories indicating geographic area and systematic class have been used extensively to provide access to publications on the basis of the source of the fossil material. The frequent use of "Paleontology" as a second-order heading under geographic terms stems from the organization of these more-inclusive geological indices. Geologic age is generally noted in second- or third-order heading. Further details are given in the Introduction to the Subject Index on p. 388.

The Synopsis of Classification has been eliminated. Taxa are allocated systematically according to the classification in the 1966 edition of A. S. Romer's "Vertebrate Paleontology" (with a few exceptions). The Systematic Index shows the author's usage when it differs from Romer's.

Publications on paleolithic archeology containing no information on fossil vertebrates have not been included in this volume. We have continued to include references on fossil hominid remains, representations of vertebrate animals in paleolithic art, and artifacts associated with vertebrate fossils.

The List of Serials is no longer a supplement, but contains all serials referred to in this publication, together with the standard abbreviations used for citations in the Author Catalogue. Festschrifts and volumes of Russian topical collected papers have been listed among the Special Publications.

Judith A. Bacskai compiled the Systematic Index and managed the day to day operation of the project. Dr. Boris Brajnikov abstracted the numerous slavic publications as well as papers in many other European languages. Kathleen Munthe prepared the Subject Index. All these participated in searching out and abstracting pertinent articles. Rachel H. Nichols, who retired from the project upon completion of Memoir 117, Susan Evans Bartlett, and Elizabeth Fulton contributed to the earlier stages of compiling this volume. The offset copy was prepared by Mayme Matsumoto.

The helpful cooperation of the staff of the University of California Library at Berkeley greatly facilitated our work and is deeply appreciated. We are likewise grateful to the staff of the Museum of Paleontology for assistance in many ways. We thank the National Science Foundation for support under extensions of Grant GN-405, and The Geological Society of America for financial aid in completing preparation of copy for publication.

Joseph T. Gregory
Museum of Paleontology
University of California
Berkeley, CA
September 10, 1973

LIST OF SERIALS

All serials cited in this volume are listed together with abbreviations used in the Author Catalogue. These abbreviations conform to the American National Standard for the Abbreviation of Titles of Periodicals.

Acad. Brasil. Ciênc., An. . . . . Academia Brasileira de Ciências, Anais. Rio de Janeiro.

Acad. Cienc. Art. Barcelona, Mem. . . . . Real Academia de Ciencias y Artes de Barcelona, Memorias. Barcelona.

Acad. Inscript. Belles-Lettres, C. R. . . . . Académie des inscriptions et belles-lettres, Paris. Comptes Rendus des séances. Paris.

Acad. Pol. Sci., Bull., Sér. Sci. Biol. . . . . Académie Polonaise des Sciences, Bulletin, Série des Sciences Biologiques. Warsaw.

Acad. Repub. Soc. Rom. Inst. Speol.
"Emil Racoviţă", Lucr. . . . . Academia Republicii Socialiste Romãnia, Institutul de Speologie "Emil Racoviţă", Lucrările. Bucharest.

Acad. Sci., C. R., Sér. D . . . . Académie des Sciences, Comptes Rendus Hebdomadaires des Séances, Série D, Sciences Naturelles. Paris.

Acad. Soc. Lorraines Sci., Bull. . . . . Académie et Société Lorraines des Sciences, Bulletin. Nancy.

Accad. Fisiocr., Siena, Atti, Sez. Agr. . . . . Accademia dei Fisiocritici, Siena, Atti, Sezione Agraria. Siena.

Accad. Gioenia Sci. Natur. Catania, Atti . . . . . . Accademia Gioenia di Scienze Naturali in Catania, Atti. Catania.

Accad. Naz. Lincei, Atti, Ser. 8, Cl. Sci. Fis.,
Mat. Natur., Mem. . . . . Accademia Nazionale dei Lincei, Atti, Classe di Scienze Fisiche, Matematiche e Naturali, Memorie. Rome.

Accad. Naz. Lincei, Atti, Ser. 8, Cl. Sci. Fis.,
Mat. Natur., Rend. . . . . Accademia Nazionale dei Lincei, Atti, Classe di Scienze Fisiche, Matematiche e Naturali, Rendiconti. Rome.

Accad. Patavina Sci. Let. Arti, Mem. Cl.
Sci. Mat. Natur., Atti Mem. . . . . Accademia Patavina di Scienze, Lettre ed Arti già Accademia dei Ricovrati, Memorie della Classe di Scienze Matematiche e Naturali, Atti e Memorie. Padova.

Acta Archaeol. Carpathica . . . . Acta Archaeologica Carpathica (Polska Akademia Nauk). Krakow.

Acta Archaeol. Hung. . . . . Acta Archaeologica (Academiae Scientiarum Hungarica). Budapest.

Acta Arctica . . . . Acta Arctica. Copenhagen.

Acta Biotheoret. Acta Biotheoretica. Leyden.

Acta Geol. Hisp. Acta Geológica Hispánica (Instituto Nacional de Geología). Barcelona.

Acta Geol. Lilloana . . . . Acta Geológica Lilloana (Universidad Nacional de Tucmán, Instituto Miguel Lillo). Tucumán.

Acta Geol. Pol. . . . . Acta Geologica Polonica. Polska Akademia Nauk, Komitet Geologiczny. Warsaw.

Acta Geol. Taiwanica . . . . Acta Geologica Taiwanica. National Taiwan University. Taipei.

Acta Mus. Macedonici Sci. Natur. . . . . Acta Musei Macedonici Scientiarum Naturalium. Prirodonaučen muzej. Skopje, Yugoslavia.

Acta Palaeontol. Pol. . . . . Acta Palaeontologica Polonica (Polska Akademia Nauk). Warsaw.

Acta Univ. Carol., Geol. . . . . Acta Universitatis Carolinae, Geologica. Universita Karlova. Prague.

Acta Zool. . . . . Acta Zoologica, International Journal for Zoology. Stockholm.

Acta Zool. Cracoviensia . . . . Acta Zoologica Cracoviensia. Krakow.

Acta Zool. Fennica . . . . Acta Zoologica Fennica, Societas pro Fauna et Flora Fennica. Helsinki.

Acta Zool. Sin. . . . . Acta Zoologica Sinica (Tung Wu Hsueh Pao). Peking.

Advan. Sci. . . . . Advancement of Science (British Association for the Advancement of Science). London.

Akad. Athenon, Prakt. . . . . Akademia Athenon, Praktika. Athens, Greece.

Akad. Nauk. Arm. SSR, Izv., Nauki Zemle . . . . Akademiia Nauk Armiãnskoi SSR, Izvestiia, Seriia Nauki o Zemle. Erevan.

xi

Akad. Nauk Azerb. SSR, Izv., Ser. Nauk Zemle .. Akademiia Nauk Azerbaĭdzhanskoĭ SSR, Izvestiia, Seriia Nauk o Zemle. Baku.

Akad. Nauk Gruz. SSR, Inst. Paleobiol.,
Nauchn. Sess. .... Akademiia Nauk Gruzinskoĭ SSR, Institut Paleobiologii, Nauchnaia Sessiia, Plan Raboty i Tezisy Dokladov. Tiflis.

Akad. Nauk Gruz. SSR, Inst. Paleobiol.,
Obshch. Vop. Evoliuts. Paleobiol. .... Akademiia Nauk Gruzinskoĭ SSR, Institut Paleobiologii, Obshchie Voprosy Evoliutsionnoĭ Paleobiologii. Tiflis.

Akad. Nauk Gruz. SSR, Soobshch. .... Akademiia Nauk Gruzinskoĭ SSR, Soobshcheniia. Tiflis.

Akad. Nauk Kaz. SSR, Inst. Zool.,
Mater. Fauny i Flory. .... Akademiia Nauk Kazakhskoĭ SSR, Institut Zoologii, Materialy po Istorii Fauny i Flory. Alma-Ata.

Akad. Nauk Kaz. SSR, Izv., Ser. Biol. .... Akademiia Nauk Kazakhskoĭ SSR, Izvestiia, Seriia Biologicheskaia. Alma-Ata.

Akad. Nauk Kaz. SSR, Izv., Ser. Geol. ...... Akademiia Nauk Kazakhskoĭ SSR, Izvestiia, Seriia Geologicheskaia. Alma-Ata.

Akad. Nauk Kaz. SSR, Izv., Ser.
Obshchest. Nauk. .... Akademiia Nauk Kazakhskoĭ SSR, Izvestiia, Seriia Obshchestvennykh Nauk. Alma-Ata.

Akad. Nauk Kaz. SSR, Vestn. .... Akademiia Nauk Kazakhskoĭ SSR, Vestnik. Alma-Ata.

Akad. Nauk Kirgiz. SSR, Izv., Ser.
Obshchest. Nauk .... Akademiia Nauk Kirgizskoĭ SSR, Izvestiia, Seriia Obshchestvennykh Nauk. Frunze.

Akad. Nauk Moldav. SSR, Izv., Ser. Biol.
Khim. Nauk .... Akademiia Nauk Moldavskoĭ SSR, Izvestiia, Seriia Biologicheskikh i Khimicheskikh Nauk. Kishinev.

Akad. Nauk Moldav. SSR, Okh. Prir. Moldav. .. Akademiia Nauk Moldavskoĭ SSR, Okhrana Prirody Moldavii. Kishinev.

Akad. Nauk Mongol. NR, Nauchn.-Issled.
Geol. Inst., Tr. .... Akademiia Nauk Mongol'skoĭ Narodnoĭ Respubliki, Nauchno-Issledovatel'skiĭ Geologicheskiĭ Institut, Trudy. Ulan-Bator.

Akad. Nauk SSSR, Dokl. .... Akademiia Nauk SSSR, Doklady. Moscow.

Akad. Nauk SSSR, Dokl., Earth Sci. Sec. .... Akademiya Nauk SSSR, Doklady, Earth Science Section (Translation published by the American Geological Institute). Washington, D.C.

Akad. Nauk SSSR, Geol. Inst., Tr. .... Akademiia Nauk SSSR, Geologicheskiĭ Institut, Trudy. Moscow.

Akad. Nauk SSSR, Inst. Arkheol., Krat.
Soobshch. .... Akademiia Nauk SSSR, Institut Arkheologii, Kratkie Soobshcheniia. Moscow.

Akad. Nauk SSSR, Inst. Okeanol., Tr. ...... Akademiia Nauk SSSR, Institut Okeanologii, Trudy. Moscow.

Akad. Nauk SSSR, Izv., Ser. Geogr. .... Akademiia Nauk SSSR, Izvestiia, Seriia Geograficheskaia. Moscow.

Akad. Nauk SSSR, Izv., Ser. Geol. .... Akademiia Nauk SSSR, Izvestiia, Seriia Geologicheskaia. Moscow.

Akad. Nauk SSSR, Kom. Izuch. Chetvertich.
Perioda, Biull. .... Academiia Nauk SSSR, Komissiia po Izucheniiu Chetvertichnogo Perioda, Biulleten'. Moscow.

Akad. Nauk SSSR, Kom. Opred. Absoliut.
Vozr. Geol. Form., Tr. .... Akademiia Nauk SSSR, Komissiia po Opredeleniiu Absoliutnogo Vozrasta Geologicheskikh Formatsii pri Otdelenii Nauk o Zemle, Trudy. Moscow.

Akad. Nauk SSSR, Komi Fil., Inst. Geol., Tr. .. Akademiia Nauk SSSR, Komi Filial. Institut Geologii, Trudy. Syktyvkar.

Akad. Nauk SSSR, Paleontol. Inst., Tr. ...... Akademiia Nauk SSSR, Paleontologicheskiĭ Institut, Trudy. Moscow.

Akad. Nauk SSSR, Sib. Otd., Inst. Geol.
Geofiz., Tr. .... Akademiia Nauk SSSR, Sibirskoe Otdelenie, Institut Geologii i Geofiziki, Trudy. Moscow.

Akad. Nauk SSSR, Sib. Otd., Izv.,
Ser. Obshchest. Nauk .... Akademiia Nauk SSSR, Sibirskoe Otdelenie, Izvestiia, Seriia Obshchestvennykh Nauk. Novosibirsk.

Akad. Nauk SSSR, Sib. Otd., Mater. Ist. Sib.,
Drevniaia Sibir' .... Akademiia Nauk SSSR, Sibirskoe Otdelenie, Materialy po Istorii Sibiri, Drevniaia Sibir'. Novosibirsk.

Akad. Nauk SSSR, Sib. Otd., Sakhalinsk.
    Kompleks. Nauch.-Issled. Inst., Tr. . . . . Akademiĭa Nauk SSSR, Sibirskoe Otdelenie, Sakhalinskiĭ
        Kompleksnyĭ Nauchno-Issledovatel'skiĭ Institut, Trudy.
        Ĭuzhno-Sakhalinsk.

Akad. Nauk SSSR, Ural. Fil., Inst. Ekol.
    Rast. Zhiv., Tr. . . . . Akademiĭa Nauk SSSR, Ural'skiĭ Filial, Institut Ekologii Rasteniĭ
        i Zhivotnykh, Trudy. Sverdlovsk.
Akad. Nauk SSSR, Vestn. . . . . Akademiĭa Nauk SSSR, Vestnik. Moscow.
Akad. Nauk SSSR, Zool. Inst., Tr. . . . . Akademiĭa Nauk SSSR, Zoologicheskiĭ Institut, Trudy.
        Leningrad.
Akad. Nauk Ukr. RSR, Dopov., Ser. B . . . . . . Akademiĭa Nauk Ukraïnskoĭ RSR, Dopovidi, Seriĭa B,
        Geologiĭa, Geofizyka, Khimiĭa, ta Biologiĭa. Kiev.
Akad. Nauk Ukr. SSR, Inst. Zool.,
    Vestn. Zool. Akademiĭa Nauk Ukraïnskoĭ RSR, Institut Zoologii, Vestnik
        Zoologii. Kiev.
Akad. Nauk Ukr. SSR, Kompl. Karst.
    Eksped., Tr. . . . . Akademiĭa Nauk Ukraïnskoĭ RSR. Kompleksnaĭa Karstovaĭa
        Ekspeditsiĭa, Trudy. Kiev.
Akad. Nauk Ukr. RSR, Nauk. Pryrod. Muz.,
    L'vov, Nauk Zap. . . . . Akademiĭa Nauk Ukraïnskoĭ RSR, Naukovo-Pryrodoznavchyĭ
        Muzeĭ, L'viv, Naukovi Zapysky. Kiev.
Akad. Nauk Ukr. RSR, Zool., Mus.,
    Zb. Prats. . . . . Akademiĭa Nauk Ukraïnskoĭ RSR, Zoologichnyĭ Muzeĭ, Zbirnyk
        Prats'. Kiev.
Akad. Nauk Uzb. SSR, Dokl. . . . . Akademiĭa Nauk Uzbekskoĭ SSR, Doklady. Tashkent.
Akad. Nauk Uzb. SSR, Inst. Ist. Arkheol., Ist.
    Mater. Kul't. Uzbekist. . . . . Akademiĭa Nauk Uzbekskoĭ SSR, Institut Istorii i Arkheologii,
        Istoriĭa Material'noĭ Kul'tury Uzbekistana. Tashkent.
Akad. Navuk BSSR, Dokl. . . . . Akademiĭa Navuk BSSR, Doklady. Minsk.
Akad. savet FNRJ., Bull. Sci., Sec. A . . . . Akademiski savet FNRJ. Bulletin Scientifique. Section A.
        Zagreb.
Akad. Wiss. Berlin, Monatsbr. . . . . Deutsche Akademie der Wissenschaften zu Berlin, Monatsberichte.
        Berlin.
Akad. Wiss. Lit. Mainz, Mat.-Naturwiss.
    Kl., Abh. . . . . Akademie der Wissenschaften und der Literatur in Mainz,
        Matematisch-Naturwissenschaftliche Klasse, Abhandlungen.
        Wiesbaden.
Alsace-Lorraine, Serv. Carte Géol., Bull. . . . . . . Alsace-Lorraine, Service de la Carte Géologique, Bulletin.
        Strasbourg.
Alsace-Lorraine, Serv. Carte Géol., Mém. . . . . . . Alsace-Lorraine, Service de la Carte Géologique, Mémoires.
        Strasbourg.
Alt-Thüring., Mus. Ur-Frühgesch., Jahresschr. . . . . Alt-Thüringen, Museum für Ur- und Frühgeschichte,
        Jahresschrift. Weimar.
Ameghiniana . . . . Ameghiniana (Asociación Paleontológica Argentina, Revista).
        Buenos Aires.
Amer. Anthropol. . . . . American Anthropologist. Menasha, Wisconsin.
Amer. Anthropol. Ass., Bull. . . . . American Anthropological Association, Bulletin. Washington, D.C.
Amer. Anthropol. Ass., Mem. . . . . American Anthropological Association, Memoirs. Washington,
        D.C.
Amer. Antiquity . . . . American Antiquity (Society for American Archaeology).
        Washington, D.C.
Amer. Ass. Petrol. Geol., Bull. . . . . American Association of Petroleum Geologists, Bulletin.
        Tulsa, Oklahoma.
Amer. Heritage . . . . American Heritage. American Heritage Publishing Co., Inc.
        New York.
Amer. J. Archaeol. . . . . American Journal of Archaeology. Concord, New Hampshire.
Amer. J. Phys. Anthropol. . . . . American Journal of Physical Anthropology. Washington, D.C.
Amer. J. Sci. . . . . American Journal of Science. New Haven, Connecticut.
Amer. Midland Natur. . . . . (The) American Midland Naturalist (University of Notre Dame).
        Notre Dame, Indiana.
Amer. Mus. Natur. Hist., Ann. Rep. . . . . American Museum of Natural History, Annual Report.
        New York City.
Amer. Mus. Natur. Hist., Bull. . . . . American Museum of Natural History, Bulletin. New York City.
Amer. Mus. Nov. . . . . American Museum Novitates. American Museum of Natural
        History. New York City.

Amer. Natur. American Naturalist   (American Society of Naturalists). Chicago.
Amer. Phil. Soc., Proc. . . . . American Philosophical Society, Proceedings.   Philadelphia.
Amer. Phil. Soc., Trans. . . . . American Philosophical Society, Transactions.   Philadelphia.
Amer. Phil. Soc., Yearb. . . . . American Philosophical Society, Yearbook.   Philadelphia.
Amer. Sch. Orient. Res., Bull. . . . . American Schools of Oriental Research, Bulletin.   Jerusalem.
Amer. Sch. Prehist. Res., Bull. . . . . American School of Prehistoric Research, Bulletin.   Peabody Museum, Harvard University.   Cambridge, Massachusetts.
Amer. Sci. . . . . American Scientist.   Society of the Sigma Xi.   New Haven, Connecticut.
Amer. Soc. Mammal., Spec. Publ. . . . . American Society of Mammalogists, Special Publications. Baltimore.
Amer. West . . . . The American West.   The magazine of Western History (Western History Association).   Menlo Park, California.
Amer. Zool. . . . . American Zoologist   (American Society of Zoologists). Utica, New York.
Ampurias . . . . Ampurias.   Revista de Arqueología, Prehistoria y Etnología (Spain.   Consejo Superior de Investigaciones Científicas). Barcelona.
An. Antropol., Mexico . . . . Anales de Antropología, Universidad Nacional Autónoma de México.
Anadolu . . . . Anadolu.   Université d'Ankara, Faculté des Lettres, Institut d'Archéologie.   Ankara   (Formerly Anatolia, Revue Annuelle d'Archéologie).
Anat. Anz. . . . . Anatomischer Anzeiger.   Jena.
Animals . . . . Animals.   London.
Ankara, Úniv., D.T.C. Fak., Yayinl. . . . . Ankara, Úniversitesi, Dil Tarih Coğrafya Fakültesi, Yayinlari.
Ann. Archéol. Arabes Syrienne . . . . Annales Archéologiques Arabes Syriennes.   Direction Générale des Antiquités de Syrie.   Damascus.
L'Ann. Biol. L'Année Biologique.   Fédération française des Sociétés des Sciences Naturelles.   Paris.
Ann. Géol. Pays Hellén . . . . Annales Géologiques des Pays Helléniques.   Athens.
Ann. Géol. Pén. Balkan. . . . . Annales Géologiques de la Péninsule Balkanique.   Belgrade.
Ann. Paléontol., Vertébrés . . . . Annales de Paléontologie, Vertébrés.   Paris.
Ann. Rev. Ecol. Syst. . . . . Annual Review of Ecology and Systematics.   Palo Alto.
Antarctic J. . . . . Antarctic Journal of the United States   (National Science Foundation, Office of Antarctic Programs - Department of Defense, U.S. Naval Support Force, Antarctica).   Washington, D.C.
Antarctic Res. Ser. . . . . Antarctic Research Series, American Geophysical Union. Washington, D.C.
Anthropol. Anz. . . . . Anthropologischer Anzeiger.   Stuttgart.
Anthropol. Ges., Mitt. . . . . Anthropologische Gesellschaft, Mitteilungen.   Vienna.
Anthropol. J. Can. . . . . Anthropological Journal of Canada, Quarterly Bulletin of the Anthropological Association of Canada.   Ottawa.
Anthropol. North . . . . Anthropology of the North: translations from Russian sources, Arctic Institute of North America.   Toronto.
Anthropol. Soc. Nippon, J. . . . . Anthropological Society of Nippon, Journal   (Jinrui-gaku zasshi).   Tokyo.
Anthropologica . . . . Anthropologica.   University of Ottawa, Research Center for Amerindian Anthropology.   Ottawa.
L'Anthropologie . . . . L'Anthropologie.   Paris.
Anthropologie, Brno . . . . Anthropologie, Moravské Muzeum, Brno   (No longer published).
Anthropos . . . . Anthropos, International Review of Ethnology and Linguistics. Freiburg, Switzerland.
Anthropos, Brno . . . . Anthropos, Brno.   Moravské Muzeum v Brně.
Antiquaries J. Antiquaries Journal   (Society of Antiquaries of London). London.
Antiquitas, Reihe 2 . . . . Antiquitas, Reihe 2.   Abhandlungen aus dem Gebiete der Vor- und Frühgeschichte. Bonn.
Antiquity . . . . Antiquity   (A quarterly review of archaeology).   Gloucester, England.
Arbor . . . . Arbor.   Revista general del Consejo Superior de Investigaciones Científicas.   Madrid, Spain.
Arch. Inst. Paléontol. Hum., Mém. . . . . Archives de l'Institut de Paléontologie Humaine, Mémoires.   Paris.

Arch. Sci. (Soc. Phys. Hist. Natur. Genève) . . . . Archives des Sciences (Société de Physique et d'Histoire Naturelle de Genève). Geneva.

Arch. Suiss. Anthropol. Gén. . . . . Archives Suisses d'Anthropologie Générale (L'Institut Suisse d'Anthropolgie Générale Genève). Geneva.

Archaeol. Austriaca . . . . Archaeologia Austriaca. Beiträge zur Paläanthropologie, Ur- und Frühgeschichte Österreichs. Vienna.

Archaeol. Értesítö . . . . Archaeologiai Értesítő. Budapest.

Archaeol., Phys. Anthropol. Oceania . . . . Archaeology and Physical Anthropology in Oceania. University of Sydney. New South Wales, Australia.

Archaeology . . . . Archaeology (Archaeological Institute of America). Cambridge, Massachusetts.

Archéocivilisation . . . . Archéocivilisation. Centre d'Études Pré- et Protohistoriques. Paris (Formerly Antiquités Nationales et Internationales).

Archeol. Polski . . . . Archeologia Polski (Polska Akademia Nauk) Warsaw.

Archeol. Rozhl. Archeologické Rozhledy. Prague.

Archeol. Soc. N. J., News. . . . . Archeological Society of New Jersey, News Letter. Trenton.

Arctic . . . . Arctic. Journal of the Arctic Institute of North America. Montreal.

Arctic Anthropol. . . . . Arctic Anthropology. Wisconsin, University, Department of Anthropology. Madison.

Ardea . . . . Ardea. Tijdschrift der Nederlandsche ornithologische Vereeniging. Leiden.

Arheol. Vestn. . . . . Arheološki Vestnik, Acta Archaeologica (Slovenska Akademija Znanosti in Umetnosti, Sekcija za Arheologijo). Ljubljana.

Ariz. Acad. Sci., J. . . . . Arizona Academy of Science, Journal. Tucson.

Ark. Zool. . . . . Arkiv för Zoologi, utgivet av k. Svenska Vetenskaps - Akademien. Stockholm.

Arkansas Acad. Sci., Proc. . . . . Arkansas Academy of Science, Proceedings. Fayetteville.

Arkt. i Antarkt. Nauchn.-Issl. Inst., Tr. . . . . . . Arkticheskiĭ i Antarkticheskiĭ Nauchno-Issledovatel'skiĭ Institut, Trudy. Leningrad.

Arnoldia . . . . Arnoldia. National Museums of Southern Rhodesia. Causeway.

Asian Pac. Archaeol. Ser. . . . . Asian and Pacific Archaeology Series. (Social Science Research Institute, University of Hawaii). Honolulu.

Asian Perspectives . . . . Asian Perspectives (Social Science Research Institute, University of Hawaii). Honolulu.

Asoc. Geol. Argent., Rev. . . . . Asociación Geológica Argentina, Revista. Buenos Aires.

Asoc. Venez. Geol., Minería, Petról., Bol. Inform. . Asociación Venezolana de Geología, Minería y Petróleo, Boletim Informativo. Caracas.

Ass. Anat., C. R. . . . . Association des Anatomistes, Comptes Rendus. Paris.

Ass. Fr. Etud. Quat., Bull. . . . . Association Française pour l'Étude du Quaternaire, Bulletin. Paris.

Ass. Géol. Carpato-Balkanique, Congr., Rapp. . . . Association Géologique Carpato-Balkanique, Congrès, Rapports.

Ass. Miner. Subalp., Boll. . . . . Associazione Mineraria Subalpina, Bollettino

Athens. Inst. Geol. Ereun. Hypedaph.,
Geol. Geophys. Mel. . . . . Institouton Geologias kai Ereunon Hypedaphous (Institute for Geology and Subsurface Research), Geologikai kai Geophysikai Meletai (Geological and Geophysical Research). Athens.

Atomes . . . . Atomes. A monthly review of vulgarization of all scientific subjects. Paris (Superseded by La Recherche, May 1970.)

Audubon Mag. . . . . Audubon Magazine. New York City.

Aufschluss . . . . Aufschluss (Zeitschrift für die Freunde der Mineralogie und Geologie). Göttingen.

Aufschluss, Sonderheft . . . . Aufschluss, Sonderheft (Vereinigung der Freunde der Mineralogie und Geologie). Rossdorf.

Auk . . . . The Auk, a quarterly Journal of Ornithology. Boston, New York City.

Ausgrabung. u. Funde . . . . Ausgrabungen und Funde Nachrichtenblatt für Vor- und Frühgeschichte. Berlin.

Austr. Geol. Bundesanst., Verh. . . . . Austria, Geologische Bundesanstalt, Verhandlungen. Vienna.

Austral., Bur. Miner. Resour., Geol.
Geophys., Bull. . . . . Australia, Bureau of Mineral Resources, Geology and Geophysics, Bulletin. Canberra.

Austral., Bur. Miner. Resour., Geol.
Geophys., Rep. . . . . Australia, Bureau of Mineral Resources, Geology and Geophysics, Reports. Canberra.

Austral. Inst. Aboriginal Stud., Manual. . . . . . . Australian Institute of Aboriginal Studies, Manual. Canberra.

Austral. J. Sci. Australian Journal of Science   (Australian National Research
Council). Sydney.

Austral. Mammal Soc., Bull. . . . . Australian Mammal Society, Bulletin   (For private circulation
only). Canberra.

Austral. Mus., Rec. . . . . Australian Museum, Records. Sydney.

Austral. Natur. Hist. . . . . Australian Natural History. Sydney.

Baden-Württemberg, Geol. Landesamt, Jahresh. . . Baden-Württemberg, Geologisches Landesamt, Jahreshefte.
Freiburg im Breisgau.

Baden-Württemberg, Staatl. Amt Denkmalpflege,
Stuttgart, Veröff., Reihe A . . . . Baden-Württemberg, Staatliches Amt für Denkmalpflege, Stuttgart.
Veröffentlichungen, Reihe A Vor- und Frühgeschichte. Stuttgart.

Baku, Azerbaidzh. Gos. Med. Inst., Uch. Zap. . . Azerbaidzhanskii Gosudarstvennyi Medifsinskii Institut, Uchenye
Zapiski. Baku.

Baku, Azerbaidzh. Inst. Nefti Khimii,
Uch. Zap. . . . . Azerbaidzhanskii Institut Nefti i Khimii, Uchenye Zapiski. Baku.

Baku, Azerbaidzh. Univ., Uch. Zap., Ser. Biol. . . Azerbaidzhanskii Gosudarstvennyi Universitet, Uchenye Zapiski,
Seriia Biologicheskikh Nauk. Baku.

Baku, Azerbaidzh. Univ., Uch. Zap., Ser.
Geol.-Geogr. . . . . Azerbaidzhanskii Gosudarstvennyi Universitet, Uchenye Zapiski,
Seriia Geologicheskaia-Geograficheskaia. Baku.

Bandung, Inst. Teknol., Proc. . . . . Bandung, Institut Teknologi, Proceedings. Indonesia.

Barcelona (Prov.), Inst. Prov. Paleontol.,
Bol. Inform. . . . . Diputación Provincial de Barcelona, Instituto Provincial de
Paleontología, Boletín Informativo. Sabadell (España).

Barcelona (Prov.), Inst. Prov. Paleontol.,
Paleontol. Evol. . . . . Diputación Provincial de Barcelona, Instituto Provincial de
Paleontología, Paleontología y Evolución. Sabadell (España).

Barcelona, Univ., Dept. Paleontol., Publ. . . . . . Barcelona, Universidad, Departmento de Paleontología,
Publicación.

Bayer. Akad. Wiss., Math.-Naturwiss. Kl., Abh. . . Bayerische Akademie der Wissenschaften, Mathematisch-
Naturwissenschaftliche Klasse, Abhandlungen. Munich.

Bayer. Akad. Wiss., Math.-Naturwiss. Kl.,
Sitz-Ber. . . . . Bayerische Akademie der Wissenschaften, Mathematisch-
Naturwissenschaftliche Klasse, Sitzungsberichte. Munich.

Bayer. Staatssamml. Paläontol. Hist. Geol., Mitt. . . Bayerische Staatssammlung für Paläontologie und Historische
Geologie, Mitteilungen. Munich.

Bayer. Vorgeschichtsblät. . . . . Bayerische Vorgeschichtsblätter, Fortschritte des Bayerisches
Vorgeschichtsfreundes. München.

Beaufortia . . . . Beaufortia Zoological Museum. Amsterdam.

Beirut, Mus. Nat. Lib., Bull. . . . . Beirut, Musée National Libanais, Bulletin.

Beitr. Ur- und Frühgesch. Archäol.
Mittelmeer-Kulturr. . . . . Beiträge zur Ur- und Frühgeschichtlichen Archäologie des
Mittelmeer-Kulturraumes. Institut für Ur- und Frühgeschichte
der Universität Heidelberg. Bonn.

Beitr. Vogelk. Beiträge zur Vogelkunde. Leipzig.

Belem, Mus. Paraen. E. Goeldi, Bol., Ser. Geol. . . Belem (Brazil), Museu Paraense Emílio Goeldi, Boletim, Série
Geologia.

Belgrad, Prirodn. Muz., Glas., Ser. A . . . . Prirodnjački Muzej u Beogradu, Glasnik, Serija A: mineralogija,
geologija, paleontologija. Belgrad.

Berkeley Daily Gazette . . . . Berkeley Daily Gazette. Berkeley, California.

Berlin, Humboldt-Univ., Wiss. Z.,
Math.-Naturwiss. Reihe . . . . Berlin, Humboldt-Universität, Wissenschaftliche Zeitschrift,
Mathematisch-Naturwissenschaftliche Reihe.

Besançon, Univ., Ann. Sci., Sér. 3 . . . . Besançon, Université, Annales Scientifiques, Série 3, Géologie.

Bijdr. Dierkunde . . . . Bijdragen tot de Dierkunde (K. Zoölogisch Genootschap, "Natura
artis magistra"). Amsterdam.

Biol. Jaarboek . . . . Biologisch Jaarboek. K. Natuurwetenschappelijk genootschap
Dodonaea te Gent. Antwerp.

Biol. Rev. . . . . Biological Reviews of the Cambridge Philosophical Society.
Cambridge, England.

Biol. Soc. Wash., Proc. . . . . Biological Society of Washington, Proceedings. Washington, D.C.

Biol. Zentralbl. . . . . Biologisches Zentralblatt. Leipzig.

Biologist . . . . The Biologist. Denver, Colorado, and Columbus, Ohio.

BioScience . . . . BioScience. American Institute of Biological Sciences, Bulletin.
Washington, D.C.

Bits and Pieces . . . . Bits and Pieces. Newcastle, Wyoming.

Blue Jay . . . . The Blue Jay. Quarterly of the Saskatchewan Natural History Society. Regina.

Bol. Geol. Min., España . . . . Boletín Geológico y Minero, Revista bimestral. Instituto Geológico y Minero de España. Madrid.

Boll. Paletnol. Ital. Bollettino di Paletnologia Italiana. Roma.

Bonner Geschichtsblätter . . . . Bonner Geschichtsblätter. Bonn.

Bonner Jahrb. . . . . Bonner Jahrbücher (Verein von Altertums-Freunden im Rheinlande, Bonn. Rheinisches Landesmuseum). Bonn.

Bonner Zool. Beitr.   . . . . Bonner Zoologische Beiträge (Zoologisches Forschungsinstitut und Museum Alexander Koenig). Bonn.

Bordeaux, Univ., Inst. Géol. Bassin Aquitaine,
    Bull. . . . . Bordeaux (City), Université, Institut de Géologie du Bassin d'Aquitaine, Bulletin. Bordeaux-Talence.

Bordeaux, Univ., Inst. Préhist., Publ., Mém. . . . . Bordeaux, Université, Institut de Préhistoire, Publications, Mémoires. Bordeaux.

Breviora . . . . Breviora. Museum of Comparative Zoology. Cambridge, Massachusetts.

Brigham Young Univ. Geol. Studies   . . . . Brigham Young University Geology Studies. Provo, Utah.

Bristol Natur. Soc., Proc. . . . . Bristol Naturalists Society, Proceedings. Bristol, England.

Brit. J. Herpetol. . . . . British Journal of Herpetology. British Herpetological Society. London.

Brit. Mus. (Natur. Hist.), Bull., Geol. . . . . British Museum (Natural History), Bulletin, Geology. London.

Brit. Mus. (Natur. Hist.), Bull., Hist. Ser. . . . . . . British Museum (Natural History), Bulletin, Historical Series. London.

Brit. Ornithol. Club, Bull. . . . . Bulletin of the British Ornithologists' Club. London.

Brünn, Moravske Mus., Časopis . . . . Brünn, Moravske Museum, Časopis, Acta Musei Moraviae. Brno.

Brünn, Univ., Prirod. Fak., Geol. . . . . Brünn, Universitata, Prirodovedecka Fakulta, Geologia. Subseries of its Folia. Brno.

Bucharest, Muz. Nat. Ist. Natur.
    "Grigore Antipa", Trav. . . . . Bucharest, Muzeul National de Istorie Naturala "Grigore Antipa", Travaux.

Bucharest, Univ., An., Ser. Ştiinţ. Natur.,
    Geol.-Geogr. Bucharest, Universitatea, Analele, Seria Ştiinţelor Naturii, Geologie-Geografie.

Budapest, Hist.-Nat. Mus. Nat. Hungarica, Ann. . . . Budapest, Historico-Naturales Musei Nationalis Hungarica, Annales.

Bŭlg. Akad. Nauk., Geol. Inst., Izv.,
    Ser. Paleontol. . . . . Bŭlgarska Akademiia na Naukite, Geologicheski Institut, Izvestiia, Seriia Paleontologiia. Sofia.

Bull. Amer. Paleontol. . . . . Bulletin of American Paleontology. Ithaca, New York.

Bull. Can. Petrol. Geol. . . . . Bulletin of Canadian Petroleum Geology. Alberta Society of Petroleum Geologists, Edmonton Geological Society, Saskatchewan Geological Society. Calgary, Alberta.

Bull. Corresp. Hellén. . . . . Bulletin de Correspondance Hellénique. École Française d'Athènes. Athens.

Bull. Sci. Bourgogne . . . . Bulletin Scientifique de Bourgogne. Dijon.

Bull. Zool. Nomencl. . . . . Bulletin of Zoological Nomenclature. International Commission on Zoological Nomenclature. London.

Caesaraugusta . . . . Caesaraugusta. Publicaciones del Seminario de Arqueología y Numismática Aragonesas. Saragossa.

Cagliari, Univ., Ist. Geol. Paleontol., Publ.   . . . . Cagliari, Università, Istituto di Geologia e Paleontologia, Publicazioni.

Cah. Étud. Biol. . . . . Cahiers d'Études Biologiques. Lyons, Facultés Catholiques, Laboratoire de Zoologie et Biologie.

Cah. Geol. . . . . Cahiers Géologiques. Paris.

Cah. Ligures Préhist. Archéol. . . . . Cahiers Ligures de Préhistoire et d'Archéologie (Institut International d'Études Ligures, Sections Françaises). Bordighera.

Cah. Paléontol. . . . . Cahiers de Paléontologie. Centre National de la Recherche Scientifique. Paris.

Caithness Notebook . . . . Caithness Notebooks. Thurso.

Calif. Acad. Sci., Ann. Rep. . . . . California Academy of Sciences, Annual Report. San Francisco.

Calif. Acad. Sci., Proc. . . . . California Academy of Sciences, Proceedings. San Francisco.

Calif., Div. Mines, Bull. . . . . California (State), Division of Mines, Bulletin. San Francisco.

Cálif., Div. Mines Geol., Miner. Inform. Serv. . . California (State), Division of Mines and Geology, Mineral Information Service. San Francisco.

Calif. Geol. . . . . California Geology (California (State), Division of Mines and Geology, Publication). Sacramento.

Calif., Univ., Archaeol. Res. Fac., Contrib. . . . . California, University, Archaeological Research Facility, Contributions. Berkeley.

Calif., Univ., Archaeol. Surv., Rep. . . . . California, University, Berkeley, Archaeological Survey, Reports. Department of Anthropology, Berkeley.

Calif., Univ., Los Angeles, Archaeol. Surv., Rep. . . California, University, Los Angeles, Archaeological Survey, Report, Department of Anthropology. Los Angeles.

Calif., Univ., Lowie Mus. Anthropol., Ann. Rep. . . California, University, Robert H. Lowie Museum of Anthropology, Annual Report. Berkeley.

Calif., Univ., Publ. Geol. Sci. . . . . California, University, Publications in Geological Sciences. Berkeley, Los Angeles.

Campus Rep. . . . . Campus Report. University of California. Berkeley.

Can. Audubon . . . . Canadian Audubon. Canadian Audubon Society. Toronto.

Can. Field-Natur. . . . . The Canadian Field Naturalist (Ottawa Field-Naturalists' Club). Ottawa.

Can. Geogr. J. Canadian Geographical Journal. Montreal.

Can., Geol. Surv., Bull. . . . . Canada, Geological Survey, Bulletin. Ottawa.

Can. J. Earth Sci. . . . . Canadian Journal of Earth Sciences (National Research Council of Canada). Ottawa.

Can. J. Zool. . . . . Canadian Journal of Zoology   (National Research Council of Canada). Ottawa.

Can., Nat. Mus. Man, Publ. Archaeol. . . . . Canada, National Museum of Man, Publications in Archaeology. Ottawa.

Can., Nat. Mus., Publ. Pal. . . . . Canada, National Museums, Publications in Paleontology. Ottawa.

Canterbury Mus., Rec. . . . . Canterbury Museum, Records (Canterbury College). Christchurch, New Zealand.

Cape Prov. Mus., Ann. . . . . Cape Provincial Museums, Annals. Grahamstown, South Africa.

Carnegie Mag. Carnegie Magazine. Carnegie Institute and Carnegie Library of Pittsburgh. Pittsburgh, Pennsylvania.

Carnegie Mus., Ann. . . . . Carnegie Museum, Annals. Pittsburgh, Pennsylvania.

Carnegie Mus., Ann. Rept. . . . . Carnegie Museum, Annual Reports. Pittsburgh, Pennsylvania.

Čas. Mineral. Geol. . . . . Časopis pro Mineralogii a Geologii. Societas Mineralogica et Geologica Bohemoslovaca. Prague.

Case West. Reserve Univ., Stud. Anthropol. . . . . Case Western Reserve University, Studies in Anthropology. Cleveland, Ohio.

Cave Res. Group Gt. Brit., Trans. . . . . Cave Research Group of Great Britain, Transactions. Ledbury (Herefordshire).

Caves Karst . . . . Caves and Karst; Research in Speleology (Cave Research Associates). Castro Valley, California.

Cent. Rech. Anthropol., Préhist., Ethnogr., Mém. . Centre de Recherches Anthropologiques, Préhistoriques et Ethnographiques, Mémoires. Algiers.

Centro Brasil. Pesquis. Fís., Notas Fís. . . . . Centro Brasileiro de Pesquisas Físicas. Notas de Física. Rio de Janeiro.

Česk. Akad. Věd, Prirodověd. Ústav Brne,
   Prace . . . . Československá Akademie Věd, Prirodovedecky Ústav Brne, Prace. Brno.

Ceylon, Ass. Advance. Sci., Ann. Sess., Proc. . . . . Ceylon, Association for Advancement of Science, Annual Sessions, Proceedings.

Chattanooga Times . . . . Chattanooga Times. Chattanooga, Tennessee.

Chercheurs Wallonie, Bull. . . . . Bulletin des Chercheurs de la Wallonie. Société Royale Belge d'Études Géologiques et Archéologiques.

Chesopiean . . . . The Chesopiean. A Journal of Atlantic Coast Archeology. Norfolk, Virginia.

Chicago Acad. Sci., Bull. . . . . Chicago Academy of Sciences, Bulletin. Chicago, Illinois.

Chicago, Field Mus. Natur. Hist., Bull. . . . . Chicago, Field Museum of Natural History, Bulletin. Chicago, Illinois.

Chigaku Kenkyū . . . . Chigaku Kenkyū. Geoscience Magazine. Tokyo.

Chigaku Zasshi . . . . Journal of Geography   (Tokyo chigaku-kyokwai). Tokyo.

Chile, Inst. Invest. Geol., Bol. . . . . Instituto de Investigaciones Geológicas, Boletín. Santiago.

Chile, Mus. Nac. Hist. Natur., Notic. Mens. . . . . Chile, Museo Nacional de Historia Natural, Noticiario Mensual. Santiago.

Chile, Univ., Bol. . . . . Chile, Universidad, Boletín. Santiago.

Chile, Univ., Fac. Cienc. Fís. Mat.,
   Dep. Geol., Publ. . . . . Chile, Universidad, Facultad de Ciencias Físicas y Matemáticas, Departamento de Geología, Publicaciones. Santiago.

Chinese Sci. Inst. Vert. Paleontol.
  Paleoanthropol., Monogr., Ser. A. . . . . Chinese Science Institute of Vertebrate Paleontology and
Paleoanthropology, Monographs, Series A. Peking.
Chronik der Grube Messel . . . . Chronik der Grube Messel. Munich.
Ciencias . . . . Ciencias, Revista Trimestral. Associación española para el
progreso de las ciencias. Madrid.
Cimbebasia . . . . Cimbebasia. S. W. A. Research Publication (Windhoek, South-
west Africa. State Museum). Windhoek.
Clausthaler Tekton. Hefte . . . . Clausthaler Tektonische Hefte. Clausthal-Zellerfeld.
Cluj, Univ., Stud., Ser. Geol.-Geogr. . . . . Cluj, Universitatea Babeş-Bolyai, Studia, Series Geologia-
Geographia.
Cluj, Univ., Stud., Ser. Geol.-Mineral. . . . . Cluj, Universitatea Babeş-Bolyai, Studia, Series Geologia-
Mineralogia.
Coimbra Univ., Mus. Mineral Geol., Publ.,
  Mem. Not. . . . . Coimbra Universidade Museu Mineralógico e Geológico,
Publicações, Memórias e Noticias.
Colo.-Wyo. Acad. Sci., J. . . . . Journal of the Colorado-Wyoming Academy of Science. Boulder,
Colorado.
Col-Pa (Madrid, Univ., Fac. Cienc.) . . . . Coloquios de la Cátedra de Paleontología Facultad de Ciencias.
Universidad de Madrid.
Comp. Biochem. Physiol. . . . . Comparative Biochemistry and Physiology. An international
journal. New York and London.
Condon Lectures . . . . Condon Lectures. Oregon State System of Higher Education.
Eugene, Oregon.
Condor . . . . The Condor, Journal of the Cooper Ornithological Society.
Lawrence, Kansas.
Conn. Geol. Natur. Hist. Surv., Bull. . . . . Connecticut State Geological and Natural History Survey,
Bulletin. Middletown.
Conservationist . . . . New York (State), Department of Environmental Conservation,
Conservationist. Albany.
Copeia . . . . Copeia (American Society of Ichthyologists and Herpetologists).
New York City.
Córdoba, Arg. Rep. Univ. Nac., Ser.
  Cienc. Natur. Córdoba, Argentine Rep. Universidad Nacional. Facultad de
Ciencias Exactas, Físicas y Naturales. Serie Ciencias Naturales.
COWA Surv. Bibliogr. . . . . COWA Surveys and Bibliographies. Published by Council for
Old World Archaeology. Cambridge, Massachusetts.
Curator . . . . Curator, a quarterly publication of the American Museum of
Natural History. New York City.
Curr. Anthropol. Current Anthropology; a World Journal of the Sciences of Man
(Wenner-Gren Foundation for Anthropological Research). Chicago.
Curr. Sci. . . . . Current Science. Bangalore, India.
Czech., Ustřed. Ústav Geol., Roz. . . . . Czechoslovakia, Ustřední Ústav Geologický, Rozpravy. Prague.
Czech., Ustřed. Ústav Geol., Sborn.
  Geol. Věd., Rada A. . . . . Czechoslovakia, Ustřední Ústav Geologický, Sborník Geologických
Věd, Rada A, Antropozoikum. Prague.
Czech., Ustřed. Ústav Geol., Věstn. . . . . Czechoslovakia, Ustřední Ústav Geologický, Věstník. Prague.
Czech., Ustřed. Ústav Geol., Zprávy
  Geol. Vyzk. . . . . Czechoslovakia, Ustřední Ústav Geologický, Zprávy o
Geologických Výzkumech. Prague.
Dan. Geol. Foren., Medd. . . . . Dansk Geologisk Forening, Meddelelser. Copenhagen.
Dan. Geol. Unders., Raekke 1 . . . . Danmarks Geologiske Undersøgelse, Raekke 1. Copenhagen.
Dan. Geol. Unders., Raekke 2 . . . . Danmarks Geologiske Undersøgelse, Raekke 2. Copenhagen.
Dan. Geol. Unders., Raekke 3 . . . . Danmarks Geologiske Undersøgelse, Raekke 3. Copenhagen.
Dan. Geol. Unders., Raekke 4 . . . . Danmarks Geologiske Undersøgelse, Raekke 4. Copenhagen.
Dan. Vidensk. Selsk., Biol. Skr. . . . . Det Kongelige Danske Videnskabernes Selskab, Biologiske
Skrifter. Copenhagen.
Decheniana . . . . Decheniana (Naturhistorischer Verein der Rheinlande und
Westfalens, Verhandlungen). Bonn.
Denver Mus. Natur. Hist., Ann. Rep. . . . . Denver Museum of Natural History, Annual Report. Denver,
Colorado.
Denver Mus. Natur. Hist., Mus. Pictorial . . . . . Denver Museum of Natural History, Museum Pictorial. Denver,
Colorado.
Desert Mag. . . . . Desert Magazine. Palm Desert, California.

Deut. Geol. Ges., Z. . . . . Deutsche Geologische Gesellschaft, Zeitschrift. Hannover.
Deut. Ges. Geol. Wiss., Ber., Reihe A,
  Geol. Paläontol. . . . . Deutsche Gesellschaft für Geologische Wissenschaften, Berichte,
    Reihe A, Geologie und Paläontologie. Berlin.
Discovery . . . . Discovery. Yale University, Peabody Museum. New Haven,
    Connecticut.
Diss. Abstr. . . . . Dissertation Abstracts. Abstracts of Dissertations and mono-
    graphs in microform. Ann Arbor, Michigan.
Dorset Natur. Hist. Archaeol. Soc., Proc. . . . . . . Dorset Natural History and Archaeological Society, Proceedings.
    Dorchester, England.
Dresden, Staatl. Mus. Mineral. Geol., Abhandl. . . Dresden, Staatliches Museum für Mineralogie und Geologie,
    Abhandlungen.
Dumfries. Galloway Natur. Hist. Antiq. Soc.,
  Trans. . . . . Dumfriesshire and Galloway Natural History and Antiquarian
    Society, Transactions. Dumfries, Scotland.
E. Anthropol. . . . . Eastern Anthropologist, Ethnographic and Folk Culture Society.
    Lucknow, India.
Earth Planet. Sci. Lett. . . . . Earth and Planetary Science Letters. Amsterdam.
Earth Sci. (Chikyū Kagaku) . . . . Earth Science (Chikyū Kagaku); Association for the Geological
    Collaboration of Japan, Journal. Tokyo.
Earth Sci. J. (Waikato Geol. Soc.) . . . . Earth Science Journal (Waikato Geological Society). Hamilton,
    New Zealand.
Earth-Sci. Rev. Earth Science Reviews. International Magazine for Geo-
    Scientists. Elsevier Publ. Co., Amsterdam.
Eclogae Geol. Helv. . . . . Eclogae Geologicae Helvetiae. Basel.
Ecology . . . . Ecology. The Ecological Society of America. Durham, North
    Carolina.
Eesti NSV Tead. Akad., Toimet., Keem. Geol. . . Eesti NSV Teaduste Akadeemia, Toimetised, Keemia Geoloogia.
    Tallinn.
Eiszeitalter Gegenwart . . . . Eiszeitalter und Gegenwart (Deutsche Quartärvereinigung,
    Jahrbuch). Öhringen.
Ekologiíā . . . . Ekologiíā. USSR.
El Palacio . . . . El Palacio. A quarterly journal of the Museum of New Mexico.
    Santa Fé.
Emu . . . . The Emu, Journal of the Royal Australian Ornithologists Union.
    Melbourne.
Endeavour . . . . Endeavour. London.
Eng., Mineração, Met. . . . . Engenharia, Mineração e Metalurgia. Rio de Janeiro.
Environ. Southwest . . . . Environment Southwest. San Diego Society of Natural Hisjtory.
    San Diego, California.
Erlanger Geol. Abhandl. . . . . Erlanger Geologische Abhandlungen. Erlangen.
Estud. Geol. (Inst. Invest. Geol.
  "Lucas Mallada") . . . . Estudios Geológicos (Instituto de Investigaciones Geológicas
    "Lucas Mallada"). Madrid.
Ethnogr.-Archäol. Z. . . . . Ethnographish-Archäologische Zeitschrift. Deutscher Verlag der
    Wissenschaften. Berlin.
Evolut. Biol. . . . . Evolutionary Biology. New York: Appleton-Century-Crofts.
Evolution . . . . Evolution. International Journal of Organic Evolution (Society
    for the Study of Evolution). Lawrence, Kansas.
Exc. Arqueol. Españ. . . . . Spain, Servicio Nacional de Excavaciones Arqueológicas,
    Excavaciones Arqueológicas en España. Madrid.
Explorer (Cleveland Mus. Natur. Hist.) . . . . The Explorer (Cleveland Museum of Natural History). Cleveland,
    Ohio.
Faith and Thought . . . . Faith and Thought (supersedes Journal and Transactions of the
    Victoria Institute).
Faune de France . . . . Faune de France. Fédération française des Sociétés des sciences
    naturelles, Revue. Paris.
Fed. Soc. Hist. Natur. Franche-Comté, Bull. . . . . Fédération des Sociétés d'Histoire Naturelle de Franche-Comté,
    Bulletin. Vésoul, France.
Ferrara, Univ., Ann., Sez. 9 . . . . Ferrara, Università, Annali (nuova serie), Sezione 9, Scienze
    Geologiche e Paleontologiche.
Ferrara, Univ., Mem. Geopaleontol. . . . . Ferrara, Università, Memorie Geopaleontologiche.
Fieldiana: Geol. . . . . Fieldiana: Geology (Field Museum of Natural History).
    Chicago, Illinois.
Fieldiana: Geol. Mem. . . . . Fieldiana: Geological Memoirs (Field Museum of Natural
    History). Chicago, Illinois.

Fieldiana: Zool. . . . . Fieldiana: Zoology (Field Museum of Natural History). Chicago, Illinois.

Fla. Acad. Sci., Quart. J. . . . . Florida Academy of Sciences, Quarterly Journal. Gainesville.

Fla. Geol. Surv., Spec. Publ. . . . . Florida Geological Survey, Special Publication. Tallahassee.

Fla. State Mus., Bull., Biol. Sci. . . . . Florida State Museum, Bulletin, Biological Sciences. Gainesville.

Földt. Közl. . . . . Földtani Közlöny, Zeitschrift der Ungarischen Geologischen Gesellschaft. Budapest.

Folia Morphol. Folia Morphologica. Czechoslovak Academy of Sciences. Prague.

Folia Primatol. . . . . Folia Primatologica, International Journal of Primatology. Basel and New York.

Folia Quaternaria . . . . Folia Quaternaria (Polska Akademia Nauk, Oddzial w Krakowie). Kraków.

Forma et Functio . . . . Forma et Functio. An International Journal of Functional Biology. Braunschweig, Germany.

Fort Burgwin Res. Cent., Publ. . . . . Fort Burgwin Research Center. Publications. Santa Fe, New Mexico.

Fort Hays Kansas, State College News . . . . Fort Hays Kansas, State College News. Hays, Kansas.

Fortschr. Evolutionsforsch. . . . . Fortschritte der Evolutionsforschung. Stuttgart: Fischer Verlag.

Fossils and Strata . . . . Fossils and Strata. University of Oslo. Oslo: University Press.

Fr., Bur. Rech. Géol. Minières, Bull. (Sér. 2), Sect. 1 . . . . France, Bureau de Recherches Géologiques et Minières, Bulletin (Série 2), Section 1 (Géologie de la France, Travaux des Collaborateurs pour la Carte Géologique). Orléans.

Fr., Bur. Rech. Géol. Minières, Bull. (Sér. 2), Sect. 4 . . . . France, Bureau de Recherches Géologiques et Minières, Bulletin (Série 2), Section 4 (Géologie Générale et Divers). Orléans.

Fr., Bur. Rech. Géol. Minières, Mém. . . . . France, Bureau de Recherches Géologiques et Minières, Mémoires. Paris.

Fr., Cent. Nat. Rech. Sci., Bull. Signal. . . . . . . France, Centre National de la Recherche Scientifique, Bulletin Signalétique. Paris.

Frankfurter Allgemeine Zeitung . . . . Frankfurter Allgemeine Zeitung. Frankfurt, Germany.

Freiberg. Forschungsh., Reihe C . . . . Freiberger Forschungshefte (Bergakademie Freiberg), Reihe C. Leipzig.

Frontiers . . . . Frontiers. Academy of Natural Sciences of Philadelphia. Philadelphia, Pennsylvania.

Fundamenta, Reihe A and Reihe B . . . . Fundamenta, Reihe A and Reihe B. Köln-Graz: Böhlau Verlag.

Fundber. Schwaben . . . . Fundberichte aus Schwaben. Stuttgart.

Gallia Préhist. Gallia Préhistoire, Centre National de la Recherche Scientifique. Paris.

Gegenbaurs Morph. Jahrb. . . . . Gegenbaurs Morphologisches Jahrbuch. Leipzig.

Genetica . . . . Nederlands Tijdschrift voor Erfelijkheids- en Afstammingsleer. The Hague.

Géobios . . . . Géobios. Paléontologie, Stratigraphie, Paléoécologie. Département des Sciences de la Terre, Faculté des Sciences, Université de Lyon. (Supersedes Travaux des Lab. de Géol. de Lyon.)

Geochronicle . . . . Geochronicle. Published by Geochron Laboratories, Inc. Cambridge, Massachusetts.

Geogr. Obshchest. SSSR, Altaĭ. Otdel, Izv. . . . . Geograficheskoe Obshchestvo SSSR, Altaĭskiĭ Otdel, Izvestiia. Biĭsk.

Geogr. Obshchest. SSSR, Khar'kov. Otd., Izv. . . Geograficheskoe Obshchestvo SSSR, Khar'kovskoe Otdelenie, Izvestiia. Khar'kov.

Geogr. Obshchest. SSSR, Vost.-Sibirsk. Otd., Izv. . . . . Geograficheskoe Obshchestvo SSSR, Vostochno-Sibirskiĭ Otdel, Izvestiia. Irkutsk.

Geogr. Obshchest. SSSR, Zabaĭkal. Fil., Izv. . . . Geograficheskoe Obshchestvo SSSR, Zabaĭkal'skiĭ Filial, Izvestiia. Chita.

Geogr. Obshchest. SSSR, Zabaĭkal'. Filial, Zap. Geograficheskoe Obshchestvo SSSR, Zabaĭkal'skiĭ Filial, Zapiski. Chita.

Geogr. Obshchest. USSR, L'vov. Otd., Dokl. Soobshch. . . . . Geograficheskoe Obshchestvo Ukr. SSR, L'vovskoe Otdelenie, Doklady i Soobshcheniia. L'vov.

Geogr. Pol. . . . . Geographia Polonica. Warsaw.

Geogr. Rev. . . . . Geographical Review. American Geographical Society of New York. New York City.

Geol. Ass. (London), Proc. . . . . Geologists' Association (London), Proceedings. Colchester.
Geol. Bavarica . . . . Geologica Bavarica. Bayerisches Geologisches Landesamt. Munich.
Geol. Bl. Nordost-Bayern . . . . Geologische Blätter für Nordost-Bayern und angrenzende Gebiete. Erlangen.
Geol. Fören. Stockholm, Förh. . . . . Geologiska Föreningen i Stockholm, Förhandlingar. Stockholm.
Geol. Geofiz. (Akad. Nauk SSSR, Sib. Otd.) . . . . Geologiĭa i Geofizika (Akademiĭa Nauk SSSR, Sibirskoe Otdelenie). Novosibirsk.
Geol. Ges. Wien, Mitt. . . . . Geologische Gesellschaft in Wien, Mitteilungen. Vienna.
Geol. J. . . . . Geological Journal. Liverpool.
Geol. Jahrb. . . . . Geologisches Jahrbuch. Bundesanstalt für Bodenforschung und die Geologische Landesämter der Bundesrepublik Deutschland. Hannover.
Geol. Mag. . . . . Geological Magazine. London: Cambridge Univ. Press.
Geol. Markmed . . . . Geologilised Markmed (Loodusuurijate selts). Eesti NSV Teaduste Akademia. Tallinn.
Geol. Mijnbouw . . . . Geologie en Mijnbouw (Koninklijk Nederlands Geologisch Mijnbouwkundig Genootschap, Maandblad). The Hague.
Geol. Mining Met. Soc. India, Quart. J. . . . . . . Geological, Mining and Metallurgical Society of India, Quarterly Journal. Calcutta.
Geol. News . . . . Geological News. London.
Geol. Obshchest. Gruz., Izv. . . . . Geologicheskoe Obshchestvo Gruzii, Izvestiĭa. Tiflis.
Geol. Palaeontol. . . . . Geologica et Palaeontologica (Marburg, Philipps-Universität, Geologisch-Paläontologisches Institut). Marburg.
Geol. Práce, Zpr. . . . . Geologické Práce, Zprávy (Czechoslovakia, Geologický Ústav Dionýza Štúra). Bratislava.
Geol., Razprave Poročila . . . . Geologija, Razprave in Poročila, Geološki Zavod. Ljubljana.
Geol. Rom. . . . . Geologica Romana (Rome, Università, Istituto di Geologia e Paleontologia - Consiglio Nazionale delle Ricerche, Centro di Studio per la Geologia dell' Italia Centrale). Rome.
Geol. Soc. Amer., Abstr. . . . . Geological Society of America, Abstracts with Programs. Boulder, Colorado.
Geol. Soc. Amer., Bull. . . . . Geological Society of America, Bulletin. Boulder, Colorado.
Geol. Soc. Amer., Mem. . . . . Geological Society of America, Memoir. Boulder, Colorado.
Geol. Soc. Amer., Proc. Vol. . . . . Geological Society of America, Proceedings Volume. Boulder, Colorado.
Geol. Soc. Amer., Spec. Pap. . . . . Geological Society of America, Special Paper. Boulder, Colorado.
Geol. Soc. Austral., J. . . . . Geological Society of Australia, Journal. Adelaide.
Geol. Soc. India, Bull. . . . . Geological Society of India, Bulletin. Bangalore.
Geol. Soc. India, J. . . . . Geological Society of India, Journal. Bangalore.
Geol. Soc. India, Mem. . . . . Geological Society of India, Memoirs. Bangalore.
Geol. Soc. Jap., J. . . . . Geological Society of Japan, Journal (Tishitsugaku dzassi). Tokyo.
Geol. Soc. London, J. . . . . Geological Society of London, Journal. London.
Geol. Soc. London, Proc. . . . . Geological Society of London, Proceedings. London.
Geol. Soc. S. Afr., Trans. . . . . Geological Society of South Africa, Transactions. Johannesburg.
Geol. Surv. India, Rec. . . . . Geological Survey of India, Records. Calcutta.
Geol. Vjesnik . . . . Geološki Vjesnik (Institut za Geološka Istraživanja u Zagrebu i Hrvatsko Geološko Društvo). Zagreb.
Geol. Zh. . . . . Geologicheskiĭ Zhurnal. Ministerstvo Geologii Ukr. SSR. Akademiĭa Nauk Ukr. SSR, Otdelenie Nauk o Zemle i Kosmose. Kiev.
Geologie, Beiheft . . . . Geologie, Beiheft. Zeitschrift für das Gesamtgebiet der Geologie und Mineralogie. Beihefte. Berlin.
Geologie (Berlin) . . . . Geologie, Zeitschrift für das Gesamtgebiet der Geologischen Wissenschaften, Mit Beiheften. Deutsche Gesellschaft für Geologische Wissenschaften. Berlin.
Geologiĭa SSSR . . . . Ministerstvo Geologii SSSR. Moscow.
Georgia Acad. Sci., Bull. . . . . Georgia Academy of Science. Athens, Georgia.
Geotimes . . . . Geotimes (American Geological Institute). Washington, D.C.
Germania . . . . Germania. Anzeiger der Römisch-Germanischen Komission des deutschen Archäologischen Instituts. Berlin.
Ges. Naturk. Württemberg, Jahresh. . . . . Gesellschaft für Naturkunde in Württemberg, Jahreshefte (Supersedes: Verein für vaterländische Naturkunde in Württemberg). Stuttgart.

G. Geol. . . . . Giornale di Geologia (Bologna. Museo geologico). Pisa.

Ghent, Rijksuniv. Fac. Wetensch., Verh. . . . . . . Ghent, Rijksuniversiteit, Faculteit der Wetenschappen, Verhandelinger.

Globe . . . . Le Globe; organe de la Société de Géographie de Genève. Geneva.

Glückauf . . . . Glückauf. Zeitschrift für Technik und wirtschaft des Bergbaus. Essen.

Goodwin Ser. . . . . The Goodwin Series. South African Archaeological Society. Claremont, Cape Province.

Göteborg, K. Vetensk. Vitterh. Samh.,
   Handl., Ser. B . . . . Göteborg, K. Vetenskaps och Vitterhets Samhälle, Handlingar. Series B, Matematiska och Naturvetenskapliga Skrifter. Göteborg.

Göttinger Arb. Geol. Paläontol. . . . . Göttinger Arbeiten zur Geologie und Paläontologie. Göttingen: Selbstverlag des Geologisch-Paläontologischen Instituts der Georg-August-Universität.

Grad. Res. Center, J., S. Methodist Univ. . . . . . . Graduate Research Center, Journal, Southern Methodist University. Dallas, Texas.

Graz, Joanneum, Mus. Berg. Geol. Techn., Mitt. . . . Graz, Museum für Bergbau, Geologie und Technik am Landesmuseum Joanneum, Mitteilungen.

Great Basin Natur. . . . . Great Basin Naturalist. Brigham Young University, Department of Zoology and Entomology. Provo, Utah.

Grenoble, Fac. Sci., Lab. Géol., Trav. . . . . Grenoble, Faculté des Sciences, Laboratoire de Géologie, Travaux.

Groupement Int. Recherch. Sci. Stomatol., Bull. . . . Groupement International pour la Recherche Scientifique en Stomatologie, Bulletin. Liège, Belgium.

Grozny, USSR, Grozn. Neft.
   Nauch.-Issled. Inst., Tr. . . . . Grozny, USSR, Groznenskiĭ Nefti͡anoĭ Nauchno-Issledovatel'skiĭ Institut, Trudy.

Gt. Brit., Geol. Surv., Bull. . . . . Great Britain, Geological Survey, Bulletin. London.

Gt. Brit., Inst. Geol. Sci., Overseas Geol.
   Miner. Resour. . . . . Great Britain. Institut of Geological Sciences. Overseas Geology and Mineral Resources. London.

Gt. Plains J. . . . . Great Plains Journal. Great Plains Historical Association. Lawton, Oklahoma.

Gt. Plains News. . . . . Great Plains Newsletter. Museum of the Great Plains. Lawton, Oklahoma.

Gulf Coast Ass. Geol. Soc., Trans. . . . . Gulf Coast Association of Geological Societies, Transactions. Jackson, Mississippi.

Hall. Jahrb. Mitteldeut. Erdgesch. . . . . Hallesches Jahrbuch für Mitteldeutsche Erdgeschichte. Leipzig.

Hanover, Tech. Hochsch., Geol. Inst., Mitt. . . . . Hanover, Technische Hochschule, Geologisches Institut, Mitteilungen.

Harvard Univ., Mus. Comp. Zool., Ann. Rep. . . Harvard University, Museum of Comparative Zoology, Annual Report. Cambridge, Massachusetts.

Harvard Univ., Mus. Comp. Zool., Bull. . . . . . . Harvard University, Museum of Comparative Zoology, Bulletin. Cambridge, Massachusetts.

Harvard Univ., Peabody Mus. Archaeol.
   Ethnol., Pap. . . . . Harvard University, Peabody Museum of Archaeology and Ethnology, Papers. Cambridge, Massachusetts.

Hays Daily News . . . . Hays Daily News. Hays, Kansas.

Helictite . . . . Helictite. Journal of Australasian Cave Research. Quarterly. Sydney.

Helinium . . . . Helinium. Revue Consacrée à l'Archéologie des Pays-Bas, de la Belgique et du Grand-Duché de Luxembourg. Wetteren, Belgium.

Hercynia . . . . Hercynia (Martin-Luther-Universität, Mathematisch-Naturwissenschaftliche Fakultät). Halle-Wittenberg.

Herpeton . . . . Herpeton. Southwestern Herpetologists Society. Pasadena, California.

Hess. Landesamt Bodenforsch., Abh. . . . . Hessisches Landesamt für Bodenforschung, Abhandlungen. Wiesbaden.

Hess. Landesamt Bodenforsch., Notizbl. . . . . . . Hessisches Landesamt für Bodenforschung, Notizblatt. Wiesbaden.

Homo . . . . Homo. Zeitschrift für die vergleichende Forschung am Menschen. Göttingen.

Human Biol. . . . . Human Biology; an International Record of Research. Baltimore.

Hung., Magy. Áll. Földt. Intéz., Évi Jelent. . . . . Hungary, Magyar Állami Földtani Intézet, Évi Jelentése. Budapest.
Hung., Magy. Áll. Földt. Intéz., Évk. . . . . Hungary, Magyar Állami Földtani Intézet, Évkönyve. Budapest.
Ibis . . . . The Ibis. A Quarterly Journal of Ornithology. London.
Idaho State Univ. Mus., Spec. Publ. . . . . Idaho State University Museum, Special Publication. Pocatello.
Ill. Acad. Sci., Trans. . . . . Illinois State Academy of Science, Transactions. Springfield, Illinois.
Ill. State Mus., Rep. Invest. . . . . Illinois State Museum, Report of Investigations. Springfield, Illinois.
Illus. London News . . . . The Illustrated London News. London.
INACH, Ser. Cient. . . . . Instituto Antártico Chileno, Serie Científica. Santiago.
Indian Geol. Ass., Bull. . . . . Indian Geologists Association, Bulletin. Calcutta.
Indian Minerals . . . . Indian Minerals. Geological Survey of India. Calcutta.
Indian Sci. Congr., Proc. . . . . Indian Science Congress. Proceedings. Calcutta.
Indiana Acad. Sci., Proc. . . . . Indiana Academy of Science, Proceedings. Indianapolis.
Inform. Sci. . . . . Information Scientifique. Paris.
Inst. Antárt. Chileno, Bol. . . . . Instituto Antártico Chileno, Boletín. Santiago.
Inst. Boliviano Petról., Bol. . . . . Instituto Boliviano del Petróleo, Boletín (IBP). La Paz.
Inst. Fond. Afr. Noire, Bull. . . . . Institut Fondamental d'Afrique Noire, Bulletin (Formerly Bulletin Institut Français de l'Afrique Noire.) Dakar.
Inst. Roy. Sci. Natur. Belg., Bull. . . . . Institut Royal des Sciences Naturelles de Belgique, Bulletin (Koninklijk Belgisch Instituut voor Natuurwetenschappen, Bulletin). Brussels.
Inst. Roy. Sci. Natur. Belg., Mém. . . . . Institut Royal des Sciences Naturelles de Belgique, Mémoires (Koninklijk Belgisch Instituut voor Natuurwetenschappen, Verhandelingen). Brussels.
Int. Geol. Rev. International Geology Review. American Geological Institute, Washington, D.C.
Int. J. Speleol. International Journal of Speleology. Amsterdam: Swets and Zeitlinger N. V.
Int. Turtle Tortoise Soc., J. . . . . International Turtle and Tortoise Society, Journal. Los Angeles, California.
Interamer. . . . . The Interamerican. Newsletter of the Instituto Interamericano. Denton, Texas.
Iowa Acad. Sci., Proc. . . . . Iowa Academy of Science, Proceedings. Des Moines, Iowa.
Ipek . . . . Ipek. Jahrbuch für prehistorische und ethnographische Kunst. Leipzig.
Iran, Geol. Surv., Rep. . . . . Iran, Ministry of Economy, Geological Survey, Reports. Teheran.
Irish Natur. J. . . . . Irish Naturalists' Journal. Belfast.
Isis . . . . Isis. Quarterly organ of the History of Science Society and of the International Academy of the History of Science. Washington, D.C.
Isr. Acad. Sci. Hum., Publ. . . . . Israel Academy of Sciences and Humanities, Publications. Jerusalem.
Isr. Explor. J. . . . . Israel Exploration Journal. Jerusalem.
Isr. J. Earth-Sci. . . . . Israel Journal of Earth-Sciences. Jerusalem.
Isr. J. Zool. . . . . Israel Journal of Zoology. Jerusalem.
Ist. Ital. Paleontol. Umana . . . . Istituto Italiano di Paleontologia Umana. Rome.
Italy, Serv. Geol., Boll. . . . . Italy, Servizio Geologico, Bollettino. Rome.
Itogi Nauki, Ser. Biol. . . . . Itogi Nauki, Seriîa Biologiîa (Akademiîa Nauk SSSR, Vsesoîuznyĭ Institut Nauchnoĭ i Tekhnicheskoĭ Informaîsii). Moscow.
Itogi Nauki, Ser. Geol. . . . . Itogi Nauki, Seriîa Geologiîa (Akademiîa Nauk SSSR, Vsesoîuznyĭ Institut Nauchnoĭ i Tekhnicheskoĭ Informaîsii). Moscow.
J. Afr. Hist. . . . . Journal of African History. London: Cambridge University Press.
J. Anat. . . . . Journal of Anatomy. London.
J. Animal Ecol. Journal of Animal Ecology. Published by the British Ecological Society. London.
J. Anthropol. . . . . Journal of Anthropology. University of the Americas. Cholula, Puebla, Mexico.
J. Anthropol. Soc. Nippon . . . . Journal of the Anthropological Society of Nippon. Zinruigaku Zassi. Tokyo.
J. Anthropol. Soc. S. Austral. . . . . Journal of the Anthropological Society of South Australia. Adelaide.

J. Comp. Neurol. . . . . Journal of Comparative Neurology. Philadelphia.
J. Dental Res. . . . . Journal of Dental Research. Published by the American Dental Association. New York City.
J. E. Afr. Nat. Hist. Soc. . . . . Journal of the East Africa Natural History Society and National Museum. Nairobi, Kenya.
J. Geol. . . . . Journal of Geology. Chicago.
J. Geol. Educ. . . . . Journal of Geological Education (Association of Geology Teachers). Columbus, Ohio.
J. Herpetol. Journal of Herpetology (Society for the study of amphibians and reptiles). Athens, Ohio.
J. Hist. Biol. . . . . Journal of the History of Biology. Harvard University. Cambridge, Massachusetts.
J. Human Evol. . . . . Journal of Human Evolution. A. B. Chiarelli, ed. New York and London: Academic Press.
J. Mammal. Journal of Mammalogy. Lawrence, Kansas.
J. Mammal. Soc. Jap. . . . . The Journal of the Mammalogical Society of Japan. Tokyo.
J. Morphol. Journal of Morphology. Philadelphia, Pennsylvania.
J. Natur. Hist., London . . . . Journal of Natural History (Supersedes Annals and Magazine of Natural History). London.
J. Ornithol. Journal für Ornithologie. Berlin.
J. Palaeontol. Soc. India . . . . Journal of the Palaeontological Society of India. Lucknow.
J. Paleontol. . . . . Journal of Paleontology. Tulsa, Oklahoma.
J. Roy. Asiatic Soc. (Ceylon Br.) . . . . Journal of the Royal Asiatic Society (Ceylon Branch). Colombo.
J. Student Pap., Anthropol. . . . . Journal of Student Papers in Anthropology. University of Victoria. Victoria, British Columbia.
J. West . . . . Journal of the West. Los Angeles.
J. Zool. . . . . Journal of Zoology (Zoological Society of London, Proceedings). London.
Jahresschrift Mitteldeutsch. Vorgesch. . . . . Jahresschrift für Mitteldeutsche Vorgeschichte. Für das Landesmuseum für vorgeschichte in Halle. Halle.
Jassy, Univ. Cuza, An. Ştiinţ., Sec. 2, b. Geol.-Geogr. . . . . Jassy (Rumania), Universitătii "Al. I. Cuza" din Iaşi, Analele Ştiinţifice, Sectiunea 2 (Ştiinţe Naturale) b. Geologie-Geografie.
Jugoslav. Akad. Znanosti i Umjetnosti, Ljetopis . . Jugoslavenska Akademija Znanosti i Umjetnosti, Ljetopis. Zagreb.
Jugoslav. Akad. Znanosti i Umjetnosti, Rad . . . . Jugoslavenska Akademija Znanosti i Umjetnosti, Rad. Zagreb.
Kagoshima Univ., Fac. Sci., Rep. . . . . Kagoshima University, Faculty of Science, Reports. Japan.
Kans. Acad. Sci., Trans. . . . . Kansas Academy of Science. Transactions. Topeka.
Kans. Anthropol. Ass., News. . . . . Kansas Anthropological Association, Newsletter. Fort Hayes.
Kans., Univ., Dept. Geol., Spec. Publ. . . . . Kansas, University, Department of Geology, Special Publication. Lawrence.
Kans., Univ., Mus. Natur. Hist., Misc. Publ. . . . . Kansas, University, Museum of Natural History, Miscellaneous Publications. Lawrence.
Kans., Univ., Mus. Natur. Hist., Publ. . . . . Kansas, University, Museum of Natural History, Publications. Lawrence.
Kans. Univ., Paleontol. Contrib. . . . . Kansas, University, Paleontological Contributions. Articles. Lawrence.
Kans., Univ., Paleontol. Contrib., Pap. . . . . Kansas, University, Paleontological Contributions, Papers. Lawrence.
Kaseki . . . . Kaseki (Fossils), Palaeontological Society of Japan. Tokyo.
Kenya Past and Present . . . . Kenya Past and Present. Kenya National Museums. Nairobi.
Kirtlandia . . . . Kirtlandia. The Cleveland Museum of Natural History. Cleveland, Ohio.
K'o Hsueh T'ung Pao . . . . K'o Hsueh T'ung Pao. Kexue Tongbao. Added titles: Nauchnyĭ Vestnik, Scientia. Peking.
Kolyma . . . . Kolyma. Magadan, SSSR.
Košice, Czech., Východosloven. Múz., Sborn., Ser. A, Geol. Vedy . . . . Košice, Czechoslovak Republic, Východoslovenske Múzeum, Sborník, Seria A, Geologické Vedy.
Košice, Czech., Východosloven. Múz., Sborn., Ser. A, Prirod. Vedy . . . . Košice, Czechoslovak Republic, Východoslovenske Múzeum, Sborník, Seria A, Prirodne Vedy.
Kosmos . . . . Kosmos. Stuttgart.
Kroeber Anthropol. Soc., Pap. . . . . Kroeber Anthropological Society, Papers. Berkeley, California.

Kush . . . . Kush. Journal of the Sudan Antiquities Service. Khartoum.
Kwart. Geol. (Pol., Inst. Geol.) . . . . Kwartalnik Geologiczny (Poland, Instytut Geologiczny).
       Warsaw.
Kyoto, Univ., Fac. Sci., Mem., Ser. Geol.
   Mineral. . . . . Kyoto, University, Faculty of Science, Memoirs, Series of
       Geology and Mineralogy.
La Habana, Univ., Fac. Cienc., Mem.,
   Ser. Cienc. Biol. . . . . La Habana, Universidad, Facultad de Ciencias, Memorias, Serie
       Ciencias Biológicas. Havana.
Lancet . . . . The Lancet. A journal of British and Foreign Medicine.
       London.
La Physiophile . . . . Revue périodique de vulgarisation des sciences naturelles et
       historiques "La Physiophile". Montceau-les-Mines (Saône-et
       Loire).
La Plata, Univ. Nac., Mus. Notas, Antropol. . . . . La Plata, Universidad Nacional, Notas del Museo, Antropologia.
       La Plata, Argentina.
La Recherche . . . . La Recherche. Société d'Éditions Scientifiques. (Supersedes
       Atomes). Paris.
Lausanne Univ., Lab. Géol., Bull. . . . . Lausanne, Université, Laboratoires de Géologie, Bulletin.
Leidse Geol. Meded. . . . . Leidse Geologische Mededelingen (Leiden, Rijksmuseum van
       Geologie en Mineralogie-Leiden Rijksuniversiteit, Geologisch-
       Mineralogisch Instituut). Leyden.
Leningrad. Univ., Vestn., Geol. Geogr. . . . . Leningradskiĭ Universitet, Vestnik; Geologiĭa, Geografiĭa.
       Leningrad.
Les Eyzies . . . . Les Eyzies. Bulletin de la Société d'Études et de Recherches
       Préhistoriques et Institut Pratique de Préhistoire. Les Eyzies.
Lethaia . . . . Lethaia. An International Journal of Palaeontology and
       Stratigraphy. Oslo: Universitetsforlaget.
Leyden, Rijksmus. Natuur. Hist.,
   Zool. Mededel. . . . . Leyden, Rijksmuseum van Natuurlijke Historie te Leiden,
       Zoologische Mededelingen.
Libyca . . . . Libyca. Série Anthropologie et Archéologie Préhistorique.
       Algiers.
Life . . . . Life Magazine. New York City.
Linn. Soc., Biol. J. . . . . Linnean Society, Biological Journal (formerly Linnean Society
       of London, Journal (Biology)). London.
Linn. Soc., Zool. J. . . . . Linnean Society, Zoological Journal (formerly Linnean Society
       of London, Journal (Zoology)). London.
Lisbon, Univ., Fac. Ciênc., Rev., Sér. 2,
   C (Ciênc. Natur.) . . . . Lisbon, Universidade, Faculdade de Ciências, Revista, Série 2,
       C, Ciências Naturais.
Lisbon, Univ., Fac. Letr., Publ. . . . . Lisbon, Universidade, Faculdade de Letras, Publicações.
Lisbon, Univ., Fac. Letr., Rev., Sér. 3 . . . . Lisbon, Universidade, Faculdade de Letras, Revista, Série 3.
London Univ., Inst. Archaeol., Bull. . . . . London University, Institute of Archaeology, Bulletin.
Loris . . . . Loris. The Journal of the Wildlife Protection Society of
       Ceylon. Colombo.
Los Angeles Cty. Mus., Contrib. Sci. . . . . Los Angeles County Museum, Contributions in Science.
Los Angeles Cty. Mus. Natur. Hist., Sci. Bull. . . Los Angeles County Museum of Natural History, Science
       Bulletin.
Los Angeles Cty. Mus., Quart. . . . . Los Angeles County Museum, Quarterly (Science and History
       Alliance).
Los Angeles Times . . . . Los Angeles Times. Los Angeles, California.
Lutra . . . . Lutra. Orgaan van de Vereniging voor Zoogdierkunde en
       Zoogdierbescherming. Gouda - Leyden.
Lychnos . . . . Lychnos. Stockholm.
Lyons, Fac. Sci., Lab. Géol., Doc. . . . . Lyons, Faculté des Sciences, Laboratoires de Géologie,
       Documents.
McGraw-Hill Yearbook Sci. Tech. . . . . McGraw-Hill Yearbook of Science and Technology. New York
       City.
Maden Tetkik Arama Enst. (Miner. Res. Explor.
   Inst. Turk.), Bull. (Foreign Ed.) . . . . Maden Tetkik ve Arama Enstitüsü (Mineral Research and
       Exploration Institut of Turkey), Bulletin, Foreign Edition.
       Ankara.
Mainzer Naturwiss. Arch. . . . . Mainzer Naturwissenschaftliches Archiv. Mainz.
Mammal. Depicta . . . . Mammalia Depicta. Hamburg and Berlin.

Mammal Soc. Brit. Isles, Bull. . . . . Mammal Society of the British Isles, Bulletin. Birmingham.
Mammalia . . . . Mammalia. Morphologie, Biologie, Systématique des
                                              Mammifères (Paris, Muséum d'Histoire Naturelle. Laboratoire
                                              de Zoologie des Mammifères). Paris.
Man in India . . . . Man in India. A quarterly record of anthropological science
                                              with special reference to India. Ranchi.
Man (J. Roy. Anthropol. Inst.) . . . . Man (Journal of the Royal Anthropological Institute of
                                              Great Britain and Ireland). London.
Manitoba Archaeol. News. . . . . Manitoba Archaeol. Newsletter (Manitoba Archaeological
                                              Society). Winnipeg.
Mankind . . . . Mankind, Journal of the Anthropological Societies of Australia.
                                              Sydney.
Mankind Quart. . . . . The Mankind Quarterly. Edinburgh, Scotland.
Mar del Plata, Mus. Munic. Cienc. Natur., Publ. . . Mar del Plata, Museo Municipal de Ciencias Naturales,
                                              Publicaciones. Mar del Plata, Argentina.
Marit. Sediments . . . . Maritime Sediments. Dalhousie University, Institute of
                                              Oceanography. Halifax, Nova Scotia.
Mass. Univ., Dept. Anthropol., Res. Reps. . . . . Massachusetts University, Department of Anthropology, Research
                                              Reports. Amherst.
Math. Naturwiss. . . . . Mathematik und Naturwissenschaft. Bonn.
Med. Newsmag. . . . . Medical Newsmagazine. New York City.
Mercian Geol. . . . . Mercian Geologist (East Midland Geological Society).
                                              Nottingham, England.
Mexico, Dep. Prehist., Publ. . . . . Mexico, Instituto Nacional de Antropología e Historia,
                                              Departamento de Prehistoria, Publicaciones. Mexico, D.F.
Mexico, Inst. Nac. Antropol. Hist.,
  Ser. Invest. . . . . Mexico, Instituto Nacional de Antropología e Historia, Serie
                                              Investigaciones. Mexico, D.F.
Mexico, Univ. Nac., Cuad. Inst. Hist.,
  Ser. Antropol. . . . . Mexico, Universidad Nacional Autónoma de México, Cuadernos
                                              del Instituto de Historia, Serie Antropológica. Mexico (city).
México, Univ. Nac., Inst. Geol.,
  Paleontol. Mex. . . . . México, Universidad Nacional Autónoma, Instituto de Geología.
                                              Paleontología Mexicana. Mexico City.
Meyniana . . . . Meyniana, Veröffentlichungen aus dem Geologischen Institut
                                              der Universität Kiel. Kiel, Germany.
Mich. Acad. . . . . Michigan Academician. Ann Arbor.
Mich. Acad. Sci., Arts, Lett., Pap. . . . . Michigan Academy of Science, Arts, and Letters, Papers.
                                              Ann Arbor.
Mich. Archaeol. . . . . Michigan Archaeologist. Michigan Archaeological Society.
                                              Ann Arbor.
Mich., State Univ., Mus., Publ., Biol. Ser. . . . . . Michigan, State University, Museum, Publications, Biological
                                              Series. East Lansing.
Mich., Univ., Mus. Paleontol., Contrib. . . . . Michigan, University, Museum of Paleontology, Contributions.
                                              Ann Arbor.
Mich., Univ., Mus. Zool., Occ. Pap. . . . . Michigan, University, Museum of Zoology, Occasional Papers.
                                              Ann Arbor.
Minn., Sci. Mus., Monogr. . . . . Minnesota, Science Museum of Minnesota, Monographs.
                                              St. Paul, Minnesota.
Monaco, Mus. Anthropol. Préhist., Bull. . . . . . Monaco, Musée d'Anthropologie Préhistorique, Bulletin.
Monogr. Biol. . . . . Monographiae Biologicae. Edited by P. Van Oye. The Hague.
Monum. Hist. Budapest. . . . . Monumenta Historica Budapestinensia. Akadémiai Kiadó.
                                              Budapest.
Morocco, Serv. Géol., Notes Mém. . . . . Morocco, Service Géologique, Notes et Mémoires. Rabat.
Mosk. Obshchest. Ispyt. Prir., Biull., Otd. Biol. . . Moskovskoe Obshchestvo Ispytatelei Prirody, Biulleten', Otdel
                                              Biologicheskii. Moscow.
Mosk. Obshchest. Ispyt. Prir., Biull., Otd. Geol. . . Moskovskoe Obshchestvo Ispytatelei Prirody, Biulleten', Otdel
                                              Geologicheskii. Moscow.
Mosk. Univ., Vestn., Ser. Geogr. . . . . Moskovskii Universitet, Vestnik, Seriia 5, Geografiia. Moscow.
Mosk. Univ., Vestn., Ser. Geol. . . . . Moskovskii Universitet, Vestnik, Seriia 4, Geologiia. Moscow.
Munibe . . . . Munibe. Suplemento de Ciencias Naturales del Boletín de la
                                              Real Sociedad Vascongada de Los Amigos del País. Sociedad
                                              de Ciencias Naturales Aranzadi. San Sebastián, Spain.
Münstersche Forsch. Geol. Paläontol. . . . . Münstersche Forschungen zu Geologie und Paläontologie.
                                              Münster.

Mus. Argent. Cienc. Natur. "Bernardino
  Rivadavia", Comun., Geol. . . . . Museo Argentino de Ciencias Naturales "Bernardino Rivadavia" –
    Instituto Nacional de Investigación de las Ciencias Naturales,
    Comunicaciones, Geología. Buenos Aires.

Mus. Argent. Cienc. Natur. "Bernardino
  Rivadavia", Comun., Paleontol. . . . . Museo Argentino de Ciencias Naturales "Bernardino Rivadavia" –
    Instituto Nacional de Investigación de las Ciencias Naturales,
    Comunicaciones, Paleontología. Buenos Aires.

Mus. Argent. Cienc. Natur. "Bernardino
  Rivadavia", Rev., Paleontol. . . . . Museo Argentino de Ciencias Naturales "Bernardino Rivadavia",
    Revista, Paleontología. Buenos Aires.

Mus. Hist. Natur. Marseille, Bull. . . . . Muséum d'Histoire Naturelle de Marseille, Bulletin. Marseille.

Mus. Hist. Natur. Montevideo, Com. Paleontol. . . Museo de Historia Natural de Montevideo, Comunicaciones
    Paleontológicas. Montevideo.

Mus. Hist. Natur. Montevideo, Com. zool. . . . . Museo de Historia Natural de Montevideo. Comunicaciones
    zoológicas. Montevideo.

Mus. Hist. Natur. Nice, Ann. . . . . Muséum d'Histoire Naturelle de Nice, Annales. Nice, France.

Mus. J. . . . . The Museums Journal. Museums Association. London.

Mus. Nat. Hist. Natur., Paris, Arch. . . . . Muséum National d'Histoire Naturelle, Paris, Archives.

Mus. Nat. Hist. Natur., Paris, Bull. . . . . Muséum National d'Histoire Naturelle, Paris, Bulletin.

Mus. Nat. Hist. Natur., Paris, Mém., Sér. C . . . . Muséum National d'Histoire Naturelle, Paris, Mémoires, Série C,
    Sciences de la Terre.

Mus. Nat. Hist. Natur., Paris, Notes Mém. . . . . Muséum National d'Histoire Naturelle, Paris, Notes et Mémoires
    sur le Moyen-Orient.

Mus. News . . . . Museum News. Journal of the American Association of
    Museums. Washington, D.C.

Mus. North. Ariz., Bull. . . . . Museum of Northern Arizona, Bulletin. Flagstaff, Arizona.

Mus. North. Ariz., Tech. Ser. . . . . Museum of Northern Arizona, Technical Series. Flagstaff,
    Arizona.

Mus. Roy. Afr. Cent., Ann., Nouv. Sér. in 4º,
  Sci. Zool. Musée Royal de l'Afrique Centrale, Annales, Nouvelle série in 4º,
    Sciences Zoologiques. Tervuren, Belgium.

Mus. Roy. Afr. Cent., Ann., Sér. in 8º,
  Sci. Géol. Musée Royal de l'Afrique Centrale, Annales. Série in 8º.
    Sciences Géologiques. Tervuren, Belgium.

Mus. Talk . . . . Museum Talk, Santa Barbara, California, Museum of Natural
    History.

Mus., UNESCO . . . . Museum. A quarterly review. Published by UNESCO (United
    Nations Educational, Scientific and Cultural Organization).
    Paris.

Museologist . . . . The Museologist (Rochester Museum of Arts and Sciences).
    Rochester, New York.

N. Mex. Geol. Soc., Guidebk., Field Conf. . . . . New Mexico Geological Society, Guidebook, Field Conference.
    Socorro.

N. Mex. Geol. Soc., Spec. Publ. . . . . New Mexico Geological Society, Special Publication. Soccorro.

N. Mex. Quart. . . . . New Mexico Quarterly. University of New Mexico.
    Albuquerque.

N. Mex., Univ., Publ. Geol. . . . . New Mexico, University, Publications in Geology. Albuquerque.

NSS News . . . . NSS News. National Speleological Society. Trenton,
    New Jersey.

N.Y. Acad. Sci., Ann. . . . . New York Academy of Sciences, Annals. New York City.

N.Y. State Mus. and Sci. Serv., Bull. . . . . New York State Museum and Science Service, Bulletin
    (Supersedes Bull. N.Y. State Mus. Nat. Hist.). Albany.

N.Y. Times . . . . New York Times. New York City.

N.Z. J. Geol. Geophys. . . . . New Zealand Journal of Geology and Geophysics. Wellington.

Nairobi Nat. Mus., Rep. . . . . Nairobi National Museum, Report. Nairobi, Kenya.

Na'pao . . . . Na'pao; a Saskatchewan Anthropology Journal (University of
    Saskatchewan). Saskatoon.

Nat. Acad. Sci., Proc. . . . . National Academy of Sciences, Proceedings. Washington, D.C.

Nat. Geogr. Mag. . . . . National Geographic Magazine. Washington, D.C.

Nat. Geogr. Soc., Res. Reps. . . . . National Geographic Society, Research Reports. Washington,
    D.C.

Nat. Mus. S. Rhodesia, Occas. Pap. . . . . National Museum of Southern Rhodesia, Occasional Papers.
    Bulawayo.

Nat. Sci. Mus., Tokyo, Bull. . . . . National Science Museum, Bulletin. Tokyo.

Nat. Sci. Mus., Tokyo, Mem. . . . . National Science Museum, Memoirs. Tokyo.
Nat. Speleol. Soc., Bull. . . . . National Speleological Society, Bulletin. Arlington, Virginia.
Nat. Wildlife . . . . National Wildlife. Published by the National Wildlife
                                                    Federation. Washington, D.C.
Natur. and Sci. . . . . Nature and Science. The American Museum of Natural
                                                    History. New York City   (Juvenile).
Natur. Belg. Naturalistes Belges. Bulletin mensuel. Brussels.
Natur. Can. . . . . Le Naturaliste Canadien (Université Laval). Quebec.
Natur. Hist. Natural History (American Museum of Natural History,
                                                    Journal). New York City.
Natur Mus. . . . . Natur und Museum. Senckenbergische Naturforschende
                                                    Gesellschaft, Bericht. Frankfurt am Main.
Natur. Sci. and Mus. . . . . Natural Science and Museums. National Science Museum
                                                    (Shizenkagaku to Hakubutsukan). Tokyo.
Natura . . . . Natura, Rivista di Scienze Naturali. Milan.
Natura, Ser. Biol. . . . . Natura, Seria Biologie. Bucharest.
Nature . . . . Nature. London.
Naturen . . . . Naturen. Bergen, Norway.
Naturforsch. Ges. Bamberg, Ber. . . . . Naturforschende Gesellschaft in Bamberg, Bericht. Bamberg.
Naturforsch. Ges. Basel, Verh. . . . . Naturforschende Gesellschaft in Basel, Verhandlungen. Basel.
Naturforsch. Ges. Baselland, Tätigkeitsber. . . . . Naturforschende Gesellschaft Baselland, Tätigkeitsberichte. Basel.
Naturforsch. Ges. Freiburg i. Br., Ber. . . . . . . Naturforschende Gesellschaft zu Freiburg i. Br., Berichte.
                                                    Freiburg.
Naturforsch. Ges. Luzern, Mitt. . . . . Naturforschende Gesellschaft in Luzern, Mitteilungen. Lucerne.
Naturforsch. Ges. Zürich, Vierteljahresschr. . . . Naturforschende Gesellschaft in Zürich, Vierteljahresschrift.
                                                    Zürich.
Naturhist. Ges. Hannover, Ber., Beih. . . . . Naturhistorische Gesellschaft zu Hannover, Bericht, Beihefte.
                                                    Hannover.
Naturhist. Mus. Wien, Ann. . . . . Naturhistorisches Museum in Wien, Annalen. Vienna.
Naturhist. Riksmus. Småskrifter . . . . Naturhistoriska Riksmuseets Småskrifter. Stockholm.
Naturk. Forsch. Südwestdeutschland, Beitr. . . . . Naturkundliche Forschungen Südwestdeutschland, Beiträge.
                                                    Karlsruhe.
Naturk. Jahrb. Linz . . . . Naturkundliches Jahrbuch der Stadt Linz (Stadtmuseum Linz).
                                                    Linz.
Naturk. Mus. "Mauritanium", Abhandl. Ber. . . . . Naturkundliches Museum "Mauritanium", Abhandlungen und
                                                    Berichte. Altenburg, Germany.
Naturwiss. . . . . Naturwissenschaften. Berlin.
Naturwiss. Ges. Bayreuth, Ber. . . . . Naturwissenschaftliche Gesellschaft Bayreuth, Berichte.
                                                    Bayreuth.
Naturwiss. Rundsch. . . . . Naturwissenschaftliche Rundschau. Stuttgart.
Naturwiss. Ver. Bielefeld u. Umgegend, Ber. . . . . Naturwissenschaftlicher Verein für Bielefeld und Umgegend,
                                                    Bericht. Bielefeld.
Naturwiss. Ver. Hamburg, Abh. Verh. . . . . Naturwissenschaftlicher Verein in Hamburg, Abhandlungen und
                                                    Verhandlungen. Hamburg.
Naturwiss. Ver. Schleswig-Holstein, Schr. . . . . . Naturwissenschaftlicher Verein für Schleswig-Holstein, Schriften.
                                                    Kiel.
Naturwiss. Ver. (Würzburg) . . . . Naturwissenschaftlicher Verein, Würzburg.
Natuur Tech. Natuur en Techniek. Tijdschrift voor Natuur, Natuur-
                                                    wetenschappen en Techniek. Deventer, Netherlands.
Natuurhist. Genoot. Limburg, Publ. . . . . Natuurhistorisch Genootschap in Limburg, Publicaties.
                                                    Maastricht.
Natuurwet. Tijdschr. . . . . Natuurwetenschappelijk Tijdschrift. Gent.
Nauch.-Issled. Inst. Geol. Arktiki, Tr. . . . . . . Nauchno-Issledovatel'skiĭ Institut Geologii Arktiki, Trudy.
                                                    Moscow.
Nauch.-Issled. Lab. Geol. Zarubezh. Stran, Tr. . . Ministerstvo Geologii SSSR, Nauchno-Issledovatel'skaiâ
                                                    Laboratoriiâ Geologii Zarubezhnykh Stran, Trudy. Geologiiâ i
                                                    Poleznye Iskopaemye Zarubezhnykh Stran. Leningrad.
Nauchn. Dokl. Vyssh. Shkoly, Biol. Nauki . . . . Nauchnye Doklady Vyssheĭ Shkoly, Biologicheskie Nauki.
                                                    Moscow.
Nauk. Zap. Kremeneťs'k. Derzh. Pedag. Inst. . . . Naukovi Zapysky, Derzhavnyĭ Pedagogichnyĭ Instytut.
                                                    Kremeneťs, URSR.
Nebr. Acad. Sci., Proc. . . . . Nebraska Academy of Science, Proceedings. University of
                                                    Nebraska. Lincoln.
Nebr. Acad. Sci., Trans. . . . . Nebraska Academy of Science, Transaction. University of
                                                    Nebraska. Lincoln.

Nebr. Univ. State Mus., Bull. . . . . Nebraska University. State Museum, Bulletin. Lincoln.
Nebr., Univ., State Mus., Univ. Nebr. News,
  Mus. Notes . . . . Nebraska, University, State Museum, University of Nebraska
                                                     News, Museum Notes. Lincoln.
Ned. Akad. Wetensch., Proc., Ser. B . . . . Koninklijke Nederlandse Akademie van Wetenschappen,
                                                     Proceedings, Series B, Physical Sciences. Amsterdam.
Ned. Akad. Wetensch., Proc., Ser. C . . . . Koninklijke Nederlandse Akademie van Wetenschappen,
                                                     Proceedings, Series C, Biological and Medical Sciences.
                                                     Amsterdam.
Neth., Geol. Dienst, Meded., Ser. C . . . . Netherlands, Rijks Geologische Dienst, Mededelingen, Serie C
                                                     (Continuation of Netherlands, Geologische Stichting,
                                                     Mededelingen, Serie C). Maastricht.
Neue Erlangen . . . . Neue Erlangen. Zeitschrift für Wissenschaft, Wirtschaft und
                                                     Kulturelles Leben. Erlangen, Germany.
Neue Mus. . . . . Neue Museumskunde (DDR, Ministerium für Kultur. Fachstelle
                                                     für Heimatmuseen). Halle.
Neues Jahrb. Geol. Paläontol., Abh. . . . . Neues Jahrbuch für Geologie und Paläontologie, Abhandlungen.
                                                     Stuttgart.
Neues Jahrb. Geol. Paläontol., Monatsh. . . . . . Neues Jahrbuch für Geologie und Paläontologie, Monatshefte.
                                                     Stuttgart.
New Sci. . . . . The New Scientist. New Science Publications. London.
New World Antiq. . . . . New World Antiquity. London.
Newsl. Stratigr. . . . . Newsletters on Stratigraphy. Published by E. J. Brill. Leyden.
Nor. Geol. Tidsskr. . . . . Norsk Geologisk Tidsskrift. Oslo.
Nor. Polarinst., Årbok . . . . Norsk Polarinstitutt, Årbok. Oslo.
Nor. Polarinst. Skr. . . . . Norsk Polarinstitutt, Skrifter. Oslo.
Nor. Vidensk.-Akad. Oslo, Årbok . . . . Norske Videnskaps-Akademi i Oslo, Årbok. Oslo.
Nor. Videsnk.-Akad. Oslo, Mat.-Natur. Kl.,
  Skr., N. Ser. Norske Videnskaps-Akademi i Oslo, Matematisk-Natur-
                                                     videnskapelig Klasse, Skrifter, Ny Serie. Oslo.
Northwest Sci. Northwest Science (Northwest scientific association). Cheney,
                                                     Washington.
Notornis . . . . Notornis, Quarterly Journal of the Ornithological Society of
                                                     New Zealand. Dunedin.
Nova Acta Leopold. . . . . Kaiserliche-Leopoldinische-Carolinische deutsche Akademie der
                                                     Naturforscher. Nova Acta Leopoldina. Leipzig.
Oberösterr. Musealver., Jahrb. . . . . Oberösterreichischer Musealverein, Jahrbuch. Linz, Austria.
Oberrhein. Geol. Ver., Jahresb. Mitt. . . . . Oberrheinischer Geologischer Verein, Jahresberichte und
                                                     Mitteilungen. Stuttgart.
Objets et Mondes . . . . Objets et mondes. La Revue du Musée de l'Homme.
                                                     Muséum National d'Histoire Naturelle. Paris.
Ohio J. Sci. . . . . Ohio Journal of Science. Ohio State University, Columbus.
Okla. Geol. Notes . . . . Oklahoma Geology Notes. Oklahoma Geological Survey,
                                                     Norman.
Okla. Geol. Surv., Circ. . . . . Oklahoma Geological Survey, Circular. University of Oklahoma.
                                                     Norman.
Opera Lilloana . . . . Opera Lilloana. Universidad Nacional de Tucumán. Fundación
                                                     e Instituto Miguel Lillo. Tucumán, Argentina.
Ore Bin . . . . The Ore Bin. Oregon, Department of Geology and Mineral
                                                     Industries. Portland.
Oreg. Acad. Sci., Proc. . . . . Oregon Academy of Sciences, Proceedings. Salem.
Oreg., Dept. Geol. Mineral. Ind., Bull. . . . . . . Oregon, State Department of Geology and Mineral Industries,
                                                     Bulletin. Portland.
Oreg., Univ., Anthropol. Pap. . . . . Oregon, University, Anthropological Papers. Eugene.
Oreg., Univ., Mus. Natur. Hist., Bull. . . . . Oregon, University, Museum of Natural History, Bulletin.
                                                     Eugene.
Oslénytani Viták . . . . Oslénytani Viták. Magyarhoni Földtani Társulat [Hungarian
                                                     Geol. Soc.]. Budapest.
Österreich. Akad. Wiss., Math.-Naturwiss. Kl.,
  Abt. I, Sitz.-Ber. . . . . Österreichische Akademie der Wissenschaften, Mathematisch-
                                                     Naturwissenschaftliche Klasse, Abteilung I. Sitzungsberichte.
                                                     Vienna.
Österreich. Akad. Wiss., Math.-Naturwiss.
  Kl., Anz. . . . . Österreichische Akademie der Wissenschaften, Mathematisch-
                                                     Naturwissenschaftliche Klasse, Anzeiger. Vienna.

Österreich. Akad. Wiss., Denk. . . . . Österreichische Akademie der Wissenschaften, Mathematisch-
Naturwissenschaftliche Klasse, Denkschriften. Vienna.

Österreich. Arbeitsgemeinsch. Ur- und
Frühgesch., Mitt. . . . . Österreichische Arbeitsgemeinschaft für Ur- und Frühgeschichte,
Mitteilungen. Vienna.

Ostrich . . . . The Ostrich. The Journal of the South African Ornithological
Society. Cape Town.

Pac. Discovery . . . . Pacific Discovery (California Academy of Sciences).
San Francisco.

Padua, Univ., Ist. Geol. Miner., Mem. . . . . Padua, Università. Istituto di Geologia e Mineralogia. Memorie.

Palaeogeogr. Palaeoclimatol. Palaeoecol. . . . . . . Palaeogeography, Palaeoclimatology, Palaeoecology; An International Journal for the Geo-Sciences. Amsterdam: Elsevier
Publ. Co.

Palaeontogr. Ital. . . . . Palaeontographia Italica. Pisa.

Palaeontographica, Abt. A . . . . Palaeontographica, Abteilung A, Paläozoologie-Stratigraphie.
Stuttgart.

Palaeontol. Afr. Palaeontologia Africana, Annals of the Bernhard Price
Institute for Palaeontological Research, University of the
Witwatersrand. Johannesburg.

Palaeontol. Jugoslav. . . . . Palaeontologia Jugoslavica. Jugoslavenska Akademija Znanosti i
Umjetnosti. Razred za Prirodne Nauke. Zagreb.

Palaeontol. Polonica . . . . Palaeontologia Polonica. Warsaw.

Palaeontol. Soc. Jap., Trans. Proc. . . . . Palaeontological Society of Japan, Transaction and Proceedings.
Tokyo.

Palaeontol. Z. Palaeontologische Zeitschrift. Stuttgart.

Palaeontology . . . . Palaeontology (Palaeontological Association). London.

Palaeovertebrata (Montpellier) . . . . Palaeovertebrata (Montpellier, Faculté des Sciences-Société
Méridionale pour l'Expansion de la Recherche Scientifique).
Montpellier.

Paläontol. Abh., Abt. A . . . . Paläontologische Abhandlungen, Abteilung A: Paläozoologie.
Deutsche Gesellschaft für Geologische Wissenschaften. Berlin.

PaleoBios . . . . PaleoBios. Contributions from the University of California
Museum of Paleontology, Berkeley.

Paleoecologia . . . . Paleoecologia (Departamento de Prehistoria, Instituto Nacional
de Antropologia e Historia). Mexico.

Paleontol. J. . . . . Paleontological Journal. A translation of Paleontologicheskiĭ
Zhurnal. American Geological Institute. Washington, D.C.

Paleontol. Sb. Paleontologicheskiĭ Sbornik. L'vov, URSR.

Paleontol. Stratigr. Pribalt. Belorus. . . . . Paleontologiiā i Stratigrafiiā Pribaltiki i Belorussii (Ministerstvo
Geologii SSSR, Institut Geologii (Vil'niŭs), Institut
Geologicheskikh Nauk (Minsk), Institut Geologii (Riga)).
Vil'niŭs, Lit. SSR: "Mintis" Press.

Paleontol. Zh. Paleontologicheskiĭ Zhurnal (Akademiiā Nauk SSSR). Moscow.

Pavia, Univ., Ist. Geol., Atti . . . . Pavia, Università, Istituto Geologico, Atti.

Pearce-Sellards Ser., Texas Mem. Mus. . . . . Pearce-Sellards series, Texas Memorial Museum, University of
Texas. Austin.

Penn ar Bed . . . . Penn ar Bed (Societé pour l'Étude et la Protection de la
Nature en Bretagne). Brest, France.

Pernambuco, Univ. Fed., Inst. Geociênc., Sér. B . . Pernambuco, Universidade Federal, Instituto de Geociências,
Série B: Estudos e Pesquisas. Recife, Brazil.

Perspect. Biol. Med. . . . . Perspectives in Biology and Medicine. University of Chicago
Press. Chicago.

Peshchery . . . . Peshchery [Caves], Permskiĭ Gosudarstvennyĭ Universitet, Perm'
(Formerly Speleologicheskiĭ Biulleten').

Peshchery Gruzii . . . . Peshchery Gruzii. Akademiiā Nauk Gruzinskoĭ SSR.
Speleologicheskaiā Komissiiā. Tiflis.

Petrol. Explor. Soc. Libya,
10th Ann. Field Conf. . . . . Petroleum Exploration Society of Libya, 10th Annual Field
Conference, 1968, Guidebook. F. T. Barr, ed. Amsterdam:
Holland-Breumelhaf N.V.

Phila., Acad. Natur. Sci., Monogr. . . . . Philadelphia, Academy of Natural Sciences, Monographs.

Plains Anthropol. . . . . Plains Anthropologist, Journal of the Plains Conference.
Lawrence, Kansas.

Plaster Jacket . . . . The Plaster-Jacket. Florida State Museum, University of
Florida, Gainesville.

Plateau . . . . Plateau, Quarterly of the Museum of Northern Arizona.
Flagstaff.

Poeyana, Ser. A. . . . . Poeyana, Series A. La Habana, Cuba.
Poitiers, Univ., Inst. Géol. Anthropol. Préhist.,
    Trav. . . . . Poitiers, Université, Institut de Géologie et d'Anthropologie
        Préhistorique, Travaux. France.
Pol. Akad. Nauk, Bull., Ser. Sci. Géol. Géogr. . . Polska Akademia Nauk, Bulletin. Série des Sciences
        Géologiques et Géographiques. Warsaw.
Port., Serv. Geol., Comun. . . . . Portugal Serviços Geológicos, Comunicações. Lisbon.
Port., Serv. Geol., Mem. . . . . Portugal, Serviços Geológicos, Memórias. Lisbon.
Porto Alegre, Escol. Geol., Notas Estud. . . . . . Porto Alegre, Universidade Federal do Rio Grande do Sul,
        Escola de Geologia, Notas e Estudos. Brazil.
Postilla . . . . Postilla (Yale Peabody Museum of Natural History).
        New Haven, Connecticut.
Prague, Národ. Muz., Čas. Odd. Přírod. . . . . . . Prague, Národni Muzeum, Časopis, Oddíl Přírodovědný.
Prague, Sborn. Národ. Muz. Praze, Rada B . . . . Prague, Národni Muzeum, Sborník (Acta Musei Nationalis
        Pragae), Rada B, Přírodovědný.
Prehist. Soc., Proc. . . . . Prehistoric Society, Proceedings. London.
Préhist. Spéléol. Ariége. . . . . Préhistoire [et] Spéléologie Ariégeoises. Société Préhistorique
        de l'Ariège, Bulletin. Etudes Préhistoriques Pyrénéennes.
        Pamiers, France.
Présence Normande . . . . Présence Normande. Rouen, France.
Priroda . . . . Priroda (Akademiia Nauk SSSR). Moscow.
Priroda (Zagreb) . . . . Priroda. Časopis Hrvatskog prirodoslovnog društva. Zagreb.
Prirodn. Obstan. i Fauny Proshl. . . . . Prirodnaia Obstanovka i Fauny Proshlogo, Institut Zoologii,
        Akademiia Nauk Ukrainskoĭ SSR. Kiev.
Provence, Univ., Ann., Sci. . . . . Université de Provence, Annales, Sciences. Marseilles.
Przegl. Antropol. . . . . Przegląd Antropologiczny. Poznań.
Przegl. Geol. Przegląd Geologiczny. Warsaw.
Przegl. Zool. Przegląd Zoologiczny. Wrocław.
Publicatie Reeks . . . . Publicatie Reeks. Netherlands.
Punjab Univ., Res. Bull., Sci. . . . . Punjab University, Research Bulletin, Science. Chandigarh,
        India.
Quarry Mine and Pit . . . . Quarry Mine and Pit. Australia.
Quart. Rev. Biol. . . . . Quarterly Review of Biology. Baltimore, Maryland.
Quartär . . . . Quartär; Jahrbuch für Erforschung des Eiszeitalters und der
        Steinzeit (Hugo Obermaier-Gesellschaft). Bonn.
Quaternaria . . . . Quaternaria. Rome.
Quaternary Res. . . . . Quaternary Research (an Interdisciplinary Journal). New York,
        London.
Queensl. Mus., Mem. . . . . Queensland Museum, Memoirs. Brisbane.
Res. Inst. Natur. Resour. (Tokyo), Misc. Rep. . . Research Institute for Natural Resources, Miscellaneous Reports.
        Tokyo.
Resp. Physiol. . . . . Respiration Physiology. Amsterdam.
Rev. de Menorca . . . . Revista de Menorca. Ateneo científico literario y artístico de
        Mahón. Mahón.
Rev. Gén. Belge . . . . Revue Générale Belge. Brussels.
Rev. Géogr. Phys. Géol. Dyn. . . . . Revue de Géographie Physique et de Géologie Dynamique.
        Paris.
Rev. Haute-Auvergne . . . . Revue de la Haute-Auvergne (Société des lettres, sciences et
        arts de "la Haute-Auvergne"). Aurillac, France.
Rev. Quest. Sci. . . . . Revue des Questions Scientifiques (Société Scientifique de
        Bruxelles). Louvain.
Rev. Roum. Géol., Géophys., Géogr., Sér. Géol. . . Revue Roumaine de Géologie, Géophysique, et Géographie,
        Série de Géologie. Bucharest.
Rev. Sci. Natur. Auvergne . . . . Revue des Sciences Naturelles D'Auvergne. Publiée par la
        Société d'Histoire Naturelle D'Auvergne. Clermont-Ferrand,
        France.
Rev. Suisse Zool. . . . . Revue Suisse de Zoologie. Annales de la Société Zoologique
        Suisse et du Muséum d'Histoire Naturelle de Genève. Geneva.
Rev. Zool. Bot. Afr. . . . . Revue de Zoologie et de Botanique Africaines (Cercle
        zoologique congolais). Brussels.
Rhein. Naturforsch. Ges., Z. . . . . Rheinische Naturforschende Gesellschaft, Zeitschrift. Mainz.
Rio de Janeiro, Univ. Fed., Inst. Geociênc.,
    Bol., Geol. . . . . Universidade Federal do Rio de Janeiro, Instituto de
        Geociências, Boletim, Geologia. Rio de Janeiro.
Riv. Antropol. . . . . Rivista di Antropologia. Atti della Societa Romana di
        Antropologia. Rome.

Riv. Ital. Paleontol. Stratigr. . . . . Rivista Italiana di Paleontologia e Stratigrafia. Milan.
Riv. Sci. Preist. . . . . Rivista di Scienze Preistoriche. Florence.
Rocks Miner. . . . . Rocks and Minerals. Peekskill, New York.
Rom., Inst. Geol., Dări . . . . Romania, Comitetul de Stat al Geologiei, Institutul Geologic,
    Dări de Seamă ale şedinţelor. Bucharest.
Rom., Inst. Geol., Stud. Teh. Econ., Ser. J. . . . . Romania, Institutul Geologic, Studii Tehnice şi Economice,
    Seria J, Stratigrafie. Bucharest.
Rotunda . . . . Rotunda, the bulletin of The Royal Ontario Museum. Toronto.
Roy. Scottish Mus., Inform. Ser., Geol. . . . . . . Royal Scottish Museum, Information Series. Geology.
    Edinburgh.
Roy. Soc. Edinburgh, Trans. . . . . (The) Royal Society of Edinburgh, Transactions. Edinburgh.
Roy. Soc. London, Biogr. Mem. . . . . Royal Society of London, Biographical Memoirs. London.
Roy. Soc. London, Phil. Trans., Ser. B . . . . . . Royal Society of London, Philosophical Transactions, Series B,
    Biological Sciences. London.
Roy. Soc. Med., Proc. . . . . Royal Society of Medicine, Proceedings. London.
Roy. Soc. N.S.W., J. Proc. . . . . Royal Society of New South Wales, Journal and Proceedings.
    Sydney.
Roy. Soc. N.Z., J. . . . . Royal Society of New Zealand, Journal. Wellington.
Roy. Soc. S. Austral., Trans. . . . . Royal Society of South Australia, Transactions. Adelaide.
Roy. Soc. Victoria, Proc. . . . . Royal Society of Victoria. Proceedings. Melbourne.
Roy. Soc. West. Austral., J. . . . . Royal Society of Western Australia, Journal. Perth.
Ruse, Bulg., Nar. Muz., Izv. . . . . Ruse, Bulgaria, Okruzhen Naroden Muzei, Izvestiia. Varna.
S. Afr. Archaeol. Bull. . . . . The South African Archaeological Bulletin. Published by the
    South African Archaeological Society, Cape Town.
S. Afr. J. Sci. . . . . South African Journal of Science. Cape Town.
S. Afr. Mus., Ann. South African Museum, Annals. Cape Town.
S. Afr. Mus. Ass., Bull. . . . . South African Museums Association, Bulletin. Cape Town.
S. Austral. Mus., Rec. . . . . South Australian Museum, Records. Adelaide.
S. Calif. Acad. Sci., Bull. . . . . Southern California Academy of Sciences, Bulletin.
    Los Angeles.
S. Calif. Paleontol. Soc., Bull. . . . . Southern California Paleontological Society, Bulletin.
    Los Angeles.
S. Dak. Acad. Sci., Proc. . . . . South Dakota Academy of Science. Proceedings. Vermillion.
S. Dak. Geol. Surv., Circ. . . . . South Dakota Geological Survey, Circular. Vermillion.
S. Dak. Geol. Surv., Guidebk. . . . . South Dakota Geological Survey, Guidebook. Vermillion.
S. Dak. Geol. Surv., Rep. . . . . South Dakota Geological Survey, Reports of Investigations.
    Vermillion.
Saito Ho-on Kai Mus., Res. Bull. . . . . Saito Ho-on Kai Museum, Research Bulletin. Sendai, Japan.
Salamandra . . . . Salamandra. Herausgegeben von der Deutchen Gesellshaft für
    Herpetologie und Terrarienkunde. Frankfurt am Main.
Salvage Archeol. Smithson. Inst., Publ. . . . . . . Salvage Archeology, Smithsonian Institution, Publications. River
    Basin Surveys. Washington, D.C.
Sammelgr. Geschiebek., Mitt. . . . . Sammelgruppe für Geschiebekunde, Mitteilungen. Hamburg.
San Diego Soc. Natur. Hist., Trans. . . . . San Diego Society of Natural History, Transactions. San Diego,
    California.
San Francisco Chron. . . . . San Francisco Chronicle. San Francisco, California.
São Paulo, Univ., Inst. Geociên. Astron., Bol. . . São Paulo, Universidade, Instituto de Geociências e Astronomia,
    Boletim.
Saragossa, Univ., Fac. Fil. Let., Dept. Prehist.
  Arqueol., Monogr. Arqueol. . . . . Saragossa, Universidad, Facultad de Filosofía y Letras,
    Departamento de Prehistoria y Arqueología, Monografías
    Arqueológicas.
Sarajevo, Zemaljski Muz., Glasnik, Arheol. . . . . Sarajevo, Zemaljski Muzej, Glasnik, Arheologija, Nova Serija.
    Yugoslavia.
Sarawak Mus. J. . . . . The Sarawak Museum Journal. Kuching, Sarawak.
Säugetierkundl. Mitt. . . . . Säugetierkundliche Mitteilungen. Stuttgart.
Schriftenr. OÖ. Musealv. . . . . Schriftenreihe des Oberösterreichschen Musealvereins. Linz.
Schweiz. Ges. Urgesch., Jahrb. . . . . Schweizerische Gesellschaft für Ur- und Frühgeschichte,
    Jahrbuch. Basel.
Schweiz. Paläontol. Abh. - Mém. Suisses
  Paléontol. . . . . Schweizerische Paläontologische Abhandlungen - Mémoires Suisses
    de Paléontologie. Basel.
Sci. Abstr. China, Earth Sci. . . . . Science Abstracts of China, Earth Sciences (Institut of
    Scientific and Technical Information of China). Peking.
Sci. Amer. . . . . Scientific American. New York.

Sci. Avenir . . . . Sciences et Avenir. Paris.

Sci. Culture . . . . Science and Culture; a Monthly Journal devoted to Natural and Cultural Sciences. Calcutta.

Sci. J. . . . . Science Journal. London.

Sci. Man . . . . Science of Man. National Association of Local Anthropology Clubs. Mentone, California.

Sci. News . . . . Science News. Washington, D.C. (Formerly Science News Letter.)

Sci. on the March . . . . Science on the March. Buffalo Society of Natural Sciences. Buffalo, New York.

Sci. Progr. . . . . Science Progress. Oxford, London, Edinburgh, Melbourne: Blackwell Scientific Publications.

Sci. Progr. Découverte . . . . Science Progrès Découverte. Paris (Formerly Science Progrès La Nature.)

Sci. Progr., Nature (Paris) . . . . Science Progrès, La Nature. Paris (Formerly La Nature.)

Sci. Record, New Ser. . . . . Science Record, New Series. Academia Sinica. Peking.

Sci. S. Afr. . . . . Scientific South Africa. Johannesburg.

Science (AAAS) . . . . Science (American Association for the Advancement of Science). Washington, D.C.

Sciences . . . . Sciences. Revue française des Sciences et des Techniques. Paris.

Scientia . . . . Scientia (Rivista di Scienza). Milan.

Scot. J. Geol. . . . . Scottish Journal of Geology. Edinburgh.

Screenings . . . . Screenings. Oregon Archaeological Society. Portland, Oregon.

Scripta Geol. . . . . Scripta Geologica. Rijksmuseum van Geologie en Mineralogie. Leiden, Netherland.

Sea Front. . . . . Sea Frontiers. Miami University, Coral Gables, Fla., Marine Laboratory. Miami, Florida.

Senckenbergiana Biol. . . . . Senckenbergiana Biologica. Wissenschaftliche Mitteilungen der Senckenbergischen Naturforschenden Gesellschaft. Frankfurt am Main.

Senckenbergiana Lethaea . . . . Senckenbergiana Lethaea (Senckenbergische Naturforschende Gesellschaft, Wissenschaftliche Mitteilungen). Frankfurt am Main.

Sev.-Kavkaz. Neft. Nauch.-Issled. Inst., Tr.   . . . . Severo-Kavkazskiĭ Neftianoĭ Nauchno-Issledovatel'skiĭ Institut, Trudy. Moscow.

Sevilla, Univ., Publ. . . . . Sevilla, Universidad de Sevilla, Publicaciones del Seminario de Antropología Americana. Spain.

Shinshu Univ., Fac. Sci., J. . . . . Shinshu University, Faculty of Science, Journal. Matsumoto, Japan.

Shūkan Asahi . . . . Shūkan Asahi [Asahi weekly]. Tokyo.

Skopje, Prirodonauč. Muz., Posebno Izd. . . . . . . Skopje, Prirodonaučen Muzej, Posebno Izdanie. Yugoslavia.

Slovenska Archeol. . . . . Slovenská Archeológia (Slovenská Akadémia Vied). Bratislava, Czekoslovakia.

Smithson. Contrib. Anthropol. . . . . Smithsonian Contributions to Anthropology. Washington, D.C.

Smithson. Contrib. Paleobiol.   . . . . Smithsonian Contributions to Paleobiology. Washington, D.C. Smithsonian Institution Press.

Smithson. Contrib. Zool. . . . . Smithsonian Contributions to Zoology. Washington, D.C.

Smithson. Inst., Smithson. Misc. Coll. . . . . Smithsonian Institution, Smithsonian Miscellaneous Collections. Washington, D.C.

Smithson. Year . . . . Smithsonian Year (Formerly: Annual Report of the Smithsonian Institution. As of 1965 issue includes all U.S. National Museum reports.) Washington, D.C.

Smolensk. Gos. Pedag. Inst., Uch. Zap.   . . . . . . Smolenskiĭ Gosudarstvennyĭ Pedagogicheskiĭ Institut, Uchenye Zapiski. Smolensk, USSR.

Soc. Anthropol. Paris, Bull. Mém.   . . . . Société d'Anthropologie de Paris, Bulletins et Mémoires. Paris.

Soc. Archéol. Hist. Charente, Mém.   . . . . Société Archéologique et Historique de la Charente, Mémoires. Angoulême, France.

Soc. Belge Géol. Paléontol. Hydrol., Bull. . . . . . . Société Belge de Géologie, de Paléontologie et d'Hydrologie, Bulletin. Brussels.

Soc. Bibliogr. Natur. Hist., J.   . . . . Society for the Bibliography of Natural History, Journal. London.

Soc. Biogéogr., C. R. . . . . Société de Biogéographie, Comptes Rendus. Paris.

Soc. Brasil. Geol., Bol.   . . . . Sociedade Brasileira de Geología, Boletim. São Paulo.

Soc. Cienc. Natur. Jalisco A.C., Bol.   . . . . Sociedad de Ciencias Naturales de Jalisco, A.C., Boletin. Jalisco, Mexico.

Soc. Écol., Bull.   . . . . Société Écologique, Bulletin. France.

Soc. Españ. Hist. Natur., Bol., Secc. Biol. .... Real Sociedad Española de Historia Natural, Boletín, Sección Biologica. Madrid.

Soc. Españ. Hist. Natur., Bol., Secc. Geol. .... Real Sociedad Española de Historia Natural, Boletín, Sección Geológica. Madrid.

Soc. Étud. Sci. Angers, Bull. . . . . Société d'Études Scientifiques d'Angers, Bulletin. Angers, France.

Soc. Géol. Fr., Bull. . . . . Société Géologique de France, Bulletin. Paris.

Soc. Géol. Fr., C. R. . . . . Société Géologique de France, Compte rendu sommaire des Séances. Paris.

Soc. Géol. Fr., Mém. . . . . Société Géologique de France, Mémoires. Paris.

Soc. Geol. Ital., Boll. . . . . Società Geologica Italiana, Bollettino. Roma.

Soc. Geol. Ital., Mem. . . . . Società Geologica Italiana, Memorie. Pisa.

Soc. Geol. Mex., Bol. . . . . Sociedad Geológica Mexicana, Boletin. Mexico.

Soc. Géol. Nord, Ann. . . . . Société Géologique du Nord, Annales. Lille, France.

Soc. Geol. Port., Bol. . . . . Sociedade Geológica de Portugal, Boletim. Lisbon.

Soc. Hist. Archéol. Périgord, Bull. . . . . Société Historique et Archéologique du Périgord, Bulletin. Périgueux, France.

Soc. Hist. Natur. Amis Mus., Autun.,
  Bull. (L'Eduen) . . . . Société d'Histoire Naturelle et Amis du Muséum, Bulletin Trimestriel (L'Eduen). Autun, France.

Soc. Hist. Natur. Ardennes, Bull. . . . . Société d'Histoire Naturelle des Ardennes, Bulletin. Charleville.

Soc. Hist. Natur. Baleares, Bol. . . . . Sociedad de Historia Natural de Baleares, Boletin. Palma de Mallorca.

Soc. Hist. Natur. Doubs . . . . Société d'Histoire Naturelle du Doubs. France.

Soc. Hist. Natur. Toulouse, Bull. . . . . Société d'Histoire Naturelle de Toulouse, Bulletin. Toulouse.

Soc. Hort. Hist. Natur. Hérault, Ann. . . . . Société d'Horticulture et d'Histoire Naturelle de l'Hérault, Annales. Montpellier.

Soc. Ital. Miner. Petrologia, Rend. . . . . Società Italiana di Mineralogia e Petrologia, Rendiconti. Milan.

Soc. Linn. Bordeaux, Actes, Sér. B . . . . Société Linnéenne de Bordeaux, Actes, Série B. Bordeaux.

Soc. Linn. Bordeaux, Bull. . . . . Société Linnéenne de Bordeaux. Bulletin. Bordeaux.

Soc. Linn. Lyon, Bull. . . . . Société Linnéenne de Lyon, Bulletin mensuel. Lyon.

Soc. Linn. Normandie, Bull. . . . . Société Linnéenne de Normandie, Bulletin. Caen, France.

Soc. Paleontol. Ital., Boll. . . . . Società Paleontologica Italiana, Bollettino. Modena.

Soc. Phys. Hist. Natur. Genève, C. R. . . . . Société de Physique et d'Histoire Naturelle de Genève, Compte Rendu des Séances. Geneva.

Soc. Préhist. Fr., Bull., C. R. . . . . Société Préhistorique Française, Bulletin, Comptes Rendus des Séances Mensuelles. Paris.

Soc. Préhist. Fr., Bull., Étud. Trav. . . . . Société Préhistorique Française, Bulletin, Études et Travaux. Paris.

Soc. Préhist. Fr., Mém. . . . . Société Préhistorique Française, Mémoires. Paris.

Soc. Roy. Belge Anthropol. Préhist., Bull. .... Société Royale Belge d'Anthropologie et de Préhistoire, Bulletin. Brussels.

Soc. Sci. Fennica, Comment. Biol. . . . . Societas Scientiarum Fennica, Commentationes Biologicae. Helsinki.

Soc. Sci. Natur. Phys., Maroc, Bull. . . . . Société des Sciences Naturelles et Physiques du Maroc, Bulletin. Rabat.

Soc. Spéléol. Préhist. Bordeaux, Bull. . . . . Société de Spéléologie et Préhistoire de Bordeaux, Bulletin. Bordeaux.

Soc. Ştiinţ. Geol. R. S. R., Bul. . . . . Societaţea de Ştiinţe Geologice din R. S. România, Buletinul. Bucharest.

Soc. Toscana Sci. Natur., Atti, Mem., Ser. A . . . Società Toscana di Scienze Naturali, Atti, Memorie, Serie A. Pisa.

Soc. Vaudoise Sci. Natur., Bull. . . . . Société Vaudoise des Sciences Naturelles, Bulletin. Lausanne.

Soc. Vert. Paleontol., News Bull. . . . . Society of Vertebrate Paleontology, News Bulletin. New Haven, Connecticut.

Soc. Zool. Fr., Bull. . . . . Société Zoologique de France, Bulletin. Paris.

Sof. Univ., Geol.-Geogr. Fak., God. . . . . Sofiĭskiiă Universitet, Geologo-Geografski Fakultet, Godishnik. Sofia, Bulgaria.

Soobshch. Gosud. Ermitazha . . . . Soobshcheniiă Gosudarstvennogo Ordena Lenina Ermitazha. Leningrad-Moscow.

Southeast. Geol. . . . . Southeastern Geology. Duke University. Durham, North Carolina.

Southwest. J. Anthropol. . . . . Southwestern Journal of Anthropology. Albuquerque, New Mexico.

Southwest. Natur. . . . . The Southwestern Naturalist. Lubbock, Texas.

Sov. Arkheol. . . . . Sovetskai͡a Arkheologii͡a. Akademii͡a Nauk SSSR, Institut Arkheologii. Moscow.

Sov. Etnogr. . . . . Sovetskai͡a Etnografii͡a, Akademii͡a Nauk SSSR. Leningrad.

Sov. Geol. . . . . Sovetskai͡a Geologii͡a. Moscow.

Sovm. Sovet.-Mongol. Nauch.-Issled.
  Geol. Eksped., Tr. . . . . Sovmestnai͡a Sovetsko-Mongol'skai͡a Nauchno-Issledovatel'skai͡a Geologicheskai͡a Ekspedit͡sii͡a, Trudy. Moscow.

Spec. Pap. Palaeontol. . . . . Special Papers in Palaeontology. Palaeontological Association, London.

Spelaion Carso . . . . Spelaion Carso. France.

Speleo Digest . . . . Speleo Digest. A collection of speleological writings taken from the publications of the Chapters of the National Speleological Society, Inc. Vienna, Virginia.

Speléon . . . . Speléon. Revista Española de Hidrologia, Morfologia Cárstica, Espeleología y Cuaternario. Oviedo.

Spolia Zeylanica . . . . Spolia Zeylanica. Bulletin of the National Museums of Ceylon. Colombo.

St. Paul Inst., Sci. Mus., Sci. Publ., New Ser. . . Saint Paul Institute, Science Museum, Scientific Publications, New Series. Saint Paul, Minnesota.

Stud. Anthropol. . . . . Studies in Anthropology. University of Kentucky Press, Lexington.

Stud. Cercet. Geol., Geofiz., Geogr., Ser. Geol. . . Studii şi Cercetări de Geologie, Geofizică, Geografie, Seria Geologie (Academia Republicii Socialiste România). Bucharest.

Stud. Geol. Pol. . . . . Studia Geologica Polonica. Polska Akademia Nauk. Zaklad Nauk Geologicznykh. Warsaw.

Stud. Speleol. . . . . Studies in Speleology (Association of the Pengelly Cave Research Centre). London.

Stuttgarter Beitr. Naturk. . . . . Stuttgarter Beiträge zur Naturkunde. Stuttgart.

Sunset . . . . Sunset Magazine. San Francisco, California.

Sverdlovsk, SSSR, Ural. Gos. Univ.,
  Uch. Zap. . . . . Sverdlovsk, SSSR, Ural'skiĭ Gosudarstvennyĭ Universitet, Uchenye Zapiski.

Svet Vedy . . . . Svet Vedy (Slovenska Akademia Vied). Bratislava, Czekoslovakia.

Syesis . . . . Syesis. British Columbia Provincial Museum. Victoria.

Syst. Zool. . . . . Systematic Zoology (Society of Systematic Zoology). Lawrence, Kansas.

Tashkent, Univ., Nauch. Tr. . . . . Tashkent, Universitet, Nauchnye Trudy. USSR.

Taxon . . . . Taxon, Journal of the International Association for Plant Taxonomy. Utrecht, Netherland.

Tebiwa . . . . Tebiwa. Journal of the Idaho State University Museum. Pocatello.

Tenn. Archaeol. . . . . Tennessee Archaeologist (Tennessee Archaeological Society). Knoxville.

Teruel . . . . Teruel. Instituto de Estudios Turolenses. Teruel, Spain.

Tex. Archeol. Soc., Bull. . . . . Texas Archeological Society, Bulletin. Dallas.

Tex. J. Sci. . . . . Texas Journal of Science (Texas Academy of Science). San Marcos.

Tex. Mem. Mus., Bull. . . . . Texas Memorial Museum Bulletin. Austin.

Tex. Tech. Univ., Mus., Occas. Pap. . . . . Texas Technical University, Museum, Occasional Papers. Lubbock.

Theol. Phil. . . . . Theologie und Philosophie. Freiburg im Breisgau (Called Scholastik until 1965.)

Time . . . . Time Magazine. New York City.

Tiraspol', Gos. Pedagog. Inst., Uch. Zap. . . . . . Tiraspol', Gosudarstvennyĭ Pedagogicheskiĭ Institut, Uchenye Zapiski. USSR.

Tohoku Univ., Sci. Rep., Ser. 2 . . . . Tohoku University, Science Reports, Series 2, Geology. Sendai, Japan.

Toimetised Eesti NSV Tead. Akad., Ser. Biol. . . . Eesti NSV Teaduste Akademia Toimetised, Series Bioloogia. Tallinn.

Tokyo Gakugei Univ., Bull., Ser. 4 . . . . Tokyo Gakugei University, Bulletin, Series 4: Mathematics, Physics, Chemistry, Biology, Astronomy, and Earth Sciences.

Tomsk, Politekh. Inst., Izv. . . . . Tomsk, Politekhnicheskiĭ Institut, Izvestii͡a. USSR.

Toronto, Roy. Ont. Mus., Life Sci., Contrib. . . . . Toronto, Royal Ontario Museum, Life Sciences, Contributions.

Toronto, Roy. Ont. Mus., Life Sci. Occas. Pap. . . . Toronto, Royal Ontario Museum, Life Sciences, Occasional Papers.

Totem Pole . . . . The Totem Pole. Bulletin of the Aboriginal Research Club. Detroit, Michigan.

Toulouse, Univ., Inst. d'Art Préhist., Trav. . . . . Toulouse, Université, Institut d'Art Préhistorique, Travaux (Faculté des Lettres).

Trans-Antarctic Exped. 1955-58, Sci. Rep. . . . . Trans-Antarctic Expedition, 1955-1958, Scientific Reports. London.

Transvaal Mus., Ann. . . . . Transvaal Museum, Annals. Pretoria, S. Africa.

Trieste, Mus. Civ. Storia Natur., Atti . . . . Trieste, Museo Civico di Storia Naturale, Atti.

Tuatara . . . . Tuatara (Journal of the Biological Society, Victoria University of Wellington). New Zealand.

Tulane Stud. Geol. Paleontol. . . . . Tulane Studies in Geology and Paleontology (Tulane University). New Orleans, Louisiana.

Tunisia, Serv. Géol., Notes . . . . Tunisia, Service Géologique, Notes. Tunis.

Türk Tarih Kurumu, Bell. . . . . Türk Tarih Kurumu, Belleten. Ankara.

U.N., Econ. Comm. Asia Far East,
   Miner. Resour. Develop. Ser. . . . . United Nations, Economic Commission for Asia and the Far East, Mineral Resources Development Series. New York City.

UNESCO (Int. Soc. Sci. J.) . . . . UNESCO (International Social Science Journal). Paris.

U.S. Geol. Surv., Bull. . . . . U.S. Geological Survey, Bulletin. Washington, D.C.

U.S. Geol. Surv., Prof. Paper . . . . U.S. Geological Survey, Professional Papers. Washington, D.C.

U.S. Nat. Mus., Ann. Rept. . . . . U.S. National Museum, Annual Report. See Smithsonian Year.

U.S. Nat. Mus., Bull. . . . . U.S. National Museum, Bulletin. Washington, D.C.

Uganda J. . . . . The Uganda Journal. Kampala.

Umsch. Wiss. Tech. . . . . Umschau in Wissenschaft und Technik. Frankfurt am Main.

Univ. Nac. Litoral, Inst. Fisiogr. Geol., Publ. . . . . Universidad Nacional del Litoral, Facultad de Ciencias, Ingeniería y Arquitectura, Instituto de Fisiografía y Geología, Publicaciones. Rosario, Argentina.

Uppsala, Univ., Geol. Inst., Bull. . . . . Uppsala, University, Geological Institutions, Bulletin. Sweden.

Ural. Univ., Uch. Zap. . . . . Ural'skiĭ Gosudarstvennyĭ Universitet, Uchenye Zapiski. Sverdlovsk, USSR.

Uzbek. Biol. Zh. Uzbekskiĭ Biologicheskiĭ Zhurnal. Akademiía Nauk Uzbekskoĭ SSR. Tashkent.

Uzbek. Geol. Zh. Uzbekskiĭ Geologicheskiĭ Zhurnal. Akademiía Nauk Uzbekskoĭ SSR . Tashkent.

Valparaiso, Mus. Hist. Natur., An. . . . . Valparaiso, Museo de Historia Natural, Anales. Chile.

Vår Fågelvärld . . . . Vår Fågelvärld. Utgiven av Sveriges Ornitologiska Förening. Stockholm.

Ver. Freunde Univ. Mainz, Jahrb. . . . . Verein "Freunde der Universität Mainz", Jahrbuch. Mainz.

Ver. Vaterländ Naturk. Württemberg, Jahresh. . . Verein für Vaterländische Naturkunde in Württemberg, Jahreshefte. Stuttgart.

Ver. Verbreitung Naturwiss. Kenntnisse
   Wien, Schrift. Verein zur Verbreitung Naturwissenschaftlicher Kenntnisse in Wien, Schriften. Vienna.

Verona, Mus. Civ. Stor. Natur., Mem. . . . . Verona, Museo Civico di Storia Naturale, Memorie. Italy.

Verona, Mus. Civ. Stor. Natur., Mem.,
   Fuori Ser. . . . . Verona, Museo Civico di Storia Naturale, Memorie, Fuori Serie.

Verständ. Wiss. Verständliche Wissenschaft. New York and Berlin: Springer Verlag.

Vert. Hungarica . . . . Vertebrata Hungarica. Musei Historico-Naturalis Hungarici. Budapest.

Vert. PalAsiat. . . . . Vertebrata PalAsiatica (Ku Chi Ch'ui Tung Wu Hsueh Pao). Institute of Vertebrate Paleontology of the Academia Sinica. Peking.

Vert. Paleontol., Mem. . . . . Vertebrate Paleontology, Memoirs. Peking.

Vet. Rec. . . . . Veterinary Record. National Veterinary Medical Association of Great Britain and Ireland. London.

Victoria, Nat. Mus., Mem. . . . . Victoria, National Museum, Memoirs. Melbourne.

Victorian Natur. Victorian Naturalist. Melbourne.

Visual . . . . Visual. Oxford, England.

Vop. Antropol. . . . . Voprosy Antropologii, Moskovskiĭ Gosudarstvennyĭ Universitet. Moscow.

Vop. Ikhtiol. . . . . Voprosy Ikhtiologii. Akademiía Nauk SSSR. Moscow.

Vop. Paleontol. Voprosy Paleontologii. Leningradskiĭ Gosudarstvennyĭ Universitet. Leningrad.

Vses. Geogr. Obshchest., Izv. . . . . Vsesoiūznoe Geograficheskoe Obshchestvo, Izvestiīa. Leningrad.

Vses. Nauch.-Issled. Geologorazved. Neft. Inst.,
Tr. . . . . Vsesoiūznyĭ Nauchno-Issledovatel'skiĭ Geologorazvedochnyĭ Neftīanoĭ Institut, Trudy (VNIGNI). Moscow.

Vses. Nauch.-Issled. Inst. Prirodn. Gazov, Tr. . . . . Vsesoiūznyĭ Nauchno-Issledovatel'skiĭ Institut Prirodnykh Gazov, Trudy (VNII Gaz). Moscow.

Vses. Nauch.-Issled. Proektn. Inst. Gal., Tr. . . . . Vsesoiūznyĭ Nauchno-Issledovatel'skiĭ i Proektnyĭ Institut Galurgii, Trudy. USSR.

Vses. Neft. Nauch.-Issled. Geologorazved.
Inst., Tr. . . . . Vsesoiūznyĭ Neftīanoĭ. Nauchno-Issledovatel'skiĭ Geologorazvedochnyĭ Institut, Trudy (VNIGRI). Leningrad.

Vses. Paleontol. Obshchest., Ezhegod. . . . . Vsesoiūznoe Paleontologicheskoe Obshchestvo, Ezhegodnik. Moscow.

Vses. Paleontol. Obshchest., Tr. . . . . Vsesoiūznoe Paleontologicheskoe Obshchestvo, Trudy. Moscow.

Vyssh. Ucheb. Zaved., Izv., Geol. Razved. . . . . Vysshoe Uchebnoe Zavedenie (Ministerstvo Vysshego i Srednego Spetsial'nogo obrazovaniīa SSSR), Izvestiīa, Geologiīa i Razvedka. Moscow.

Vyssh. Ucheb. Zaved. Lit. SSR, Nauch. Tr.,
Geogr. Geol. . . . . Vysshoe Uchebnoe Zavedenie Litovskoĭ SSR, Nauchnye Trudy, Geografiīa i Geologiīa. Vil'niūs.

W. Afr. Archaeol. Newsletter . . . . The West African Archaeological Newsletter. Institute of African Studies, University of Ibadan, Nigeria.

W. Austral. Natur. . . . . Western Australian Naturalist (Western Australian Naturalists' Club). Perth.

Walkabout . . . . Walkabout. Australian Geographical Magazine. Published by the Australian National Travel Association. Melbourne.

Ward's Bull. . . . . Ward's Bulletin. Ward's Natural Science Establishment, Inc., Rochester, New York.

Warsaw, Muz. Ziemi, Pr. . . . . Warsaw, Muzeum Ziemi, Prace. Polska Akademia Nauk.

Weimar, Hochsch. Architekt. Bauw., Wiss. Z. . . . . Weimar. Hochschule für Architektur und Bauwesen, Wissenschaftliche Zeitschrift. Germany.

Werkgroep. Tert. Kwart. Geol., Meded. . . . . . . Werkgroep voor tertiarie en kwartaire geologie, Mededelingen. Holland.

Wilson Bull. . . . . The Wilson Bulletin; an Illustrated Quarterly Magazine devoted to the Study of Birds in the Field. Sioux City, Iowa.

World Archaeol. . . . . World Archaeology. London.

Wyo. Archaeol. Wyoming Archaeologist. Wyoming Archaeological Society. Cheyenne.

Wyo. Geol. Assoc., Guidebk., Field Confer. . . . . Wyoming Geological Association, Guidebook, Annual Field Conference. Casper.

Wyo., Univ., Contrib. Geol. . . . . Wyoming, University, Contributions to Geology. Laramie.

Wyo., Univ., Contrib. Geol., Spec. Pap. . . . . . . Wyoming, University, Contributions to Geology, Special Paper. Laramie.

Yager Mus., Publ. Anthropol., Bull. . . . . Yager Museum, Publications in Anthropology, Bulletin. Hartwick College, Oneonta, New York.

Yale Alumni Mag. . . . . Yale Alumni Magazine. Yale University. New Haven, Connecticut.

Yale Univ., Peabody Mus. Natur. Hist., Bull. . . . . Yale University, Peabody Museum of Natural History, Bulletin. New Haven, Connecticut.

Yale Univ., Peabody Mus. Natur. Hist.,
Spec. Publ. . . . . Yale University, Peabody Museum of Natural History, Special Publication. New Haven, Connecticut.

Yearb. Phys. Anthropol. . . . . Yearbook of Physical Anthropology. New York.

Ymer . . . . Ymer (Svenska Sällskapet för Antropologi och Geografi). Stockholm.

Yokohama Nat. Univ., Sci. Repts., Sect. II . . . . Yokohama National University, Science Reports, Section II Biological and Geological Sciences (Yokohama Kokuritsu Daigaku).

Z. Morphol. Anthropol. . . . . Zeitschrift für Morphologie und Anthropologie. Stuttgart.

Z. Säugetierkunde . . . . Zeitschrift für Säugetierkunde. Berlin.

Z. Tierzücht. Züchtungsbiol. . . . . Zeitschrift für Tierzüchtung und Züchtungsbiologie. Hamburg and Berlin.

Z. Zool. Syst. Evolut.-Forsch. . . . . Zeitschrift für Zoologische Systematik und Evolutionsforschung. Hamburg, Berlin.

Zambia, Geol. Surv., Mem. . . . . Zambia, Geological Survey. Memoirs. Lusaka.

Zentralbl. Geol. Paläontol., Teil 2 . . . . Zentralblatt für Geologie und Paläontologie, Teil 2, Historische Geologie, und Paläontologie. Stuttgart.

Zephyrus . . . . Zephyrus. Seminario de Arqueología, Universidad de Salamanca. Spain.

Zh. Obshch. Biol. . . . . Zhurnal Obshcheĭ Biologii (Akademiiâ Nauk SSSR). Moscow.

Zitteliana . . . . Zitteliana. Abhandlungen der Bayerischen Staatssammlung für Paläontologie und historische Geologie. München.

Zool. Anz. . . . . Zoologischer Anzeiger (Zoologische Jahrbücher). Jena, Germany.

Zool.-Bot. Ges. Wien, Verh. . . . . Zoologisch-Botanische Gesellschaft in Wien, Verhandlungen. Vienna.

Zool. Jahrb., Abt. Syst. Ökol. Geogr. Tiere . . . . Zoologische Jahrbücher. Abteilung für Systematik Ökologie und Geographie der Tiere. Jena, Germany.

Zool. Scripta . . . . Zoologica Scripta. Stockholm: Royal Swedish Acad. Sci. Publ.

Zool. Soc. India, J. . . . . Zoological Society of India, Journal. Calcutta.

Zool. Zh. . . . . Zoologicheskiĭ Zhurnal (Akademiiâ Nauk SSSR). Moscow.

Zürich, Univ., Paläontol. Inst., Mitt. . . . . Zürich, Universität, Paläontologisches Institut, Mitteilungen.

SPECIAL PUBLICATIONS

A.A.P.G.–S.E.P.M. Symp.
  The Pacific Coast Miocene Biostratigraphic Symposium. Pacific Section S.E.P.M. March 9–10, 1972. Bakersfield, California. Proceedings. Edwin H. Stinemeyer, ed. 364 p.
Atas Simp. Biota Amazônica
  Atas do Simpósio sôbre a Biota Amazônica (Geociências). Brazil. 1967.
Biostratigrafícheskie i paleobiofatsial'nye issledovanifá i ikh prakticheskoe znachenie [Biostratigraphic and paleobiofacies research and its practical significance]. Vses. Paleontol. Obshchest., Tr., X and XI sess., 1970 (Russian).
Chetvertichnafá geologifá i geomorfologifá Sibiri [Quaternary geology and geomorphology of Siberia]. Collected Papers: Novosibirsk: "Nauka" Press, Trudy Inst. Geol. Geofiz., Part 1, 195 pp., illustr., 1969 (Russian).
Colloque sur l'Éocène, Paris, mai 1968: Fr., Bur. Rech. Géol. Minières, Mém.
  Colloque sur l'Éocène, Paris, mai 1968 (3 vols.): France, Bureau de Recherches Géologiques et Minières, Mémoires. 1968, 1969.
Colorado, Univ. Mus., Field Confer. Guidebk.
  Colorado, University Museum, Field Conference Guidebook for the high altitude and mountain deposits of Miocene age in Wyoming and Colorado. August, 1968.
Committee on Mediterranean Neogene Stratigraphy, Proceedings of the Fourth Session in Bologna, 19–30 September 1967. See: G. Geol., 35:1–4.
Congr. Intern. Stud. Sardi, Cagliari, Atti
  Congresso Internazionale di Studi Sardi, Cagliari, Atti. VI, 1955 (1962); X, 1966–67 (1968).
Congr. Nat. Soc. Savantes, C. R.
  Congrès National des Sociétés Savantes de Paris et des départements, Comptes Rendus. France.
Congr. Panafr. Préhist., 6ᵐᵉ, Dakar, Actes
  Congrès Panafricain de Préhistoire, 6ᵐᵉ, Dakar, 1967, Actes.
Congr. Préhist. France, 16ᵉ. Sess., Monaco 1959, C. R.
  Congrès Préhistorique de France, 16ᵉ Session, Principauté de Monaco 28 Août - 5 Septembre 1959, Comptes Rendus. Paris: Soc. Préhist. Fr. Publ., 1067 pp.
Fauna kaĭnozoĭá Moldavii [Cenozoic fauna of Moldavia.] (K. N. Negadaev-Nikonov, ed.). Collected Papers: Kishinev: Akad. Nauk Moldav. SSR Press, 131 pp., 31 figs., 7 pls., 23 tables, 1970 (Russian).
Fauna mezozoĭá i kaĭnozoĭá Gruzii i ee geoistoricheskoe znachenie [Mesozoic and Cenozoic fauna of Georgia and its geohistorical significance.] (L. Sh. Davitashvili, ed.). Collected Papers: Tbilisi: "Meĭsniereba" Press, 138 pp., 17 figs., 9 pls., 15 tables, 1970 (Russian; Georgian summaries).
Field Conf. Tert. Bios., S. and W. Wyo., Guidebk.
  Field Conference on Tertiary Biostratigraphy of Southern and Western Wyoming. August 5–10, 1972. Robert M. West, Coordinator.
Galogennye formatsii Ukrainy i svĭazannye s nimi poleznye iskopaemye [Halogen formations of Ukraine and related mineral deposits.] Collected Papers: Kiev: "Naukova Dumka" Press, 1971 (Russian).
Gandert, O.-F. – Festschrift.
  Zum sechzigsten Geburtstag von Otto-Friedrich Gandert am 8. August 1958. Herausgegeben von Adriaan von Müller und Wolfram Nagel. Berliner Beit. Vor- und Frühgesch., 2, 178 pp., figs., 47 pls., portr. 1959.
Geologifá, geokhimifá i razrabotka neftĭánykh i gazovykh mestorozhdeniĭ [Geology, geochemistry and development of oil and gas deposits]. Collected Papers: Kuĭbyshev, 1969 (Russian).
Geologifá i fauna nizhnego i srednego pleĭstofsena Evropy [Geology and fauna of the lower and middle Pleistocene of Europe]. Collected Papers: Moscow: "Nauka" Press, 264 pp., illustr., 1972 (Russian).
Geologifá i poleznye iskopaemye Urala [Geology and economic ores of the Urals]. Collected Papers: Sverdlovsk: 1971 (Russian).
Gidrogeologifá i inzhenernafá geologifá aridnoĭ zony SSSR [Hydrogeology and engineering geology of the arid zone of USSR]. Collected Papers: Tashkent: "Fan" Press, 1969 (Russian).
Gondwana Symp., 2nd, Proc., Pap.
  Gondwana Symposium, Second. Proceedings and Papers. Cape Town, Johannesburg, Pretoria, South Africa, July 3–25, 1970 (1972).
Granifsa tretichnogo i chetvertichnogo periodov [Tertiary-Quaternary boundary] (V. I. Gromov, E. A. Vangengeĭm, V. P. Grichuk, I. K. Ivanova, and K. V. Nikiforova, eds.). Collected Papers: Moscow: "Nauka" Press, Reports of Soviet Geologists at the 23rd. Internat. Geol. Congr., Prague, 1968, Problem 10, 118 pp., 1968 (Russian; English summaries).
Handb. Mid. Amer. Ind.
  Handbook of Middle American Indians. Austin: Univ. of Texas Press. 1966.
Handb. Paläoherp.
  Handbuch der Paläoherpetologie O. Kuhn, Ed. Encyclopedia of Paleoherpetology. Stuttgart-Portland, USA: G. Fischer Verlag. 1969, 1970, 1971, 1972.
Handb. Strat. Geol.
  Handbuch der Stratigraphischen Geologie. F. Lotze, ed. Stuttgart: F. Enke Verlag.

Handb. Zool.
 Handbuch der Zoologie Eine Naturgeschichte der Stämme des Tierreiches. J.-G. Helmcke, D. Stark, H. Wermuth
 (eds.) Berlin: W. de Gruyter & Co. 1969.
Hist. Mallorca
 História de Mallorca. Edited by J. Mascaró Pasarius. Palma de Mallorca: Gráfica Miramar, 5 vols. (Spanish).
 1971.
Int. Ass. Quaternary Res., 6th Congr. (1961), Rept.
 International Association for Quaternary Research, 6th Congress (1961), Report. Warsaw. 1964.
Int. Ass. Quaternary Res., 7th Congr. (1965), Proc.
 International Association for Quaternary Research, 7th Congress (1965), Proceedings. U.S. National Academy of
 Sciences — National Research Council. Univ. Utah Press, Salt Lake City. 1968.
Int. Ass. Quaternary Res., 8th Congr. (1969), Étud. Fr. Quat.
 International Association for Quaternary Research, 8th Congress, 1969, Études françaises du Quaternaire. Paris.
Int. Congr. Amer., Proc.
 International Congress of Americanists, Proceedings. 36th, Sevilla, 1964 (1966); 37th, Buenos Aires, 1966 (1968).
Int. Congr. Anthropol. Ethnol. Sci., 7th, Moscow, 1964, Proc.
 International Congress of Anthropological and Ethnological Sciences, 7th, Moscow, 1964, Proceedings. Moscow.
Int. Congr. Anthropol. Ethnol. Sci., 8th, Tokyo, 1968, Proc.
 International Congress of Anthropological and Ethnological Sciences, 8th, Tokyo and Kyoto, 1968, Proceedings.
 Tokyo: Science Council of Japan.
Int. Congr. Prehist. Protohist. Sci.
 International Congress of Prehistoric and Protohistoric Sciences. 7th, Prague, 1966, Doklady i soobshcheniĩa
 arkheologov SSSR. Les rapports et les informations des archéologues de l'URSS (B. A. Rybakov, ed.)
 Moscow, "Nauka" Press. 1966.
Int. Congr. Primat., 2nd, Atlanta, Ga. 1968, Proc.
 International Congress of Primatology, Second, Atlanta, Ga. 1968, Proceedings (3 vols.). Basel, New York:
 S. Karger. 1969.
Int. Congr. Primat., 3rd, Zürich, 1970, Proc.
 International Congress of Primatology, Third, Zürich, 1970, Proceedings (3 vols.). Basel, New York: S. Karger.
 1971.
Int. Geol. Congr., 22nd, India, 1964
 International Geological Congress, 22nd session, New Delhi, India, 1964.
Int. Geol. Congr., 23rd, Czech., Guidebk.
 International Geological Congress, 23rd, Prague, Czechoslovakia, 1968, Guidebook, 50 vols.
Int. Geol. Congr., 23rd, Czech., Rep., Abstr.
 International Geological Congress, 23rd, Czechoslovakia, 1968, Report, Abstracts. Prague.
Int. Geol. Congr., 23rd, Czech., Rep., Proc.
 International Geological Congress, 23rd, Czechoslovakia, 1968, Report, Proceedings, 20 vols., Prague.
Int. Geol. Congr., 24th, Canada, Abstr.
 International Geological Congress, 24th, Canada, 1972, Abstracts. Montreal.
Int. Geol. Congr., 24th, Canada, Guidebk. Field Excursion A59
 International Geological Congress, 24th, Canada, 1972, Guidebook. Field Excursion A59. Montreal.
Int. Geol. Congr., 24th, Canada, Proc.
 International Geological Congress, 24th, Canada, 1972, Proceedings, 19 vols. Montreal.
Int. Ornith. Congr., 12th, Proc.
 International Ornithological Congress, 12th, Proceedings, 1958. Helsinki.
Int. Ornith. Congr., 15th, Abs.
 International Ornithological Congress, XV, Abstracts. The Hague, 1970.
Int. Radiocarb. Tritium Dating Confer., 6th, Proc.
 International Radiocarbon and Tritium Dating Conference, 6th, Proceedings. Pullman, Washington, 1965.
Int. Paleontol. Union, Congr., Prague, 1968, Abstr.
 International Paleontological Union, Congress, Prague, 1968, Abstracts.
Int. Speleol. Conf., Brno 1964, Proc., Probl. Speleol. Res.
 International Speleological Conference, Brno 1964, Proceedings. Problems of the Speleological Research
 (O. Štelcl, ed.) Brno, Czekoslovakia.
Int. Union Geol. Sci., 1st Symp. Gondwana Stratigr., Rev.
 International Union of Geological Sciences, First Symposium on Gondwana Stratigraphy, Reviews. Mar Del
 Plata, Argentina, 1967.
Internationales Paläontologisches Kolloquium, 2nd, 1966 in Weimar. See Pal. Abh., Abt. A, 1969, Band III,
 Heft 3/4.
Investigations arquéologiques en Tchécoslovaquie (Jan Filip, editor). VII-ème Congrès International des Sciences
 préhistoriques et protohistoriques, Prague, 1966. Prague: Academia, 317 pp., 24 figs., 44 pls., 7 maps, 1966
 (French).
Kaĭnozoĭ Zapadnoĭ Sibiri [Cenozoic of western Siberia] (V. A. Nikolaev, ed.) Collected Papers: Novosibirsk:
 "Nauka" Press, Sib. Otd. Akad. Nauk SSSR, Inst. Geol. Geof., 168 pp., illustr., 1968 (Russian).

Kat. Geol. Paläontol. Linz.
  Katalog Geologie und Paläontologie des Linzer Raumes. Vienna.
Khronologii͡a lednikovogo veka. Materialy k simposiumu, Leningrad, mart 1972g [Chronology of the Ice Age.
  Materials for the symposium, Leningrad, March 1972] Collected Papers: Leningrad: 167 pp., illustr., 1971
  (Russian).
Kontinental'nye obrazovanii͡a vostochnykh rai͡onov Srednei͡ Azii i Kazakhstana (Litologii͡a i biostratigrafii͡a)
  [Continental formations of eastern regions of Central Asia and Kazakhstan (Lithology and biostratigraphy)]
  (Barkhatova, ed.). Collected Papers: Leningrad: "Nauka" Press, 152 pp., 11 figs., 3 charts, 21 pls., 3 tables,
  1969 (Russian).
Krapina
  Krapina 1899–1969. Vorträge der wissenschaftlichen Versammlung. Zagreb. 1970.
Less-Perigliatsial-Paleolit na territorii Srednei͡ i Vostochnoi͡ Evropy (VIII Kongress INKVA, Parizh, 1969) [Loess-
  Periglacial-Paleolithic on the territory of middle and eastern Europe (For the VIII Congress INQUA, Paris,
  1969)]. Collected Papers: Moscow: (Akad. Nauk VNR, GDR, PNR, SSSR, Ch. SSR), "Nauka" Press, 742 pp.,
  illustr., 1969 (Russian; French summary).
Lexique Stratigraphique International. Congrès Géologique International – Commission de Stratigraphie. Centre
  National de la Recherche Scientifique. Paris.
McGraw-Hill Encycl. Sci. Technol.
  McGraw-Hill Encyclopedia of Science and Technology. Third edition. New York: McGraw-Hill, 15 vols.,
  illustr., 1971.
Martin, H. – Festschrift.
  Göttinger Arb. Geol. Paläontol., 5, VIII + 166 pp., illustr. 1970.
Materialy i͡ubilei͡noi͡ Nauchnoi͡ Sessii po voprosam geologii i͡uzhnogo Urala i Russkoi͡ platformy. Tezisy dokladov
  [Materials of the jubilean scientific session on the problems of the geology of southern Urals and Russian
  Platform. Theses of reports]. Collected Papers: Ufa: 1967 (Russian).
Materialy nauchnoi͡ konferent͡sii molodykh uchenykh geologov Litvy [Materials of the scientific conference of
  young students of geology of Lithuania]. Collected Papers: Vil'ni͡us: 1968 (Russian).
Materialy pervoi͡ nauchnoi͡ konferent͡sii molodykh uchenykh AN Kaz SSR [Materials of the first scientific
  conference of young scientists of the AN Kaz. SSR]. Collected Papers: Alma-Ata: 1968 (Russian).
Materialy po arkheologii Severnogo Prichernomor'i͡a [Materials on the archeology of northern Black Sea region].
  Collected Papers: Odessa: 1962 (Russian).
Materialy po chetvertichnomu periodu Ukrainy. K VIII kongressu Mezhdunar. assot͡s. po izuch. chetvertuchn.
  perioda (INQUA), Parizh, 1969 [Materials on the Quaternary period of Ukraine. For the VIII INQUA
  Congress. Paris, 1969] (V. G. Bondarchuk, ed.). Collected Papers: Kiev: "Naukova dumka" Press, 318 pp.,
  illustr., 1969 (Russian).
Materialy po evoli͡ut͡sii nazemnykh pozvonochnykh [Materials on evolution of terrestrial vertebrates] (K. K.
  Flerov, ed.). Collected Papers: Moscow: "Nauka" Press (Akad. Nauk SSSR, Otd. Obshch. Biol., Nauchn. Sov.
  po probleme "Puti i zakonomernosti istoricheskogo razvitii͡a zhivotnykh i rastitel'nykh organizmov"), 160 pp.,
  illustr., 1970 (Russian).
Materialy po faunam antropogena SSSR [Materials on the Quaternary faunas of USSR] (B. E. Bykhovskii͡, ed.).
  Collected Papers: Leningrad: Akad. Nauk SSSR, Zool. Inst., Tr., 49, 275 pp., 84 figs., 33 pls., 65 tables,
  1971 (Russian; English summaries).
Materialy po geologii i poleznym iskopaemym i͡uzhnogo Kazakhstana [Materials on the geology and economic
  ores of southern Kazakhstan]. Collected Papers: Alma-Ata: "Nauka" Press, 1971 (Russian).
Materialy po geologii i poleznym iskopaemym i͡uzhnogo Urala [Materials on the geology and economic ores of
  south Urals]. Collected Papers: Moscow: "Nedra" Press, 1956–1965 (Russian).
Materialy po geologii i poleznym iskopaemym t͡sentral'nykh rai͡onov Evropei͡skoi͡ chasti SSSR [Materials on
  geology and economic ores of central areas of the European part of USSR]. Collected Papers: Moscow: M-vo
  geologii RSFSR, vyp. 6, 331 pp., illustr., 1970 (Russian).
Materialy po geologii kai͡nozoi͡a i novei͡shei͡ tektonike Ti͡an'-Shani͡a [Materials on geology of the Cenozoic and
  newest tectonics of Tian-Shan]. Collected Papers: Frunze: "Ilim" Press, 1970 (Russian).
Materialy po geologii Ti͡an'-Shani͡a [Materials on the geology of Tian-Shan] Collected Papers: Frunze: 1964
  (Russian).
Materialy po geologii T͡sentral'nogo Kazakhstana [Materials on the geology of Central Kazakhstan] (E. M.
  Velikovskai͡a, ed.). Collected Papers: Moscow: Univ. Press, 7, 351 pp., illustr., 1967 (Russian).
Materialy 1-i͡ Respublikanskoi͡ nauchno-teoreticheskoi͡ konferent͡sii molodykh geologov Kaz SSR [Materials of the
  1-st. Republican scientific-theoretical conference of young geologists of the Kaz SSR]. Collected Papers:
  Alma-Ata: "Nauka" Press, 1968 (Russian).
Mezhdunarodnyi͡ kollokvium po geologii i faune nizhnego i srednego plei͡stot͡sena Evropy. Tezisy dokladov
  [International colloquium on the geology and fauna of Lower and Middle Pleistocene of Europe. Theses of
  reports] (K. V. Nikiforova, ed.). Collected Papers: Moscow: 86 pp., illustr., 1969 (Russian).
Mezhdunar. Simp. Litol. Genez. Less. Porod.
  Mezhdunarodnyi͡ simposium po litologii i genezisu lessovykh porod [International symposium on the lithology
  and origin of loessic rock]. Tashkent: "Fan" Press, 1970 (Russian).

Mezozoĭskie i kaĭnozoĭskie ozera Sibiri   [Mesozoic and Cenozoic lakes of Siberia] (A. P. Zhuze and N. A. Florensov, eds.). Collected Papers: Moscow: "Nauka" Press, Akad. Nauk SSSR, Sibirskoe Otd., Limnologicheskiĭ Inst., 258 pp., illustr., 1968 (Russian).

N. Amer. Paleontol. Conv., Proc.
North American Paleontological Convention, Proceedings, Chicago, September 1969   (E. L. Yochelson, ed.)

N. England Geol. Conf., 60th Ann. Meeting, Guidebk.
New England Intercollegiate Geological Conference, 60th Annual Meeting, October 1968, Guidebook. New Haven, Connecticut.

Nauch. Konf. Molod. Uch. Moldavii, 3-rd, Kishinev, Tr., Biol. Sel'sko-Khoz. Nauki
Nauchnaĭa Konferentsiĭa Molodykh Uchenykh Moldavii, 3-rd, Kishinev, 1964 [Scientific conference of young Moldavian students, 3rd, Kishinev, 1964] Trudy, Biologicheskie i Sel'sko-Khoziaĭstvennye Nauki. Kishinev.

Nauchnye itogi VI kongressa mezhdunarodnoĭ assotsiatsii po izucheniĭu chetvertichnogo perioda (INQUA) (Varshava, 1961) [Scientific results of the VI Congress of the International Association for Quaternary Research (INQUA) (Warsaw 1961)]. Moscow: "Nauka" Press, Akad. Nauk SSSR, Kom. Izuch. Chetvert. Per., 134 pp., illustr., 1964 (Russian).

Nazemni khrebetni Ukrainy   [Land vertebrates of Ukraine]. Kiev: "Naukova Dumka" Press, 1965 (Ukrainian).

Neogenovye i chetvertichnye otlozheniĭa Zapadnoĭ Sibiri   [Neogene and Quaternary deposits of western Siberia]. Collected Papers: Moscow: "Nauka" Press, Akad. Nauk SSSR, Sibirskoe Otd., Inst. Geologii i Geofiziki., 164 pp., illustr., 1968 (Russian).

Nobel Symp., 4th, Stockholm, 1967, Proc.
Nobel Symposium, 4th, Stockholm, June 1967, Proceedings, 1968. T. Ørvig, ed.   New York and London: Wiley Interscience, and Stockholm: Almqvist and Wiksell, 1968, 539 pp., illustr.

Nobel Symp., 12th, Uppsala Univ., 1969, Proc.
Nobel Symposium, 12th, Uppsala University, 1969, Proceedings. Ingrid U. Olsson, editor. New York and London: Wiley Interscience, and Stockholm: Almqvist and Wiksell, 1970, 652 pp., illustr.

Noveĭshaĭa tektonika, noveĭshie otlozheniĭa i chelovek   [Newest tectonics, newest deposits and man]. Collected Papers: Moscow: Moscow University Press, Vol. 1, 223 pp., 39 figs., 46 tables; Vol. 2, 201 pp., 41 figs., 7 tables, 1969; Vol. 3, 1972 (Russian).

Novosti ornitologii. Materialy chetvertoĭ vsesoĭuznoĭ ornitologicheskoĭ konferentsii. Alm-Ata, 1965   [News of ornithology. Materials of the fourth All-Union Ornithological Conference. Alma-Ata, 1965]   (I. A. Dolgushin, et al., eds.). Alma-Ata: "Nauka" Press, 451 pp., 1965 (Russian).

Ocherki po filogenii i sistematike iskopaemykh ryb i bezchelĭustnykh   [Outlines on the phylogeny and systematics of fossil fishes and Agnatha] (D. V. Obruchev, ed.). Collected Papers: Moscow: "Nauka" Press, 211 pp., illustr., 1968 (Russian).

Ocherki po geologii Kuznetskogo i Donetskogo basseĭnov   [Outlines of geology of the Kuznetsk and Donets basins] (V. I. Ĭavorskiĭ, ed.) Collected Papers: Leningrad: "Nedra" Press, 436 pp., illustr., 1970 (Russian).

Orlov, Ĭuriĭ Aleksandrovich — Festschrift.
Akad. Nauk SSSR, Paleontol. Inst., Tr., 130, 380 pp., illustr. 1971.

Osnovnye problemy geologii antropogena Evrazii. K VIII kongressu INQUA, Parizh, 1969   [Fundamental problems of Anthropogene geology of Eurasia. For the VIII INQUA congress. Paris, 1969] (A. V. Peĭve, ed.). Collected Papers: Moscow: "Nauka" Press, Geol. Inst. AN SSSR, 133 pp., illustr., 1969 (Russian).

Paleontologicheskie issledovaniĭa verkhnego kaĭnozoĭa Moldavii   [Paleontological research on upper Cenozoic of Moldavia]. Collected Papers: Kishinev: 1970 (Russian).

Paleontologicheskie kriterii ob"ema i ranga stratigraficheskikh podrazdeleniĭ   [Paleontological criteria of the scope and rank of stratigraphical subdivisions] Vses. Paleontol. Obshchest., Tr., VIII sess., 1966. Collected Papers, 216 pp., illustr. (Russian).

Parrington, F. R. — Festschrift.
Studies in vertebrate evolution. Edited by K. A. Joysey and T. S. Kemp. Edinburgh: Oliver and Boyd, 284 pp., illustr. 1972.

Pasa, A. — Festschrift.
Scritti sul quaternario in onore di Angelo Pasa. Verona, Mus. Civ. Stor. Natur., Mem., Fuori Ser., 3, vi + 305 pp., illustr. 1969.

Pleĭstotsen Tiraspolĭa   [Pleistocene of Tiraspol'] (K. V. Nikiforova, ed.). Collected Papers: Kishinev: "Ştiinţa" Press, 187 pp., illustr., 1971 (Russian).

Pozvonochnye neogena i pleĭstotsena Moldavii   [Neogene and Pleistocene vertebrates of Moldavia]. Collected Papers: Kishinev: "Ştiinţa" Press, 80 pp., illustr., 1972 (Russian).

Pribalt. Ornitol. Konf., 5th, Tartu, 1963, Tr.
Pribaltiĭskaĭa Ornitologicheskaĭa Konferentsiĭa [Baltic ornithological conference] 5th, Tartu, 1963, Trudy. Tallinn: "Valgus" Press, 270 pp., illustr., 1967 (Russian).

Pribalt. Ornitol. Konf., 6th, Vil'nĭus, 1966, Mater.
Pribaltiiskaĭa Ornitologicheskaĭa Konferentsiĭa [Baltic ornithological conference], 6th, Vil'nĭus, 1966, Materialy. Vil'nĭus, Lit. SSR.

Prirodnye i trudovye resursy Levoberezhnoĭ Ukrainy i ikh ispol'zovanie   [Natural and manpower resources of the left-bank Ukraine and their utilization] Moscow: "Nedra" Press, 1971 (Russian).

Problemy chetvertichnoĭ geologii Sibiri. K VIII kongressu INQUA, Parizh, 1969 [Problems of the Quaternary geology of Siberia. For the VIII INQUA Congress. Paris, 1969] Collected Papers: Moscow: "Nauka" Press, 156 pp., illustr., 1969 (Russian).

Problemy evoliutsii. T. I. [Problems of evolution. V. I.] (N. N. Vorontsov, ed.) Collected Papers: Novosibirsk: "Nauka" Press, Akad. Nauk SSSR, Sib. Otd., Otd. Obshch. Biol., 275 pp., illustr., 1968 (Russian; English summaries).

Problemy geologii Zapadnogo Kazakhstana [Problems of the geology of western Kazakhstan] Collected Papers: Alma-Ata: "Nauka" Press, 1971 (Russian).

Problemy izucheniia chetvertichnogo perioda. Tezisy [Problems of Quaternary research. Theses] Khabarovsk: Khabarovskiĭ Kompleksnyĭ Nauchn.-Issl. Institut, Sibirskoe Otd. AN SSSR, Priamurskiĭ (Khabarovskiĭ) Filial Geogr. Obshch. SSSR, 274 pp., illustr., 1968 (Russian).

Problemy ornitologii. Trudy tret'eĭ vsesoiuznoĭ ornitologicheskoĭ konferentsii. Sentiabr' 1962 [Problems of ornithology. Transactions of the third All-Union Ornithological Conference] (F. I. Strautman, et al., eds.). Collected Papers: L'vov: Univ. Press, 224 pp., illustr., 1964 (Russian).

Problemy paleontologii [Problems of paleontology] (R. F. Gekker, ed.). Collected Papers: Moscow: "Nauka" Press, Reports of soviet geologists, XXIII International Geological Congress, Prague, 124 pp., illustr., 1968 (Russian; English summaries).

Problemy stratigrafii kaĭnozoĭa. Mezhdunarodnyĭ geologicheskiĭ kongress XXII sessiia. Doklady sovetskikh geologov. Problema 16 [Problems of Cenozoic stratigraphy. International geological congress 22nd session. Reports of soviet geologists. Problem 16]. Collected Papers: Moscow: "Nedra" Press, 143 pp., illustr., 1965 (Russian).

Problemy zoologicheskikh issledovaniĭ v Sibiri [Problems of zoological research in Siberia]. Collected Papers: Gorno-Altaĭsk: "Knigoizdat" Press, 1962 (Russian).

Resheniia i trudy Mezhvedomstvennogo soveshchaniia po dorabotke i utochneniiu unifitsirovannoĭ i korreliatsionnoĭ skhem Zapadno-Sibirskoĭ nizmennosti. Tiumen', 21–27 marta 1967g [Resolutions and transactions of the interdepartmental Conference on the revision and precise definition of the unified correlation scheme of west-Siberian lowlands. Tiumen', 21–27 March, 1967]. Collected Papers: Tiumen': 274 pp., illustr., 1970 (Russian).

Romer, A. S. — Festschrift.
Forma et Functio, Vol. 3. 1970.

Saller, K. — Festschrift.
Anthropologie und Humangenetik. Festschrift zum 65. Geburtstag von Professor Karl Saller. Stuttgart: Gustav Fischer Verlag, x + 196 pp., 99 figs. 1968.

Schwarzbach, M. — Festschrift.
Miscelanea in honorem M. Schwarzbach. Cologne, Univ., Geol. Inst., Sonderveröff., 13, Ahorner, L., and Jux, U. (eds.), 187 pp., illustr. 1967.

Severnyĭ Ledovityĭ Okean i ego poberezh'e v kaĭnozoe. Symposium [The Arctic Ocean and its coastal regions during the Cenozoic. Symposium] (A. I. Tolmachev, ed.). Collected Papers: Leningrad: "Gidrometeizdat" Press, 562 pp., illustr., 1970 (Russian).

Simpósio Brasileiro de Paleontologia, Rio de Janeiro, GB, 20 a 25 de setembro de 1970. Acad. Brasil. Ciênc., An., 43 Suppl., 661 pp., illustr. 1971.

Simposium "Vozniknovenie roda Homo i ego evoliutsiia." [Symposium "The origin of the genus Homo and its evolution".] Moscow, 14–15 December, 1971. Vop. Antropol., 41, 146–163 (Russian).

Simpson, G. G. — Festschrift.
Evolutionary Biology, volume 6. Edited by T. Dobzhansky, M. K. Hecht, and W. G. Steere. New York: Appleton-Century-Crofts, 445 pp. 1972.

Soc. Vert. Paleontol. Ann. Meeting, 32nd, 1972, Abstr.
Society of Vertebrate Paleontology Annual Meeting, 32nd, 1972, Abstracts. Lincoln, Nebraska.

Soc. Vert. Paleontol., Bibliogr.
Society of Vertebrate Paleontology, Bibliography. New Haven, Conn. 1969, 1970, 1971, 1972.

Sovremennye problemy ornitologii. Chetvertaia vsesoiuznaia ornitologicheskaia konferentsiia. Alma-Ata, 1965 [Modern problems of ornithology. Fourth All-Union Ornithological Conference. Alma-Ata, 1965] (I. A. Dolgushin, et al., eds.). Collected Papers: Frunze: "Ilim" Press, Akad. Nauk Kirgiz. SSR, 243 pp., 1965 (Russian).

Stratigrafiia i fauna siluriĭskikh otlozheniĭ Vaĭgacha [Stratigraphy and fauna of Silurian deposits of Vaigach] Collected Papers: Leningrad: NII geol. Arktiki, 241 pp., illustr., 1970 (Russian).

Stratigrafiia neogena Moldavii i iuga Ukrainy [Neogene stratigraphy of Moldavia and southern Ukraine] Collected Papers: Kishinev: 1969 (Russian).

Stratigrafiia neogena Vostoka Evropeĭskoĭ chasti SSSR. Materialy soveshchaniia po stratigrafii neogena. Kazan', 1966 [Neogene stratigraphy of the east of the European part of USSR. Materials of the conference on Neogene stratigraphy. Kazan', 1966] Collected Papers: Moscow: "Nedra" Press, 327 pp., illustr., 1971 (Russian).

Stratigrafiia nizhnego paleozoia Pribaltiki i korreliatsiia s drugimi regionami [Stratigraphy of the lower Paleozoic of Pribaltika and correlation with other regions]. Collected Papers: Vil'nius: "Mintis" Press, Int. Geol. Congr., 23rd, Prague, 318 pp., illustr., 1968 (Russian; English summaries).

Stratigrafiíà nizhnego paleozoíà T́sentral'noĭ Evropy [Stratigraphy of the Lower Paleozoic of Central Europe] (B. S. Sokolov, ed.). Int. Geol. Congr., 23rd, Czech., Rep. Sov. Geol., Collected Papers, Problem 9, 154 pp., illustr., 1968 (Russian; English summaries).

Sushkin, Petr Petrovich — Festschrift.
   Coletania Ornithologica. 100 years since the birthday of P. P. Sushkin (1868–1928). Akad. Nauk SSSR, Zool. Inst., Trudy, 47, 264 pp., illustr., portr. (Russian). 1970.

Symp. Biol. Hungarica
   Symposia Biologica Hungarica Akadémiai Kiadó. Budapest.

Symp. 4th Field Conf.
   Four Corners Geological Society. A symposium. Shelf carbonates of the Paradox Basin (Ralph O. Bass and Seymour L. Sharps, eds.) 4th Field Conference, June 12–16, 1963. Durango, Colorado 273 p. 1963.

Symp. Gondwana Stratigr.
   Gondwana Stratigraphy. I.U.G.S. Symposium, Buenos Aires, 1–15 October 1967. International Union of Geological Sciences, Subcommission on Gondwana Stratigraphy. Paris: UNESCO, Coll. Earth Sci., no. 2, 1969, 1 vol. in -4o, xvi + 1173 pp., illustr. (English and Spanish).

Symp. Soc. Stud. Human Biol.
   Symposia of the Society for the Study of Human Biology. New York. 1968.

Systematic biology (Charles G. Sibley, editor): Proceedings of an international conference. National Academy of Sciences, Publication 1692, Washington, D.C., 1969.

Teriologiíà [Theriology] Collected Papers: Novosibirsk: 1971 (Russian).

Tezisy dokladov 1-go Vsesoíùznogo soveshchaniíà po paleobiogeokhimii i paleoekologii, 1969 [Abstracts of reports 1-st All-Union Conference on Paleobiogeochemistry and Paleoecology, 1969]. Collected Papers: Baku: Azerbaĭdzhan Univ. Press, 1969 (Russian).

Tezisy dokladov XVII sessii Vsesoíùznogo paleontologicheskogo obshchestva, 25–29 íànv. 1971g [Abstracts of reports. XVII session of the All-Union Paleontological Society, 25–29 January, 1971] Collected Papers: Leningrad: "Nedra" Press, 113 pp., 1971 (Russian).

Tobien, Heinz — Festschrift.
   Heinz Tobien zum 60. Geburtstag. Hess. Landesamt Bodenforsch., Abh., 60, 308 pp., 58 figs., 32 pls., 12 tables, portr., bibl. 1971.

U istokov chelovechestva (Osnovnye problemy antropogeneza) [At the sources of mankind (Fundamental problems of anthropogenesis)] (V. P. Íàkimov, ed.). Collected Papers: Moscow: MGU Press, 317 pp., illustr., 1964 (Russian).

Union Internationale pour l'Étude du Quaternaire, 8e Congrès, Paris. Rev. Géogr. Phys. Géol. Dyn., 11:3, 247–380, illustr. 1969.

Vaufray, Raymond — Festschrift.
   La Préhistoire. Problèmes et tendances. Paris: Éditions du Centre National de la Recherche Scientifique, XVI + 528 pp., illustr. 1968.

Verkhnepaleozoĭskie i mezozoĭskie zemnovodnye i presmykaíùshchiesíà SSSR [Upper Paleozoic and Mesozoic amphibians and reptiles of the USSR]. Collected Papers: Moscow: "Nauka" Press, 142 pp., illustr., 1968 (Russian).

Voprosy geologii antropogena [Problems of Quaternary geology]. Collected Papers: Minsk: "Nauka i tekhnika" Press, Vol. 1, 156 pp., illustr., 1968; Moscow: "Nedra" Press, Vol. 2, 1972 (Russian).

Voprosy geologii íùzhnogo Urala i Povolzh'íà [Problems of the geology of southern Urals and Povolzh'e]. Collected Papers: Saratov: Saratov Univ. Press, Vols. 5 and 6, 1969, Vol. 7, 1970 (Russian).

Voprosy geologii Kartlĭskoĭ depressii [Problems of the geology of Kartli depression]. Collected Papers: Tbilisi: "Meṫsniereba" Press, 1970 (Russian).

Voprosy geologii Kazakhstana [Problems of the geology of Kazakhstan]. Collected Papers: Alma-Ata: 1964 (Russian).

Voprosy geologii Pribaĭkal'íà i Zabaĭkal'íà [Problems of the geology of Baikal and Transbaikal regions] Collected Papers: Chita: Vol. 3, 1968, Vol. 6, 1969 (Russian).

Voprosy geologii vostochnoĭ okrainy Russkoĭ Platformy i íùzhnogo Urala [Problems of the geology of the eastern margin of Russian Platform and of south Urals]. Collected Papers: Ufa. Vols. 4–13, 1959–1971.

Voprosy gerpetologii. Materialy gerpetologicheskoĭ konferenṫsii [Problems of herpetology. Materials of herpetological conference]. Collected Papers: Leningrad, 1964 (Russian).

Vsesoíùznoe Soveshchanie po Izucheniíù Chetvertichnogo Perioda, Novosibirsk, 1964, Tezisy Dokladov, Sektsiíà Istorii Flory, Fauny i Drevnego Cheloveka [All-Union conference on the study of the Quaternary Period Novosibirsk, 1964. Abstracts. Section on history of flora, fauna, and ancient man] 94 pp. Sektsiíà Paleogeografii [Section on Paleogeography], 115 pp. Novosibirsk 1964 (Russian).

II Vsesoíùznoe soveshchanie po paleontologii mlekopitaíùshchikh kaĭnozoíà [II All-Union Conference on Paleontology of Cenozoic mammals]. Collected Papers: Tbilisi: 1966 (Russian).

Vykopni fauny Ukrainy i sumizhnykh terytoriĭ [Fossil faunas of Ukraine and adjacent territories] (I. G. Pidoplichko, ed.). Kiev: Akad. Nauk URSR Press, 171 pp., 65 figs., 4 pls., 45 tables, 1962 (Ukrainian; Russian summaries).

Wistar Inst. Symp. Monogr.
   The Wistar Institute Symposium Monographs. Philadelphia.

Zakonomernosti razvitiĭa organicheskogo mira po dannym paleontologii   [Laws of the evolution of organic world according to paleontological data] (G. Îa. Krymgol'ts, ed.). Vses. Paleontol. Obshchest., Tr., XII sess., 1968, Collected Papers: 148 pp., illustr. (Russian).

Zoologiĭa pozvonochnykh. Voprosy ornitologii   [Vertebrate zoology. Problems of ornithology] Itogi Nauki, 1971 (Russian).

AUTHOR CATALOGUE

AUTHOR CATALOGUE

Names of authors are most often listed as they appear in the publications. Names not so listed are cross-referenced to a more common spelling. Works of an author whose name has been spelled differently in different publications have, in some cases, been brought together under one spelling of the name. Variant transcriptions or spellings which are not cross-indexed are listed below together with the spelling which has been followed in this bibliography.

Names and titles published in the Cyrillic alphabet have been transliterated according to the Library of Congress system. Transliterated titles of articles in Russian, etc., and titles in certain other languages, e.g. Polish, are accompanied by an English translation in brackets. Japanese and Chinese titles are given in English translation only.

Review of books indexed in previous volumes refer to the earlier citation by author and year.

Alexandrova = Aleksandrova
Alexeev = Alekseev
Alexeeva = Alekseeva
Baygusheva = Baĭgusheva
Beliajeva = Beliaeva
Belyaeva = Beliaeva
Boĭarskaĭa = Bojarskaja
Borchwardt = Borkhvardt
Burczak-Abramowicz = Burchak-Abramovich
Čkhikvadze = Chkhikvadze
Crusafont = Crusafont Pairó
Daniltshenko, P. G. = Danil'chenko, P. G.
Daxner-Höck, G. = Daxner, G.
Dementjev = Dement'ev
Devjatkin = Deviatkin
Dmitrijeva, Y. L. = Dmitrieva, E. L.
Erbajeva = Erbaeva
Flerow, C. C. = Flerov, K. K.
Forsten, A. = Forstén, A.-M.
Gabunia, L. C. = Gabuniia, L. K.
Ganea = Gania
Glickman = Glikman
Hecker = Gekker
Heptner, W. G. = Geptner, V. G.
Ivachnenko = Ivakhnenko
Ivanjev = Ivan'ev
Ivan'yev = Ivan'ev
Jegallo = Zhegallo
Kurotchkin = Kurochkin
Lytschev = Lychev

Manzyĭ = Manziĭ
Mark, E. = Mark-Kurik, E. Iu.
Minich = Minikh
Obrutchev = Obruchev
Odintzov = Odintsov
Otschev = Ochev
Odintzov = Odint͡sov
Piszov = Pist͡sov
Rzebik-Kowalska, B. = Rzebik, B.
Ržonsnickaja = Rzhonsnit͡skaĭa
Schevtschenko = Shevchenko
Schmidt, N. = Schmidt-Kittler, N.
Stęślicka, W. = Stęślicka-Mydlarska, W.
Suchov = Sukhov
Švažaite = Shvazhaĭte
Switchenska = Svichenskaĭa
Sytchevskaya = Sychevskaĭa
Tchudinov = Chudinov
Topatshevsky = Topachevs'kyĭ
Torres, T. de = Torres Perezhidalgo, T. J. de
Tverdochlebova = Tverdokhlebova
Vereščagin = Verestchagin = Vereshchagin
Woronzow = Vorontzow = Voront͡sov
Yablokov = Ĭablokov
Yakimov = Ĭakimov
Yakovlev = Ĭakovlev
Yanovskaya = Ĭanovskaĭa
Yatzko, I. Ya. = Ĭat͡sko, I. Ĭa
Yerbayeva = Erbaeva
Yudin = Ĭudin

ABBIE, ANDREW A.
    1969A   The original Australians. London: Frederick Muller Ltd., 288 pp., 28 figs.
              Rev.: Comas in An. Antropol., Mexico, 8, 281–283; Giles in Amer. J. Phys. Anthropol., 34:2, 307–
              308; Parsons in Mankind, 7:4, 316.

ABEL, MARIANNE
    1972A   Women and evolution. Frontiers, 36:4, 18–21, illustr.

ABELIN, P. G.
    1972A   Letaiushchiĭ iashcher. [Flying lizard.] Priroda, 1972:2, 109, 2 figs. (Russian).

ABRAMOVA, E. A.
    1966B   Lokal'nye osobennosti Paleoliticheskikh kul'tur Sibiri. [Local particularities of the Paleolithic cultures
              of Siberia.] Int. Congr. Prehist. Protohist. Sci., VII, Moscow 1966, 46–55 (Russian).

ABRAMOVA, Z. A.
    1968B   Periodizatsiia paleoliticheskikh pamiatnikov Sibiri. [Periodization of the Paleolithic of Siberia.]
              In: Problemy izucheniia chetvertichnogo perioda. Tezisy, 100–101 (Russian).
    1969A   Issledovanie eniseĭskogo paleolita. [Research on the Paleolithic of Eniseĭ.] In: Rybakov, B. A. (ed.),
              1969A, 212–214 (Russian).

ACCORDI, FIORENZA S. and PALOMBO, MARIA R.
    1971A   Morfologia endocranica degli elefanti nani pleistocenici di Spinagallo (Siracusa) e comparazione con
              l'endocranio di *Elephas antiquus*. Accad. Naz. Lincei, Atti, Ser. 8, Cl. Sci. Fis. Mat. Natur.,
              Rend., 51:1–2, 111–124, 4 figs., 1 pl., 3 tables (Italian; English summary).

ACSÁDI, GY. and NEMESKÉRI, J.
    1970A   History of human life span and mortality. Budapest: Akad. Kiadó, 346 pp., 58 figs., 130 tables.
              Rev.: Preuschoft in Zentralbl. Geol. Paläontol., Teil 2, 1972:3, 179–180.

ADAM, H.   See: Ehrenberg, K., Ruckensteiner, E., Adam, H. and Friedl, H., 1969A.

ADAM, KARL DIETRICH
    1965C   Neue Flusspferd-Funde am Oberrhein. Baden-Württemberg, Geol. Landesamt, Jahresh., 7, 621–631,
              2 figs., 5 pls., 2 tables (German; English summary).
    1966D   Die Teufels- oder Fuchsenlucken bei Eggenburg (NÖ.). 4. Die Mammutreste. Österreich. Akad. Wiss.,
              Denk., 112, 39–60, 4 pls., 1 table (German).
    1969A   Urmensch-Museum Steinheim an der Murr. Ver. Vaterländ. Naturk. Württemberg, Jahresh., 124,
              54–57, 3 figs. (German).

ADAMENKO, O. M.
    1968A   O vozraste i raschlenenii krasnodubrovskoĭ svity Ob'-Chumyshskogo plato. [On the age and sub-
              division of Krasnodubrovskaia formation of the Ob'-Chumysh plateau.] In: Neogenovye i
              chetvertichnye otlozheniia Zapadnoĭ Sibiri, 33–37 (Russian).
    1969A   O nakhodke cherepa rannego mamonta v basseĭne reki Kudy (pravogo pritoka Angary). [On the find
              of a skull of early mammoth in the basin of Kuda river (right tributary of Angara).] Geogr.
              Obshchest. SSSR, Zabaĭkal'. Filial, Izv., 5:6, 144–146 (Russian).
    1970A   O geologicheskikh usloviiakh zaleganiia nizhnepaleoliticheskikh orudiĭ na r. Ulalinke (g. Gorno-Altaĭsk).
              [On the geological conditions of occurrence of lower Paleolithic tools on Ulalinka R. (Gorno-
              Altaĭsk).] Akad. Nauk SSSR, Sib. Otd., Mater. Ist. Sib., Drevniaia Sibir', 3, 57–59, 1 fig.
              (Russian).
    1971A   Raschlenenie eopleĭstotsenovykh otlozheniĭ Predaltaĭskoĭ ravniny v sviazi s problemoĭ nizhneĭ
              granitsy chetvertichnoĭ sistemy. [Subdivision of Early Pleistocene deposits of the Cis-Altaĭ
              plain in relation to the problem of the lower boundary of the Quaternary system.] Geol.
              Geofiz. (Akad. Nauk SSSR, Sib. Otd.), 1971:8, 82–87, 1 chart (Russian).

ADAMENKO, O. M. and GAĬDUK, I. M.
    1967A   O novykh nakhodkakh paleolita v predgor'iakh Altaia. [New finds of Paleolithic artifacts in the
              Altaĭ foothills.] Geogr. Obshchest. SSSR, Altaĭsk. Otd., Izv., 8, 24–28 (Russian).

ADAMIĬA, SH.A., DZOTSENIDZE, N. M., MATSKHONASHVILI, K. G. and MELADZE, G. K.
    1965A   O vozraste "Bazaletskoĭ serii". [On the age of "Bazaleti series".] Geol. Obshchest. Gruz., Izv., 4:2,
               69–71 (Russian).

ADAMS, FRED T.
    1968A   The way to modern man: an introduction to human evolution. New York: Teachers College Press,
               Columbia University, 284 pp., 25 figs., 3 tables.
               Rev.: Holloway in Amer. J. Phys. Anthropol., 33:1, 120–121; Miller in Amer. Anthrop., 71, 1191–
               1192.

ADAMS, S. J.   See: Carreck, J. N. and Adams, S. J., 1969A.

ADEGOKE, OLUWAFAYISOLA S.
    1969A   Eocene stratigraphy of southern Nigeria. Colloque sur l'Éocène, Paris, mai 1968, Vol. III: Fr., Bur.
               Rech. Géol. Minières, Mém., 69, 23–48, 6 figs., 3 tables.
    1969B   Stratigraphy and paleontology of the marine Neogene formations of the Coalinga region, California.
               Calif., Univ., Publ. Geol. Sci., 80, 241 pp., 6 figs., 13 pls., 3 maps.

ADLER, KRAIG
    1968A   Synonymy of the Pliocene turtles Pseudemys hilli Cope and Chrysemys limnodytes Galbreath.
               J. Herpetol., 1:1–4, 32–38, 3 figs.

ADROVER, RAFAEL
    1966B   Dos nuevos mustelidos de Teruel para la ciencia. Uno de ellos el mas antiguo que se conozca en el
               mundo. Teruel, 35, 131–138 (Spanish).
    1967A   Estudio comparativo de los restos craneanos de Myotragus procedente de la sima de Génova (Palma
               de Mallorca). Soc. Hist. Natur. Baleares, Bol., 13, 99–109, 111–114, 1 pl. (Spanish; French
               and English summaries).
    1967B   Nuevos micromamíferos en Mallorca. Soc. Hist. Natur. Baleares, Bol., 13, 117–127, 1 pl. (Spanish).
    1969A   Los micromamíferos del Plioceno inferior de los lignitos de Alcoy. I. Ruscinomys. Soc. Españ. Hist.
               Natur., Bol., Secc. Geol., 67:3, 245–272, 15 figs., 3 tables (Spanish; French and English
               summaries).
    1969B   Estudio de las raíces en los molares de "Ruscinomys schaubi", en su aspecto morfológico y evolutivo.
               Teruel, 42, 95–125, 6 figs., 6 tables (Spanish; French summary).

ADROVER, RAFAEL and ANGEL, BASILIO
    1967A   El Myotragus de Can Sion: primer esqueleto completo (no compuesto) del rupicáprido endémico de
               Baleares. Soc. Hist. Natur. Baleares, Bol., 13, 75–95, 2 figs. (Spanish; French and English
               summaries).

ADROVER, RAFAEL and CUERDA BARCELÓ, JUAN
    1969A   Mandíbula de Myotragus de "Es Bufador" (Mallorca), con dos incisivos y dos premolares. Acta Geol.
               Hisp., 4:4, 99–103, 1 fig. (Spanish; French summary).
    1969B   Mandíbula de Myotragus con dos incisivos y dos premolares. Soc. Hist. Natur. Baleares, Bol. (1968),
               14, 125–142 (Spanish; French and English summaries).

ADROVER, RAFAEL   See also: Ballmann, P. and Adrover, R., 1970A; Crusafont Pairó, M., and
               Adrover, R., 1966A.

AGADZHANIĂN, A. K.
    1970A   Rannepleĭstotsenovye gryzuny Priazov'ia. [Early Pleistocene rodents of the Azov Sea area.] Mosk.
               Univ., Vestn., Ser. Geog., 1970:3, 74–78, 2 figs. (Russian; English summary).
    1971A   Lemmingi likhvinskogo razreza. [Lemmings of Likhvin section.] Mosk. Obshchest. Ispyt. Prir., Biull.,
               Otd. Geol., 46:2, 154–155 (Russian).
    1971B   Lemmingi dneprovskogo oledeneniĭa Russkoĭ ravniny. [Lemmings of the Dnepr glaciation of the
               Russian Plain.] Akad. Nauk SSSR, Dokl., 201:1, 208–211, 2 figs. (Russian).
    1972A   Rannepleĭstotsenovye gryzuny Priazov'ia i Dona. [Early Pleistocene rodents of Priazov'e and Don.]
               In: Noveĭshaia tektonika, noveĭshie otlozheniĭa i chelovek, 3, 162–172, 3 figs. (Russian).

AGADZHANIĂN, A. K. and BOĬARSKAIĂ, T. D.
    1969A   Prirodnaĭa obstanovka nizhnealdanskoĭ vpadiny vo vtoroĭ polovine pleĭstotsena. [The natural
               environment of lower Aldan depression in the second half of Pleistocene.] In: Noveĭshaia
               tektonika, noveĭshie otlozheniĭa i chelovek, 1, 68–79, 1 fig. (Russian).

AGADZHANIĂN, A. K., DOBREDEEV, O. P., KURSALOVA, V. I. and MOTUZKO, A. N.
    1972A   Paleofaunisticheskaĭa kharakteristika opornogo razreza pleĭstotsena Priazov'ia u s. Veselo-
               Voznesenskogo. [Paleofaunal characteristic of the Pleistocene key section of Priazov'e at the

Veselo-Voznesenskoe village.] In: Noveĭshaia tektonika, noveĭshie otlozheniia i chelovek, 3, 147—154 (Russian).

AGADZHANÍAN, A. K. and MOTUZKO, A. N.
1971A   Fauna chetvertichnykh melkikh mlekopitaiushchikh iz razreza u s. Voronovo na r. Obi. [Quaternary small mammals fauna from a section near Voronovo village on Ob' River.] Geol. Geofiz. (Akad. Nauk SSSR, Sib. Otd.), 1971:1, 134—137, 1 fig. (Russian).
1972A   Ranneplei̇stotsenovye gryzuny doliny Irtysha. [Early Pleistocene rodents of the Irtysh valley.] In: Noveĭshaia tektonika, noveĭshie otlozheniia i chelovek, 3, 188—195, 2 figs. (Russian).

AGENTOV, VLADIMIR BORISOVICH   See: Kudriavtsev, G. A., Agentov, V. B., Gatinskiĭ, Íu.G. and Mishina, A. V., 1969A.

AGOGINO, GEORGE A.
1968B   Archeological excavations at Blackwater Draw locality no. 1, New Mexico, 1963—64. Nat. Geogr. Soc., Res. Reps., 1963, 1—7.
1969A   Paleontological and zoological materials from the Blackwater Draw locality number one. Amer. Phil. Soc., Yearb., 1968, 275.

AGOGINO, GEORGE A. and EGAN, GAIL NOEL
1972A   Indians of eastern New Mexico. N. Mex. Geol. Soc., Guidebk., Field Conf., 23, 137—140, 4 figs.

AGOGINO, GEORGE A. and ROVNER, IRWIN
1969A   Preliminary report of a stratified post-Folsom sequence at Blackwater Draw Locality No. 1. Amer. Antiquity, 34, 175—176, 1 table.

AGOGINO, G. A.   See also: Rovner, I. and Agogino, G. A., 1969A.

AGUADO, MAXIMO MARTIN
1968A   Versuch eines chrono-stratigraphischen Vergleichs des Unteren und Mittleren Pleistozäns beiderseits des Tajo. Deut. Ges. Geol. Wiss., Ber., Reihe A, Geol. Paläontol., 13:3, 289—298, 3 figs. (German).

AGUIRRE ENRÍQUEZ, EMILIANO DE (= AGUIRRE, EMILIANO DE)
1962A   Problemática paleontológica y selección natural. Discussions. Soc. Españ. Hist. Nat., Bol., Secc. Biol., 60, 177—192 (Spanish).
1968B   Revisión sistemática de los Elephantidae por su morfología y morfometría dentaria. (Primera parte). Estud. Geol. (Inst. Invest. Geol. "Lucas Mallada"), 24:3/4, 109—167, 48 figs., 2 tables (Spanish; French and English summaries).
1969A   Revisión sistemática de los Elephantidae por su morfología y morfometría dentaria. (Segunda parte). Estud. Geol. (Inst. Invest. Geol. "Lucas Mallada"), 25, 123—177, 9 figs., 36 tables (Spanish).
1969B   Revisión sistemática de los Elephantidae por su morfología y morfometría dentaria. (Tercera parte). Estud. Geol. (Inst. Invest. Geol. "Lucas Mallada"), 25:3/4, 317—367, 15 figs., 1 table (Spanish).
1969C   Evolutionary history of the elephant. Science (AAAS), 164, 1366—1376, 8 figs.
1970A   Diez años de descubrimientos en los lagos africanos. El valle de la Grieta y la genesis humana. Ciencias, 35:3, 163—177 (Spanish).

AGUIRRE ENRÍQUEZ, EMILIANO DE   See also: Alberdi, M. T. and Aguirre, E., 1970A; Crusafont Pairó, M. and Aguirre, E., 1971A, 1971B, 1972A; Crusafont Pairó, M., Aguirre, E. and Michaux, J., 1969A; Crusafont Pairó, M., Meléndez, B. and Aguirre, E., 1966A; Pérez González, A., Fuentes Vidarte, C. and Aguirre, E., 1970A.

AIGNER, JEAN S.
1972A   The archaeology of Pleistocene China. Diss. Abstr., 32:11, 6173B—6174B.

AIR, G. M., THOMPSON, O. P., RICHARDSON, B. J. and SHARMAN, G. B.
1971A   Amino-acid sequences of kangaroo myoglobin and hemoglobin and the date of marsupial-eutherian divergence. Nature, 229:5284, 391—394, 2 figs., 6 tables.

AISH, P. J., DEWHIRST, J. T. and FOLAN, W. J.
1968A   Dry-cleaning tags in the archaeological laboratory. Amer. Antiquity, 33, 504—505.

AĬZENBERG, D. M. and ROGINSKIĬ, ÍA. ÍA.
1970A   Polovoĭ otbor i ... moda. [Sexual selection and ... fashion.] Priroda, 1970:5, 121—122 (Russian).

AĬZENVERG, DAVID EFREMOVICH and LAGUTIN, P. K.
1970A   Stratigrafiia devonskikh otlozheniĭ Donetskogo basseĭna. [Stratigraphy of Devonian deposits of Donets basin.] In: Ocherki po geologii Kuznetskogo i Donetskogo basseĭnov, 419—434 (Russian).

AKERS, J. P.   See: Repenning, C. A., Cooley, M. E. and Akers, J. P., 1969A.

AKERSTEN, WILLIAM A.
1972A   Red Light local fauna (Blancan) of the Love formation, southeastern Hudspeth County, Texas. Tex.
          Mem. Mus., Bull., 20, 53 pp., 16 figs., 21 tables.

AKHUNDOV, M. A. and MAMEDOV, M. A.
1968A   Neobkhodimosti i sluchaĭnosti v uchenii G. Mendelia. [Necessity and chance in G. Mendel's doctrine.]
          Baku, Azerbaĭdzh. Univ., Uch. Zap., Ser. Biol., 1968:2, 3–11 (Azerbaĭdzhani; Russian summary).

AKOPIAN, G. M., VEGUNI, A. T. and PTUKHIAN, A. E.
1970A   Paleogenovaia sistema. [Paleogene system.] Geologiia SSSR, 43, Armenian SSR, 113–165, 7 figs.
          (Russian).

ALBERDI, MARÍA TERESA
1971A   Primer ejemplar completo de un *Tetralophodon longirostris* Kaup, 1835, encontrado en España. Estud.
          Geol. (Inst. Invest. Geol. "Lucas Mallada"), 27:2, 181–191, 2 figs., 5 pls. (Spanish).

ALBERDI, M. T. and AGUIRRE, E.
1970A   Adiciones a los mastodontes del Terciario español. Estud. Geol. (Inst. Invest. Geol. "Lucas Mallada"),
          26:4, 401–415, 11 figs. (Spanish).

ALBERDI, M. TERESA   See also: García, J. and Alberdi, M. T., 1968A.

ALBERT, ETHEL M.   See: Mandelbaum, D. G., Lasker, G. W. and Albert, E. M. (eds.), 1963B.

ALBERTI, GIORGIO
1968-69A Ritrovamento di resti fossili di elefante (*Elephas s.l.*) sul carso triestino. Trieste, Mus. Civ. Storia
          Natur., Atti, 26:56, 77–80, 4 figs. (Italian).

ALEKSANDROV, I. M.
1971A   Formy zameshcheniia organicheskikh ostatkov v permskikh solenosnykh otlozheniiakh. [Forms of
          substitution of organic remains in Permian saliferous deposits.] In: Galogennye formatsii
          Ukrainy i sviazannye s nimi poleznye iskopaemye, 29–30 (Russian).

ALEKSANDROVA, LIDIIA PETROVNA (= ALEXANDROVA, L. P.)
1969A   Gryzuny tiraspol'skogo faunisticheskogo kompleksa. [Rodents of the Tiraspol' faunistic complex.]
          In: Mezhdunarodnyĭ kollokvium po geologii i faune nizhnego i srednego pleĭstotsena Evropy.
          Tezisy dokladov, 15–17 (Russian).
1971A   Mammalia. Mlekopitaiushchie. [Mammalia.] In: Pleĭstotsen Tiraspolia, 71–169 (Russian).

ALEKSANDROVA, LIDIIA PETROVNA   See also: Krasnenkov, R. V. and Aleksandrova, L. P., 1967A;
          Krasnenkov, R. V., Aleksandrova, L. P., Shcherbakova, L. A. and Chepalyga, A. L., 1970A.

ALEKSEEV, M. N.
1969A   O printsipakh korreliatsii antropogenovykh otlozheniĭ Vostochnoĭ Azii. [On the principles of corre-
          lation of Anthropogene deposits of East Asia.] In: Osnovnye problemy geologii antropogena
          Evrazii. K VIII kongressu INQUA, Parizh, 1969, 121–128, 2 tables (Russian; English summary).
1970A   Nekotorye osobennosti pleĭstotsenovogo osadkonakopleniia v Leno-Kolymskoĭ zone poberezh'ia
          Arkticheskogo basseĭna. [Some special features of the Pleistocene sedimentation in the Lena-
          Kolyma zone of the coastal area of the Arctic Basin.] In: Severnyĭ Ledovityĭ Okean i ego
          poberezh'e v kaĭnozoe, 480–484, 1 fig. (Russian).
1970B   An occurrence of Tiraspolian fauna at the Vilyuy River (Eastern Siberia). Palaeogeogr., Palaeoclimatol.,
          Palaeoecol., 8:2–3, 209–214, 1 fig., 1 table.

ALEKSEEV, M. N., GITERMAN, R. E. and DUBROVO, I. A.
1972A   Mestonakhozhdenie fauny tiraspol'skogo kompleksa na r. Viliue (Vostochnaia Sibir'). [Faunal locality
          of Tiraspol' complex on the Viliuĭ R. (east Siberia).] In: Geologiia i fauna nizhnego i srednego
          pleĭstotsena Evropy, 240–244 (Russian).

ALEKSEEV, M. N.   See also: Menner, V. V., et al., 1972A.

ALEKSEEV, VALERIĬ PAVLOVICH
1968C*   Simposium. Metody antropologicheskogo analiza, faktory v obrazovanii rasovykh priznakov i printsipy
          rasovoĭ klassifikatsii. [Symposium. Methods of anthropological analysis, factors in the formation
          of racial characters, and principles of racial classifications. Introductory allocution. Discussion.]
          Int. Congr. Anthropol. Ethnol. Sci., 7th, Moscow, 1964, Proc., 3, 549–578 (Russian).

1969A Ot zhivotnykh k cheloveku. [From animals to man.] Moscow: "Sovetskaia Rossiia", 191 pp., illustr. (Russian).

Rev.: Uryson in Vop. Antropol., 34, 160—161 (Russian).

1969B O pervoĭ differentsiatsii chelovechestva na rasy. Pervichnye ochagi rasoobrazovaniia. [On the primary differentiation of mankind into races. Primary foci of race formation.] Sov. Etnogr., 1969:1, 12—24, 2 figs. (Russian; English summary).

1969C O pervichnoĭ differentsiatsii chelovechestva na rasy. Vtorichnye ochagi rasoobrazovaniia. [On the primary differentiation of mankind into races. Secondary foci of race formation.] Sov. Etnogr., 1969:6, 21—29, 1 fig. (Russian; English summary).

1970A Chto my dumaem o proiskhozhdenii cheloveka. Dva ochaga proiskhozhdeniia cheloveka. [What do we think about the origin of man. Two centers of origin of man.] Priroda, 1970:10, 37—40, 5 figs., portr. (Russian).

ALEKSEEV, VALERIĬ PAVLOVICH and DEBETS, GEORGIĬ FRANTSEVICH

1964A Kraniometriia. Metodika antropologicheskikh issledovaniĭ. [Craniometry. Methods of anthropological research.] Moscow: "Nauka" Press, 128 pp., 36 figs., 14 tables (Russian).

Rev.: Uryson in Vop. Antropol., 22, 180—182 (Russian).

ALEKSEEVA, E. V.

1970A Pleĭstotsenovaia teriofauna Kuzbassa. [Pleistocene theriofauna of Kuznetsk Basin.] Geogr. Obshchest. SSSR, Altaĭ. Otdel, Izv., 14, 118—120 (Russian).

ALEKSEEVA, E. V. and VERESHCHAGIN, N. K.

1969A Gigantskoe kladbishche mamontov. [A gigantic cemetery of mammoths.] Priroda, 1969:8, 115 (Russian).

1970A Okhotniki na mamontov v Barabinskoĭ stepi. [Mammoth hunters in Barabinskaia steppe.] Priroda, 1970:1, 71—74, 4 figs. (Russian).

ALEKSEEVA, E. V. and VOLKOV, I. A.

1969A Stoianka drevnego cheloveka v Barabinskoĭ stepi (Volch'ia Griva). [A settlement of ancient man in Barabinskaia steppe (Volch'ia Griva).] In: Problemy chetvertichnoĭ geologii Sibiri, 142—150, 4 figs. (Russian; English summary).

ALEKSEEVA, LIUDMILA IVANOVNA (= ALEXEEVA, L. I.)

1964B Vliianie aziatskikh elementov na formirovanie fauny mlekopitaiushchikh eopleĭstotsena iuga evropeĭskoĭ chasti SSSR. [Influence of asiatic elements on the constitution of mammalian fauna of the Eopleistocene of the south of European part of USSR.] In: Vsesoiuznoe Soveshchanie po Izucheniiu Chetvertichnogo perioda, Novosibirsk, 1964, Tezisy Dokladov, Sektsiia Istorii Flory, Fauny i Drevnego Cheloveka, 9—10 (Russian).

1968A Die asiatischen Elemente in der Säugetierfauna des osteuropäischen Anthropogens. Deut. Ges. Geol. Wiss., Ber., Reihe A, Geol. Paläontol., 13:3, 299—303, 1 table (German).

1969A Po povodu verbliuda iz tiraspol'skogo graviia. [Concerning the camel from Tiraspol' gravel.] In: Mezhdunarodnyĭ kollokvium po geologii i faune nizhnego i srednego pleĭstotsena Evropy. Tezisy dokladov, 14—15 (Russian).

1969B Posledovatel'nost' smeny kompleksov mlekopitaiushchikh v Antropogene Vostochnoĭ Evropy. [Sequence in the change of mammalian complexes during the east European Anthropogene.] In: Osnovnye problemy geologii antropogena Evrazii. K VIII kongressu INQUA, Parizh, 1969, 36—46, 1 table (Russian; English summary).

1969C O kuial'nitskoĭ faune mlekopitaiushchikh. [On the Kuial'nik mammalian fauna.] In: Stratigrafiia neogena Moldavii i Iuga Ukrainy, 106—112 (Russian).

1970A Rannechetvertichnye khobotnye Evropy. [Early Quaternary proboscideans of Europe.] Itogi Nauki, Ser. Geol., 21 (1969), Obshch. Geol., Stratigr., Paleontol., 120—135, 1 fig., 1 table (Russian).

1971A O mastodonte iz mestonakhozhdeniia Oshi (Zapadnaia Mongoliia). [On the mastodont from Oshi (Western Mongolia).] Sovm. Sovet.-Mongol. Nauch.-Issled. Geol. Eksped., Tr., 3, 71—77, 3 pls. (Russian).

ALEKSEEVA, L. I. See also: Garutt, V. E. and Alekseeva, L. I., 1964A; Tchoumakov, I. S. and Alekseeva, L. I., 1971A; Timofeev, E. M., Steklov, A. A. and Alekseeva, L. I., 1970A; Vereshchagin, N. K., Alekseeva, L. I., David, A. I. and Baĭgusheva, V. S., 1969A.

ALEKSEEVA, T. I.

1971A Pamiati Mikhaila Mikhaĭlovicha Gerasimova (1907—1970). [In memoriam M. M. Gerasimov (1907—1970).] Vop. Antropol., 37, 158—159, portr. (Russian).

ALEŠINSKAJA, Z. V. and BONDAREV, L. G.

1969A Le Pleistocène de la depression d'Issyk-Koul et l'histoire du climat du Tien-Chan. Ass. Fr. Etud. Quat., Bull., 18, 43—61, 5 figs., 1 chart, 2 tables (French; Russian summary).

ALEXANDER, RICHARD D.
1971A   The search for an evolutionary philosophy of man. Roy. Soc. Victoria, Proc., 84:1, 99–119.

ALIEV, S. D.   See: Gadzhiev, D. V. and Aliev, S. D., 1966B, 1969A, 1971A.

ALIMEN, MARIE-HENRIETTE, RADULESCO, C. and SAMSON, P.
1968B   Précisions paléontologiques et indices climatiques relatifs aux couches pléistocènes de la dépression de
            Braşov (Roumanie). Soc. Géol. Fr., Bull., 10:5, 549–560, 4 figs., 1 pl. (French).

ALIMEN, MARIE-HENRIETTE and STEVE, MARIE-JOSEPH
1966A*   Fischer Weltgeschichte. Band I. Vorgeschichte. Frankfurt: S. Fischer, 399, illustr. (German).
            Rev.: Kurth in Homo, 19:3–4, 242.

ALISON, D. and CARROLL, R.
1972A   Catalogue of type and figured fossils in the Redpath Museum, McGill University. Montreal: McGill
            University, 173 pp.

ALIZADE, KAMBAĬ ASKEROVICH
1966A   Stratigrafiia oligotsenovykh otlozheniĭ Azerbaĭdzhana. [Stratigraphy of Oligocene deposits of
            Azerbaĭdzhan.] Akad. Nauk Azerb. SSR, Izv., Ser. Nauk Zemle, 1966:1, 22–29 (Azerbaĭdzhani;
            Russian summary).
1968A   Oligotsenovye otlozheniia vostochnoĭ chasti Malogo Kavkaza. [Oligocene deposits of the eastern part
            of Little Caucasus.] Baku: "Nauka" Press, 128 pp., illustr. (Russian).

ALIZADE, K. A. and GADZHIEV, D. V.
1970A   Izuchenie iskopaemykh pozvonochnykh zhivotnykh Azerbaĭdzhana. [The study of fossil vertebrate
            animals of Azerbaĭdzhan.] Akad. Nauk Azerb. SSR, Izv., Ser. Nauk Zemle, 1970:1, 114–119
            (Azerbaĭdzhani; Russian summary).

ALKER, JULIUS
1969A   *Paciculus* (Cricetinae, *incertae sedis*) teeth from the Miocene of Nebraska. J. Paleontol., 43, 171–174,
            1 fig., 3 tables.

ALLAIN, JACQUES
1970A   Informations archéologiques. Circonscription du Centre. Gallia Préhist., 13:2, 345–363, 22 figs.
            (French).

ALLAND, ALEXANDER, JR.
1967A   Evolution and human behavior. Garden City, New York: Natural History Press, xiii + 243 pp.,
            37 figs.
            Rev.: Roberts in Amer. Anthropol., 70, 1033–1034; Washburn in Amer. J. Phys. Anthropol., 29, 105.
1972A   The human imperative. New York: Columbia University Press, 185 pp.
            Rev.: Montague in Natur. Hist., 81:7, 92–95.

ALLEGRANZI, A.   See: Leonardi, P. and Allegranzi, A., 1965A.

ALLEN, GLENN T., JR.   See: Dolan, E. M. and Allen, G. T., Jr., 1961A.

ALLEN, HARRY   See: Bardetti, M. and Allen, H., 1972A; Bowler, J. M., Jones, R., Allen, H. and Thorne,
                    A. G., 1970A.

ALLIN, EDGAR F.
1972A   Origin of the mammalian middle ear: how and why? Soc. Vert. Paleontol. Ann. Meeting, 32nd, 1972,
            Abstr. (abs.).

ALLISON, IRA S.
1966   Rev.: Anon. in Calif., Div. Mines Geol., Miner. Inform. Serv., 20:5, 54.

ALLISON, IRA S. and BOYD, HAROLD A.
1954A   A fossil camel from Oregon. Oreg. Acad. Sci., Proc., 3, 31.

ALLISON, IRA S.   See also: Packard, E. L., Allison, I. S. and Cressman, L. S., 1951A.

ALMAGRO, MARTÍN
1959A   La datación del pasado por el carbono 14 y sus resultados. Rev. Arch. Bib. Mus., 67:1, 275–297
            (Spanish).
1969A   En el aniversario del descubrimiento de la Cueva de Altamira. Atlántida, Madrid, 37, 104–111
            (Spanish).

ALPYSBAEV, KH.A.
1968A   Paleoliticheskie izdeliiã kak markiruiũshchiĩ indikator antropogenovykh otlozheniĩ Kazakhstana.
[Paleolithic artifacts as stratigraphic indexes of Anthropogene deposits in Kazakhstan.] Akad.
Nauk Kaz. SSR, Izv., ser. Obshchest. Nauk, 1968:4, 34–38 (Russian; Kazakh summary).

ALTEIRAC, ANDRÉ and CHEMIN, J.
1968A   Étude de sept dents humaines magdaléniennes provenant de la Grotte du Mas-d'Azil. Préhist. Spéléol.
Ariége., 23, 131–142, 2 figs. (French).

ALTNER, GÜNTER
1969A*   Kreatur Mensch. Moderne Wissenschaft auf der Suche nach dem Humanum. München: H. Moos
Verlag, 192 pp., 178 figs. (German).
Rev.: Kleinschmidt in Kosmos (Stuttgart), 1970:5, 183; Schwidetzky in Homo, 21:1, 61.

ALTUNA, JESÚS
1967A   Hallazgo de un esqueleto de león de las cavernas en la cueva de Arrikrutz (Oñate-Guipúzcoa). Munibe,
19, 331–332 (Spanish).
1970A   Fauna de mamíferos del yacimiento prehistórico de Aitzbitarte IV (Renteria, Guipúzcoa). II. Carnívoros
y micromamíferos. Munibe, 22:1–2, 3–41, 15 figs., 1 map (Spanish; English summary).
1970B   Hallazgo de una liebre ártica (Lepus timidus L.) en el yacimiento prehistórico de Urtiaga (Guipúzcoa).
Munibe, 22:3–4, 165–168 (Spanish).

ALTUNA, JESÚS   See also: Barandiaran, J. M. and Altuna, J., 1969A.

ALVARADO, RAFAEL
1962A   Las adaptaciones orgánico-funcionales. I. La convergencia adaptativa. Discussions. Soc. Españ.
Hist. Natur., Bol., Secc. Biol., 60, 193–204 (Spanish).

ALVARADO, SALUSTIO
1962A   Las adaptaciones orgánico-funcionales. II. Factores somáticos de las adaptaciones. Discussions. Soc.
Españ. Hist. Natur., Bol., Secc. Biol., 60, 205–216 (Spanish).

ALVAREZ, JOSÉ
1966A   Contribución al conocimiento de los bagres fósiles de Chapala y Zacoalco, Jalisco, México. Paleoecologia, 1, 1–26, 9 figs. (Spanish).

ALVAREZ, JOSÉ and ARREOLA, JULIO
1972A   Primer goodeido fósil. Soc. Cienc. Natur. Jalisco, A.C., Bol., 6, 6–15, 4 figs. (Spanish; English
summary).

ALVAREZ, TICUL
1965A   Catálogo paleomastozoológico Mexicano. Mexico, Dep. Prehist., Publ., 17, 70 pp. (Spanish).
1969A   Restos fósiles de mamíferos de Tlapacoya, Estado de México (Pleistoceno-Reciente). Kans., Univ.,
Mus. Natur. Hist., Misc. Publ., 51, 93–112, 6 figs., 1 table (Spanish; English summary).

ALVAREZ LÓPEZ, ENRIQUE
1961A   La especie en "The Origin of Species". Soc. Españ. Hist. Natur., Bol., Secc. Biol., 59, 5–24
(Spanish).

AMARAL, SÉRGIO ESTANISLAU DE
1971A   Geología e petrología da Formação Iratí (Permiano) no Estado de São Paulo. São Paulo, Univ., Inst.
Geociên. Astron., Bol., 1971:2, 3–81, 27 figs. (Portuguese).

AMARÉ, RICARDO FERRÉ D'
1965A   El Antropogeno de Siberia y el hombre americano. Mexico, Inst. Nac. Antropol. Hist., Ser. Invest.,
8, 97 pp., 25 pls., 5 maps, 8 tables (Spanish).

AMBROSE, W. R.
1968A   Conservation in the field and laboratory. In: Mulvaney, D. J. (ed.), 1968A, 157–173.

AMBROSETTI, PIERLUIGI
1967A   Cromerian fauna of the Rome area. Quaternaria, 9, 267–283, 3 figs., 2 pls. (Italian and German
summaries).
1968A   The Pleistocene dwarf elephants of Spinagallo (Siracusa, southeastern Sicily). Geol. Rom., 7, 277–
397, 54 figs., 15 pls., 12 tables (Italian summary).
1969A   Rappresentanti del genere Leithia nel Pleistocene della Sicilia. Verona, Mus. Civ. Stor. Natur., Mem.,
Fuori Ser., 3, 75–80, 3 figs. (Italian; English summary).

AMBROSETTI, P., AZZAROLI, A., BONADONNA, F. P. and FOLLIERI, M.
   1972A   A scheme of Pleistocene chronology for the Tyrrhenian side of central Italy. Soc. Geol. Ital., Boll.,
             91, 169—184, 2 tables (Italian summary).

AMBROSETTI, P. and BONADONNA, F. P.
   1967A   Revisione dei dati sul Plio-Pleistocene di Roma. Accad. Gioenia Sci. Natur. Catania, Atti, 18 suppl.,
             33—72, 6 figs., 9 pls., 1 table (Italian; English summary).

AMBROSETTI, P. and SALOMONI, E.
   1966A   Radiological research on the structure of Elephas falconeri Busk. Soc. Paleontol. Ital., Boll., 5:2,
             197—201, 1 fig., 2 pls.
             Rev.: Albanesi in Riv. Ital. Paleontol. Stratigr., 74:3, 991.

AMBROSETTI, P.   See also: Azzaroli, A. and Ambrosetti, P., 1970A, 1972A.

AMSTUTZ, G. C.   See: Häntzschel, W., El-Baz, F. and Amstutz, G. C., 1968A.

ANATI, EMMANUEL
   1969A   Magourata Cave: a prehistoric sanctuary cave in Bulgaria. Archaeology, 22:2, 92—100.

ANATI, EMMANUEL and HAAS, NICU
   1967B   The Hazorea Pleistocene site: a preliminary report. Man (J. Roy. Anthropol. Inst.), 2, 454—456, 7 pls.

ANÐELKOVIĆ, JELENA S.
   1967A   Sardinella beogradensis n. sp. iz donjeg sarmata teritorije Beograda. [Sardinella beogradensis nov. sp.
             from the Lower Sarmatian of the Beograd area.] Ann. Géol. Pén. Balkan., 33, 233—236, 1 pl.
             (Serbian and English).
             Rev.: B.B.M. in Akad. Savet FNRJ, Bull. Sci., Sec. A, 16:9—10, 306.
   1969A   Fosilne ribe iz donjeg sarmata teritorije Beograda. [Fossil fishes from the Lower Sarmatian of
             Belgrad.] Belgrad, Prirodn. Muz., Glas., Ser. A, 24, 127—167, 1 map, 6 pls. (Serbian; English
             summary).
   1969B   Prilog poznavanju fosilnih predstavnika familije Mullidae - Mullus gorjanovici n. sp. [Contribution to
             the knowledge of fossil representatives of the Mullidae family - Mullus gorjanovici n. sp.] Ann.
             Géol. Pén. Balkan., 34, 435—438, 1 pl. (Serbian and English).
   1970A   Tercijarne ribe Srbije. [Tertiary fishes of Serbia.] Ann. Géol. Pén. Balkan., 35, 281—366, 9 figs.,
             25 pls., 9 tables (Serbian; English summary).

ANDERSON, CHARLES A.   See: McKee, E. D. and Anderson, C. A., 1971A.

ANDERSON, ELAINE
   1967   Rev.: Thenius in Zentralbl. Geol. Paläontol., Teil 2, 1970:6, 520.
   1968   Rev.: Thenius in Zentralbl. Geol. Paläontol., Teil 2, 1970:6, 517—518.
   1970A   Quaternary evolution of the genus Martes (Carnivora, Mustelidae). Acta Zool. Fennica, 130, 1—132,
             51 figs., 38 tables.
             Rev.: Hall in J. Mammal., 52:3, 643—644.
   1972A   Pleistocene ferrets. Soc. Vert. Paleontol. Ann. Meeting, 32nd, 1972, Abstr. (abs.).

ANDERSON, HANS-JOACHIM, et al.
   1969A*   Führer zur Oligozän-Exkursion 1969. Köln-Münster-Hannover-Göttingen-Mainz, 20—27 April 1969.
             Marburg: Landesausschuss der Bundesrepublik Deutschland, 112 pp., 33 figs., tables (German).

ANDERSON, H. M. and ANDERSON, J. M.
   1970A   A preliminary review of the biostratigraphy of the uppermost Permian, Triassic, and lowermost
             Jurassic of Gondwanaland. Palaeontol. Afr., 13, suppl., 22 pp., 6 tables, charts.

ANDERSON, J. E.
   1968A   Late Paleolithic skeletal remains from Nubia. In: Wendorf, Fred (ed.), 1968D, 996—1040, 17 figs.,
             17 tables.

ANDERSON, J. M.   See: Anderson, H. M. and Anderson, J. M., 1970A.

ANDERSON, ROBERT T.
   1972A   Anthropology: a perspective on man. Belmont, California: Wadsworth Publishing Co., Inc., 133 pp.

ANDERSON, ROGER Y.
   1959A   Floral and faunal changes at the Cretaceous-Tertiary boundary, San Juan Basin, New Mexico. N. Mex.
             Geol. Soc., Guidebk., Field Conf. 10, 159 (abs.).

ANDERSON, ROGER Y. and KIRKLAND, DOUGLAS W.
1969A*   Paleoecology of an Early Pleistocene lake on the High Plains of Texas. Geol. Soc. Amer., Mem., 113,
          215 pp., illustr.

ANDERSON, SYDNEY
1968A   A new craniometer and suggestions for craniometry. J. Mammal., 49:2, 221—228, 1 fig.

ANDERSON, S., et al.
1972A   Recent literature of mammalogy. J. Mammal., 53:1, suppl., 64 pp.

ANDERSSON, J. GUNNAR
1967A   The Peking man. In: Rapport, S. and Wright, H. (eds.), 1967A, 19—32, illustr. (reprinted from
         Andersson, J. G., 1934, Children of the yellow earth).

ANDREWS, PETER
1970A   Two new fossil primates from the Lower Miocene of Kenya. Nature, 228:5271, 537—540, 2 figs.,
         1 table.
1971A   Ramapithecus wickeri mandible from Fort Ternan, Kenya. Nature, 231:5299, 192—194, 3 figs.,
         1 table.

ANDREWS, S. MAHALA
1972A   The shoulder girdle of 'Eogyrinus'. In: Joysey, K. A. and Kemp, T. S. (eds.), 1972A, 35—48, 7 figs.,
         2 pls.

ANDREWS, S. MAHALA and WESTOLL, T. STANLEY
1970A   The postcranial skeleton of Eusthenopteron foordi Whiteaves. Roy. Soc. Edinburgh, Trans., 68:9,
         207—329, 32 figs., 5 pls.
1970B   The postcranial skeleton of rhipidistian fishes excluding Eusthenopteron. Roy. Soc. Edinburgh, Trans.,
         68:12, 391—489, 23 figs., 15 pls., 1 table.

ANDRIEUX, CLAUDE   See: Roussot, A., Andrieux, C. and Chauffriasse, A., 1968A.

ANFOSSI, G. and MOSNA, S.
1969A   Otoliti del bacino terziario ligure-piemontese (Tortoniano e Miocene superiore). Pavia, Univ., Ist.
         Geol., Atti, 20, 22—49, 2 figs., 5 pls., 2 tables (Italian; English, French and German summaries).
         Rev.: Robba in Riv. Ital. Paleontol. Stratigr., 75:4, 884; Weiler in Zentralbl. Geol. Paläontol., Teil 2,
         1970:5, 414—415.
1969B   Ulteriori contributi allo studio degli otoliti del bacino terziario ligure-piemontese. Pavia, Univ., Ist.
         Geol., Atti, 20, 57—66, 2 pls., 1 table (Italian; English, French and German summaries).
         Rev.: Robba in Riv. Ital. Paleontol. Stratigr., 76:1, 177; Weiler in Zentralbl. Geol. Paläontol., Teil 2,
         1970:5, 415.
1971A   Alcuni otoliti del Miocene medio-superiore tortonese. Pavia, Univ., Ist. Geol., Atti, 21, 138—147,
         4 pls. (Italian; French, English and German summaries).
         Rev.: Robba in Riv. Ital. Paleontol. Stratigr., 77:3, 429.

ANFRAY, FRANCIS
1968A   Aspects de l'archéologie éthiopienne. J. Afr. Hist., 9, 345—366, 2 figs., 10 pls. (French).

ANGEL, B.   See: Adrover, R. and Angel, B., 1967A.

ANGEL, J. LAWRENCE
1966A   Early skeletons from Tranquillity, California. Smithson. Contrib. Anthropol., 2:1, III + 19 pp., 4 pls.,
         3 tables.
         Rev.: Anderson in Amer. Anthropol., 70, 169; Anderson in Amer. Antiquity, 33, 113; Schwidetzky
         in Homo, 19:3—4, 240; Vallois in L'Anthropologie, 72, 166—167.

ANGST, RALF
1970A   Über die Schädelkämme der Primaten. Natur Mus., 100:7, 293—302, 5 figs.

ANISIUTKIN, N. K. and ASTAKHOV, S. N.
1970A   K voprosu o drevneĭshikh pamiatnikakh Altaia. [On the question of the oldest relics of Altai.]
         Akad. Nauk SSSR, Sib. Otd., Mater. Ist. Sib., Drevniaia Sibir', 3, 27—33, 1 fig., 3 tables
         (Russian).

ANKEL, FRIDERUN
    1970A   Einführung in die Primatenkunde. Stuttgart: G. Fischer Verlag, Grundbegriffe der modernen
                   Biologie, Bd. 6, viii + 139 pp., 112 figs. (German).
                   Rev.: Preuschoft in Zentralbl. Geol. Paläontol., Teil 2, 1972:3, 180—181.
    1972A   Vertebral morphology of fossil and extant primates. In: Tuttle, R. (ed.), 1972A, 223—240, 7 figs.,
                   3 tables.

ANON.
    1961DA   Pleistocene antlers. Conservationist, 15:3, 31, 1 photo.
    1961DB   Jubilé scientifique de M. le Professeur H. V. Vallois. Les Eyzies, 10, 38—39, 1 fig. (French).
    1961DC   Extracts from news letters. Sci. of Man, 1, 211.
    1961DD   Old New World. Sci. of Man, 1, 213.
    1961DE   Chicago Natural History Museum holds open house. Sci. of Man, 2, 17, 29.
    1961DF   Abbé Henri Breuil (1877—1961). Toulouse, Univ., Inst. d'Art Préhist., Trav., 4, 3, portr. (French).
    1961DG   How old is man in the Western Hemisphere? Wyo. Archaeol., 4:3, 3—5.
    1961DH   The newest oldest man. Wyo. Archaeol., 4:5, 5.
    1961DI   National Geographic sponsors Wyoming site. Wyo. Archaeol., 4:5, 5.
    1961DJ   Intimations of immortality in childhood. Wyo. Archaeol., 4:6, 1.
    1961DK   New Zinjanthropos date. Wyo. Archaeol., 4:7, 10.
    1961DL   Rawlins site yields bison. Wyo. Archaeol., 4:9, 12.
    1962CP   L'Abbé Breuil. 1877—1961. Les Eyzies, 11, 25—28, 2 portr. (French).
    1963CS   Inauguration du médaillon Henri Breuil à Rouffignac (21 juillet 1963). Toulouse, Univ., Inst. d'Art
                   Préhist., Trav., 6, 279—285, 2 figs. (French).
    1963CT   Ancient slaughterhouse excavated. Wyo. Archaeol., 6:2, 19 (reprinted from South African Summary,
                   2, 17).
    1964CA   The evolution of man. Natur. and Sci., 2:7, 8—9, illustr. (juvenile).
    1964CB   The palaeontological expedition to north Rhodesia and Tanganyika. S. Afr. Mus. Ass., Bull., 8:3, 81.
    1965CX   Stanford fossil — studied by U.S.G.S. Calif., Div. Mines Geol., Miner. Inform. Serv., 18:6, 124—125,
                   5 figs.
    1965CY   Man's origin: mystery deepens. Med. Newsmag., 9:7, 99—101, 7 figs.
    1965CZ   The ages of the earth. Natur. and Sci., 2:11, 8—9, illustr. (juvenile).
    1965DA   Back yard mastodon. Natur. and Sci., 3:3, 4—5, illustr. (juvenile).
    1965DB   Last major gap in evolution story filled? Sci. S. Afr., 2:12, 577.
    1966BS   Chanoine Jean Bouyssonie [1878—1966]. Les Eyzies, 15, 9—10 (French).
    1966BT   Dinosaurios. Mexico: Organización Editorial Novaro, S.A., 6 illustr. pp. (juvenile; Spanish).
    1966BU   Mammoths back in pits. Mus. News, 45:3, 7.
    1966BV   The horse's first 55 million years. Natur. and Sci., 3:9, 8—9, illustr. (juvenile).
    1966BW   "Fossil" marsupial found alive. New Sci., 31:515, 713.
    1966BX   Paleo-Indian bison kill. Totem Pole, 49, 57—59, illustr.
    1966BY   Kayenta tritylodonts related to late Triassic genera. U.S. Geol. Surv., Prof. Paper, 550—A, 114.
    1966BZ   Muskox from Big Bone Lick dated as Tazewell. U.S. Geol. Surv., Prof. Paper, 550—A, 116.
    1966CA   Early Miocene mammals in Nevada. U.S. Geol. Surv., Prof. Paper, 550—A, 117.
    1967BL   Dr. Louis B. Leakey lectures at Virginia Polytechnic Institute. Chesopiean, 5, 14.
    1967BM   News release: new evidence for great age of man in the New World. Chesopiean, 5, 60.
    1967BN   Blackwater Draw Museum soon to be completed. Gt. Plains News., 3:6, 1.
    1967BO   Dam threatens Domebo Canyon. Gt. Plains News., 3:6, 2.
    1967BP   The Walker Mammoth site in Montana. Gt. Plains News., 3:7, 13.
    1967BQ   Othmar Kühn. Jugoslav. Akad. Znanosti i Umjetnosti, Ljetopis, 72, 202—203 (Serbocroatian).
    1967BR   More dinosaur tracks. Natur. and Sci., 5:1, 11, illustr. (juvenile).
    1967BS   Bat fossil is 50 million years old. New Sci., 33:528, 8—9.
    1967BT   What became of the mammoths? New Sci., 33:529, 71.
    1967BU   What makes giant animals? New Sci., 33:535, 447.
    1967BV   Elephants once roamed Japan. New Sci., 33:537, 599—600.
    1967BW   The artless hunters of the Palaeolithic. New Sci., 33:538, 654—655.
    1967BX   Taking an extinct animal's temperature. New Sci., 35:559, 375.
    1967BY   The lion that used to live down under. New Sci., 36:568, 209.
    1967BZ   Editorial. S. Afr. Archaeol. Bull., 22, 1—2.
    1967CA   Editorial. S. Afr. Archaeol. Bull., 22, 71—72.
    1967CB   Editorial. S. Afr. Archaeol. Bull., 22, 127—128.
    1967CC   Archaeology in South Africa 1952—67. S. Afr. Archaeol. Bull., 22, 154.
    1967CD   New World man — twice as old as thought. Sci. J., 3:7, 7, 3 figs.
    1967CE   Man's earliest known ancestor. Sci. News, 92:22, 514, 1 fig.
    1967CF   Paleobiology. Smithson. Year, 1967, 99—104, illustr.
    1967CG   Ape skull 28 million years old reported found by scholar. Wyo. Archaeol., 10:3, 10. Rocky
                   Mountain News, Nov. 16, 1967.
    1968AJ   Bibliography of C. J. van der Klaauw. Acta Biotheoret., 18, 5—8.
    1968AK   Fossil bone of amphibian found in Transantarctic Mountains. Antarctic J., 3:2, 52, 1 photo.

1968AL   Remains of *Pithecanthropus* discovered in Israel. Archaeology, 21:1, 65.
1968AM   Bericht über die VFMG-Sommertagung 1968 in Göttingen. Aufschluss, 19, 283–289, 7 figs. (German).
1968AN   Vertebrate fossils. Carnegie Mus., Ann. Rept., 71, 15–17.
1968AO   Mammoth bone shaft wrench. Chesopiean, 6, 26.
1968AP   News release: oldest human remains in North America found. Chesopiean, 6, 56.
1968AQ   News release: Leakey finds 12 million year old hammerstone. Chesopiean, 6, 61.
1968AR   Vertebrate paleontology. Discovery, 4:1, 65–66, 2 figs.
1968AS   Newly redesigned fossil reptile exhibits. Discovery, 4:1, 70–72, 3 figs.
1968AT   Radiocarbon dating of bones. Geochronicle, 2:3, 3–4.
1968AU   Pocket-sized geological time scales. Geochronicle, 2:4, 7, fig.
1968AV   Lindsay mammoth site being investigated. Gt. Plains News., 3:8, 9.
1968AW   Cooperton project underway. Gt. Plains News., 3:8, 14.
1968AX   Bibliographie des travaux de Raymond Vaufrey. In: R. Vaufrey Festschrift, XIII–XVI (French).
1968AY   Acquisitions. Mus. News, 46:7, 3, 3 photos.
1968AZ   Geological bibliography of the Netherlands. Neth., Geol. Dienst., Meded., Ser. C, 19, 83 pp.
1968BA   A fossil amphibian from Antarctica. New Sci., 37:588, 580.
1968BB   Search for early man in India. New Sci., 38:601, 561.
1968BC   Jubilé scientifique du Professeur P. P. Grassé. Paris: Masson et Cie, 81 pp. (French).
         Rev.: Leroy in Soc. Zool. Fr., Bull., 95:4, 874–875.
1968BD   Rare fish fossil found. Sci. News, 93:5, 127.
1968BE   Teeth link man and ape. Sci. News, 94:2, 32, 1 fig.
1968BF   Flower children of the dawn of man. Screenings, 17:10, 3.
1968BG   Paleobiology. Smithson. Year, 1968, 351–367, illustr.
1968BH   Giant bison from Colorado. U.S. Geol. Surv., Prof. Paper, 600–A, 119.
1968BI   Origin of arvicoline rodents. U.S. Geol. Surv., Prof. Paper, 600–A, 119.
1968BJ   Un eslabon de la cadena evolutiva humana. Univ. Chile, Bol., 87–88, 22, 1 fig. (Spanish).
1968BK   Mikhailu Mikhailovichu Gerasimovu — 60 let. [Mikhail Mikhailovich Gerasimov — 60 years
         anniversary.] Vop. Antropol., 29, 181–182, portr. (Russian).
1969AA   Edmund Iosifovich Ravskiĭ. Akad. Nauk SSSR, Kom. Izuch. Chetvertich. Perioda, Byull., 36,
         152–153, portr. (Russian).
1969AB   Une sépulture contenant le squelette d'un enfant de l'époque moustérienne. Atomes, 269, 597
         (French).
1969AC   Colloque sur l'origine de l'homme moderne. Atomes, 270, 677 (French).
1969AD   *Camptosaurus*. Carnegie Mag., 43:11, 305.
1969AE   Archaeologists honor Paul Martin. Chicago, Field Mus. Natur. Hist., Bull., 40:1, 4, illustr.
1969AF   Museum hosts first convention of North American paleontologists. Chicago, Field Mus. Natur. Hist.,
         Bull., 40:9, 5.
1969AG   [The skull of a new fossil reptile...] Discovery, 4:2, 127, 2 figs.
1969AH   Vertebrate paleontology. Discovery, 5:1, 55–56.
1969AI   George F. Sternberg (1883–1969). Fort Hays Kansas, State College News, 913, 625–5611.
1969AJ   D. N. Wadia (1883–1969). Geol. Soc. India, Bull., 6:3, 77–78, portr.
1969AK   Marmes man. Geotimes, 14:6, 28.
1969AL   George F. Sternberg (1883–1969). Hays Daily News, Oct. 24.
1969AM   Dorothy Garrod. 1892–1968. Interamer., 16:1, 3.
1969AN   The Talgai skull is an ancient mineralized skull. Interamer., 16:1, 3.
1969AO   Art and archaeology. Interamer., 16:2, 6.
1969AP   *Homo habilis*. Interamer., 16:6, 1.
1969AQ   *Ramapithecus*. Interamer., 16:6, 3.
1969AR   The red lady of Paviland. Interamer., 16:6, 3.
1969AS   Venezuela. Interamer., 16:6, 5.
1969AT   Maladie verte. Interamer., 16:6, 8.
1969AU   Prof. J. A. Orlov — an obituary. 1899 to 1966. J. Palaeontol. Soc. India, 12, portr.
1969AV   Faune de Blanzy-Montceau et note sur un poisson fossile de ce bassin. La Physiophile, 45:70,
         43–50 (French).
1969AW   W. K. Gregory, paleontologist, dies. N.Y. Times, 1969, Dec. 30, 28.
1969AX   Darwin's questions. Nature, 221:5178, 313.
1969AY   Lobe finned fishes. Nature, 221:5183, 803–804.
1969AZ   Centenary for museum. Nature, 222:5190, 214–215.
1969BA   Another place for digging. Nature, 222:5199, 1117.
1969BB   Dichotomies in mammal history. Nature, 223:5205, 450–451.
1969BC   History and the Omo Valley. Nature, 223:5212, 1199–1200.
1969BD   New fauna found. Nature, 224:5214, 14–15.
1969BE   Archive for data. Nature, 224:5220, 636.
1969BF   Not a turtle after all. Nature, 224:5224, 1057–1058, 1 fig.
1969BG   Reptiles of Gondwanaland. Nature, 224:5224, 1059.
1969BH   How the physicist helps. Nature, 224:5226, 1252.
1969BI   Ariadne. New Sci., 42:652, 548.

1969BJ   *Homo sapiens et al.* New Sci., 44:668, 629.
1969BK   News notes. Plaster Jacket, 10, 14 pp., 1 fig.
1969BL   Arma di Nasino (Albenga). Riv. Sci. Preist., 24:2, 349 (Italian).
1969BM   Arma delle Manie (Finale Ligure). Riv. Sci. Preist., 24:2, 349–350 (Italian).
1969BN   Techniques for cleaning fossils. Rocks Miner., 44:7, 492–493.
1969BO   Ice Age bison's remains unearthed. Rocks Miner., 44:12, 839.
1969BP   The growing collections. Rotunda, 2:2, 34–35, illustr.
1969BQ   Report on Ranche House College. S. Afr. Archaeol. Bull., 23, 23.
1969BR   Obituary. Dr. A. C. Hoffman. S. Afr. Mus. Ass., Bull., 9:9, 287–288.
1969BS   Rare find in Baja California. S. Calif. Paleontol. Soc., Bull., 1:3, 1 (reprinted from Los Angeles Times).
1969BT   Prehistoric condor found. S. Calif. Paleontol. Soc., Bull., 1:7, 8 (reprinted from the Sacramento Bee, Feb. 14, 1969).
1969BU   Body of Stone Age man found in Spain. S. Calif. Paleontol. Soc., Bull., 1:10, 5 (reprinted from Los Angeles Times, Sept. 1969).
1969BV   The age of man. S. Calif. Paleontol. Soc., Bull., 1:11, 6–8 (reprinted from Time Mag., Aug. 29, 1969).
1969BW   Old australopithecines. Sci. Amer., 220:6, 56–57.
1969BX   Did an earth "flip" kill the dinosaurs? Sci. and Culture, 35, 47–49.
1969BY   Man gets older and older. Screenings, 18:12, 3.
1969BZ   Paleobiology. Smithson. Year, 1969, 156–170, illustr.
1969CA   Georgiĭ Frantsevich Debets. 1905–1969. Sov. Etnogr., 1969:1, 184–189, portr. (Russian).
1969CB   Ice Age dig in Hancock Park and you are invited. Sunset, Oct. 1969, 58, 61, 2 figs.
1969CC   The age of man. Time, 94:9, 50, 3 figs.
1969CD   Saving the cave paintings. Time, 94:12, 74, 1 fig.
1969CE   The missing *Ammosaurus.* Time, 94:19, 53.
1969CF   New vertebrate faunas from Colorado. U.S. Geol. Surv., Prof. Paper, 650–A, 135.
1969CG   Adaptive radiation of Cetacea. U.S. Geol. Surv., Prof. Paper, 650–A, 136.
1969CH   Descubren dientes fosilizados de simios gigantes en China central. Univ. Chile, Bol., 91, 31, 1 fig. (Spanish).
1969CI   100 let so dnia rozhdeniia Alesha Grdlichki. [100th anniversary of Aleš Hrdlička's birthday.] Vop. Antropol., 33, 3–5, portr. (Russian).
1970AA   85-letie akademika AN Kaz. SSR B. A. Dombrovskogo. [85th anniversary of the academician of AN Kaz. SSR B. A. Dombrovskiĭ.] Akad. Nauk Kaz. SSR, Vestn., 1970:2, 75 (Russian).
1970AB   Recent discoveries in the Soviet Union. Archaeology, 23:2, 156–160, 8 figs., 1 map.
1970AC   Ioanni Filip septuagenario. Archeol. Roz., 22:6, 639–642 (Latin).
1970AD   Problemen in verband met vroeg-menselijke fossielen in Africa. Biol. Jaarboek, 38, 40 (Dutch).
1970AE   Vertebrate fossils. Carnegie Mus., Ann. Rept., 73, 17–20.
1970AF   El Ramapiteco, ¿ predecesor del Australopiteco? Chile, Univ., Bol., 104, 59 (Spanish).
1970AG   *Archaeopteryx lithographica.* Discovery, 6:1, 44, 1 fig.
1970AH   Fossil turtle found in New Jersey. Frontiers, 35:2, 8–9, 3 figs.
1970AI   A. Tindell Hopwood. Geotimes, 15:6, 30.
1970AJ   Russia invented it? Interamer., 17:3, 1.
1970AK   More than 35,000 year old American man? Interamer., 17:3, 1.
1970AL   Daniel W. Josselyn, 25 February 1970. Interamer., 17:3, 4.
1970AM   The dinosaurs finally win one. Life, 69:24, 73–74, illustr.
1970AN   40,000 year old cat tooth. Los Angeles Cty. Mus., Quart., 8:3, 2, 1 fig.
1970AO   Professeur J. Viret, 1894–1970. Lyons, Fac. Sci., Lab. Géol., Doc., 42, 8 (French).
1970AP   40,000 years old skeleton found. Mankind Quart., 11:2, 118–119.
1970AQ   The oldest Australian. Nature, 225:5229, 216.
1970AR   Signs of early man. Nature, 225:5233, 589–590.
1970AS   Leaping dinosaur. Nature, 226:5241, 109, 1 fig.
1970AT   Mammalian dark ages. Nature, 227:5253, 17–18.
1970AU   Archosaurs. Divergent evolution. Nature, 227:5263, 1089–1090, 1 fig.
1970AV   Should palaeoanthropology be big science? Nature, 228:5269, 315–316, 1 fig.
1970AW   Neuer Fossilienfund in Antarktis. [New fossil find in Antarctica.] Naturwiss. Rundsch., 23, 334 (German and English).
1970AX   A molecular view of man's evolution. New Sci., 45:683, 49.
1970AY   Museum of Northern Arizona geologists with science team in Antarctica; "truly great" fossil find reported. Plateau, 42:3, 76–78, 1 fig.
1970AZ   Un objet gravé acheuléen. La Recherche, 1:7, 666 (French).
1970BA   Rol' prirodnoĭ sredy v evoliutsii cheloveka. [The role of natural environment in the evolution of man.] Priroda, 1970:2, 115 (Russian).
1970BB   A clue to the past. S. Calif. Paleontol. Soc., Bull., 2:2, 7–8 (reprinted from Science News, Dec. 13, 1969).
1970BC   Dinosaurs under stress. S. Calif. Paleontol. Soc., Bull., 2:3, 7 (reprinted from Science News, Nov. 22, 1969).

1970BD   Australian fossil finds. S. Calif. Paleontol. Soc., Bull., 2:4, 5 (reprinted from Science News, 96, 1969).
1970BE   More about the La Jolla dinosaur. S. Calif. Paleontol. Soc., Bull., 2:4, 5 (reprinted from the
          Fossileer, 5:3, 1970).
1970BF   Giving a big bird a lift. S. Calif. Paleontol. Soc., Bull., 2:6, 7 (reprinted from Time, March 16, 1970).
1970BG   New Paleozoic animal fossils found in West Virginia. S. Calif. Paleontol. Soc., Bull., 2:6, 7—8
          (reprinted from W. Va. Geol. Surv., Newsletter, Dec. 1969).
1970BH   Fossilized elephant skull unearthed. S. Calif. Paleontol. Soc., Bull., 2:8, 8 (reprinted from Palo Alto
          Times, June 4, 1970).
1970BI   Boneyard's a career for 2 civil servants. S. Calif. Paleontol. Soc., Bull., 2:9, 5—6 (reprinted from
          Los Angeles Times, May 28, 1970).
1970BJ   Early man in America. Sci. News, 98:19, 364, 1 fig.
1970BK   Whole fossils in Antarctica. Sci. News, 98:23, 428, 1 fig.
1970BL   History of Gondwanaland. Sci. News, 98:26, 479.
1970BM   Mikhail Mikhaĭlovich Gerasimov (1907—1970). Sov. Etnogr., 1970:5, 171—173, portr. (Russian).
1970BN   Giving a big bird a lift. Time, 95:11, 51, 1 fig.
1970BO   How birds began to fly. Time, 96:23, 50, 2 figs.
1970BP   New toothed whale from the Yorktown formation in Virginia. U.S. Geol. Surv., Prof. Paper, 700—A,
          145.
1970BQ   Giant pig from Alabama. U.S. Geol. Surv., Prof. Paper, 700—A, 145.
1970BR   New Cenozoic vertebrate finds on the high plains. U.S. Geol. Surv., Prof. Paper, 700—A, 146.
1971AA   Ancient skull 'fills big gap'. Berkeley Daily Gazette, Oct. 15, 1971, 1, 1 photo.
1971AB   A whale skull or a shrew's tooth. Campus Rep., 6:1, 3, 1 photo.
1971AC   Teeth of a saber-toothed tiger. Frontiers, 35:5, 28, 1 fig.
1971AD   Hisakatsu Yabe (1878—1969). Geol. Soc. London, Proc., 1664B, 373—374.
1971AE   Late Quaternary frog. GeoTimes, 16:4, 3, cover illustr.
1971AF   La Brea. Interamer., 18:1, 7.
1971AG   Avery Island. Interamer., 18:2, 7.
1971AH   Oldest hominid? Interamer., 18:4, 4.
1971AI   Buffalo bones. Interamer., 18:7, 3.
1971AJ   Cave man. Interamer., 18:8, 8.
1971AK   Tautavel man. Interamer., 18:9, 2.
1971AL   Darwin shares with Eve and Adam. Nature, 229:5279, 6—7.
1971AM   Changing dinosaurs — but not in mid-stream. Nature, 229:5281, 153, 2 figs.
1971AN   A current trend in palaeoanthropology. Nature, 230:5295, 489.
1971AO   Early man in the east Rudolf basin. Nature, 231:5300, 213.
1971AP   Sir W. Le Gros Clark. Nature, 232:5310, 429—430.
1971AQ   Mammalian evolution. Nature, 223:5320, 451.
1971AR   Darwin centenary. Nature, 234:5328, 325—326.
1971AS   Labyrinthodonts. Amphibians of the coal. Nature, 234:5331, 508.
1971AT   Dinosaurier — Eier in der Wüste Gobi. Naturwiss. Rundsch., 24:2, 80 (German).
1971AU   Der Neandertaler und Rachitis. Naturwiss. Rundsch., 24:5, 223—224 (German).
1971AV   Unterkieferformen bei Menschen und Affen. Naturwiss. Rundsch., 24:7, 306, 1 fig. (German).
1971AW   Marsupialier — Migration und Kontinentaldrift. Naturwiss. Rundsch., 24:7, 310—312, 2 figs.
          (German).
1971AX   Tautavel man: oldest human skull in Europe. New Sci., 51:766, 449.
1971AY   Academically speaking. Pac. Discovery, 24:5, 32—33, illustr.
1971AZ   Sushchestvoval li avstralopitek s Homo sapiens? [Did the australopithecines coexist with Homo
          sapiens?] With a comment by V. P. Alekseev. Priroda, 1971:4, 78—79, 3 figs. (Russian).
1971BA   Otlozhenie urana v kostiakh zhivotnykh. [Uranium deposition in animal bones.] Priroda, 1971:5,
          107 (Russian).
1971BB   Novaia iskopaemaia reptiliia. [A new fossil reptile.] Priroda, 1971:7, 108, 1 fig. (Russian).
1971BC   Le crâne de l'Arago. La Recherche, 2:16, 862 (French).
1971BD   Bones of huge dinosaur found. Rocks Miner., 46:4, 231.
1971BE   Rich fossil finds. Rocks Miner., 46:9, 523.
1971BF   Fossil teeth from California. Rocks Miner., 46:9, 558, 1 fig.
1971BG   Bare bones of evolution. Rotunda, 4:1, 18—25, illustr.
1971BH   50,000-year-old remains of whale found by youth. S. Calif. Paleontol. Soc., Bull., 3:7, 8—9.
1971BI   Eastbluff's fabulous fossil finds. S. Calif. Paleontol. Soc., Bull., 3:7, 9.
1971BJ   Bones uncovered. San Francisco Chron., Aug. 17, 1971, 34.
1972BK   Ancient jawbone found in France. San Francisco Chron., Oct. 13, 1971, 14.
1971BL   Old fellow. San Francisco Chron., Oct. 15, 1971, 11.
1971BM   Oldest fossil bird a good runner but a poor flier. Sci. J., 7:1, 13, 2 photos.
1971BN   Swamp-dweller or landlubber? Sci. News, 99:3, 79, 1 fig.
1971BO   The search for New World man. Sci. News, 99:6, 98—100, 7 figs.
1971BP   Record duckbill dinosaur. Sci. News, 99:6, 103.
1971BQ   More complete view of man's ancestors. Sci. News, 99:9, 141, 2 figs.
1971BR   New Gondwana reconstruction. Sci. News, 99:9, 150.

1971BS   Lake Rudolf fossils. Two distinct hominids? Sci. News, 99:24, 398, 1 fig.
1971BT   The earliest ape. Sci. News, 100:2, 24, 1 fig.
1971BU   Once more into the past. Leakey wants to start a new dig in East Africa... Sci. News, 100:16, 259, portr., map.
1971BV   Reconstruction of the jaws of the giant fossil shark, *Carcharodon megalodon*. Science, 174:4005, cover.
1971BW   Upgrading Neanderthal man. Time, 97:20, 75–76, 1 fig.
1971BX   Publications of the United States National Museum (1947–1970). U.S. Nat. Mus. Bull., 298, 77 pp.
1971BY   Archäologischer Fund in der Ud SSR. Umschau, 71:4, 140 (German).
1971BZ   "Neues" *Archaeopteryx* — Exemplar. Umschau, 71:8, 285, 1 fig. (German).
1971CA   Vosem'desiat let so dniâ rozhdeniiâ G. A. Bonch-Osmolovskogo. [Eighty years since the birthday of G. A. Bonch-Osmolovskiĭ.] Vop. Antropol., 38, 165 (Russian).
1971CB   Pamiâti Veroniki Ivanovny Kochetkovoĭ [1927–1971]. [In memoriam Veronika Ivanovna Kochetkova [1927–1971].] Vop. Antropol., 39, 156–159, portr. (Russian).
1972AA   When the "monsters" roamed nearby parks. Berkeley Daily Gazette, Nov. 17, 1972, 10.
1972AB   Dinosaur National Monument. Calif. Geol., 25:8, 181.
1972AC   Rare snake fossil. Calif. Geol., 25:8, 182.
1972AD   A taste for the Triassic. Campus Rep., 6:10, 1–2, 1 photo.
1972AE   El *Lystrosaurus*: fosil Antartico. Chile, Univ., Bol., 108, 26 (Spanish).
1972AF   Neanderthal in Urals. Interamer., 19:2, 8.
1972AG   Neanderthal mute? Interamer., 19:2, 8.
1972AH   Kurt W. Marek, 1915–1972. Interamer., 19:3, 1.
1972AI   *Homo erectus*? Interamer., 19:5, 3 (reprinted from Western Australian, August 22, 1972).
1972AJ   L. S. B. Leakey, 1903–1972. Interamer., 19:5, 5.
1972AK   Yuha man. Interamer., 19:5, 8 (reprinted from Los Angeles Times, October 8, 1972, A–19).
1972AL   Oldest man? Interamer., 19:6, 6.
1972AM   Obituary notice. Sergio Sergi (1878–1972). J. Human Evol., 1:5, 513.
1972AN   Sierra yields bones of prehistoric sloth. Los Angeles Times, March 7, 1972, 20.
1972AO   Mammoths in the Arctic. Nature, 235:5337, 299.
1972AP   Gogo placoderms. Nature, 236:5340, 12.
1972AQ   Fossil lungfish from Australia. Nature, 236:5343, 143, 1 fig.
1972AR   More early hominids from East Rudolf. Nature, 237:5353, 250–251.
1972AS   Late Pleistocene man at Kow Swamp. Nature, 238:5363, 308–309.
1972AT   Sir Gavin de Beer [1899–1972]. Nature, 239:5368, 179–180, portr.
1972AU   Caecilian fossil found. Nature, 239:5369, 190–191.
1972AV   Evolution of elephants and suids in East Africa. Nature, 239:5372, 365.
1972AW   Prehistoric man built mammoth houses. New Sci., 55:803, 9.
1972AX   When dinosaurs strolled hand in hand... New Sci., 55:813, 550.
1972AY   News notes. Plaster Jacket, 18, 14 pp.
1972AZ   [Note on trogontherian elephant.] Priroda, 1972:2, 113, 1 fig. (Russian).
1972BA   Paléontologie au bois de Vincennes. La Recherche, 3:26, 768, 1 fig. (French).
1972BB   Remains of an ancient panda found in China. San Francisco Chron., March 29, 1972, 11.
1972BC   A small footprint — "Stone Age". San Francisco Chron., June 22, 1972, 4.
1972BD   Archeologist Leakey dies in London. San Francisco Chron., Oct. 2, 1972, 2, 1 photo.
1972BE   21,500-year-old skeleton in desert. San Francisco Chron., Oct. 9, 1972, 5.
1972BF   "Oldest human skull" reported. San Francisco Chron., Nov. 10, 1972, 1.
1972BG   The oldest man unearthed. San Francisco Chron., This World, Nov. 19, 1972, 16, 2 photos.
1972BH   Last Adam. Sci. Amer., 227:4, 48.
1972BI   What did in the dinosaurs: warm blood or soft eggs? Sci. News, 102:4, 53, 1 fig.
1972BJ   Australia yields possible oldest vertebrate print. Sci. News, 102:8, 117.
1972BK   Footprints in the sand(stone). Sci. News, 102:12, 182, 1 photo.
1972BL   Man from Olduvai Gorge, L. S. B. Leakey (1903–72). Sci. News, 102:15, 230, 1 photo.
1972BM   Leakey's new skull changes our pedigree and lengthens our past. Sci. News, 102:21, 324, illustr.
1972BN   Two superlatives. Time, 100:8, 56–57, photo.
1972BO   A new clock. Time, 100:10, 46–47, photo.
1972BP   Milestones. Time, 100:16, 74.
1972BQ   The petite monster. Time, 100:23, 89, 1 photo.

d'ANS, CHRISTIANE   See: Petit-Maire Heintz, N., Dricot, J.-M. and d'Ans, C., 1970A.

ANTAK, MARIO
1972A   Context, possible australopithecine affinity, and significance of *Meganthropus palaeojavanicus*. J. Student Pap., Anthropol., 1, 57–67, 4 figs.

ANTHONY, JEAN
1970A   Hommage à Georges Cuvier. Allocations prononcées à l'occasion des cérémonies du bi-centenaire de la naissance de Georges Cuvier. Mus. Nat. Hist. Natur., Paris, Bull., 42:1, 97–101 (French).

ANTHONY, JEAN and HEIM, JEAN-LOUIS
    1970A   La morphologie encéphalique de l'Homme de La Ferrassie I. Acad. Sci., C.R., Sér. D, 271:2, 176–179, 1 pl. (French).

ANTOSHCHENKO-OLENEV, I. V.   See: Bazarov, D. B., Antoshchenko-Olenev, I. V. and Gurulev, S. A., 1969A.

ANTYPKO, B. E.
    1964A   Neogenovaiā sistema. Mioťsen. Plioťsen. [Neogene system. Miocene, Pliocene.] Geologiiā SSSR, 44:1, West Siberian Lowlands, 177–189 (Russian).

ANTYPKO, B. E. and KRASNOV, I. I.
    1964A   Plioťsen-nizhniĭ otdel chetvertichoĭ sistemy (neraschlenennye). [Pliocene – lower part of Quaternary system (undivided).] Geologiiā SSSR, 44:1, West Siberian Lowlands, 189–192 (Russian).

AOKI, NAOAKI
    1968A   Some Pleistocene fish-otoliths from the Boso and Miura Peninsulas. Palaeontol. Soc. Jap., Trans. Proc., 71, 296–307, 14 figs., 1 table (Japanese summary).

APOSTOL, LEONID
    1960A   Contributions à l'étude des restes de *Hesperoloxodon* (Falc.) découvert dans la commune de Buciumeni-région Bucarest. Anthropos, Brno, 1960 suppl., 43–50, 2 pls., 2 tables (French; Russian summary).
    1967C   De ce dispar unele specii animale? [Why have some animal species disappeared?] Natura, Ser. Biol., 19:2, 82–86, 8 figs. (Rumanian).
    1968A   Particularités morphologiques des molaires de proboscidiens fossiles quaternaires de Roumanie, conservés dans la collection du Musée d'Histoire Naturelle "Grigore Antipa". Bucharest, Muz. Nat. Ist. Natur. "Grigore Antipa", 9, 581–612, 2 figs., 4 pls., 3 tables (Rumanian and Russian summaries).
    1970A   L'étude de l'espèce *Coelodonta antiquitatis* (Blumb.) du Quaternaire de Chiṣcani (Dép. Braila), point fossilifère situé à l'Est de la plaine Roumaine. Bucharest, Muz. Nat. Ist. Natur. "Grigore Antipa", Trav., 10, 383–396, 13 figs. (Rumanian and Russian summaries).
    1971A   Données sur le squelette de *Mammuthus trogontherii* (Pohlig) découvert dans la plaine roumaine. Bucharest, Muz. Nat. Ist. Natur. "Grigore Antipa", Trav., 11, 459–480, 23 figs., 5 tables (Rumanian summary).

APOSTOL, L. and VICOVEANU, D.
    1970A   L'étude des Éléphantidés, des Rhinocéridés et des Bovidés des dépots quaternaires de la vallée inférieure du Bîrlad, existants au Musée de Tecuci (Dép. Galatzi). Bucharest, Muz. Nat. Ist. Natur. "Grigore Antipa", Trav., 10, 365–382, 62 figs. (French; Rumanian and Russian summaries).

APPLEGATE, SHELTON P.
    1968A   A large fossil sand shark of the genus *Odontaspis* from Oregon. Ore Bin, 30:2, 32–36, 3 figs.
    1969-
    1970A   Digging fossil whales in Mississippi with southern hospitality. Los Angeles Cty. Mus., Quart., 8:3, 26–31, 8 figs.
    1970A   The vertebrate fauna of the Selma Formation of Alabama. Part VIII. The fishes. Fieldiana: Geol. Mem., 3:8, 383–433, 31 figs.
            Rev.: Westphal in Zentralbl. Geol. Paläontol., Teil 2, 1971:1, 52.
    1971A   Spectacular jaw. Science, 174:4012, 893.

ARAMBOURG, CAMILLE
    1966A   Les poissons oligocènes de l'Iran. Mus. Nat. Hist. Natur., Paris, Notes Mém., 8, 11–247, 65 figs., 17 pls., 6 tables (French).
            Rev.: Weiler in Zentralbl. Geol. Paläontol., Teil 2, 1968:6, 640–641.
    1966B   Réflexions sur la systématique des hominiens fossiles. Soc. Anthropol. Paris, Bull. Mém., Sér. 11, 9:4, 445–458, 1 fig., 1 table (French).
    1966C   Continental vertebrate faunas of the Tertiary of North Africa. In: Howell, F. C. and Bourliere, F. (eds.), 1966A, 55–64, 1 fig.
            Rev.: Maier in Z. Säugetierkunde, 36:2, 124.
    1967B   A propos du genre *Clupavus* Aramb. (Rectification de nomenclature). Mus. Nat. Hist. Natur. Paris, Bull., 39:6, 1236 (French).
    1967C   Observations sur la faune des Grottes d'Hercule près de Tanger, Maroc. In: Howe, B., 1967A, 181–186, 2 tables (French).
    1969A   Les corrélations paléontologiques et chronologiques entre le Pléistocène inférieur de l'Europe et celui de l'Afrique. Soc. Géol. Fr., C.R., 1969:3, 92 (French).
    1969B   Les corrélations paléontologiques et chronologiques entre le Pléistocène inférieur de l'Europe et celui de l'Afrique. Soc. Géol. Fr., Bull., 11:1, 106–115, 4 figs. (French).

1969C   La nouvelle expédition scientifique de l'Omo. Riv. Sci. Preist., 24:1, 3–13, 3 figs. (French; Italian and English summaries).

1970A   Les vertébrés du Pléistocène de l'Afrique du Nord. Tome I. Les faunes villafranchiennes. Fascicule 1. Historique-Stratigraphie-Paléontologie (Proboscidiens et Périssodactyles). Mus. Nat. Hist. Natur. Paris, Arch., 7e sér., 10, 1–126, 67 figs., 24 pls., 78 tables (French).
      Rev.: Thenius in Zentralbl. Geol. Paläontol., Teil 2, 1971:4, 335–337.

ARAMBOURG, C., et al.
1968A   Definición del genero humano. Mexico: Instituto Nacional de Antropología e Historia, Departamento de Investigaciones Antropológicas, 129 pp., 22 figs. (Spanish).
      Rev.: Vargas in An. Antropol., Mexico, 6, 302–304.

ARAMBOURG, CAMILLE, CHAVAILLON, JEAN and COPPENS, YVES
1969A   Résultats de la Nouvelle Mission de l'Omo (2-e campagne 1968). Acad. Sci., C.R., Sér. D, 268:5, 759–762, 1 map, 1 chart (French).

ARAMBOURG, C. and WOLFF, R. G.
1969A   Nouvelles données paléontologiques sur l'âge des "grès du Lubur" (Turkana grits) à l'Ouest du lac Rodolphe. Soc. Géol. Fr., C.R., 1969:6, 190–191, 2 figs. (French).

ARCHER, MICHAEL
1971A   A re-evaluation of the Fromm's Landing thylacine tooth. Roy. Soc. Victoria, Proc., 84:2, 229–233, 2 figs.

ARCHIVES SUISSES d'ANTHROPOLOGIE GÉNÉRALE
1968C   Eugène Pittard. In Memoriam 1867–1967. Arch. Suiss. Anthropol. Gén., 32, 137, portr.

ARDREY, ROBERT
1966A   Rev.: Alexander and Tinkle in BioScience, 18:3, 245–248; Cole in New Sci., 33:538, 688.
1967A   Adam kam aus Africa. Vienna: F. Molden, 351 pp. (German).
      Rev.: Knussmann in Homo, 20:1, 71.

ARDREY, ROBERT   See also: Leopold, C. A. and Ardrey, R. 1972A.

ARIMA, E. See: Gaherty, G., Kettel, D., MacDonald, J., Niemann, L., Von Graeve, B. and Arima, E., 1969A.

ARIPOV, A. A. See: Kambariddinov, R. K., Kadyrov, M. Kh., Aripov, A. A. and Sharakhmedov, Sh. Sh., 1971A.

ARKHIPOV, STANISLAV ANATOL'EVICH and MATVEEVA, OL'GA VLADIMIROVNA
1964A   Antropogen iuzhnoĭ okrainy Eniseĭskoĭ depressii. [Anthropogene of the southern margin of the Eniseĭ depression.] Akad. Nauk SSSR, Sib. Otd., Inst. Geol. Geofiz., Tr., 29, 128 pp., 35 figs., 3 tables (Russian).

ARMANET, F. See: Rahmouni, O., Roussillot, C. and Armanet, F., 1970A.

ARMELAGOS, GEORGE J.
1968A   Aikens' Fremont hypothesis and use of skeletal material in archaeological interpretation. Amer. Antiquity, 33, 385–386.

ARMELAGOS, GEORGE J. and DEWEY, JOHN R.
1970A   Evolutionary response to human infectious diseases. BioScience, 20:5, 271–275.

ARMELAGOS, G. J., MIELKE, JAMES H. and WINTER, JOHN
1971A   Bibliography of human paleopathology. Mass. Univ., Dept. Anthropol., Res. Reps., 8, 159 pp.
      Rev.: Anon. in Interamer., 18:8, 3.

ARMENT, HORACE L.
1961A   The outsized points of southern Oregon. Screenings, 10:2, 2–3, 2 figs.

ARMSTRONG, AUGUSTUS K.
1959A   Mississipian strata on the east side of the Datil Plateau. N. Mex. Geol. Soc., Guidebk., Field Conf. 10, 52–56, 2 figs.

ARNOLD, WALTER
1968A   The evolution of man in relation to that of the earth. Part I. Mankind Quart., 9:2, 43–87.
1969A   The evolution of man in relation to that of the earth. Part II. Mankind Quart., 9:3, 91–105.

ARREOLA, JULIO   See: Alvarez, J. and Arreola, J., 1972A.

ARTEM'EV, GEORGIĬ VASIL'EVICH
1970A   Evoliūt͡sionnaia teoriia, Darvin i Lamark. [The theory of evolution, Darwin and Lamarck.] Priroda,
           1970:5, 39—47 (Russian).
1971A   Vydaiūshchiisia vklad v antologiiū evoliūt͡sionizma. Et'en Zhoffrua Sent-Iler. Izbrannye trudy.
           [An outstanding contribution to the anthology of evolutionism. Etienne Geoffroy Saint-Hilaire.
           Selected works.] Priroda, 1971:9, 113—116 (Russian).

ARTEM'EVA, V. I.   See: Speranskiĭ, V. S., Artem'eva, V. I., Osipova, V. A. and Rodionova, V. A., 1971A.

ARTHUR, DON R.
1969A   Man and his environment. New York: American Elsevier, 218 pp., illustr.
           Rev.: Cook in Amer. Sci., 58:4, 441—442.

ARUTIŪNOV, S. A.   See: Averkieva, I͡u. P., Arutiūnov, S. A. and Bromleĭ, I͡u. V., 1969A.

ARZUMANIĀN, S. K., VEGUNI, A. T. and DAVTIĀN, A. R.
1970A   Neogenovaia sistema. [Neogene system.] Geologiia SSSR, 43, Armenian SSR, 165—203, 3 figs.
           (Russian).

ASAMA, KAZUO
1971A   On the exhibition of evolution at the British Museum (Natural History). Natur. Sci. and Mus.,
           38:5—6, 118—134, 16 figs. (Japanese).

ASCENZI, ANTONIO and SEGRE, ALDO G.
1971A   A new Neanderthal child mandible from an Upper Pleistocene site in southern Italy. Nature,
           233:5317, 280—283, 4 figs., 2 tables.
1971B   Il giacimento con mandibola neandertaliana di Archi (Reggio Calabria). Accad. Naz. Lincei, Atti,
           Ser. 8, Cl. Sci. Fis., Mat. Natur., Rend., 50:1:6, 763—771, 2 figs., 5 pls., 2 tables (Italian;
           English summary).

ASCHER, ROBERT   See: Hockett, C. F. and Ascher, R., 1972A.

ASH, SIDNEY R.
1964A   Bibliography and index of the New Mexico Geological Society Guidebooks, 1950—1963. N. Mex.
           Geol. Soc., Spec. Publ., 1, 31 pp., 1 pl.

ASIMOV, ISAAC
1972A   At stake: 500,000,000 years of life. Nat. Wildlife, 10:3, 4—13, illustr.

ASLANIĀN, A. T.
1970A   Chetvertichnaia sistema. Tufy-tufolavy (ignimbrity). Lednikovye otlozheniia. Travertiny.
           [Quaternary system. Tuffs-welded tuffs (ignimbrites). Glacial deposits. Travertines.]
           Geologiia SSSR, 43, Armenian SSR, 220—234, 1 fig. (Russian).

ASLANOVA, SEVIL MUTALIBOVNA and BURCHAK-ABRAMOVICH, NIKOLAĬ IOSIFOVICH
1968A   A fossil swan from the Maykopian series of Azerbaydzhan. Acta Zool. Crac., 13:14, 325—347,
           1 fig., pls. 11—14, 3 tables (Polish and Russian summaries).

ASMUS, GISELA
1967A   Zur Datierung der Menschenfunde aus dem Paläolithikum des nahen Ostens. Akten des Anthro-
           pologischen Kongresses, Brno, 1965. Anthropos, Brno, 19, 15—17 (German).
1967B   Ergebnisse einer erneuten Untersuchung der altsteinzeitlichen Menschenfunde aus Palästina.
           Fundamenta, Reihe B, 2, 290—305, 1 table (German).

ASTAKHOV, S. N.
1966C   O putiakh pervonachal'nogo zaseleniia chelovekom doliny Eniseia. [On the ways of first settlement
           of Eniseĭ Valley by man.] Int. Congr. Prehist. Protohist. Sci., VII, Moscow 1966, 56—67
           (Russian).
1968B   Voprosy khronologii paleoliticheskikh pamiātnikov Tuvy. [Problems of the chronology of
           Paleolithic of Tuva.] In: Problemy izucheniia chetvertichnogo perioda. Tezisy, 101—102
           (Russian).

ASTAKHOV, S. N.   See also: Anisiūtkin, N. K. and Astakhov, S. N., 1970A.

ASTANIN, L. P.
    1968A   Proporísii ruki cheloveka i primatov. [Proportions of the hand of man and of Primates.]
            Discussion. Int. Congr. Anthropol. Ethnol. Sci., 7th, Moscow, 1964, Proc., 3, 485–491,
            2 tables (Russian).

ASTRE, GASTON
    1968A   Faune aurignacienne et périgordienne de Tarté. Soc. Hist. Natur. Toulouse, Bull., 104:3–4,
            351–364 (French).
    1968B   Ossements fossiles de l'aven de Mano (Ariège). Soc. Hist. Natur. Toulouse, Bull., 104:3–4, 365–366
            (French).

ATKINS, EDWARD G.   See: West, R. M. and Atkins, E. G., 1970A.

ATKINSON, TIM
    1969A   A horse astragalus from the Hand Hills conglomerate of Alberta. (Copied from Russell, L. S., 1958B).
            Rocks Miner., 44:7, 536–537.

ATTRIDGE, JOHN and CHARIG, ALAN J.
    1967A   Crisis in evolution: the Stormberg series. Sci. J., 3:7, 48–54, 4 figs., 2 pls.
    1967B   Sediments and skulls. New Sci., 35:556, 260.

AUBEKEROV, B. Zh., AUBEKEROVA, PIRUZA ABLAEVNA, BIRIUKOV, MIKHAIL DENISOVICH, LYCHEV,
GENNADIĬ FEDOROVICH and SAVINOV, PETR FEDOROVICH
    1970A   Stratigraficheskoe polozhenie i fauna pozvonochnykh serozelenykh glin levoberezh'ia Pavlodarskogo
            Priirtysh'ia. [Stratigraphic position and vertebrate fauna of the grayish-green clays of the left
            bank of Pavlodar Irtysh area.] In: Resheniia i trudy Mezhvedomstvennogo soveshchaniia po
            dorabotke i utochneniiu unifitsirovannoĭ i korreliatsionnoĭ skhem Zapadno-Sibirskoĭ
            nizmennosti, 2, 76–81 (Russian).

AUBEKEROVA, PIRUZA ABLAEVNA
    1965A   Novye dannye ob iskopaemykh ptitsakh Kazakhstana. [New data on fossil birds of Kazakhstan.]
            In: Novosti ornitologii. Materialy chetvertoĭ vsesoiuznoĭ ornitologicheskoĭ konferentsii,
            Alma-Ata, 1965, 18–19 (Russian).
    1968A   Pliotsenovaia fauna mlekopitaiushchikh iugo-vostoka Kazakhstana. [Pliocene mammalian fauna of
            the south-east of Kazakhstan.] In: Materialy pervoĭ nauchnoĭ konferentsii molodykh
            uchenykh AN Kaz SSR (Russian).
    1969A   Novyĭ predstavitel' semeĭstva Entelodontidae. [A new representative of the family Entelodontidae.]
            Akad. Nauk Kaz. SSR, Izv., Ser. Biol., 1969:4, 47–52, 2 figs., 1 table (Russian; Kazakh
            summary).

AUBEKEROVA, P. A.   See also: Aubekerov, B. Zh., Aubekerova, P. A., Biriukov, M. D., Lychev, G. F. and
            Savinov, P. F., 1970A; Lychev, G. F. and Aubekerova, P. A., 1971A; Tolochko, V. V. and
            Aubekerova, P. A., 1971A.

AUBOIN, JEAN, BROUSSE, ROBERT and LEHMAN, JEAN-PIERRE
    1967A   Précis de géologie. Paris: Dunod Ed., 3 vols., 1790 pp., illustr. (French).

AUDLEY-CHARLES, MICHAEL GEOFFREY
    1970A   Triassic palaeogeography of the British Isles. (Discussions). Geol. Soc. London, Quart. J., 126:1–2,
            49–89, 2 figs., 7 pls.

AUFFENBERG, WALTER
    1969A   Statistical study of fossil tortoises. Amer. Phil. Soc., Yearb., 1968, 278.
    1971A   A new fossil tortoise, with remarks on the origin of South American testudinines. Copeia, 1971:1,
            106–117, 9 figs., 4 tables.
    1972A   Fossil turtles. Plaster Jacket, 16, 1–10, 4 figs.

AUGUST, O.
    1968A   Bibliographie zur Vor- und Frühgeschichte. Ausgrabung. u. Funde, 13, 294–333 (German).

AVAKIAN, LEVON AVETISOVICH and DAVTIAN, A. R.
    1970A   Chetvertichnaia sistema. Ozernye i ozerno-rechnye otlozheniia. [Quaternary system. Lake and
            lake-fluviatile deposits.] Geologiia SSSR, 43, Armenian SSR, 203–210, 2 figs. (Russian).

AVELEYRA ARROYO de ANDA, LUIS
    1966A   The second mammoth and associated artifacts at Santa Isabel Iztapan, Mexico. In: Graham, J. A.
            (ed.), 1966A, 15–31, 10 figs.

AVERKIEVA, ĪU. P., ARUTĪUNOV, S. A. and BROMLEĬ, ĪU. V.
   1969A   VIII Mezhdunarodnyĭ kongress antropologicheskikh i etnograficheskikh nauk. [VIIIth International
              Congress of Anthropological and Ethnographic Sciences.] Sov. Etnogr., 1969:1, 3—11
              (Russian; English summary).

AVNIMELECH, M. A.
   1967A   A preliminary account of the geological situation of the prehistoric site near Hazorea. Man (J. Roy.
              Anthropol. Inst.), 2, 457—461, 2 figs.

AZZAROLI, AUGUSTO
   1966B   Rev.: Schäfer in Säugetierkundl. Mitt., 18, 283—284.
   1970A   Villafranchian correlations based on large mammals. G. Geol., 35:1, 111—131, 3 tables.
              Rev.: Thenius in Zentralbl. Geol. Paläontol., Teil 2, 1971:1, 61—62.

AZZAROLI, A. and AMBROSETTI, P.
   1970A   Late Villafranchian and early Mid-Pleistocene faunas in Italy. Palaeogeogr., Palaeoclimatol.,
              Palaeoecol., 8:2—3, 107—111, 1 fig.
              Rev.: Thenius in Zentralbl. Geol. Paläontol., Teil 2, 1971:4, 337.
   1972A   Pozdnevillafrankskie i rannie srednepleĭstotšenovye fauny Italii. [Late Villafranchian and early middle
              Pleistocene faunas of Italy.] In: Geologiiā i fauna nizhnego i srednego pleĭstotšena Evropy,
              40—45 (Russian).

AZZAROLI, A. and BERZI, A.
   1970A   On an Upper Villafranchian fauna at Imola, northern Italy, and its correlation with the marine
              Pleistocene sequence of the Po plain. Palaeontogr. Ital., 66, 1—12, 2 figs., 3 pls.
              Rev.: Albanesi in Riv. Ital. Paleontol. Stratigr., 77:4, 551.

AZZAROLI, AUGUSTO   See also: Ambrosetti, P., Azzaroli, A., Bonadonna, F. P. and Follieri, M., 1972A.

B., W. R. P.
   1971A   James Maxwell McConnell Fisher [1912 — September 25, 1970]. Ibis, 113:1, 112—114, portr.

BAADSGAARD, HALFDAN   See: Folinsbee, R. E., Baadsgaard, H., and Cumming, G. L., 1970A.

BABIN, CLAUDE
   1971A   Éléments de paléontologie. Paris: Armand Colin, 408 pp., 300 figs., 4 tables (French).
              Rev.: Ager in Palaeogeogr. Palaeoclimatol. Palaeoecol., 11:3, 226—228.

BACHINSKIĬ, GEORGIĬ ALEKSEEVICH (= BACHYNS'KYĬ, G. O.) and DUBLIĀNSKIĬ, V. N.
   1963A   Novye dannye o zakhoroneniiākh iskopaemykh pozvonochnykh v karstovykh polostiākh Kryma.
              [New data on burials of fossil vertebrates in karst cavities of Crimea.] Akad. Nauk Ukr. SSR,
              Kompl. Karst. Eksped., Tr., 1, 93—106 (Russian).

BACHINSKIĬ, G. A.   See also: Tatarinov, K. A. and Bachinskiĭ, G. A., 1968A.

BACHMAYER, FRIEDRICH
   1967B   Eine Riesenschildkröte aus den altpleistozänen Schichten von Pikermi (Griechenland). Ann. Géol.
              Pays Hellén., 18, 512—526, 3 figs., 6 pls., 2 tables (German ; Greek summary).

BACHMAYER, FRIEDRICH, KOLLMANN, HEINZ A., SCHULTZ, ORTWIN and SUMMESBERGER, HERBERT
   1971A   Eine Mammutfundstelle im Bereich der Ortschaft Ruppersthal (Gross-Weikersdorf) bei Kirchberg am
              Wagram, NÖ. Naturhist. Mus. Wien, Ann., 75, 263—282, 7 figs., 6 pls., 3 tables (German).

BACHMAYER, FRIEDRICH and WILSON, ROBERT W.
   1970A   Die Fauna der altpliozänen Höhlen- und Spaltenfüllungen bei Kohfidisch, Burgenland (Österreich).
              Small mammals (Insectivora, Chiroptera, Lagomorpha, Rodentia) from the Kohfidisch
              fissures of Burgenland, Austria. Naturhist. Mus. Wien, Ann., 74, 533—587, 13 pls. (English;
              German summary).

BACHMAYER, FRIEDRICH and ZAPFE, HELMUTH
   1969A   Die Fauna der altpliozänen Höhlen- und Spaltenfüllungen bei Kohfidisch, Burgenland (Österreich).
              Geologische und biostratinomische Verhältnisse der Fundstelle, Ausgrabungen. Naturhist. Mus.
              Wien, Ann., 73, 123—139, 2 figs., 5 pls. (German; English summary).

1969B*   Schätze im Boden. Bilder aus Österreichs geologischer vergangenheit. Second edition. Vienna: Naturhistorisches Museum, 181 pp., 218 figs., 1 map.
Rev.: Bogsch in Földt. Közl., 100:4, 404–405 (Hungarian).

BACHYNS'KYĬ, G. O. (= BACHINSKIĬ, G. A.)
1965A   Tafonomichni osoblyvosti Syniakivs'kogo i Tarkhankuts'kogo mistenakhodzhen' vykopnykh nazemnykh khrebetnykh. [Taphonomic peculiarities of Siniakhov and Tarkhankut cave deposits of fossil land vertebrates.] Akad. Nauk Ukr. RSR, Dopov., Ser. B, 1965:5, 658–661, 2 tables (Ukrainian; Russian and English summaries).
1967A   Tafonomiia antropogenovykh i neogenovykh mistseznakhodzhen' nazemnykh khrebetnykh Ukrainy. [Taphonomy of Quaternary and Neogene localities of terrestrial vertebrates in Ukraine.] Kiev: "Naukova Dumka" Press, 131 pp., 21 figs., 6 tables (Ukrainian).

BACKUS, RICHARD H.   See: Lineaweaver, T. H. and Backus, R. H., 1970A.

BACON, EDWARD
1971A   Archaeology. Discoveries in the 1960's. New York and Washington: Praeger Publishers, 293 pp., illustr.
Rev.: Savory in Mus. J., 71:2, 79.

BACSKAI, JUDITH A.
1969A   Miocene porcupine fishes in California. Geol. Soc. Amer., Abstr., Part 3, 3 (abs.).

BACSKAI, J., BARTLETT, S., BRAJNIKOV, B. MUNTHE, K., NICHOLS, R. and MATSUMOTO, M.
1972A*   Bibliography of vertebrate paleontology and related subjects. 1970–1971. Soc. Vert. Paleontol., Bibliog., 26, 163 pp.

BACSKAI, J. A.   See also: Camp, C. L., Nichols, R. H., Brajnikov, B., Fulton, E. and Bacskai, J. A. (eds.), 1972A.

BADA, JEFFREY L.   See: Turekian, K. K. and Bada, J. L., 1972A.

BADAM, G. L.   See: Tewari, B. S. and Badam, G. L., 1969A.

BADER, OTTO NIKOLAEVICH (= BAHDER, O. N.)
1966D   Paleoliticheskoe pogrebenie na stoianke Sungir'. (Tezisy doklada). [Paleolithic burial on Sungir' site. (Theses of the report).] Int. Congr. Prehist. Protohist. Sci., VII, Moscow 1966, 44–45 (Russian).
1966E   Pitture rupestri paleolitiche negli Urali. Riv. Sci. Preist., 21:2, 365–378, 7 figs., 2 pls. (Italian; French and English summaries).
1968D   New data on the original inhabitation of north-east Europe. Quartär, 19, 181–197, 9 figs.
1969A   Severnaia paleoliticheskaia ekspeditsiia. [Northern Paleolithic Expedition.] In: Rybakov, B. A. (ed.), 1969A, 145–146 (Russian).
1969B   Polevoi seminar po stratigrafii antropogena i paleolitu pechorskogo Pripoliar'ia v 1968g. [Field seminar on Quaternary stratigraphy and on Paleolithic of Pechora Polar region in 1968.] Sov. Arkheol., 1969:4, 305–310, 1 fig. (Russian).
1969C   G. F. Debets (7.XII.1905–19.I.1969). Sov. Arkheol., 1969:4, 313–315, portr. (Russian).
1969D   Novye raboty v Volch'ei Peshchere. [New works in Volchii Cave.] In: Rybakov, B. A. (ed.), 1969A, 259–261 (Russian).
1970A   Vtoraia paleoliticheskaia mogila na Sungire. [Second Paleolithic burial on Sungir'.] In: Rybakov, B. A. (ed.), 1970A, 41–43, 1 fig. (Russian).
1970B   Das zweite Grab in der paläolithischen Siedlung Sungir' im mittleren Russland. Quartär, 21, 103–104, 1 pl. (German).
1970C   Le Paléolithique dans l'Oural et le peuplement du Nord. Discussion. Int. Congr. Anthropol. Ethnol. Sci., 7th, Moscow, 1964, Proc., 5, 385–392 (French).
1971A   Chelovek paleolita u severnykh predelov oikumeny. [Paleolithic man at the northern limits of the ecumene.] Priroda, 1971:5, 30–39, 11 figs. (Russian).
1971B   Drevneishee zaselenie Severnoi Evropy chelovekom v svete novykh dannykh. [Oldest peopling of northern Europe by man in the light of new data.] Akad. Nauk SSSR, Inst. Arkheol., Krat. Soobshch., 126, 3–13, 4 figs. (Russian).

BADER, O. N., ERDELI, I. and RANOV, V. A.
1969A   László Vértes (1914–1968). Sov. Arkheol., 1969:4, 316–317, portr. (Russian).

BAER, JAMES L.
1969A   Paleoecology of cyclic sediments of the lower Green River formation, central Utah. Brigham Young Univ. Geol. Studies, 16:1, 3–95, 23 figs., 7 pls., 6 tables.

BAHLO, EKKEHARD
1971A   Cerviden — (Mammalia) Reste aus den Oberen Mosbacher Sanden (Mittelpleistozän) bei Wiesbaden
             (Hessen). Hess. Landesamt Bodenforsch., Abh., 60, 17—24, 3 figs. (German).

BAHLO, EKKEHARD and MALEC, FRANZ
1969A   Insectivoren (Mammalia) aus den Oberen Mosbacher Sanden (Mittelpleistozän) bei Wiesbaden-Biebrich/
             Hessen. Mainz. Naturwiss. Arch., 8, 56—76, 5 figs., 2 pls. (German; French and English
             summaries).
1971A   Rodentia (Mammalia) aus den Oberen Mosbacher Sanden (Mittelpleistozän) bei Wiesbaden (Hessen).
             Mainz. Naturwiss. Arch., 10 (German).

BAĬBULATOVA, RAISA BEKTIMIROVNA   See: Didenko-Kislitsina, L. K., Biriukov, M. D. and
             Baĭbulatova, R. B., 1971A.

BAĬGUSHEVA, V. S. (= BAYGUSHEVA, V. S.)
1971A   Iskopaemaia teriofauna Liventsovskogo kar'era (Severo-Vostochnoe Priazov'e). [Fossil theriofauna
             of Liventsovka quarry (northeastern Azov region).] Akad. Nauk SSSR, Zool. Inst., Tr., 49,
             5—29, 2 figs., 6 pls., 1 table (Russian; English summary).

BAĬGUSHEVA, V. S.   See also: Vereshchagin, N. K., Alekseeva, L. I., David, A. I. and Baĭgusheva, V. S., 1969A.

BAILIT, HOWARD L.
1966A   Tooth size variability, inbreeding, and evolution. N.Y. Acad. Sci., Ann., 134:2, 616—623, 1 fig.,
             2 tables.

BAILIT, HOWARD L. and FRIEDLAENDER, J. S.
1967A   Reply to Oppenheimer. Amer. Anthropol., 69, 515.

BAILIT, HOWARD L.   See also: Sofaer, J. A., Bailit, H. L. and MacLean, C. J., 1971A.

BAILLOUD, M. G.
1969A   Informations archéologiques. Circonscription de la Région parisienne. Gallia Préhist., 12:2, 401—415,
             20 figs. (French).

BAIRD, DONALD
1970A   Type specimen of the Oligocene frog Zaphrissa eurypelis Cope, 1866. Copeia, 1970:2, 384—385.

BAIRD, DONALD   See also: Carroll, R. L. and Baird, D., 1972A; Carroll, R. L., Belt, E. S., Dineley, D. L.,
             Baird, D. and McGregor, D. C., 1972A, 1972B; West, R. M. and Baird, D., 1970A.

BAIRD, IRWIN L.
1970A   The anatomy of the reptilian ear. In: Gans, C. (ed.), 1970A, 193—275, 34 figs., 1 table.

BAKER, A. N.   See: Climo, F. M. and Baker, A. N., 1972A.

BAKER, JOHN
1969A   The Cro-Magnon discovery. Man (J. Roy. Anthropol. Inst.), 4:1, 135—136.

BAKHMUTOV, V. A.   See: Gashev, N. S. and Bakhmutov, V. A., 1968A.

BAKKER, ROBERT T.
1968A   The superiority of dinosaurs. Discovery, Yale, 3:2, 11—22, 8 figs.
1971A   Ecology of the Brontosaurs. Nature, 229:5281, 172—174, 1 fig.
1971B   Dinosaur physiology and the origin of mammals. Evolution, 25:4, 636—658, 8 figs.
1972A   Anatomical and ecological evidence of endothermy in dinosaurs. Nature, 238:5359, 81—85, 2 figs.,
             2 tables.

BALABAĬ, PAVEL PAVLOVICH
1956D   Do klasyfikatsii rodu Poraspis Kiaer. [On the classification of the genus Poraspis Kiaer.] Akad. Nauk
             Ukr. RSR, Nauk. Pryrod. Muz., L'vov, Nauk. Zap., 5, 3—13, 9 figs., 2 tables (Ukrainian;
             Russian summary).
1959B   Do vyvchennia pteraspid nyzhn'ogo devonu Podillia. [On the study of Pteraspidae from the lower
             Devonian of Podolia. Communication I.] Akad. Nauk Ukr. RSR, Nauk. Pryrod. Muz., L'vov,
             Nauk. Zap., 7, 3—21 (Ukrainian).

BALAKHMATOVA, VALENTINA TIMOFEEVNA
    1957A   Tretichnaia sistema. Severnye Karakumy, Sarykamyshskaia vpadina i iugo-vostochnyi Ustiurt.
        [Tertiary system. Northern Karakumy, Sarykamysh depression and southeastern Ustiurt.]
        Geologiia SSSR, 22, Turkmenian SSR, 236–240, 1 fig. (Russian).

BALCELLS R., E.
    1962A   Evolución y biogeografía. Discussions. Soc. Españ. Hist. Natur., Bol., Secc. Biol., 60, 219–229
        (Spanish).

BALLÉSIO, RONALD
    1964A   Monographie d'un machairodus du gisement villafranchien de Senèze. *Homotherium crenatidens*
        Fabrini. Saint-Etienne: Le Hénaff Ed., 138 pp., illustr. (French).

BALLÉSIO, R.   See also: Guérin, C., Ballésio, R. and Méon-Vilain, H., 1969A; Mein, P., Truc, G. and Ballésio, R.,
        1972A.

BALLESTEROS-GAIBROIS, M. and FRANCH, J. A.
    1964A*   El americanismo en las revistas. Antropología: 4. Sevilla, Univ., Publ., 8, 148 pp. (Spanish).
    1965A*   El americanismo en las revistas. Antropología: 5. Sevilla, Univ., Publ., 10, 161 pp. (Spanish).

BALLMANN, PETER
    1969A   Les oiseaux miocènes de la Grive-Saint-Alban (Isère). Geobios, 2, 157–204, 26 figs., 3 pls. (French;
        German summary).
        Rev.: Kuhn in Zentralbl. Geol. Paläontol., Teil 2, 1970:1, 70–71.
    1969B   Die Vögel aus der altburdigalen Spaltenfüllung von Wintershof (West) bei Eichstätt in Bayern.
        Zitteliana, 1, 5–60, 14 figs., 2 pls. (French; English summary).
        Rev.: Kuhn in Zentralbl. Geol. Paläontol., Teil 2, 1971:5, 410–411.
    1970A   Ein neuer Vertreter der Musophagidae (Aves) aus dem Chattium von Gaimersheim bei Ingolstadt
        (Bayern). Bayer. Staatssamml. Paläontol. Hist. Geol., Mitt., 10, 271–276, 2 figs. (German;
        English summary).
        Rev.: Kuhn in Zentralbl. Geol. Paläontol., Teil 2, 1971:5.

BALLMANN, PETER and ADROVER, RAFAEL
    1970A   Yacimiento paleontológico de la cueva de Son Bauzá (Mallorca). Acta Geol. Hisp., 5:2, 58–63,
        3 figs. (Spanish; French summary).

BALOGH, KÁLMÁN
    1970A   Dr. Schréter Zoltán emlékezete (1882–1970). Földt. Közl., 100:3, 238–242, portr., bibliog.
        (Hungarian).

BALOUT, L.
    1969A   Mosché Stékélis [1898–1967]. L'Anthropologie, 73:1–2, 135–138.

BAŁUK, WACŁAW
    1970A   Dolny torton Niskowej koło Nowego Sącza. [The Lower Tortonian at Niskowa near Nowy Sącz,
        Polish Carpathians.] Acta Geol. Pol., 20:1, 101–157, 3 figs., 14 pls., 6 tables (Polish;
        English summary).

BANDI, HANS-GEORG
    1968A   Les origines du peuplement de l'Amérique. Préhist. Spéléol. Ariége., 23, 99–119, 7 figs. (French).
        Rev.: Balout in L'Anthropologie, 73:5–6, 423–425.
    1969A   Esquimo prehistory. Translated from German by Ann E. Keep. College, Alaska: Univ. Alaska Press,
        xii + 228 pp., illustr.
        Rev.: Chard in Science (AAAS), 165, 1247; Lee in Anthropol. J. Can., 9:2, 29–32; McKennan in
        Arctic, 23, 65–66.
    1968-69B   Eiszeitkunst und Zoologie. Anthropos, 63/64:1/2, 22–32, 8 figs. (German).
    1969C   Le Paléolithique supérieur en Suisse. Préhist. Spéléol. Ariége., 24, 55–71, 10 figs. (French).

BANDI, M.
    1969A   Recherches archéologiques en Alaska. Globe, 109, 12–13 (French).

BANDRABUR, T.   See: Ghenea, C., Bandrabur, T. and Mihăilă, N., 1967A.

BÁNESZ, LADISLAV
    1969A   Zomrel László Vértes [1914–1968]. Sloven. Archeol., 17:1, 259–260, portr. (Czechoslovakian).

BANTI, M.
    1969A   Reconstruction de la denture de l'adolescent de Grimaldi. Discussion. Soc. Anthropol. Paris, Bull.
                Mém., Sér. 12, 4, 386–388 (French).

BARANDIARÁN, IGNACIO
    1968A   El doctor André Cheynier. Caesaraugusta, 31–32, 262–267 (Spanish).
    1969-70A   El paleontólogo F. Ed. Koby. Caesaraugusta, 33-34, 183–185 (Spanish).

BARANDIARÁN, JOSE MIGUEL and ALTUNA, JESÚS
    1969A   La cueva de Ekain y sus figuras rupestres. Munibe, 21:4, 331–386, 64 figs.. 54 pls., 2 maps.
                (Spanish).

BARANOV, A. S.
    1969A   Cheliustnaiа kost' "sviazyvaet" ... kontinenty. [A jaw bone "ties together" ... the continents.]
                Priroda, 1969:2, 109–110, 1 fig. (Russian).

BARANOVA, IU. P., BISKE, S. F., GONCHAROV, V. F., KUL'KOVA, I. A. and TITKOV, A. S.
    1968A   Kainozoi Severo-Vostoka SSSR. [Cenozoic of the northeast of USSR.] Akad. Nauk SSSR, Sib. Otd.,
                Inst. Geol. Geofiz., Tr., 38, 124 pp., 19 figs., 7 maps, 3 tables (Russian).

BARBERENA, M. C.
    1970A   A presença de *Loxomma* na formação Palermo. Porto Alegre, Escol. Geol., Notas Estud., 2:1, 45–49,
                1 fig. (Portuguese; English summary).
                Rev.: Westphal in Zentralbl. Geol. Paläontol., Teil 2, 1971:1, 52–53.
    1971A   Algumas considerações sôbre o desenvolvimento de rincossáurios. Acad. Brasil. Ciênc., An., 43
                suppl., 403–409, 1 fig. (Portuguese; English summary).

BARBETTI, M. and ALLEN, H.
    1972A   Prehistoric man at Lake Mungo, Australia, by 32,000 years BP. Nature, 240:5375, 46–48, 2 figs.,
                1 table.

BARDACK, DAVID
    1970A   A new teleost from the Oldman formation (Cretaceous) of Alberta. Can., Nat. Mus., Publ. Pal., 3,
                viii + 8 pp., 2 figs.

BARDACK, DAVID and SPRINKLE, GLORIA
    1969A   Morphology and relationships of saurocephalid fishes. Fieldiana: Geol., 16:12, 297–340, 8 figs.,
                3 tables.

BARDACK, D. and ZANGERL, R.
    1971A   Lampreys in the fossil record. In: Hardisty, M. W. and Potter, I. C. (eds.), 1971A, 67–84, 7 figs.

BARDON, L.   See: Bouyssonie, A., Bouyssonie, J. and Bardon, L., 1971A.

BARGHUSEN, HERBERT R.   See: DeMar, R. and Barghusen, H. R., 1972A.

BARJON, LOUIS and LEROY, PIERRE
    1964A   La carrière scientifique de Pierre Teilhard de Chardin. Monaco: Editions du Rocher (French).
                Rev.: L.-R. N. in Toulouse, Univ., Inst. d'Art Prehist., Trav., 7, 210.

BARLOW, NORA
    1967A   Rev.: deBeer in New Sci., 36:566, 114.

BARNABAS, JOHN   See: Goodman, M., Barnabas, J., Matsuda, G. and Moore, G. W., 1971A.

BARNES, B., EDWARDS, B. J. N., HALLAM, J. S. and STUART, A. J.
    1971A   Skeleton of a Late Glacial elk associated with barbed points from Poulton-le-Fylde, Lancashire.
                Nature, 232:5311, 488–489, 2 figs.

BARNES, LAWRENCE G.
    1969A   Miocene Desmatophocinae from California. Geol. Soc. Amer., Abstr., Part 3, 3 (abs.).
    1970A   A re-evaluation of mandibles of *Allodesmus* (Otariidae, Carnivora) from the Round Mountain Silt,
                Kern County, California. PaleoBios, 10, 24 pp., 11 figs., 5 tables.
    1971A   *Imagotaria* (Mammalia: Otariidae) from the Late Miocene Santa Margarita Formation near Santa Cruz,
                California. PaleoBios, 11, 10 pp., 3 figs., 1 table.
                Rev.: Thenius in Zentralbl. Geol. Paläontol., Teil 2, 1971:5, 414.

1971B   Comments on the Phocoenidae. Geol. Soc. Amer., Abstr., 3:2, 79 (abs.).
1972A   Miocene Desmatophocinae (Mammalia: Carnivora) from California. Calif., Univ., Publ. Geol. Sci., 89,
          68 pp., 25 figs., 6 pls., 9 tables.

BARNES, LAWRENCE G.   See also: Savage, D. E. and Barnes, L. G., 1972A.

BARNETT, S. A.
1971A   The human species. A biology of man. New York and London: Harper and Row, 333 pp., illustr.
          Rev.: Glanville in Amer. J. Phys. Anthropol., 37:2, 315.

BARR, F. T.
1968A*   Geology and archaeology of Northern Cyrenaica, Libya. Petrol. Explor. Soc. Libya, 10th Ann.,
          Field Conf., 215 pp., illustr.
          Rev.: Marchetti in Amer. Ass. Petrol. Geol., Bull., 52:10, 2067–2068.

BARR, THOMAS C., JR.
1957A   The bones of Big Bone Cave, Tennessee. Speleo Digest, 1957, 4–6 – 4–8, 1 fig. (reprinted from
          Speleonews, 4:12, 1).

BARRAL, LOUIS
1965A   La grotte de l'Observatoire. Congr. Préhist. France, 16ᵉ Sess., Monaco 1959, C.R., 101–103, 1 fig.
          (French).
1965B   Le Musée d'Anthropologie Préhistorique de Monaco. Congr. Préhist. France, 16ᵉ Sess., Monaco 1959,
          C.R., 104–107, 1 fig. (French).
1965C   Les grottes de Grimaldi (Italie). Congr. Préhist. France, 16ᵉ Sess., Monaco 1959, C.R., 108–116,
          3 figs. (French).
1968A   Techniques scientifiques en préhistoire. Sciences, 56, 14–21, 6 figs. (French).
1970A   Grotta del Principe (Grimaldi di Ventimiglia, Prov. di Imperia). Riv. Sci. Preist., 25:2, 397–398
          (Italian).

BARRAL, LOUIS and SIMONE, SUZANNE
1968A   Découverte de Paléolithique inférieur dans la grotte du Prince (Grimaldi, Ligurie italienne).
          L'Anthropologie, 72:5–6, 531–536, 3 figs. (French).
1968B   Nouvelles fouilles à la grotte du Prince (Grimaldi, Ligurie italienne). Découverte de Paléolithique
          inférieur. Monaco, Mus. Anthropol. Préhist., Bull., 14, 5–23, 6 figs. (French).
1968C   Scavi nella Grotta del Principe (Grimaldi, Liguria). Campagna 1968. Riv. Sci. Preist., 23:2, 389–392,
          1 fig. (Italian).
1969A   Sur la présence à la grotte du Prince (Grimaldi, Ligurie italienne) de brèches à ossements rissiennes et
          de formations attribuables à la mer du Mindel-Riss. Acad. Sci., C.R., Sér. D, 268:4, 637–640,
          1 fig. (French).
1970A   Scavi nella grotta del Principe (Grimaldi, Liguria). Riv. Sci. Preist., 25:1, 301–308, 3 figs. (Italian;
          French and English summaries).

BARRIÈRE, CLAUDE
1962A   L'utilisation des reliefs rocheux dans l'art paléolithique supérieur (deux nouveaux exemples). Toulouse,
          Univ., Inst. d'Art Préhist., Trav., 5, 21–22, 1 pl. (French).
1962B   Les gravures de la grotte du Gazel, Sallèles-Cabardès (Aude). Toulouse, Univ., Inst. d'Art Préhist.,
          Trav., 5, 23–31, 6 figs. (French).
1969A   Une scène anthropomorphique à Font-de-Gaume. Préhist. Spéléol. Ariége., 24, 39–53, 6 figs., 7 photos
          (French).

BARRIÈRE, CLAUDE   See also: Nougier, L. R. and Barrière, C., 1965B.

BARRIÈRE, JEAN, CAPPETTA, HENRI and MICHAUX, JACQUES
1970A   Nouvelles données stratigraphiques et paléontologiques sur les "calcaires de Frontignan". Signification
          de ces formations lagunaires et lacustres dans le Plio-Pleistocène inférieur languedocien. Soc.
          Géol. Fr., C.R., 1970:6, 200–202, 1 fig. (French).

BARRIÈRE, JEAN and MICHAUX, JACQUES
1970A   La formation détritique villafranchienne de la Mosson (Montpellier) et son paléosol. Ass. Fr. Étud.
          Quat., Bull., 23–24, 93–103, 2 figs., 3 tables (French; English summary).

BARROWS, ALLEN
1970A   New excavations for fossils at Rancho La Brea, Los Angeles. Calif., Div. Mines Geol., Miner. Inform.
          Serv., 23:1, 14–15, 1 photo, 1 map.

BARRY, DAVID G.
1971A   The Darwinian synthesis. In: Holmes, L. D. (ed.), 1971A, 61—70 (reprinted from Midwest
          Quarterly, 1:4, 1960).

BARRY, T. H.
1968A   Sound conduction in the fossil anomodont *Lystrosaurus*. S. Afr. Mus., Ann., 50:11, 275—281,
          3 figs., 1 pl.
1972A   Terrestrial vertebrate fossils from Ecca defined beds in South Africa. Gondwana Symp., 2nd, Proc.,
          Pap., 653—657, 3 figs.

BARSBOLD, R., VORONIN, IU. I. and ZHEGALLO, V. I.
1971A   O rabote Sovetsko-Mongol'skoi paleontologicheskoi ekspedifsii v 1969—1970 g. [On the work of the
          Soviet-Mongolian paleontological expedition in 1969—1970.] Paleontol. Zh., 1971:2, 139—143
          (Russian).

BARSBOLD, R.   See also: Martinson, G. G., Sochava, A. V. and Barsbold, R., 1969A, 1970A.

BARSKOV, IGOR' SERGEEVICH and KOROLEVA, N. V.
1969A   O konodontakh, ostatkakh ryb i problematicheskikh iskopaemykh dzhul'finskogo iarusa verkhnei
          permi Zakavkaz'ia. [On conodonts, fish remains and problematic fossils of Dzhul'fa stage of
          Upper Permian in Transcaucasia.] Mosk. Obshchest. Ispyt. Prir., Biull., Otd. Geol., 44:6, 144
          (Russian).

BÁRTA, JURAJ
1965E   Poznámky k paleolitu Rumunska. [Notes on Rumanian Paleolithic.] Czech., Ustred. Ústav. Geol.,
          Sborn. Geol. Ved, Rada A, 3, 123—140, 4 pls. (Czech; English and Russian summaries).

BARTH, T. F. W. and HEINTZ, A.
1970A   Geologisk museum ved Universitetet i Oslo — Femtiår. Naturen, 94, 252—265, 1 fig. (Norwegian).

BARTHEL, K. WERNER
1966A   Mounting a skeleton of *Smilodon californicus* Bovard. Curator, 9:2, 119—124, 2 figs.
1970A   Fossil-Lagerstätten, Nr. 6: On the deposition of the Solnhofen lithographic limestone (Lower
          Tithonian, Bavaria, Germany). Neues Jahrb. Geol. Paläontol., Abh., 135:1, 1—18, 2 figs.,
          4 pls., 1 table (German summary).
          Rev.: Author's summary in Geol. Bl. Nordost-Bayern, 21:2/3, 153—154.

BARTHEL, K. W. and JANICKE, V.
1970A   Aptychen als Verdauungsrückstand. Ein Fund aus den Solnhofener Plattenkalken, unteres Untertithon,
          Bayern. Neues Jahrb. Geol. Paläontol., Monatsh., 1970:2, 65—68, 1 fig. (German; English
          summary).

BARTHELD, F. VON, ERDBRINK, D. P. and KROMMENHOEK, W.
1970A   A fossil incisor from Lake Edward, and a method for its determination. Uganda J., 34:1, 75—78, 3 pls.
1970B   A fossil incisor from Uganda and a method for its determination. Ned. Akad. Wetensch., Proc., Ser. B,
          73, 426—431, 1 fig., 4 pls.

BARTHOLOMAI, ALAN
1969A   The Lower Cretaceous elopid fish *Pachyrhizodus marathonensis* (Etheridge Jnr.). In: Campbell, K. S. W.
          (ed.), 1969A, 249—263, figs. 46—49, pls. 14—15.
1970A   The extinct genus *Procoptodon* Owen (Marsupialia: Macropodidae) in Queensland. Queensl. Mus., Mem.,
          15:4, 213—233, 1 fig., 6 pls., 7 tables.
1971A   *Dasyurus dunmalli*, a new species of fossil marsupial (Dasyuridae) in the upper Cainozoic deposits of
          Queensland. Queensl. Mus., Mem., 16:1, 19—26, 1 pl., 3 tables.
1972A   Some upper cheek teeth in *Propleopus oscillans* (de Vis). Queensl. Mus., Mem., 16:2, 211—213, 1 pl.

BARTHOLOMAI, ALAN and HOWIE, ANNE
1970A   Vertebrate fauna from the Lower Trias of Australia. Nature, 225:5237, 1063, 2 figs.

BARTHOLOMEW, GEORGE A., JR.
1970A   A model for the evolution of pinniped polygyny. Evolution, 24:3, 546—559, 1 fig.

BARTHOLOMEW, G. A., JR. and BIRDSELL, J. B.
1969A   Ecology and the protohominids. In: Ehrlich, P. R., *et al.* (eds.), 1969A, 541—558.

BARTLETT, SUSAN   See: Bacskai, J., Bartlett, S., Brajnikov, B., Munthe, K., Nichols, R. and Matsumoto, M. (eds.),
          1972A.

BARTOLOMEI, GIORGIO
1969A   Rinvenimento di un sirenio nei Colli Berici (Vicenza). Accad. Naz. Lincei, Atti, Ser. 8, Cl. Sci. Fis., Mat.
                    Natur., Rend., 47:1–2, 39–40, 2 pls. (Italian).
                    Rev.: Albanesi in Riv. Ital. Paleontol. Stratigr., 76:1, 176.
1969B   Rinvenimento di resti de elefante presso Citerna (Perugia). Ferrara, Univ., Ann., Sez. 9, 4:17, 267–274,
                    4 figs. (Italian; French and English summaries).
1969C   Considerazioni ecologiche sulle faune pleistoceniche dell' Europa contenenti scimmie ed istrici. Verona,
                    Mus. Civ. Stor. Natur., Mem., Fuori Ser., 3, 39–52, 1 fig., 1 table (Italian; English summary).
1970A   Considerazioni sul probabile significato ecologico del roditore pleistocenico Dolomys lenki Heller.
                    [Considerations on the probable ecological significance of the Pleistocene rodent Dolomys lenki
                    Heller.] Ferrara, Univ., Ann., Sez. 9, 4:19, 299–304, 1 table (Italian; English and French
                    summaries).
1970B   Primi contributi alla conoscenza dei Dolomys pleistocenici del Veneto e del Carso. Verona, Mus. Civ.
                    Stor. Natur., Mem., 17 (1969), 79–139, 32 figs. (Italian).

BARTOLOMEI, GIORGIO and PASA, ANGELO
1970A   La breccia ossifera di Boscochiesanuova nei Monti Lessini (Verona): I depositi e la fauna. Verona, Mus.
                    Civ. Stor. Natur., Mem., 17 (1969), 475–494, 3 figs., 1 table (Italian; English summary).

BASABE, JOSÉ Mª.
1969A   Nouvelles découvertes anthropologiques dans le Moustérien Basque espagnol. Int. Congr. Anthropol.
                    Ethnol. Sci., 8th, Tokyo, 1968, Proc., Vol. I, Anthropology, 99–101, 3 tables (French).
1970A   Dientes humanos del paleolítico de Lezetxiki (Mondragón). Munibe, 22:3–4, 113–124, 12 figs.
                    (Spanish).

BASS, WILLIAM M.
1969A   Recent developments in the identification of human skeletal material. Amer. J. Phys. Anthropol., 30,
                    459–462.

BASSO, G.   See: Bucci, G., Nebbia, L., Sacchi Vialli, G., Savi, A. and Basso, G., 1969A.

BASSOULLET, JEAN-PAUL
1971A   Découverte d'empreintes de pas de reptiles dans l'Infralias de la région d'Aïn-Sefra (Atlas saharien–
                    Algérie). Soc. Géol. Fr., C.R., 1971:7, 358–359, 1 fig. (French).

BATTAIL, BERNARD
1972A   Une famille très primitive de Cynodontes sud-africains: les Procynosuchidae. Acad. Sci., C.R., Sér. D,
                    274:17, 2463–2466 (French).

BATTEN, R. L.   See: Dott, R. H. and Batten, R. L., 1971A.

BATTETTA, J.
1969A   Compte rendu du remaniement de la reconstitution du crâne de Dolichopithecus arvernensis Depéret,
                    type. Soc. Linn. Lyon, Bull., 38:8, 279–284, 3 pls. (French).

BAUDELOT, SABINE
1968A   A propos des Talpidés (Insectivores) de Sansan. Soc. Géol. Fr., C.R., 1968:4, 124–126, 2 figs. (French).
                    Rev.: Fahlbusch in Zentralbl. Geol. Palä ontol., Teil 2, 1969:3, 291–292.
1969A   Sur une faune de petits Mammifères récoltés dans le Miocène de La Romieu (Gers). Soc. Géol. Fr., C.R.,
                    1969:6, 224–226 (French).
1970A   Compléments à l'étude des micromammifères du gisement miocène de Sansan (Gers). Soc. Géol. Fr.,
                    C.R., 1970:8, 303–304, 2 figs. (French).

BAUDELOT, SABINE and BONIS, LOUIS DE
1968A   Contribution à l'étude des rongeurs de l'Aquitanien moyen et supérieur de l'Agenais. Soc. Hist. Natur.
                    Toulouse, Bull., 104:1–2, 160–164, 1 fig. (French).

BAUDELOT, SABINE and CROUZEL, FERNAND
1969A   Sur un nouveau gisement aquitanien de vertébrés près de Colomiers (Haute-Garonne). Soc. Géol. Fr.,
                    C.R., 1969:2, 58–59, 1 fig. (French).

BAUDELOT, SABINE See also: Crouzel, F. and Baudelot, S., 1970A.

BAUMHOF, MARTIN A.   See: Heizer, R. F. and Baumhof, M. A., 1970A.

BAUZÁ RULLÁN, JUAN
1967A   Contribuciones al conocimiento de la ictiología actual y fósil de Menorca. Rev. de Menorca, 3, 197–210,
                    18 figs. (Spanish).

Rev.: Weiler in Zentralbl. Geol. Paläontol., Teil 2, 1970:3/4, 220.
1971A   Contribuciones al conocimiento de la fauna ictiológica fósil de Cataluña. Acta Geol. Hisp., 6:1, 1–3, 2 figs. (Spanish).
1971B   Paleontología de Mallorca. Ciento ochento milliones de años de la flora y fauna de Mallorca. Hist. Mallorca, 331–340, 67 figs. (Spanish).
Rev.: Weiler in Zentralbl. Geol. Paläontol., Teil 2, 1971:5, 397.
1971C   Contribuciones al conocimiento de la fauna ictiológica fósil de España. II. Acta Geol. Hisp., 6:5, 149–151, 1 fig., 1 table (Spanish; French summary).

BAY, ROLAND
1966B   Les fouilles dans le gisement villafranchien à Ubeidiya, près de Tibériade, en Israel. Les Eyzies, 15, 120–123, 1 fig. (French).
1967A   La morphologie comparée de la dentition des Hominidés. Les Eyzies, 16, 55–66 (French).
1969A   Le Paléolithic et le Mésolithique de la vallée de la Birse. Les Eyzies, 18, 15–24 (French).

BAZAROV, DASHI-DONDOK BAZAROVICH
1964A   Chetvertichnyĭ period v Selenginskom srednegor'e. [Quaternary period in the Selenga mountain region.] In: Vsesoĭuznoe Soveshchanie po Izucheniĭu Chetvertichnogo perioda, Novosibirsk, 1964, Tezisy Dokladov, Sektsiĭa Paleogeografii, 98–102 (Russian).
1968A   Chetvertichnye otlozheniĭa i osnovnye etapy razvitiĭa rel'efa selenginskogo srednegor'ĭa. [Quaternary deposits and main stages in relief development of Selenga middle-height mountains.] Ulan-Ude: Burĭatskoe Publish., 166 pp., 50 figs., 1 chart, 4 tables (Russian).
Rev.: Kozhevnikov and Laukhin in Geol. Geofiz., 1970:2, 146–148 (Russian).
1970A   K voprosu o genezise i vozraste otlozheniĭ razreza Oshurkovo (Zapadnoe Zabaĭkal'e). [On the question of the genesis and age of deposits of the Oshurkovo section (western Transbaĭkalia).] Akad. Nauk SSSR, Sib. Otd., Mater. Ist. Sib., Drevniaia Sibir', 3, 53–56, 1 fig. (Russian).

BAZAROV, D. B., ANTOSHCHENKO-OLENEV, I. V. and GURULEV, S. A.
1969A   Osnovnye problemy paleogeografii antropogena Pribaĭkal'ĭa i Zapadnogo Zabaĭkal'ĭa. [Basic problems of Anthropogene paleogeography of Baĭkalia and west Transbaĭkalia.] In: Problemy chetvertichnoĭ geologii Sibiri, 121–130 (Russian; English summary).

BAZHANOV, O. V.
1971A   Chetvertichnaĭa sistema. Zailiĭskiĭ raĭon. [Quaternary system. Trans-Ili region.] Geologiĭa SSSR, 40:1, Southern Kazakhstan, 509–516 (Russian).

BAZHANOV, O. V., DIDENKO-KISLITSINA, L. K. and KOSTENKO, N. N.
1971A   Paleogenovaĭa sistema. Zailiĭskiĭ raĭon, Severnaĭa i Ĭuzhnaĭa Dzhungariĭa. [Paleogene system. Trans-Ili region, northern and southern Dzhungaria.] Geologiĭa SSSR, 40:1, Southern Kazakhstan, 445–454 (Russian).

BAZHANOV, O. V., BOCHAROVA, N. I., DIDENKO-KISLITSINA, L. K. and KOSTENKO, N. N.
1971A   Neogenovaĭa sistema. Zailiĭskiĭ raĭon, Ĭuzhnaĭa i Severnaĭa Dzhungariĭa. [Neogene system. Trans-Ili region, southern and northern Dzhungaria.] Geologiĭa SSSR, 40:1, Southern Kazakhstan, 472–493, 2 figs. (Russian).

BAZHANOV, O. V. and KOSTENKO, N. N.
1971A   Melovaĭa sistema. Zailiĭskiĭ raĭon, Severnaĭa i Ĭuzhnaĭa Dzhungariĭa. [Cretaceous system. Trans-Ili region, northern and southern Dzhungaria.] Geologiĭa SSSR, 40:1, Southern Kazakhstan, 414–417 (Russian).

BAZHANOV, VALERIAN SEMENOVICH
1971A   Pervoe mezozoĭskoe mlekopitaĭushchee iz Sovetskogo Soĭuza. [First Mezozoic mammalian from the Soviet Union.] In: Teriologiĭa (Russian).

BAZHANOV, V. S., BIRĬUKOV, M. D., VETROV, F. E., KOZHAMKULOVA, B. S., LYCHEV, G. F., MUSAKULOVA, L. T. and SAVINOV, P. F.
1971A   Osobennosti arealov neskol'kikh faun mlekopitaĭushchikh kaĭnozoĭa. [Particularities of the areas of some Cenozoic mammalian faunas.] Akad. Nauk Kaz. SSR, Inst. Zool., Mater. Fauny i Flory, 5, 5–11, 4 figs. (Russian).

BAZHANOV, V. S. and EROFEEV, V. S.
1971A   Smena teriofaun kaĭnozoĭa basseĭna Verkhnego Irtysha na fone tektonicheskogo rezhima i klimaticheskoĭ obstanovki. [Change of Cenozoic theriofaunas of the upper Irtysh basin on the background of tectonic conditions and climatic environment.] Akad. Nauk. Kaz. SSR, Inst. Zool., Mater. Fauny i Flory, 5, 63–65, 1 table (Russian).

BAZHANOV, VALERIAN SEMENOVICH and KOSTENKO, N. N.
1964A   Korreliat͡sii͡a otlozheniĭ kaĭnozoi͡a Kazakhstana i Indii po faune mlekopitai͡ushchikh. [Correlation of Cenozoic deposits of Kazakhstan and India by mammalian fauna.] In: Voprosy geologii Kazakhstana, 82—95 (Russian; English summary).

BAZILE, F.   See: Ravoux, G. and Bazile, F., 1967A.

BEALS, RALPH L. and HOIJER, HARRY
1965A   Rev.: Kurth in Homo, 20:3, 197.
1971A   An introduction to anthropology. Fourth edition. New York: MacMillan Co., xix + 711 pp., illustr.
          Rev.: Wetherington in Amer. J. Phys. Anthropol., 37:3, 411—423.

BEAUFORT, F. DE and JULLIEN, R.
1968A   Les ours de la grotte d'Haristoi-Isturitz. Mammalia, 32:2, 225—227, 1 pl. (French; English summary).

BEAUMONT, GÉRARD DE
1968B   Une intéressante mandibule de Hyaenidae (Carnivora) du Pontien de Samos. Arch. Sci. (Soc. Phys. Hist. Natur. Genève), 21:1, 21—26, 1 fig., 1 pl. (French).
          Rev.: Thenius in Zentralbl. Geol. Paläontol., Teil 2, 1970:3/4, 237.
1968C   Note sur l'ostéologie crânienne de Plesiogale Pomel (Mustelidae, Carnivora). Arch. Sci. (Soc. Phys. Hist. Natur. Genève), 21:1, 27—34, 5 figs., 1 pl., 1 table (French).
1968D   Note sur la région auditive de quelques carnivores. Arch. Sci. (Soc. Phys. Hist. Natur. Genève), 21:2, 213—223, 1 pl. (French).
          Rev.: Thenius in Zentralbl. Geol. Paläontol., Teil 2, 1970:3/4, 237.
1969A   Brèves remarques à propos d'un crâne de Hyaenidae (Carnivora) du Musée de Vienne. Arch. Sci. (Soc. Phys. Hist. Natur. Genève), 22:1, 49—53, 1 pl. (French).
1969B   Brèves remarques sur Plioviverrops Kretzoi (Carnivora). Soc. Vaudoise Sci. Natur, Bull., 70:6, 247—253, 2 figs., 1 pl. (French).
1970A   Brèves remarques sur Plioviverrops Kretzoi (Carnivora). Lausanne Univ., Lab. Géol., Bull., 180, 7 pp., 2 figs., 1 pl. (French).
1970B   Observations sur Orycteropus gaudryi Major (Mammalia, Tubulidentata). Lausanne Univ., Lab. Géol., Bull., 183, 10 pp., 2 figs. (French).

BEAUMONT, P. B.   See: Vogel, J. C. and Beaumont, P. B., 1972A.

BECH BORRÁS, JAIME
1970A   Nuevo hallazgo de Hippopotamus amphibius major en Banyoles (Gerona). Acta Geol. Hisp., 5:2, 51—53, 2 figs. (Spanish; English summary).

BECKER-PLATEN, JENS DIETER
1970A   Lithostratigraphische Untersuchungen im Känozoikum Südwest-Anatoliens (Türkei). Geol. Jahrb., Suppl. 97, 243 pp., 12 figs., 11 pls., 22 tables (German; English and French summaries).

BECKER-PLATEN, J. D., and SICKENBERG, O.
1968A   Die unterpleistozänen Kiese von Eskişehir (Anatolien) und ihre Säugetierfauna. Hanover, Tech. Hochsch., Geol. Inst., Mitt., 8, 7—20, 2 figs. (German).

BECKHAM, REXFORD S.
1963A   A basic list of books and periodicals for college libraries. (Compiled with the assistance of Marie P. Beckham.) In: Mandelbaum, D. G., Lasker, G. W. and Albert, E. M. (eds.), 1963B, 77—316.

BEDDALL, BARBARA G.
1969A*   Wallace and Bates in the tropics. An introduction to the theory of natural selection. London: Macmillan Co., xii + 241 pp., illustr.
          Rev.: Oppenheimer in Quart. Rev. Biol., 45, 394—395.
1972A   Wallace, Darwin, and Edward Blyth: further notes on the development of evolution theory. J. Hist. Biol., 5:1, 153—158.

BEDEN, MICHEL
1969A   Étude et reconstitution des restes de Palaeoloxodon (Elephas) antiquus du Chatelard (Charente). Poitiers, Univ., Inst. Géol. Anthropol. Préhist., Trav., 10, 43—56, 4 pls. (French; German and English summaries).
1970A   Contribution à la connaissance des terrasses du Clain: morphologie et faune. Poitiers, Univ., Inst. Géol. Anthropol. Préhist., Trav., 9, 1—161, 22 pls., tables (French).
1970B   Découverte d'un squelette de Cervus philisi Schaub 1941 dans le gisement villafranchien de Chilhac (Haute-Loire). Poitiers, Univ., Inst. Géol. Anthropol. Préhist., Trav., 11, 15 pp., 4 figs., 2 pls., 8 tables (French; German summary).

BEDEN, MICHEL and GUTH, CHRISTIAN
  1970A   Nouvelles découvertes de restes de mammifères dans le gisement villafranchien de Chilhac (Haute-Loire). Acad. Sci., C.R., Sér. D, 270:17, 2065—2067 (French).
           Rev.: Thenius in Zentralbl. Geol. Paläontol., Teil 2, 1971:2—3, 188.
  1970B   Un nouveau gisement de vertébrés du villafranchien de la vallée de l'Allier. Acad. Sci., C.R., Sér. D, 271:2, 168—171 (French).
           Rev.: Thenius in Zentralbl. Geol. Paläontol., Teil 2, 1971:2—3, 188.

BEDISH, G.   See: Duguid, J. and Bedish, G., 1968A.

BEDROSSIAN, TRINDA L.
  1971A   Fossils... the living past. Calif. Geol., 24:12, 227—239, 13 figs., 2 tables.

BEDWELL, STEPHEN F.
  1971A   New evidence for the presence of turkey in the early postglacial period of the northern Great Basin. Great Basin Natur., 31, 48—49.

BEDWELL, S. F. and CRESSMAN, L. S.
  1971A   Fort Rock report: prehistory and environment of the pluvial Fort Rock Lake area of south-central Oregon. Oreg., Univ., Anthropol. Pap., 1, 1—25, 9 figs.

BEECHER, WILLIAM J.
  1969A   Possible motion detection in the vertebrate middle ear. Chicago Acad. Sci., Bull., 11:6, 155—210, 23 figs.

BEER, GAVIN R. DE
  1963A   Rev.: Cannon in Isis, 55:4, 446—447.
  1964D   Rev.: Halliday in New Sci., 26:448, 812.
  1966C   Hominisation, humanisation, civilisation: réponse à Jean-Jacques Rousseau. Archéocivilisation, 1:1—2, 2—10 (French).

BEERBOWER, JAMES R.
  1968A   Rev.: R. M. B. in Geol. Mag., 106:5, 501—502;   Reiss in Isr. J. Earth-Sci., 19:1, 39—40.

BEGG, E. L.   See: Hansen, R. O. and Begg, E. L., 1970A.

BEGINES RAMÍREZ, A.   See: González Echegaray, P. J., García Guinea, M. A. and Begines Ramírez, A., 1963A; González Echegaray, P. J., García Guinea, M. A., Begines, A., Madariaga de la Campa, B. and Leroi-Gourhan, A., 1966A.

BEHRENS, M., FRANK, H., HÖLLEIN, K., SPAETH, W. V. and WURSTER, P.
  1970A   Geologische Untersuchungen im Ostteil der Murnauer Mulde. Deut. Geol. Ges., Z., 121, 197—224, 15 figs. (German).

BEHRENSMEYER, A. K.
  1970A   Preliminary geological interpretation of a new hominid site in the Lake Rudolf basin. Nature, 226: 5242, 225—226, 2 figs.

BEHRENSMEYER, A. K.   See also: Isaac, G. L., Leakey, R. E. F. and Behrensmeyer, A. K., 1971A; Patterson, B., Behrensmeyer, A. K. and Sill, W. D., 1970A; Vondra, C. F., Johnson, G. D., Bowen, B. E. and Behrensmeyer, A. K., 1971A.

BEKENI, SH.
  1969A   Novyĭ metod vychisleniĭa kolichestva osobeĭ zhivotnykh v osteologicheskom materiale iz arkheologicheskikh mestonakhozhdeniĭ. [A new method for calculating the number of individual animals in osteological material from archeological sites.] Mosk. Obshchest. Ispyt. Prir., Bĭull., Otd. Biol., 74:6, 69—71 (Russian; English summary).

BELDEN, L. BURR
  1968A   50,000 years ago. Desert Mag., 31:12, 8—11, 6 figs.

BELIAEV, G. M. and GLIKMAN, LEONID SERGEEVICH
  1965A   O massovykh nakhozhdeniĭakh zubov akul na dne Tikhogo i Indiĭskogo okeanov. [On mass finds of shark teeth at the bottom of the Pacific and Indian oceans.] In: Problemy stratigrafii kaĭnozoĭa, 74—79 (Russian; English summary).

1970A   O geologicheskom vozraste zubov akuly *Megaselachus megalodon* (Ag.). [On the geological age of
           teeth of the shark *Megaselachus megalodon* (Ag.).] Akad. Nauk SSSR, Inst. Okeanol., Tr.,
           88, 277—280, 1 pl. (Russian; English summary).
1970B   Zuby akul na dne Tikhogo okeana. [Shark teeth at the bottom of the Pacific Ocean.] Akad. Nauk
           SSSR, Inst. Okeanol., Tr., 88, 252—276, 4 pls. (Russian; English summary).

BELIAEVA, ELIZAVETA IVANOVNA (= BELIAJEVA, E. I. = BELYAEVA, Y. I.)
1970A   O nakhodke aminodonta v oligotsene Kazakhstana. [On the finding of an amynodont in the
           Oligocene of Kazakhstan.] Paleontol. Zh., 1970:3, 155—156, 1 fig., 1 table (Russian).
           Rev.: Thenius in Zentralbl. Geol. Paläontol., Teil 2, 1971:4, 341.
1971A   O nekotorykh nosorogakh semeistva Rhinocerotidae iz neogena Zapadnoi Mongolii. [On some
           rhinoceroses of the family Rhinocerotidae from the Neogene of West Mongolia.] Sovm.
           Sovet.-Mongol. Nauch.-Issled. Geol. Eksped., Tr., 3, 78—97, 11 tables (Russian).
1971B   Novye dannye po aminodontam SSSR [New data on the aminodonts of the USSR.] Akad. Nauk
           SSSR, Paleontol. Inst., Tr., 130, 39—61, 12 figs., 3 tables (Russian).

BELIAEVA, ELIZAVETA IVANOVNA and DAVID, ANATOLII IVANOVICH
1969A   Nosorogi (Rhinocerotidae) tiraspol'skogo faunisticheskogo kompleksa. [Rhinoceroses (Rhinocerotidae)
           in the Tiraspol faunistic complex.] In: Mezhdunarodnyi kollokvium po geologii i faune
           nizhnego i srednego pleistotsena Evropy, Tezisy dokladov, 10—11, and 66—67 (Russian and
           English).

BELL, K. N. and DE MERLO, J. A.
1969A   Some fossil bird tracks. Victorian Natur., 86:5, 134—135, 2 pls., map.

BELL, ROBERT E.
1968A   Dating the prehistory of Oklahoma. Gt. Plains J., 7, 42—52, 1 fig.

BELLAIRS, ANGUS D'A.
1969A   The life of reptiles. London: Weidenfield and Nicolson, 2 vols., 590 pp., 149 figs.
           Rev.: Cave in J. Anat., 108:1, 197.
1972A   Comments on the evolution and affinities of snakes. In: Joysey, K. A. and Kemp, T. S. (eds.),
           1972A, 157—172, 3 figs., 1 pl.

BELOUSOVA, ZOIA DMITRIEVNA and RIABUKHINA, SVETLANA GEORGIEVNA
1971A   Indskii iarus Solianogo kriazha i ego kontinental'nyi analog — vetluzhskaia seriia Evropeiskoi chasti
           SSSR. [Indian stage of the Salt Range and its continental analogue — the Vetlugian series of
           the European part of the USSR.] Vses. Nauch.-Issled. Geologorazved. Neft. Inst., Tr., 84,
           50—54 (Russian).

BEL'SKAIA, TAT'IANA NIKOLAEVNA
1960A   Pozdnedevonskoe more Kuznetskoi kotloviny, istoriia ego razvitiia, naselenie i osadki. [Late
           Devonian sea of Kuznetsk basin, the history of its development, population and deposits.]
           Akad. Nauk SSSR, Paleontol. Inst., Tr., 82, 184 pp., 54 figs., 17 pls., 5 tables (Russian).

BELT, E. S.   See: Carroll, R. L., Belt, E. S., Dineley, D. L., Baird, D. and McGregor, D. C., 1972A, 1972B.

BELTAN, LAURENCE
1968A   La faune ichthyologique de l'Éotrias du N.W. de Madagascar: le neurocrâne. Paris: Cah. Paléontol.,
           Eds. CNRS, 135 pp., 44 figs., 50 pls. (French).

BELTRÁN, ANTONIO
1967A   Las pinturas de las "Eglises inférieures" en Ussat-les-Bains (Ariège). Caesaraugusta, 29—30, 81—98,
           3 figs., 25 pls. (Spanish).
1969-70A   Novedades en arte rupestre 1969—1970. Caesaraugusta, 33—34, 156—165 (Spanish).

BELTRÁN, A., ROBERT, R., and GAILLI, R.
1967A   La Cueva de Bédeilhac. Saragossa, Univ., Fac. Fil. Let., Dept. Prehist. Arqueol., Monogr. Arqueol.,
           2, 148 pp., 76 pls., 1 map.
           Rev.: Jordá Cerdá in Zephyrus, 18, 155—156.

BENDIX-ALMGREEN, SVEND ERIK
1968A   The bradyodont elasmobranchs and their affinities; a discussion. Nobel Symp., 4th, Stockholm,
           1967, Proc., 1968, 153—170.
1969A   Notes on the Upper Cretaceous and lower Tertiary fish faunas of northern West Greenland. Dan.
           Geol. Foren., Medd., 19, 204—217 (Danish summary).

1971A   The anatomy of *Menaspis armata* and the phyletic affinities of the menaspid bradyodonts. Lethaia,
             4:1, 21—49, 9 figs.

BENDIX-ALMGREEN, SVEND E. and MALZAHN, ERICH
1969A   Über neue oder wenig bekannte Elasmobranchier aus dem deutschen Kupferschiefer. Hess. Landesamt
             Bodenforsch., Notizbl., 97. 44—45 (German).

BENDUKIDZE, O. G.
1971A   Novyǐ predstavitel' semeǐstva Geranoididae (Aves, Gruiformes) iz eoĕenovykh otlozheniǐ Zaǐsana.
             [A new representative of the family Geranoididae (Aves, Gruiformes) from the Eocene deposits
             of Zaǐsan.] Akad. Nauk Guz. SSR, Soobshch., 63:3, 749—751, 1 fig. (Russian; Georgian and
             English summaries).

BENDUKIDZE, O. G.   See also: Burchak-Abramovich, N. I. and Bendukidze, O. G., 1969A, 1971A.

BENEDETTO, J. L. and SANCHEZ, T. M.
1971A   El hallazgo de peces Pycnodontiformes (Holostei) en la Formación Yacoraite (Cretácico superior) de
             la Provincia de Salta (Argentina) y su importancia paleoecológica. Acta Geol. Lilloana, 11:8,
             151—176, 4 figs., 3 pls., 1 table (English summary).

BENEŠ, JOSEF
1970A   Pleistocénní savci z Chlumu u Srbska (Čechy). [Pleistocene mammals from Chlum near Srbsko
             (Bohemia).] Prague, Národ. Muz., Čas., Odd. Přírod., 137:3—4, 17—26, 8 figs. (Czech;
             German summary).
1972A   Lišky evropského pleistocénu. [Die Füchse im mitteleuropäischen Pleistozän.] Prague, Národ, Muz.,
             Čas., Odd. Přírod., 140:3/4, 191—196, 6 figs. (Czech and German).

BENOIST, JEAN
1968A   On the origin of Races. Current Anthropol., 9:1, 65—66.

BENSCH, CL.
1971A   Caractères généraux de la macrofaune mammalienne de la grotte de la Bergerie, à Caniac (Lot).
             Soc. Spéléol. Préhist. Bordeaux, Bull., 1969—1970, 20—21, 93—114 (French).

BERA, AL.
1968A   Studiul unor resturi de *Ursus spelaeus* din peştera "Colţul Suprat " de pe valea Dîmboviţei (Com.
             Podul Dîmboviţei-Muscel). [Study of some remains of *Ursus spelaeus* from the "Coltul Suprat"
             Cave in the Dimboviţa valley.] Soc. Ştiinţ. Geol. R.S.R., Bull., 10, 205—216, 9 figs., 1 table
             (Rumanian; French and English summaries).

BERBERIAN, PAUL   See: Estes, R. and Berberian, P., 1969A, 1970A; Estes, R., Berberian, P. and Meszoely,
             C. A. M., 1969A.

BERCIU, DUMITRU
1967A   Romania. London: Thames and Hudson, Ancient Peoples and Places, 57, 215 pp., 127 figs.,
             10 maps, 5 tables.
             Rev.: Ehrich in Amer. Anthropol., 71, 348; Thomas in Archaeology, 23:4, 364.

BERDAR, A.   See: Bonfiglio, L. and Berdar, A., 1969A.

BERDZENISHVILI, N. Z.
1970A   Okumskaĭa verkhnepaleoliticheskaĭa stoĭanka. [Okumi upper Paleolithic locality.] In: Rybakov,
             B. A. (ed.), 1970A, 357—358 (Russian).

BERENGUERAS ALSINA, MARÍA TERESA
1969A*   Boletín Informativo. Barcelona (Prov.), Inst. Prov. Paleontol., Bol. Inform., 1, 27 pp. (Spanish).
1971A*   Boletín Informativo. Barcelona (Prov.), Inst. Prov. Paleontol., Bol. Inform., 3:1, 1—30; 3:2—3, 1—32,
             2 figs.; 3:4—5, 1—23 (Spanish).

BERG, DIETRICH E.
1967A   Aquitane Krokodile vom "Hessler" (Wiesbaden-Biebrich) und anderen rheinhessischen Fundstellen.
             Mainz. Naturwiss. Arch., 5/6, 186—193, 4 figs. (German).
1969A   Characteristic crocodiles of the Paleogene in Europe. Colloque sur l'Eocène, Paris, mai 1968, Vol. III,
             Fr., Bur. Rech. Géol. Minières Mém., 69, 73—75, 1 fig.
1969B   *Charactosuchus kugleri*, eine neue Krokodilart aus dem Eozän von Jamaica. Eclogae Geol. Helv.,
             62:2, 731—735, 1 fig., 1 pl. (German; English summary).

1971A   Oligozäne Vertreter der alligatorinen Krokodilgattung *Diplocynodon*. Hess. Landesamt Bodenforsch., Abh., 60, 25–30, 2 pls. (German).

BERG, D. E. and CRUSAFONT, M.
1970A   Note sur quelques crocodiliens de l'Éocène prépyrénaïque. Acta Geol. Hisp., 5:2, 54–57, 1 fig. (French; English and Spanish summaries).

BERG, LEO S.
1969A   Nomogenesis, or evolution determined by law. Translated from the Russian edition (1922) by J. N. Rostovtsov. Foreword by Th. Dobzhansky. Cambridge, Mass.: M.I.T. Press, 512 pp. Rev.: Bock in Science (AAAS), 164, 684–685.

BERGER, RAINER, *et al.*
1971A   New radiocarbon dates based on collagen of California Paleo-Indians. Calif., Univ., Archaeol. Res. Fac., Contrib., 12, 43–49.

BERGER, RAINER   See also: Heizer, R. F. and Berger, R., 1970A; Ho, T. Y., Marcus, L. F. and Berger, R., 1969A; Taylor, R. E., Berger, R. and Dimsdale, B., 1968A.

BERGOUNIOUX, FRÉDÉRIC M.
1967A   L'abbé André Glory. 1906–1966. Les Eyzies, 16, 10–12, portr., biog. (French).
1967B   L'abbé Jean-Louis Villeveygoux. 1940–1966. Les Eyzies, 16, 12–14, portr., biog. (French).
1967C   Le problème anthropien. (Réflexions d'un paléontologiste). Les Eyzies, 16, 46–54, 1 fig. (French).

BERGOUNIOUX, F. M. and CROUZEL, F.
1964B   Mastodontes et éléphants villafranchiens de France. Int. Ass. Quaternary Res., 6th Congr. (1961), Rept., 2, 511–515 (French).
1968A   Deux tortues fossiles d'Afrique. Soc. Hist. Natur. Toulouse, Bull., 104:1–2, 179–186, 3 figs. (French).
1968B   Sur deux gisements stampiens du bassin d'Aquitaine Saint-Martin-de-Casselvi (Tarn) et Launaguet (Haute-Garonne). Soc. Hist. Natur. Toulouse, Bull., 104:3–4, 367–380, 6 figs. (French).
1970A   Trois gisements de mammifères vindoboniens au pied des Petites Pyrénées. Soc. Hist. Natur. Toulouse, Bull., 106:1–2, 54–58 (French).
1971A   Un gisement fossilifère oligocène à Saverdun (Ariège). Soc. Hist. Natur. Toulouse, Bull., 107:1–2, 89–92 (French).

BERGSTROM, ROBERT E.
1968A*   The Quaternary of Illinois. A symposium in observance of the centennial of the University of Illinois. Urbana: Illinois State Geological Survey, 179 pp., illustr.

BERMAN, DAVID S.
1969A   Vertebrate fossils from the Lueders Formation, Lower Permian of north-central Texas. Diss. Abstr., 30:6, 2955B (abs.).
1970A   Vertebrate fossils from the Lueders Formation, Lower Permian of north-central Texas. Calif., Univ., Publ. Geol. Sci., 86, 39 pp., 4 figs., 10 pls.
1971A   Stone bone. Carnegie Mag., 45:3, 93–96, 4 figs.
1971B   A small skull of the lower Permian reptile *Diadectes* from the Washington formation, Dunkard group, West Virginia. Carnegie Mus., Ann., 43:3, 33–46, 3 figs.

BERRY, J. ALLAN and KING, JUDITH E.
1970A   The identity of the Pliocene seal from Cape Kidnappers, New Zealand, previously known as *Arctocephalus caninus*. Tuatara, 18:1, 13–18, 3 pls., 1 map.

BERRY, R. J. and SOUTHERN, H. N.
1970A*   Variation in mammalian populations. Symp. Zool. Soc. London, 26, xvi + 403 pp., illustr.

BERRY, WILLIAM B. N.
1968A   Rev.: Anon. in Calif., Div. Mines Geol., Miner. Inform. Serv., 21:12, 187; Durden in Asian Perspectives, 11, 189–190; Gray in Bioscience, 19:5, 482.

BERRY, W. B. N.   See also: Floyd, D. N., Miller, T. H. and Berry, W. B. N., 1958A.

BERSENEV, I. I. and SOKHIN, V. K.
1969A   Chetvertichye otlozheniia. [Quaternary deposits] Geologiia SSSR, 32:1, Maritime Province, 373–399, 4 figs., 1 table (Russian).

BERSENEV, I. I., USTINOVSKIĬ, ĬU. B., BUR'ĬANOVA, I. Z., NEVOLINA, S. I. and MEDVEDEV, V. V.
  1969A   Paleogenovaĭa sistema. [Paleogene system.] Geologiĭa SSSR, 32:1, Maritime Province, 317–350,
            1 fig., 1 table (Russian).

BERTMAR, GUNNAR
  1968A   Lungfish phylogeny. Nobel Symp., 4th, Stockholm, 1967, Proc., 1968, 259–283, 9 figs.
  1968B   Phylogeny and evolution in Lungfishes. Acta Zool., 49:3, 189–201, 5 figs.
  1969A   The vertebrate nose, remarks on its structural and functional adaptation and evolution. Evolution,
            23:1, 131–152, 12 figs.

BERTOUILLE, H. and BOUCHUD, J.
  1969A   Étude préliminaire de la faune de la grotte de Fustié (Ariège). Préhist. Spéléol. Ariége., 24, 87–95,
            3 figs. (French).

BERTOUILLE, H., BERTOUILLE, M. and BOUCHUD, J.
  1968A   La prospection géologique et paléontologique des avens. Études préliminaires faites dans la grotte
            Bernard (Ariège). Soc. Préhist. Fr., Bull., C.R., 65:5–6, 139–143 (French).

BERTOUILLE, M.   See: Bertouille, H.. Bertouille, M. and Bouchud, J., 1968A.

BERZI, ANNALISA
  1970A   Lagomorphs from the type Villafranchian of Villafranca d'Asti (Italy). G. Geol., 35:1, 137–152,
            17 figs., 1 pl., 1 table.

BERZI, A., MICHAUX, J., HUTCHISON, J. H. and LINDSAY, E.
  1970A   The Arondelli local fauna, an assemblage of small vertebrates from the Villafranchian stage near
            Villafranca d'Asti, Italy. G. Geol., 35:1, 133–136.

BERZI, ANNALISA   See also: Azzaroli, A. and Berzi, A.. 1970A.

BESAIRIE, HENRI
  1967A   Progrès dans l'étude du Gondwana de Madagascar de 1960 à 1966. Int. Union Geol. Sci.. 1st Symp.
            Gondwana Stratigr., Rev., 1967, 197–200 (French).

BESANÇON, J.. COPELAND, L. and HOURS, F.
  1970A   L'Acheuléen de Joub Jannine II. Compte-rendu d'un sondage effectué en 1968. Beirut, Mus. Nat.
            Lib., Bull., 23, 9–24, 6 figs. (French).

BESSONNAT, GILBERT, DUGHI, R. and SIRUGUE, F.
  1969A   Un important gisement d'empreintes de pas de mammifères dans le Paléogène du bassin d'Apt-
            Forcalquier. Acad. Sci., C.R., Sér. D, 268:10, 1376–1379, 1 pl. (French).

BEURLEN, KARL
  1967A   Die Periodizität im erd- und lebensgeschichtlichen Entwicklunggang. Naturwiss. Ver. Hamburg, Abh.
            Verh., 12, 5–25 (German).
  1972A   Zeugnis der Kontinentaldrift. Kosmos, 68:10, 298, 1 photo (German).

BEZNOSIKOV, ĬA. N.
  1970A   [Some results of the archeological research at the Komi Filial AN SSSR.] Sov. Arkheol., 1970:1,
            306–309 (Russian).

BHALLA, S. N. and DEV, PRAMENDRA
  1972A   A note on the occurrence of fossil vertebra from Baripada beds (Miocene), Orissa. Geol. Soc. India,
            J., 13:3, 298–299, 1 fig.

BIANCHINI, G. and MASCLE, G.
  1971A   Nouvelles observations sur le Quaternaire de Sicile méridionale. Acad. Sci., C.R., Sér. D, 272:2,
            200–202, 1 fig. (French).

BIASUTTI, RENATO, et al.
  1959A*   Le razze e i popoli della terra. Third edition, revised. Turín: Unione Tipografico-Editrice Torinese,
            4 vols., 2914 pp., illustr. (Italian).

BIBERSON, PIERRE
  1966B   Human evolution in Morocco in the framework of the paleoclimatic variations of the Atlantic
            Pleistocene. In: Howell, F. C. and Bourliere, F. (eds.), 1966A, 417–447, 3 figs.. 1 table.

1968A   Les gisements Acheuléens de Torralba et Ambrona (Espagne). Nouvelles précisions. L'Anthropologie,
           72:3—4, 241—278, 6 figs., 5 pls. (French).
1969A   Le problème des correlations entre l'Europe méridionale et l'Afrique du Nord au Pléistocène. In:
           Mezhdunarodnyĭ kollokvium po geologii i faune nizhnego i srednego pleĭstofŝena Evropy.
           Tezisy dokladov, 49—51 (French).
1969B   Récentes découvertes de nouveaux gisements acheuléens en Adrar de Mauritanie. L'Anthropologie,
           73:5—6, 446—456, 4 figs., 2 pls. (French).
1970A   Index-cards on the marine and continental cycles of the Moroccan Quaternary. Quaternaria, 13,
           1—76, 4 figs., 1 table (German and French summaries).
1970B   Colloque international sur la Géologie et la fauna du Pléistocène inférieur et moyen d'Europe
           (U.R.S.S., 25 mai—5 juin 1969). L'Anthropologie, 74:5—6, 443—449 (French).

BIBIKOV, S. N.
1969A   Paleolit Kryma. [The Paleolithic of Crimea.] Geologiĭâ SSSR, 8:1, 289—300, 6 figs. (Russian).
1969B   Nekotorye aspekty paleoekonomicheskogo modelirovaniĭâ paleolita. [Some aspects of paleoeconomic
           modeling of the Paleolithic.] Sov. Arkheol., 1969:4, 5—22, 1 fig. (Russian; French summary).
1971A   Plotnost' naseleniĭâ i velichina okhotnich'ikh ugodiĭ v paleolite Kryma. [Density of population and
           the extent of hunting grounds in the Paleolithic of Crimea.] Sov. Arkheol., 1971:4, 11—22,
           1 fig. (Russian; French summary).

BICKEL, LEONARD
1970A   Ancient man in Kow swamp. Sci. News, 97:10, 254—255, 5 figs.

BIDAR, ALAIN, DEMAY, L. and THOMEL, G.
1971A   Sur la présence du dinosaurien Compsognathus dans le Portlandien de Canjuers (Var). Acad. Sci.,
           C.R., Sér. D, 275:21, 2327—2329, 1 pl. (French).
1972B   Compsognathus corallestris, nouvelle espèce de dinosaurien théropode du Portlandien de Canjuers
           (Sud-Est de la France). Mus. Hist. Natur. Nice, Ann., 1:1, 34 pp., 21 figs.. 3 tables (French;
           English, German, and Spanish summaries).

BIDDITTU, I. and CASSOLI, P.
1968A   Una stazione del Paleolitico inferiore a Pontecorvo in Provincia di Frosinone. Quaternaria, 10,
           167—197, 15 figs. (Italian; French and English summaries).

BIDDITTU, I., CASSOLI, P. and MALPIERI, L.
1967A   Stazione Musteriana in Valle Radice nel Comune di Sora (Frosinone). Quaternaria, 9, 321—348,
           9 figs.. 1 table (Italian; French and English summaries).

BIELICKI, TADEUSZ
1965A   The intensity of feedbacks between physical and cultural evolution. Unesco (Int. Soc. Sci. J.), 17:1,
           97—99.

BIELICKI, TADEUSZ and MISZKIEWICZ, BRUNON
1968A   Variability of the internal mandibular contour. In: K. Saller Festschrift, 1968, 11—17, 3 figs.

BIELICKI, TADEUSZ   See also: Fryxell, R., Bielicki, T., Daugherty, R. D., Gustafson, C. E., Irwin, H. T. and
           Keel, B. C., 1968A; Fryxell, R., Bielicki, T., Daugherty, R. D., Gustafson, C. E., Irwin, H. T.,
           Keel, B. C. and Krantz, G. S., 1968A.

BIESE, WALTER
1961A   El Jurássico de Cerritos Bayos. Chile, Univ., Fac. Cienc. Fís. Mat., Dep. Geol., Publ., 19, 61 pp.,
           5 figs., 4 pls., 2 maps, 2 tables (Spanish; English summary).

BIGARELLA, JOÃO JOSÉ and SALAMUNI, RIAD
1967A   A review of South American Gondwana geology. Int. Union Geol. Sci., 1st Symp. Gondwana Stratigr.,
           Rev., 1967, 7—137, 51 figs.. 2 tables.

BIGELOW, R.
1970A   Und willst du nicht mein Bruder sein. Stuttgart: Englishe Deutsche Verlags-Anstalt, 248 pp.
           (German).
           Rev.: Kurth in Naturwiss. Rundsch., 24:2, 87—88.

BIGGERSTAFF, ROBERT H.
1968A   On the groove configuration of mandibular molars: the unreliability of the "Dryopithecus pattern"
           and a new method for classifying mandibular molars. Amer. J. Phys. Anthropol., 29, 441—444.

BILELO, MARIA A. M.
1969A   The fossil fish *Lepidotes* in the Paluxy formation, north-central Texas. Amer. Midland Natur., 81,
             405—411, 3 figs., 2 tables.
1969B   The fossil shark genus *Squalicorax* in north-central Texas. Tex. J. Sci., 20:4, 339—348, 3 figs.,
             1 table.

BILLY, GINETTE
1969A   Le squelette post-cranien de l'Homme de Chancelade. L'Anthropologie, 73:3—4, 207—246, 10 figs.,
             24 tables (French).
1971A   Les restes humains proto-magdaléniens de l'Abri Pataud. Acad. Sci., C.R., Sér. D, 273:25, 2482—
             2484, 1 fig. (French).

BILSBOROUGH, ALAN
1969A   Rates of evolutionary change in the hominid dentition. Nature, 223:5202, 146—149, 2 figs., 2 tables.
1971A   Early hominids and artifacts in South Africa. Antiquity, 45:179, 210—213.
1972A   Cranial morphology of Neanderthal man. Nature, 237:5354, 351—352, 1 table.

BINFORD, LEWIS, *et al.*
1968A   Discussion: the magic numbers "25" and "500": determinants of group size in modern and
             Pleistocene hunters. In: Lee, R. B., and DeVore, I. (eds.), 1968A, 245—248.

BINFORD, LEWIS   See also: Binford, S. R. and Binford, L., 1966A.

BINFORD, SALLY R.
1967A   Human ecology in the upper Pleistocene: another try at the "Neanderthal problem." Amer.
             Anthropol. Ass., Abstr., 1967, 9 (abs.).
1968B   Early upper Pleistocene adaptations in the Levant. Amer. Anthropol., 70, 707—717, 1 map.
             Rev.: Anon. in Anthropos, 63/64:3/4, 576—577.
1970A   Late middle Paleolithic adaptations and their possible consequences. BioScience, 20:5, 280—283.

BINFORD, SALLY R. and BINFORD, LEWIS
1966A   Burial practices in the Mousterian and upper Paleolithic. Amer. Anthropol. Ass., Abstr., 1966, 6
             (abs.).

BINGE, H. G.
1964A   Über die vermutliche Ursache der Korrelation zwischen der phylogenetischen Entwicklung der
             Säugetiere und Klimawechseln in geologischen Vergangenheit. Naturwiss. Ver. Hamburg, Abh.
             Verh., 8, 21—28, 1 fig. (German).

BIRD, JUNIUS B.
1968A   More about earth-shaking equipment. Amer. Antiquity, 33, 507—509, 1 fig.

BIRDSELL, J. B.
1972A   Human evolution. An introduction to the new physical anthropology. Chicago: Rand McNally
             and Co., xiv + 546 pp., illustr.

BIRDSELL, J. B.   See also: Bartholomew, G. A. and Birdsell, J. B., 1969A.

BIRIUKOV, MIKHAIL DENISOVICH
1962A   Iskopaemye tapiroobraznye sopredel'nykh s Zapadnoǐ Sibir'iù chasteǐ Kazakhstana. [Fossil
             tapiromorphs of the parts of Kazakhstan contiguous to west Siberia.] In: Problemy
             zoologicheskikh issledovaniǐ v Sibiri, 28—29 (Russian).
1971A   Novye dannye o faune tapiroobraznykh Kazakhstana. [New data on the fauna of tapiromorphs of
             Kazakhstan.] In: Teriologiia (Russian).

BIRIUKOV, MIKHAIL DENISOVICH   See also: Bazhanov, V. S., Biriùkov, M. D., Vetrov, F. E., Kozhamkulova,
             B. S., Lychev, G. F., Musakulova, L. T. and Savinov, P. F., 1971A; Kuznetsov, V. V. and
             Biriùkov, M. D., 1969A, 1969B; Didenko-Kislitsina, L. K., Biriùkov, M. D. and Baǐbulatova,
             R. B., 1971A; Aubekerov, B. Zh., Aubekerova, P. A., Biriùkov, M. D., Lychev, G. F. and
             Savinov, P. F., 1970A.

BIRKELAND, P. W., CRANDELL, D. R. and RICHMOND, G. M.
1971A   Status of correlation of Quaternary stratigraphic units in the western conterminous United States.
             Quaternary Res., 1:2, 208—227, 2 charts.

BIRKENMAJER, KRZYSZTOF
1964A   Devonian, Carboniferous and Permian formations of Hornsund, Vestspitsbergen. Stud. Geol. Pol., 11,
             47—124, 27 figs., 11 pls., 2 tables (Polish summary).

BIRMAN, A. S. and RASTSVETAEV, L. M.
1967A   O skheme raschleneniïa pliotsenovykh molass Tsentral'nogo i Giaurskogo Kopet-Daga. [On the scheme for subdivision of Pliocene molass of central and Giaurian Kopet-Dagh.] Mosk. Univ., Vestn., ser. Geol., 1967:6, 52–56, 2 figs. (Russian).
1969A   Novye dannye po stratigrafii neogenovykh otlozheniï vostochnogo Kopetdaga. [New data on the stratigraphy of Neogene deposits of eastern Kopet-Dagh.] In: Noveïshaïa tektonika, noveïshie otlozheniïa i chelovek, 2, 194–200, 1 fig. (Russian).

BIRMAN, A. S., ZHEGALLO, V. I., RASTSVETAEV, L. M., KHOZATSKIĬ, L. I. and SHEVYREVA, N. S.
1971A   O nakhodke pliotsenovykh pozvonochnykh v molassovykh otlozheniïakh vostochnogo Kopetdaga. [On the find of Pliocene vertebrates in the molassic deposits of eastern Kopet-Dagh.] Mosk. Obshchest. Ispyt. Prir., Biull., Otd. Geol., 46:2, 99–106, 3 figs. (Russian).

BISHOP, GALE A.
1972A   Crab bitten by a fish from the upper Cretaceous Pierre shale of South Dakota. Geol. Soc. Amer., Bull., 83:12, 3823–3825, 2 figs.

BISHOP, RICHARD C.
1969A   Early Miocene selachian faunas from Kern County, California. Geol. Soc. Amer., Abstr., Part 3, 6 (abs.).

BISHOP, WALTER WILLIAM
1966A   The later Tertiary and Pleistocene in eastern equatorial Africa. In: Howell, F. C. and Bourliere, F. (eds.), 1966A, 246–275.
         Rev.: Maier in Z. Säugetierkunde, 36:2, 125.
1966B   Decade of Quaternary studies in Africa. Sci. S. Afr., 3:5, 17–19.
1968A   Means of correlation of Quaternary successions in East Africa. In: Morrison, R. B. and Wright, H. E. (eds.), 1968A, 161–172.
1971A   The late Cenozoic history of East Africa in relation to hominoid evolution. In: Turekian, K. K. (ed.), 1971A, 493–527, 7 figs., 3 tables.
1972A   Stratigraphic succession 'versus' calibration in East Africa. In: Bishop, W. W. and Miller, J. A. (eds.), 1972A, 219–246, 7 figs., 2 tables.

BISHOP, W. W. and CHAPMAN, G. R.
1970A   Early Pliocene sediments and fossils from the northern Kenya rift valley. Nature, 226:5249, 914–918, 4 figs., 1 table.

BISHOP, W. W., CHAPMAN, G. R., HILL, A. and MILLER, J. A.
1971A   Succession of Cainozoic vertebrate assemblages from the northern Kenya rift valley. Nature, 233:5319, 389–394, 4 figs., 1 table.

BISHOP, W. W. and CLARK, DESMOND
1967A*   Rev.: Lippert in Anthropol. Ges., Mitt., 99, 242–243; Parkington in S. Afr. Archaeol. Bull., 25:97, 48–50; Smolla in Homo, 19:3–4, 242.

BISHOP, W. W. and MILLER, JOHN A.
1972A*   Calibration of hominoid evolution. Toronto: University of Toronto Press; Edinburgh: Scottish Academic Press, viii + 487 pp., illustr.
         Rev.: Molleson in New Sci., 55:811, 454.

BISHOP, W. W., MILLER, J. A. and FITCH, F. J.
1969A   New potassium-argon age determinations relevant to the Miocene fossil mammal sequence in East Africa. Amer. J. Sci., 267:6, 669–699, 4 figs., 6 tables.

BISKE, SERGEĬ FELIKSOVICH   See: Baranova, Iu. P., Biske, S. F., Goncharov, V. F., Kul'kova, I. A. and Titkov, A. S., 1968A.

BJERRING, HANS C.
1968A   The second somite with special reference to the evolution of its myotomic derivatives. Nobel Symp., 4th, Stockholm, 1967, Proc., 341–357, 6 figs.
1972A   Morphological observations on the exoskeletal skull roof of an osteolepiform from the Carboniferous of Scotland. Acta Zool., 53:1, 73–92, 9 figs. (Russian summary).
1972B   The nervus rarus in coelacanthiform phylogeny. Zool. Scripta, 1:2, 57–68, 7 figs., 1 table (Russian summary).

BJORK, PHILIP REESE
1968A   New records of helaletid tapiroids from the Oligocene of South Dakota. Mich. Acad. Sci., Arts, Lett., Pap., 53, 73–78, 2 figs., 1 table.

1969A   The Carnivora of the Hagerman local fauna (late Pliocene) of southwestern Idaho. Diss. Abstr.,
         30:2, 763B—764B (abs.).
1970A   The Carnivora of the Hagerman local fauna (late Pliocene) of southwestern Idaho. Amer. Phil. Soc.,
         Trans., 60:7, 1—54, 26 figs., 19 tables, 1 chart.
         Rev.: Galbreath in J. Paleontol., 46:5, 785—786.

BJORK, P. R.   See also: Hibbard, C. W. and Bjork, P. R., 1971A.

BLACK, CRAIG C.
1968C   Small mammals from the Colter formation, Jackson Hole, Wyoming. Colorado, Univ. Mus., Field
         Confer. Guidebk., 10—12.
1968D   Late Oligocene vertebrates from the northeastern Wind River basin. Colorado, Univ. Mus., Field
         Confer. Guidebk., 50—54.
1969A   North African safari for fossils. Carnegie Mag., 43:1, 25—33, 5 figs.
1969B   The fossil rodent genera Horatiomys and Palustrimus — juvenile geomyoid rodents. J. Mammal.,
         50:4, 815—817.
1970A   A new Pareumys (Rodentia: Cylindrodontidae) from the Duchesne River formation, Utah. Fieldiana:
         Geol., 16:17, 453—459, 2 figs.
1970B   Paleontology and geology of the Badwater Creek area, central Wyoming. Part 5. The cylindrodont
         rodents. Carnegie Mus., Ann., 41:6, 201—214.
1971A   Paleontology and geology of the Badwater Creek area, central Wyoming. Part 7. Rodents of the
         Family Ischyromyidae. Carnegie Mus., Ann., 43:6, 179—217, 73 figs., 2 tables.
1972A   Review of fossil rodents from the Neogene Siwalik beds of India and Pakistan. Palaeontology,
         15:2, 238—266, 11 figs., 1 table.
1972B   Holarctic evolution and dispersal of squirrels (Rodentia: Sciuridae). In: Dobzhansky, Th., Hecht,
         M. K. and Steere, W. C. (eds.), 1972B, 305—322, 3 figs., 2 tables.

BLACK, CRAIG C.   See also: Dawson, M. R. and Black, C. C., 1970A; Robinson, P. and Black, C. C., 1969A;
                    Sutton, J. F. and Black, C. C., 1972A.

BLACK, DAVIDSON
1971A   Tertiary man in Asia: the Chou Kou Tien discovery. In: Leakey, L. S. B., Prost, J. and Prost, S.
         (eds.), 1971A, 219—220 (reprinted from Nature, 118, 1926).
1971B   On the adolescent skull of Sinanthropus pekinensis. In: Leakey, L. S. B., Prost, J. and Prost, S.
         (eds.), 1971A, 221—223 (reprinted from Palaeontologica Sinica, 7, 1930).

BLACK, RHONA M.
1970A   The elements of paleontology. London and New York: Cambridge University Press, ix + 339 pp.,
         202 illustr.
         Rev.: A.R.I.C. in S. Afr. J. Sci., 67:5, 326; Anon. in Geotimes, 16:3, 36; Boné in Rev. Quest. Sci.,
         32:2, 297; Hubbard in Nature, 230:5288, 64; J. C. H. in Geol. J., 7:2, xi; Lipparini in
         Scientia, 107:3—4, 331—332; M. R. H. in Geol. Mag., 108:4, 349—350; Olson in Quart. Rev.
         Biol., 46:3, 285—286; Shotwell in Earth-Sci. Rev., 7:3, A131; Skevington in New Sci., 49:742,
         577; Staplin in Palaeogeogr. Palaeoclimatol. Palaeoecol., 11:2, 148—149; Westphal in Zentralbl.
         Geol. Paläontol., Teil 2, 1971:2—3, 97.

BLAGONRAVOV, V. A.   See: Vladimirskaïa, E. V. and Blagonravov, V. A., 1966A.

BLANC, A. C.
1964A   Sur le facteur fondamental des mouvements des cultures pré- et protohistoriques en Afrique du Nord:
         La fuite du désert. In: Pericot García, L. and Ripoll Perelló, E. (eds.), 1964A, 179—184,
         (French; English summary).

BLANC, M.   See: Théobald, N., Blanc, M. and David, E., s.d.

BLANC, SÉVERIN
1963A   Chronologie relative et chronologie absolue. Les Eyzies, 12, 23—26 (French).

BLANCHARD, JACQUES
1964B   Informations recherchées d'après les équides européens figurés. In: Pericot García, L., and Ripoll
         Perelló, E. (eds.), 1964A, 3—34, 8 pls. (French; English summary).

BLANCHARD, VÉRONIQUE
1967A   L'abbé Glory au travail. Les Eyzies, 16, 15—16 (French).

BLEIBTREU, HERMANN K.
1969A*   Evolutionary anthropology. Boston: Allyn and Bacon, Inc., vii + 456 pp., illustr.

Rev.: Holloway in Amer. Anthropol., 72:4, 952–953; Otten in Amer. J. Phys. Anthropol., 33:2, 275–276; Rösing in Homo, 21:2, 123.

BLEIBTREU, HERMANN K.   See also: Downs, J. F. and Bleibtreu, H. K., 1969A.

BLIAKHOVA, SOF'IA MEEROVNA and MARTYNOVA, MARIIA IAKOVLEVNA
1971A   Paleogenovaiā sistema. Vostochnye Kyzylkumy, Bol'shoi Karatau, otrogi Talasskogo Alatau.
            [Paleogene system. Eastern Kyzylkumy, Great Karatau, offshoots of Talas Alatau.] Geologiiā
            SSSR, 40:1, Southern Kazakhstan, 421–428 (Russian).

BLICK, JOHN C.   See: Galusha, T. and Blick, J. C., 1971A.

BLINDERMAN, CHARLES S.
1971A   The great bone case. Perspectives Biol. Med., 14:3, 370–393, 2 figs.

BLODGETT, ROBERT H.
1971A   Southeastern Michigan: the land the glaciers left behind. Explorer (Cleveland Mus. Natur. Hist.),
            13:1, 4–10, illustr.

BLOM, GEORGII IVANOVICH
1967A   Triasovaiā sistema. [Triassic system.] Geologiiā SSSR, 11, Povolzh'e and Prikam'e, 427–462, 5 figs.,
            1 table (Russian).
1968A   Katalog mestonakhozhdenii faunisticheskikh ostatkov v nizhnetriasovykh otlozheniiākh Srednego
            Povolzh'iā i Prikam'iā. [Catalogue of localities of faunal remains in the lower Triassic deposits
            of middle Povolzh'e and Prikam'e.] Kazan': Kazan' University Press, 375 pp., illustr. (Russian).

BLOT, JACQUES
1969A   Holocéphales et Élasmobranches. Systématique. In: Piveteau, J. (ed.), Traité de Paléo., T. IV,
            vol. 2, 702–776, 56 figs., 1 table (French).
1969B   Les poissons fossiles du Monte Bolca classés jusqu'ici dans les familles des Carangidae-Menidae-
            Ephippidae-Scatophagidae. Mem. Mus. Civ. Storia Nat. Verona, Mem. out of normal series
            no. 2, in - 4⁰, Tome I text, x + 525 pp., 160 figs., 58 tables; Tome II pls., 84 photos.,
            16 graph. reconstructions (French).
            Rev.: Albanesi in Riv. Ital. Paleontol. Stratigr., 76:1, 178; Lehman in Soc. Géol. Fr., C.R., 1970:3,
            93; Patterson in Copeia, 1971:1, 187–189; Weiler in Zentralbl. Geol. Paläontol., Teil 2,
            1970:5, 415–420.

BLOT, JACQUES and VORUZ, CATHERINE
1970A   Les poissons fossiles du Monte Bolca la famille des Zanclidae. Verona, Mus. Civ. Stor. Natur., Mem.,
            18, 31–42 (French; Italian summary).

BLOXAM, T. W.   See: Rhodes, F. H. T. and Bloxam, T. W., 1971A.

BLUMENSTOCK, DAVID I.
1966A*   Pleistocene and post-Pleistocene climatic variations in the Pacific area. A symposium. Honolulu:
            Bishop Museum Press, x + 182 pp., illustr.
            Rev.: Tilley in Archaeol., Phys. Anthropol. Oceania, 3:1, 74.

BOBOEDOVA, A. A.
1968A   Kustanaiskaiā svita Turgaiskogo progiba i ee sopostavlenie s bitekeiskimi sloiāmi Priishim'iā.
            [Kustanai suite of Turgai depression and its correlation with Biteke beds of Ishim region.]
            In: Neogenovye i chetvertichnye otlozheniiā Zapadnoi Sibiri, 41–51, 1 fig. (Russian).
1971A   Neogenovaiā sistema. Verkhnii mioŝen-plioŝen. [Neogene system. Upper Miocene-Pliocene.]
            Geologiiā SSSR, 34:1, Turgai trough, 425–461, 3 figs., 1 table (Russian).
1971B   Chetvertichnaiā sistema. [Quaternary system.] Geologiiā SSSR, 34:1, Turgai trough, 461–500,
            4 figs. (Russian).

BOCHAROVA, N. I.   See: Bazhanov, O. V., Bocharova, N. I., Didenko-Kislitŝina, L. K. and Kostenko, N. N., 1971A.

BOCK, WALTER J.
1969A   Comparative morphology in systematics. Discussions. In: Sibley, Ch. G. (ed.), 1969A, 411–458,
            17 figs.
1969B   Nonvalidity of the "phylogenetic fallacy". Syst. Zool., 18:1, 111–115.
1969C   The origin and radiation of birds. N.Y. Acad. Sci., Ann., 167:1, 147–155.
1972A   Species interactions and macroevolution. In: Dobzhansky, Th., Hecht, M. K. and Steere, W. C. (eds.),
            1972A, 1–24.

BOCQUET, AIMÉ and LEQUATRE, PAUL
    1968A   Le Moustérien de la grotte des Eugles en Chartreuse.   Grenoble, Fac. Sci., Lab. Géol., Trav., 44,
              89–93, 4 figs. (French).

BODA, JENÖ
    1964A   A Magyar Állami Földtani Intézet öslénytani tipusgyüjteménye.   [Collection of paleontological type
              specimens of the Hungarian Geological Institute.]   Hung., Magy. Áll. Földt. Intéz., Évi Jelent.,
              1961:2, 139–142 (Hungarian; French, German, English and Russian summaries).
    1964B   Catalogus originalium fossilium Hungariae.   Pars zoologica.   Budapest: M. Áll. Földtani Intézet,
              229 pp., bibliog. (Hungarian, French, German, English and Russian).

BODILY, NORMAN M.
    1969A   An armored dinosaur from the lower Cretaceous of Utah.   Brigham Young Univ. Geol. Studies, 16:3,
              35–60, 4 figs., 5 pls., 2 tables.

BOECKER, MAXIMILIAN, LEHMANN, E. VON and REMY, H.
    1972A   Über eine Wirbeltierfauna aus den jüngsten würmzeitlichen Ablagerungen am Michelberg bei
              Ochtendung/Neuwieder Becken.   Decheniana, 124:2, 119–134, 4 figs., 2 pls., 11 tables
              (German).

BOEKSCHOTEN, G. J.
    1969A   Fossilführung und Stratigraphie des Oligo-Miozäns von fünf norddeutschen Bohrungen.   Meyniana, 19,
              1–77, 9 figs., 3 pls., 24 tables (German; English summary).

BOESIGER, E.   See: Dobzhansky, Th. and Boesiger, E., 1968A.

BOEUF, ODILE
    1970A   Faune et nouveaux restes humains du gisement Moustérien.   Soc. Archéol. Hist. Charente, Mém.,
              1969, 53–128, 26 pls. (French).

BOGACHEVA, MARIÍA IVANOVNA, VASIL'EV, ÍU. M., PROSHLÍAKOV, B. K., CHARYGIN, M. M. and
SHLEÍFER, A. G.
    1965A   Unikal'nyĭ razrez triasa v Aralsorskoĭ sverkhglubokoĭ skvazhine (Prikaspñskaía vpadina).   [A unique
              Triassic section in the Aralsorsk super-deep well (the Near-Caspian depression).]   Akad. Nauk
              SSSR, Dokl., 165:3, 629–632 (Russian).

BÖGER, HORST
    1970A   Bildung und Gebrauch von Begriffen in der Paläoökologie.   Lethaia, 3:3, 243–269 (German).
              Rev.:   Rossi Ronchetti in Riv. Ital. Paleontol. Stratigr., 76:4, 627.

BOGSCH, LÁSZLÓ
    1968A   Ergebnisse der paläozoologischen Forschung in Ungarn seit 1945.   Austr. Geol. Bundesanst., Verh.,
              1968:1–2, 203–213 (German).
    1968B   Általános öslénytan.   [General paleontology.]   Budapest: Tankönyvkiadó, 281 pp., 156 figs.,
              9 tables (Hungarian).
    1969A   Kühn, Othmar.   (1892–1969).   Földt. Közl., 99:4, 388–389 (Hungarian).

BÖHME, GOTTFRIED
    1963A   Über den Skelettfund eines Pliocerviden aus dem Pliozän von Kaltensundheim/Rhön.   Paläontol.
              Abhandl., Abt. A, 1:4, 353–373, 12 figs., 5 pls. (German; Russian and English summaries).

BOHN, P.
    1966   Rev.:   Bogsch in Zentralbl. Geol. Paläontol., Teil 2, 1971:1, 54.

BOJARSKAJA, T. D. (= BOÍARSKAÍA, T. D.)
    1969A   Le Pleistocène de la Sibérie Orientale (d'après les données de l'étude de la coupe du mont Mamontova).
              Ass. Fr. Étud. Quat., Bull., 18, 63–73, 4 charts, 1 table (French; Russian summary).

BOJARSKAJA, T. D.   See also: Agadzhaniân, A. K. and Boíarskaía, T. D., 1969A.

BOLT, JOHN R.
    1969A   Lissamphibian origins: possible protolissamphibian from the lower Permian of Oklahoma.   Science
              (AAAS), 166:3907, 888–891, 4 figs.
              Rev.:   Westphal in Zentralbl. Geol. Paläontol., Teil 2, 1970:3/4, 227.

BOLTEN, ROLF and MÜLLER, DIETER
    1969A   Das Tertiär im Nördlinger Ries und in seiner Umgebung.   Geol. Bavarica, 61, 87–130, 1 table
              (German).

BONADONNA, F. P.   See: Ambrosetti, P., Azzaroli, A., Bonadonna, F. P. and Follieri, M.. 1972A; Ambrosetti, P. and Bonadonna, F. P., 1966A, 1967A.

BONAPARTE, JOSÉ F.

1965A   Nuevas icnitas de la Quebrada del Yeso (La Rioja) y reconsideración de la edad de los afloramientos. Acta Geol. Lilloana, 7, 5–16, 3 figs. (Spanish; English summary).

1966F   Cronología de algunas formaciones triásicas argentinas. Basada en restos de tetrápodos. Rev. Asoc. Geol. Argentina, 21:1, 20–38, 5 tables (Spanish; English summary).

1967B   Reptilia fossilis. McGraw-Hill Yearbook, Sci. Tech., 1967, 5 pp., 3 figs.

1969A   Cynognathus minor n. sp. (Therapsida-Cynodontia), nueva evidencia de la vinculación faunística Afro-Sudamericana a principios del Triásico. Symp. Gondwana Stratigr., 273–281, 2 figs. (Spanish; English summary).

1969B   'Dos nuevas "faunas" de reptiles triásicos de Argentina. Symp. Gondwana Stratigr.. 283–306, 12 figs. (Spanish; English summary).

1969C   Los tetrápodos triásicos de Argentina. Symp. Gondwana Stratigr., 307–325, 1 map, 2 charts (Spanish English summary).

1969D   Comments on early saurischians. Linn. Soc., Zool. J., 48:4, 471–480.

1969E   Datos sobre la evolución paleoecológica en las formaciones triásicas de Ischigualasto – Villa Unión. (San Juan – La Rioja). Acta Geol. Lilloana, 10, 191–205 (Spanish; English summary).

1969F   Pterodaustro guiñazui gen. et sp. nov. pterosáurio de la formación Lagarcito, provincia de San Luis, Argentina, y su significado en la geología regional (Pterodactylidae). Acta Geol. Lilloana, 10, 209–225 (Spanish; English summary).

1971A   Cerritosaurus binsfeldi Price, tipo de una nueva familia de tecodontes (Pseudosuchia-Proterochampsia). Acad. Brasil. Ciênc., An., 43 Suppl., 417–422, 1 fig. (Spanish; English summary).

1971B   Los tetrápodos del sector superior de la formación Los Colorados, La Rioja, Argentina. (Triásico Superior). I Parte. Opera Lilloana, 22, 183 pp., 74 figs., 4 pls., 3 tables (Spanish; English summary).

1971C   Descripción del cráneo y mandíbulas de Pterodaustro guiñazui (Pterodactyloidea-Pterodaustriidae nov.) de la formación Lagarcito, San Luis, Argentina. Mar del Plata, Mus. Munic. Cienc. Natur., Publ., 1:9, 263–272, 2 figs., 1 pl. (Spanish; English summary).

1972A   Annotated list of the South American Triassic tetrapods. Gondwana Symp., 2nd., Proc., Pap., 665–682, 45 figs.

BONAPARTE, JOSÉ F. and BOSSI, GERARDO

1967A   Sobre la presencia de dinosáurios en la formación Pirgua del grupo Salta y su significado cronológico. Acta Geol. Lilloana, 9, 25–44, 4 figs., 1 chart, 2 tables (Spanish; English summary).

BOND, GEOFFREY

1966A   Pleistocene environments in southern Africa. In: Howell, F. C. and Bourliere, F. (eds.), 1966A, 308–334, 3 tables.

1972A   Milestones in Rhodesian palaeontology (1901–1971). Geol. Soc. S. Afr., Trans., 75:2, 151–158.

BOND, GEOFFREY and BROMLEY, K.

1970A   Sediments with the remains of dinosaurs near Gokwe, Rhodesia. Palaeogeogr., Palaeoclimatol., Palaeoecol.. 8:4, 313–327, 1 map, 3 pls.

BOND, GEOFFREY, WILSON, J. F. and RAATH, M. A.

1970A   Upper Karroo pillow lava and a new sauropod horizon in Rhodesia. Nature, 227:5265, 1339, 1 fig.

BOND, GEOFFREY   See also: Raath, M. A.. Smith, C. C. and Bond, G., 1970A.

BONDAREV, L. G.   See: Alešinskaja, Z. V. and Bondarev, L. G., 1969A.

BONÉ, ÉDOUARD L.

1971A   Reconnaissance paléontologique en Iran – Septembre 1970. Soc. Roy. Belge. Anthropol. Préhist.. Bull., 82, 9–23 (French).

BONFIGLIO, L. and BERDAR, A.

1969A   Elefanti pleistocenici del litorale dello Stretto di Messina, revisione e nuove osservazioni. Quaternaria, 11, 255–261, 1 fig. (Italian; English and French summaries).

BONIFAY, EUGÈNE

1962A   Rev.: Ferrer Morrón in Ampurias, 29, 353–355.

1968A   Stratigraphie et industries lithiques de la grotte no. 1 du Mas des Caves à Lunel-Viel (Hérault). In: R. Vaufray Festschrift, 37–46, 4 figs. (French; English summary).

BONIFAY, MARIE-FRANÇOISE

1967A   Étude paléontologique de la grotte de la Balauzière (Gard). Monaco, Mus. Anthropol. Préhist., Bull., 13, 91–139, 18 figs., 14 tables (French).

1968B   La faune de l'abri Cornille (Istres, Bouches-du-Rhône). In: R. Vaufray Festschrift, 47–57, 5 figs.. 5 tables (French; English summary).

1968C   Principales formes caractéristiques du Quaternaire moyen du Sud-Est de la France (Grands Mammifères). Monaco, Mus. Anthropol. Préhist., Bull., 14, 49–62, 4 figs., 2 tables (French).

1969A   Les grand mammifères découverts sur le sol de la cabane acheuléenne du Lazaret. In: Lumley, H. de (ed.), 1969B, 59–73, 1 fig., 9 tables (French).

1969B   Relations entre les paléoclimats et les migrations des grands mammifères quaternaires en Europe méridionale. Quaternaria, 11, 155–160, 1 table (French; English and Italian summaries).

1969C   Faunes quaternaires de France. Int. Ass. Quaternary Res., 8th Congr. (1969), Etud. Fr. Quat., 127–142 (French).

        Rev.: Thenius in Zentralbl. Geol. Paläontol., Teil 2, 1970:6, 516.

1971A   Carnivores quaternaires du sud-est de la France. Mus. Nat. Hist. Natur., Paris, Mém., Sér. C, 21:2, 43–377, 76 figs., 27 pls., 109 tables (French).

        Rev.: Thenius in Zentralbl. Geol. Paläontol.. Teil 2, 1971:6, 507–508.

BONIS, LOUIS DE

1969A   Mise au point sur la répartition stratigraphique des grands rhinocéros oligocènes. Acad. Sci., C.R., Sér. D, 269:3, 316–318 (French).

1969B   Remarques sur la position systématique des Amphicyon. Acad. Sci., C.R., Sér. D, 269:18, 1748–1750, 1 table (French).

1969C   Les vertébrés fossiles de Saint-Paul-des-Landes près d'Aurillac. Rev. Haute-Auvergne, 41, 393–400 (French).

1970A   Contribution à l'étude des rhinocérotidés aquitaniens d'Europe occidentale. Acad. Sci., C.R., Sér. D, 270:6, 764–766 (French).

1971A   Deux nouveaux carnassiers des Phosphorites du Quercy. Ann. Paléontol., Vertébrés, 57:1, 117–129, 2 figs., 1 pl. (French; English summary).

        Rev.: Thenius in Zentralbl. Geol. Paläontol., Teil 2, 1971:6, 517.

1972A   Découverte d'un nouveau gisement de mammifères dans la "molasse de l'Agenais". Son intérêt pour la stratigraphie de l'Oligocène supérieur du Bassin d'Aquitaine. Acad. Sci., C.R., Sér. D, 275:21, 2323–2326.

BONIS, LOUIS DE, LEBEAU, M.-O and RICQLÈS, A. DE

1972A   Étude de la répartition des types de tissus osseux chez les vertébrés tétrapodes au moyen de l'analyse factorielle des correspondances. Acad. Sci., C.R., Sér. D, 274:23, 3084–3087, 1 fig. (French).

BONIS, L. DE   See also: Baudelot, S. and Bonis, L. de, 1968A.

BONNEFILLE, RAYMONDE, CHAVAILLON, J. and COPPENS, Y.

1970A   Résultats de la nouvelle mission de l'Omo (3e campagne 1969). Acad. Sci., C.R., Sér. D, 270:7, 924–927, 1 fig. (French).

BONNEFILLE, RAYMONDE, CHAVAILLON, N. and TAÏEB, M.

1970A   Formations volcano-lacustres quaternaires de la vallée supérieure du Webi-Schebelli (Ethiopie): données stratigraphiques, préhistoriques et palynologiques. Acad. Sci., C.R., Sér. D, 271:2, 161–164, 2 figs. (French).

BONNET, ANDRÉ

1970A   Sur l'importance du gisement de mammifères rissiens de Châtillon — St.-Jean (Drôme) pour la stratigraphie du Quaternaire rhodanien. Soc. Géol. Fr., C.R., 1970:2, 36–38 (French).

BONNET, ANDRÉ and BORNAND, M.

1970A   Pédologie et Quaternaire dans la vallée du Rhône moyen. Ass. Fr. Étud. Quat., Bull., 23–24, 105–116, 2 pls., 2 tables (French).

BONNICHSEN, ROBSON   See: Hopkins, M. L., Bonnichsen, R. and Fortsch, D., 1969A.

BOONSTRA, L. D.

1968B   The braincase, basicranial axis and median septum in the Dinocephalia. S. Afr. Mus., Ann., 50:10, 195–273, 58 figs.

1969A   The fauna of the Tapinocephalus zone (Beaufort beds of the Karoo). S. Afr. Mus., Ann., 56:1, 73 pp., 22 figs., 1 table.

1969B   The terrestrial reptile fauna of Tapinocephalus — zone age and Gondwanaland. (Abstract). Symp. Gondwana Stratigr., 327–330 (English and Spanish).

1971A   The early therapsids. S. Afr. Mus., Ann., 59:2, 17–46, 3 figs.

BORDES, FRANÇOIS
1968A   Rev.: Serizawa in Asian Perspectives, 11, 190–191; Walker in New Sci., 44:663, 393.
1968B   In memory of Raymond Vaufrey, 1890–1967. Current Anthropol., 9:4, 337–338.
1969A   Colloque sur l'origine de l'homme moderne (Paris, UNESCO, 2–5 Septembre 1969). Quaternaria, 11, 281–282 (French).
1970A   Informations archéologiques. Circonscription d'Aquitaine. Gallia Préhist., 13:2, 485–511, 31 figs. (French).
1972A*   The origin of Homo sapiens. New York: UNESCO, Ecology and Conservation Series, 3, 321 pp. Rev.: Molleson in New Sci., 54:800, 647.

BORDES, FRANÇOIS and SONNEVILLE-BORDES, DENISE DE
1967B   Raymond Vaufrey, 1890–1967. Soc. Préhist. Fr., Bull., Étud. Trav., 64:1, 3–14 (French).

BORESKE, JOHN R. A., JR.
1972A   Taxonomy and taphonomy of the North American amiid fishes. Geol. Soc. Amer., Abstr., 4:1, 3–4 (abs.).

BORESKE, JOHN R., JR., GOLDBERG, LEONARD and CAMERON, BARRY
1972A   A reworked cetacean with clam borings: Miocene of North Carolina. J. Paleontol., 46:1, 130–139, 6 figs., 1 pl., 1 table.

BORESKE, JOHN R. A., JR.   See also: Cameron, B. and Boreske, J. R., 1972A.

BORGOGNINI-TARLI, S. M.
1972A   The Seventh Panafrican Congress on Prehistory and Quaternary Studies. Addis Ababa, 6–11 December 1971. J. Human Evol., 1:4, 429–430.

BORISKOVSKIĬ, P. I.
1966B   Basic problems of the prehistoric archaeology of Vietnam. Asian Perspectives, 9, 83–85.
1969A   C. S. Nicolăescu-Plopşor (1900–1968). Sov. Arkheol., 1969:3, 314–315, portr. (Russian).
1970A   Zamechaniia v sviazi so stat'eĭ G. P. Grigor'eva "Novye aspekty proplemy proiskhozhdeniia Homo sapiens'. [Comments on the article by G. P. Grigor'ev "New aspects of the problem of origin of Homo sapiens'.] Vop. Antropol., 34, 50–51 (Russian).

BORISKOVSKIĬ, P. I. and OKLADNIKOV, A. P.
1970A   D. N. Lev (1905–1969). Sov. Arkheol., 1970:3, 298–299, portr. (Russian).

BORISOV, B. A.
1967A   Paleogenovaia i neogenovaia sistemy. Zaĭsanskaia vpadina. [Paleogene and Neogene. Zaĭsan basin.] Geologiia SSSR, 41:1, Eastern Kazakhstan, 191–199, 1 fig., 1 table (Russian).
1967B   Paleogenovaia i neogenovaia sistemy. Tarbagataĭ. [Paleogene and Neogene. Tarbagataĭ.] Geologiia SSSR, 41:1, Eastern Kazakhstan, 209–211 (Russian).

BORISOV, B. A. and CHUMAKOV, I. S.
1967A   Paleogenovaia i neogenovaia sistemy. Rudnyĭ Altaĭ. [Paleogene and Neogene. Rudnyĭ Altaĭ.] Geologiia SSSR, 41:1, Eastern Kazakhstan, 201–206, 1 fig. (Russian).

BORISOV, B. A. and KLEIMAN, G. P.
1967A   Paleogenovaia i neogenovaia sistemy. Saurskaia zona. [Paleogene and Neogene. Saur zone.] Geologiia SSSR, 41:1, Eastern Kazakhstan, 199–200 (Russian).

BORISOV, B. A. and SEVRIUGIN, N. A.
1967A   Paleogenovaia i neogenovaia sistemy. Zapadnaia Kalba (Charskaia i Zharminskaia zony). [Paleogene and Neogene. West Kalba (Char and Zharmin zones).] Geologiia SSSR, 41:1, Eastern Kazakhstan, 206–209 (Russian).

BORISOV, B. A.   See also: Zhegallo, V. I. and Borisov, B. A., 1968A.

BORKHVARDT, V. G. (= BORCHWARDT, V. G.)
1969A   Ob osobennostiakh stroeniia pozvonkov khroniozukhid. [Peculiarities in the structure of vertebrae in chroniosuchids.] Paleontol. Zh., 1969:3, 146–148, 2 figs. (Russian).
1969B   Structural features of chroniosuchid vertebrae. Paleontol. J., 3:3, 421–422, 2 figs.

BORKIN, L. ÎA.   See: Khozatskiĭ, L. I. and Borkin, L. ÎA., 1971A.

BORNAND, M.   See: Bonnet, A. and Bornand, M., 1970A.

BOROS, I. and DELY, O. G.
1968A   Einige Vertreter der ungarischen Zoologie an der Wende des 19.–20. Jahrhunderts und die wissenschaftschistorische Bedeutung ihrer Tätigkeit II. Géza Gyula Fejérváry (1894–1932). Vert. Hungarica, 10, 45–142 (German; Hungarian summary).

BORRELLO, ANGEL V.
1966A*   Paleontografía Bonaerense. La Plata: Provincia de Buenos Aires, Comisión de Investigación Científica, nos. 1–5, illustr. (Spanish).

BORSUK-BIAŁYNICKA, B. and WYSOCZAŃSKI-MINKOWICZ, T.
1969A   Mammuthus trogontherii from Rzochów. Pol. Akad. Nauk, Bull., Sér. Sci. Géol. Géogr., 17, 143–147, 3 photos, 3 tables.

BORSUK-BIAŁYNICKA, MAGDALENA
1968A   Allacerops minor Belayeva, 1954 (Rhinocerotidae) from the Oligocene of Ulan Ganga, western Gobi Desert. Palaeontol. Polonica, 19, 153–159, 2 pls., 2 tables.
    Rev.: Thenius in Zentralbl. Geol. Paläontol., Teil 2, 1970:5, 439.
1970A   Lower Pliocene rhinocerotids from Altan Teli, western Mongolia. In: Kielan-Jaworowska, Z. (ed.), 1970B, 73–92, 2 figs., 6 pls., 8 tables.

BORSUK-BIAŁYNICKA, MAGDALENA and MŁYNARSKI, MARIAN
1968A   The first finding of the Mesozoic marine turtle Tretosternon aff. punctatum Owen, 1848 in Poland. Warsaw, Muz. Ziemi, Pr., 12, 217–222, 2 figs. (Polish summary).

BORZATTI VON LÖWENSTERN, EDOARDO
1965C   La grotta-riparo di Uluzzo C. (Campagna di scavi 1964). Riv. Sci. Preist., 20:1, 1–31, 9 figs. (Italian; English and French summaries).
1966A   Gli strati pleistocenici della grotta delle Prazziche (Novaglie-Lecce). Bull. Paletnol. Ital., n.s. 17, 75, 7–12, 1 fig. (Italian; French and English summaries).
1966B   Industria musteriana a Rhinoceros mercki a Santa Caterina (Lecce). Riv. Sci. Preist., 21:1, 185–193, 3 figs. (Italian; French and English summaries).
1966C   Alcuni aspetti del Musteriano nel Salento. Riv. Sci. Preist., 21:2, 203–287, 23 figs. (Italian; French and English summaries).
1970A   Prima campagna di scavi nella grotta "Mario Bernardini" (Nardò-Lecce). Riv. Sci. Preist., 25:1, 89–125, 11 figs. (Italian; French and English summaries).
1970B   Grotta Mario Bernardini (Prov. di Lecce). Riv. Sci. Preist., 25:2, 407 (Italian).

BORZATTI VON LÖWENSTERN, E. and DANI, A.
1968A   Grotta di Rigoli (Gavorrano, Prov. di Grosseto). Riv. Sci. Preist., 23:2, 397–398 (Italian).

BORZATTI VON LÖWENSTERN, E. and MAGALDI, D.
1967A   Ultime ricerche nella Grotta dell' Alto (S. Caterina-Nardò). Riv. Sci. Preist., 22:2, 205–250, 16 figs., 3 tables (Italian; French and English summaries).

BOSCH, M. VAN DEN
1964D   Haientanden uit de fosforietenlaag aan de basis van het Oligoceen in Overijssel en Gelderland. Natuurhist. Genoot. Limburg, Publ., 13, 61–78, 4 pls. (Dutch).
1969A   Het Mioceen van Delden. — III. De Selachierfauna uit de miocene afzetingen in het Twente-Kaanal bij Delden. Publicatie Reeks, 19, 25–36, 2 figs., 3 pls. (Dutch).
    Rev.: Weiler in Zentralbl. Geol. Paläontol., Teil 2, 1970:5, 430; Weiler in Zentralbl. Geol. Paläontol., Teil 2, 1971:5, 397.
1971A   Elasmobranchii uit het Rupelien van Lintorf bij Düsseldorf (Westdeutschland). Werkgroep Tert. Kwart. Geol., Meded., 8, 46–61, 3 pls., 1 map (Dutch; German summary).
    Rev.: Weiler in Zentralbl. Geol. Paläontol., Teil 2, 1971:5, 397–398.

BOSCH Y GIMPERA, PEDRO
1967A   L'Amérique avant Cristophe Colomb. Paris: Payot, Bibliothèque Historique, 238 pp., 76 figs. (French).
    Rev.: Vallois in L'Anthropologie, 72, 131–133.
1968B   Nuevos aspectos del paleolítico eurasiático en relación con el origen de los cazadores americanos. An. Antropol., Mexico, 5, 163–179, 15 figs. (Spanish; English summary).
1971A   L'America precolumbiana. Translated by Paolo Pignota. Turin, Italy: Unione Tipografico, Editrice Torinese, 578 pp., 30 pls. (Italian).
    Rev.: Anon. in Interamer., 18:5, 2.

BOSCHMA, H.
1968A   Short biography of Professor Dr. C. J. van der Klaauw. Acta Biotheoret., 18, 3–4, portr.

BOSINSKI, GERHARD
1967A   Die mittelpaläolithischen Funde im westlichen Mitteleuropa. Fundamenta, Reihe A, 4, 206 pp.,
                    16 figs., 197 and XV pls., 7 maps (German).
               Rev.: Anisíutkin and Grigor'ev in Sov. Arkheol., 1971:3, 290–292 (Russian); Felgenhauer in Archaeol
                    Austriaca, 44, 99; Freund in Quartär, 20, 238–242; Smolla in Germania, 47:1–2, 205–209.
1968A   Ein Magdalénien-Fundplatz in Feldkirchen-Gönnersdorf, Kreis Neuwied. Eiszeitalter Gegenwart, 19,
                    268–269 (German).
1969A   Der Magdalénien-Fundplatz Feldkirchen-Gönnersdorf, Kr. Neuwied. Germania, 47:1–2, 1–38, 17 figs.,
                    10 pls., 2 maps (German).

BOSINSKI, GERHARD and BRUNNACKER, KARL
1969A   Ein Halbkeil von Hoengen-Warden, Kr. Aachen-Land. Bonner Jahrb., 169, 29–43, 7 figs. (German).

BOSINSKI, G.   See also: Wetzel, R. and Bosinski, G., 1969A.

BOSMA, ANNEKE A.
1968A   The influence of attrition on the dental pattern of Pleistocene *Acanthion brachyurus* (Hystricidae,
                    Rodentia, Mammalia) from Java. Ned. Akad. Wetensch., Proc., Ser. B, 71:4, 336–341, 2 figs.,
                    2 tables.

BOSMA, ANNEKE A. and INSOLE, A. N.
1972A   Theridomyinae (Rodentia, Mammalia) from the Osborne beds (late Eocene), Isle of Wight, England.
                    Ned. Akad. Wetensch., Proc., Ser. B, 75:2, 233–244, 5 figs., 1 pl.

BOSMA, ANNEKE and SCHMIDT-KITTLER, NORBERT
1972A   *Ectropomys exiguus* n. gen., n. sp., member of the Oltinomyinae n. subfam. (Theridomyidae,
                    Rodentia), from Paleogene deposits of the Isle of Wight (England) and southern Germany.
                    Ned. Akad. Wetensch., Proc., Ser. B., 75:3, 181–192, 4 figs., 1 pl.

BOSSI, GERARDO   See: Bonaparte, J. and Bossi, G., 1967A.

BOSSY, K. H.   See: Thomson, K. S. and Bossy, K. H., 1970A.

BOTTLEY, E. P.
1961A   *Drepanaspis*. New discoveries. Geol. News, 18, 6.

BOTTOMS, EDWARD
1969A   Notes on the geology, Pleistocene paleontology, and archaeology of Saltville, Virginia. Chesopiean,
                    7:4–5, 80–89, 2 figs.

BOUBELÍK, M.   See: Špinar, Z. V., Boubelík, M. and Romanovský, A., 1971A.

BOUCHUD, JEAN
1957A   Notions de Géologie et de Paléontologie Quaternaire. Les Eyzies, 1957:1, 36–40 (French).
1957B   Le renne Quaternaire français. Les Eyzies, 1957:1, 41–50, 4 figs. (French).
1959B   La faune de la basse terrasse de l'Allier à Pont-du-Château (Puy-de-Dôme). Les Eyzies, 9, 36–39
                    (French).
1961B   Le Professeur Edouard Bourdelle. 1876–1960. Les Eyzies, 10, 44–46, portr. (French).
1961C   Étude de la microfaune de la grotte de Lascaux. Les Eyzies, 10, 60–62, 2 tables (French).
1961D   La détermination des Éléphants fossiles. Les Eyzies, 10, 157–165, 2 pls. (French).
1961E   Histoire des idées relatives aux origines de l'Humanité et des êtres vivants. Les Eyzies, 10, 166–187
                    (French).
1962B   Découverte d'un squelette d'enfant moustérien. Les Eyzies, 11, 34 (French).
1962C   Notions de géologie du Quaternaire. Les Eyzies, 11, 83–98, 3 figs., 3 tables (French).
1962D   Notions de paléontologie du Quaternaire. Les Eyzies, 11, 101–106, 2 figs. (French).
1964B   Présence d'*Elephas meridionalis* mutation *cromerensis* à Wissant (Pas-de-Calais). Les Eyzies, 13, 135–
                    138, 1 fig. (French).
1965C   Mises au point récentes en Géologie du Quaternaire. Les Eyzies, 14, 92–108, 2 tables (French).
1966F   La restoration de l'abri de Cro-Magnon aux Eyzies (Dordogne). Les Eyzies, 15, 25–27 (French).
1966G   Remarques sur les fouilles de L. Lartet à l'abri de Cro-Magnon. (Dordogne). Les Eyzies, 15, 28–36,
                    5 figs. (French).
1966H   Les acquisitions récentes en Paléontologie Humaine et le problème de l'*Homo habilis*. Les Eyzies, 15,
                    50–59, 1 fig. (French).
1966I   Étude préliminaire de la faune des abris sous roche de la Baume (Haute-Loire). Rev. Sci. Natur.
                    Auvergne, 32:1–4, 35–43 (French).
1966J   Essai sur le renne et la climatologie du Paléolithique moyen et supérieur. Périgueux: Impr. Magne,
                    300 pp., 55 figs., 13 pls., 71 tables (French).

Rev.:   Delporte in Soc. Préhist. Fr., Bull., C.R., <u>64</u>:6, 165—167.

1967B   L'alimentation carnée des hominidés fossiles. Les Eyzies, <u>16,</u> 67—76 (French).

1968C   L'abri du Facteur à Tursac (Dordogne) II: La faune et sa signification climatique. Gallia Préhist., <u>11</u>:1, 113—121, 5 figs., 5 tables (French).

1968D   Étude préliminaire de la faune des abris sous roche de la Baume (Haute-Loire). Rev. Sci. Natur. Auvergne (1966), <u>32,</u> 35—43, 2 figs. (French).

1969A   La faune moustérienne de Carigüela. L'Anthropologie, <u>73</u>:5—6, 361—364, 2 pls. (French).

1969B   L'avifaune découverte sur le sol de la cabane acheuléenne du Lazaret. In: Lumley, H. de (ed.), <u>1969B</u>, 97—106, 3 figs., 3 tables (French).

BOUCHUD, J. and DESBROSSE, R.

1972A   Cartilages costaux dans les niveaux préhistoriques. Soc. Préhist. Fr., Bull., <u>69</u>:2, 38—39 (French).

BOUCHUD, J.   See also: Bertouille, H. and M. and Bouchud, J., 1968A; Bertouille, H. and Bouchud, J., 1969A; Bouchud, P. and Bouchud, J., 1957A.

BOUCHUD, PAULETTE and BOUCHUD, JEAN

1957A   La microfaune de l'abri sous roche de Fontalès près Saint-Antonin (Tarn-et-Garonne). Les Eyzies, <u>7,</u> 13—15 (French).

BOUGHEY, ARTHUR S.

1971A   Man and the environment. An introduction to human ecology and evolution. New York: Macmillan Co., London: Collier-Macmillan Ltd., viii + 472 pp., illustr. Rev.:   Weiner in New Sci., <u>51</u>:767, 536.

BOUILLON, E.

1969A   Biface épais amygdaloid en quartzite de Gondreville (M.-et-M.). Acad. Soc. Lorraines Sci., Bull., <u>8</u>:3, 236—240, 3 figs. (French).

BOULE, MARCELLIN

1971A   The fossil man of La Chapelle-aux-Saints (Correze). In: Leakey, L. S. B., Prost, J. and Prost, S. <u>1971A</u>, 179—181 (reprinted from Boule, M., 1908).

BOULINIER, G.

1968A   Le colloque du centenaire de la découverte de l'Homme de Cro-Magnon. (Les Eyzies, 15—17 juillet 1968). L'Anthropologie, <u>72</u>:5—6, 622—624 (French).

1969A   Le colloque du centenaire de la découverte de l'Homme de Cro-Magnon. Les Eyzies, <u>18,</u> 56—59 (French).

BOURDELLE, ED.

1955A   Les parentés morphologiques des Equidés Caballins d'après les gravures rupestres du Sud-Ouest de la France. Les Eyzies, <u>5,</u> 23—30, 13 figs. (French).

BOURDIER, FRANK

1967A   Rev.:   Verger in Sciences, <u>58/59,</u> 34.

1969A   Sur la position chronologique du paléolithique de Sangatte, Wissant et Wimereux (Pas-de-Calais). Soc. Préhist. Fr., Bull., C.R., <u>66</u>:8, 230—231 (French).

1969B   Geoffroy Saint-Hilaire versus Cuvier: the campaign for paleontological evolution (1825—1838). In: Schneer, C. J. (ed.), <u>1969A</u>, 36—61.ˋ

BOURLIERE, F.   See: Howell, F. C. and Bourliere, F. (eds.), 1966A.

BOUT, PIERRE

1967A   Observations sur le Villafranchien d'Auvergne et du Velay. Assoc. Franç. Étude Quat., Bull., <u>10,</u> 3—64, 27 figs. (French).

1968A   La limite Pliocène-Quaternaire en Europe occidentale. Assoc. Franç. Étude Quat., Bull., <u>14,</u> 55—78, 1 map, 1 table (French; English summary).

1970A   Absolute ages of some volcanic formations in the Auvergne and Velay areas and chronology of the European Pleistocene. Palaeogeogr., Palaeoclimatol., Palaeoecol., <u>8</u>:2—3, 95—106, 3 figs., 2 tables.

1972A   Absoliutnyĭ vozrast vulkanogennykh formatsiĭ Overni i Vele i khronologiia chetvertichnoĭ fauny mlekopitaiushchikh Evropy. [Absolute age of volcanic formations of Auvergne and Velay and the chronology of the Quaternary mammalian fauna of Europe.] In: Geologiia i fauna nizhnego i srednego pleistotsena Evropy, 7—24 (Russian).

BOUVIER, JEAN-MARC
    1969A   Existence de Magdalénien supérieur sans harpon: preuves stratigraphiques. Acad. Sci., C.R., Sér. D, 268:24, 2865–2866 (French).
    1969B   Godet en stéatite et collier magdalénien de la "Chaire à Calvin" Mouthiers (Charente). Soc. Archéol. Hist. Charente, Mém., 1968, 65–72, 7 figs. (French).
    1971A   Fossilisation différentielle des restes humains würmiens. Acad. Sci., C.R., Sér. D, 272:12, 1613–1615 (French).

BOUVIER, J. M., DEBENATH, A., DELPECH, F. and DUPORT, L.
    1969A   Les restes humains de la Grotte Duport à La Chaise de Vouthon (Charente) dans leur contexte stratigraphique et paléontologique. Soc. Anthropol. Paris, Bull. Mém., Série 12, 4, 405 (French)

BOUYSSONIE, A., BOUYSSONIE, J. and BARDON, L.
    1971A   The discovery of a human Mousterian skeleton at La Chapelle-aux-Saints (Correze). In: Leakey, L. S. B., Prost, J. and Prost, S. (eds.), 1971A, 177–178 (reprinted from Bouyssonie, A., Bouyssonie J. and Bardon, L., 1908).

BOUYSSONIE, J.   See: Bouyssonie, A., Bouyssonie, J. and Bardon, L., 1971A.

BOWEN, B. E.   See: Vondra, C. F., Johnson, G. D., Bowen, B. E. and Behrensmeyer, A. K., 1971A.

BOWEN, D. Q.
    1970A   The palaeoenvironment of the 'Red Lady' of Paviland. Antiquity, 44:174, 134–136.

BOWEN, ROBERT N.
    1969A   Comments. Curr. Anthropol., 10:4, 407–408.

BOWERS, ALFRED W.   See: Jones, R. W. and Bowers, A. W., 1968A.

BOWLER, J. M., JONES, R., ALLEN, H. and THORNE, A. G.
    1970A   Pleistocene human remains from Australia: a living site and human cremation from Lake Mungo, western New South Wales. World Archaeol., 2:1, 39–60, 5 figs., 5 tables.

BOWLER, J. M., THORNE, A. G. and POLACH, H. A.
    1972A   Pleistocene man in Australia: age and significance of the Mungo skeleton. Nature, 240:5375, 48–50, 3 figs.. 1 table.

BOWN, THOMAS M. and GINGERICH, PHILIP D.
    1972A   Dentition of early Eocene primates Niptomomys and Absarokius. Postilla, 158, 10 pp., 4 figs.

BOY, JÜRGEN A.
    1971A   Zur Problematik der Branchiosaurier (Amphibia, Karbon-Perm). Paläontol. Z., 45:3/4, 107–119, 2 figs., 1 table (German; English summary).
             Rev.: Westphal in Zentralbl. Geol. Paläontol.. Teil 2, 1971:6, 505.
    1971B   Ein bemerkenswerter Schädelrest eines unterpermischen Labyrintodontiers (Amphibia) aus dem Saargebiet. Hess. Landesamt Bodenforsch., Abh., 60, 31–43, 5 figs. (German).
    1971C   Paläontologie. Geol. Karte Rheinland-Pfalz, 1:25,000, Erläut., Blatt 6410, Kusel, 52-59, 1 table (German).
    1972A   Palökologischer Vergleich zweier berühmter Fossillagerstätten des deutschen Rotliegenden (Unterperm, Saar-Nahe-Gebiet). Hess. Landesamt Bodenforsch., Notizbl., 100, 46–59, 2 figs. (German).
    1972B   Die Branchiosaurier (Amphibia) des saarpfälzischen Rotliegenden (Perm, SW-Deutschland). Hess. Landesamt Bodenforsch., Abh., 65, 137 pp., 70 figs., 2 pls.. 2 tables (German).

BOYD, HAROLD A.   See: Allison, I. S. and Boyd, H. A., 1954A.

BOYER, S. J.   See: Simons, E. L., Pilbeam, D. and Boyer, S. J., 1971A.

BOYLAN, PATRICK J.
    1970A   An unpublished portrait of Dean William Buckland, 1784–1856. Soc. Bibliogr. Natur. Hist., J., 5:5, 350–354, 1 pl.

BOYNTON, K. L.
    1971A   The artful armadillo. Desert Mag.. 34:8, 6–9, 3 figs.

BOZHICH, S. P.
    1971A   O vymiranii vidov (popytka matematicheskogo analiza). [On extinction of species (an attempt at mathematical analysis).] Zh. Obshch. Biol., 32:1, 45–55, 9 tables (Russian; English summary).

BRABB, EARL E.
1969A   Eocene colloquium. Geotimes, 14:3, 19—20, 2 tables.

BRACE, C. LORING
1962E   The fate of the "classic" Neanderthals. Amer. Anthropol. Ass., Abstr., 1962, 5 (abs.).
1964B   Hominid catastrophism — australopithecine version? Amer. Anthropol. Ass., Abstr., 1964, 9 (abs.).
1967A   Rev.: Buettner-Janusch in Amer. J. Phys. Anthropol., 32:1, 155—156; Hughes in Man, 4:1, 137—138.
1967B   Environment, tooth form, and size in the Pleistocene. Jour. Dental Res., 46:5, 809—816, 7 figs.,
             3 tables.
1969A   The australopithecine range of variation. Amer. J. Phys. Anthropol., 31, 255 (abs.).
1969B   Sexual dimorphism and the australopithecine range of variation. Amer. Anthropol. Ass., Bull., 2:3,
             12 (abs.).
1970A   The origin of man. Natur. Hist., 79:1, 46—49, 1 fig.

BRACE, C. L., NELSON, H. and KORN, N.
1971A   Atlas of fossil man. N.Y. and London: Holt, Rinehart and Winston, Inc., x + 150 pp., illustr.
             Rev.: Steegman in Amer. J. Phys. Anthropol., 37:1, 159—160; Villiers in J. Human Evol., 1:4,
             431—432.

BRAESTRUP, F. W.
1968A   Evolution der Wirbeltiere. Ökologische und ethologische Gesichtspunkte. Zool. Anz., 181:1/2, 1—22,
             1 fig. (German).

BRAHIMI, CLAUDE
1968A   L'Ibéromaurusien littoral de la région d'Alger. Cent. Rech. Anthropol., Préhist., Ethnogr., Mém., 13,
             154 pp., 53 figs., 1 map (French).

BRAIDWOOD, ROBERT J.
1967A   A note on the present status of radioactive carbon age determination. Sumer, 23, 39—44.
1967B   Prehistoric men. Seventh edition. Glenview, Illinois: Scott, Foresman, and Co., 181 pp., 47 illustr.
             Rev.: Birmingham in Mankind, 7:1, 78.
1970A   Prehistory into history in the Near East. Nobel Symp., 12th, Uppsala Univ., 1969, Proc., 81—91.

BRAIN, C. K.
1968A   New light on old bones. S. Afr. Mus. Ass., Bull., 9:1, 22—27 (Dutch summary).
1968B   Who killed the Swartkrans ape-men? S. Afr. Mus. Ass., Bull., 9:4, 127—139 (Dutch summary).
1969A   The probable role of leopards as predators of the Swartkrans australopithecines. S. Afr. Archaeol.
             Bull., 24:95—96, 170—171, 1 fig.
1969B   Zoological aspects. S. Afr. Archaeol. Bull., 24:95—96, 208.
1970A   Comments. Curr. Anthropol., 11:1, 31—32.

BRAIN, C. K.   See also: Freedman, L. and Brain, C. K., 1972A.

BRAJNIKOV, BORIS See: Bacskai, J., Bartlett, S., Brajnikov, B., Munthe, K., Nichols, R. and Matsumoto, M. (eds.),
             1972A; Camp, C. L., Nichols, R. H., Brajnikov, B., Fulton, E. and Bacskai, J. A. (eds.), 1972A.

BRAMBLE, DENNIS M. and HUTCHISON, J. H.
1971A   Biogeography of continental Tertiary Chelonia and Crocodilia of far-western United States. Geol.
             Soc. Amer., Abstr., 3:2, 86—87 (abs.).

BRAME, ARDEN H., JR.
1967A   A list of the world's Recent and fossil salamanders. Herpeton, 2, 1—26.
             Rev.: Thomas in Salamandra, 6, 141.

BRAME, ARDEN H., JR. and MURRAY, KEITH F.
1968A   Three new slender salamanders (Batrachoseps) with a discussion of relationships and speciation within
             the genus. Los Angeles Cty. Mus. Natur. Hist. Sci., Bull., 4, 35 pp., 15 figs., 5 tables.

BRAMWELL, CHERRIE D.
1971A   Flying ability of Archaeopteryx. Nature, 231:5298, 128.
1971B   Aerodynamics of Pteranodon. Linn. Soc., Biol. J., 3:4, 313—328, 12 figs., 4 tables.

BRAMWELL, CHERRIE D. and WHITFIELD, G. R.
1970A   Flying speed of the largest aerial vertebrate. Nature, 225:5233, 660, 1 fig.
             Rev.: Anon. in Priroda, 1970:10, 104—105.

BRAMWELL, CHERRIE D.   See also: Whitfield, G. and Bramwell, C., 1971A.

BRANDT, KARL
    1968A   Über neue Steinwerkzeugfunde in Australien. Quartär, 19, 353–367, 4 figs., 1 pl. (German).

BRANISA, LEONARDO
    1968A   Hallazgo del amonite *Neolobites* en la caliza Miraflores y de huellas de dinosáurios en la Formación
               El Molino y su significado para la determinación de la edad del Grupo Puca. Inst. Boliviano
               Petról., Bol., 8:1, 16–29 (Spanish).

BRANTLEY, ALBERT G.
    1971A   Paleoenvironmental significance of bone orientation in Watkin's quarry (late Pleistocene), Glynn
               County, Georgia. Georgia Acad. Sci., Bull., 29:2, 128.

BRANTS, A.   See: Haghipour, A. and Brants, A., 1971A.

BRAUNITZER, G. and FUJIKI, H.
    1969A   Zur Evolution der Vertebraten. Die Konstitution und Tertiärstruktur des Hämoglobins des
               Flussneunaugens. Naturwiss., 56:6, 322–323, 1 fig. (German).

BRAY, WARWICK and TRUMP, DAVID
    1970A   A dictionary of archaeology. London: Penguin Press, 269 pp., 211 figs., 104 pls.
               Rev.: Thompson in Antiquaries J., 51:2, 333; Walker in New Sci., 48:728, 397–398.

BREED, WILLIAM J.
    1968A   The age of dinosaurs in northern Arizona. Flagstaff: Mus. No. Arizona, vi + 45 pp., 29 figs.
               Rev.: Johnston in J. West, 9:2, 305.

BREED, WILLIAM J.   See also: Elliot, D. H., Colbert, E. H., Breed, W. J., Jensen, J. A. and Powell, J. S., 1970A;
               McKee, E. D. and Breed, W. J., 1969A.

BRENNER, PATRICK
    1969A   Fossil and mineral collecting in northwest Iowa. Rocks Miner., 44:1, 12–16, 5 figs., 1 map.

BRESLAV, S. L.
    1971A   Chetvertichnaía sistema. [Quaternary system.] Geologiía SSSR, 4, Center of the European part of
               the USSR, 489–636, 20 figs., 9 tables (Russian).

BRETERNITZ, DAVID A.
    1969A   Radiocarbon dates: eastern Colorado. Plains Anthropol., 14:44 pt. 1, 113–124, 1 fig., 5 tables.

BREUIL, ABBÉ HENRI
    1961A   Alberto-Carlo Blanc. [1906–1960]. Les Eyzies, 10, 46–49 (French).

BREW, J. O.
    1968A*   One hundred years of anthropology. Cambridge: Harvard Univ. Press, viii + 176 pp., illustr.
               Rev.: Billy in L'Anthropologie, 74:1–2, 105–106; Hallowell in Amer. Anthropol., 71, 725–726;
               Hoebel in Amer. J. Phys. Anthropol., 34:3, 453; MacLachlan in J. West, 8, 291–292; Rock in
               Archaeology, 25:2, 160–163; Shapiro in Science (AAAS), 165, 886; Swazey in J. Hist. Biol.,
               2:2, 451.
    1968B   Introduction. In: Brew, J. O. (ed.), 1968A, 5–25.

BREWER, RICHARD
    1968A   Two birds new to the Pleistocene of Reddick, Florida. Fla. Acad. Sci., Quart. J., 31:1, 79–80.

BREYER, JOHN
    1972A   An application of theoretical concepts of population dynamics to the fossil record. Soc. Vert.
               Paleontol. Ann. Meeting, 32nd, 1972, Abstr. (abs.).

BRÉZILLON, MICHEL
    1969A   Dictionnaire de la préhistoire. Paris: Librairie Larousse, 256 pp., illustr. (French).

BŘEZINOVÁ, D., LOSOS, L. and MAJZNER, Z.
    1968A   Die Methode der Reproduktion von Silikonabgüssen des paläontologischen Materials. Prague, Sborn.
               Národního Muz. Praze, Rada B, 24:1, 89–92, 4 pls. (German; Czech and English summaries).

BRIAL, G.
    1957A   Odontologie et Paléontologie. Les Eyzies, 1957:1, 8–29, 13 figs., 2 tables (French).

BRIAN, L.
    1966A   Sintesi storica degli ominidi nel quadro dei fondamentali problemi antropologici. Milan: Marzorati,
                115 pp., 2 pl. (Italian).
                Rev.: Billy in L'Anthropologie, 72, 162; Martiny in L'Anthropologie, 72:3—4, 363.

BRIDGE, T. E., LEISMAN, G. A. and LOCKARD, W.
    1972A   Vertebrate, invertebrate, and plant fossils of the Hamilton quarry. Geol. Soc. Amer., Abstr., 4:4,
                275 (abs.).

BRIGGS, LLOYD CABOT
    1967A   The human remains. In: Howe, B., 1967A, 188—191, 1 fig., 2 tables.
    1968A   Hominid evolution in northwest Africa and the question of the north African "Neanderthaloids".
                Amer. J. Phys. Anthropol., 29, 377—385.

BRIGGS, LLOYD CABOT and HENCKEN, HUGH
    1967A*   The Palaeolithic of Tangier, Morocco. Excavations at Cape Ashakar, 1939—1947. Amer. Sch.
                Prehist. Res., Bull., 22, xi + 200 pp., frontispiece, 68 illustr., 5 tables.

BRINK, A. S. and HAUGHTON, S. H.
    1967A   Vertebrate palaeontology of Karroo system in South Africa. Int. Union Geol. Sci., 1st Symp.
                Gondwana Stratigr., Rev., 1967, 149—153.

BROAD, D. S., DINELEY, D. L. and MIALL, A. D.
    1968A   The Peel Sound formation (Devonian) of Prince of Wales and adjacent islands: a preliminary report.
                Arctic, 21:2, 84—91, 2 figs. (French and Russian summaries).

BROAD, D. S. and LENZ, A. C.
    1972A   A new Silurian species of Vernonaspis (Heterostraci) from Yukon Territory, Canada. J. Paleontol.,
                46:3, 415—420, 4 figs., 1 pl.

BROADHURST, FREDERICK M. and DUFFY, LOUIS
    1970A   A plesiosaur in the geology department, University of Manchester. Mus. J., London, 70, 30—31,
                figs. 28—29.

BROCK, ANTONY
    1969A   Neanderthal man — not our direct ancestor? Sci. Culture, 35:11, 615—617.

BROCK, P. W. G. and MACDONALD, R.
    1969A   Geological environment of the Bukwa mammalian fossil locality, eastern Uganda. Nature, 223:5206,
                593—596, 1 fig.

BROCK, P. W. G.   See also: Walker, A., Brock, P. W. G. and Macdonald, R., 1969A.

BRODAR, MITJA
    1964-65A   Poročilo o paleolitskih poskusnih izkopavanjih. [Report on experimental excavations for Paleolithic.]
                Arheo. Vestn., 15—16, 167—174 (Slovenian; German summary).

BRODAR, SREČKO
    1967A   Lothar F. Zotz (6.12.1899—12.2.1967). Arheo. Vestn., 18, 465—466, portr. (Russian).

BRODKORB, PIERCE
    1968A   An extinct Pleistocene owl from Cuba. Fla. Acad. Sci., Quart. J., 31:2, 112—114, 1 fig.
                Rev.: Kuhn in Zentralbl. Geol. Paläontontol., Teil 2, 1971:5, 411.
    1968B   An ancestral mourning dove from Rexroad, Kansas. Fla. Acad. Sci., Quart. J., 31:3, 173—176, 1 fig.
                Rev.: Kuhn in Zentralbl. Geol. Paläontol., Teil 2, 1971:5, 411.
    1969A   Two fossil owls from the Aquitanian of France. Fla. Acad. Sci., Quart. J., 32:2, 159—160.
                Rev.: Kuhn in Zentralbl. Geol. Paläontol., Teil 2, 1971:5, 412.
    1969B   H. James Gut, February 29, 1904 — March 20, 1969. Soc. Vert. Paleontol., News Bull., 86, 42.
    1969C   The generic position of a Cretaceous bird. Fla. Acad. Sci., Quart. J., 32:3, 239—240.
                Rev.: Kuhn in Zentralbl. Geol. Paläontol., Teil 2, 1971:5, 411.
    1970A   An Eocene puffbird from Wyoming. Wyo., Univ., Contrib. Geol., 9:1, 13—15, 1 fig., 2 tables.
                Rev.: Kuhn in Zentralbl. Geol. Paläontol., Teil 2, 1971:5, 411.
    1970B   The paleospecies of woodpeckers. Fla. Acad. Sci., Quart. J., 33:2, 132—136, 1 fig.
                Rev.: Kuhn in Zentralbl. Geol. Paläontol., Teil 2, 1971:5, 412.
    1970C   New discoveries of Pliocene birds in Florida. Int. Ornith. Congr., 15th, Abs., 74.
    1971A   Catalogue of fossil birds: part 4 (Columbiformes through Piciformes). Fla. State Mus., Bull., Biol.
                Sci., 15:4, 163—266, 1 fig.

Rev.: Kuhn in Zentralbl. Geol. Paläontol., Teil 2, 1971:5, 412.
1971B   Origin and evolution of birds. In: Farner, D. S., King, J. R. and Parkes, K. C. (eds.), 1971A, 19–55, 2 figs., 7 tables.
1972A   Neogene fossil jays from the Great Plains. Condor, 74:3, 347–349, 2 figs., 2 tables.

BRODRICK, ALAN HOUGHTON
1971A   Man and his ancestors. New edition. London: Hutchison, viii + 238 pp., frontispiece, 26 figs., 3 maps.

BROGLIO, ALBERTO
1965B   Colloquio sul Paleolitico della Slovenia. Riv. Sci. Preist., 20:2, 359–362, 1 fig. (Italian; French and English summaries).

BROIN, FRANCE DE
1969A   Sur la présence d'une tortue, Pelusios sinatus (A. Smith), au Villafranchien inférieur du Tchad. Soc. Géol. Fr., C.R., 1969:8, 324 (French).
1969B   Sur la présence d'une tortue, Pelusios sinuatus (A. Smith), au Villafranchien inférieur du Tchad. Soc. Géol. Fr.. Bull., 11:6, 909–916, 1 fig., 1 pl., 1 table (French).
1970A   Découverte d'une tortue (Ptychogaster sp.) dans le Sannoisien (Lattorfien) des mines de potasse d'Alsace. Alsace-Lorraine, Serv. Carte Géol., Bull., 23:2, 79–84, 1 fig., 1 pl. (French).

BROIN, F. DE, GRENOT, C. and VERNET, R.
1971A   Sur la découverte d'un nouveau gisement de vertébrés dans le Continental Intercalaire saharien: la Gara Samani (Algérie). Acad. Sci., C.R., Sér. D, 272:9, 1219–1221, 1 fig. (French).

BROMLEĬ, Ĭu. V.   See: Averkieva, ĬU. P.. Arutĭunov, S. A. and Bromleĭ, ĬU. V., 1969A.

BROMLEY, K.   See: Bond, G. and Bromley, K., 1970A.

BROOKS, SHEILAGH
1970A   Theodore Doney McCown, 1908–1969. Amer. J. Phys. Anthropol., 32:2, 165–168.

BROOM, ROBERT
1971A   A new fossil anthropoid skull from South Africa. In: Leakey, L. S. B., Prost, J. and Prost, S. (eds.), 1971A, 239–243, 4 figs. (reprinted from Nature, Sept. 1936).
1972A   On Australopithecus and its affinities. In: McCown, T. D. and Kennedy, K. A. R. (eds.), 1972A, 322–327, 3 figs. (reprinted from Early Man, 1937).

BROSE, DAVID S. and WOLPOFF, MILFORD H.
1971A   Early upper Paleolithic man and late middle Paleolithic tools. Amer. Anthropol., 73:5, 1156–1194, 8 tables.

BROTHWELL, DON R.
1968A*   The skeletal biology of earlier human populations. Symposia of the Society for the Study of Human Biology, no. 8. Oxford, New York: Pergamon Press, 288 pp.. illustr.
Rev.: Ashton in J. Anat.. 104:2, 394; Khrisanfova in Vop. Antropol., 36, 173 (Russian); Merbs in Amer. Anthropol., 71, 168–170; Sublett in Amer. J. Phys. Anthropol. 32:1, 152–155; Tétry in L'Ann. Biol., 8:3–4, 261–262; Vallois in L'Anthropologie, 73:3–4, 287–288.
1968B   Introduction to the field. In: Brothwell, D. R. (ed.), 1968A, 1–18, 2 figs., 1 table.

BROTHWELL, DON R. and BROTHWELL, PATRICIA
1969A   Food in antiquity. London: Thames and Hudson, 248 pp., 109 figs., 7 tables, 4 maps.
Rev.: Renfrew in Nature, 224, 928.

BROTHWELL, D. R., MOLLESCON, T. and METREWELI, C.
1968A   Radiological aspects of normal variation in earlier skeletons: an exploratory study. In: Brothwell, D. R. (ed.), 1968A, 149–172, 9 figs.. 1 table.

BROTHWELL, D. R., SANDISON, A. T. and GRAY, P. H. K.
1969A   Human biological observations on a Guanche mummy with anthracosis. Amer. J. Phys. Anthropol.. 30, 333–348, 9 figs.

BROTHWELL, DON R.   See also: Clark, J. D.. Brothwell, D. R.. Powers, R. and Oakley, K. P., 1968A.

BROTHWELL, PATRICIA   See: Brothwell, D. and Brothwell, P., 1969A.

BROUSSE, R.   See: Auboin, J., Brousse, R. and Lehman, J.-P., 1967A.

BROUWER, A.
1962A   Historische Paleontologie. Leiden: E. J. Brill, 39 pp. (German).
1967A   Rev.: Corgan in BioScience, 18:3, 250; Heinzelin de Braucourt in Natuurwet. Tijdschr., 42:1–2,
         51–62.

BROWN, D. A.
1968A   Some problems of distribution of late Paleozoic and Triassic terrestrial vertebrates. Austral. J. Sci.,
         30:11, 434–445.

BROWN, FRANCIS H.
1969A   Observations on the stratigraphy and radiometric age of the "Omo beds", lower Omo basin, southern
         Ethiopia. Quaternaria, 11, 7–14, 2 figs., 1 table (German and Italian summaries).

BROWN, F. H., HEINZELIN, J. DE and HOWELL, F. C.
1970A   Pliocene/Pleistocene formations in the lower Omo Basin, southern Ethiopia. Quaternaria, 13, 247–268,
         3 figs., 3 tables (Italian and German summaries).

BROWN, F. H. and LAJOIE, K. R.
1971A   Radiometric age determinations on Pliocene/Pleistocene formations in the lower Omo Basin, Ethiopia.
         Nature, 229:5285, 483–485, 2 tables.

BROWN, F. H.   See also: Butzer, K. W., Brown, F. H. and Thurber, D. L., 1969A; Heinzelin de Braucourt,
                J. de and Brown, F. H., 1969A.

BROWN, JAMES and CLELAND, CHARLES
1968A   The late glacial and early postglacial faunal resources in midwestern biomes newly opened to human
         adaptation. In: Bergstrom, R. E. (ed.), 1968A, 114–122, 1 table.

BROWN, MABEL E.
1968A   Wyoming boneyard. Bits and Pieces, 4:7, 11–13, 7 photos.

BRUES, ALICE M.
1968A   The spearman and the archer. In: Cohen, Y. A. (ed.), 1968A, 186–196 (reprinted from Brues, A. M.,
         1959).

BRUIJN, H. DE
1966B   Rev.: Adrover in Teruel, 37, 139–140.
1967A   Gliridae, Sciuridae y Eomyidae (Rodentia, Mammalia) miocenos de Calatayud (provincia de Zaragoza,
         España) y su relación con la bioestratigrafía del área. Bol. Geol. Min. España, 78, 189–373,
         18 figs., 11 pls., 1 chart, 1 map (Spanish).

BRUIJN, H. DE, DAWSON, M. R. and MEIN, P.
1970A   Upper Pliocene Rodentia, Lagomorpha and Insectivora (Mammalia) from the Isle of Rhodes (Greece).
         I, II, III. Ned. Akad. Wetensch., Proc., Ser. B, 73, 535–584, 5 figs., 11 pls.

BRUIJN, H. DE and MEIN, P.
1968A   Rev.: Adrover in Teruel, 40, 243.

BRUIJN, H. DE and MEULENKAMP, J. E.
1972A   Late Miocene rodents from the Pandanassa formation (Prov. Rethymnon), Crete, Greece. Ned. Akad.
         Wetensch., Proc., Ser. B, 75:1, 54–60, 1 fig., 1 pl.

BRUIJN, H. DE and MEURS, A. P. H. VAN
1967A   Rev.: Adrover in Teruel, 38, 225–226.

BRUIJN, H. DE, SONDAAR, P. Y. and ZACHARIASSE, W. J.
1971A   Mammalia and Foraminifera from the Neogene of Kastellios Hill (Crete), a correlation of continental
         and marine biozones. I and II. Ned. Akad. Wetensch., Proc., Ser. B, 74:5, 1–22, 5 figs., 4 pls.
         Rev.: Thenius in Zentralbl. Geol. Paläontol., Teil 2, 1971:6, 508–509.

BRUNDIN, LARS
1972A   Evolution, causal biology, and classification. Zool. Scripta, 1:3–4, 107–120.

BRUNET, JEAN
1969A   The Pliocene rhinoceroses of México. Geol. Soc. Amer., Abstr., 121, 40 (abs.).

1970A   Oiseaux de l'Éocène supérieur du Bassin de Paris. Ann. Paléontol., Vertébrés, 56:1, 3–65, 6 figs., 4 pls., 2 tables (French).
        Rev.: Kuhn in Zentralbl. Geol. Paläontol.. Teil 2, 1970:6, 515–516.

BRUNET, MICHEL
1967A   Contribution à la connaissance des genres *Dinictis* et *Hoplophoneus* (Carnivora-Felidae). Poitiers, Univ., Inst. Géol. Anthropol. Préhist.. Trav.. 8, 1–37, 28 figs., 8 pls. (French; German and English summaries).
1969A   Note préliminaire sur une faune de vertébrés du Callovien des environs de Poitiers. Acad. Sci., C.R., Sér. D, 268:22, 2667–2670, 1 pl. (French).
1970A   Villebramar (Lot-et-Garonne): très important gisement de vertébrés Stampien inférieur du Bassin d'Aquitaine. Acad. Sci., C.R., Sér. D, 270:21, 2535–2538 (French).
1970B   Nouvelles découvertes concernant la faune et la position stratigraphique du gisement de vertébrés de Comberatière (Lot-et-Garonne). Acad. Sci., C.R., Sér. D, 270:23, 2776–2779 (French).
1972A   Première découverte en Europe d'un crâne d'Entelodontidae (Mammalia, Artiodactyla). Acad. Sci., C.R., Sér. D, 275:25, 2849–2852, 1 pl. (French).

BRÜNING, HERBERT
1970A   Aus dem Naturhistorischen Museum Erkenntnisse und Darstellungen. Mainz 1966–69. Mainzer Naturwiss. Arch.. 9, 335–360, 17 figs. (German).

BRUNNACKER, KARL   See: Bosinski, G. and Brunnacker, K.. 1969A; Jánossy, D., Krolopp, E. and Brunnacker, K., 1968A.

BRYAN, ALAN L.
1968A   Some problems and hypotheses relative to the early entry of man into America. Anthropologica, 10:2, 157–177, 2 figs., 1 map.
1969A   Early man in America and the late Pleistocene chronology of western Canada and Alaska. With comments and reply. Current Anthropol., 10:4, 339–365, 2 figs.

BRZOBOHATÝ, ROSTISLAV
1966A   Zpráva o výzkumu rybích otolitů z pouzdřanských vrstev. [Report on the research on fish otoliths from Pouzdřany strata.] Czech.. Ustřed. Ústav Geol., Zprávy Geol. Výzk., 1964:1, 278–280 (Czech).
1967C   Die Otolithenfauna der Karpathischen Serie. In: Cicha, I., Seneš, J., and Tejkal, J., *et al.* (eds.), 1967A, 231–243, 2 pls. (German).
        Rev.: Weiler in Zentralbl. Geol. Paläontol., Teil 2, 1968:6, 642–643.
1969A   Die Fischfauna des südmärischen Untermiozäns. Brünn, Univ., Prirod. Fak., Geol., 10, 1–49, 8 pls., 1 map (German).
        Rev.: Weiler in Zentralbl. Geol. Paläontol., Teil 2, 1969:6, 509–510.

BUACHIDZE, TSISANA IOSIFOVNA   See: Gabuniiă, L. K. and Buachidze, T. I.. 1970A.

BUBENIK, ANTON B.
1966A   Das Geweih (Entwicklung, Aufbau und Ausformung der Geweihe und Gehörne und ihre Bedeutung für das Wild und für die Jagd). Hamburg and Berlin: Paul Parey Verlag, 214 pp.. 87 figs., 11 tables (German).
        Rev.: Kühnelt in Zool.-Bot. Ges. Wien, Verh.. 107, 198–199.

BUCCI, G., NEBBIA, L.. SACCHI VIALLI, G., SAVI, A. and BASSO, G.
1969A   Ricerca di aminoacidi in ossa fossili con gascromatografia e altri metodi. Pavia, Univ., Ist. Geol.. Atti, 20, 87–101, 3 figs., 1 pl., 2 tables (Italian; English, French, and German summaries).

BÜCHNER, MARTIN
1967A   Fossilerhaltung in rhätischen Bonebeds. Naturwiss. Ver. Bielefeld u. Umgegend, Ber., 18, 5–24, 4 pls. (German).
        Rev.: Hollmann in Zentralbl. Geol. Paläontol., Teil 2, 1968, 9–10.

BUCKLAND-WRIGHT, J. C.
1969A   Craniological observations on *Hyaena* and *Crocuta* (Mammalia). J. Zool., 159:1, 17–29, 7 figs., 3 pls., 1 table.

BUCUR, ION
1971A   Noi date faunistice şi structurale în flişul cretacic şi paleogen de la nord de depresiunea Breţcu - Tg. Secuiesc. [New data on fauna and structure concerning the Cretaceous and Paleogene flysch of the north of the Breţcu - Tîrgu Secuiesc depression.] Rom., Inst. Geol., Dari, 57:4, 27–33, 2 pls., 1 map (Rumanian; French and English summaries).

BUDDING, A. J., PITRAT, C. W. and SMITH, C. T.
1960A   Geology of the southeastern part of the Chama basin. N. Mex. Geol. Soc., Guidebk., Field Conf., 11, 78–92, 1 table, 1 map.

BUDKER, PAUL
1971A   The life of sharks. New York: Columbia Univ. Press, xviii + 222 pp., 49 figs., 8 pls. Rev.: Tyler in Frontiers, 36:2, 31.

BUERKLI, MARIA   See: Smith, C. L. and Buerkli, M., 1969A.

BUETTNER-JANUSCH, JOHN
1964B   Hemoglobin and primate phylogeny. Amer. Anthropol. Ass., Abstr., 1964, 10 (abs.).
1966A   Rev.: Comas in An. Antropol., Mexico, 4, 205–209; Grimm in Biol. Zentralbl., 87:6, 792–793; Kloiber in Anthropol. Ges., Mitt., 100, 446–447; Roth-Lutra in Anat. Anz., 123:4, 478–479.

BUFFARD, R., DEMATHIEU, G. and DEMATHIEU, P.
1969A   Mise en évidence de deux niveaux bien individualisés à empreintes théromorphoïdes, lacertoïdes et crocodiloïdes dans le grès bigarré de Haute-Saône. Besançon, Univ., Ann. Sci., Sér. 3, 8, 13–20, 5 figs., 1 pl. (French).

BUFFARD, ROLAND   See also: Courel, L., Demathieu, G. and Buffard, R., 1968A, 1968B.

BUFFINGTON, JOHN D.
1971A   Predation, competition, and Pleistocene megafauna extinction. BioScience, 21:4, 167–170, 4 figs.

BUKATCHUK, P. D., BURDENKO, B. V. and VOLOSHIN, V. E.
1968A   Novye dannye o nalichii drevnealluvial'nykh otlozheniĭ na territorii mezhdurech'iā Prut-Dnestr (v predelakh Moldavskikh Kodr). [New data on the presence of old alluvial deposits on the Prut-Dnestr interfluve (in the Moldavskie Kodry area).] Akad. Nauk SSSR, Dokl., 178:6, 1371–1373, 1 fig., 1 table (Russian).
1968B   More information on the presence of old alluvium in the Prut-Dneister interfluve (in the Moldavskiye Kodry area). Akad. Nauk SSSR, Dokl., Earth Sci. Sec., 178, 90–92, 1 fig., 1 table. (Translated from Russian: Akad. Nauk SSSR, Dokl., 1968, 178:6, 1371–1373).

BUKATCHUK, P. D.   See also: Negadaev-Nikonov, K. N. and Bukatchuk, P. D., 1969A.

BULEĬSHVILI, D. A.
1964A   Verkhniĭ miotsen – sarmat. [Upper Miocene – Sarmatian.] Geologiiā SSSR, 10, Georgian SSR, 284–308, 3 figs. (Russian).
1964B   Pliotsen. Vostochnaiā zona pogruzheniiā Gruzinskoĭ glyby. [Pliocene. Eastern zone of submersion of the Georgian block.] Geologiiā SSSR, 10, Georgian SSR, 324–331, 3 figs. (Russian).

BUNAK, VICTOR VALER'IĀNOVICH
1969A   Sur l'évolution de la forme du crâne humain. Symp. Biol. Hungarica, 9, 51–63, 2 tables (French).

BURACHEK, A. R. and CHIKHACHEV, P. K.
1959A   Kontinental'nye neogenovye otlozheniiā. [Continental Neogene deposits.] Geologiiā SSSR, 24, Tadzhik SSR, 319–333, 10 figs. (Russian).

BURCHAK-ABRAMOVICH, NIKOLAĬ IOSIFOVICH (= BURCZAK-ABRAMOWICZ, N.)
1960A   Materialy k izucheniiū peshchernykh medvedeĭ vostochnogo chernomorskogo poberezh'iā. [Materials for the study of cave bears of the eastern Black Sea coast.] Anthropos, Brno, 1960 Suppl., 51–53, 1 table (Russian).
1965C   Istoriiā chetvertichnoĭ ornitofauny Kavkaza. [History of the Quaternary ornithofauna of Caucasus.] In: Novosti ornitologii. Materialy chetvertoĭ vsesoiūznoĭ ornitologicheskoĭ konferentsii, Alma-Ata, 1965, 50–52 (Russian).
1965D   Fauna peshchernykh stoiānok iūzhnoi Abkhaziĭ. [Cave fauna of southern Abkhazia.] Peshchery Gruzii, 3, 9–13 (Russian).
1966F   K poznaniiū ekogeneza iskopaemykh bykov i ovtsebykov Starogo Sveta i Severnoĭ Ameriki [On the ecogenesis of fossil oxen and musk oxen of the Old World and North America.] Akad. Nauk Gruz. SSR, Inst. Paleobiol., Nauchn. Sess., 12, 37–39 (Russian and Georgian).
1966G   Fossil birds in the caves of the U.S.S.R. Int. Speleol. Conf., Brno 1964, Probl. Speleol. Res., Part 2, 231–245 (German summary).
1966H   K izucheniiū pleĭstotsenovoĭ fauny Kavkaza (iskopaemye ptitsy). [Research on Pleistocene fauna of Caucasus (fossil birds).] Akad. Nauk Azerb. SSR, Izv., Ser. Nauk Zemle, 1966:6, 38–42 (Russian).

1967B   K izucheniiu progressivnykh putei evoliutsii v klasse ptits. [On the progressive evolution in the class
          of birds.] Akad. Nauk Gruz. SSR, Inst. Paleobiol., Obshch. Vop. Evoliuts. Paleobiol., 3,
          100–125, 4 figs. (Russian; Georgian and English summaries).
1967C   Iskopaemye ptitsy i ikh vozmozhnoe znachenie dlia geokhronologii. [Fossil birds and their significance
          for geochronology.] Akad. Nauk Gruz. SSR, Inst. Paleobiol., Nauchn. Sess., All-Union Meeting,
          18–21 (Russian).
1968A   K poznaniiu iavlenii izmenchivosti u pleistotsenovykh binagadinskikh ptits. [On the phenomena of
          variability in the Pleistocene birds from Binagady.] Akad. Nauk Gruz. SSR, Inst. Paleobiol.,
          Obshch. Vop. Evoliuts. Paleobiol., 4, 75–96, 1 pl. (Russian; Georgian and English summaries).
1969A   Iskopaemye pozvonochnye peshcher Kavkaza. [Fossil vertebrates of Caucasian caves.] Acta Mus.
          Macedonici Sci. Natur., 11:7, 131–145 (Russian; Macedonian summary).
1970A   K izucheniiu ekogeneza iskopaemykh bykov i ovtsebykov Starogo Sveta i Ameriki. [On the ecogenesis
          of oxen and musk oxen of the Old World and America.] Akad. Nauk Gruz. SSR, Inst. Paleo-
          biol., Obshch. Vop. Evoliuts. Paleobiol., 5, 50–68 (Russian; Georgian and German summaries).
1971A   Materialy k izucheniiu pleistotsenovykh ptits Gruzii (peshchera Tsona). [Materials for the study of
          Pleistocene birds of Georgia (Tsona Cave).] Paleontol. Sb., 7:2, 45–51, 4 figs., 2 tables
          (Russian; English summary).

BURCHAK-ABRAMOVICH, N. I. and BENDUKIDZE, O. G.
1969A   Fauna epipaleoliticheskoi stoianki Zurtaketi. [Fauna of the Zurtaketi Epipaleolithic settlement.]
          Akad. Nauk Gruz. SSR, Soobshch., 55:3, 741–744, 1 table (Russian; Georgian and English
          summaries).
1971A   O proiskhozhdenii domashnikh kur Gruzii. [On the origin of domestic fowl of Georgia.] Akad. Nauk
          Gruz. SSR, Soobshch., 61:2, 497–500 (Russian; Georgian and English summaries).

BURCHAK-ABRAMOVICH, N. I. and LIUBIN, V. P.
1972A   Ornitofauna peshchery Kudaro I (Zakavkaz'e). [Ornithofauna of Kudaro I Cave (Transcaucasia).]
          Sov. Arkheol., 1972:2, 159–164 (Russian).

BURCHAK-ABRAMOVICH, N. I. and VEKUA, A. K.
1971A   The fossil ostrich from the Akchagil layers of Georgia. Acta Zool. Cracoviensia, 16:1, 1–28, 2 figs.,
          2 pls., 2 tables (Polish and Russian summaries).

BURCHAK-ABRAMOVICH, N. I.   See also: Aslanova, S. M. and Burchak-Abramovich, N. I., 1968A; Liubin,
          V. P., Burchak-Abramovich, N. I. and Klapchuk, M. N., 1971A.

BURDENKO, B. V.   See: Bukatchuk, P. D., Burdenko, B. V. and Voloshin, V. Ye., 1968A, 1968B.

BUR'IANOVA, I. Z.   See: Bersenev, I. I., Ustinovskii, Iu. B., Bur'ianova, I. Z., Nevolina, S. I. and Medvedev, V. V.,
          1969A.

BURKE, J. J.
1969A   An antiacodont from the Green River Eocene of Utah. Kirtlandia, 5, 1–7, 1 fig.

BURNS, PETER E.
1971A   New determination of australopithecine height. Nature, 232:5309, 350.

BURNSTEIN, ALBERT H.   See: Lovejoy, C. O., Burnstein, A. H. and Heiple, K. G., 1972A.

BURYCHENKO, A. I.   See: Danilova, E. I. and Burychenko, A. I., 1969A.

BUSH, HELEN
1969A   Hope Johnson — prairie fossil collector. Can. Audubon, 31:1, 10–13, 3 figs.

BUSHNELL, HUGH P.
1955A   Mesozoic stratigraphy of south-central New Mexico. N. Mex. Geol. Soc., Guidebk., Field Conf. 6,
          81–87, 3 figs.

BUTLER, B. ROBERT
1966A   A guide to understanding Idaho archaeology. Idaho State Univ. Mus., Spec. Publ., viii + 143 pp.,
          29 figs.
          Rev.: Gruhn in Amer. Antiquity, 33, 263–264.
1968A   A guide to understanding Idaho archaeology. Second edition. Idaho State Univ. Mus., Spec. Publ.,
          v + 117 pp., 25 figs.
1971A   The origin of the upper Snake County buffalo. Tebiwa, 14:2, 1–20.

BUTLER, HOWARD K.
1968A   The study of fossils in the last half of the seventeenth century. Diss. Abstr., 29:4, 1182A (abs.).

BUTLER, JAY J.   See: Römisch-Germanisches Zentralmuseum, Mainz and Butler, J. J. (eds.), 1964A.

BUTLER, PERCY M.
1969A   Insectivores and bats from the Miocene of East Africa: new material. In: Leakey, L. S. B. (ed.), 1969C, 1—37, 13 figs., 1 table.
1972A   Some functional aspects of molar evolution. Evolution, 26:3, 474—483, 6 figs., 1 table.
1972B   The problem of insectivore classification. In: Joysey, K. A. and Kemp, T. S. (eds.), 1972A, 253—265, 6 figs.

BUTZER, KARL W.
1967B   Late Pleistocene deposits of the Kom Ombo plain, upper Egypt. Fundamenta, Reihe B, 2, 213—227, 4 figs., 2 tables.
1969A   Geological interpretation of two Pleistocene hominid sites in the lower Omo basin. Nature, 222:5199, 1133—1135, 2 figs.
1969B   Geochronology of primitive Homo sapiens fossils from the lower Omo Valley (southwest Ethiopia). Amer. Anthropol. Ass., Bull., 2:3, 17 (abs.).
1971A   The lower Omo basin: geology, fauna and hominids of Plio-Pleistocene formations. Naturwiss., 58:1, 7—16, 8 figs., 1 table.
1971B   Another look at the Australopithecine cave breccias of the Transvaal. Amer. Anthropol., 73:5, 1197—1201.
1971C   Environment and archeology. An ecological approach to prehistory. Second edition. Chicago: Aldine-Atherton, xviii + 704 pp., 95 figs., 23 tables.
          Rev.: Jelinek in Science (AAAS), 176:4035, 665; Savory in Mus. J., 72:2, 70; Sparks in Nature, 239:5366, 55—56.

BUTZER, K. W., BROWN, F. H. and THURBER, D. L.
1969A   Horizontal sediments of the lower Omo Valley: the Kibish formation. Quaternaria, 11, 15—29, 1 fig., 1 table (German and Italian summaries).

BUTZER, K. W. and HANSEN, CARL L.
1968A   Desert and river in Nubia. Geomorphology and prehistoric environments at the Aswan reservoir. Madison, Milwaukee, and London: The Univ. of Wisconsin Press, xxi + 562 pp., 170 illustr., 44 tables.
          Rev.: Fairbridge in Amer. Anthropol., 71, 345—347; Stearns in Amer. Sci., 56:4, 501A.

BUTZER, K. W. and THURBER, D. L.
1969A   Some late Cenozoic sedimentary formations of the lower Omo basin. Nature, 222:5199, 1138—1143, 2 figs., 1 table.

BUTZER, K. W.   See also: Howell, F. C. and Butzer, K. W., 1968A.

BUVALKIN, A. K., ZHAĬMIN, M. I., MURAKHOVSKAĬA, E. I., ORLOVSKAĬA, E. R. and SAKULINA, G. V.
1971A   Triasovaĭa i ĭurskaĭà sistemy. [Triassic and Jurassic systems.] Geologiĭà SSSR, 40:1, Southern Kazakhstan, 366—389, 1 fig. (Russian).

BŮZEK, ČESTMIR   See: Šantrůček, P., Bůzek, Č., Kopecký, L., Malecha, A. and Václ, J., 1968A.

BYERS, DOUGLAS S.   See: MacNeish, R. S., Byers, D. S., et al., 1967A.

C., S.
1969A   Les défenses du mammouth: une erreur séculaire. Sci. Progrès La Nature, 3410, 233 (French).

CADENAT, PIERRE
1966A   Les industries et les hommes du Paléolithique Nord-Africain. Les Eyzies, 15, 37—49, 2 figs., 1 table (French).
1966B   Atlas préhistorique de l'Algérie. Feuille No. 33P. Tiaret. Libyca, 14, 21—113, 1 map (French).

CAILLAUD, PIERRE
1968A   Extension, vers Rennes-le-Château (Aude), des gisements d'oeufs de dinosaures dans le Crétacé supérieur des Corbières. Soc. Géol. Fr., C.R., 1968:4, 111—112 (French).

CAILLEUX, ANDRÉ DE (= CAYEUX, A. DE)
 1969A   Observations sur des gastrolites d'oiseaux holocènes et tertiaires. Soc. Géol. Fr., C.R., 1969:3, 73–75,
           1 fig. (French).
 1969B   Pierres de gésier au microscope électronique à balayage. Sci. Progrès La Nature, 3410, 224–226,
           6 figs. (French).
 1969C   Three billion years of life. Translated by Joyce E. Clemow. New York: Stein and Day, 239 pp.,
           illustr.

CAJORI, FLORIAN A.
 1968A   Department of geology. Denver Mus. Natur. Hist., Ann. Rep., 1967, 15–19, illustr.

CALABY, J. H.
 1971A   Man, fauna, and climate in aboriginal Australia. In: Mulvaney, D. J. and Golson, J. (eds.), 1971A,
           80–93.

CALABY, J. H.   See also: Firth, H. J. and Calaby, J. H., 1969A.

CALAS, GEORGES
 1969A   Découverte d'un créodonte dans le Lutétien du bassin d'Aquitaine. Soc. Géol. Fr., C.R., 1969:8,
           299–300, 1 fig. (French).
 1970A   Les carnivores du gisement lutétien de Lissieu (Rhône). Soc. Géol. Fr., C.R., 1970:6, 226–227
           (French).

CALCATERRA, ARMANDO
 1972A   Dos roedores fósiles nuevos para Uruguay y confirmación de otro. Mus. Hist. Natur. Montevideo, Com.
           Paleontol., 1:2, 11–21, 2 pls. (Spanish).

CALLEN, ERIC O.
 1969A   Les coprolithes de la cabane acheuléenne du Lazaret. II. - Analyse et diagnostic. In: Lumley, H. de
           (ed.), 1969B, 123–124 (French).

CALVOCORESSI, DAVID
 1969A*   West Africa. COWA, Surv. Bibliogr., Area 11, 4, 1–13.

CALZADA BADÍA, SABASTIÁN
 1969A   Litoestratigrafía y paleontología de unas arenas del Mioceno de Sant Pere de Ribes. (Garraf,
           Barcelona). Acta Geol. Hisp., 4:2, 29–34, 4 figs. (Spanish; French summary).
           Rev.: H.-P. in Soc. Españ. Hist. Natur., Bol., Secc. Geol., 67:3, 350–351.

CAMERON, BARRY and BORESKE, JOHN R.
 1972A   Clam borings in reworked whale skull, shark teeth and oysters: Miocene of Maryland and North
           Carolina. Geol. Soc. Amer., Abstr., 4:1, 7 (abs.).

CAMERON, BARRY and ESTES, RICHARD
 1971A   Fossil and Recent "tadpole nests": a discussion. J. Sediment. Petrology, 41:1, 171–178, 1 fig.

CAMERON, BARRY   See also: Boreske, J. R., Goldberg, L. and Cameron, B., 1972A.

CAMP, CHARLES L.
 1966   Rev.: Wissler in J. West, 6:3, 504–505.
 1969A   Paleontology in the west: an introduction   J. West, 8, 165–168.
 1969B *   The letters of William Diller Matthew. J. West, 8, 263–290, 8 pls.
 1969C *   The letters of William Diller Matthew. Part II. J. West, 8, 454–476.
 1970A   Earth song. A prologue to history. Second edition. Illustrated by Margaret M. Colbert. Palo Alto,
           Calif.: American West Publ. Co., 192 pp., 30 figs., 12 pls., 7 charts.
 1970B   Prologue – Orinda, twelve million years ago. In: Sorrick, M., 1970A, vii–x.

CAMP, C. L., ALLISON, H. J., NICHOLS, R. H. and McGINNIS, H.
 1968A*   Rev.: Albanesi in Riv. Ital. Paleontol. Stratigr., 76:2, 343; B. in Przegl. Geol., 1970:7, 351 (Polish);
           Egenhoff in Calif., Div. Mines Geol., Miner. Inform. Serv., 23:10, 208; Westphal in Zentralbl.
           Geol. Paläontol., Teil 2, 1970:1, 67.

CAMP, CHARLES L., NICHOLS, R. H., BRAJNIKOV, B., FULTON, E. and BACSKAI, J. A.
 1972A*   Bibliography of fossil vertebrates, 1964–1968. Geol. Soc. Amer., Mem., 134, lxi + 1119 pp.

CAMP, L. SPRAGUE DE
 1969A   The end of the monkey war. Sci. Amer., 220:2, 15–21, illustr.

CAMP, L. SPRAGUE DE and CAMP, C. C. DE
1968A   Rev.: Asimov in Natur. Hist., 78:2, 107—108.

CAMPBELL, BERNARD GRANT
1965A   Rev.: Roth-Lutra in Anat. Anz., 122:2, 183.
1966A   Rev.: Kloiber in Anthropol. Ges., Mitt., 100, 447; Marcozzi in Anthropos, 62:3—4, 575—577.
1968B   The use of nomenclature in the study of recent and fossil man. In: Brothwell, D. R. (ed.), 1968A,
             19—29, 1 table.
1968C   The evolution of the human hand. In: Cohen, Y. A. (ed.), 1968A, 128—130 (reprinted from
             Campbell, B. G., 1966).
1969A   Early man in southern Africa. S. Afr. Archaeol. Bull., 24:95—96, 212.

CAMPBELL, BERNARD G.   See also: Mayr, E. and Campbell, B., 1971A; Oakley, K. P., Campbell, B. G. and
             Molleson, T. I. (eds.), 1971A.

CAMPBELL, COLIN R.
1971A   Some comments on Australian dasyurid marsupials. Geol. Soc. Amer., Abstr., 3:2, 91—92 (abs.).

CAMPBELL, KENNETH E., JR.
1969A   Comparing postcranial skeletons of Pliocene rabbits. Mich. Acad., 1:1, 99—115, 2 pls., 2 tables.
1972A   The late Pleistocene avifauna of the Tulara seeps, Peru. Soc. Vert. Paleontol., Ann. Meeting, 32nd,
             1972, Abstr. (abs.).

CAMPBELL, K. S. W.
1969A*   Stratigraphy and palaeontology. Essays in honour of Dorothy Hill. Canberra: Australian National
             University Press, xxiv + 390 pp., illustr.
             Rev.: Browne in Austral. J. Sci., 32:8, 337; Harrington in Bull. Can. Petrol. Geol., 18, 566—567;
             Oliver in J. Geol., 79:1, 127; Stehli in Palaeogeogr. Palaeoclimatol. Palaeoecol., 9, 149—150;
             Teichert in J. Paleontol., 44, 1147—1148.

CAMPBELL, K. S. W.   See also: Dasch, E. J. and Campbell, K. S. W., 1970A; Thomson, K. S. and Campbell,
             K. S. W., 1971A.

CAMPONESCHI, BIAGIO
1970A   Sul renvenimento di alcuni reperti fossili nelle vulcaniti del fosso delle Ferriere (Cerveteri). Soc.
             Ital. Miner. Petrologia, Rend., 26:1, 43—52, 3 figs. (Italian; English summary).

CAMPS, G.
1966A   In memoriam R. Vaufrey. (1880—1967). Libyca, 14, 417—419, bibliog. (French).
1966B   Le gisement de Rachgoun (Oranie). Libyca, 14, 161—188, 21 figs., 3 tables (French).
1966C   La préhistoire en Algérie et les activités du C.R.A.P.E. durant l'année 1966. Libyca, 14, 437—468,
             13 figs., 1 map (French).

CAMPS, G., DELIBRIAS, G. and THOMMERET, J.
1968A   Chronologie absolue et successions des civilisations préhistoriques dans le nord de l'Afrique. Libyca,
             16, 9—28, 6 tables (French).
             Rev.: Mauny in Inst. Franç. Afr. Noire, Bull., 31:4, 1215—1216.

ČANADJIJA, S.
1970A   Die Bedeutung des Urmenschen von Krapina in der Evolution der Hominiden. Krapina, 147—152
             (Serbocroatian; German summary).
             Rev.: Kochansky-Devidé in Zentralbl. Geol. Paläontol., Teil 2, 1971:5, 417.

CANNARELLA, DANTE and CREMONESI, GIULIANO
1967A   Gli scavi nella Grotta Azzurra di Samatorza nel Carso triestino. Riv. Sci. Preist., 22:2, 281—330,
             12 figs., 3 tables (Italian; French and English summaries).

CANTALUPPI, GIAMMARIO
1969A   Il rinoceronte di San Colombano al Lambro. Pavia, Univ., Ist. Geol., Atti, 20, 67—81, 3 figs., 2 pls.,
             1 table (Italian; French, English, German summaries).
             Rev.: Fantini Sestini in Riv. Ital. Paleontol. Stratigr., 76:1, 177—178.

CANTWELL, R. J.
1969A   Fossil Sigmodon from southeastern Arizona. Geol. Soc. Amer., Abstr., 121, 494 (abs.).
1969B   Fossil Sigmodon from the Tusker locality, 111 Ranch, Arizona. J. Mammal., 50:2, 375—378, 2 figs.

CAPITANO, MARIANTONIA   See: Corrain, C. and Capitano, M., 1969A.

CAPPETTA, HENRI C.
1969A   Les gisements de vertébrés de la région montpelliéraine. 2. Gisements miocènes. Bur. Rech. Géol.
         Minières, Bull. (Sér. 2), Sect. 1, 1969:1, 19–29, 1 table (French; English summary).
1969B   L'ichthyofaune (Euselachii, Teleostei) miocène de la région de Montpellier (Hérault). Montpellier:
         University of Montpellier, Fac. Sci. Thèse Doctor., xviii + 373 pp., 26 pls., 5 tables (French).
         Rev.: Weiler in Zentralbl. Geol. Paläontol., Teil 2, 1970:3/4, 220–221; Weiler in Zentralbl. Geol.
         Paläontol., Teil 2, 1970:5, 420–422.
1970A   Les sélaciens du Miocène de la région de Montpellier. Palaeovertebrata (Montpellier), Mémoire
         extraordinaire 1970, part 1 text, part 2 plates, 139 pp., 22 figs., 27 pls., 6 tables (French;
         English and German summaries).
         Rev.: Weiler in Zentralbl. Geol. Paläontol., Teil 2, 1971:5, 398–399.
1970B   Découverte de nouvelles faunes de poissons dans le Crétacé et le Tertiaire du Niger. Soc. Géol. Fr.,
         C.R., 1970:7, 258–259 (French).
1972A   Les Sélaciens du Burdigalien de Lespignan (Hérault). Soc. Géol. Fr., C.R., 1972:1, 17 (French).
1972B   Les poissons crétacés et tertiaires du bassin des Iullemmeden (République du Niger). Palaeovertebrata
         (Montpellier), 5:5, 179–251, 10 figs., 13 pls., 5 tables (French; German and English summaries).

CAPPETTA, H. C., HARTENBERGER, J.-L., SIGÉ, B. and SUDRE, J.
1968A   Une faune de vertébrés de la zone de Cuis dans l'Éocène continental du Bas-Languedoc (gisement du
         Mas de Gimel, Grabels, Hérault). Bur. Rech. Géol. Minières, Bull. (Sér. 2), Sect. 1, 1968:3,
         45–48, 1 fig. (French).

CAPPETTA, H. and SIGÉ, B.
1969A   Pour un inventaire systématique des gisements de vertébrés. Bur. Rech. Géol. Minières, Bull. (Sér. 2),
         Sec. 1, 1969:1, 1–5, 2 figs. (French; English summary).

CAPPETTA, HENRI C.   See also: Barrière, J., Cappetta, H. and Michaux, J., 1970A.

CARALP, É., NOUGIER, L.-R. and ROBERT, R.
1970A   L'intérêt archéologique du nouveau réseau "René Clastres" dans la caverne de Niaux. Préhist. Spéléol.
         Ariége., 25, 145–168, 9 figs. (French).

CARETTO, P. G.
1970A   La balenottera delle sabbie plioceniche di Valmontasca (Vigliano d'Asti). Soc. Paleontol. Ital., Boll.,
         9:1, 3–75, 9 figs., 20 pls., 3 tables (Italian; English summary).
         Rev.: Albanesi in Riv. Ital. Paleontol. Stratigr., 77:1, 132.

CAREY, D. J.
1972A   Flying ability of Archaeopteryx. Nature, 239:5374, 525.

CARITE, D.   See: Michel, J. P. and Carite, D., 1971A.

CARLES, J.
1970A   Le premier homme. Paris: Presses Universitaires de France, "Que sais-je", 128 pp. (French).
         Rev.: Cheval in Rev. Quest. Sci., 33:2, 298.

CARLSON, KEITH J.
1968A   The skull morphology and estivation burrows of the Permian lungfish, Gnathorhiza serrata. J. Geol.,
         76:6, 641–663, 3 figs., 1 pl., 5 tables.

CARNEY, J., HILL, A., MILLER, J. A. and WALKER, A.
1971A   Late australopithecine from Baringo district, Kenya. Nature, 230:5295, 509–514, 3 figs., 3 tables.

CARPENTER, C. R. and HOFER, H. O.
1969A*   Proceedings of the Second International Congress of Primatology. Basel and New York: S. Karger,
         3 vols., 708 pp., 278 figs., 72 tables.
         Rev.: Bramblett in Man (J. Roy. Anthropol. Inst.), 5:4, 705.

CARRECK, J. N.
1966A   Microtine remains from the Norwich Crag (lower Pleistocene) of Easton Bavents, Suffolk. Geol. Ass.
         (London), Proc., 77, 491–496, 1 fig.

CARRECK, J. N. and ADAMS, S. J.
1969A   Field extraction and laboratory preparation of fossil bones and teeth, using expanded polyurethane.
         Geol. Ass. (London), Proc., 80, 81–89.

CARROLL, ROBERT L.
1969A   Problems of the origin of reptiles. Biol. Rev., 44:3, 393—432, 14 figs.
1969B   A middle Pennsylvanian captorhinomorph, and the interrelationships of primitive reptiles. J. Paleontol.,
           43, 151—170, 12 figs.
1969C   Origin of reptiles. In: Gans, C. (ed.), 1969A, 1—44, 14 figs.
1969D   A new family of Carboniferous amphibians. Palaeontology, 12:4, 537—548, 2 figs.
           Rev.: Westphal in Zentralbl. Geol. Paläontol., Teil 2, 1970:3/4, 227.
1970A   The ancestry of reptiles. Roy. Soc. London, Phil. Trans., Ser. B, 257:814, 267—308, 20 figs., 3 tables.
1970B   The origin and early evolution of reptiles. Amer. Phil. Soc., Yearb., 1969, 293—294.
1970C   Quantitative aspects of the amphibian-reptilian transition. Forma et Functio, 3, 165—178, 5 figs.,
           2 tables (French and German summaries).
1972A   Gephyrostegida, Solenodonsauridae. Handb. Paläoherp, 5B, 1—19, 11 figs.

CARROLL, R. L. and BAIRD, DONALD
1972A   Carboniferous stem-reptiles of the family Romeriidae. Harvard Univ., Mus. Comp. Zool., Bull., 143:5,
           321—363, 14 figs., 2 pls., 1 table.

CARROLL, R. L., BELT, E. S., DINELEY, D. L., BAIRD, D. and McGREGOR, D. C.
1972A   Vertebrate paleontology of eastern Canada. Int. Geol. Congr., 24th, Canada, 1972, Guidebk., Field
           Excursion A59, Montreal, 113 pp., 22 figs., 3 tables.

CARROLL, R. L. and GASKILL, PAMELA
1971A   A captorhinomorph reptile from the lower Permian of Europe. J. Paleontol., 45:3, 450—463, 7 figs.,
           1 table.

CARROLL, ROBERT L.   See also: Alison, D. and Carroll, R., 1972A.

CARTER, C. O.
1968A   Origin of man. New Sci., 37:578, 40.

CARTER, GEORGE F.
1968A   Uhle's mastodon. ·Anthropol. J. Can., 6:2, 21—24.

CARTMILL, MATT
1967A   The early Pleistocene mammalian microfaunas of sub-Saharan Africa and their ecological significance.
           Quaternaria, 9, 169—198, 3 figs. (German and Italian summaries).
1971A   Ethmoid component in the orbit of primates. Nature, 232:5312, 566—567, 1 fig.
1972A   Arboreal adaptions and the origin of the order Primates. In: Tuttle, R. (ed.), 1972A, 97—122, 3 figs.,
           2 pls.

CASAMIQUELA, RODOLFO
1968A   Noticia sobre la presencia de Glossotherium (Xenarthra, Mylodontidae) en Chile central. Valparaiso,
           Mus. Hist. Natur., Ann., 1, 59—75, 3 pls. (Spanish).

CASAMIQUELA, R. M., CORVALÁN, J. and FRANQUESA, F.
1969A   Hallazgo de dinosaurios en el Cretácico superior de Chile. Chile, Inst. Invest. Geol., Bol., 25, 31 pp.,
           illustr. (Spanish; English summary).

CASAMIQUELA, R. M. and FASOLA, A.
1968A   Sobre pisadas de dinosaurios del Cretácico inferior de Colchagua (Chile). Chile, Univ., Fac. Cienc. Fís.
           Mat., Dep. Geol., Publ., 30, 24 pp., 3 figs., 7 pls., 1 table (Spanish; English summary).

CASANOVA, RICHARD
1970A   An illustrated guide to fossil collecting. Healdsburg, Calif.: Naturegraph Publishers, 128 pp., illustr.
           Rev.: Anon. in Amer. Midland Natur., 85:2, 541; Anon. in Rocks Miner., 45:12, 781.

CASANOVAS CLADELLAS, MARÍA LOURDES and SANTAFÉ LLOPIS, JOSÉ-VICENTE
1971A   Icnitas de reptiles mesozoicos en la provincia de Logroño. Acta Geol. Hisp., 6:5, 139—142, 6 figs.
           (Spanish; French summary).

CASE, GERARD R.
1967A   Rev.: Zídekin Prague, Národ. Muz. Prague, Čas., Odd. Přírod., 137:3—4, 90.

CASE, GERARD R. and BIGBIE, CLYDE E.
1972A   Eugene Paul Wilson. May 4, 1904 — July 9, 1970. Soc. Vert. Paleontol., News Bull., 94, 81—82.

CASE, GERARD R.   See also: Lundberg, J. G. and Case, G. R., 1970A.

CASEY, D. A. and DARRAGH, T. A.
1970A   Excavation of the Green Gully burial. Victoria, Nat. Mus., Mem.. 30, 3–13, 4 figs., 1 pl.

CASIER, EDGARD
1957C   Sur la découverte d'épines pectorales de siluroides dans le Quaternaire de la Belgique. Soc. Roy. Belge
                    Étud. Géol. Archéol. "Cherch. Wallonie", Bull., 16, 343–347, 2 figs. (French).
1967B   Le Landénien de Dormaal (Brabant) et sa faune ichthyologique. Inst. Roy. Sci. Natur. Belg., Mém.,
                    156, 1–66, 10 figs., 8 pls. (French).
                    Rev.: Weiler in Zentralbl. Geol. Paläontol., Teil 2, 1968:6, 643–644.
1968A   Le squelette céphalique de Eochelone brabantica L. Dollo, du Bruxellien (Lutétien inférieur) de
                    Belgique, et sa comparaison avec celui de Chelone mydas Linné. Inst. Roy. Sci. Natur. Belg.,
                    Bull., 44:9, 22 pp., 6 figs., 5 pls. (French).
1969A   Addenda aux connaissances sur la faune ichthyologique de la série de Bokungu (Congo). Mus. Roy.
                    Afr. Cent., Ann., Sér. in 8°, Sci. Géol., 62, 1–22, 4 figs., 2 pls., 1 table (French).
                    Rev.: Weiler in Zentralbl. Geol. Paläontol., Teil 2, 1970:5, 422–423.

CASIER, EDGARD, et al.
1966A   Het Fossielhoudend Ieperiaan van Merelbeke. Natuurwet. Tijdschr., 48:6–8, 202–227, 1 fig. (Dutch).

CASIER, EDGARD and TAVERNE, LOUIS
1971A   Note préliminaire sur le matériel paléoichthyologique éocrétacique récolté par la Spanish Gulf Oil
                    Company en Guinée Equatoriale et au Gabon. Rev. Zool. Bot. Afr., 83:1–2, 16–20, 1 fig.
                    (French).

CASSOLI, P.   See: Biddittu, I. and Cassoli, P., 1968A; Biddittu, I., Cassoli, P. and Malpieri, L., 1967A.

CASSON, MARGARETHE
1972A   The fossil mystery. Rocks Miner., 47:9, 532–533.

CASTANET, J., GASC, J.-P., MEUNIER, F. and RICQLÈS, A. DE
1970A   Calcium et nature des zones de croissance cyclique dans l'os des vertébrés poïkilothermes. Acad. Sci.,
                    C.R., Sér. D, 270:23, 2853–2856, 2 pls. (French).

CASTELLANOS, ALFREDO
1969A   Notas de estratigrafía terciaria del valle de Yocahuil en las provincias de Catamarca, Tucuman y Salta
                    (Argentina). Univ. Nac. Litoral, Inst. Fisiogr. Geol., Publ., 54, 38 pp. (Spanish).

CASTILLO, H. DE   See: Comas, J., Castillo, H. de and Méndez, B., 1971A.

CATZIGRAS, F., GUÉRIN, C. and ONORATINI, G.
1971A   Découverte d'une dent de Rhinocerotidae dans le Néogène du littoral de la Nerthe (Bouches-du-Rhône).
                    Soc. Géol. Fr., C.R., 1971:6, 314–316, 2 figs. (French).

CAUVIN, JEAN   See: Cauvin, M.-C. and Cauvin, J., 1969A.

CAUVIN, MARIE-CLAIRE and CAUVIN, JEAN
1969A   Découverte de restes humains moustériens à l'abri de Hauteroche, Chateauneuf-sur-Charente. Acad. Sci.,
                    C.R., Sér. D, 268:1, 37–40, 2 figs. (French).

CAVAILLÉ, A.
1970A   L'évolution des grottes au Quaternaire dans la France méridionale. Soc. Hist. Natur. Toulouse, Bull.,
                    106:1–2, 41–53, 2 figs. (French).

CAVENDER, TED M.
1968A   Freshwater fish remains from the Clarno formation Ochoco Mountains of north-central Oregon. Ore
                    Bin, 30:7, 125–141, 5 figs., 4 pls.
1969A   An Oligocene mudminnow (family Umbridae) from Oregon with remarks on relationships within the
                    Esocoidei. Mich., Univ., Mus. Zool., Occ. Pap., 660, 33 pp., 6 figs., 2 pls.

CAVENDER, T. M., LUNDBERG, J. G. and WILSON, R. L.
1970A   Two new fossil records of the genus Esox (Teleostei, Salmoniformes) in North America. Northwest Sci.,
                    44:3, 176–183, 3 figs.

CAVENDER, T. M. and MILLER, ROBERT RUSH
1972A   *Smilodonichthys rastrosus*, a new Pliocene salmonid fish from western United States. Oreg., Univ.,
Mus. Natur. Hist., Bull., 18, 44 pp., 14 figs., 3 tables.

CAYEUX, ANDRÉ DE   See: Cailleux, André de.

CELERIER, G.
1967A   Le gisement périgordien supérieur des "Jambes" commune de Périgueux (Dordogne). Soc. Préhist. Fr.,
Bull., Étud. Trav., 64:1, 53–68, 4 figs., 1 table (French).

CERAM, C. W. (= MAREK, KURT W.)
1971A   The first American. Translated from German by Richard and Clara Winston. New York: Harcourt
Brace Jovanovich, Inc., xxi + 357 pp., illustr.
Rev.:   Anon. in Die Zeit, Dec. 31, 1971, 32; Barrett in Time, 98:21, 110, 112, 114; McKusick in
Amer. Sci., 60:3, 387; MacLachlan in J. West, 11:4, 696–697; Willey in Antiquity, 46:181,
159–160.

CÉROU, E.   See: Clottes, J. and Cérou, E., 1970A.

CEUCA, TRAIAN
1971A   Cele trei exemplare de *Archaeopteryx*. [The three specimens of *Archaeopteryx*.] Natura, Ser. Biol.,
23:3, 77–80, 4 figs. (Rumanian).

CHAKRAVARTI, D. K.
1968A   Fauna and stratigraphy of the *Gangamopteris* beds. J. Palaeontol. Soc. India, 5–9, 9–15, 1 table.

CHALINE, JEAN
1968A   Utilisation du microscope électronique à balayage dans l'étude des dents de micromammifères.
Mammalia, 32:2, 211–218, 1 fig., 2 pls. (French; English summary).
1969A   Les rongeurs découverts sur le sol de la cabane acheuléenne du Lazaret. In: Lumley, H. de (ed.),
1968B, 85–93, 6 figs., 3 tables.
1970A   *Pliomys lenki*, forme relique dans la microfaune du Würm ancien de la grotte de Lezetxiki (Guipúzcoa-
Espagne). Munibe, 22:1–2, 43–49, 1 pl., 3 tables (French).
1970B   La signification des rongeurs dans les dépôts quaternaires. Ass. Fr. Étud. Quat., Bull., 7:25, 229–241,
6 pls. (French; English summary).
1971A   L'âge des Hominiens de la Caune de l'Arago à Tautavel (Pyrénées-Orientales), d'après l'étude des
rongeurs. Acad. Sci., C.R., Sér. D, 272:13, 1743–1746, 3 tables (French).
1972A   Gryzuny srednego i verkhnego pleĭstotŝena Franŝii. [Rodents of the middle and upper Pleistocene of
France.] Akad. Nauk SSSR, Kom. Izuch. Chetvertich. Perioda, Biull., 38, 56–71, 3 figs.,
2 tables (Russian).

CHALINE, J., CLAIR, A. and PUISSÉGUR, J.-J.
1970A   Mise au point sur le Villafranchien de Chagny (Saône-et-Loire). Soc. Géol. Fr., C.R., 1970:4, 114–116,
1 fig. (French).

CHALINE, J. and MATTHEY, R.
1971A   Hypothèses relatives à la formule chromosomique d'*Allophaiomys pliocaenicus* (Rodentia, Arvicolidae)
et à la diversification de cette espèce. Acad. Sci., C.R., Sér. D, 272:8, 1071–1074, 1 fig.
(French).

CHALINE, J. and MICHAUX, JACQUES
1969A   Les gisements de vertébrés de la région montpelliéraine. 4. Gisements quaternaires. Bur. Rech. Géol.
Minières, Bull. (Sér. 2), Sec. 1, 1969:1, 39–42, 1 table (French; English summary).
1969B   Évolution et signification stratigraphique des arvicolidés du genre *Mimomys* dans le Plio-Pleistocène de
France. Acad. Sci., C.R., Sér. D, 268:25, 3029–3032, 1 fig., 2 tables (French).

CHALYSHEV, VASILIĬ IVANOVICH and VARĬUKHINA, LILIĬA MIKHAĬLOVNA
1966A   Biostratigrafiiā triasa Pechorskoĭ oblasti. [Biostratigraphy of Triassic of the Pechora region.] Moscow:
"Nauka" Press, 155 pp., 4 figs., 6 pls., 6 tables (Russian).
1968A   Biostratigrafiiā verkhneĭ permi severo-vostoka evropeĭskoĭ chasti SSSR. [Biostratigraphy of upper
Permian of the northeast of the European part of USSR.] Leningrad: "Nauka" Press, 244 pp.,
1 map, 3 charts, 9 pls., 16 tables (Russian).

CHAMBERLAIN, A. P.
1968A   The Piltdown "forgery". New Sci., 40:625, 516.

CHAMLA, M.-C.
1966A   Note sur les restes humains (H4) découvert à Rachgoun, en Février 1964. In: Camps, G., 1966B, 182–185, 2 figs., 3 tables (French).

CHAMPAGNE, F. and ESPITALIÉ, R.
1970A   L'abri du Roc d'Abeilles à Calviac (Dordogne). Annexe: Bouchud, J., Détermination de la faune du Roc d'Abeilles. Gallia Préhist., 13:1, 1–23, 10 figs., 1 table (French).

CHANG, HSI-CHIH
1964A   Abs.: Sci. Abstr. China, Earth Sci., 2:2, 8.
1964B   Abs.: Sci. Abstr. China, Earth Sci., 2:4, 8.

CHANG, HSI-CHIH and LIU, HOU
1964   Abs.: Sci. Abstr. China, Earth Sci., 2:3, 9.

CHANG, KUO-JUI
1963   Abs.: Sci. Abstr. China, Earth Sci., 2:2, 6.

CHANG, KUO-WEI   See: Wang, Y-y., Hsueh, H-h., Ho, J-c. and Chang, K-w., 1969A.

CHANG, KWANG-CHIH
1968   Rev.: Smalley in Man (J. Roy. Anthropol. Inst.), 4:2, 297.

CHANG, MI-MAN
1963   Abs.: Sci. Abstr. China, Earth Sci., 2:1, 3–4.

CHANG, YU-PING and TUNG, YUNG-SHENG
1963A   Abs.: Sci. Abstr. China, Earth Sci., 2:1, 1.

CHANTELL, CHARLES J.
1970A   Upper Pliocene frogs from Idaho. Copeia, 1970:4, 654–664, 8 figs., 1 table.
1971A   Fossil amphibians from the Egelhoff local fauna in north-central Nebraska. Mich., Univ., Mus. Paleontol., Contrib., 23:15, 239–246, 1 pl., 3 tables.

CHAO, TZE-KUEI and BI, CHU-ZHEN
1964   Abs.: Sci. Abstr. China, Earth Sci., 2:2, 9.

CHAPLIN, RAYMOND E.
1971A   The study of animal bones from archaeological sites. New York: Seminar, International Series of Monographs on Science in Archaeology, No. 1. x + 170 pp., illustr.
        Rev.: deSaussure in Caves Karst, 14:5, 35; Heath in Mus. J., 72:1, 32–33; Herre in Z. Zool. Syst. Evolut.-Forsch., 10:1, 80; Jarman in Antiquity, 46:182, 167–168; Perkins in Science (AAAS), 176:4038, 1008–1009.

CHAPMAN, G. R.   See: Bishop, W. W. and Chapman, G. R., 1970A; Bishop, W. W., Chapman, G. R., Hill, A. and Miller, J. A., 1971A.

CHAPPELL, W. M., DURHAM, J. W. and SAVAGE, D. E.
1970A   Rhinoceros mold in basalt. S. Calif. Paleontol. Soc., Bull., 2:12, 9 (reprinted from Geol. Soc. Amer., Abstr., 1949).

CHAPSKIĬ, K. K.
1970A   Kontseptsiia arkticheskogo proiskhozhdeniia lastonogikh i drugie puti resheniia etoĭ problemy. [The concept of the Arctic origin of the pinnipeds and other ways for solving this problem.] In: Severnyĭ Ledovityĭ Okean i ego poberezh'e v kainozoe, 166–173 (Russian).

CHARD, CHESTER S.
1967A   Northeast Asia. Bibliography. Asian Perspectives, 10, 23–37.
1969A   Man in prehistory. New York, London and Sydney: McGraw-Hill Book Co., vii + 351 pp., illustr.
        Rev.: Motyková in Archeol. Roz., 23:2, 232.

CHARD, CHESTER S. and MORLAN, RICHARD E.
1970A   Absoliutnaia khronologiia kamennogo veka Iaponii. [Absolute chronology of the Stone Age in Japan.] Akad. Nauk SSSR, Sib. Otd., Mater. Ist. Sib., Drevniaia Sibir', 3, 109–138, 1 fig., 3 tables (Russian).

CHARD, CHESTER S. and POWERS, ROGER
    1968A   Soviet archaeological radiocarbon dates: III. Arctic Anthropol., 5:1, 224–233.

CHARIG, ALAN J.
    1966B   Stance and gait in the archosaur reptiles. Advan. Sci., 22, 537 (abs.).
    1972A   The evolution of the archosaur pelvis and hind-limb: an explanation in functional terms. In: Joysey,
                K. A. and Kemp, T. S. (eds.), 1972A, 121–155, 11 figs., 8 pls., 1 table.

CHARIG, A. J. and REIG, O. A.
    1970A   The classification of the Proterosuchia. Linn. Soc., Biol. J., 2:2, 125–171, 6 figs., 3 tables.

CHARIG, ALAN J.   See also: Attridge, J. and Charig, A. J., 1967A, 1967B.

CHARLES-DOMINIQUE, PIERRE and MARTIN, ROBERT D.
    1970A   Evolution of lorises and lemurs. Nature, 227:5255, 257–260, 2 figs., 1 table.

CHARON, M.   See: Petit-Maire Heinz, N. and Charon, M., 1972A.

CHARRIER, G. and GIGLIO, A.
    1969A   Primi risultati di una campagna di rilevamento geologico nell'isola di Coo. Assoc. Miner. Subalp.,
                Boll., 6:3, 482–516, illustr. (Italian; French and English summaries).

CHARTKOFF, JOSEPH L.
    1966A   Color coding: a laboratory aid for archaeology. Calif., Univ., Los Angeles, Archaeol. Surv., Rep., 8,
                283–286.

CHARYGIN, M. M.   See: Bogacheva, M. I., Vasil'ev, Iù. M., Proshliàkov, B. K., Charygin, M. M. and Shleĭfer, A. G.,
                1965A.

CHATTERJEE, SANKAR
    1967B   New discoveries contributing to the stratigraphy of the continental Triassic sediments of the Pranhita-
                Godavari Valley. Geol. Soc. India, Bull., 4:2, 37–41, 1 fig., 1 table.
    1969A   Rhynchosaurs in time and space. Geol. Soc. London, Proc., 1658, 203–208, 1 fig., 1 table.
    1969B   Dr. D. N. Wadia, F. R. S. [1883–1969]. Geol. Mining Met. Soc. India, Quart. J., 39:3, 137–138,
                portr.

CHATTERJEE, S., JAIN, S. L., KUTTY, T. S. and CHOWDHURY, T. K. R.
    1969A   On the discovery of Triassic cynodont reptiles from India. Sci. Culture, 35:8, 411–413.

CHATTERS, ROY M.
    1963A   The application of physical techniques to age-dating. Wash. Archaeol., 7:2, 42–45.

CHATURVEDI, M. N.   See: Tewari, B. S., Chaturvedi, M. N. and Singh, M. P., 1968A.

CHAUDHURY, R. S.   See: Gupta, V. J. and Chaudhury, R. S., 1969A.

CHAUFFRIASSE, ANDRÉ   See: Roussot, A., Andrieux, C. and Chauffriasse, A., 1968A.

CHAVAILLON, JEAN
    1970A   Découverte d'un niveau oldowayen dans la basse vallée de l'Omo (Ethiopie). Soc. Préhist. Fr., Bull.,
                C.R., 67:1, 7–11, 6 figs. (French; English summary).

CHAVAILLON, JEAN and CHAVAILLON, NICOLE
    1969A   Les habitats oldowayens de Melka Kontouré (Ethiopie): premiers resultats. Acad. Sci., C.R., Sér. D,
                268:18, 2244–2247 (French).
    1969B   Les habitats oldowayens (pebble culture) de Melka Kontouré, Ethiopie: résultats des missions de 1967
                et 1968. Soc. Préhist. Fr., Bull., C.R., 66:4, 98 (French).
    1971A   Présence éventuelle d'un abri oldowayen dans le gisement de Melka-Kontouré (Ethiopie). Acad. Sci.,
                C.R., Sér. D, 273:6, 623–625, 1 pl. (French).

CHAVAILLON, JEAN   See also: Arambourg, C., Chavaillon, J. and Coppens, Y., 1969A; Bonnefille, R.,
                Chavaillon, J. and Coppens, Y.

CHAVAILLON, NICOLE   See: Bonnefille, R., Chavaillon, N. and Taieb, M., 1970A; Chavaillon, J. and Chavaillon,
                N., 1969A, 1969B, 1971A.

CHAVAN, A. and CAILLEUX, A. DE
1957A   Rev.: A. Hacquart in Natuurwet. Tijdschr., 39:4–5, 134.

CHAVANON, S. and SAUBADE, A. M.
1970A   Découverte d'un squelette d'*Halitherium* Kaup aux environs de Saint-Émilion (Gironde). Bordeaux, Univ., Inst. Géol. Bassin Aquitaine, Bull., 8, 261–262, 3 figs. (French; English summary).

CHEATUM, ELMER P.   See: Schultz, G. E. and Cheatum, E. P., 1969A, 1970A.

CHEDD, GRAHAM
1967A   How close are we to the apes? New Sci., 36:575, 673–674, 2 figs.

CHEDD, G. and STUBBS, P.
1969A   New fossil finds push back the ages of man. New Sci., 42:655, 678.

CHEDD, G., STUBBS, P. and WICK, G.
1970A   There's mammals in them thar hills! New Sci., 46:706, 569.

CHELNOKOV, F. G.
1969A   Ostatki skeleta morskoĭ korovy. [Remains of sea cow skeleton.] Priroda, 1969:1, 71–73, 3 figs. (Russian).

CHEMEKOV, Iu. F.
1966A   Chetvertichnaĭa sistema. [Quaternary system.] Geologiĭa SSSR, 19, Khabarovsk area and Amur Province, 342–363, 6 figs., 1 table (Russian).

CHEMIN, J.   See: Alteirac, A. and Chemin, J., 1968A.

CHÊNG, TÊ-K'UN
1966A   Archaeology in China. Vol. 1 suppl. 1. New light on prehistoric China. Cambridge: Heffer and Sons, Univ. of Toronto Press, viii + 55 pp., 25 figs., 1 table.
          Rev.: Chang in Asian Perspectives, 10, 163; Starr in Amer. Anthropol., 70, 414–415.

CHEPALYGA, ANDREĬ LEONIDOVICH   See: Konstantinova, N. A. and Chepalyga, A. L., 1972A; Krasnenkov, R. V., Aleksandrova, L. P., Shcherbakova, L. A. and Chepalyga, A. L., 1970A.

CHERDYNTSEV, V. V.
1970A   Absoliutnaĭa geokhronologiĭa pleĭstotšena. [Absolute geochronology of the Pleistocene.] Akad. Nauk SSSR, Kom. Opred. Absoliut. Vozr. Geol. Form., Tr., 15th. Sess. (1967), 392–398, 1 fig., 2 tables (Russian).

CHERKESOV, S. V.
1970A*   Stratigrafiĭa i fauna siluriĭskikh otlozheniĭ Vaĭgacha. [Stratigraphy and fauna of Silurian deposits of Vaĭgach.] Leningrad: NII geol. Arktiki, 241 pp., illustr. (Russian).

CHERNIĀVSKIĬ, F. B.
1970A   Analiz sovremennykh teriokompleksov Chukotki i arkticheskoĭ Aliaski v sviazi s problemoĭ Beringii. [Analysis of Modern therian complexes of Chukotka and Arctic Alaska in connection with the problem of Beringia.] In: Severnyĭ Ledovityĭ Okean i ego poberezh'ev Kaĭnozoe, 525–529 (Russian).

CHERNYKH, I. I. and MALEEVA, A. G.
1971A   Uzkocherepnaĭa polevka (*Microtus (Stenocranius) gregalis* Pall.) iz sostava pozdnepleĭstotšenovoĭ "smeshannoĭ fauny" iuga Tiumenskoĭ oblasti. [The narrow-skulled vole (*Microtus (Stenocranius) gregalis* Pall.) from the Late Pleistocene "mixed fauna" of the south of Tiumen' Province.] Sverdlovsk, Ural. Gos. Univ., Uch. Zap., 115, 15–24 (Russian).

CHERNYSH, A. P.
1969A   Issledovaniĭa v Oselivke na Dnestre. [Research at Oselivka on Dnestr.] In: Rybakov, B. A. (ed.), 1969A, 266–267.
1970A   Issledovaniĭa v Kormane na Dnestre. [Research in Korman on the Dnestr.] In: Rybakov, B. A. (ed.), 1970A, 220–221 (Russian).
1971A   Issledovaniĭa stoĭanki Oselivka I v 1966–1967gg. [Research at the station Oselivka I in 1966–1967.] Akad. Nauk SSSR, Inst. Arkheol., Krat. Soobshch., 126, 68–77, 5 figs. (Russian).

CHERNYSH, E. K.   See: Grigor'eva, G. B., Markevich, V. I., Popova, T. A. and Chernysh, E. K.. 1969A.

CHESNOVA, L. V.
   1966A   K stoletiiu so dnía opublikovaniía E. Gekkelem pervogo filogeneticheskogo dreva zhizni. [Centenary of
             the publication of the first phylogenetic system of life by E. Haeckel.] Zool. Zh., 45:12, 1753–
             1758 (Russian).

CHEYNIER, ANDRÉ and BREUIL, ABBÉ HENRI
   1963A   Rev.: Llongueras Campañá in Ampurias, 31–32, 381–383.

CHIA, LAN-PO
   1965A   Discovery of a hominid skull and stratigraphical observation at Gongwangling in Lantian, Shensi. K'o
             Hsueh T'ung Pao, 6, 477–81, 2 figs. (Chinese).
             Abs.: Sci. Abstr. China, Earth Sci., 4:2, 7.

CHIAPPELLA, GINETTA V.
   1962A   La Grotta della "Basua" di Toirano (SV). Congr. Intern. Stud. Sardi, VI, Cagliari, 1955, Atti, 2, 25–
             41, 14 figs. (Italian).

CHIARELLI, BRUNETTO
   1968C*   Taxonomy and phylogeny of Old World primates with references to the origin of man. Torino, Italy:
             Rosenberg and Sellier, xi + 323 pp., illustr.
             Rev.: Ankel in Homo, 20:1, 72; Ashton in Endeavor, 28:105, 153; Billy in L'Anthropologie, 73:5–6,
             425–426; Comas in An. Antropol., Mexico, 6, 305–308; Gavan in Human Biol., 42:1, 140–144;
             Jolly in Man, 4:3, 461–463; M.S. in Archeol. Roz., 22:2, 231; Pilbeam in Amer. Anthropol.,
             988–990; Roth-Lutra in Anat. Anz., 126:4, 472–473; Starck in Folia Primatol., 11:3, 239–
             240; Tuttle in Amer. J. Phys. Anthropol., 33:1, 118–119.

CHIARELLI, BRUNETTO   See also: Fedele, F., Chiarelli, B. and Masali, M., 1966A.

CHIJI, MANZO
   1971A   Pleistocene Proboscidea from Kinki district, central Japan, I. In: Minato, M., et al. (eds.), 1968A, 98,
             1 fig.
   1971B   Pleistocene Proboscidea from Kinki district, central Japan, II. In: Minato, M., et al. (eds.), 1968A, 99,
             3 figs.
   1971C   Pleistocene Proboscidea from Kinki district, central Japan, III. In: Minato, M., et al. (eds.), 1968A·
             100, 2 figs.
   1971D   Pleistocene Proboscidea from Kinki district, central Japan, IV. In: Minato, M., et al. (eds.), 1968A,
             101, 2 figs.
   1971E   Pleistocene Proboscidea from Kinki district, central Japan, V. In: Minato, M., et al. (eds.), 1968A,
             102, 2 figs.

CHIJI, M.   See also: Ikebe, N., Chiji, M. and Nakaseko, K., 1969A.

CHIKHACHEV, P. K.
   1959A   Tretichnye otlozheniía Tadzhikistana. [Tertiary deposits of Tadzhikistan.] Geologiía SSSR, 24,
             Tadzhik SSR, 292–316, 4 figs., 1 table (Russian).

CHIKHACHEV, P. K.   See also: Burachek, A. R. and Chikhachev, P. K., 1959A.

CHINZEI, K.   See: Hamada, T. and Chinzei, K., 1971A.

CHIU, CHAN-SIANG
   1965A   First discovery of Lophiomeryx in China. Vert. PalAsiat., 9:4, 397–398.
             Abs.: Sci. Abstr. China, Earth Sci., 4:2, 6–7.

CHIU, H. T.
   1972A   Occurrence of whale bone fossils in Taiwan. Acta Geol. Taiwanica, 15, 23–26, 2 figs., 3 pls.

CHKHIKVADZE, VIACHESLAV MIKHAÍLOVICH (= ČKHIKVADZE, V. M.)
   1968B   O vzaimosvîazi filogeneza i ontogeneza nekotorykh iskopaemykh cherepakh. [On the relationship of
             phylogenesis and ontogenesis in some fossil turtles.] Akad. Nauk Gruz. SSR, Inst. Paleobiol.,
             Nauchn. Sess., 14, 10–12 (Russian).
   1969A   Novye cherepakhi iz paleogenovykh otlozhenií Zaísanskoi kotloviny i Tsentral'nogo Kazakhstana. [New
             turtles from Paleogene deposits of Zaísan trough and central Kazakhstan.] Mosk. Obshchest.
             Ispyt. Prir., Biull., Otd. Geol., 44:6, 145–146 (Russian).
   1970A   O proiskhozhdenii sovremennykh sukhoputnykh cherepakh Palearktiki. [On the origin of modern
             Palearctic land tortoises.] Akad. Nauk Gruz. SSR, Soobshch., 57:1, 245–247 (Russian;
             Georgian and English summaries).

1970B   Drevneĭshie kaĭnozoĭskie cherepakhi SSSR. [Earliest Cenozoic tortoises of the USSR.] Akad. Nauk Gruz. SSR, Soobshch., 60:3, 749–752, 3 figs. (Russian; Georgian and English summaries).

1970C   Novye pozdneeotsenovye cherepakhi Zaĭsana i oligomerizat͡siia rogovykh shchitkov plastrona nekotorykh Testudinata. [New late Eocene turtles from Zaĭsan and the oligomerization of the horny scutes of plastron of some Testudinata.] In: Materialy po evoliut͡sii nazemnykh pozvonochnykh, 58–62, 4 figs. (Russian).

1971A   K istorii cherepakh semeĭstva Chelydridae. [On the history of the tortoise family Chelydridae.] Akad. Nauk Gruz. SSR, Soobshch., 61:1, 237–240, 2 figs. (Russian; Georgian and English summaries).

1971B   Novye cherepakhi iz oligot͡sena Kazakhstana i sistematicheskoe polozhenie nekotorykh iskopaemykh vidov Mongolii. [New tortoises from the Oligocene of Kazakhstan and the systematic position of some fossil species of Mongolia.] Akad. Nauk Gruz. SSR, Soobshch., 62:2, Akad. Nauk Gruz. SSR, Soobshch., 62:2, 489–492, 3 figs. (Russian; Georgian and English summaries).

1971C   Pervai͡a nakhodka tretichnoĭ cherepakhi semeĭstva Platysternidae. [First find of a Tertiary turtle of the family Platysternidae.] Paleontol. Zh., 1971:4, 137–139, 1 fig. (Russian).

1971D   Tri novykh iskopaemykh vida sukhoputnykh cherepakh iz Zaĭsanskoĭ kotloviny (Vostochnyĭ Kazakhstan) [Three new fossil species of land tortoises from Zaĭsan basin (east Kazakhstan).] Akad. Nauk Gruz. SSR, Soobshch., 54:1, 245–248, 3 figs. (Russian; Georgian and English summaries).

1971E   First find of a Tertiary turtle of the family Platysternidae. Paleontol. J., 5:4, 546–547, 1 fig.

1972A   O sistematicheskom polozhenii tretichnykh gigantskikh sukhoputnykh cherepakh Palearktiki. [On the systematic position of the Tertiary gigantic land turtles of Palearctic.] Akad. Nauk Gruz. SSR, Soobshch., 65:3, 745–748, 2 figs. (Russian; Georgian and English summaries).

CHMIELEWSKI, WALDEMAR (= KHMELEVSKIĬ, V. V.)
  1969A   Influence exercée par le milieu périglaciaire sur l'habitat au Pléistocène supérieur de Pologne. Biul. Peryglac., 20, 9–27, 1 map, 1 chart (French).

CHOATE, JERRY R.
  1970A   Systematics and zoogeography of middle American shrews of the genus Cryptotis. Kan., Univ., Mus. Natur. Hist., Publ., 19:3, 195–317, 20 figs.

CHOCHIA, N. G. and DOMRACHEV, S. M.
  1969A   Devonskai͡a sistema. Zapadnyĭ sklon Urala i Priural'e. [Devonian system. Western versant of Urals and Priural'e.] Geologii͡a SSSR, 12:1, Perm, Sverdlov, Cheli͡abinsk, and Kurgan Provinces, 199–217 (Russian).

CHOPRA, S. R. K.   See: Simons, E. L. and Chopra, S. R., 1969A, 1969B.

CHORN, J. D.   See: Rasmussen, D. L., Martin, L. D., Chorn, J. D. and Slimmer, D. F., 1971A.

CHOW, BEN- SHUN
  1963A   Abs.: Sci. Abstr. China, Earth Sci., 1:4, 7.

CHOW, MIN-CHEN
  1958G   A record of the earliest sabre-toothed cats from the Eocene of Lushih, Honan. Sci. Record, New Ser., 2:10, 347–349, 2 figs.
  1961D   Abs.: Sci. Abstr. China, Earth Sci., 1:2, 9.
  1962A   Abs.: Sci. Abstr. China, Earth Sci., 1:2, 10–11.
  1963B   Abs.: Sci. Abstr. China, Earth Sci., 2:1, 4–5.
  1964A   Abs.: Sci. Abstr. China, Earth Sci., 2:4, 8.
  1964B   Abs.: Sci. Abstr. China, Earth Sci., 2:4, 9.
  1965A   Abs.: Sci. Abstr. China, Earth Sci., 3:4, 9–10.
  1965B   Abs.: Sci. Abstr. China, Earth Sci., 3:4, 9.

CHOW, M.-C. and CHIU, CHAN-SIANG
  1963A   Abs.: Sci. Abstr. China, Earth Sci., 2:2, 5.
  1964A   Abs.: Sci. Abstr. China, Earth Sci., 2:4, 8.

CHOW, M.-C. and CHOW, BEN-SHUNG
  1965A   Abs.: Sci. Abstr. China, Earth Sci., 3:3, 10–11.

CHOW, M.-C., HU, C.-K. and LEE, Y.-C.
  1965A   Abs.: Sci. Abstr. China, Earth Sci., 3:4, 9.

CHOW, M.-C. and LI, CHUAN-KUEI
  1965A   Abs.: Sci. Abstr. China, Earth Sci., 3:2, 7.
  1965B   Mammalian fossils in association with the mandible of Lantian man at Chen-Chia-Ou, in Lantian, Shensi. Vert. PalAsiat., 9:4, 387–394, 1 pl.

CHOW, M.-C. and TUNG, YUNG-SHENG
    1965A   Abs.: Sci. Abstr. China, Earth Sci., 3:2, 5—6.

CHOW, M.-C. and XU, YU-XUAN
    1965A   Abs.: Sci. Abstr. China, Earth Sci., 3:3, 9—10.

CHOWDHURY, TAPAN ROY
    1970A   A new capitosaurid amphibian from the Triassic Yerrapalli formation of the Pranhita-Godavari Valley. Geol. Soc. India, J., 11:2, 155—162, 2 figs., 1 table.
    1970B   Two new dicynodonts from the Triassic Yerrapalli formation of central India. Palaeontology, 13:1, 132—144, 7 figs.
        Rev.: Chrulew in Zentralbl. Geol. Paläontol., Teil 2, 1972:3, 165.

CHOWDHURY, T. R.   See also: Chatterjee, S., Jain, S. L., Kutty, T. S., and Chowdhury, T. K. R., 1969A.

CHRISTIAN, JOHN J.
    1970A   Social subordination, population density, and mammalian evolution. Science (AAAS), 168:3927, 84—90.

CHRISTIANSEN, E. A.
    1972A   Stratigraphy of the Fort Qu'Appelle vertebrate fossil locality, Saskatchewan. Can. J. Earth Sci., 9:2, 212—218, 5 figs. (French summary).

CHRZANOWSKA, WIESŁAWA
    1971A   Kilka uwag o czaszkach tura (Bos primigenius Bojanus, 1827). [Some remarks on skulls of aurochs (Bos primigenius Bojanus, 1827).] Przegl. Zool., 15:1, 91—97, 8 figs., 3 tables (Polish; English summary).

CHUDINOV, PETR KONSTANTINOVICH (= TCHUDINOV, P. K.)
    1968C   Novye dinotsefaly iz Ochera. [New deinocephalians from Ocher.] In: Verkhnepaleozoĭskie i mezozoĭskie zemnovodnye i presmykaĭushchiesiâ SSSR, 16—31, 4 figs. (Russian).
    1968D   Itogi i perspektivy izucheniiâ permskikh pozvonochnykh Priural'iâ. [Results and prospects of the research of Permian vertebrates of Priural'e.] In: Verkhnepaleozoĭskie i mezozoĭskie zemnovodnye i presmykaĭushchiesiâ SSSR, 65—71 (Russian).
    1968E   Structure of the integuments of theromorphs. Akad. Nauk SSSR, Dokl., Earth Sci. Sec., 179, 226—229, 2 figs. (Translated from Russian: Akad. Nauk SSSR, Dokl., 1968, 179:1, 207—210).
    1969A   O stratigraficheskom raspredelenii permskikh pozvonochnykh na vostoke Evropeĭskoĭ chasti SSSR. [On the stratigraphic distribution of permian vertebrates in the east of the European part of USSR.] In: Voprosy geologii iûzhnogo Urala i Povolzh'iâ, 6:1, 96—105 (Russian).
    1970A   O kozhnom pokrove terapsid. [On the dermal integument of therapsids.] In: Materialy po evoliûtsii nazemnykh pozvonochnykh, 45—50, 1 fig., 1 pl. (Russian).

CHUDINOV, P. K.   See also: Kalandadze, N. N., Ochev, V. G., Tatarinov, L. P., Chudinov, P. K. and Shishkin, M. A., 1968A; Sigogneau, D. and Tchudinov, P. K., 1972A; Trofimov, B. A. and Chudinov, P. K., 1970A.

CHUMAKOV, I. S. (= TCHOUMAKOV, I. S.)
    1967B   Chetvertichnaiâ sistema. Rudnyĭ Altaĭ. [Quaternary. Rudnyĭ Altaĭ.] Geologiiâ SSSR, 41:1, Eastern Kazakhstan, 224—227 (Russian).

CHUMAKOV, I. S.   See also: Borisov, B. A. and Chumakov, I. S., 1967A.

CHURCHER, CHARLES S.
    1968B   Pleistocene ungulates from the Bow River gravels at Cochrane, Alberta. Can. J. Earth Sci., 5:6, 1467—1488, 20 figs., 13 tables.
    1968C   Portrait of a paleontologist. Rotunda, 1:2, 22—29, 5 photos.
    1970A   The fossil Equidae from the Krugersdorp caves. Transvaal Mus., Ann., 26:6, 145—168, 5 pls., 8 tables.
    1970B   Two new upper Miocene giraffids from Fort Ternan, Kenya, East Africa: Palaeotragus primaevus n. sp. and Samotherium africanum n. sp. In: Leakey, L. S. B., and Savage, R. J. G. (eds.), 1970A, 1—105, 89 figs., 3 pls., 24 tables.
        Rev.: Thenius in Zentralbl. Geol. Paläontol., Teil 2, 1971:4, 341—342.
    1972A   Return to Africa. Rotunda, 5:3, 40—44, illustr.
    1972B   Imperial mammoth and Mexican half-ass from near Bindloss, Alberta. Can. J. Earth Sci., 9:11, 1562—1567, 1 fig., 3 tables.
    1972C   Late Pleistocene vertebrates from archaeological sites in the plain of Kom Ombo, upper Egypt. Toronto, Roy. Ont. Mus., Life Sci., Contrib., 82, 172 pp., 44 figs., 5 tables (French summary).

CHURCHER, C. S. and SMITH, P. E. L.
1972A   Kom Ombo: Preliminary report on the fauna of late Paleolithic sites in upper Egypt. Science (AAAS) 177:4045, 259–261, 1 fig., 1 table.

CHURCHER, C. S. and STALKER, A. MAC S.
1970A   A late, postglacial horse from Pashley, Alberta. Can. J. Earth Sci., 7:3, 1020–1026, 3 figs., 2 tables.

CHURCHER, C. S.   See also: Stalker, A. Mac S. and Churcher, C. S., 1972A.

CHURILOVA, EMILIĨA VASIL'EVNA   See: Zhizhchenko, B. P., Serezhenko, V. A. and Churilova, E. V., 1968.

CICHA, IVAN
1970A   Stratigraphical problems of the Miocene in Europe. Czech., Ustřed. Ústav. Geol., Roz., 35, 134 pp., 10 figs., 12 pls., 16 tables (Czech summary).

CICHA, I., FAHLBUSCH, V. and FEJFAR, O.
1972A   Die biostratigraphische Korrelation einiger jungtertiärer Wirbeltierfaunen Mitteleuropas. Neues Jahrb. Geol. Paläontol., Abh., 140:2, 129–145, 2 tables (German; English summary).

CICHA, I., SENEŠ, J. and TEJKAL, J., et al.
1967A   Chronostratigraphie und Neostratotypen, Miozän der zentralen Paratethys; Bd. I, M₃ (Karpatien). Die Karpatische Serie und ihr Stratotypus. Bratislava: Vydavatel'stvo Slovenskej Akadémie Vied, 312 pp., illustr., maps (German).

CIESARIK, MILAN
1970A   *Emys orbicularis* (L.) from the limnoquartzites of the Žiar depression. Geol. Práce, Zpr., 53, 167–172 1 fig.

CIOBANU, M.
1969A   Date noi asupra peştilor fosili din Oligocenul de la Piatra-Neamţ. [New data on fossil fishes from the Oligocene of Piatra-Neamţ.] Rom., Inst. Geol., Dări, 54:2, 47–85, 2 figs., 5 pls., 7 tables (Rumanian; French and English summaries).

ČIŽEK, F. and HODÁNOVÁ, D.
1971A   Evolution als Selbstregulation. Jena: Gustav Fischer Verlag, 316 pp., 21 figs., 3 tables (German). Rev.: Reinig in Kosmos, 68:6, 195.

CLAIR, ANDRÉ and PUISSÉGUR, JEAN-JACQUES
1969A   Découverte de faunes villafranchiennes entre la vallée de la Saône et Dijon (Côte-d'Or). Acad. Sci., C.R., Sér. D, 268:25, 3033–3035, 1 fig. (French).

CLAIR, ANDRÉ   See also: Chaline, J., Clair, A. and Puisségur, J.-J., 1970A.

CLARK, GRAHAME
1969A   World prehistory: a new outline. Cambridge: University Press, xvi + 331 pp., 16 pls., 10 maps. Rev.: Fritz in Amer. Antiquity, 36:4, 485–486; Mulvaney in Antiqutiy, 43:171, 237–239; Piggott in Antiquaries J., 50:1, 105; Pittioni in Archaeol. Austriaca, 46, 120; Ruttkay in Anthropol. Ges., Mitt., 100, 441–442; Trigger in Man (J. Roy. Anthropol. Inst.), 4:3, 465–466.
1970A   Aspects of prehistory. Berkeley: University of California Press, xiii + 161 pp., 23 figs., 4 pls. Rev.: Hencken in Antiquity, 45:180, 306–307.

CLARK, G. and PIGGOTT, S.
1965   Rev.: Bosch-Gimpera in An. Antropol., Mexico, 4, 226–230.

CLARK, GRAHAME   See also: Howell, F. C., Turnbull, C., Sharp, L., Clark, J. G. D. and DeVore, I., 1968A.

CLARK, JANET K.
1969A*   Bibliography of vertebrate paleontology and related subjects. 1967–1968. Soc. Vert. Paleontol., Bibliogr., 23, 101 pp.

CLARK, JOHN
1968A   Cymaprimadontidae, a new family of insectivores. Fieldiana: Geol., 16:8, 241–254, 6 figs., 1 table.
1969A   Treasures in the attic. Chicago, Field Mus. Natur. Hist., Bull., 40:7, 10–11, 4 figs.

CLARK, JOHN and GUENSBURG, THOMAS E.
1970A   Population dynamics of *Leptomeryx*. Fieldiana: Geol., 16:16, 411–451, 13 figs., 4 tables.
1972A   Arctoid genetic characters as related to the genus *Parictis*. Fieldiana: Geol., 26:1, 1–71, 17 figs., 6 tables, appendix.

CLARK, JOHN DESMOND
1964D   Acheulian occupation sites in Syria and Africa: a study in cultural variability. Amer. Anthropol. Ass.,
        Abstr., 1964, 12 (abs.).
1967A   Rev.: Anon. in Biologist, 51:1, 40; Jelinek in Amer. J. Phys. Anthropol., 33:1, 115—116; Lippert in
        Anthropol. Ges., Mitt., 99, 243.
1967D   The middle Acheulian occupation site at Latamne, northern Syria (first paper). Quaternaria, 9, 1—68,
        13 figs., 25 pls., 6 tables (German and French summaries).
1968A   Studies of hunter-gatherers as an aid to the interpretation of prehistoric societies. In: Lee, R. B., and
        DeVore, I. (eds.), 1968A, 276—280.
1968B   The middle Acheulian occupation site at Latamne, northern Syria (second paper). Further excavations:
        general results, definition and interpretation. With contributions by J. de Heinzelin and A. van
        Dusen Eggers. Quaternaria, 10, 1—60, 24 figs., 9 pls., 8 tables (French and German summaries).
1968C   New field investigations in the Malawi rift, south central Africa. Amer. Anthropol. Ass., Bull., 1:3,
        23 (abs.).
1970A   The prehistory of Africa. London: Thames and Hudson, 302 pp., 62 figs., 48 pls., 10 maps.
        Rev.: Fagan in Antiquity, 45:177, 72—73.
1970B   The prehistoric origins of African culture. In: Fage, J. D. and Oliver, R. A. (eds.), 1970A, 1—23,
        8 figs.

CLARK, J. D., BROTHWELL, D. R., POWERS, R. and OAKLEY, K. P.
1968A   Rhodesian man: notes on a new lemur fragment. Man (J. Roy. Anthropol. Inst.), 3, 105—111, 2 figs.,
        2 tables.

CLARK, J. D. and HAYNES, C. VANCE, JR.
1970A   An elephant butchery site at Mwanganda's Village, Karonga, Malawi, and its relevance for Palaeolithic
        archaeology. World Archaeol., 1:3, 390—411, 11 figs., 4 pls., 1 table.

CLARK, ROBERT E. D.
1968A   The origin of life. Faith and Thought, 97:2, 35—40.

CLARK, RONALD W.
1968A   The Huxleys. New York: McGraw-Hill Book Co., 398 pp.
        Rev.: Hatch in Biologist, 51:3, 120.

CLARK, WILFRID E. LE GROS
1967B   Rev.: Ashton in New Sci., 34:548, 607; Roth-Lutra in Anthropos, 62:3—4, 594-595.
1968A   Rev.: Day in Man (J. Roy. Anthropol. Inst.), 4:1, 168; Gurley in BioScience, 20:12, 729.
1969A   The crucial evidence for human evolution. In: Ehrlich, P. R., et al. (eds.), 1969A, 482—495, 1 fig.
1971A   The antecedents of man. Third edition. Edinburgh: University Press; Chicago: Quadrangle Books,
        ix + 394 pp., 152 figs.
        Rev.: Roth-Lutra in Anat. Anz., 131:3—4, 343—344.
1971B   Observations on the anatomy of the fossil Australopithecinae. In: Leakey, L. S. B., Prost, J. and
        Prost, S. (eds.), 1971A, 293—314, 13 figs. (reprinted from J. Anat., 81:3, 1947).
1972A   History of the primates. Tenth edition. London: British Museum (Natural History), 127 pp.,
        frontispiece, 45 figs.

CLARKE, R. J. and HOWELL, F. CLARK
1972A   Affinities of the Swartkrans 847 hominid cranium. Amer. J. Phys. Anthropol., 37:3, 319—336, 4 figs.,
        1 table.

CLARKE, R. J.   See also: Leakey, M. D., Clarke, R. J. and Leakey, L. S. B., 1971A.

CLASON, A. T.
1968A   The subfossil bones from Bunde reconsidered. Natuurhist. Genoot. Limburg, Publ., 18:3—4, 50—51,
        2 figs.

CLEGG, E. J.
1968A   The study of man. An introduction to human biology. London: The English Universities Press;
        New York: American Elsevier Pub. Co., viii + 212 pp., 51 figs., 27 tables.
        Rev.: Day in Man (J. Roy. Anthropol. Inst.), 3, 661; Fry in Human Biol., 43:1, 179—181; Roth-Lutra
        in Anat. Anz., 128:5, 503—504; Schwidetzky in Homo, 20:3, 197; Straus in Amer. Sci., 57:1,
        76A; Tyagi in E. Anthropol., 22:2, 262—263.

CLELAND, CHARLES   See: Brown, J. and Cleland, C., 1968A.

CLEM, RICHARD   See: Scott, W. F. and Clem, R., 1967A.

CLEMENS, WILLIAM A., JR.
    1966A   Rev.: J. C. in Austral. Mammal Soc., Bull., 2:5, 134.
    1970A   Mesozoic mammalian evolution. Ann. Rev. Écol. Syst., 1, 357–390, 10 figs.
    1970B   Mammalian evolution in the Cretaceous. Linn. Soc., Biol. J., 2:4, 321 (abs.).
    1971A   Mesozoic evolution of mammals with tribosphenic dentitions. In: Dahlberg, A. A. (ed.), 1971A,
            181–192, 4 figs.
    1971B   Mammalian evolution in the Cretaceous. Linn. Soc., Zool. J., 50:suppl. 1, 165–180, 3 figs.
            Rev.: Krebs in Zentralbl. Geol. Paläontol., Teil 2, 1972:3, 174.

CLEMENS, W. A. and LEES, PATRICIA M.
    1971A   A review of English early Cretaceous mammals. Linn. Soc., Zool. J., 50:suppl. 1, 117–130, 1 fig.,
            5 pls.
            Rev.: Krebs in Zentralbl. Geol. Paläontol., Teil 2, 1972:3, 172.

CLEMENS, W. A. and MILLS, JAMES R. E.
    1971A   Review of *Peramus tenuirostris* Owen (Eupantotheria, Mammalia). Brit. Mus. (Natur. Hist.), Bull.,
            Geol., 20:3, 87–113, 3 figs., 4 pls.

CLERCQ, S. W. G. DE and HOLST, H. K. H.
    1971A   Footprints of birds and sedimentary structures from the subalpine molasse near Flühli (Canton of
            Luzern). Eclogae Geol. Helv., 64:1, 63–69, 7 figs.

CLERMONT, NORMAN
    1965A   L'hominisation de la mandibule. Anthropologica, 7:1, 13–26, 3 figs., 1 table (French).

CLEWLOW, C. WILLIAM, JR.   See: Heizer, R. F., Elsasser, A. B. and Clewlow, C. W., Jr., 1970A.

CLIMO, F. M. and BAKER, A. N.
    1972A   A new shark-toothed dolphin (Cetacea: Squalodontidae) from the upper Oligocene of New Zealand.
            Roy. Soc. N. Z., J., 2:1, 61–68, 2 figs., 3 tables.

CLOPINE, G.   See: DuBar, J. R. and Clopine, G., 1961A.

CLOT, ANDRÉ
    1970A   Note préliminaire sur la Grotte de la Carrière, à Gerde (Hautes-Pyrénées). Soc. Préhist. Fr., Bull.,
            Étud. Trav., 67:2, 427–434, 5 figs., 2 tables (French).

CLOTTES, J.
    1970A   In memoriam Louis Méroc (1904–1970). Préhist. Spéléol. Ariége., 25, 176 (French).
    1971A   La découverte d'une statuette féminine paléolithique à Monpazier (Dordogne). Préhist. Spéléol. Ariége
            26, 77–82, 3 pls. (French).

CLOTTES, J. and CÉROU, E.
    1970A   La statuette féminine de Monpazier (Dordogne). Soc. Préhist. Fr.. Bull., Étud. Trav., 67:2, 435–444,
            5 figs. (French; English summary).

CLOUD, PRESTON
    1970A*   Adventures in earth history. San Francisco: W. H. Freeman and Co.. xv + 992 pp., frontispiece, illust
            Rev.: B. W. T. in Calif. Geol., 24:6, 110; Laufeld in Geol. Fören. Stockholm, Förh., 94:1, 119–120;
            Ospovat in Isis, 63:1, 112–113; White in Science, 171:3977, 1234.

CLOUDSLEY-THOMPSON, J. L.
    1966A   Fossil site at Saqqai. Kush, 16, 328–330.

CLUTTON-BROCK, JULIET
    1970A   The fossil fauna from an upper Pleistocene site in Jordan. J. Zool., 162:1, 19–29, 5 figs., 2 tables.

CLUVER, M. A.
    1969A   *Zorillodontops*, a new scaloposaurid from the Karoo. S. Afr. Mus., Ann., 52:8, 183–188, 2 figs.
    1970A   The palate and mandible in some specimens of *Dicynodon testudirostris* Broom & Haughton
            (Reptilia, Therapsida). S. Afr. Mus., Ann., 56:4, 133–153, 12 figs.

COATES, D. R., LANDRY, S. O. and LIPE, W. D.
    1971A   Mastodon bone age and geomorphic relations in the Susquehanna valley. Geol. Soc. Amer., Bull., 82:7
            2005–2009, 2 figs.

COBBAN, WILLIAM A.   See: Gill, J. R. and Cobban, W. A., 1966A.

COCHRAN, WENDELL
    1972A   International Geological Congress. Geotimes, 17:10, 21- 22.

COE, MICHAEL D. and FLANNERY, KENT V.
    1966A   Microenvironments and Mesoamerica prehistory. In: Graham, J. A. (ed.), 1966A, 46—50, 3 figs.

COHEN, DANIEL M. and CRESSEY, ROGER F.
    1969A*   A symposium on natural history collections past, present, future. Biol. Soc. Wash., Proc., 82, 559—762,
               illustr.
    1969B*   Natural history collections, past-present-future. Washington: Biol. Society, 202 pp., 8 pls.
               Rev.: Stansfield in Mus. J., London, 70, 34.

COHEN, DAVID
    1969A   The age of giant mammals. New York: Dodd, Mead and Co., illustr. (juvenile).
               Rev.: Moore in Archaeology, 24:2, 177.

COHEN, YEHUDI A.
    1968A*   Man in adaptation. The biosocial background. Chicago: Aldine Publishing Co., xii + 386 pp.
               Rev.: Faulhaber in An. Antropol., Mexico, 6, 308—312; Hulse in Amer. J. Phys. Anthropol., 33:2,
               279—280.

COLBERT, EDWIN HARRIS
    1964F   El libro de los dinosaurios. Los reptiles dominantes y sus distintos parientes. Translated from English.
               Buenos Aires: Eudeba, 160 pp., illustr. (Spanish).
    1965H   Rev.: Dahlskog in Ymer, 1966, 246 (Swedish).
    1968A   Rev.: Charig in New Sci., 42:649, 372—373; Morrison in Sci. Amer., 220:1, 134.
    1968C   Later fossil reptiles. In: Moore, R. C., et al., 1968A, 1375.
    1969A   A Jurassic pterosaur from Cuba. Amer. Mus. Nov., 2370, 26 pp., 14 figs., 2 tables.
    1969B   Evolution of the horned dinosaurs. In: Ehrlich, P. R., et al. (eds.), 1969A, 314—332, 7 figs., 2 tables.
    1969C   Evolution of the vertebrates. A history of the backboned animals through time. Second edition.
               New York: John Wiley & Sons, Inc., 535 pp., 144 figs.
               Rev.: Charig in Naturwiss., 58:2, 107—108; Deflandre in Soc. Géol. Fr., C.R., 1970:1, 21; Fantini
               Sestini in Riv. Ital. Paleontol. Stratigr., 76:1, 182—183; Haltenorth in Säugetierkundl. Mitt.,
               18, 285; Lundelius in Quart. Rev. Biol., 45:2, 190; Montalenti in Scientia, 106:11—12, 1121;
               Olson in J. Geol., 79:1, 126—127; Russell in Earth-Sci. Rev., 7:1, A30; Thomson in Amer. Sci.,
               58:3, 338; White in Austral. J. Sci., 32:12, 484.
    1969D   Gondwanaland and the distribution of Triassic tetrapods. Symp. Gondwana Stratigr., 355—374,
               2 figs., 1 table (Spanish summary).
    1969E   Amphibian fossil. McGraw-Hill Yearbook Sci. Tech., 1969, 98—99, 2 figs.
    1970A   Antarctic Triassic tetrapods. Geol. Soc. Amer., Abstr., 2:7, 523 (abs.).
    1970B   What happened in Antarctica. Soc. Vert. Paleontol., News Bull., 89, 51—54.
    1970C   Arizona and Antarctica. Plateau, 42:4, 118—124, 4 figs.
    1970D   The Triassic gliding reptile Icarosaurus. Amer. Mus. Natur. Hist., Bull., 143:2, 142 pp., 46 figs.,
               3 tables.
    1970E   The fossil tetrapods of Coalsack Bluff. Antarctic J., 5:3, 57—61, illustr.
    1970F   A saurischian dinosaur from the Triassic of Brazil. Amer. Mus. Nov., 2405, 39 pp., 14 figs., 2 tables.
    1970G   Paleontological investigations at Coalsack Bluff. Antarctic J., 5:4, 86.
    1971A   Triassic tetrapods from McGregor Glacier. Antarctic J., 6:5, 188—189, 1 photo.
    1971B   Tetrapods and continents. Quart. Rev. Biol., 46:3, 250—269, 8 figs.
    1971C   Antarctic fossil vertebrates and Gondwanaland. In: Quam, L. O. (ed.), 1971A, 685—701, 7 figs.
    1972A   Antarctic fossils and the reconstruction of Gondwanaland. Natur. Hist., 81:1, 66—73, illustr.
    1972B   Present knowledge concerning Antarctic Triassic tetrapods. Soc. Vert. Paleontol., Ann. Meeting, 32nd,
               1972, Abstr. (abs.).
    1972C   Lystrosaurus and Gondwanaland. In: Dobzhansky, Th., Hecht, M. K. and Steere, W. C. (eds.), 1972B,
               157—177, 6 figs., 1 table.

COLBERT, E. H. and RUSSELL, DALE A.
    1969A   The small Cretaceous dinosaur Dromaeosaurus. Amer. Mus. Nov., 2380, 49 pp., 15 figs., 3 tables.

COLBERT, EDWIN H.   See also: Elliot, D. H., Colbert, E. H., Breed, W. J., Jensen, J. A. and Powell, J. S.,
               1970A; Kitching, J. W., Collinson, J. W., Elliot, D. H. and Colbert, E. H., 1972A.

COLE, GLEN H.   See: Howell, F. C., Cole, G. H., Kleindienst, M. R., Szabo, B. J. and Oakley, K. P., 1972A.

COLEMAN, ROBERT G.
    1951A   A recently discovered entelodont from the John Day Basin. Oreg. Acad. Sci., Proc., 2, 40.

COLES, JOHN M.
1968A   Ancient man in Europe. In: Coles, J. M. and Simpson, D. D. A. (eds.), 1968A, 17–43, 6 figs.

COLES, J. M. and HIGGS, E. S.
1969A   The archaeology of early man. London: Faber, 454 pp., 12 pls., 183 figs.
               Rev.: Binford in Amer. Anthropol., 73, 925–927; Clark in Antiquity, 44:174, 156–158; Dimbleby
               in New Sci., 44:670, 87; Grosjean in Soc. Préhist. Fr., Bull., C.R., 67:5, 133–134; Hillers in
               Amer. Sch. Orient. Res., Bull., 198, 45; Howell in Nature, 224:5217, 388; Roe in Prehist. Soc.
               Proc., 36, 386–388; Searle in Advan. Sci., 26:129, 329; Thomas in Archaeology, 25:4, 314;
               Trigger in Man (J. Roy. Anthropol. Inst.), 4:4, 654–655; Wendorf in Science, 170:3961, 963.

COLES, J. M. and SIMPSON, D. D. A.
1968A *   Studies in ancient Europe: essays presented to Stuart Piggott. Leicester University Press, 367 pp.,
               frontispiece, 77 figs., 16 pls., 4 tables.
               Rev.: Powell in Antiquity, 43:169, 82–83.

COLLESS, DONALD H.
1969A   The phylogenetic fallacy revisited. Syst. Zool., 18:1, 115–126.
1971A   "Phenetic," "phylogenetic," and "weighting." Syst. Zool., 20, 73–76.

COLLINGS, G. E.
1972A   A new species of machaerodont from Makapansgat. Palaeontol. Afr., 14, 87–92, 7 figs., 1 table.

COLLINS, DESMOND
1969A   Culture traditions and environment of early man. With comments and reply. Current Anthropol.,
               10:4, 267–316, 15 figs., 16 tables.

COLLINS, JANICE I.
1970A   The chelonian Rhinochelys Seeley from the upper Cretaceous of England and France. Palaeontology,
               13:3, 355–378, 16 figs., 3 pls., 3 tables.

COLLINSON, JAMES W.   See: Kitching, J. W., Collinson, J. W., Elliot, D. H. and Colbert, E. H., 1972A.

COMAS, JUAN
1966A   Rev.: Díaz Ungría in An. Antropol., Mexico, 4, 209–213.
1968A   Distinción al doctor P. Bosch-Gimpera. An. Antropol., Mexico, 5, 236 (Spanish).
1968B   El doctor Bosch-Gimpera en Europa. An. Antropol., Mexico, 5, 238–239 (Spanish).
1971A   Introducción a la prehistorica general. Second edition. México: Universidad Nacional Autonoma de
               México, 273 pp., illustr. (Spanish).
               Rev.: Anon. in Interamer., 18:5, 1; Bárcena in An. Antropol., Mexico, 9, 308–311.

COMAS, J., CASTILLO, H. DE and MÉNDEZ, B.
1971A   Biología humana y/o antropología física (resultados de una encuestra). Mexico, Univ. Nac., Cuad.
               Inst. Hist., Ser. Antropol., 24, 119 pp. (Spanish).
               Rev.: Anon. in Interamer., 18:4, 4; Gavan in Human Biol., 44:3, 583–584; Hiernaux in An. Antropol
               Mexico, 9, 281.

COMASCHI CARIA, IDA
1968A   Fossili marini e continentali del Quaternario della Sardegna. Congr. Intern. Stud. Sardi, X, Cagliari,
               1966–67, Atti, 141–229, 8 pls., 1 map (Italian).
1970A   Prima segnalazione di Scomberomorus (pesce teleosteo) nel Miocene della Sardegna. Cagliari, Univ.,
               Ist. Geol. Paleontol., Publ. (1968), 8, 4 pp., 2 pls. (Italian).
               Rev.: Robba in Riv. Ital. Paleontol. Stratigr., 77:1, 132.
1970B   Nuova segnalazione di resti di scimmia nel Quaternario della Sardegna. Cagliari, Univ., Ist. Geol.
               Paleontol., Publ. (1968–69), 8, 7 pp., 1 fig. (Italian).
               Rev.: Albanesi in Riv. Ital. Paleontol. Stratigr., 77:1, 133.

COMBÉMOREL, R., GUÉRIN, C. and MÉON-VILAIN, H.
1970A   Un nouveau gisement de vertébrés mio-pliocènes à Priay (Ain). Fr., Bur. Rech. Géol. Minières, Bull.
               (Sér. 2), Sect. 1, 1970:4, 33–47, 4 figs., 1 pl., 2 tables (French; English summary).

COMBIER, J., DROUOT, E. and HUCHARD, P.
1959A   Les grottes solutréennes à gravures pariétales du canyon inférieur de l'Ardèche. Soc. Préhist. Fr., Mém.
               (1958), 5, 61–117, 29 figs., 2 tables (French).

COMPTON, CARL B.
1969A   Paleoanthropology. Interamer., 16:8, 2.

CONKLIN, EDWIN G.
    1971A   A brief history of the American Philosophical Society. Amer. Phil. Soc., Yearb., 1970, 37—63.

CONNALLY, G. GORDON
    1970A   Caribou and Paleo-Indian in New York State: a presumed association. Amer. J. Sci., 269:3, 314—315.

CONOLLY, J. R., HALL, L. R. and ROSE, G.
    1969A   The geology of New South Wales. Southern and central highlands fold belt. Upper Devonian series. Geol. Soc. Austral., J., 16:1, 150—178, 7 figs., 5 tables.

CONROY, GLENN C. and FLEAGLE, JOHN G.
    1972A   Locomotor behaviour in living and fossil pongids. Nature, 237:5350, 103—104.

COOK, SHERBURNE F.   See: Heizer, R. F. and Cook, S. F., 1966A.

COOKE, H. B. S.
    1966A   Pleistocene mammal faunas of Africa, with particular reference to southern Africa. In: Howell, F. C. and Bourliere, F. (eds.), 1966A, 65—116, 6 figs., 8 tables.
            Rev.: Maier in Z. Säugetierkunde, 36:2, 124.
    1968B   Preservation of the Sterkfontein ape-man cave site, South Africa. Stud. Speleol., 2:1, 25—34, 3 figs., 3 pls.
    1972A   Pleistocene chronology: long or short? Marit. Sediments, 8:1, 1—12, 3 tables.
    1972B   The fossil mammal fauna of Africa. In: Keast, A., Erk, F. C. and Glass, B. (eds.), 1972A, 89—139, 17 figs., 2 tables.

COOKE, H. B. S. and CORYNDON, S. C.
    1970A   Pleistocene mammals from the Kaiso formation and other related deposits in Uganda. In: Leakey, L. S. B. and Savage, R. J. G. (eds.), 1970A, 107—224, 17 figs., 18 pls., 46 tables.
            Rev.: Thenius in Zentralbl. Geol. Paläontol., Teil 2, 1971:4, 337—338.

COOKE, H. B. S. and EWER, R. F.
    1972A   Fossil Suidae from Kanapoi and Lothagam, northwestern Kenya. Harvard Univ., Mus. Comp. Zool., Bull., 143:3, 295 pp., 21 figs., 30 pls., 59 tables.

COOKE, H. B. S. and MAGLIO, V. J.
    1972A   Plio-Pleistocene stratigraphy in East Africa in relation to proboscidean and suid evolution. In: Bishop, W. W. and Miller, J. A. (eds.), 1972A, 303—329, 8 figs., 2 tables.

COOLEY, M. E.   See: Repenning, C. A., Cooley, M. E. and Akers, J. P., 1969A.

COOMBS, MARGERY CHALIFOUX
    1971A   Status of Simidectes (Insectivora, Pantolestoidea) of the late Eocene of North America. Amer. Mus. Nov., 2455, 41 pp., 14 figs., 5 tables.

COOMBS, WALTER P., JR.
    1971A   The Ankylosauria. Diss. Abstr., 32:6, 3542B (abs.).
    1972A   The bony eyelid of Euoplocephalus (Reptilia, Ornithischia). J. Paleontol., 46:5, 637—650, 10 figs., 3 pls.

COON, CARLETON S.
    1962B   Rev.: Chaplin in London Univ., Inst. Archaeol., Bull., 5, 91.
    1966A   The taxonomy of human variation. N.Y. Acad. Sci., Ann., 134:2, 516—523, 2 figs.
    1968A   The taxonomy of human variation. In: Genovés Tarazaga, S., et al. (eds.), 1968A, 61—69, 2 figs. (reprinted from N.Y. Acad. Sci., Ann., 1966).
    1972A   New findings on the origin of races. In: McCown, T. D. and Kennedy, K. A. R. (eds.), 1972A, 360—371 (reprinted from Harper's Mag., Dec., 1962).

COON, C. S. and HUNT, E. E.
    1965   Rev.: Sauter in An. Antropol., Mexico, 4, 213—216.

COORAY, P. G.
    1967A   An introduction to the geology of Ceylon. Spolia Zeylanica, 31:1, xxiii + 324 pp., 102 figs., 39 pls., 22 tables.

COPE, E. D.
    1870Y   Verbal communication on pythonomorphs. Amer. Phil. Soc., Proc., 11, 571—572.

1885FG   Marsh on American Jurassic Dinosauria, Part VIII. Amer. Natur., <u>19</u>, 67–68.

COPE, J. C. W.
1971A   A Bathonian crocodile new to Dorset. Dorset Natur. Hist. Archaeol. Soc., Proc., <u>92</u>, 43–44.
1972A   Geology. Dorset Natur. Hist. Archaeol. Soc., Proc., <u>93</u>, 38–40.

COPELAND, L.   See: Besançon, J., Copeland, L. and Hours, F., 1970A.

COPPENS, YVES
1965E   Les éléphants du Quaternaire français. Dentition, systématique, signification en préhistoire. Congr. Préhist. France, 16ᵉ Sess., Monaco 1959, C.R., 403–431, 10 figs., 2 charts (French).
1966B   Le point des connaissances en Paléontologie humaine. Soc. Préhist. Franç., Bull., Étud. Trav., <u>63</u>:3, 475–484, 1 table (French).
    Abs.: Anon. In Anthropos, <u>62</u>:3–4, 563.
1966C   Rev.: Knussmann in Homo, <u>19</u>:1, 49.
1970A   Les restes d'Hominidés des séries inférieures et moyennes des formations plio-villafranchiennes de l'Omo en Ethiopie. Acad. Sci., C.R., Sér. D, <u>271</u>:25, 2286–2289, 3 pls. (French).
1970B   Localisation dans le temps et dans l'espace des restes d'hominidés des formations plio-pleistocènes de l'Omo (Ethiopie). Acad. Sci., C.R., Sér. D, <u>271</u>:22, 1968–1971, 2 maps, 2 charts (French).
1971A   Une nouvelle espèce de suidé du Villafranchien de Tunisie, *Nyanzachoerus jaegeri* nov. sp. Acad. Sci., C.R., Sér. D, <u>272</u>:26, 3264–3267, 2 pls. (French).
1971B   Les vertébrés villafranchiens de Tunisie: gisements nouveaux, signification. Acad. Sci., C.R., Sér. D, <u>273</u>:1, 51–54, 3 pls. (French).
1971C   Les restes d'Hominidés des séries supérieures des formations plio-villafranchiennes de l'Omo en Ethiopie. Acad. Sci., C.R., Sér. D, <u>272</u>:1, 36–39, 1 pl. (French).
1972A   Tentative de zonation du Pliocène et du Pleistocène d'Afrique par les grands mammifères. Acad. Sci., C.R., Sér. D, <u>274</u>:2, 181–184, 2 pls. (French).
1972B   Un nouveau proboscidien du Pliocène du Tchad, *Stegodibelodon schneideri* nov. gen. nov. sp., et le phylum des Stegotetrabelodontinae. Acad. Sci., C.R., Sér. D, <u>274</u>:22, 2962–2965, 2 pls. (French).

COPPENS, Y., GOUZES, R., LE FLOCH, R. and PAQUET, M.
s.d.   Découverte d'un gisement de vertébrés fossiles avec industrie acheuléenne près de Zouérat en Mauritanie. Congr. Panafr. Préhist., 6me, Dakar, Actes (French).

COPPENS, YVES   See also: Arambourg, C., Chavaillon, J. and Coppens, Y., 1969A; Bonnefille, R., Chavaillon, J. and Coppens, Y., 1970A; Servant, M., Ergenzinger, P. and Coppens, Y., 1969A; Taieb, M., Coppens, Y., Johanson, D. C. and Kalb, J., 1972A.

CORDY, J.-M.
1972A   Étude de la variabilité des crânes d'ours des cavernes de la collection Schmerling. Ann. Paléontol., Vertébrés, <u>58</u>:2, 151–207, 16 figs., 11 tables (French; English summary).

CORNWALL, IAN W.
1964A   Rev.: Parkington in S. Afr. Archaeol. Bull., <u>24</u>:94, 70.
1968A   Rev.: Butzer in Amer. Anthropol., <u>72</u>:4, 933; Fagg in New Sci., <u>41</u>:632, 144; Hemmer in Homo, <u>20</u>:4, 262; Hendey in S. Afr. Archaeol. Bull., <u>26</u>:101–102, 84.
1970A   Ice ages. Their nature and effects. London: John Baker; New York: Humanities, 180 pp., illustr.
    Rev.: West in Nature, <u>228</u>:5272, 690.
1971A   Geology and early man in central Mexico. Geol. Ass. (London), Proc., <u>82</u>:3, 379–391, 4 figs.

CORRAIN, CLETO and CAPITANO, MARIANTONIA
1969A   Recherches sur la substance organique d'os humains antiques. La composition, en amino-acides, du collagène. Int. Congr. Anthropol. Ethnol. Sci., 8th, Tokyo, 1968, Proc., Vol. I. Anthropology, 112–113, 1 table (French).

CORRENTI, VENERANDO
1967A   Risultati di uno studio perigrafico sui crani di S. Teodoro (Sicilia). Riv. Antropol., <u>54</u>, 5–22, 11 figs., 1 pl. (Italian; English summary).

CORRO, GUILLERMO DEL
1966A   Un nuevo dinosáurio carnívoro del Chubut (Argentina). Mus. Argent. Cienc. Natur. "Bernardino Rivadavia", Comun., Paleontol., <u>1</u>:1, 4 pp., 1 pl. (Spanish).
1968A   La presencia de *"Madtsoia"* Simpson (Boidae) en el Eoceno de Patagonia y en el Cretácico de Madagascar y algunos ejemplos de distribución disyunta. Mus. Argent. Cienc. Natur. "Bernardino Rivadavia", Comun., Paleontol., <u>1</u>:3, 21–26 (Spanish).

1971A   Nueva contribución al conocimiento de la biota gondwánica fósil. Mus. Argent. Cienc. Natur.
         "Bernardino Rivadavia", Comun., Paleontol., 1:4, 27—35 (Spanish).

CORVALÁN, J.   See: Casamiquela, R. M., Corvalán, J. and Franquesa, F., 1969A.

CORVINUS, GUDRUN K.
1968-69A   Stratigraphy and geological background of an Acheulean site at Chirki-on-Pravara, India. Anthropos,
            63/64:5/6, 921—940, 4 figs., 1 pl., 3 tables.

CORYNDON, SHIRLEY C.
1970A   The extent of variation in fossil *Hippopotamus* from Africa. In: Berry, R. J., and Southern, H. N.
         (eds.), 1970A, 135—147, 7 figs.

CORYNDON, S. C., GENTRY, A. W., HARRIS, J. M., HOOIJER, D. A., MAGLIO, V. J. and HOWELL, F. C.
1972A   Mammalian remains from the Isimila prehistoric site, Tanzania. Nature, 237:5353, 292.

CORYNDON, S. C. and SAVAGE, R. J. G.
1972A   The origin and affinities of African mammal faunas. In: Hughes, N. F. (ed.), 1972A, illustr.

CORYNDON, S. C.   See also: Cooke, H. B. S. and Coryndon, S. C., 1970A.

COSGRIFF, JOHN W., JR.
1967B   Triassic vertebrates from Western Australia. Diss. Abstr., 27:8, 2743—B (abs.).
1969A   *Blinasaurus*, a brachyopid genus from Western Australia and New South Wales. Roy. Soc. West
         Austral., J., 52:3, 65—88, 11 figs., 2 tables.
1972A   *Parotosaurus wadei*, a new capitosaurid from New South Wales. J. Paleontol., 46:4, 545—555, 2 figs.,
         2 tbls., 1 pl.

COSMOVICI, N. L., ŞOVA, C. and TĂRĂBUŢĂ, C.
1964A   Cuiburi fosilifere in jurul oraşului Piatra Neamt. [Fossil localities in the neighborhood of Piatra Neamt.]
         Natura, Ser. Biol., 16:5, 80—83, 6 figs. (Rumanian).

COUCHARD, J.
1963A   Le gisement paléontologique de La Fage à Noailles (Corrèze). Les Eyzies, 12, 48—50 (French).

COULONGES, L.
1963A   Vues sur la préhistoire. Les Eyzies, 12, 51—57 (French).

COUNCIL FOR BRITISH ARCHAEOLOGY and LUCAS, A. T.
1964A*   COWA surveys and bibliographies. British Isles. COWA Surv. and Bibliog., Area 1, 3, 21 pp.

COUPATEZ, P.   See: Plisnier-Ladame, F. and Coupatez, P., 1969A; Quinet, G. E., Coupatez, P. and Wouters, G.,
               1970A; Quinet, G. E., Verlinden, W. and Coupatez, P., 1971A.

COUREL, L., DEMATHIEU, G. and BUFFARD, R.
1968A   Empreintes de pas de Vertébrés et stratigraphie du Trias. Soc. Géol. Fr., Bull., 10:3, 275—281, 1 pl.,
         1 table (French).
1968B   Empreintes de pas de reptiles et stratigraphie du Trias. Soc. Géol. Fr., C.R., 1968:5, 142 (French).

COVACEVICH C., VLADIMIR and LAMPEREIN R., CARLOS
1969A   Nota sobre el hallazgo de icnitas fósiles de aves en Península Fildes, Isla Rey Jorge, Shetland del Sur,
         Antártica. Inst. Antárt. Chileno, Bol., 4, 26—28 (Spanish).
1970A   Hallazgo de icnitas en península Fildes, Isla Rey Jorge, Archipiélago Shetland del Sur, Antártica.
         INACH, Ser. Cient., 1:1, 55—74, 8 figs., 3 pls. (Spanish; English summary).

COWAN, RICHARD S.
1966A   Paleobiology. Smithson. Year, 1966, 105—111.

COWGILL, GEORGE L.
1968A   Archaeological applications of factor, cluster, and proximity analysis. Amer. Antiquity, 33, 367—375.

COWLES, GRAHAM S.
1970A   The original description by H. O. Forbes of the extinct New Zealand musk duck *Biziura delautouri*.
         Brit. Ornithol. Club, Bull., 90:6, 166—168.

COX, ALLAN and DOELL, R. R.
1968A   Paleomagnetism and Quaternary correlation. In: Morrison, R. B., and Wright, H. E. (eds.), 1968A,
         253—265, 2 figs.

COX, C. BARRY

1968A   The Chañares (Argentina) Triassic reptile fauna. IV. The dicynodont fauna. Breviora, 295, 27 pp., 12 figs.

1969A   Two new dicynodonts from the Triassic Ntawere formation, Zambia. Brit. Mus. (Natur. Hist.), Bull., Geol., 17:6, 257–294, 23 figs., 1 table.

1969B   The problematic Permian reptile Eunotosaurus. Brit. Mus. (Natur. Hist.), Bull., Geol., 18:5, 167–196, 13 figs., 1 pl., 3 tables.

1969C   Prehistoric animals. London: Hamlyn; Melbourne: Sunbooks (Hamlyn all-colour paperbacks), 160 pp illustr.

    Rev.: Tooze in Nature, 224:5216, 293–294.

1970A   Migrating marsupials and drifting continents. Nature, 226:5247, 767–770, 2 figs.

1972A   A new digging dicynodont from the upper Permian of Tanzania. In: Joysey, K. A. and Kemp, T. S. (eds.), 1972A, 173–189, 8 figs.

1972B   Systematics and plate tectonics in the spread of marsupials. In: Hughes, N. F. (ed.), 1972A, illustr.

1972C   Triassic tetrapods. In: Hallam, A. (ed.), 1972C, illustr.

CRACRAFT, JOEL

1968B   A review of the Bathornithidae (Aves, Gruiformes) with remarks on the relationship of the suborder Cariamae. Amer. Mus. Nov., 2326, 1–46, 14 figs.

1968C   Reallocation of the Eocene fossil Palaeophasianus meleagroides Shufeldt. Wilson Bull., 80, 281–285, 1 fig.

1969A   Systematics and evolution of the Gruiformes (Class Aves). 1. The Eocene family Geranoididae and the early history of the Gruiformes. Amer. Mus. Nov., no. 2388, 1–41, 11 figs., 7 tables.

    Rev.: Kuhn in Zentralbl. Geol. Paläontol., Teil 2, 1970:3/4, 233.

1969B   Notes on fossil hawks (Accipitridae). Auk, 86:2, 353–354.

1970A   Mandible of Archaeopteryx provides an example of mosaic evolution. Nature, 226:5252, 1268, 1 fig.

1971A   Systematics and evolution of the Gruiformes (Class Aves). 2. Additional comments on the Bathornithidae, with descriptions of new species. Amer. Mus. Nov., 2449, 14 pp., 6 figs.

1971B   Caenagnathiformes: Cretaceous birds convergent in jaw mechanism to dicynodont reptiles. J. Paleontol. 45:5, 805–809, 2 figs., 1 pl., 1 table.

1971C   The role of continental drift in the biogeography of birds. Geol. Soc. Amer., Abstr., 3:7, 532 (abs.).

1972A   A new Cretaceous charadriiform family. Auk, 89:1, 36–46, 3 figs., 2 tables.

1972B   Continental drift and Australian avian biogeography. Emu, 72:4, 171–174.

CRACRAFT, JOEL and RICH, PAT VICKERS

1972A   The systematics and evolution of the Cathartidae in the Old World Tertiary. Condor, 74:3, 272–283, 10 figs., 4 tables.

CRAIN, IAN K.

1971A   Possible direct causal relation between geomagnetic reversals and biological extinctions. Geol. Soc. Amer., Bull., 82:9, 2603–2606, 1 fig.

CRANDELL, D. R.   See: Birkeland, P. W., Crandell, D. R. and Richmond, G. M., 1971A.

CRANE, J. M.

1966   Rev.: Weiler in Zentralbl. Geol. Paläontol., Teil 2, 1971:5, 399.

CRAWFORD, MICHAEL H.

1970A   Trends in genetics and biological anthropology. In: Siegel, B. J. (ed.), 1970A, 191–251.

CREMONESI, GIULIANO   See: Cannarella, D. and Cremonesi, G., 1967A.

CRESSEY, ROGER F.   See: Cohen, D. M. and Cressey, R. F. (eds.), 1969A.

CRESSMAN, LUTHER S.   See: Bedwell, S. F. and Cressman, L. S., 1971A; Packard, E. L., Allison, I. S. and Cressman, L. S., 1951A.

CROCHET, JEAN-YVES

1969A   Révision du genre Peratherium Aymard 1849 (Marsupialia). Acad. Sci., C.R., Sér. D, 268:16, 2038–2041, 2 figs., 2 tables (French).

1971A   Les vertébrés de l'Oligocène supérieur du Pech du Fraysse, poche à phosphate du Quercy (commune de Saint-Projet, Tarn-et-Garonne). Soc. Géol. Fr., C.R., 1971:6, 316–317, 1 fig. (French).

CROCHET, JEAN-YVES and HEINTZ, EMILE

1970A   Insectivora (Mammalia) de la faune villafranchienne de la Puebla de Valverde (Prov. Teruel. Espagne). Mus. Nat. Hist. Natur., Paris, Bull., 42:4, 776–779, 1 pl., 1 table (French).

CROCKETT, CHARLES T.
1970A   Department of paleontology: vertebrate paleontology. Denver Mus. Natur. Hist., Ann. Rep., 1969,
               24—25, illustr.
1970B   Department of paleontology: vertebrate paleontology. Denver Mus. Natur. Hist., Ann. Rep., 1970,
               43—44.

CROIZAT, LÉON
1958   Rev.: Kiriakoff in Natuurwet. Tijdschr., 41:2—3, 100—101.

CROMPTON, ALFRED WALTER
1968A   In search of the "insignificant." Discovery, Yale, 3:2, 23—32, 21 figs.
1968B   Studying function by X-ray. Discovery, Yale, 3:2, 50—51, 1 fig.
1969A   The late Triassic terrestrial fauna of southern Africa. (Abstract). Symp. Gondwana Stratigr., 331—332
               (English and Spanish).
1970A   Continental drift and a strange fossil reptile. Discovery, Yale, 5:2, 105—108, 4 figs.
1970B   The relationship between form and function in the molars of therian mammals of the Mesozoic. Linn.
               Soc., Biol. J., 2:4, 318—319 (abs.).
1971A   The origin of the tribosphenic molar. Linn. Soc., Zool. J., 50:suppl. 1, 65—87, 8 figs.
               Rev.: Krebs in Zentralbl. Geol. Paläontol., Teil 2, 1972:3, 170—171.
1972A   The evolution of the jaw articulation of cynodonts. In: Joysey, K. A. and Kemp, T. S. (eds.), 1972A,
               231—251, 10 figs., 4 pls.

CROMPTON, A. W. and HIIEMÄE, KAREN
1969A   How mammalian molar teeth work. Discovery, Yale, 5, 23—34, 9 figs.
               Rev.: Thenius in Zentralbl. Geol. Paläontol., Teil 2, 1971:1, 61.

CROMPTON, A. W. and JENKINS, F. A.
1968A   Rev.: Krebs in Zentralbl. Geol. Paläontol., Teil 2, 1970:1, 71—73.

CROMPTON, A. W.   See also: Hopson, J. A. and Crompton, A. W., 1969A.

CROSS, FRANK B.
1970A   Fishes as indicators of Pleistocene and Recent environments in the central plains. In: Dort, W., Jr.
               and Jones, J. K., Jr. (eds.), 1970A, 241—257, 9 figs., 1 table.

CROSSMAN, E. J. and HARINGTON, C. R.
1970A   Pleistocene pike, Esox lucius, and Esox sp., from the Yukon Territory and Ontario. Can. J. Earth Sci.,
               7:4, 1130—1138, 5 figs., 1 table.

CROUZEL, FERNAND
1971A   Essai sur la dynamique d'une population fossile: les cervidés de Sansan (Miocène du Gers). Soc. Géol.
               Fr., C.R., 1971:2, 111 (French).
1971B   Sur un Testudo canetotiana du gisement de Sansan (Gers) (Helvétien moyen). Soc. Hist. Natur.
               Toulouse, Bull., 107:3—4, 534—539, 1 fig. (French).
1972A   Sédimentologie et paléoécologie du Miocène continental aquitain (France). Int. Geol. Congr., 24th,
               Canada, Proc., Sec. 7, 496—502 (French).

CROUZEL, FERNAND and BAUDELOT, SABINE
1970A   Deux gisements fossilifères Helvétiens de la région de Lombez (Gers). Soc. Hist. Natur. Toulouse, Bull.,
               106, 459—462 (French).

CROUZEL, FERNAND and VIALLARD, PIERRE
1968A   Sur un nouveau gisement de mammifères fossiles dans la province de Cuenca (Chaîne ibérique, Espagne).
               Soc. Géol. Fr., C.R., 1968:1, 14—15 (French).
               Rev.: H.-P. in Soc. Españ. Hist. Natur., Bol., Secc. Geol., 66:2, 188.

CROUZEL, FERNAND   See also: Baudelot, S. and Crouzel, F., 1969A; Bergounioux, F. M. and Crouzel, F.,
               1964B, 1968A, 1968B, 1970A, 1971A.

CROZIER, E. A.
1970A   Preliminary report on two Triassic dicynodonts from Zambia. Palaeontol. Afr., 13, 39—45, 11 figs.

CRUICKSHANK, A. R. I.
1970A   Taxonomy of the Triassic anomodont genus Kannemeyeria. Palaeontol. Afr., 13, 47—55, 4 figs.,
               1 table.
1972A   The proterosuchian thecodonts. In: Joysey, K. A. and Kemp, T. S. (eds.), 1972A, 89—119, 10 figs.,
               1 pl., 4 figs.

1972B   A note on the genus *Proplacerias*. Palaeontol. Afr., 14, 17.

CRUSAFONT PAIRÓ, MIGUEL (= CRUSAFONT, M.)
1960A   Le Quaternaire espagnol et sa faune de mammifères — essai de synthèse. Anthropos, Brno, 1960
                 suppl., 55—64, 3 figs. (French; Russian summary).
1962E   — Algunos principios teóricos derivados del estudio masterométrico. Discussions. Soc. Españ. Hist.
                 Natur., Bol., Secc. Biol., 60, 167—176, 3 figs. (Spanish).
1963C   Perspectivas de la biocenótica en paleontología. Soc. Españ. Hist. Natur., Bol. Secc. Biol., 61, 149—15¶
                 5 figs. (Spanish).
1965D   Rev.: Adrover in Teruel, 35, 168—169.
1965Q   La teoria de la información en la evolución biológica. Col-Pa (Madrid, Univ., Fac. Cienc.), 1965:2
                 (Spanish).
1965R   Singularidad del *phylum* homínido, singularidad del hombre. Col-Pa (Madrid, Univ., Fac. Cienc.),
                 1965:6 (Spanish).
1967C   Bioquímica, paleobioquímica y evolución. Col-Pa (Madrid, Univ., Fac. Cienc.), 1967:11, 3—4 (Spanish)
1969A   Sobre la edad del yacimiento de mamíferos fósiles de Buñol (Valencia). Acta Geol. Hisp., 4:3, 64—66
                 (Spanish; French summary).
                 Rev.: H.-P. in Soc. Españ. Hist. Natur., Bol., Secc. Geol., 69:1, 126.
1970A   Observaciones a unos trabajos sobre fauna cuaternaria de Mallorca. Acta Geol. Hisp., 5:3, 67—69
                 (Spanish; French summary).
                 Rev.: H.-P. in Soc. Españ. Hist. Natur., Bol., Secc. Geol., 69:2, 206.
1971A   El conjunto "Pontiense" de mamíferos de España y su significación ecológica y paleobiológica.
                 Barcelona (Prov.), Inst. Prov. Paleontol., Paleontol. Evol., 3, 2—9 (Spanish).
1971B   Campañas de excavaciones paleontológicas en Túnez. Barcelona (Prov.), Inst. Prov. Paleontol.,
                 Paleontol. Evol., 3, 50—53 (Spanish).
1971C   Evolución: ¿ azar o direccionismo? Barcelona (Prov.), Inst. Prov. Paleontol., Bol. Inform., 3:4—5.
                 I—IV (Spanish).
1971D   Estado actual de los estudios paleomastológicos en España. Acad. Cienc. Art. Barcelona, Mem., 41:5,
                 139—159 (Spanish; English summary).
1972A   Les *Ischyrictis* de la transition Vindobonien-Vallésien. Palaeovertebrata (Montpellier), 5:5, 253—260,
                 1 fig., 1 pl. (French).
1972B   Rdo. P. Máximo Ruiz de Gaona Sch. P. Barcelona (Prov.), Inst. Prov. Paleontol., Bol. Inform., 4:1,
                 24—25 (Spanish).
1972C   William King Gregory. Barcelona (Prov.), Inst. Prov. Paleontol., Bol. Inform., 4:1, 26—27 (Spanish).
1972D   Josef Augusta. Barcelona (Prov.), Inst. Prov. Paleontol., Bol. Inform., 4:1, 27—28 (Spanish).
1972E   Paleontología y biología: análisis y síntesis. Barcelona (Prov.), Inst. Prov. Paleontol., Bol. Inform.,
                 4:2—3, I—V (Spanish).

CRUSAFONT PAIRÓ, M. and ADROVER, R.
1965A   El primer mamífero del Mesozoico español. Fossilia, 1965:5—6, 28—33, 1 fig. (Spanish).
1966A   El primer representante de la clase mamíferos hallado en el Mesozoico de España. Teruel, 35, 139—143
                 (Spanish).

CRUSAFONT PAIRÓ, M. and AGUIRRE, EMILIANO DE
1971A   *Euryboas lunensis* et *Hyaena donnezani* associées, en Espagne, dans le gisement d'âge pliocène terminal
                 de Layna (Soria). Acad. Sci., C.R., Sér. D, 273:25, 2476—2478, 2 tables (French).
1971B   A new species of *Percrocuta* from the middle Miocene of Kenya. Hess. Landesamt Bodenforsch., Abh.,
                 60, 51—58, 1 fig., 2 pls., 1 table.
1972A   *Stenailurus*, félidé nouveau, du Turolien d'Espagne. Ann. Paléontol., Vertébrés, 58:2, 211—225, 2 figs.,
                 1 pl., 1 table (French; English summary).

CRUSAFONT PAIRÓ, M., AGUIRRE, E. DE and MICHAUX, J.
1969A   Un nouveau gisement de mammifères d'âge villafranchien inférieur (Pliocène terminal) découvert à Layna¶
                 (Soria, Espagne). Acad. Sci., C.R., Sér. D, 268:17, 2174—2176 (French).
                 Rev.: Thenius in Zentralbl. Geol. Paläontol., Teil 2, 1971:6, 509—510.

CRUSAFONT PAIRÓ, M., GAUTIER, M. and GINSBURG, L.
1966A   Rev.: Adrover in Teruel, 37, 138—139.

CRUSAFONT PAIRÓ, M. and GOLPE POSSE, JUANA MARÍA
1964A   En el primer centenario de la paleomastología española. (Los tipos de mamíferos españoles). Soc.
                 Españ. Hist. Natur., Bol., Secc. Geol., 62:3—4, 371—375 (Spanish).
                 Rev.: Fernández-Galiano in Teruel, 33, 204—205.
1968A   Los nuevos yacimientos de mamíferos del Eoceno español. Bol. Geol. Min., España, 79:4, 341—353,
                 1 table (Spanish; English summary).
1968B   *Dissacus progressus*, nova sp., el primer creodonto de España. Bol. Geol. Min., España, 79:4, 354—357,
                 1 fig. (Spanish; English summary).

1969A   Los primeros cercopithécidos fósiles de España (nota preliminar). Barcelona, Univ., Dept. Paleontol.,
         Publ., 15:1–2, 1–2 (Spanish).
1972A   Los yacimientos de mamíferos fósiles del Vallès. Barcelona (Prov.), Inst. Prov. Paleontol., Bol. Inform.,
         4:2–3, 20–24 (Spanish).

CRUSAFONT PAIRÓ, M., GOLPE, J.-M., GIBERT, J. and THALER, L.
1971A   El yacimiento sanoisiense de Calaf tres cuartos de siglo despues. Barcelona (Prov.), Inst. Prov.
         Paleontol., Paleontol. Evol., 3, 64–65 (Spanish).

CRUSAFONT PAIRÓ, M. and HÜRZELER, JOHANNES
1969A   Catálogo comentado de los Póngidos fósiles de España. Acta Geol. Hisp., 4:2, 44–48 (Spanish; English
         summary).

CRUSAFONT PAIRÓ, M., MELÉNDEZ, B. and AGUIRRE, E. DE
1966A   La evolución. Madrid: Biblioteca de Autores Cristianos, 1014 pp. (Spanish).
         Rev.: Faulhaber in An. Antropol., Mexico, 5, 254–258.

CRUSAFONT PAIRÓ, M. and PETTER, FRANCIS
1964A   Un muriné géant fossile des iles Canaries Canariomys bravoi gen. nov. sp. nov. (Rongeurs, Muridés).
         Mammalia, 28:4, 607–612, 1 fig. (French; English summary).

CRUSAFONT PAIRÓ, M. and PETTER, GERMAINE
1969A   Contribution à l'étude des Hyaenidae. La sous-famille des Ictitheriinae. Ann. Paléontol., Vertébrés,
         55:1, 89–127, 6 figs., 4 pls., 3 tables (French).
         Rev.: Thenius in Zentralbl. Geol. Paläontol., Teil 2, 1970:3/4, 237–238.

CRUSAFONT PAIRÓ, M. and PONS, JOSÉ MARÍA
1969A   Nuevos datos sobre el Aquitaniense del N de la provincia de Huesca. Acta Geol. Hisp., 4:5, 124–125
         (Spanish; English summary).
         Rev.: L. in Spain, Inst. Geol. Minero, Bol. Geol. Minero, 81:4, 109.

CRUSAFONT PAIRÓ, M. and QUINTERO, INDALECIO
1970A   Noticia preliminar acerca de un nuevo yacimiento de mamíferos fósiles de la provincia de Guadalajara.
         Acta Geol. Hisp., 5:4, 102–104 (Spanish; English summary).

CRUSAFONT PAIRÓ, M. and REMY, JEAN-ALBERT
1970A   Les Equoidea (Perissodactyla) de l'Éocène préaxial pyrénéen espagnol. Mus. Nat. Hist. Natur., Paris,
         Bull., 42:2, 428–434, 2 figs., 1 table (French).

CRUSAFONT PAIRÓ, M. and SONDAAR, PAUL Y.
1971A   Une nouvelle espèce d'Hipparion du Pliocène terminal d'Espagne. Palaeovertebrata (Montpellier), 4:2,
         59–66, 1 pl. (French; English and German summaries).

CRUSAFONT PAIRÓ, M.   See also: Berg, D. E. and Crusafont, M., 1970A; Kühne, W. G. and Crusafont
         Pairó, M., 1968A; Montenat, C. and Crusafont Pairó, M., 1970A.

CRUXENT, JOSÉ M.
1970A   Projectile points with Pleistocene mammals in Venezuela. Antiquity, 45:175, 223–225, 3 figs.

CRUXENT, JOSÉ M. and ROUSE, IRVING
1969A   Early man in the West Indies. Sci. Amer., 221:5, 42–52, illustr.

CSÁNK, VERA G.
1968A   Archäologische Forschungen im Jahre 1967. Urzeit. Budapest III (Csillaghegy), Hegyalja u. 18 (V).
         Archaeol. Értesitö, 95:1, 126 (German).

CSERGEZÁN, P.   See: Tasnádi-Kubácska, A. and Csergezán, P., 1968A.

ČTYROKÝ, PAVEL and FEJFAR, OLDŘICH
1963A   Fauna písků a pískovců karpatské formace u Dolních Nětčic v karpatské čelní hlubině. [Fauna from
         sands and sandstones of the Carpathian formation near Dolní Nětčice in the Carpathian foredeep.]
         Geol. Práce, Zpr., 27, 143–168, 5 figs., 2 pls., 2 tables (Czechoslovakian; German summary).

CUERDA, ALFREDO
1971A   Professor Dr. Angel V. Borrello (1918–1971). Asoc. Geol. Argent., Rev., 26:4, 529–530, portr.
         (Spanish).

CUERDA BARCELÓ, JUAN   See: Adrover, R. and Cuerda Barceló, J., 1969A, 1969B.

CULTURAL RELICS WORKING PARTY OF THE AUTONOMOUS REGION OF INNER MONGOLIA
    1963A   [Selected cultural relics excavated in Inner Mongolia.] Peking, 45 pp., 144 pls. (Chinese).
           Rev.: Cheng Te-K'un in Man (J. Roy. Anthropol. Inst.), 65, 133—134.

CUMMING, GEORGE L.   See: Folinsbee, R. E., Baadsgaard, H. and Cumming, G. L., 1970A.

CUNNINGHAM, JOHN E.
    1966A   A Cretaceous vertebrate from the Big Burro Mountains, Grant County, New Mexico. N. Mex. Geol.
           Soc., Guidebk., Field Conf., 17, 119 (abs.).

CURNELLE, ROBERT   See: Lapparent, A. F. de, Curnelle, R., Defaut, B., Miroschedji, A. de and
           Pallard, B., 1969A.

CURNOW, A. G.
    1968A   Some thoughts on religion and science. Faith and Thought, 97:1, 41—57.

CURTISS, GARNISS H.   See: Jacob, T. and Curtiss, G. H., 1971A; Savage, D. E. and Curtiss, G. H., 1970A.

CUSCANI POLITI, P.
    1960-61A   Ancora una nuova specie di *Balaenula* pliocenica — con considerazioni introduttive su alcuni Misticeti
           dei nostri musei. Accad. Fisiocr., Siena, Atti, Sez. Agr., ser. 2, 8, 31 pp. (Italian).
    1963D   Resti di *Rhinoceros (Dicerorhinus) etruscus* rinvenuti nel Pliocene del Senese. Accad. Fisiocr., Siena,
           Atti, Sez. Agr., ser. 2, 10, 35 pp., 2 figs. (Italian).

CUSHING, E. J. and WRIGHT, H. E., JR
    1967A*   Rev.: Harris in Earth Sci. J., 2:2, 187—88; Judson in Amer. Sci., 56:3, 330A—331A.

CUVIER, GEORGES
    1969A   Recherches sur les ossemens fossiles de quadrupedes. Photographic reproduction of the 1812 edition.
           Brussels: Impression Anastaltique, Culture et Civilisation, 115 Avenue Gabriel Lebon, 4 vols.
           (French).

CYS, JOHN M.
    1971A   The palate and affinities of *Mirotenthes* (Reptilia: Theriodontia). J. Paleontol., 45:1, 122—125, 1 fig.

CZARNETZKI, A.
    1968A   Ein Knochenartefakt beim Skelettfund aus dem Neandertal? Anthropol. Anz., 31:1—2, 51—54, 1 fig.,
           1 pl. (German).

CZYŻEWSKA, TERESA
    1968A   Deer from Węże and their relationship with the Pliocene and Recent Eurasiatic Cervidae. Study on the
           Tertiary bone breccia fauna from Węże near Działoszyn in Poland. Part 20. Acta Palaeontol.
           Pol., 13:4, 537—604, 21 figs., 8 pls., 3 tables (Polish and Russian summaries).
    1970A   Remains of the lower Pliocene Bovidae from Altan Teli, western Mongolia. In: Kielan-Jaworowska, Z.
           (ed.), 1970B, 95—104, 2 figs., 2 pls., 4 tables.

DABER, RUDOLF
    1971A   Probleme der Wechselbeziehungen zwischen Lebens-und Erdgeschichte. Deut. Ges. Geol. Wiss., Ber.,
           Reihe A, Geol. Paläontol., 16:3—5, 435—443 (German).

DACHEV, DETELIN M.
    1967A   Novi danni za taneta v Plevensko. [New data on Thanetian of Plevna region.] Sof. Univ., Geol.-Geogr.
           Fak., God., 60:1, 107—125 (Bulgarian; French summary).
    1971A   Za filogeniïata i razprostranenieto na rod *Otodus* v Bŭlgariïa. [On the phylogeny and distribution of
           the genus *Otodus* in Bulgaria.] Sof. Univ., Geol.-Geogr. Fak., God., 63:1, 11—18, 3 pls.
           (Bulgarian; French summary).

DAHLBERG, ALBERT A.
    1971A*   Dental morphology and evolution. Chicago and London: University of Chicago Press, x + 350 pp.,
           illustr.
           Rev.: McKenna in Science (AAAS), 176:4039, 1115—1116; Osborn in Evolution, 26:4, 676—677.

DAL PIAZ, GIORGIO
    1971A   Guida dell'Istitudo e del Museo di Geologia e Paleontologia [Università di Padova]. Publicata postuma, con Introduzione di Giambattista Dal Piaz e Giuliano Piccoli. Padova: Società Cooperativa Tipografica, 149 pp., illustr., portrs. (Italian).

DALLMAN, JOHN E.
    1969A   Giant beaver from a post-Woodfordian lake near Madison, Wisconsin. J. Mammal., 50:4, 826—830, 2 pls., 1 table.

DALQUEST, WALTER W.
    1967A   Mammals of the Pleistocene Slaton local fauna of Texas. Southwest. Natur., 12:1, 1—30, 3 figs., 16 tables.
    1968A   The bone-eating dog, Borophagus diversidens Cope. Fla. Acad. Sci., Quart. J., 31:2, 115—129, 4 figs.
    1969A   Pliocene carnivores of the Coffee Ranch (type Hemphill) local fauna. Tex. Mem. Mus., Bull., 15, 44 pp., 11 figs., 1 pl., 31 tables.
    1972A   A new genus and species of shrew from the upper Pliocene of Texas. J. Mammal., 53:3, 570—573, 1 fig.

DALQUEST, W. W. and ROTH, EDWARD
    1970A   Late Pleistocene mammals from a cave in Tamaulipas, Mexico. Southwest. Natur., 15:2, 217—230.

DALQUEST, W. W., ROTH, E. and JUDD, F.
    1969A   The mammal fauna of Schulze Cave, Edwards County, Texas. Fla. State Mus., Bull., Biol. Sci., 13:4, 205—276, 4 figs., 3 tables.

DALRYMPLE, G. BRENT and LANPHERE, MARVIN A.
    1969A   Potassium-argon dating. Principles, techniques and applications to geochronology. San Francisco: Freeman, xiv + 258 pp., illustr.
              Rev.: Anon. in Rocks Miner., 45:3, 197; Damon in Science (AAAS), 170, 54—55; Hanson in Amer. Sci., 58:5, 556; I. R. P. in Geol. J., 7:1, v—vi; Šmejkal in Čas. Mineral. Geol., 15:3, 225—226.

DALY, ELEANOR
    1969A   A new procolophonoid reptile from the lower Permian of Oklahoma. J. Paleontol., 43:3, 676—687, 7 figs.

DALY, ELEANOR   See also: Olson, E. C. and Daly, E., 1972A.

DALY, PATRICIA
    1969A   Approaches to faunal analysis in archaeology. Amer. Antiquity, 34, 146—153, 1 fig., 1 table.

DALZELL, BONNIE B.
    1969A   Characters of the pelvis in cursorial mammals. Geol. Soc. Amer., Abstr., Part 3, 13—14 (abs.).

DANI, A.   See: Borzatti von Löwenstern, E. and Dani, A., 1968A.

DANIEL, GLYN
    1968A   László Vértes. [1914 — Sept. 20, 1968]. Antiquity, 42:168, 252—253.
    1968B   One hundred years of Old World prehistory. In: Brew, J. O. (ed.), 1968A, 57—93, 237—242.
    1968C   Man discovers his past. New York: Thomas Y. Crowell, viii + 95 pp., 58 illustr., 8 maps.
              Rev.: Whallon in Amer. Anthropol., 71, 566—567.
    1969A   Dorothy Garrod. [1892—1968]. Antiquity, 43:169, 1—2.

DANIEL, J. A.   See: Prasad, K. N. and Daniel, J. A., 1968A.

DANIEL, RAOUL
    1969A   Quelques précisions sur le remplissage archéologique de la grotte de Liveyre commune de Tursac (Dordogne). Soc. Préhist. Fr., Bull., C.R., 66:4, 112—116, 5 figs. (French).

DANIELS, GEORGE
    1968A*   Darwinism comes to America. Waltham, Mass. and London: Blaisdell (Ginn), xix + 137 pp.
              Rev.: Smith in Nature, 222:5193, 599.

DANIL'CHENKO, PAVEL GEORGIEVICH (= DANILTSHENKO, P. G.)
    1968B   Ryby verkhnego paleotsena Turkmenii. [Upper Paleocene fishes of Turkmenia.] In: Ocherki po filogenii i sistematike iskopaemykh ryb i bezchelfiustnykh, 113—156, 20 figs., 14 pls. (Russian).
              Rev.: Weiler in Zentralbl. Geol. Paläontol., Teil 2, 1970:5, 423—426.

DANIL'CHENKO, P. G.   See also: Iosifova, Iu. I. and Danil'chenko, P. G., 1970A, 1970B.

DANIL'CHENKO, V. P.
1969A   Rod *Sardinops* v srednem miotsene Kavkaza. [The genus *Sardinops* in the middle Miocene of
        Caucasus.] Vop. Ikhtiol., 9:4(57), 757–758, 1 fig. (Russian).
1972A   Sel'devye (Clupeidae) v paleogen-neogenovykh moriakh Tetisa. [Clupeidae in the Paleogene-Neogene
        seas of Thetis.] Vop. Ikhtiol., 12:2, 226–232, 1 fig., 1 table (Russian).

DANILEVICH, A. M. and VASIL'EV, V. I.
1966A   Kamennougol'naia sistema. [Carboniferous system.] Geologiia SSSR, 29, Tuvinskaia ASSR, 201–209,
        3 figs. (Russian).

DANILOV, A. I.
1971A   Novyi ditsinodont iz srednego triasa iuzhnogo Priural'ia. [A new dicynodont from the middle Triassic
        of southern Cisuralia.] Paleontol. Zh., 1971:2, 132–135, 1 fig. (Russian).
1971B   A new dicynodont from the middle Triassic of southern Cisuralia. Paleontol. J., 5:2, 265–268, 1 fig.

DANILOV, A. I. and KALANDADZE, N. K.
1970A   Cherep triasovogo teriodonta na territorii SSSR. [A skull of Triassic theriodont on the territory of
        the USSR.] Priroda, 1970:5, 70–72, 2 figs. (Russian).

DANILOV, N. N.
1968A   Petr Petrovich Sushkin (1868–1928) (100 let so dnia rozhdeniia i 40 let so dnia smerti). [Petr
        Petrovich Sushkin (1868–1928) (to the centenary of the birth and to the fortieth anniversary
        of the death).] Mosk. Obshchest. Ispyt. Prir., Biull., Otd. Biol., 73:6, 149–153 (Russian).

DANILOVA, E. I.
1968A   Particularités morphologiques de la main des Hominidés fossiles en rapport avec certains problèmes
        d'anthropogenèse. Int. Congr. Anthropol. Ethnol. Sci., 7th, Moscow, 1964, Proc., 3, 479–484
        (French).
1971A   K evoliutsii kisti i stopy v sviazi s proiskhozhdeniem cheloveka. [On the evolution of hand and foot
        in connection with the origin of man.] Vop. Antropol., 37, 19–32, 7 figs. (Russian).

DANILOVA, E. I. and BURYCHENKO, A. I.
1969A   Locomotion and tool function of primates as reflected in the hominid hand. Int. Congr. Anthropol.
        Ethnol. Sci., 8th, Tokyo, 1968, Proc., Vol. I. Anthropology, 251–252.

DANILOVA, E. I. and SVISTUN, V. I.
1969A   [Morpho-functional analysis of the pectoral extremities of *Dinotherium* from vil. Gusiatin, Ternopol'
        Province.] Akad. Nauk Ukr. SSR, Inst. Zool., Vestn. Zool., 1969:5, 37–41, 1 fig., 1 table
        (Russian; English summary).

DANON, J.   See: Mattievich, E., and Danon, J., 1971A.

DARLINGTON, C. D.
1969A   The evolution of man and society. London: George Allen and Unwin Ltd., 753 pp., 22 figs.,
        44 tables.
        Rev.: Birch in Austral. J. Sci., 32:10, 410; Burt in New Sci., 44:665, 489; Clark in Nature, 224:5215,
        193; Padoa in Scientia, 106:3–4, 305–306; Quigley in Amer. Anthropol., 73:2, 434–439.

DARLINGTON, PHILIP J., JR.
1957A   Rev.: Kiriakoff in Natuurwet. Tijdschr., 39:4–5, 130–131.
1968A   Biogeography of the southern end of the world. Paperback edition. New York and London: McGraw-
        Hill Book Co., x + 236 pp., 38 figs., 5 tables.

DARRAGH, T. A.   See: Casey, D. A. and Darragh, T. A., 1970A.

DART, RAYMOND A.
1966D   List of publications, 1920–1966. Compiled with additional matter by Marjorie Dart. 10 pp.,
        mimeographed.
1967C   Mousterian osteodontokeratic objects from Geula Cave (Haifa, Israel). Quaternaria, 9, 105–140,
        10 figs.
1971A   *Australopithecus africanus*: the man-ape of South Africa. In: Leakey, L. S. B., Prost, J. and Prost, S.
        (eds.), 1971A, 201–209, 4 figs. (reprinted from Nature, 115, 1925).

DARWIN, CHARLES ROBERT
1972A   On the affinities and genealogy of man. General summary and conclusions. In: McCown, T. D. and
         Kennedy, K. A. R. (eds.), 1972A, 149–158 (reprinted from Darwin, 1871).

DAS, MANMOHAN
1967A   Prithibir Katha. [The story of the earth.] Calcutta: Orient Book Co., 383 pp.
         Rev.: Bose in Man in India, 48:1, 92.

DASCH, E. JULIUS and CAMPBELL, K. S. W.
1970A   Strontium-isotope evidence for marine or freshwater origin of fossil dipnoans and arthrodires. Nature,
         227:5263, 1159.

DASHZEVEG, DEMBERELIYN
1969A   More information on the age of the lower Paleogene in the Nemebeta basin, Mongolia. Akad. Nauk
         SSSR, Dokl., Earth Sci., Sec., 182, 45–46. (Translated from Russian: Akad. Nauk SSSR, Dokl.,
         182:2, 415–417.)
1970A   Novye dannye o stratigrafii sredneoligofsenovykh otlozheniĭ MNR. [New data on the stratigraphy of
         middle Oligocene deposits of MPR.] Sovm. Sovet.-Mongol. Nauch.-Issled. Geol. Eksped., Tr., 2,
         37–43, 1 fig. (Russian).
1970B   Stratigrafiĭa i fauna verkhnego paleogena Mongol'skoĭ Narodnoĭ Respubliki. [Stratigraphy and fauna
         of upper Paleogene of the Mongolian People's Republic.] Akad. Nauk Mongol. NR, Nauchn.-
         Issled. Geol. Inst., Tr., 1, 45–56 (Russian).
1971A   Novyĭ Tachyoryctoides (Mammalia, Rodentia, Cricetidae) iz oligofsena Mongolii. [A new
         Tachyoryctoides (Mammalia, Rodentia, Cricetidae) from the Oligocene of Mongolia.] Sovm.
         Sovet.-Mongol. Nauch.-Issled. Geol. Eksped., Tr., 3, 68–70 (Russian).

DASTUGUE, J.
1967B   Pathologie du "vieillard" de Cro-Magnon. (Summary). Discussion. Soc. Anthropol. Paris, Bull. Mém.,
         Sér. 12, 1:4, 495–496 (French).
1969A   Les lésions pathologiques du squelette de Chancelade. L'Anthropologie, 73:3–4, 247–252, 3 figs.
         (French).
1969B   Réflexions sur la communication de M. Vallois sur le temporal des Néandertaliens. Discussion. Soc.
         Anthropol. Paris, Bull. Mém., Sér. 12, 4, 380–381 (French).

DAUGHERTY, RICHARD D.   See: Fryxell, R., Bielicki, T., Daugherty, R. D., Gustafson, C. E., Irwin, H. T.
         and Keel, B. C., 1968A; Fryxell, R., Bielicki, T., Daugherty, R. D., Gustafson, C. E., Irwin,
         H. T., Keel, B. C. and Krantz, G. S., 1968A.

DAUVILLIER, A.
1971A   L'importance des lois de Dubois et des faits géographiques dans la phylogénèse humaine. Cah. Géol.,
         87, 1175–1176 (French).

DAVENPORT, LAWRENCE C. and GOLDBRANDSEN, JEAN
1963A   Barstowian fossil beds at Barstow, Calif. Victorville, Calif.: 16 pp., illustr.

DAVID, ANATOLIĬ IVANOVICH
1964B   Ostatki slonov v antropogenovykh otlozheniĭakh Moldavii. [Remains of elephants from Anthropogene
         deposits of Moldavia.] Nauch. Konf. Molod. Uch. Moldavii, 3-rd., Kishinev, Tr., Biol. Sel'sko-
         Khoz. Nauki, 2, 187–188 (Russian).
1966B   [Fossil rhinoceroses (Rhinocerotidae) from the Anthropogene of Moldavia.] Akad. Nauk Moldav. SSR,
         Izv., 1966:10, 3–15, 7 figs., 5 tables (Russian).
1966C   [Distribution of beaver (Castor fiber L.) in Moldavia.] Akad. Nauk Moldav. SSR, Izv., 1966:10, 16–19,
         2 figs., 1 table (Russian).
1969A   [Early Anthropogene mammals of Moldavia.] Akad. Nauk Moldav. SSR, Izv., Ser. Biol. Khim. Nauk,
         1969:2, 18–44, 4 figs., 11 pls., 14 tables (Russian).
1969B   Fauna paleoliticheskoĭ stoĭanki Rashkov – VII. [The fauna of the Paleolithic site Rashkov – VII.]
         Priroda, 1969:5, 104–105, 1 fig., 1 table (Russian).
1970A   Rasprostranenie burogo medvedĭa (Ursus arctos L.) v antropogene Moldavii. [Distribution of the brown
         bear (Ursus arctos L.) in the Anthropogene of Moldavia.] Akad. Nauk Moldav. SSR, Izv., Ser.
         Biol. Khim. Nauk, 1970:1, 67--72, 1 fig., 1 table (Russian).
1970B   Rasprostranenie, chislennost' i izmenchivost' kosuli (Capreolus capreolus L.) v antropogene Ĭugo-
         Vostochnoĭ Evropy. [Distribution, number and variability of the roedeer (Capreolus capreolus L.)
         in the Quaternary of southeastern Europe.] In: Paleontologicheskie issledovaniĭa verkhnego
         kaĭnozoĭa Moldavii, 3–21, 1 map, 3 pls. (Russian).

DAVID, A. I. and KAHLKE, HANS-DIETRICH
1969A   Die Cervidenreste aus den Kiesen von Tiraspol. In: Mezhdunarodnyĭ kollokvium po geologii i faune nizhnego i srednego pleĭstofŝena Evropy. Tezisy dokladov, 80–82 (German).

DAVID, A. I. and KETRARU, N. A.
1966A   Predvaritel'nye dannye ob issledovanii stoĭanki "Rashkov VII". [Preliminary data of research on the site "Rashkov VII".] Akad. Nauk Moldav. SSR, Okh. Prir. Moldav., 4, 163–170, 6 figs., 1 table (Russian).
1970A   Fauna mlekopitaĭushchikh paleolita Moldavii. [Mammalian fauna of the Paleolithic of Moldavia.] In: Fauna kaĭnozoĭa Moldavii, 3–53, 26 figs., 10 tables (Russian).

DAVID, A. I. and LUNGU, ALEKSANDR NIKOLAEVICH
1972A   Ostatki mlekopitaĭushchikh iz Karagashskogo kar'era. [Mammal remains from Karagash quarry.] In: Pozvonochnye neogena i pleĭstofŝena Moldavii, 19–24 (Russian).

DAVID, A. I. and SHUSHPANOV, K. I.
1972A   Ostatki mlekopitaĭushchikh iz neogenovykh otlozheniĭ Moldavii. [Mammal remains from the Neogene deposits of Moldavia.] In: Pozvonochnye neogena i pleĭstofŝena Moldavii, 3–18, 2 pls. (Russian).

DAVID, A. I.   See also: Belĭaeva, E. I. and David, A. I., 1969A; Dubrovo, I. A. and David, A. I., 1969A; Negadaev-Nikonov, K. N., David, A. I. and Khubka, A. N., 1970A; Vereshchagin, N. K., Alekseeva, L. I., David, A. I. and Baĭgusheva, V. S., 1969A; Vereshchagin, N. K. and David, A. I., 1968A, 1971A.

DAVID, E., and DUPLESSIS-KERGOMARD, D.
1967A   A propos de la découverte de défenses de Proboscidiens dans la gravière de Vincent (Jura); quelques
  /   remarques sur le Pliocène bressan. Soc. Hist. Natur. Doubs, no. 69:4, 8 pp., 1 fig., 1 pl. (French).

DAVID, E., FRACHON, J.-C. and SATTONNET, R.
1968A   Les "massacres" de boeuf primitif du gouffre de Cornerives (Jura) et les restes des grands bovidés disparus de Franche-Comté. Féd. Soc. Hist. Natur. Franche-Comté, Bull., 70:1, 10–16 (French).

DAVID, E.   See also: Théobald, N., Blanc, M. and David, E., s.d.

DAVID, L., EVIN, J., GUÉRIN, C., MONGEREAU, N. and WALTER, B.
1972A   Datation par le radiocarbone de la terrasse quaternaire de Saint-Rambert-d'Albon (Drôme). Würm de la moyenne vallée du Rhône. Acad. Sci., C.R., Sér. D, 274:14, 2007–2008 (French).

DAVID, PIERRE
1952A   Grotte Suard (Moustérien ancien). Les Eyzies, 2, 27 (French).

DAVID, PIERRE and DUPORT, LOUIS
1955A   Fouille de la Grotte Duport à La Chaise de Vouthon (Charente). Les Eyzies, 5, 48–49 (French).

DAVID, PIERRE and PIVETEAU, JEAN
1953A   Étude d'une portion de calotte cranienne néanderthalienne provenant de La Chaise (Charente). Les Eyzies, 3, 34–37, 2 figs. (French).

DAVIES, A. MORLEY
1971A   Tertiary faunas. A text-book for oilfield palaeontologists and students of geology. Revised and brought up to date by F. E. Eames. Section on Vertebrata contributed by R. J. G. Savage. Vol. I. The composition of Tertiary faunas. Second edition. New York: American Elsevier Publ. Co., 571 pp., 1030 figs.
          Rev.: Anon. in Calif. Geol., 25:8, 183; Sastry in Geol. Soc. India, J., 13:2; Wilson in Geotimes, 17:6, 30–31.

DAVIES, GORDON L.
1970A   The palaeontological collection of Lord Cole, Third Earl of Enniskillen (1807–1886), at Florence Court, Co. Fermanagh. Irish Natur. J., 16:12, 379–381.

DAVIES, OLIVER
1968A   Reply to the three reviews ["the Quaternary in the Coastlands of Guinea" reviewed by Biberson, Clark, and Folster]. W. Afr. Archaeol. News., no. 9, 45–47 (French summary).
1969A   Modern archaeological research in Africa and the possibilities in Natal. S. Afr. Archaeol. Bull., 23, 9–12.

1970A The eighth INQUA congress at Paris, 1969. S. Afr. Archaeol. Bull., 25:97, 45.

DAVIES, P. L.
1968A An 8,000 to 12,000 years old human tooth from Western Australia. Archaeol., Phys. Anthropol. Oceania, 3:1, 33—40, 1 table, 1 pl.

DAVIS, LEO CARSON
1969A The biostratigraphy of Peccary Cave, Newton County, Arkansas. Arkansas Acad. Sci., Proc., 23, 192—196, 1 fig.
1972A The herpetofauna of Peccary Cave, Newton County, Arkansas. Soc. Vert. Paleontol., Ann. Meeting, 32nd, 1972, Abstr. (abs.).

DAVITASHVILI, LEO SHIOVICH
1967A Vzaimozavisimost' mezhdu paleobiologiei i geokhronologiei. [Mutual dependence between paleobiology and geochronology.] Akad. Nauk Gruz. SSR, Inst. Paleobiol., Nauchn. Sess., All-Union Meeting, 3—5 (Russian).
1967B Perspektivy dal'neishei razrabotki ucheniia ob evoliutsionnom progresse. [Prospects of further development of the doctrine on evolutionary progress.] Akad. Nauk Gruz. SSR, Inst. Paleobiol., Obshch. Vop. Evoliuts. Paleobiol., 3, 5—26 (Russian; Georgian and English summaries).

1968A Dopolnitel'nye dannye k biografii osnovatelia evoliutsionnoi paleontologii V. O. Kovalevskogo. [New data for the biography of the founder of evolutionary paleontology V. O. Kovalevskii.] Akad. Nauk Gruz. SSR, Inst. Paleobiol., Obshch. Vop. Evoliuts. Paleobiol., 4, 117—137 (Russian; Georgian and English summaries).
1968B Voprosy metodologii v izuchenii evoliutsii organicheskogo mira. [Problems of methodology in the study of the evolution of the organic world.] Tbilisi: "Metsniereba" Press, 216 pp. (Russian; Georgian and English summaries).
1969A Deficiencies of the synthetic theory of evolution. Evolution, 23:3, 513—516.
1969B Prichiny vymiraniia organizmov. [Causes of extinction of the organisms.] Moscow: "Nauka" Press, 440 pp., 28 figs. (Russian).
    Rev.: Pidoplichko in Akad. Nauk Ukr. SSR, Inst. Zool., Vestn. Zool., 1971:2, 88—90 (Russian).
1970A Izmenchivost' organizmov v geologicheskom proshlom. [Variability of organisms in the geological past.] Tbilisi: "Metsniereba" Press, 255 pp., 55 figs., 14 pls. (Russian).

DAVTIAN, A. R.
1970A Novye nakhodki iskopaemykh mlekopitaiushchikh v Pambakskoi doline. [New finds of fossil mammals in Pambak Valley.] Akad. Nauk Arm. SSR, Izv., Nauki Zemle, 23:2, 75—77 (Russian).

DAVTIAN, A. R. See also: Arzumanian, S. K., Veguni, A. T. and Davtian, A. R., 1970A; Avakian, L. A. and Davtian, A. R., 1970A.

DAWSON, CHARLES and WOODWARD, ARTHUR SMITH
1971A On the discovery of a Palaeolithic human skull and mandible in flint-bearing gravel overlying the Wealden (Hastings beds) at Piltdown, Fletching (Sussex). In: Leakey, L. S. B., Prost, J. and Prost, S. (eds.), 1971A, 183—194, 6 figs. (reprinted from Geol. Soc. Quart. J., March 1913).
1971B Supplementary note on the discovery of a Palaeolithic human skull and mandible at Piltdown (Sussex). In: Leakey, L. S. B., Prost, J. and Prost, S. (eds.), 1971A, 195—199, 2 figs. (reprinted from Geol. Soc. Quart. Rev., April 1914).

DAWSON, MARY R.
1969A Restoration of a Sardinian fossil. Carnegie Mag., 43:3, 83—84, 2 figs.
1969B Osteology of Prolagus sardus, a Quaternary ochotonid (Mammalia, Lagomorpha). Palaeovertebrata (Montpellier), 2:4, 158—190, 38 figs., 1 pl., 1 table (German and French summaries).
1969C The Quaternary lagomorph Prolagus sardus. Amer. Phil. Soc., Yearb., 1968, 289—290.
1970A Paleontology and geology of the Badwater Creek area, central Wyoming. Part 6. The leporid Mytonolagus (Mammalia, Lagomorpha). Carnegie Mus., Ann., 41:7, 215—230.
1971A Fossil mammals of Java. I. Notes on Quaternary Leporidae (Mammalia, Lagomorpha) from central Java. Ned. Akad. Wetensch., Proc., Ser. B, 74:1, 27—32, 1 pl.

DAWSON, MARY R. and BLACK, CRAIG C.
1970A The North American cricetid rodent "Eumys" exiguus, once more. J. Paleontol., 44:3, 524—526, 2 figs.

DAWSON, MARY R. See also: Bruijn, H. de, Dawson, M. R. and Mein, P., 1970A; Emry, R. J. and Dawson, M. R., 1972A; Guilday, J. and Dawson, M., 1969A, 1971A; Stevens, M. S., Stevens, J. B. and Dawson, M. R., 1969A.

DAXNER, GUDRUN (= DAXNER-HÖCK, G.)
1968A   Die Wildziegen (Bovidae, Mammalia) aus der altpleistozänen Karstspalte von Hundsheim in
          Niederösterreich. Deut. Ges. Geol. Wiss., Ber., Reihe A, Geol. Paläontol., 13:3, 305–334,
          12 figs., 2 tables (German).
1970A   Die Wirbeltierfauna aus dem Alt-Pliozän (O-Pannon) vom Eichkogel bei Mödling (NÖ). III. Rodentia.
          Naturhist. Mus. Wien, Ann., 74, 597–605 (German).
1972A   Cricetinae aus dem Alt-Pliozän vom Eichkogel bei Mödling (Niederösterreich) und von Vösendorf bei
          Wien. Palaeontol. Z., 46:3–4, 133–150, 3 figs., 2 pls., 6 diagrams (German; English summary).

DAXNER-HÖCK, GUDRUN and RABEDER, GERND
1971A   Vorläufige Ergebnisse der paläontologischer Grabung 1968 im Altpliozän (O-Pannon) des Eichkogels
          (NÖ). Österreich. Akad. Wiss., Math.-Naturwiss, Kl., Anz. (1970), 107:1–2, 47–50 (German).

DAY, MICHAEL H.
1965A   Rev.: Leakey in New Sci., 30:490, 45.
1967B   Guide to fossil man. Second edition. London: Cassell, 289 pp., illustr.
          Rev.: Schwidetzky in Homo, 19:3–4, 233.
1969A   Fossil man. London: Hamlyn; Melbourne: Sunbooks; New York: Grosset and Dunlap, Inc., 159 pp.,
          illustr.
          Rev.: Tooze in Nature, 224:5216, 293–294.
1969B   Femoral fragment of a robust australopithecine from Olduvai Gorge, Tanzania. Nature, 221:5177,
          230–233, 3 figs.
1969C   Omo human skeletal remains. Nature, 222:5199, 1135–1138, figs. 3–6, 1 table.
1969D   Der Mensch der Vorgeschichte. Stuttgart and Zürich: Delphin Verlag, Delphin-Taschenbuch, 159 pp.,
          illustr. (German).
          Rev.: Preuschoft in Zentralbl. Geol. Paläontol., Teil 2, 1971:5, 417.
1971A   Postcranial remains of Homo erectus from Bed IV, Olduvai Gorge, Tanzania. Nature, 232:5310,
          383–387, 4 figs., 2 tables.

DAY, M. H. and MOLLESON, T.
1971A   The Trinil femora. Amer. J. Phys. Anthropol., 35:2, 276 (abs.).

DAY, M. H. and WALKER, A. C.
1969A   New prosimian remains from early Tertiary deposits of southern England. Folia Primatol., 10:1–2,
          139–145, 4 figs., 1 table.

DAY, M. H. and WOOD, B. A.
1968A   Functional affinities of the Olduvai Hominid 8 talus. Man (J. Roy. Anthropol. Inst.), 3, 440–455,
          8 figs., 6 tables.
1969A   Hominoid tali from East Africa. Nature, 222:5193, 591–592, 3 figs.

DEACON, H. J.
1966A   An annotated list of radiocarbon dates for sub-Saharan Africa. Cape Prov. Mus., Ann., 5, 5–84,
          2 figs., 2 tables, 1 map.
1969A*   South Africa. COWA, Surv. Bibliogr., Area 13, 4, 1–15.
1972A   A review of the post-Pleistocene in South Africa. Goodwin Ser., 1, 26–45, 3 figs., 2 tables.

DEASON, HILARY J.
1970A*   The AAAS science book list. Third edition. Washington: American Association for the Advancement
          of Science, xiii + 439 pp.

DEB, S.
1969A   Darashaw Nosherwan Wadia, F.R.S. [1883–1969]. Sci. Culture, 35:7, 306–309, portr.

DEBÉNATH, ANDRÉ
1968A   Découvertes récentes de restes humains fossiles à La Chaise de Vouthon, Charente. Soc. Anthropol.
          Paris, Bull. Mém., Sér. 12, 3:4, 387 (French).
1969A   La Chaise de Vouthon, un siècle de recherches dans un gisement préhistorique charentais. Préhistoire-
          Géologie. Soc. Archéol. Hist. Charente, Mém., 1968, 49–64, 8 figs. (French).
1970A   Nouvelles découvertes de restes humains à La Chaise-de-Vouthon (Charente). Soc. Archéol. Hist.
          Charente, Mém., 1969, 145, 1 fig. (French).

DEBÉNATH, ANDRÉ and PIVETEAU, JEAN
1969A   Nouvelles découvertes de restes humains fossiles à La Chaise-de-Vouthon (Charente). Position
          stratigraphique des restes humains de La Chaise (abri Bourgeois-Delaunay). Acad. Sci., C.R.,
          Sér. D, 269:1, 24–28, 1 pl. (French).

DEBÉNATH, ANDRÉ   See also: Bouvier, J. M., Debénath, A., Delpech, F. and Duport, L., 1969A.

DEBETŠ, GEORGIĬ FRANTŠEVICH   See: Alekseev, V. P. and Debetš, G. F., 1964A.

DECHASEAUX, COLETTE
1966A   Un crocodile en Charente. Soc. Archéol. Hist. Charente, Mém., 1965, 91—94, 2 figs. (French).
1969A   Moulages endocraniens d'Artiodactyles primitifs. Essai sur l'histoire du néopallium. Ann. Paléontol.,
                    Vertébrés, 55:2, 195—248, 21 figs. (French).
1969B   Réflexions sur l'intelligence des oiseaux et des mammifères. Acad. Sci., C.R., Sér. D, 268:22, 2671—
                    2673 (French).
1970A   Moulages endocraniens d'oiseaux de l'Éocène supérieur du Bassin de Paris. Ann. Paléontol., Vertébrés,
                    56:1, 69—72, 1 fig. (French).
                    Rev.: Kuhn in Zentralbl. Geol. Paläontol., Teil 2, 1970:6, 516.
1970B   Cérébralisation croissante chez le courlis (Numenius) au cours de la période qui va de l'Éocène
                    supérieur à l'époque actuelle. Acad. Sci., C.R., Sér. D, 270:6, 771—773, 1 fig. (French).
1970C   Récents résultats en paléoneurologie. Acad. Soc. Lorraines Sci., Bull., 9:1, 223—232, 5 figs. (French).
1971A   Oreomylodon wegneri, édenté gravigrade du Pléistocène de l'Equateur, crâne et moulage endocranien.
                    Ann. Paléontol., Vertébrés, 57:2, 243—285, 24 figs. (French).

DEETZ, JAMES
1968A   Discussion: hunters in archeological perspective. In: Lee, R. B., and DeVore, I. (eds.), 1968A,
                    281—285.

DEEVEY, EDWARD and WHITING, JOHN W. M.
1968A   Discussion: Pleistocene family planning. In: Lee, R. B., and DeVore, I. (eds.), 1968A, 248—249.

DEFAUT, BERNARD   See: Lapparent, A. F. de, Curnelle, R., Defaut, B., Miroschedji, A, de and Pallard, B., 1969A.

DEGERBØL, MAGNUS and FREDSKILD, BENT
1970A   The Urus (Bos primigenius Bojanus) and Neolithic domesticated cattle (Bos taurus domesticus Linné)
                    in Denmark. Dan. Vidensk. Selsk., Biol. Skr., 17:1, 234 pp., 27 figs., 14 pls., 28 tables.

DE GIULI, C., FICCARELLI, G. and TORRE, D.
1970A   Missione paleontologica nella provincia di Sokoto (NW Nigeria). Nota preliminare. Soc. Geol. Ital.,
                    Boll., 89:4, 547—556, 6 figs. (Italian).

DEHM, RICHARD
1969A   Bericht Über die Arbeit von Herrn Volker Fahlbusch "Populationsverschiebungen bei tertiären
                    Nagetieren, eine Studie an oligozänen und miozänen Eomyidae Europas". Bayer. Akad. Wiss.,
                    Math.-Naturwiss. Kl., Sitz-Ber., 145, 1—3 (German).
1970A   Bericht über die Arbeit von Herrn Wighart v. Koenigswald "Peratherium (Marsupialia) im Ober-Oligozän
                    und Miozän von Europa". Bayer. Akad. Wiss., Math.-Naturwiss, Kl., Sitz.-Ber., 1969, 6—8
                    (German).
1970B   Bericht über die Arbeit von Herrn Peter Wellnhofer "Die Pterodactyloidea (Pterosauria) der Oberjura-
                    Plattenkalke Süddeutschlands". Bayer. Akad. Wiss., Math.-Naturwiss. Kl., Sitz.-Ber., 1969,
                    15—18 (German).
1970C   Bericht über die Arbeit von Herrn Volker Fahlbusch "Populationsverschiebungen bei tertiären
                    Nagetieren, eine Studie an oligozänen und miozänen Eomyidae Europas". Bayer. Akad. Wiss.,
                    Math.-Naturwiss. Kl., Sitz.-Ber., 1969, 19—21 (German).
1970D   Oligozäne Spaltenfüllungen im Weissjura-Massenkalk bei Ehingen (Donau). Bayer. Staatssamml.
                    Paläontol. Hist. Geol., Mitt., 10, 321—330, 1 fig. (German; English summary).
1971A   Professor Dr. Ernst Freiherr Stromer von Reichenbach, Lebensdaten und Schriftenverzeichnis.
                    Bayer. Staatssamml. Paläontol. Hist. Geol., Mitt., 11, 3—10 (German).

DEHM, R. and FAHLBUSCH, VOLKER
1970A   Zur Bezeichnung fossilführender Spaltenfüllungen. Bayer. Staatssamml. Paläontol. Hist. Geol., Mitt.,
                    10, 351—364, 1 fig. (German; English summary).

DEHM, RICHARD   See also: German, R., Filzer, P., Dehm, R., Freude, H., Jung, W. and Witt, W., 1968A.

DELAIR, J. B.
1969A   North of the hippopotamus belt: a brief review of Scottish fossil mammals. Mammal Soc. Brit. Isles,
                    Bull., 31, 4 pp., 1 map.
1969B   The first record of the occurrence of ichthyosaurs in the Purbeck. Dorset Natur. Hist. Archaeol. Soc.,
                    Proc., 90, 128—132, 3 figs.
1969C   A history of the early discoveries of Liassic ichthyosaurs in Dorset and Somerset (1779—1835). Dorset
                    Natur. Hist. Archaeol. Soc. Proc., 90, 115—127, 3 figs.

1970A   Preliminary notice of vertebrate footprints from the Trias of Dumfriesshire. Dumfries. Galloway
                     Natur. Hist. Antiq. Soc., Trans., 46, 178–179, 3 figs.

DELARAI, J.
1957A   Les formations quaternaires des basses et moyennes vallées de la Tardoire et du Bandiat. Inst. Géol.
                     Anthropol. Préhist. Poitiers, Trav., 1, 61–101, 23 figs. (French).

DELATTRE, A. and FENART, R.
1966A   Tentative de définition du genre *Homo*. Le crâne humain. Soc. Anthropol. Paris, Bull. Mém., Sér. 11,
                     9:4, 377–392, 6 figs., 1 table (French).

DELCOURT, ABBÉ A.
1964A   Techniques simples pour la préparation des spores et des grains de pollen des gisements préhistoriques.
                     Les Eyzies, 13, 146–152 (French).
1967A   Alimentation de l'homme préhistorique. Les Eyzies, 16, 77–83 (French).

DELPECH, FRANÇOISE
1968A   Faunes du Magdalénien VI et de l'Azilien du gisement de Duruthy, commune de Sorde-l'Abbaye
                     (Landes). Soc. Linn. Bordeaux, Actes, Sér. B, 105:6, 25 pp., 2 figs., 3 pls., 4 tables (French).
1969A   Étude paléontologique du Roc de la Belle. Soc. Hist. Archéol. Périgord, Bull., 96:3, 224–230, 1 fig.
                     (French).
1970A   Faune aurignacienne de Caminade-Est, commune de La Canéda (Dordogne). Quaternaria, 13, 137–140
                     (French).
1970B   Faune du Magdalénien IV du gisement de Duruthy, commune de Sorde-l'Abbaye (Landes). Ass. Fr.
                     Étud. Quat., Bull., 22, 13–26, 3 figs., 6 tables (French).
1970C   L'abri magdalénien du Flageolet II – Paléontologie (Bézenac-Dordogne). Soc. Préhist. Fr., Bull., Étud.
                     Trav., 67:2, 494–499, 2 pls. (French).
1971A   L'abri Faustin, commune de Cessac (Gironde). Étude paléontologique. Soc. Préhist. Fr., Bull. Étud.
                     Trav., 68:1, 328–332, 1 fig., 3 tables (French).

DELPECH, F., LACHASTRE, J., PRAT, F. and SUIRE, C.
1970A   Un gisement à faune pléistocène: la Grotte de la Martine à Domme (Dordogne). Quaternaria, 13,
                     141–168, 5 pls., 5 tables (French; English and Italian summaries).

DELPECH, F.   See also: Bouvier, J. M., Debénath, A., Delpech, F. and Duport, L., 1969A.

DELPORTE, HENRI
1969A   Docteur André Cheynier (1893–1968). Soc. Préhist. Fr., Bull., C.R., 66:2, 34–35, portr. (French).
1970A   Informations archéologiques. Circonscription d'Auvergne et Limousin. Gallia Préhist., 13:2, 459–484,
                     34 figs. (French).

DELSON, ERIC
1971A   Estudio preliminar de unos restos de simios pliocénicos procedentes de "Cova Bonica" (Gavá) (Prov.
                     Barcelona). Acta Geol. Hisp., 6:2, 54–57, 3 figs., 2 tables (Spanish).

DELY, O. G.
1968A   Die wissenschaftliche und literarische Tätigkeit von Géza Gyula Fejérváry auf dem Gebiet der Zoologie.
                     [1894–1932]. Vert. Hungarica, 10, 13–43 (German; Hungarian summary).

DELY, O. G.   See also: Boros, I. and Dely, O. G., 1968A.

DEMAR, ROBERT
1970A   A primitive pelycosaur from the Pennsylvanian of Illinois. J. Paleontol., 44:1, 154–163, 8 figs.

DEMAR, ROBERT and BARGHUSEN, HERBERT R.
1972A   Mechanics and the evolution of the synapsid jaw. Evolution, 26:4, 622–637, 13 figs.

DEMARCQ, GÉRARD
1970A   Étude stratigraphique du Miocène rhodanien. Fr., Bur. Rech. Géol. Minières, Mém., 61, 257 pp.,
                     56 figs., 4 pls., 4 tables (French).

DEMARCQ, G. and TRUC, G.
1969A   Le bassin d'Apt à l'Éocène. Colloque sur l'Éocène, Paris, mai 1968, Vol. III. Fr., Bur. Rech. Géol.
                     Minières, Mém., 69, 406–407 (French).

DEMARCQ, G.   See also: Mein, P., Truc, G. and Demarcq, G., 1971A.

DEMATHIEU, GEORGES
1967A Nouvelles empreintes de vertébrés triasiques dans l'Autunois. Soc. Hist. Natur. Amis Mus. Autun, Bull. (L'Eduen), 44, 11—15, 3 figs. (French).
1969A Contribution de l'ichnologie à la connaissance de l'évolution des reptiles pendant le Trias. Soc. Géol. Fr., C.R., 1969:7, 255 (French; abs.).
1970A Contribution de l'ichnologie à la connaissance de l'évolution des reptiles pendant la période triasique. Soc. Géol. Fr., C.R., 1970:4, 122—123 (French).
1970B Les empreintes de pas de vertébrés du Trias de la bordure nord-est du Massif Central. Cah. Paléontol., 211 pp., 76 figs., 8 pls., 83 tables (French).
1971A Cinq nouvelles espèces d'empreintes de reptiles du Trias de la bordure nord-est du Massif Central. Acad. Sci., C.R., Sér. D., 272:6, 812—814 (French).

DEMATHIEU, G. and SAMAMA, J. C.
1970A Les empreintes de pas fossiles des grès triasiques de la mine de Largentière (Ardèche). Bull. Sci. Bourgogne, 25, 347—367, 10 figs., 3 pls., 3 tables (French).

DEMATHIEU, G. See also: Buffard, R., Demathieu, G. and Demathieu, P., 1969A; Courel, L., Demathieu, G. and Buffard, R., 1968A, 1968B.

DEMATHIEU, P. See: Buffard, R., Demathieu, G. and Demathieu, P., 1969A.

DEMAY, LOUIS See: Bidar, A., Demay, L. and Thomel, G., 1972A, 1972B.

DEMENT'EV, G. P. (= DEMENTJEV, G. P.)
1960A Espèces aviennes récentes trouvées à l'état fossile au post-Tertiaire dans l'USSR. Int. Ornith. Congr., 12th, Proc., 162—166 (French).
1965A Sistematika ptits (sovremennoe sostoīanie i nekotorye problemy). [Systematics of birds (present state and some problems]. In: Sovremennye problemy ornitologii. Chetvertaīa vsesoīuznaīa ornitologicheskaīa konferentsiīa, 11—64 (Russian).

DE MERLO, J. A. See: Bell, K. N. and De Merlo, J. A., 1969A.

DEMING, LOUISE M.
1966A The history of the Uganda Museum. Uganda Mus. Occ. Paper, 10, 23 pp., 4 pls.

DENISON, ROBERT H.
1968B Middle Devonian fishes from the Lemhi Range of Idaho. Fieldiana: Geol., 16:10, 269—288, 12 figs.
1968C The evolutionary significance of the earliest known lungfish, Uranolophus. Nobel Symp., 4th, Stockholm, 1967, Proc., 1968, 247—257, 9 figs.
1969A New Pennsylvanian lungfishes from Illinois. Fieldiana: Geol., 12:12, 193—211, 8 figs.
1970A The origin of skeletons in animals. Chicago, Field Mus. Natur. Hist., Bull., 41:12, 11—13, 2 figs.
1970B Revised classification of Pteraspididae with description of new forms from Wyoming. Fieldiana: Geol., 20:1, 41 pp., 26 figs.
1971A The origin of the vertebrates: a critical evaluation of current theories. N. Amer. Paleontol. Conv., Proc., Part H, 1132—1146, 1 fig.
1971B On the tail of Heterostraci (Agnatha). Forma et Functio, 4, 87—99, 10 figs. (German and French summaries).

DENIZOT, GEORGES
1965A Sur la définition et la valeur du terme de Chelléen. Congr. Préhist. France, 16ᵉ Sess., Monaco 1959, C.R., 521—529, 2 figs. (French).

DENNY, CHARLES S. See: Ray, C. E., Denny, C. S. and Rubin, M., 1970A.

DERANIYAGALA, P. E. P.
1965B A pygmy stegodont elephant from China. Spolia Zeylanica, 30:2, 195—197, 1 fig.
1965C A stone-age human and a fossil rhinoceros from the Turkana district, East Africa, that are in the Colombo Museum. Spolia Zeylanica, 30:2, 199—204, 2 figs., 3 pls., 1 table.
1965D Some aspects of the fauna of Ceylon. J. Roy. Asiatic Soc. (Ceylon Br.), 9:2, 165—219, 9 figs., 7 pls.
1966A Ceylon bibliography. Asian Perspectives, 9, 45—47.
1967A Ceylon: 1965—1966. Annotated bibliography. Asian Perspectives, 10, 67—68.
1967B Some new Miocene vertebrates from Ceylon. Ceylon, Ass. Advance. Sci., Ann. Sess., 23rd, Proc., part 1, 50 (abs.).
1968A Three extinct mammals from Africa. J. Palaeontol. Soc. India, 5—9, 16—20, 3 figs.
1969A Some aspects of the Tertiary period in Ceylon. J. Roy. Asiatic Soc. (Ceylon Br.), 12 (1968), 86—108, 5 figs., 3 pls.

1969B   Some Miocene vertebrates from Ceylon. J. Palaeontol. Soc. India, <u>13</u> (1968), 20—23, 1 pl.
1969C   Some of the earliest vertebrates of Ceylon. Loris, <u>11</u>:5, 235—237, 8 figs.
1969D   A Miocene vertebrate faunule from the Malu member of Ceylon. Spolia Zeylanica, <u>31</u>:2, 551—570.
1970A   Elephants. Loris, <u>12</u>:1, 21—27, 8 figs.

DEREVIANKO, A. P. and OKLADNIKOV, A. P.
1969A   Drevnie kul'tury vostochnykh raĭonov MNR. [Ancient cultures of eastern Mongolian People's
           Republic.] Sov. Arkheol., <u>1969</u>:4, 141—156, 6 figs. (Russian; French summary).

DEREVIANKO, A. P.   See also: Okladnikov, A. P. and Derevianko, A. P., 1968A; Okladnikov, A. P.,
           Vasil'evskiĭ, R. S., Larichev, V. E., Derevianko, A. P., Gogolev, Z. V. and Toshchakova, E. M.,
           1969A.

DESBROSSE, R.   See: Bouchud, J. and Desbrosse, R., 1972A.

DESSAUER, HERBERT C.
1969A   Molecular data in animal systematics. Discussions. In: Sibley, Ch. G. (ed.), <u>1969A</u>, 325—365,
           6 figs.

DESTEXHE JAMOTTE, J.
1970A   Le trou Dubois à Moha (Vallée de Mehaigne). Chercheurs Wallonie, Bull. (1969—1970), <u>21</u>, 75—103,
           32 figs. (French).

DEV, PRAMENDRA   See: Bhalla, S. N. and Dev, P., 1972A.

DEVIATKIN, E. V. (= DEVYATKIN, YE. V. = DEVJATKIN, JE. V.)
1970A*   Geologiia mezozoia i kaĭnozoia Zapadnoĭ Mongolii. [Geology of the Mesozoic and Cenozoic of
           western Mongolia.] Sovm. Sovet.-Mongol. Nauch.-Issled. Geol. Eksped., Tr., <u>2</u>, 190 pp., illustr.
           (Russian).
1970B   Geologiia kaĭnozoia Zapadnoĭ Mongolii. [Geology of the Cenozoic of western Mongolia.] Sovm.
           Sovet.-Mongol. Nauch.-Issled. Geol. Eksped., Tr., <u>2</u>, 44—102, 16 figs., 2 tables (Russian).

DEVIATKIN, E. V. and STRELKOV, S. A.
1968A   Stratigrafiia kaĭnozoia v Altae-Saĭanskoĭ gornoĭ oblasti i Zapadnoĭ Mongolii i vopros o nizhneĭ granitse
           antropogena. [Cenozoic stratigraphy in the Altaĭ-Saĭan Mountains region and western Mongolia,
           and the problem of the lower limit of Anthropogene.] In: Granitsa tretichnogo i
           chetvertichnogo periodov, 86—89 (Russian; English summary).

DEVIATKIN, E. V., ZAZHIGIN, V. S. and LISKUN, I. G.
1969A   First find of small mammals in the Pliocene of Tuva and Mongolia. Akad. Nauk SSSR, Dokl., Earth
           Sci. Sec., <u>183</u>, 45—47. (Translated from Russian: Akad. Nauk SSSR, Dokl., 1968, <u>183</u>:2,
           404—407).

DEVIATKIN, E. V.   See also: Liskun, I. G. and Deviatkin, E. V., 1964A, 1965A.

DEVILLERS, CH.   See: Saint-Seine, P. de and Devillers, Ch., 1969A.

DEVORE, IRVEN
1971A   The evolution of human society. In: Eisenberg, J. F. and Dillon, W. J. (eds.), <u>1971A</u>, 299—311.
1971B   From ape toward man. In: Holmes, L. D. (ed.), <u>1971A</u>, 83—95 (reprinted from the Primates, 1965).

DEVORE, IRVEN and WASHBURN, SHERWOOD L.
1966A   Baboon ecology and human evolution. In: Howell, F. C. and Bourliere, F. (eds.), <u>1966A</u>, 335—367,
           14 figs., 1 table.
1972A   Baboon ecology and human evolution. In: Jennings, J. D. and Hoebel, E. A. (eds.), <u>1972A</u>, 159—169
           (reprinted from African Ecology and Human Evolution, 1963).

DEVORE, IRVEN   See also: Howell, F. C., Turnbull, C., Sharp, L., Clark, J. G. D. and DeVore, I., 1968A;
           Lee, R. B. and DeVore, I., 1968A, 1968B.

DEWEY, JOHN R.   See: Armelagos, G. J. and Dewey, J. R., 1970A.

DEWHIRST, J. T.   See: Aish, P. J., Dewhirst, J. T. and Folan, W. J., 1968A.

DEWOLF, Y.
1970A   Premières observations sur deux coupes de la vallée de l'Eure. Ass. Fr. Ét. Quat., Bull., <u>23—24</u>,
           191—198 (French).

DEY, A. K.   See: Randhawa, M. S., Singh, J., Dey, A. K. and Mittre, V., 1969A.

DEZSÖ, GYULA   See: Nemeskéri, J. and Dezsö, G. (eds.), 1969A.

DIACONU, P.
1972A   150 de ani de la nasterea lui Gregor Iohann Mendel. [150 years of the date of birth of Gregor Johann Mendel.] Natura, Ser. Biol., 24:4, 90-92, portr. (Rumanian).

DÍAZ DE GAMERO, MARÍA L.   See: Pascual, R. and Díaz de Gamero, M. L., 1969A; Wood, R. C. and Díaz de Gamero, M. L. 1971A.

DIBBLE, DAVID S. and LORRAIN, DESSAMAE
1968A   Bonfire shelter: a stratified bison kill site, Val Verde County, Texas. 1965 paper republished. Austin: Texas Memorial Museum, Misc. Papers, 1, 138 pp., 64 figs., 24 tables.
        Rev.: Davis in Archaeology, 23:3, 262–264; Forbis in Amer. Antiquity, 34, 90–91; Warnicka in Amer. Anthropol., 70, 1023–1024.

DIDENKO-KISLITSINA, L. K.
1971A   Chetvertichnaiā sistema. Iūzhnaiā i Severnaiā Dzhungariiā. [Quaternary system. Southern and northern Dzhungaria.] Geologiiā SSSR, 40:1, Southern Kazakhstan, 516–522, 1 fig. (Russian).

DIDENKO-KISLITSINA, L. K., BIRIUKOV, M. D. and BAIBULATOVA, R. B.
1971A   Novye dannye o stratigrafii paleogenovykh otlozheniĭ Dzhungarskogo Alatau. [New data on the stratigraphy of Paleogene deposits of Dzhungarian Alatau.] In: Materialy po geologii i poleznym iskopaemym Iūzhnogo Kazakhstana, 4 (29), 140–149 (Russian).

DIDENKO-KISLITSINA, L. K.   See also: Bazhanov, O. V., Didenko-Kislitsina, L. K. and Kostenko, N. N., 1971A; Bazhanov, O. V., Bocharova, N. I., Didenko-Kislitsina, L. K. and Kostenko, N. N., 1971A.

DIDKOVSKIĬ, VALENTIN IAKOVLEVICH
1958A   Neogenovye otlozheniiā Moldavskoĭ SSR. [Neogene deposits of Moldavian SSR.] Geologiiā SSSR, 5, Ukrainian SSR, Moldavian SSR, 729–742.

DIEBEL, KURT and HEINRICH, WOLF-DIETER
1970A   Pisede - eine einmalige Fundstelle quartärer Wirbeltiere in Mecklenburg; Probleme und erste Ergebnisse einer neuen Ausgrabung des Paläontologischen Museums Berlin. Berlin, Humboldt-Univ., Wiss. Z., Math.-Naturwiss, Reihe, 19:2–3, 236–243 (German).

DIENI, IGINIO
1968A   Gli otoliti del Pliocene inferiore di Orosei (Sardegna). Accad. Patavina Sci. Let. Arti, Cl. Sci. Mat. Natur., Atti Mem., 80:2, 243–291, 2 figs., 3 pls., 2 tables (Italian; English summary).
        Rev.: Weiler in Zentralbl. Geol. Paläontol., Teil 2, 1969:3, 283.

DIETERLEN, FRITZ
1969A   Aspekte zur Herkunft und Verbreitung der Muriden. Bedeutung der systematischen Stellung der Otomyinae. Z. Zool. Syst. Evolut.-Forsch., 7:4, 237–242 (German; English and French summaries).

DIKOV, N. N.
1969A   Verkhniĭ paleolit Kamchatki. [The upper Paleolithic of Kamchatka.] Sov. Arkheol., 1969:3, 93–109, 11 figs. (Russian; French summary).

DILLON, WILTON S.   See: Eisenberg, J. F. and Dillon, Wilton, S., 1971A.

DIMSDALE, B.   See: Taylor, R. E., Berger, R. and Dimsdale, B., 1968A.

DINELEY, DAVID L.
1968A   Osteostraci from Somerset Island. Can., Geol. Surv., Bull., 165, 47–63, 5 figs., 6 pls., 1 map.
1971A   A pteraspidid in the Dalhousie formation (l. Devonian) at Dalhousie, New Brunswick. Can. J. Earth Sci., 8:12, 1603–1605, 2 figs. (French summary).
1972A   Devonian vertebrates and north "Atlantis". Int. Geol. Congr., 24th, Canada, Abstr., 222.
1972B   Devonian vertebrates and north "Atlantis". Int. Geol. Congr., 24th, Canada, Proc., Sec. 7, 273.

DINELEY, D. L. and RUST, B. R.
1968A   Sedimentary and paleontological features of the Tertiary-Cretaceous rocks of Somerset Island, Arctic Canada. Can. J. Earth Sci., 5:4, 791-799, 21 figs.

DINELEY, D. L.   See also: Broad, D. S., Dineley, D. L. and Miall, A. D., 1968A; Carroll, R. L., Belt, E. S.,
                        Dineley, D. L., Baird, D. and McGregor, 1972A, 1972B.

DINGMAN, R. J. and GALLI, C.
    1965A   Geology and ground-water resources of the Pica area, Tarapaca province, Chile. U.S. Geol. Surv.,
                   Bull., 1189, 111 pp., 19 figs., 2 maps, 11 tables.

DIOP, CHEIKH ANTA
    1970A   L'apparition de l'*Homo sapiens.* Inst. Fond. Afr. Noire, Bull., ser. B, 32:3, 623–641 (French).

DIPESO, CHARLES C.
    1966A   Archaeology and ethnohistory of the northern Sierra. Handbk. Mid. Amer. Ind., 4, 3–25, 9 figs.

DISLER, N. N.
    1966A   O filogeneze Elasmobranchii. [On the phylogenesis of Elasmobranchii.] Zool. Zh., 45:11, 1673–
                   1685, 7 figs. (Russian; English summary).

DIXIT, P. C., KACHROO, R. K., RAI, H. and SHARMA, N. L.
    1971A   Discovery of vertebrate fossils from the Kargil basin, Ladakh (Jammu and Kashmir). Curr. Sci.,
                   40:23, 633–644.

DIXON, JAMES   See: Turner, S. and Dixon, J., 1971A.

DJOSHKIN, W. W. and SAFONOW, W. G.
    1972A   Die Biber der alten und neuen Welt. Wittenberg Lutherstadt: J. Neumann Verlag, "Die Neue Brehm
                   Bücherei", 167 pp., 75 figs. (German).
                   Rev.: Haltenorth in Kosmos, 68:9, 280–281.

DMITRIEV, GEORGIĬ ANDREEVICH and ROZHDESTVENSKIĬ, ANATOLIĬ KONSTANTINOVICH
    1968A   Kostenosnye faĭsii ozerno-rechnykh otlozheniĭ verkhnego mezozoiă Buriătii. [Bone-bearing facies in
                   fluvio-lacustrine deposits of upper Mesozoic of Buriătia.] In: Mezozoĭskie i kaĭnozoĭskie ozera
                   Sibiri, 39–48, 5 figs. (Russian).

DMITRIEV, GEORGIĬ ANDREEVICH and SKOBLO, VLADIMIR MAKSIMOVICH
    1966A   Vozmozhnosti primeneniiă paleontologicheskogo metoda v praktike stratigraficheskikh issledovaniĭ
                   mezozoĭskikh i kaĭnozoĭskikh porod, razvitykh na territorii Buriătskoĭ ASSR. [Possibilities of
                   applying the paleontological method in stratigraphic research on Mesozoic and Cenozoic rocks
                   of the Buriăt ASSR.] Vses. Paleontol. Obshchest., Tr., VIII sess., 172–179 (Russian).

DMITRIEVA, E. A.   See: Nikonov, A. A., Pen'kov, A. V., Trofimov, B. A., Vangengeĭm, E. A., Dmitrieva, E. A.
                          and Sotnikova, M. V., 1971A.

DMITRIEVA, E. L. (= DMITRIYEVA, Y. L. = DMITRIJEVA, Y. L.)
    1969A   O gazeli iz kalmakpaĭskoĭ fauny Vostochnogo Kazakhstana. [On the gazelle from Kalmakpaĭ fauna
                   of eastern Kazakhstan.] Mosk. Obshchest. Ispyt. Prir., Biŭll., Otd. Geol., 44:6, 146–147
                   (Russian).
    1970A   Ob ob'eme *Gazella deperdita* (Gervais), 1848. [On the volume of *Gazella deperdita* (Gervais), 1848.]
                   In: Materialy po evoliŭĭsii nazemnykh pozvonochnykh, 141–151, 4 figs., 3 tables (Russian).
    1971A   K sistematike i filogenii gazeleĭ podroda *Procapra.* [On the systematics and phylogeny of the gazelle
                   subgenus *Procapra.*] Paleontol. Zh., 1971:2, 135–137, 4 figs. (Russian).
    1971B   Neogenovye gazeli Zapadnoĭ Mongolii. [Neogene gazelles of western Mongolia.] Sovm. Sovet.-Mongol.
                   Nauch.-Issled. Geol. Eksped., Tr., 3, 124–131 (Russian).
    1971C   Systematics and phylogeny of the gazelle subgenus *Procapra.* Paleontol. J., 5:2, 268–270, 4 figs.

DOBIN, M. A.   See: Kokurichev, P. I. and Dobin, M. A., 1972A.

DOBREDEEV, O. P.   See: Agadzhanian, A. K., Dobredeev, O. P., Kursalova, V. I. and Motuzko, A. N., 1972A.

DOBRORUKA, L. J.
    1971A   On the identity of *Cervus nigricans* Brooke, 1877, with remarks upon other deer from the Philippines.
                   Leyden, Rijksmus. Natuur. Hist., Zool. Mededel., 45:7, 91–97, 2 figs., 2 pls.

DOBZHANSKY, THEODOSIUS
    1966A   Rev.: Weninger in Anthropol. Ges., Mitt., 98, 86.
    1966B   Rev.: Boesinger in L'Ann. Biol., 6:9–10, 589–590.
    1967B   Mankind evolving; the evolution of human species. New Haven: Yale Univ. Press, xiii + 381 pp.,
                   10 figs., 27 tables (reprint of 1962 edition).

1968A   On some fundamental concepts of Darwinian biology. In: Dobzhansky, T., *et al.* (eds.), 1968A, 1-34.
1969A   Man and natural selection. In: Ehrlich, P. R., *et al.* (eds.), 1969A, 467—481.
1970A   Genetics of the evolutionary process. New York: Columbia Univ. Press, ix + 505 pp., illustr.
    Rev.: Roth-Lutra in Anat. Anz., 131:1—2, 174—175.

DOBZHANSKY, TH. and BOESIGER, E.
1968A   Essais sur l'évolution: collection "Les grands problèmes de la Biologie". Paris: Masson et Cie, x + 182 pp., 32 figs., 21 tables (French).
    Rev.: Hublé in Natuurwet. Tijdschr., 51:3—8, 223—224; Jolicoeur in Syst. Zool., 18:4, 450; Labeyrie in Atomes, 266, 366; Mayr in Evolution, 24:2, 480—481;Schwanitz in Biol. Zentralbl., 90:4, 520—521; Tintant in Soc. Zool. Fr., Bull., 95:1, 180—181; Vandel in L'Ann. Biol., 9:1—2, 107—109.

DOBZHANSKY, TH., HECHT, M. K. and STEERE, W. C.
1967A*   Rev.: Alvarado in Soc. Españ. Hist. Natur., Bol., Secc. Biol., 65:3—4, 493—494; Rühle in Biol. Zentralbl., 87:4, 519—520.
1968A*   Evolutionary biology. Vol. II. Amsterdam: North-Holland, 452 pp., illustr.
    Rev.: Alvarado in Soc. Españ. Hist. Natur., Bol., Secc. Biol., 66:3—4, 212—213; Clark in Austral. J. Sci., 31:10, 374; Olson in Quat. Rev. Biol., 46:1, 75—76; Rühle in Biol. Zentralbl., 89:1, 113; Sheppard in J. Animal Ecol., 38:3, 791—792.
1969A*   Evolutionary biology. Vol. III. New York: Appleton-Century-Crofts, 309 pp., illustr.
    Rev.: Anon. in Biologist, 52:3, 120; Rühle in Biol. Zentralbl., 90:2, 241—242.
1970A*   Evolutionary biology. Vol. IV. New York: Appleton-Century-Crofts, ix + 312 pp., illustr.
    Rev.: Anon. in Biologist, 53, 163.
1972A*   Evolutionary biology. Vol. V. New York: Appleton-Century-Crofts, ix + 317 pp., illustr..
1972B*   Evolutionary biology. Vol. VI. New York: Appleton-Century-Crofts, xiii + 445 pp., illustr.

DOCLADAL, M.
1967A   Eksperimental'noe izuchenie vliĭaniĭa zhevatel'nykh mysht͡s na formu cherepa. K probleme brakhit͡sefalizat͡sii u cheloveka. [Experimental study of the influence of masticatory muscles on the skull shape. The problem of brachycephalization in man.] Discussion. Int. Congr. Anthropol. Ethnogr. Sci., 7th,Moscow, 1964, Proc., 2, 358—360 (Russian).

DODSON, PETER
1971A   Sedimentology and taphonomy of the Oldman formation (Campanian), Dinosaur Provincial Park, Alberta (Canada). Palaeogeogr. Palaeoclimatol. Palaeoecol., 10, 21—74, 15 figs., 6 tables.
1972A   Ontogenetic phenomena in dinosaurs. Soc. Vert. Paleontol., Ann. Meeting, 32nd, 1972, Abstr. (abs.).

DOELL, R. R.   See: Cox, A. and Doell, R. R., 1968A.

DOIZE, RENÉE L.
1967A   Comment travaillait l'abbé Breuil? Objets et Mondes, 7:1, 79—82, 4 figs. (French).

DOLAN, EDWARD M. and ALLEN, GLENN T., JR.
1961A   An investigation of the Darby and Hornsby Spring sites, Alachua County, Florida. Fla. Geol. Surv., Spec. Publ. 7, 124 pp., 10 figs., 16 pls., 1 table.

DOLHINOW, PHILLIS
1972A*   Primate patterns. New York: Holt, Rinehart and Winston, 425 pp.

DOLHINOW, PHILLIS and SARICH, VINCENT M.
1971A*   Background for man. Readings in physical anthropology. Boston: Little, Brown and Co., viii + 405 pp., illustr.
    Rev.: Cartmill in Amer. J. Phys. Anthropol., 37:2, 314—315.
1971B   Physical anthropology: theory and methods. In: Dolhinow, P. and Sarich, V. M. (eds.), 1971A, 2—6.

DOLINAR, ZLATA
1967A   Novi pogled na razvoj človeka. [The new views on human evolution.] Archeol. Vestn., 18, 301—305 (Slovenian; English summary).

DOLLÉ, P., LAPPARENT, A. F. DE and MONTENAT, C.
1970A   Sur une dalle à empreintes de pas lacertoïdes du houiller du bassin Nord-Pas-de-Calais. Soc. Géol. Nord, Ann., 90:2, 63—68, 2 figs. (French; English summary).

DOLUKHANOV, P. M.
1970A   Sergeĭ Ivanovich Rudenko. Sov. Arkheol., 1970:2, 303—304, portr. (Russian).

DOLUKHANOV, P. M.   See also: Semenfsov, A. A., Romanova, E. N. and Dolukhanov, P. M., 1969A.

DOMNING, DARYL P.
  1969A   A list, bibliography, and index of the fossil vertebrates of Louisiana and Mississippi. Gulf Coast Ass.
               Geol. Soc., Trans. 1969, 385–422.
  1971A   Sirenians as guide fossils in west coast late Tertiary correlation – a prospectus. Geol. Soc. Amer.,
               Abstr., 3:2, 110–111 (abs.).
  1972A   Sirenians and desmostylians in west coast Miocene stratigraphy. AAPG-SEPM Symp., 146–149,
               1 table.
  1972B   Steller's sea cow and the origin of North Pacific aboriginal whaling. Syesis, 5, 187–189.

DOMNING, DARYL P.   See also: Shikama, T. and Domning, D., 1970A.

DOMRACHEV, S. M.   See: Chochia, N. G. and Domrachev, S. M., 1969A.

DONG, ZHI-MING
  1965A   Abs.: Sci. Abstr. China, Earth Sci., 3:2, 6.

DONG, ZHI-MING   See also: Young, C. C. and Dong, Z.-m., 1972A.

DORR, JOHN A., JR.
  1969A   Mammalian and other fossils, early Eocene Pass Peak formation, central western Wyoming. Mich.,
               Univ., Mus. Paleontol., Contrib., 22:16, 207–219, 2 figs., 1 pl.

DORR, JOHN A., JR. and ESCHMAN, DONALD F.
  1970A   Geology of Michigan. Illustrated by Derwin Bell. Ann Arbor: University of Michigan Press, viii +
               476 pp., illustr.
               Rev.: Steidtman in Wyo., Univ., Contrib. Geol., 9:1, 53.

DORR, JOHN A., JR. and STEIDTMANN, J. R.
  1970A   Stratigraphic-tectonic implications of a new, earliest Eocene, mammalian faunule from central
               western Wyoming. Mich. Acad., 3:1, 25–41, 5 figs.

DORT, WAKEFIELD, JR. and JONES, J. KNOX, JR.
  1970A*   Pleistocene and Recent environments of the central Great Plains. Kans., Univ., Dept. Geol., Spec.
               Publ., 3, 433 pp., illustr.
               Rev.: Anon. in Biologist, 54:2, 94; Flint in Amer. Sci., 59:4, 485; Heusser in Geogr. Rev., 62:4,
               595–597; Jameson in BioSci., 21, 751; King in Ecology, 52:4, 735–736; Lundelius in Quart.
               Rev. Biol., 46:4, 414; Pearson in Evolution, 25:4, 738–739; Schultz in J. Paleontol., 46:1,
               157–158.

DOTT, ROBERT H. and BATTEN, ROGER L.
  1971A   Evolution of the earth. New York and London: McGraw-Hill, xiii + 649 pp., illustr.
               Rev.: Dewey in J. Geol., 80:3, 369–370; Feldmann in Geotimes, 16:11, 41–42; Traverse in
               J. Paleontol., 46:6, 925–927.

DOUGHTY, P. S.
  1968A   Ballyrudder mammoth tooth. Irish Natur. J., 16:4, 105–106.
  1969A   Equine teeth from the stratified deposits of the Curran, Larne. Irish Natur. J., 16:6, 168–171.

DOUGLAS, CHARLES L.
  1969A   Catfish spines from archeological sites in Texas. Tex. Archeol. Soc., Bull., 40, 263–265, 2 figs.

DOVCHIN, NAYDIN   See: Kielan-Jaworowska, Z. and Dovchin, N., 1968A.

DOWLEN, R. J.   See: Kern, J. P., Stump, T. E. and Dowlen, R. J., 1971A.

DOWNEY, JOE S.
  1968A   Late Pliocene lagomorphs of the San Pedro Valley, Arizona. U.S. Geol. Surv., Prof. Pap., 600–D,
               169–173, 2 figs., 1 table.
  1970A   Middle Pleistocene Leporidae from the San Pedro Valley, Arizona. U.S. Geol. Surv., Prof. Pap.,
               700–B, 131–136, 4 figs., 1 table.

DOWNS, JAMES F. and BLEIBTREU, HERMANN K.
  1969A   Human variation: an introduction to physical anthropology. Beverly Hills, Calif.: Glencoe Press,
               xv + 269 pp., 93 figs.

Rev.: Fry in Human Biol., 43:1, 179—181; Mann in Amer. J. Phys. Anthropol., 34:3, 454.

DOWNS, THEODORE
1969A   The Ray Alf Museum and Science Center. Soc. Vert. Paleontol., News Bull., no. 85, 57, 1 photo.

DOWNS, THEODORE and WHITE, J. A.
1968B   A vertebrate faunal succession in superposed sediments from Pliocene to middle Pleistocene in
            California. Int. Geol. Congr., 23rd, Czech., Rep., Abstr., 1968, sect. 10, 272 (abs.).

DOWNS, THEODORE   See also: Miller, W. E. and Downs, T., 1971A.

DRAKE, ELLEN T.
1968A*   Rev.: Roth-Lutra in Anat. Anz., 126:3, 334—336.

DREIMANIS, A.
1968A   Extinction of mastodons in eastern North America: testing a new climatic environmental hypothesis.
            Ohio Jour. Sci., 68:6, 257—272, 2 figs., 4 tables.

DREW, L. C.
1968A   New exhibits. Discovery, Yale, 3:2, 55—56, 1 fig.

DREZ, PAUL   See: Ray, C. E., Wetmore, A., Dunkle, D. H. and Drez, P., 1968A.

DRICOT, JEAN-MARIE   See: Petit-Maire-Heintz, N. and Dricot, J.-M., 1970A; Petit-Maire-Heintz, N., Dricot,
                     J.-M. and d'Ans, C., 1970A.

DROBNE, KATICA
1967A   Izkopavanje mastodonta v Škalah pri Velenju. [The excavation of mastodon at Škale.] Geol.,
            Razprave Poročila, 10, 305—312, 5 figs. (Slovenian; English summary).

DRÖSSLER, R.
1967A   Die Venus der Eiszeit. Entdeckung und Erforschung altsteinzeitlicher Kunst. Leipzig: Prisma Verlag,
            270 pp., 111 figs., 92 pls. (German).
            Rev.: Franzen in Natur Mus., 101:5, 226; k.v. in Archeol. Roz., 21:5, 686 (Czech); Pittioni in
            Archaeol. Austriaca, 46, 122—123; Züchner in Quartär, 19, 409—410.

DROUOT, EDOUARD   See: Combier, J., Drouot, E. and Huchard, P., 1959A.

DRUMMOND, A. H., JR.
1970A   Mastodons at sea. Sea Front., 16:3, 151—153, 3 figs.
1970B   Mastodons at sea. S. Calif. Paleontol. Soc., Bull., 2:9, 3—4 (reprinted from Sea Frontiers, 16:3, 1970).

DRUSHITS, VLADIMIR VASIL'EVICH and OBRUCHEVA, OL'GA PAVLOVNA
1971A   Paleontologiiâ. Uchebnik. [Paleontology. Textbook.] Moscow: Univ. Press, 414 pp., illustr.
            (Russian).

DUBAR, JULES R.
1958B   Neogene stratigraphy of southwestern Florida. Gulf Coast Ass. Geol. Soc., Trans., 8, 129—155,
            14 figs., 5 tables.

DUBAR, J. R. and CLOPINE, G.
1961A   Late Pleistocene deposits in the vicinity of Houston, Texas: a preliminary investigation. Gulf Coast
            Ass. Geol. Soc., Trans., 11, 83—108, 6 figs., 1 table.

DUBAR, MICHEL
1969A   Le Quaternaire du plateau de Valensole. Étude préliminaire de la région de Puimoisson (Basses-Alpes).
            Ass. Fr. Étud. Quat., Bull., 6:21, 269—273 (French).

DUBECQ, X. J., MICHELET, F. and VERGER-PRATOUCY, J.
1966A   L'apparition de l'éminence mentonnière chez l'homme. (Summary). Soc. Anthropol. Paris, Bull.
            Mém., Sér. 11, 9:4, 484 (French).

DUBEĬKOVSKIĬ, S. G.   See: Ochev, V. G., Lozovskiĭ, V. R. and Dubeĭkovskiĭ, S. G., 1972A.

DUBLIĂNSKIĬ, V. N.   See: Bachinskiĭ, G. A. and Dubliânskiĭ, V. N., 1963A.

DUBOIS, EUGENE
    1971A   *Pithecanthropus erectus* – a form from the ancestral stock of mankind. In: Leakey, L. S. B.,
                Prost, J. and Prost, S. (eds.), 1971A, 165–175, 5 figs. (reprinted from Dubois, E., 1896).
    1972A   The place of *Pithecanthropus* in the genealogical tree. In: McCown, T. D. and Kennedy, K. A. R.
                (eds.), 1972A, 195–197 (reprinted from Nature, 53, 245–247).

DUBROVO, IRINA ALEKSANDROVNA
    1970A   Novye dannye o miofsenovykh mastodontakh Vnutrennei Mongolii. [New data on Miocene
                mastodonts of Inner Mongolia.] In: Materialy po evoliutsii nazemnykh pozvonochnykh, 135–
                140, 3 figs. (Russian).
    1971A   Novyi rod kitoobraznykh (*Sachalinocetus cholmicus* gen. et sp. nov.) iz miofsena o-va Sakhalin.
                [A new genus of Cetacea (*Sachalinocetus cholmicus* gen. et sp. nov.) from the Miocene of
                Sakhalin Island.] Akad. Nauk SSSR, Paleontol. Inst., Tr., 130, 87–103, 10 figs., 3 pls.
                (Russian).

DUBROVO, I. A. and DAVID, ANATOLII IVANOVICH
    1969A   Iskopaemye slony tiraspol'skogo faunisticheskogo kompleksa. Die fossilen Elephanten aus den Kiesen
                von Tiraspol. In: Mezhdunarodnyi kollokvium po geologii i faune nizhnego i srednego
                pleistotsena Evropy. Tezisy dokladov, 7–8, and 63–64 (Russian and German).

DUBROVO, I. A. and SHARKOV, A. A.
    1971A   Kit iz verkhnego oligofsena Mangyshlaka. [Whale from upper Oligocene of Mangyshlak.] Akad. Nauk
                SSSR, Dokl., 198:6, 1403–1406, 3 figs. (Russian).

DUBROVO, I. A. and SINEL'NIKOVA, VALENTINA NIKOLAEVNA
    1971A   Desmostilidy neogena Kamchatki. [Neogene desmostylids from Kamchatka.] Akad. Nauk SSSR,
                Dokl., 199:3, 670–673, 2 figs. (Russian).

DUBROVO, I. A.   See also: Alekseev, M. N., Giterman, R. E. and Dubrovo, I. A., 1972A; Gromova, V. I. and
                Dubrovo, I. A., 1969A; Siryk, I. M. and Dubrovo, I. A., 1970A.

DUCOS, PIERRE
    1968A   Remarques sur l'alternance daim-gazelle en Palestine. In: R. Vaufray, Festschrift, 161–164, 3 figs.
                (French; English summary).

DUFFY, L.   See: Broadhurst, F. M. and Duffy, L., 1970A.

DUGHI, R., PLAZIAT, J.-C. and SIRUGUE, F.
    1969A   La répartition stratigraphique des oeufs d'oiseaux du groupe d'*Ornitholothus arcuatus* D. et S. par
                rapport aux faunes d'eau douce et marines du Sparnacien et du Thanétien de l'Aude. Soc.
                Géol. Fr., C.R., 1969:1, 9–10, 1 fig. (French).

DUGHI, R. and SIRUGUE, FRANÇOIS
    1968B   Marnes à oeufs d'oiseaux du Paléocène de Basse-Provence. Soc. Géol. Fr., Bull., 10:5, 542–548,
                1 fig., 1 table (French).

DUGHI, RAYMOND   See also: Bessonnat, G., Dughi, R. and Sirugue, F., 1969A.

DUGUID, JAMES and BEDISH, G.
    1968A   An analysis of the Spanish diggings region of Wyoming during Paleolithic inhabitance. Wyo.
                Archaeol., 11:1, 3 figs., 2 pls., 4 maps.

DUISEBAEV, ZH. D. and MUSAKULOVA, LIAILIA TALIPOVNA
    1968A   Novaia nakhodka *Sivatherium* v Kazakhstane. [Newfind of *Sivatherium* in Kazakhstan.] In:
                Materialy 1-i Respublikanskoi nauchno-teoreticheskoi konferentsii molodykh geologov Kaz SSR,
                57 (Russian).

DUISEBAEV, ZH. D.   See also: Gus'kova, A. I., Duisebaev, Zh. D., Zhylkibaev, K. Zh. and Varnavskikh,
                B. E., 1971A.

DULHUNTY, J. A. and EADIE, J.
    1969A   Geology of the Talbragar fossil fish bed area . Roy. Soc. N.S.W., J., Proc., 102, 1–4, 1 fig.

DUMITRESCU, M., SAMSON, P., TERZEA, E., RĂDULESCU, C. and GHICA, M.
    1962-   Peştera "La Adam", staţiune pleistocenă. ["La Adam" Cave, a Pleistocene site.] Acad. Repub. Soc.
    1963A   Rom., Inst. Speol. "Emil Racoviţă", Lucr., 1–2, 229–284, 30 figs. (Rumanian; Russian and
                French summaries).

DUMITRESCU, MARGARETA   See also: Orghidan, T. and Dumitrescu, M., 1962–1963A.

DUNBAR, C. O. and WAAGE, K. M.
 1969A   Historical geology. Third edition. London: John Wiley, x + 556 pp., illustr.
                Rev.: Hammond in Sci. J., 6:6, 112; Wolf and Copper in Earth-Sci. Rev., 7:2, A85–A86.

DUNCAN, PETER M.   See: Talent, J. A., Duncan, P. M. and Handby, P. L., 1966A.

DUNKLE, DAVID H.
 1969A   A new amioid fish from the upper Cretaceous of Kansas. Kirtlandia, 7, 6 pp., 1 pl.
 1971A   Notes on an addition to the fish fauna of the Mowry shale (Cretaceous) of Wyoming. Kirtlandia,
                14, 8 pp., 2 figs.

DUNKLE, DAVID H. and LANE, N. GARY
 1971A   Devonian fishes from California. Kirtlandia, 15, 5 pp., 1 fig.

DUNKLE, DAVID H.   See also: Ray, C. E., Wetmore, A., Dunkle, D. H. and Drez, P., 1968A.

DUNN, DOROTHY
 1968A   American Indian painting of the southwest and plains areas. Albuquerque: Univ. of New Mexico
                Press, xxvii + 429 pp., 124 figs., 32 pls.
                Rev.: Howard in Amer. Antiquity, 34, 191–192.

DUPHORN, K., et al.
 1969A   Der VIII. INQUA – Kongress in Paris 1969. Eiszeitalter Gegenwart, 20, 252–267, 2 figs. (German).

DUPLESSIS-KERGOMARD, D.   See: David, E. and Duplessis-Kergomard, D., 1967A.

DUPORT, LOUIS
 1966A   Les gisements préhistoriques de la vallée des Eaux-Claires. Soc. Archéol. Hist. Charente, Mém., 1965,
                95–100, 1 fig., 5 pls. (French).
 1968A   Le gisement préhistorique de Montgaudier (Charente). Soc. Archéol. Hist. Charente, Mém., 1967,
                63–80, 3 pls. (French).
 1970A   Note sur la découverte de deux crânes humains Magdaléniens dans la Grotte de Montgaudier. Soc.
                Archéol. Hist. Charente, Mém.. 1969, 140–143, 1 fig., 3 pls. (French).
 1971A   Découverte de deux crânes humains dans la grotte de Montgaudier (Charente). Acad. Sci., C.R.,
                Sér. D, 273:12, 1015–1016 (French).
 1972A   Découverte d'un sol aménagé (vraisemblablement un lieu cultuel) à l'abri E. Lartet, grotte de
                Montgaudier, commune de Montbron (Charente). Acad. Sci., C.R., Sér. D, 274:6, 818–821,
                1 fig., 1 pl. (French).

DUPORT, LOUIS and VANDERMEERSCH, BERNARD
 1972A   La grotte de Montgaudier. La Recherche, 3:21, 280–281, 2 figs. (French).

DUPORT, L.   See also: Bouvier, J. M., Debénath, A., Delpech, F. and Duport, L., 1969A; David, P. and
                Duport, L., 1955A.

DURHAM, J. WYATT
 1971A   Correlation by fossils. Geotimes, 16, 33–34.
 1971B   Evolution of communities. Geotimes, 16, 34–35.
 1971C   The fossil record and the origin of the Deuterostomata. N. Amer. Paleontol. Conv., Proc., Part H,
                1104–1132, 25 figs.

DURHAM, J. WYATT   See also: Chappell, W. M., Durham, J. W. and Savage, D. E., 1970A.

DURRANT, STEPHEN D.
 1969A   Eugene Raymond Hall – biography and bibliography. Kans., Univ., Mus. Natur. Hist., Misc. Publ.,
                51, 9–24, portr.

DUTRO, J. THOMAS, JR.
 1970A   Paleontology. GeoTimes, 15:1, 20–21.
 1971A   Paleontology. GeoTimes, 16:1, 20–21.

DUTTA, PRATAP C.
 1971A   Earliest Indian human remains found in a late Stone Age site. Nature, 233:5320, 500–501, 1 fig.

DUTUIT, JEAN-MICHEL
 1971A   Quelques aspects techniques des recherches sur les vertébrés triasiques de l'Atlas Occidental. Soc. Sci.
          Natur. Phys. Maroc, Bull. (1970), 50:1—2, 9—25, 3 figs., 3 pls. (French).
 1972A   Découverte de pleurocentres dans les vertèbres de Stégocéphales métoposauridés. Acad. Sci., C. R.,
          Sér. D, 274:4, 536—537, 1 fig. (French).
 1972B   Découverte d'un dinosaure ornithischien dans le Trias supérieur de l'Atlas occidental marocain. Acad.
          Sci., C.R.. Sér. D, 275:25, 2841—2844, 1 fig. (French).

DZHAFAROVA, ZHANNET DZHAMIL'KYZY
 1968A   Ryby maĭkopskikh otlozheniĭ Azerbaĭdzhana i ikh stratigraficheskoe znachenie. [Fishes of Maĭkop
          deposits of Azerbaĭdzhan and their stratigraphical significance.] In: Granitsa tretichnogi i
          chetvertichnogo periodov, 56—59 (Russian; English summary).

DZHAFAROVA, ZH. D.   See also: Sultanov, K. M. and Dzhafarova, Zh. D., 1967A.

DZHAMBAZOV, N.
 1970A   Paleolitni nakhodki v peshterata Peshketo pri s. Liliàche, Vrachanski okrug. [Paleolithic findings in
          Peshketo cave near Liliàche village, Vrache district.] Arkheologiià, Sofia, 1970:1, 58—66,
          6 figs. (Bulgarian; French summary).

DZIEDZIC, KAZIMIERZ
 1961A   Utwory dolnopermskie w niecce śródsudeckiej. [Lower Permian of the intra-Sudetic basin.] Stud.
          Geol. Pol., 6, 121 pp. (Polish).

DZOTSENIDZE, N. M.   See: Adamiià, Sh. A., Dzotsenidze, N. M., Matskhonashvili, K. G. and Meladze,
          G. K., 1965A.

EADIE, J.   See: Dulhunty, J. A. and Eadie, J., 1969A.

EAKIN, RICHARD M.
 1970A   A third eye. Amer. Sci., 58:1, 73—79, 7 figs.

EASTHAM, ANNE
 1968A   The avifauna of Gorham's Cave, Gibraltar. London Univ., Inst. Archaeol., Bull., 7, 37—42, 1 table.

EATON, THEODORE H., JR.
 1970A   The stem-tail problem and the ancestry of chordates. J. Paleontol., 44:5, 969—979, 8 figs.
 1970B   Evolution. London: Nelson, xi + 270 pp.
          Rev.: Ballal in Amer. Sci., 58:3, 340; George in Nature, 228:5270, 481; McDowell in Quart. Rev.
          Biol., 45, 393—394.

EBERZIN, ANATOLIĬ GEORGIEVICH
 1957A   Tretichnaià sistema. Iuzhnyĭ Mangyshlak, Ustiùrt, Tuarkyr, Sarykamyshskaià vpadina, Uzboĭ i
          Kuniàdar'inskaià del'ta Amu-Dar'i. [Tertiary system. Southern Mangyshlak, Ustiùrt, Tuarkyr,
          Sarykamysh depression, Uzboĭ and Kuniàdar'ià delta of Amu-Dar'ià.] Geologiià SSSR, 22,
          Turkmenian SSR, 250—260, 1 fig. (Russian).

ECHOLS, BETTY JOAN
 1972A   Biostratigraphy and reptile faunas of the upper Austin and Taylor groups (upper Cretaceous) of
          Texas, with special reference to Hunt, Fannin, Lamar and Delta Counties, Texas. Diss. Abstr.,
          33:5, 2240B—2241B (abs.).
 1972B   Biostraigraphy and reptile faunas of the upper Austin and Taylor groups, upper Cretaceous, of
          northeast Texas. Soc. Vert. Paleontol., Ann. Meeting, 32nd, 1972, Abstr. (abs.).

ECK, G.   See: Howell, F. C., Fichter, L. S. and Eck, G., 1969A.

ECKHARDT, ROBERT B.
 1972A   Population genetics and human origins. Sci. Amer., 226:1, 94—103, illustr.
 1972B   Hominoid dental variation and hominid origins. Diss. Abstr., 32:7, 3755B (abs.).

EDITORIAL BOARD
 1970A   Georgiĭ Frantsevich Debets (7.XII 1905—19.I 1969). Akad. Nauk SSSR, Kom. Izuch. Chetvertich.
          Perioda, Biull., 37, 139—141, portr. (Russian).

EDITORS
1972A   P. P. Efimenko in memoriam [1880–1965]. Akad. Nauk SSSR, Inst. Arkheol., Krat. Soobshch., 131, 3–4, portr. (Russian).

EDITORS OF LIFE
1972A   Life before man. New York: Time-Life Books, 160 pp., illustr.

EDMUND, A. GORDON
1968A   Paleontology: from horse hobbles to bulldozers. Rotunda, 1:4, 14–20, 9 photos.
1969A   Dentition. In: Gans, C. (ed.), 1969A, 117–200, 51 figs., 8 tables.
1972A   Royal Ontario Museum, Toronto. Soc. Vert. Paleontol., News Bull., 96, 4–5.

EDWARDS, B. J. N.   See: Barnes, B., Edwards, B. J. N., Hallam, J. S. and Stuart, A. J., 1971A.

EDWARDS, NICHOLAS
1970A   The Hastings collection (fossil vertebrates): history of additions made by the Marchioness of Hastings between 1845–1851 from the upper Eocene beds at Hordle Cliff, Hampshire. Soc. Bibliogr. Natur. Hist., J., 5:5, 340–343.

EDWARDS, N. and STINTON, F. C.
1971A   A fish fauna from the lower Tertiary marine bed, Clapham Common, west Sussex. Geol. Ass. (London), Proc., 82:4, 449–453.

EDWARDS, ROBERT
1968A   Field photography. In: Mulvaney, D. J., 1968A, 63–110, 4 pls.

EDWARDS, W. N.
1967A   The early history of palaeontology. London: Trustees Brit. Mus. (Natur. Hist.), 658, V–VIII and 59 pp., 19 figs.
         Rev.: Hölder in Zentralbl. Geol. Paläontol., Teil 2, 1969:2, 116.

EGAN, GAIL NOEL   See: Agogino, G. A. and Egan, G. N., 1972A.

EGOROV, A. E., ZARUBIN, S. I. and SIRYK, I. M.
1968A   O nakhodke skeleta kitoobraznogo v otlozheniíakh kholmskoĭ svity (miofsen) na o. Sakhaline. [On the finding of a cetacean skeleton in the deposits of Kholmsk suite (Miocene) on Sakhalin Island.] Akad. Nauk SSSR, Sibirsk. Otd., Sakhalinsk. Kompleks. Nauch.-Issled. Inst., Trudy, 18, 188–190, 1 fig. (Russian).

EHARA, AKIYOSHI and SEILER, ROLF
1970A   Die Strukturen der Überaugenregion bei den Primaten, Deutungen und Definitionen. Z. Morphol. Anthropol., 62:1, 1–29, 7 figs. (German; English summary).

EHRENBERG, KURT
1966F*   Die Teufels- oder Fuchsenlucken bei Eggenburg (NÖ.). Österreich. Akad. Wiss., Denk., 112, 158 pp., 6 figs., 15 pls., 19 tables (German).
1966G   Die Teufels- oder Fuchslucken bei Eggenburg (NÖ.). I. Die bisher veröffentlichten Ergebnisse über die Erforschung der Höhle und die Untersuchung ihrer Funde nebst einigen Ergänzungen. Österreich. Akad. Wiss., Denk., 112, 7–14, 1 fig. (German).
1966H   Die Teufels- oder Fuchsenlucken bei Eggenburg (NÖ.). II. Der Fundbestand in seiner Gesamtheit. Eine biospeläologisch-biohistorische Schlussbetrachtung. Österreich. Akad. Wiss., Denk., 112, 137–158, 1 fig., 5 tables (German).
1967B   Der Höhlenbär, sein Vorkommen und seine Beziehungen zur Umwelt. Österreich. Arbeitsgemeinsch. Ur- und Frühgesch., 18:3–4, 34–50, 3 pls. (German).
         Rev.: Ehrenberg in Zentralbl. Geol. Paläontol., Teil 2, 1968:6, 662.
1968A   Paläobiologische und biohistorische Bemerkungen zu Artefakt-Problemen des Paläolithikums. Quartär, 19, 81–92 (German).

EHRENBERG, K. and MAIS, KARL
1968A   Die Forschungen in der Schlenkendurchgangshöhle bei Vigaun im Sommer 1967. Österreich. Akad. Wiss., Math-Natur. Kl., Anz., 105, 105–122, 4 figs. (German).
1970A   Die Forschung in der Schlenkendurchgangshöhle im Sommer 1968. Österreich. Akad. Wiss., Math.-Naturwiss. Kl., Anz., 106 (1969), 35–46 (German).
1970B   Die Expedition in die Schlenkendurchgangshöhle im Sommer 1969. Österreich. Akad. Wiss., Math.-Naturwiss. Kl., Anz., 106 (1969), 301–312 (German).

EHRENBERG, K., RUCKENSTEINER, E., ADAM, H. and FRIEDL, H.
1969A   Ein fossiler Knochentumor aus der Schlenkendurchgangshöhle in Salzburg. Österreich. Akad. Wiss.,
           Math.-Naturwiss. Kl., Abt. I, Sitz.-Ber., 178:1—4, 63—76, 5 pls. (German).
           Rev.: Ehrenberg in Zentralbl. Geol. Paläontol., Teil 2, 1970:3/4, 238.

EHRLICH, P. R., HOLM, R. W. and RAVEN, P. H.
1969A*   Papers on evolution. Boston: Little, Brown & Co., 564 pp., illustr.
           Rev.: Martin and Steinberg in Quart. Rev. Biol., 45, 396.

EHRMAN, LEE   See: Levene, H., Ehrman, L. and Richmond, R., 1970A.

EIDSON, REX
1961A   Last days of Petroglyph Canyon. Sci. of Man, 1, 184—188, illustr.

EÍNOR, OL'GERD LEONARDOVICH
1968A   Problema vida v paleontologii. [The problem of species in paleontology.] In: Problemy paleontolog⁀
           57—72, 1 fig. (Russian; English summary).

EISELEY, LOREN
1970A   The star dragon. Natur. Hist., 79:6, 18—26, 74—77.
1970B   How man became natural. In: Young, L. B. (ed.), 1970A, 234—237 (reprinted from Eiseley, L.,
           1960, "The firmament of time").
1971A   Creature from the marsh. Natur. Hist., 80:8, 24, 26—28, 32, 34.

EISENBERG, J. F. and DILLON, WILTON S.
1971A*   Man and beast. Comparative social behavior. Washington, D.C.: Smithsonian Institution Press,
           Smithsonian Annual 3, 401 pp., illustr.
           Rev.: Brown in Science, 174:4013, 1013.

EISENBERG, LEONARD
1971A   The earliest hominid. Man (J. Roy. Anthropol. Inst.), 6:1, 118—119.
           Rev.: Anon. in Interamer., 18:6, 6.

EISENMANN, VÉRA
1969A   Sur l'existence d'un type "mustélidé" d'humérus chez les fissipèdes des Phosphorites du Quercy. Aca⁀
           Sci., C.R., Sér. D, 268:26, 3164—3166, 1 fig. (French).

EKHOLM, GORDON F. and WILLEY, GORDON R.
1966A*   Archaeological frontiers and external connections. Handbk. Mid. Amer. Ind., 4, 367 pp., 143 figs.,
           7 maps, 3 tables.
           Rev.: Winning in Amer. J. Archaeol., 72:1, 91—94.

EKLUND, RAYMOND R., JR.
1969A   Oligocene mammals common to the Brule formation in western Nebraska. Rocks Miner., 44:6,
           456—457.

EL-BAZ, FAROUK   See: Häntzschel, W., El-Baz, F. and Amstutz, G. C., 1968A.

ELDREDGE, NILES and GOULD, STEPHEN JAY
1972A   Punctuated equilibria: an alternative to phyletic gradualism. In: Schopf, T. J. M. (ed.), 1972A,
           82—115, 10 figs., 1 table.

ELDREDGE, NILES   See also: Schaeffer, B., Hecht, M. K. and Eldredge, N., 1972A.

ELLENBERGER, F., ELLENBERGER, P. and GINSBURG, L.
1969A   The appearance and evolution of dinosaurs in the Trias and Lias: a comparison between South African
           upper Karroo and western Europe based on vertebrate footprints. Symp. Gondwana Stratigr.,
           333—354, 3 figs. (Spanish summary).
1970A   Les dinosaures du Trias et du Lias en France et en Afrique du Sud, d'après les pistes qu'ils ont laissées.
           Soc. Géol. Fr., C.R., 1970:2, 43 (French).
1970B   Les dinosaures du Trias et du Lias en France et en Afrique du Sud, d'après les pistes qu'ils ont laissées.
           Soc. Géol. Fr., Bull., 12:1, 151—159, 3 figs. (French).

ELLENBERGER, PAUL   See: Ellenberger, F., Ellenberger, P. and Ginsburg, L., 1969A, 1970A, 1970B.

ELLERN, SEMEN SAMUILOVICH   See: Sereda, T. T., Ellern, S. S. and Lîashenko, A. I., 1967A.

ELLIOT, D. H., COLBERT, E. H., BREED, W. J., JENSEN, J. A. and POWELL, J. S.
  1970A   Triassic tetrapods from Antarctica: evidence for continental drift. Science (AAAS), 169:3951,
            1197–1201, 4 figs., 1 table.

ELLIOT, DAVID H.   See also: Kitching, J. W., Collinson, J. W., Elliot, D. H. and Colbert, E. H., 1972A.

ELLIOT-SMITH, GRAFTON
  1972A   Man's pedigree. In: McCown, T. D. and Kennedy, K. A. R. (eds.), 1972A, 228–239, 4 figs.
            (reprinted from Evolution of Man, 1924).

ELLIS, RICHARD P.
  1966A   The founding, history, and significance of Peale's Museum in Philadelphia, 1785–1841. Curator, 9:3,
            235–258, 6 figs.

ELLWOOD, BROOKS   See: Swift, C. and Ellwood, B., 1972A.

ELSASSER, ALBERT B.   See: Heizer, R. F., Elsasser, A. B. and Clewlow, C. W., Jr., 1970A.

ELTING, MARY and FOLSOM, FRANKLIN
  1971A   In the days of the wild mammoth hunters. New York: Four Winds Press, 71 pp. (juvenile).
            Rev.: Moore in Archaeology, 24:2, 176; Anon. in Archeol. Soc. N. J., News., 84, 7.

EMEL'IANOV, S. V.
  1968A   Razrabotka v SSSR idei A.N. Severtšova ob individual'nom i istoricheskom razvitii organizmov.
            [Elaboration in the USSR of A.N. Severtšov's ideas on ontogenesis and phylogenesis.]
            Zh. Obshch. Biol., 29:1, 3–11 (Russian; English summary).
  1969A   Professor Boris Stepanovich Matveev (k 80–letiîu so dniâ rozhdeniîa). [Professor B. S. Matveev
            (to the 80th anniversary).] Zool. Zh., 48:9, 1421–1422, portr. (Russian).

EMILIANI, CESARE
  1968A   The Pleistocene epoch and the evolution of man. With comments and reply. Current Anthropol.,
            9:1, 27–47, 4 figs.
            Rev.: Anon. in Anthropos, 63/64:1/2, 265.

EMMONS, EBENEZER
  1969A   Report of the North Carolina Geological Survey; agriculture of the eastern counties; together with
            descriptions of the fossils of the marl beds. Bull. Amer. Paleontol., 56:249, 68–230, 256 figs.
            (reprint in part of the 1858 edition).

EMPEREUR-BUISSON, R.   See: Fenart, R. and Empereur-Buisson, R., 1970A.

EMRY, ROBERT J.
  1970A   A North American Oligocene pangolin and other additions to the Pholidota. Amer. Mus. Natur. Hist.,
            Bull., 142:6, pp. 455–510, 32 figs.
            Rev.: Thenius in Zentralbl. Geol. Paläontol., Teil 2, 1971:4, 340–341.
  1971A   Stratigraphy and paleontology of the Flagstaff rim area, Natrona County, Wyoming. Diss. Abstr., 32:1,
            459B (abs.).
  1972A   A new heteromyid rodent from the early Oligocene of Natrona County, Wyoming. Biol. Soc. Wash.,
            Proc., 85:14, 179–190, 2 figs., 1 table.

EMRY, ROBERT J. and DAWSON, MARY R.
  1972A   A unique cricetid (Rodentia, Mammalia) from the early Oligocene of Natrona County, Wyoming.
            Amer. Mus. Nov., 2508, 14 pp., 3 figs., 1 table.

ENDO, BANRI
  1967A   Mechanical analysis of the form of the human facial skeleton. Discussion. Int. Congr. Anthropol.
            Ethnol. Sci., 7th, Moscow, 1964, Proc., 2, 346–353, 8 figs.
  1971A   Some characteristics of the deltoid tuberosity of the humerus in the west Asian and the European
            "classic" Neanderthals. Anthropol. Soc. Nippon, J., 79:3, 249–258, 3 figs., 2 tables
            (Japanese summary).

ENDO, BANRI and KIMURA, TASUKU
  1970A   Postcranial skeleton of the Amud man. In: Suzuki, H. and Takai, F. (eds.), 1970A, 231–406, 44 figs.,
            18 pls., 47 tables.

ENGELBRECHT, D. VAN Z.
 1969A The annelid ancestry of the chordates and the origin of the chordate central nervous system and the notochord. Z. Zool. Syst. Evolut.-Forsch., 7:1, 18—30, 5 figs. (German summary).
 1971A The phylogenetic origin of the lateral eyes and the optic chiasma of vertebrates. Z. Zool. Syst. Evolut.-Forsch., 9:1, 30—48, 3 figs. (German summary).

ENGESSER, BURKART
 1972A Die obermiozäne Säugetierfauna von Anwil (Baselland). Naturforsch. Ges. Baselland, Tätigkeitsber., 28, 37—363, 134 figs., 6 pls., 8 tables, 38 diagrams (German; French and English summaries).

ENGOÎAN, M. A. See: Garkusha, M. P., Engoîan, M. A., Oganesîan, D. A. and Sukiasîan, S. S., 1971A.

ENLOW, DONALD H.
 1969A The bone of reptiles. In: Gans, C. (ed.), 1969A, 45—80, 29 figs.

ENNOUCHI, ÉMILE
 1969A Présence d'un enfant néanderthalien au Jebel Irhoud (Maroc). Ann. Paléontol. Vertébrés, 55:2, 251—265, 10 figs., 1 table (French).
 1969B Découverte d'un pithécanthropien au Maroc. Acad. Sci., C.R., Sér. D, 269:7, 763—765 (French).
 1969C Les empreintes des cerveaux des Néanderthaliens marocains. Morocco, Serv. Géol., Notes Mém., 29, no. 213, 63—70, 6 figs. (French).
 1970A Un nouvel archanthropien au Maroc. Ann. Paléontol. Vertébrés, 56:1, 95—107, 4 figs., 2 tables (French).
 1971A Camille Arambourg (1885—1969). Soc. Sci. Natur. Phys. Maroc, Bull. (1970), 50:1—2, 1—7, portr. (French).
 1972A Nouvelle découverte d'un Archanthropien au Maroc. Acad. Sci., C.R., Sér. D, 274:23, 3088—3090 (French).

EPSTEIN, H.
 1971A The origin of the domestic animals of Africa. New York, London and Munich: Africana Publishing Corporation, 2 vols., 1292 pp., 1297 figs.
    Rev.: Evans in Amer. Sci., 60:5, 618—619; Matthews in Nature, 237:5354, 354.

ERBAEVA, MARGARITA ALEKSANDROVNA (= ERBAJEVA, M. A. = YERBAYEVA, M. A.)
 1964A Usloviiā nakopleniiā ostatkov melkikh mlekopitaiūshchikh v verkhnem sloe Tologoĭskogo mestonakhozhdeniiā (Zapadnoe Zabaĭkal'e) i osobennosti sostava ego fauny. [Conditions of accumulation of small mammal remains in the upper layer of Tologoĭ faunal locality (western Transbaikalia) and particularities in the composition of its fauna.] In: Vsesoiūznoe Soveshchanie po Izucheniiū Chetvertichnogo perioda, Novosibirsk, 1964, Tezisy Dokladov, Sektŝiiā Istorii Flory, Fauny i Drevnego Cheloveka, 16—18 (Russian).
 1968A Taphonomie der Fundstellen von Kleinsäugerresten des Anthropogens in Westtransbaikalien. Deut. Ges. Geol. Wiss., Ber., Reihe A, Geol. Paläontol., 13:3, 335—340, 1 fig., 1 table (German).
 1968B Ranneantropogenovaiā fauna melkikh mlekopitaiūshchikh Zapadnogo Zabaĭkal'iā. [Early Anthropogene fauna of small mammals of the western Transbaikalia.] In: Problemy izucheniiā chetvertichnogo perioda. Tezisy, 112 (Russian).
 1969A Die Besonderheiten der Pleistozänfauna im westlichen Transbaikalien (Ud SSR). Deut. Ges. Geol. Wiss., Ber., Reihe A, Geol. Paläontol., 14:4, 477—480 (German).
 1970A Istoriiā antropogenovoĭ fauny zaĭŝeobraznykh i gryzunov Selenginskogo srednegor'iā. [History of the Anthropogene fauna of lagomorphs and rodents from Selenga mountains.] Moscow: "Nauka" Press, 132 pp., 2 figs., 24 pls., 17 tables (Russian).
 1972A Bol'shoĭ tushkanchik (Allactaga jaculus Pall.) iz alliuviiā srednego techeniiā Obi. [A large jerboa (Allactaga jaculus Pall.) from the alluvium of the middle course of the Ob' R.] Akad. Nauk SSSR, Kom. Izuch. Chetvertich. Perioda, Biūll., 38, 148—150, 1 fig. (Russian).

ERBAEVA, M. A. See also: Vangengeĭm, E. A., Erbaeva, M. A., Zhegallo, V. I. and Sotnikova, M. V., 1968A.

ERBEN, H. K.
 1971A Otto Heinrich Schindewolf (7.6.1896—10.6.1971). Paläontol. Z., 45:3/4, 95—96, portr. (German).
 1971B Otto Heinrich Schindewolf. [1896—1971]. Palaeontographica, Abt. A, 138:5—6, 131—132, portr. (German).

ERDBRINK, D. P.
 1964B Comparaison des ramures récentes et fossiles du Cerf élaphe. Mammalia, 28, 628—650, 2 figs. (French; English summary).
 1968A A collection of mammalian fossils from S.E. Shansi, China. II. Natuurhist. Genoot. Limburg, Publ., 18:3—4, 17—48, 2 figs., 7 pls. (Dutch summary).

1968B   The bones from Bunde reconsidered: a reply. Natuurhist. Genoot. Limburg, Publ., 18:3—4, 52—55.
1972A   A new find of a cave hyaena from the Netherlands. Geol. Mijnbouw, 51:4, 487—490, 3 figs., 1 table.
1972B   Two late Pleistocene pinnipede remains in a private collection. Lutra, 14:1—3, 24—32, 2 pls., 1 table.

ERDBRINK, D. P. and TACOMA, J.
1967A   Another fossil human femur from the Meuse valley near Beegden. Natuurhist. Genoot. Limburg,
            Publ., 17, 1—4, 4 figs. (Dutch summary).
1968A   Another human skull from Rees, Germany. Ned. Akad. Wetensch., Proc., Ser. C, 71:5, 487—494,
            1 fig., 1 pl., 1 table.

ERDBRINK, D. P., TACOMA, J. and VISSER, H.
1966A   A fossil human bone from Anatolia. Ned. Akad. Wetensch., Proc., Ser. C, 69:4, 490—501, 4 figs.,
            4 pls.

ERDBRINK, D. P. and VAN ASCH, TH. W. J.
1972A   Çakil Kaya (Halevik) and its fossil elephant. I. Ned. Akad. Wetensch., Proc., Ser. C, 75:3, 185—199,
            4 figs., 5 pls.

ERDBRINK, D. P.   See also: Bartheld, F. von, Erdbrink, D. P. and Krommenhoek, W., 1970A, 1970B.

ERDELI, I.   See: Bader, O. N., Erdeli, I. and Ranov, V. A., 1969A.

ERGENZINGER, PETER   See: Servant, M., Ergenzinger, P. and Coppens, Y., 1969A.

ERICKSON, BRUCE R.
1968A   A claw of Megalonyx (ground sloth) from Minnesota. St. Paul Inst., Sci. Mus., Sci. Publ., New Ser.,
            1:3, 6 pp., 1 fig., 2 pls.
1969A   A new species of crocodile, Teleorhinus mesabiensis, from the Iron Range Cretaceous. St. Paul Inst.,
            Sci. Mus., Sci. Publ., New Ser., 1:4, 8 pp., 1 fig., 3 pls.
1972A   The lepidosaurian reptile Champsosaurus in North America. Minn., Sci. Mus., Monogr., 1, 91 pp.,
            65 figs., 2 tables.
1972B   Alligator ancestors. Explorer (Cleveland Mus. Natur. Hist.), 14:3, 18—21, 3 figs.
1972C   Albertochampsa langstoni, gen. et sp. nov., a new alligator from the Cretaceous of Alberta. St. Paul
            Inst., Sci. Mus., Sci. Publ., New Ser., 2:1, 1—13, 6 figs.

ERIKSON, G. E.
1962A   Adaptive radiation in the New World primates. Amer. Anthropol. Ass., Abstr., 1962, 11 (abs.).

ERITSIAN, B. G. and SEMENOV, S. A.
1971A   Novaîa nizhnepaleoliticheskaîa peshchera "Erevan". [New lower Paleolithic cave "Erevan".] Akad.
            Nauk SSSR, Inst. Arkheol., Krat. Soobshch., 126, 32—36, 4 figs. (Russian).

ERK, FRANK C.   See: Keast, A., Erk, F. C. and Glass, B. (eds.), 1972A.

ERMOLOVA, N. M.
1971A   K izucheniîu fauny mlekopitaîushchikh paleolita Eniseîa (verkhnepaleoliticheskaîa stoîanka Kokorevo I).
            [A study on the mammal fauna of Enisei Paleolithic (upper Paleolithic station Kokorevo I).]
            Akad. Nauk SSSR, Inst. Arkheol., Krat. Soobshch., 126, 22—24, 1 fig., 1 table (Russian).

EROFEEV, V. S.
1969A   Geologicheskaîa istoriîa îuzhnoî periferii Altaîa v paleogene i neogene. [Geological history of the
            southern periphery of Altaî in Paleogene and Neogene.] Alma-Ata: "Nauka" Press, 164 pp.,
            illustr. (Russian).

EROFEEV, V. S.   See also: Bazhanov, V. S. and Erofeev, V. S., 1971A.

EROSHKIN, A. F. and SAVINOV, P. F.
1971A   O vozraste shurysaîskoî ritmosvity Severo-Vostochnoî Fergany. [On the age of Shury-Saî rhythm-suite
            of northeastern Fergana.] Tashkent Univ., Nauchn. Tr., 407, 98—99 (Russian).

ESCALON DE FONTON, MAX
1970A   Informations archéologiques. Circonscription Languedoc-Roussillon. Gallia Préhist., 13:2, 513—549,
            62 figs. (French).

ESCHMAN, DONALD F.   See: Dorr, J. A., Jr. and Eschman, D. F., 1970A.

ESHELMAN, RALPH E.
  1972A   Early Pleistocene vertebrates from the Belleville formation, Republic County, Kansas. Soc. Vert.
                 Paleontol. Ann. Meeting, 32nd, 1972, Abstr. (abs.).

ESPEJO, J. A. and TORRES, T. DE
  1969A   Nota previa sobre el descubrimiento de un yacimiento de fósiles cuaternarios en la ría de Ea (Vizcaya).
                 [Preliminary note on the discovery of a locality containing Quaternary fossils in the ría de Ea
                 (Vizcaya).] Spain, Inst. Geol. Minero, Bol. Geol. Minero, 80:2, 25–26 (Spanish; English and
                 French summaries).
                 Rev.: H.-P. in Soc. Españ. Hist. Natur., Bol., Secc. Geol., 67:3, 355.

ESPITALIÉ, R.   See: Champagne, F. and Espitalié, R., 1970A.

ESTES, RICHARD
  1969A   Relationships of two Cretaceous lizards (Sauria, Teiidae). Breviora, 317, 8 pp., 3 figs.
  1969B   The fossil record of amphiumid salamanders. Breviora, 322, 11 pp., 5 figs.
                 Rev.: Westphal in Zentralbl. Geol. Paläontol., Teil 2, 1970:1, 67.
  1969C   A new fossil discoglossid frog from Montana and Wyoming. Breviora, 328, 7 pp., 4 figs.
                 Rev.: Westphal in Zentralbl. Geol. Paläontol., Teil 2, 1970:1, 67–68.
  1969D   A scincoid lizard from the Cretaceous and Paleocene of Montana. Breviora, 331, 9 pp., 5 figs.
  1969E   Two new late Cretaceous fishes from Montana and Wyoming. Breviora, 335, 15 pp., 4 pls.
  1969F   The Batrachosauroididae and Scapherpetontidae, late Cretaceous and early Cenozoic salamanders.
                 Copeia, 69:2, 225–234, 7 figs.
                 Rev.: Westphal in Zentralbl. Geol. Paläontol., Teil 2, 1970:1, 68.
  1969G   Studies on fossil phyllodont fishes: interrelationships and evolution in the Phyllodontidae (Albuloidei).
                 Copeia, 69:2, 317–331, 8 figs.
  1969H   Studies on fossil phyllodont fishes: Casierius, a new genus of albulid from the Cretaceous of Europe
                 and North America. Eclogae Geol. Helv., 62:2, 751–755, 2 pls.
  1969I   Prosirenidae, a new family of fossil salamanders. Nature, 224:5214, 87–88, 2 figs.
                 Rev.: Westphal in Zentralbl. Geol. Paläontol., Teil 2, 1970:6, 513–514.
  1969J   Die Fauna der miozänen Spaltenfüllung von Neudorf an der March (ČSSR) Reptilia (Lacertilia).
                 Österreich. Akad. Wiss., Math.-Naturwiss. Kl., Abt. I, Sitz-Ber., 178, 77–82, 2 pls. (German;
                 English summary).
  1970A   The status of Palaeosiren beinerti, a supposed Permian aïstopod amphibian. J. Paleontol., 44:1,
                 140–141.
                 Rev.: Westphal in Zentralbl. Geol. Paläontol., Teil 2, 1970:3/4, 227–228.
  1970B   New fossil pelobatid frogs and a review of the genus Eopelobates. Harvard Univ., Mus. Comp. Zool.,
                 Bull., 139:6, 293–339, 31 figs., 2 tables.
                 Rev.: Westphal in Zentralbl. Geol. Paläontol., Teil 2, 1971:4, 334.
  1970C   Origin of the recent North American lower vertebrate fauna: an inquiry into the fossil record. Forma
                 et Functio, 3, 139–163, 5 figs. (French and German summaries).
  1971A   Evidence from Cretaceous and Cenozoic herpetofaunas bearing on continental drift. Geol. Soc.
                 Amer., Abstr., 3:7, 559 (abs.).
  1972A   Paleocene amphibians and reptiles from Brazil. Soc. Vert. Paleontol., Ann. Meeting, 32nd, 1972,
                 Abstr. (abs.).

ESTES, R. and BERBERIAN, PAUL
  1969A   Amia (= Kindleia) fragosa (Jordan), a Cretaceous amiid fish, with notes on related European forms.
                 Breviora, 329, 14 pp., 4 figs., 1 pl., 1 table.
  1970A   Paleoecology of a late Cretaceous vertebrate community from Montana. Breviora, 343, 35 pp., 3 figs.,
                 5 tables.
                 Rev.: Westphal in Zentralbl. Geol. Paläontol., Teil 2, 1970:6, 514.

ESTES, R., BERBERIAN, P. and MESZOELY, C. A. M.
  1969A   Lower vertebrates from the late Cretaceous Hell Creek formation, McCone County, Montana. Breviora,
                 337, 33 pp., 4 figs., 1 pl., 2 tables.
                 Rev.: Westphal in Zentralbl. Geol. Paläontol., Teil 2, 1970:6, 514.

ESTES, R., FRAZZETTA, T. H. and WILLIAMS, E. E.
  1970A   Studies on the fossil snake Dinilysia patagonica Woodward. Part 1. Cranial morphology. Harvard
                 Univ., Mus. Comp. Zool., Bull., 140:2, 25–73, 12 figs., 5 pls.

ESTES, R. and WAKE, MARVALEE H.
  1972A   The first fossil record of caecilian amphibians. Nature, 239:5369, 228–231, 1 fig., 1 table.

ESTES, RICHARD   See also: Cameron, B. and Estes, R., 1971A; Welles, S. P. and Estes, R., 1969A;
                 Nevo, E. and Estes, R., 1969A.

ETTEL, PETER C.   See: Simons, E. L. and Ettel, P. C., 1970A; Simons, E. L., Pilbeam, D. and Ettel,
P. C., 1969A.

EVERNDEN, JACK F. and EVERNDEN, ROBERTA K. SMITH
1970A   The Cenozoic time scale. Geol. Soc. Amer., Spec. Pap., 124, 71—90, 4 figs., 1 table.

EVERNDEN, R. K. S.   See: Evernden, J. F. and Evernden, R. K. S., 1970A.

EVERY, RONALD G.
1965A   The teeth as weapons. Their influence on behaviour. Lancet, 1:7387, 685—688.
1970A   Sharpness of teeth in man and other primates. Postilla, 143, 30 pp., 5 figs., 5 pls.

EVERY, RONALD G. and KÜHNE, WALTER G.
1970A   Funktion und Form der Säugerzähne I. Thegosis, Usur und Druckusur. Z. Säugetierkunde, 35:4,
247—252, 3 figs. (German; English summary).
Rev.: Thenius in Zentralbl. Geol. Paläontol., Teil 2, 1971:1, 61.
1970B   Biomodal wear in the mammalian dentition. Linn. Soc., Biol. J., 2:4, 318 (abs.).
1971A   Bimodal wear of mammalian teeth. Linn. Soc., Zool. J., 50:suppl. 1, 23—27, 1 fig., 1 pl.

EVIN, J.   See: David, L., Evin, J., Guérin, C., Mongereau, N. and Walter, B., 1972A.

EWER, R. F.   See: Cooke, H. B. S. and Ewer, R. F., 1972A.

EYLES, JOAN MARY
1969A   William Smith (1769—1839). A chronology of significant dates in his life. Geol. Soc. London, Proc.,
1657, 173—176.

FABRE, FRED
1970A   Paléo-climats et coéfficients thermiques. Mus. Hist. Natur. Marseille, Bull., 30, 205—220, 2 pls.
(French).

FABRI, K. E.
1968A   Khvatatel'naîa funktsiîa ruki primatov i faktory ee evolîutsionnogo razvitiîa. [Prehensile function of
the hand of Primates and the factors of its evolution.] Discussion. Int. Congr. Anthropol.,
Ethnol. Sci., 7th, Moscow, 1964, Proc., 3, 496—502 (Russian).

FACCHINI, FIORENZO
1969A   Sul pensiero e l'opera di Pierre Teilhard de Chardin in paleontologia umana. Verona, Mus. Civ. Stor.
Natur., Mem., Fuori ser., 3, 229—248 (Italian; English summary).

FAGAN, BRIAN M.
1966A*   A short history of Zambia (from the earliest times until A.D. 1900). Nairobi: Oxford Univ. Press,
xii + 164 pp., 43 figs., 17 pls., 3 tables.
Rev.: Vilakazi in Amer. Anthropol., 70, 413—414.
1970A*   Introductory readings in archaeology. Boston: Little, Brown and Co., xi + 366 pp., illustr.
Rev.: Kellar in Amer. Anthropol., 73:6, 1394—1395.
1972A   In the beginning. An introduction to archaeology. Boston: Little, Brown and Co., xvi + 356 pp.,
illustr.

FAGE, J. D. and OLIVER, R. A.
1970A*   Papers in African prehistory. Cambridge: Cambridge University Press, xii + 331 pp., illustr.
Rev.: Pittioni in Archaeol. Austriaca, 50, 387—388.

FAGE, J. D.   See also: Oliver, R. and Fage, J. D., 1962A.

FAGG, BERNARD
1969A   Recent work in West Africa: new light on the Nok culture. World Archaeol., 1:1, 41—50, 2 figs.
Rev.: Mauny in Inst. Fond. Afr. Noire, Bull., 31:4, 1218.

FAHLBUSCH, VOLKER
1968A   Neue Eomyidae (Rodentia, Mamm.) aus einer aquitanen Spaltenfüllung von Weissenburg in Bayern.
Bayer. Staatssamml. Paläontol. Hist. Geol., Mitt., 8, 219—245, 9 figs., 2 pls. (German; English
summary).

1969A   Pliozäne und Pleistozäne Cricetinae (Rodentia, Mammalia) aus Polen. Acta Zool. Crac., 14:5, 99—138,
          4 figs., pls. 8—18 (German; Polish and Russian summaries).
1969B   *Pseudotheridomys pusillus* n. sp., ein neuer Eomyide (Rodentia, Mam.) aus dem Oligozän
          Süddeutschlands. Neues Jahrb. Geol. Paläontol., Monatsh., 1969:11, 673—679, 1 fig. (German;
          English summary).
1970A   Populationsverschiebungen bei tertiären Nagetieren, eine Studie an oligozänen und miozänen Eomyidae
          Europas. Bayer. Akad. Wiss., Math.-Naturwiss. Kl., Abh., 145, 136 pp., 42 figs., 11 pls.,
          26 tables (German; English summary).
          Rev.: Groiss in Geol. Bl. Nordost-Bayern, 21:1, 62.
1970B   Carnegie fossils in Bavaria. Carnegie Mag., 44:3, 111—113, 3 figs.
1970C   Phylogenie und stratigraphische Bedeutung der miozänen Cricetiden (Mamm., Rodentia) Südbayerns.
          G. Geol., 35:1, 153—159 (German).

FAHLBUSCH, V. and GALL, HORST
1970A   Die obermiozäne Fossil-Lagerstätte Sandelzhausen. 1. Entdeckung, Geologie, Faunenübersicht und
          Grabungsbericht für 1969. Bayer. Staatssamml. Paläontol. Hist. Geol., Mitt., 10, 365—396,
          9 figs., 1 pl. (German; English summary).

FAHLBUSCH, V., GALL, H. and SCHMIDT-KITTLER, N.
1972A   Die obermiozäne Fossil-Lagerstätte Sandelzhausen. 2. Sediment und Fossilinhalt-Probleme der Genese
          und Ökologie. Neues Jahrb. Geol. Paläontol., Monatsh., 1972:6, 331—343, 1 fig. (German;
          English summary).

FAHLBUSCH, V. and SCHMIDT-KITTLER, N.
1969A   Über eine weitere unteroligozäne Spaltenfüllung von Weissenburg in Bayern. Bayer. Staatssamml.
          Paläontol. Hist. Geol., Mitt., 9, 209—211 (German; English summary).

FAHLBUSCH, VOLKER   See also: Cicha, I., Fahlbusch, V. and Fejfar, O., 1972A; Dehm, R. and Fahlbusch,
          V., 1970A; Freudenthal, M. and Fahlbusch, V., 1969A.

FARB, PETER
1968A   The exploiters. Audubon Mag., 70:6, 32—45, illustr.

FARNER, D. S., KING, J. R. and PARKES, K. C.
1971A*   Avian biology. Vol. 1. New York: Academic Press, xx + 586 pp., illustr.
          Rev.: D. L. in Isis, 114:3, 405; Johnston in Auk, 89:2, 465—467; Keast in Science, 175:4027, 1233.

FARRINGTON, BENJAMIN
1966A   What Darwin really said. London: Macdonald, 124 pp.
          Rev.: Eriksson in Lychnos, 1967—1968, 381—382 (Swedish).
1967A   El evolucionismo. Iniciación a la teoría del origen de las especies. Translated from English.
          Barcelona: Ed. Cultura Popular, 124 pp. (Spanish).
          Rev.: Templado in Arbor, 269, 106—107.

FASOLA, ARMANDO
1966A   Hallazgo de huellas de dinosáurios en el Alto Tinguiririca. Chile, Mus. Nac. Hist. Natur., Notic. Mens.,
          119 (Spanish).

FASOLA, ARMANDO   See also: Casamiquela, R. M. and Fasola, A., 1968A.

FASSETT, JAMES E. and HINDS, JIM S.
1971A   Geology and fuel resources of the Fruitland formation and Kirtland shale of the San Juan Basin,
          New Mexico and Colorado. U.S. Geol. Surv., Prof. Paper, 676, iv + 76 pp., 27 figs., 3 pls.,
          8 tables.

FAUL, HENRY
1971A   Potassium-argon dating. In: Michael, H. N. and Ralph, E. K. (eds.), 1971A, 157—163, 1 table.

FAUL, HENRY and WAGNER, GÜNTHER A.
1971A   Fission track dating. In: Michael, H. N. and Ralph, E. K. (eds.), 1971A, 152—156, 1 fig., 1 table.

FAY, GEORGE E.
1969A   A bibliography of fossil man of the Old World. Suppl. 1: 1963—1968. Greely, Colo.: Mus. of
          Anthropology, Colorado State College, Mimeo., 71 pp.
          Rev.: Compton in Interamer., 16:8, 1.

FEDELE, FRANCESCO
1968A Deuxième campagne de fouilles sur le Monfenera (Borgosesia) effectuée par l'Institut et Musée d'Anthropologie et d'Ethnographie de l'Université de Turin (juillet, 1967). L'Anthropologie, 72:3–4, 413 (French).

FEDELE, F., CHIARELLI, B. and MASALI, M.
1966A Ricerche sui giacimenti quaternari del Monfenera. Nuovo scavo nella grotta "Ciota Ciara". Riv. Antropol., 53, 101–111, 3 figs., 1 table (Italian; English summary).

FEDORENKO, E. N.
1970A Paleogenovaîa sistema. [Paleogene system.] Geologiîa SSSR, 46, Rostov, Volgograd, Astrakhan' Provinces and Kalmyk ASSR, 361–409, 6 figs., 1 table (Russian).

FEDORENKO, O. A. See: Kostenko, N. N., Nikitin, E. A., Polumiskova, L. A. and Fedorenko, O. A., 1971A.

FEDOROV, A. V.
1970A Faunisticheskie kompleksy presnovodnykh ryb basseîna verkhnego Dona i puti formirovaniîa donskoî ikhtiofauny. [Faunistic complexes of the fresh-water fishes of the upper Don basin and the ways of formation of the Don ichthyofauna.] Vop. Ikhtiol., 10:2(61), 290–299, 3 tables (Russian).

FEDOROV, V. V.
1963A K voprosu o vremeni vozniknoveniîa rybolovstva na territorii evropeîskoî chasti SSSR. [The beginnings of fishing on the territory of the European part of USSR.] Akad. Nauk SSSR, Sborn. Muz. Antropol. Etnogr., 21, 172–184, 6 pls. (Russian).

FEDOROVICH, B. A.
1957A Kontinental'nye chetvertichnye otlozheniîa ravninnykh oblasteî. [Continental Quaternary deposits of plains.] Geologiîa SSSR, 22, Turkmenian SSR, 318–332 (Russian).

FEDOTOV, V. F.
1970A Novyî vid roda *Palaeogadus* (treskovye) iz oligofSena Severnogo Kavkaza. [A new species of the cod genus *Palaeogadus* from the Oligocene of north Caucasus.] Paleontol. Zh., 1970:4, 117–119, 2 figs. (Russian).
1971A O filogeneticheskikh otnosheniîakh treskovykh (Gadidae). [On phylogenetic relationships of cod fishes (Gadidae).] Mosk. Obshchest. Ispyt. Prir., Biûll., Otd. Geol., 46:2, 150–151 (Russian).
1971B Novyî iskopaemyî rod semeîstva treskovykh. [A new fossil genus of the family Gadidae.] Paleontol. Zh., 1971:3, 121–124, 2 figs. (Russian).
1971C A new fossil genus of the cod family. Paleontol. J., 5:3, 393–396, 2 figs.

FEDOTOV, V. F. See also: Lebedev, V. D. and Fedotov, V. F., 1969A.

FEDUCCIA, J. ALAN
1968A The Pliocene rails of North America. Auk, 85:3, 441–453, 3 figs., 5 tables.
       Rev.: H. E. W. in J. Ornithol., 110:1, 117.
1970A The avifauna of the Sand Draw local fauna (Aftonian) of Brown County, Nebraska. Wilson Bull., 82, 332–334, 1 fig.
1970B A new shorebird from the upper Pliocene. Grad. Res. Center, J., S. Methodist Univ., 38:4, 58–60, 1 fig.
1971A The origin of terrestrial Amphibia. Texas J. Sci., 22:2–3, 255–263.
1972A The Pleistocene avifauna of Klein Cave, Kerr County, Texas. Southwest. Natur., 17:3, 295–296.

FEDUCCIA, J. ALAN and RICH, PAT VICKERS
1972A Early Pleistocene pre-glacial and glacial rocks and faunas of north-central Nebraska. Class Aves. Amer. Mus. Natur. Hist., Bull., 148:1, 72–76.

FEJFAR, OLDŘICH
1966D Výzkum fosilních obratlovců. [Finds of fossil vertebrates.] Czech., Ustřed. Ústav Geol., Zprávy Geol. Vyzk., 1964:1, 375–376, 1 table (Czech).
1968A The Cenozoic mammals in Czechoslovakia and their relations. Int. Geol. Congr., 23rd, Czech., Rep., Abstr., sec. 10, 273 (abs.).
1969A Das Pleistozän von Süssenborn. Die Nager aus den Kiesen von Süssenborn bei Weimar. Paläontol. Abh., Abt. A, 3:3–4, 761–770, 5 figs., II Internat. Paläont. Kolloquium 1966 in Weimar (German; Russian and English summaries).

1969B   Human remains from the early Pleistocene in Czechoslovakia. Current Anthropol., 10:1, 170—173, 9 figs.

1970A   Die plio-pleistozänen Wirbeltierfaunen von Hajnácka und Ivanovce (Slowakei, CSSR). VI. Cricetidae (Rodentia, Mammalia). Bayer. Staatssamml. Paläontol. Hist. Geol., Mitt., 10, 277—296, 7 figs. (German; English summary).

1972A   Ein neuer Vertreter der Gattung *Anomalomys* Gaillard, 1900 (Rodentia, Mammalia) aus dem europäischen Miozän (Karpat). Neues Jahrb. Geol. Paläontol., Abh., 141:2, 168—193, 6 figs. (German).

FEJFAR, OLDŘICH   See also: Cicha, I., Fahlbusch, V., and Fejfar, O., 1972A; Čtyroký, P., and Fejfar, O., 1963A; Šibrava, V., Fejfar, O., Kovanda, J. and Valoch, K., 1969A.

FENART, RAPHAËL
1969A   Le crâne de l'enfant du Pech-de-l'Azé, étudié dans les axes vestibulaires d'orientation. Acad. Sci., C.R., Sér. D, 268:16, 2042—2045, 2 figs. (French).

1969B   Le vestibulographe. Soc. Anthropol. Paris, Bull. Mém., sér. 12, 4, 363—370, 1 fig. (French).

FENART, R. and EMPEREUR-BUISSON, R.
1970A   Application de la méthode "vestibulaire" d'orientation au crâne de l'enfant du Pech-de-l'Azé et comparaison avec d'autres crânes néandertaliens. Arch. Inst. Paléontol. Hum., Mém., 33, 89—148, 17 figs., 5 tables (French).

FENART, RAPHAËL   See also: Delattre, A. and Fenart, R., 1966A.

FENIKSOVA, V. V.
1970A   Istoriiã razvitiiã vnelednikovoĭ zony Zapadno-Sibirskoĭ nizmennosti v pozdnem kaĭnozoe. [History of development of the extra-glacial zone of west Siberian lowlands in late Cenozoic.] Sov. Geol., 13:1, 28—47, 7 figs. (Russian).

FEREMBACH, DENISE
1963B   Les hommes du Paléolithic supérieur de l'Europe. Les Eyzies, 12, 64—75 (French).
          Rev.: Jelínek in Anthropologie, 2:3, 91.

1964B   Les Australopithécinés. Les Eyzies, 13, 158—183, 4 figs. (French).

1965E   *Homo erectus.* Les Eyzies, 14, 144—158, 2 figs. (French).

1967A   A propos de l'origine de la brachycranie. Discussion. Int. Congr., 7th, Anthropol. Ethnol. Sci., Moscow, 1964, 2, 337—345, 3 figs. (French).

1969A   Les affinités morphologiques de l'enfant néandertalien du Pech-de-l'Azé (Dordogne). Acad. Sci., C.R., Sér. D, 268:11, 1485—1488, 2 tables (French).

1970A   Le crâne de l'enfant du Pech-de-l'Azé. Arch. Inst. Paléontol. Hum., Mém., 33, 13—51, 10 figs., 3 pls., 3 tables (French).

FEREMBACH, D., LEGOUX, P., FENART, R., EMPEREUR-BUISSON, R. and VLČEK, E.
1970A   L'enfant du Pech-de-l'Azé. Arch. Inst. Paléontol. Hum., Mém., 33, 186 pp., 36 figs., 8 pls. (French). Rev.: Billy in L'Anthropologie, 74:3—4, 282—284; Stewart in Amer. J. Phys. Anthropol., 36:2, 303—304.

FERRARI, A.
1970A   Report on the discussion during the session on "mammal phylogeny". G. Geol., 35:1, 105—109.

FERRIER, JEAN   See: Roussot, A. and Ferrier, J., 1970A, 1971A.

FERRUSQUÍA-VILLAFRANCA, ISMAEL
1969A   Rancho Gaitan local fauna, early Chadronian, northeastern Chihuahua. Soc. Geol. Mex., Bol., 30:2, 99—138, 6 figs., 10 tables (French summary).

FERRUSQUÍA-VILLAFRANCA, ISMAEL and WOOD, ALBERT E.
1969A   New fossil rodents from the early Oligocene Rancho Gaitan local fauna, northeastern Chihuahua, Mexico. Pearce-Sellards Ser., Texas Mem. Mus., 16, 13 pp., 3 figs., 2 tables.

FETTER, V.
1969A   Stoletie rozhdeniiã Alesha Grdlichki. [Aleš Hrdlička's birthday centenary.] Vop. Antropol., 33, 6—8 (Russian).

FETTER, V., PROKOPEC, M., SUCHY, J. and TITLBACHOVÁ, S.
1967A   Antropologie. Prague: Academie des Sciences de Tchecoslovaquie, 704 pp., 354 figs., 98 pls.

Rev.: Mentl in An. Antropol., Mexico, 6, 316–320; Schwidetzky in Homo, 19:1, 44.

FEUSTEL, RUDOLF
1968B Evolution und Revolution im Ablauf der Steinzeit. Ethnogr.-Archäol. Z., 9:2, 120–147, 2 figs. (German).
1969A Menschen, Affenmenschen, Affen. Ein Abriss der Hominisation. Weimar: H. Böhlaus Nachf., 62 pp., 46 figs. (German).
Rev.: Fridrich in Archeol. Roz., 22:4, 479–480; Helmuth in Z. Morphol. Anthropol., 62:3, 342;
1969B Kurth in Kosmos (Stuttgart), 1970:9, 311.
1969B Zur Problematik der "Protolitischen Knochenkultur" und der "Osteodontokeratic Culture". Alt-Thüring., Mus. Ur. Frügesch., Jahresschr., 10, 7–67, 4 figs., 23 pls. (German).
Rev.: Károlyi in Z. Morphol. Anthropol., 62:3, 347.
1970A Statuettes féminines paléolithiques de la République Démocratique Allemande. Soc. Préhist. Fr., Bull., C.R., 67:1, 12–16, 7 figs. (French).

FEUSTEL, R., KERKMANN, K., SCHMID, E., MUSIL, R. and JACOB, H.
1971A Der Bärenkeller bei Königsee-Garsitz, eine jungpaläolithische Kulthöhle. (I). Alt-Thüring., Mus. Ur-Frühgesch., Jahresschr., 11, 81–130, 17 figs., 14 pls., 8 tables (German).

FEUSTEL, R., KERKMANN, K., SCHMID, E., MUSIL, R., MANIA, D., KNORRE, D. VON and JACOB, H.
1971B Die Urdhöhle bei Döbritz. Alt-Thüring., Mus. Ur-Frühgesch., Jahresschr., 11, 131–226, 9 figs., 15 pls., 18 tables (German).

FICAT, CH.
1963A Découverte d'un crâne intact de renne. Toulouse, Univ., Inst. d'Art Préhist., Trav., 6, 261, 3 figs. (French).

FICCARELLI, GIOVANNI and TORRE, D.
1967B Una mandibola di *Euryboas lunensis* (Del Campana) nel giacimento Villafranchiano di Olivola (Val di Magra). Soc. Toscana Sci. Natur., Atti, Mem., Ser. A, 74:1, 193–198, 1 fig., 1 pl. (Italian; English summary).
Rev.: Albanesi in Riv. Ital. Paleontol. Stratigr., 74:4, 1321.
1968A Upper Villafranchian panthers of Tuscany. Palaeontogr. Ital., 64, 173–184, 6 figs., 16 pls.
Rev.: Albanesi in Riv. Ital. Paleontol. Stratigr., 75:1, 193; Thenius in Zentralbl. Geol. Paläontol., Teil 2, 1969:6, 517.
1970A Remarks on the taxonomy of Hyaenids. Palaeontogr. Ital., 66, 13–33, 19 pls.
Rev.: Albanesi in Riv. Ital. Paleontol. Stratigr., 77:4, 551; Thenius in Zentralbl. Geol. Palàontol., Teil 2, 1972:3, 176–177.

FICCARELLI, GIOVANNI   See also: De Giuli, C., Ficcarelli, G. and Torre, D., 1970A.

FICHTER, LYNN S.
1969A Geographical distribution and osteological variation in fossil and recent specimens of two species of *Kinosternon* (Testudines). J. Herpetol., 3:3–4, 113–119, 5 figs., 1 table.

FICHTER, L. S.   See also: Howell, F. C., Fichter, L. S. and Eck, G., 1969A; Howell, F. C., Fichter, L. S. and Wolff, R., 1969A.

FIELDS, ROBERT W.   See: Kuenzi, W. D. and Fields, R. W., 1971A; Petkewich, R. M. and Fields, R. W., 1971A.

FIENNES, R. N.
1972A* Biology of nutrition. Oxford and New York: Pergamon Press, x + 681 pp.
Rev.: Florkin in Nature, 239:5368, 177.

FIERRO, G. and VANOSSI, M.
1965A Nuovi elementi per la stratigrafia del "Brianzonese Ligure" tra il T. Corsaglia e il T. Pennavaira. Pavia, Univ., Ist. Geol., Atti, 16, 17–35, 4 figs., 4 pls. (Italian).

FIERSTINE, H. L.
1968A Rev.: Weiler in Zentralbl. Geol. Paläontol., Teil 2, 1971:5, 399.

FILIP, JAN
1966A Rev.: G. T. in Anthropos, 63/64:5/6, 1048.
1966B* Investigations archéologiques en Tchécoslovaquie. État actuel des recherches et leur organisation. VII ème Congrès International des Sciences préhistoriques et protohistoriques, Prague, 1966. Prague: Éditions de l'Académie Tchécoslovaque des Sciences, 317 pp., 24 figs., 40 pls., 7 maps (French).

Rev.: Leube in Ethnogr.-Archäol. Z., 9:2, 161.

1969A [Fifty years of Czechoslovakian archeology and of the Archeological Institute.] Archeol. Rozhl., 21:1, 3–6 (Czech; German summary).

1969B Enzyklopädisches Handbuch zur Ur-und Frühgeschichte Europas. Band II (L–Z). Mainz: w. Kohlhammer Verlag, 1092 pp., illustr. (German).
Rev.: Schwidetzky in Homo, 20:4, 262.

FILIPESCU, M. G.
1968A Phénomènes de radiation dans les restes fossiles de certains animaux. (Note préliminaire). Rev. Roum. Géol., Géophys., Géogr., Sér. Géol., 12:1, 61–63, 1 pl. (French).

FILIPPOV, A. K.
1969A O vozniknovenii esteticheskogo otnosheniiâ i pervykh uslovnykh sredstv izobrazheniiâ v paleolite (po arkheologicheskim dannym). [On the emergence of esthetical attitude and on the first conventional means of representation in the Paleolithic (according to archeological data).] Vop. Antropol., 31, 99–112, 3 figs. (Russian).

FILZER, P. See: German, R., Filzer, P., Dehm, R., Freude, H., Jung, W. and Witt, W., 1968A.

FINCH, EILEEN
1971A *Thylacoleo,* marsupial lion or marsupial sloth? Austral. Natur. Hist., 17:1, 7–11, 5 figs.

FINDLAY, G. H.
1970A The role of the skin in the origin of mammals. S. Afr. J. Sci., 66, 277–283, 1 table.
1970B Skin structures of small pareiasaurs. Palaeontol. Afr., 13, 15–23, 6 figs., 3 tables.

FIRBY, JEAN B.
1969A Fauna of the type Irvingtonian mammal age. Geol. Soc. Amer., Abstr., 121, 96 (abs.).
1972A Type vertebrates from Lompoc, California now at the California Academy of Sciences. J. Paleontol., 46:3, 450.

FIRBY, JEAN B. and LUCAS, KENNETH
1970A A dinosaur by the tail. Pac. Discovery, 23:1, 1–10, 16 figs.

FIRBY, JEAN B. See also: Mawby, J. E. and Firby, J. B., 1970A.

FISCHER, KARL-HEINZ
1967B Zur systematischen Stellung des *Chasmotherium* Rütimeyer 1862 (Mammalia, Perissodactyla). Deut. Ges. Geol. Wiss., Ber., Reihe A, Geol. Paläontol., 12:5, 595–600, 1 fig. (German).
1967C Ein neuer grosser Laufvogel aus dem Eozän des Geiseltales bei Halle (Saale). Deut. Ges. Geol. Wiss., Ber., Reihe A, Geol. Paläontol., 12:5, 601–605, 1 fig., 2 pls. (German).
1970A Riesensaurier, Urvögel und Ursäuger – drei Endzweige am Reptilienstammbaum. Berlin, Humboldt-Univ., Wiss. Z., Math.-Naturwiss. Reihe, 19:2–3, 191–204, 2 pls. (German).
1971A Riesenfaultiere (Megalonychidae, Edentata, Mammalia) aus Pleistozän der Pio-Domingo-Höhle in Kuba. Berlin, Humboldt-Univ., Wiss. Z., Math.-Naturwiss. Reihe, 20:4–5, 609–673 (German; Spanish, Russian, and English summaries).

FISCHER, KARL-HEINZ and STEPHAN, BURKHARD
1971A Ein flugunfähiger Kranich (*Grus cubensis* n. sp.) aus dem Pleistozän von Kuba – Eine Osteologie der Familie der Kraniche (Gruidae). Berlin, Humboldt-Univ., Wiss. Z., Math.-Naturwiss, Reihe, 20:4–5, 541–592 (German; Spanish, Russian, and English summaries).
1971B Weitere Vogelreste aus dem Pleistozän der Pio-Domingo Höhle in Kuba. Berlin, Humboldt-Univ., Wiss. Z., Math.-Naturwiss. Reihe, 20:4–5, 593–607 (German; Spanish, Russian, and English summaries).

FISHER, DONALD W.
1972A An ethic for fossil collectors. Conservationist, 26:6, 28–29.

FISHER, DONALD W. See also: Funk, R. E., Fisher, D. W. and Reilly, E. M., Jr., 1970A.

FITCH, FRANK JOHN
1972A Selection of suitable material for dating and the assessment of geological error in potassium-argon age determination. In: Bishop, W. W. and Miller, J. A. (eds.), 1972A, 77–91.

FITCH, F. J. and MILLER, J. A.
1970A Radioisotopic age determinations of Lake Rudolf artefact site. Nature, 226:5242, 226–228, 3 tables.

FITCH, F. J.   See also: Bishop, W. W., Miller, J. A. and Fitch, F. J., 1969A.

FITCH, JOHN E.
1968A   Otoliths and other fish remains from the Timms Point silt (early Pleistocene) at San Pedro,
             California. Los Angeles Cty. Mus., Contrib. Sci., 146, 29 pp., 4 figs., 1 table.
1969A   Fossil lanternfish otoliths of California, with notes on fossil Myctophidae of North America.
             Los Angeles Cty. Mus., Contrib. Sci., 173, 20 pp., 4 figs., 2 tables.
             Rev.: Weiler in Zentralbl. Geol. Paläontol., Teil 2, 1970 :3/4, 222.
1970A   Fish remains, mostly otoliths and teeth, from the Palos Verdes sand (late Pleistocene) of California.
             Los Angeles Cty. Mus., Contrib. Sci., 199, 41 pp., 6 figs., 4 tables.

FITCH, JOHN E. and LAVENBERG, ROBERT J.
1971A   Marine food and game fishes of California. Berkeley, Los Angeles, London: University of California
             Press, 179 pp., 60 figs., 8 pls., 1 map.

FITTING, JAMES E.
1968A   Environmental potential and the postglacial readaptation in eastern North America. Amer. Antiquity,
             33, 441—445.

FITTKAU, E. J., ILLIES, J., KLINGE, H., SCHWABE, G. H. and SIOLI, H.
1969A*   Biogeography and ecology in South America. Vol. 2. Monogr. Biol., 19, 449—946, illustr.

FLANNERY, KENT V.   See: Coe, M. D. and Flannery, K. V., 1966A.

FLEAGLE, JOHN C.   See: Conroy, G. C. and Fleagle, J. G., 1972A.

FLEISCHER, ROBERT L. and HART, HOWARD R., JR.
1972A   Fission track dating: techniques and problems. In: Bishop, W. W. and Miller, J. A. (eds.), 1972A,
             135—170, 7 figs., 1 table.

FLEMING, C. A.
1968A   New Zealand fossil seals. N.Z.J. Geol. Geophys., 11:5, 1184—1187.

FLEMING, C. A., GREGG, D. R. and WELLES, S. P.
1971A   New Zealand ichthyosaurs — a summary, including new records from the Cretaceous. N.Z.J. Geol.
             Geophys., 14:4, 734—741, 4 figs.

FLEROV, KONSTANTIN KONSTANTINOVICH (= FLEROW, C. C.)
1964A   O proiskhozhdenii fauny Kanady v sviazi s istorieĭ Beringiĭskoĭ sushi. [On the origin of Canadian fauna
             in connection with the history of Beringian land.] In: Vsesoiuznoe Soveshchanie po Izucheniĭu
             Chetvertichnogo perioda, Novosibirsk, 1964, Tezisy Dokladov, Sektsiiā Istorii Flory, Fauny i
             Drevnego Cheloveka, 94 (Russian).
1967B   Dinocerata of Mongolia. Translated from Trudy Pal. Inst. Akad. Nauk SSSR, 67, 1957A . Jerusalem:
             Israel Program for Scientific Translations.
1969A   Nekotorye adaptivnye izmeneniiā kostnogo neba i khoany u mlekopitaĭushchikh. [Some adaptive
             modifications of the bony palate and choanae in mammals.] Mosk. Obshchest. Ispyt. Prir.,
             Biull., Otd. Biol., 74:5, 21—27, 2 fig. (Russian).
1969B   Das Pleistozän von Süssenborn. Die Bison-Reste aus den Kiesen von Süssenborn bei Weimar. Paläontol.
             Abh., Abt. A, 3:3—4, 489—520, 17 figs., 10 pls., 1 table. II Internat. Paläont. Kolloquium 1966
             in Weimar (German; Russian and English summaries).
1969C   Iskopaemye bizony tiraspol'skogo faunisticheskogo kompleksa. [Fossil bisons of Tiraspol' faunal
             complex.] In: Mezhdunarodnyĭ kollokvium po geologii i faune nizhnego i srednego
             pleĭstotsena Evropy. Tezisy dokladov, 11—12 (Russian).
1970A   Mlekopitaĭushchie i prirodnaiā sreda pleĭstotsena. [Mammals and Pleistocene natural environment.]
             Priroda, 1970:11, 50—54, 4 figs. (Russian).
1970B   Obraz zhizni i morfologicheskie adaptatsii v evoliutsii kopytnykh. [Mode of life and morphological
             adaptations in the evolution of ungulates.] In: Materialy po evoliutsii nazemnykh
             pozvonochnykh, 63—70 (Russian).
1971A   On the history of Bison. Hess. Landesamt Bodenforsch., Abh., 60, 59—63, 1 table.
1971B   The evolution of certain mammals during the late Cenozoic. In: Turekian, K. K. (ed.), 1971A,
             479—491.

FLEROV, K. K. and IANOVSKAIA, N. M.
1971A   Ekologicheskie kompleksy mlekopitaĭushchikh oligotsena Azii i ikh zoogeograficheskaiā kharakteristika.
             [Mammalian ecological complexes in Asia during the Oligocene, and their zoogeographical
             characteristics.] Akad. Nauk SSSR, Paleontol. Inst., Tr., 130, 7—31 (Russian).

FLEROV, K. K. and KUROCHKIN, EVGENIĬ NIKOLAEVICH
    1971A   Pervyĭ vsesoĭuznyĭ paleornitologicheskiĭ simposium. [First all-union paleoornithological symposium.]
        Paleontol. Zh., 1971:3, 132–133 (Russian).

FLETCHER, FRANK W.   See: Woodrow, D. L. and Fletcher, F. W., 1969A.

FLINT, ROBERT F.
    1971A   Glacial and Quaternary geology. New York and London: John Wiley and Sons, Inc., frontispiece,
        illustr.
        Rev.: Bourdier in Soc. Géol. Fr., C.R., 1971:6, 330; McDonald in Amer. Sci., 60:3, 375.

FLOREI, NICOLAE
    1970A   Analiza faunei tortoniene de la Zorlenţu Mare-Delineşti-Rugi, consideraţii paleobionomice. [Analysis
        of the Tortonian fauna from Zorlenţu Mare-Delineşti-Rugi, paleobionomic considerations.]
        Soc. Stiint. Geol. R.S.R., Bul., 12, 141–147, 10 pls. (Rumanian; French and English summaries).

FLOYD, D. N., MILLER, T. H. and BERRY, W. B. N.
    1958A   Miocene paleoecology in the Burkeville area, Newton County, Texas. Gulf Coast Ass. Geol. Soc.,
        Trans., 8, 157–161, 1 fig.

FLUGEL, H. and MAURIN, V.
    1959A   Ein Vorkommen vulkanischer Tuffe bei Eibiswald (Südweststeiermark). Österreich. Akad. Wiss., Math.-
        Naturwiss. Kl., Abt. I, Sitz-Ber., 168:1, 1–5 (German).

FOLAN, W. J.   See: Aish, P. J., Dewhirst, J. T. and Folan, W. J., 1968A.

FOLDVARY, G. Z. and SANDERSON, J. L.
    1972A   Catalogue of palaeontological type specimens located in the Department of Geology and Geophysics,
        University of Sydney. Austral., Bur. Miner. Resour., Geol. Geophys., Rep., 149, 74 pp.

FOLEY, ROBERT
    1969A   A boreal fauna from Bat Cave, Pulaski County, Missouri. Abstract from Proceedings, August 1968.
        Nat. Speleol. Soc., Bull., 31:2, 44.

FOLINSBEE, R. E., BAADSGAARD, H. and CUMMING, G. L.
    1970A   Geochronology of the Cretaceous-Tertiary boundary of the western plains of North America. Summary.
        Eclogae Geol. Helv., 63:1, 91.

FOLLIERI, MARIA   See: Ambrosetti, P., Azzaroli, P., Bonadonna, F. P. and Follieri, M., 1972A.

FOLSOM, FRANKLIN   See: Elting, M. and Folsom, F., 1971A.

FOMICHEV, V. D.
    1967A   Permskaĭa sistema. Kuznetskiĭ basseĭn. [Permian system. Kuznetsk basin.] Geologiĭa SSSR, 14,
        Western Siberia (southern part), 274–286, 1 fig., 1 table (Russian).
    1967B   Chetvertichnaĭa sistema. Kuznetskiĭ basseĭn. [Quaternary system. Kuznetsk basin.] Geologiĭa SSSR,
        14, Western Siberia (southern part), 409–413, 1 table (Russian).

FONDI, R.
    1970A   *Prolagus sardus* Wagner (Ochotonidae, Lagomorpha, Mammalia) da una breccia ossifera della
        Montagnola senese. Soc. Toscana Sci. Natur., Atti, Mem., Ser. A, 77, 260–285, 4 figs., 1 table
        (Italian; English summary).

FONIN, VIKTOR DMITRIEVICH
    1966A   Metody preparirovaniĭa iskopaemykh organicheskikh ostatkov. [Methods of preparing fossil organic
        remains.] Itogi Nauki, Ser. Geol., 10, Stratigr. Paleontol., 101–122, 3 figs. (Russian).

FOODEN, JACK
    1972A   Breakup of Pangaea and isolation of relict mammals in Australia, South America, and Madagascar.
        Science, 175:4024, 894–898, 1 fig., 2 tables.

FORBIS, RICHARD G.
    1968A   Fletcher: a Paleo-Indian site in Alberta. Amer. Antiquity, 33, 1–10, 3 figs., 2 tables.
    1970A   A review of Alberta archaeology to 1964. Can., Nat. Mus. Man, Publ. Archaeol., 1, ix + 49 pp.,
        8 figs., 15 pls. (French summary).

FORMOZOV, A. A.
    1965C   The rock paintings of Zaraut-Kamar, Uzbekistan. Riv. Sci. Preist., 20:1, 63–84, 10 figs. (Italian
              and French summaries).

FORMOZOV, A. A.   See also: Nasimovich, A. A. and Formozov, A. A., 1970A.

FORNACA-RINALDI, G. and RADMILLI, A. M.
    1968A   Datazione con il metodo Th^{230}/U^{238} di stalagmiti contenute in depositi mousteriani. Soc. Toscana
              Sci. Natur., Atti Mem., Ser. A, 75:2, 639–646 (Italian; English summary).

FORSTÉN, ANN-MARIE   (= FORSTEN, A.)
    1970A   Variation in and between three populations of *Mesohippus bairdii* Leidy from the Big Badlands,
              South Dakota. Acta Zool. Fennica, 126, 1–16, 1 fig., 5 tables.
              Rev.: Thenius in Zentralbl. Geol. Paläontol., Teil 2, 1970:6, 520–521.
    1970B   The late Miocene Trail Creek mammalian fauna. Wyo., Univ., Contrib. Geol., 9:1, 39–51, 6 figs.
              Rev.: Thenius in Zentralbl. Geol. Paläontol., Teil 2, 1971:6, 510.
    1970C   *Mesohippus* from the Chadron of South Dakota, and a comparison with Brulean *Mesohippus bairdii*
              Leidy. Comment. Biol., Soc. Sci. Fennica, 31:11, 1–22, 9 tables.
              Rev.: Thenius in Zentralbl. Geol. Paläontol., Teil 2, 1971:6, 519.
    1971A   *Epihippus* from the Vieja group, trans-Pecos Texas. Pearce-Sellards Ser., Texas Mem Mus., 18, 1–5,
              2 figs., 1 table.
              Rev.: Thenius in Zentralbl. Geol. Paläontol., Teil 2, 1971:6, 519.
    1971B   Comparison of populations of *Mesohippus* from trans-Pecos Texas and Big Badlands, South Dakota.
              Pearce-Sellards Ser., Texas Mem. Mus., 18, 12–15, 4 tables.
              Rev.: Thenius in Zentralbl. Geol. Paläontol., Teil 2, 1971:6, 519.
    1972A   *Hipparion primigenium* from southern Tunisia. Tunisia, Serv. Géol., Notes, 35, 7–28, 1 fig., 15 tables
              (French summary).

FORTSCH, DAVID   See: Hopkins, M. L., Bonnichsen, R. and Fortsch, D., 1969A.

FOSTER, COLIN A.
    1969A   Hairy Russian fossil. New Sci., 42:654, 655.

FOURNIER, A.   See: Lumley, H. de, Gagnières, S. and Fournier, A., 1969A.

FOX, GEORGE R.
    1963A   The magic that is Cass County. Totem Pole, 46, 26–34.

FOX, RICHARD C.
    1968A   Studies of late Cretaceous vertebrates. I. The braincase of *Champsosaurus* Cope (Reptilia: Eosuchia).
              Copeia, 68:1, 100–109, 8 figs.
    1968B   Therian and quasi-mammals. Evolution, 22:4, 839–840.
    1968C   A new Paleocene mammal (Condylarthra: Arctocyonidae) from a well in Alberta, Canada. J. Mammal.,
              49:4, 661–664, 2 figs., 1 table.
    1968D   Studies of late Cretaceous vertebrates. II. Generic diversity among multituberculates. Syst. Zool.,
              17:3, 339–342.
    1968E   Early Campanian (late Cretaceous) mammals from Alberta, Canada. Nature, 220:5171, 1046.
    1969A   Studies of late Cretaceous vertebrates. III. A triconodont mammal from Alberta. Can. J. Zool.,
              47:6, 1253–1256, 1 pl., 1 table.
    1970A   Eutherian mammal from the early Campanian (late Cretaceous) of Alberta, Canada. Nature, 227:5258,
              630–631, 1 fig.
    1970B   A bibliography of Cretaceous and Tertiary vertebrates from western Canada. Bull. Can. Petrol. Geol.,
              18:2, 263–281.
    1970C   Marsupial mammals from the early Campanian (late Cretaceous) Milk River formation, Alberta, Canada.
              Linn. Soc., Biol. J., 2:4, 320–321 (abs.).
    1971A   Early Campanian multituberculates (Mammalia: Allotheria) from the upper Milk River formation,
              Alberta. Can. J. Earth Sci., 8:8, 916–938, 8 figs., 3 tables (French summary).
    1971B   Marsupial mammals from the early Campanian Milk River formation, Alberta, Canada. Linn. Soc.,
              Zool. J., 50:suppl. 1, 145–164, 6 pls., 7 tables.
              Rev.: Krebs in Zentralbl. Geol. Paläontol., Teil 2, 1972:3, 173–174.
    1972A   The University of Alberta. Soc. Vert. Paleontol., News Bull., 94, 16–18.
    1972B   An upper Cretaceous symmetrodont from Alberta, Canada. Nature, 239:5368, 170–171, 1 fig.
    1972C   A primitive therian mammal from the upper Cretaceous of Alberta. Can. J. Earth Sci., 9:11, 1479–
              1494, 6 figs., 2 tables (French summary).

FOX, ROBIN
    1967A   In the beginning: aspects of hominid behavioural evolution. Man (J. Roy. Anthropol. Inst.), 2,
              415–433, 1 fig., 1 table.

FOX, ROBIN   See also: Tiger, L. and Fox, R., 1971A.

FRACHON, J.-CL.
1965A   Paléontologie souterraine du département du Jura. Spelaion Carso, 3, 12—15 (French).

FRACHON, J.-CL.   See also: David, E., Frachon, J.-CL., and Sattonnet, R., 1968A.

FRADKIN, E. E.
1969A   Polieĭkonicheskaĭa skul'ptura iz verkhnepaleoliticheskoĭ stoĭanki Kostenki 1. [Polyeikonic sculpture
               from the upper Paleolithic site Kostenki 1.] Sov. Etnogr., 1969:1, 135—142, 5 figs. (Russian).

FRADKIN, G. S.   See: Menner, Vl. Vl., Krylova, A. K., Kolodeznikov, K. E. and Fradkin, G. S., 1970A.

FRAILEY, CARL DAVID
1972A   Additions to the Pleistocene avifauna of Arredondo, Florida. Fla. Acad. Sci., Quart. J., 35:1, 53—54.

FRANCH, JOSÉ ALCINA
1964A*   El americanismo en las revistas. Antropología: 3. Sevilla, Univ., Publ., 6, 120 pp. (Spanish).

FRANCH, J. A.   See also: Ballesteros-Gaibrois, M. and Franch, J. A., 1964A, 1965A.

FRANK, H.   See: Behrens, M., Frank, H., Höllein, K., Spaeth, W.v. and Wurster, P., 1970A.

FRANK, RICHARD VAN   See: Hecht, M. K., Schaeffer, B., Patterson, B., Frank, R. van and Wood, F. D., 1972A.

FRANK, RUBEN M.
1961B   Cave paleontology. Speleo Digest, 1961, 2—77 — 2—84 (reprinted from Texas Caver, 6:7—8, 85—86,
               93—96).

FRANKE, H. W.
1969A   Methoden der Geochronologie. Verständ. Wiss., 98, viii + 132 pp., 73 figs. (German).
               Rev.: Medwenitsch in Geol. Ges. Wien, Mitt., 62, 209; Metz in Aufschluss, 21:5, 188—189.

FRANKFORTER, W. D.
1971A   The Turin local fauna, evidence for the medial Pleistocene age of the original "Aftonian" vertebrate
               fauna in western Iowa. Nebr. Acad. Sci., Proc., 81, 48—49.

FRANQUESA, F.   See: Casamiquela, R. M., Corvalán, J. and Franquesa, F., 1969A.

FRANZEN, JENS L.
1968A   Revision der Gattung Palaeotherium Cuvier 1804 (Palaeotheriidae, Perissodactyla, Mammalia).
               Freiburg i. Br.: Inaugural-Dissertation, Naturwiss.-math. Fak., Albert-Ludwigs-Univ., Vol. 1
               (text), 181 pp., 20 figs., 7 tables; Vol. 2, 35 pls., 15 tables (German).
               Rev.: Thenius in Zentralbl. Geol. Paläontol., Teil 2, 1970:3/4, 244—245.
1970A   Zur Lystrosaurus-Ausstellung. Natur Mus., 100 :4, 179—184, 2 figs. (German).
1972A   Der aufrechte Gang. Kosmos, 68:1, 1—9, 8 figs. (German).

FRAUNFELTER, GEORGE H.
1970A   Cephalaspids from the middle Ordovician Platteville limestone. Ill. Acad. Sci., Trans., 63, 14—17,
               3 figs.

FRAYER, DAVID W.
1971A   Gigantopithecines and their relationship to the australopithecines. Amer. J. Phys. Anthropol., 35:2,
               278 (abs.).

FRAZIER, KENDRICK
1970A   California fossil marine vertebrates. Rocks Miner., 45:6, 384—385, 1 fig.; S. Calif. Paleontol. Soc.,
               Bull., 3:2, 5.
1970B   The world of Antarctic paleontology. Sci. News, 97:13, 324—326, 5 figs., cover.
1970C   Horizons for Antarctic paleontology. Sci. News, 97:14, 350—352, 7 figs.

FRAZZETTA, THOMAS H.
1968A   Adaptive problems and possibilities in the temporal fenestration of tetrapod skulls. J. Morph., 125:2,
               145—157, 7 figs.
1970A   Studies on the fossil snake Dinilysia patagonica Woodward. Part II. Jaw machinery in the earliest
               snakes. Forma et Functio, 3, 205—221, 5 figs. (French and German summaries).

FRAZZETTA, T. H.   See also: Estes, R., Frazzetta, T. H. and Williams, E. E., 1970A.

FREDSKILD, BENT   See: Degerbøl, M. and Fredskild, B., 1970A.

FREEDMAN, LEONARD
1970A   A new checklist of fossil Cercopithecoidea of South Africa. Palaeontol. Afr., 13, 109—110.

FREEDMAN, LEONARD and BRAIN, C. K.
1972A   Fossil cercopithecoid remains from the Kromdraai australopithecine site (Mammalia: Primates).
              Transvaal Mus., Ann., 28:1, 1—16, 9 tables.

FREEDMAN, LEONARD and STENHOUSE, N. S.
1972A   The Parapapio species of Sterkfontein, Transvaal, South Africa. Palaeontol. Afr., 14, 93—111, 2 figs.,
              2 pls., 6 tables.

FRENKEL, HANNA
1970A   Hystrix angressi sp. nov. A large fossil porcupine from the Levalloiso-Mousterian of the Geula Cave.
              Isr. J. Zool., 19:1, 51—82, 7 pls., 17 tables.

FRENZEL, B.
1969A   Hugo Otto Gross. Quartär, 20, 195—202.

FREUDE, H.   See: German, R., Filzer, P., Dehm, R., Freude, H., Jung, W. and Witt, W., 1968A.

FREUDENTHAL, M.
1966A   Rev.: Adrover in Teruel, 37, 140.
1967A   Rev.: Adrover in Teruel, 38, 226—227.
1968A   Rev.: Adrover in Teruel, 39, 143.
1971A   Neogene vertebrates from the Gargano peninsula, Italy. Scripta Geol., 3, 10 pp.
              Rev.: Thenius in Zentralbl. Geol. Paläontol., Teil 2, 1971:6, 510.
1972A   Deinogalerix koenigswaldi nov. gen., nov. spec., a giant insectivore from the Neogene of Italy.
              Scripta Geol., 14, 17 pp., 7 pls.

FREUDENTHAL, M. and FAHLBUSCH, V.
1969A   Cricetodon minus Lartet, 1851 (Mammalia, Rodentia): Request for a decision on interpretation.
              Z.N. (S.) 1854. Bull. Zool. Nomencl., 25:4—5, 178—183.

FREUDENTHAL, M.   See also: Mein, P. and Freudenthal, M., 1971A and B.

FREUND, GISELA and GUENTHER, EKKE W.
1968A   Lothar Zotz. 1899—1967. Quartär, 19, 1—21, portr.

FREY, D. G.   See: Wright, H. E. and Frey, D. G. (eds.), 1969A.

FREYBERG, BRUNO v.
1965B   Der Coburger Bausandstein (Mittl. Keuper) von Zeil-Ebelsbach als Beispiel einer epikontinentalen
              Schichtenfolge. Erlanger Geol. Abhandl., 58, 60 pp., 16 figs., 20 pls. (German).

FRIANT, MADELEINE
1965C   L'évolution des molaires chez les rongeurs. Interprétation des dents jugales des Castoridae d'Europe.
              Soc. Geol. Nord, Ann., 85, 49—64, 5 figs., 1 pl., 3 tables (French).
1967B   Sur les molaires des Condylarthres et des Litopternes Sud-Américains. Ferrara, Univ., Mem.
              Geopaleontol., 2:1, 135—144, 14 figs. (French; Italian and English summaries).
              Rev.: Thenius in Zentralbl. Geol. Paläontol., Teil 2, 1970:5, 443.
1968A   Sur les affinités d'un Rongeur de l'Éocène d'Europe, Maurimontia. Acta Zool., 49:1—2, 35—46,
              12 figs. (French; English summary).
1969A   Carterodon, a living-fossil rodent of Brazil. J. Palaeontol. Soc. India, 12, 1—8, 5 figs. (French
              summary).
1969B   Sur la morphologie et l'évolution des Oreodontidae, Ruminants primitifs. Folia Morphol., 17, 441—
              449, 6 figs. (French; English summary).
1970A   About the jugal teeth of the Pleistocene European shrews (Soricidae). J. Palaeontol. Soc. India, 14,
              11—13, 2 figs. (French summary).
1970B   Morphologie et évolution des molaires des Titanotheriidae, Périssodactyles de l'ère tertiaire. Folia
              Morphol., 18:3, 282—292, 9 figs. (French; English summary).
1971A   A propos du "cerf géant des cavernes". Ferrara, Univ., Mem. Geopaleontol., 2:2, 181—184, 1 fig.
              (French; Italian and English summaries).

1971B   Sur les molaires de quelques phyla d'ongulés sélénodontes encore actuels. Ferrara, Univ., Mem.
           Geopaleontol., 2:2, 211–218, 9 figs. (French; Italian and English summaries).
1971C   A propos des molaires d'un insectivore (Erinaceidae) d'Europe, le *Neurogymnurus* de l'ère tertiaire.
           Folia Morphol., 19:2, 198–204, 7 figs. (French; English summary).

FRICK, CHILDS and TAYLOR, BERYL E.
1971A   *Michenia*, a new protolabine (Mammalia, Camelidae) and a brief review of the early taxonomic history
           of the genus *Protolabis*. Amer. Mus. Nov., 2444, 24 pp., 4 figs., 3 tables.
           Rev.: Thenius in Zentralbl. Geol. Paläontol., Teil 2, 1971:6, 519–520.

FRIDENBERG, E. O.   See: Vekilova, E. A., Muratov, V. M. and Fridenberg, E. O., 1969A.

FRIED, MORTON HERBERT
1972A   The study of anthropology. New York: Crowell, vii + 263 pp.

FRIEDL, H.   See: Ehrenberg, K., Ruckensteiner, E., Adam, H. and Friedl, H., 1969A.

FRIEDLANDER, J. S.   See: Bailit, H. L. and Friedlander, J. S., 1967A.

FRIEND, P. F., HEINTZ, N. and MOODY-STUART, M.
1966A   New unit terms for the Devonian of Spitsbergen and a new stratigraphical scheme for the Wood Bay
           formation. Nor. Polarinst., Årbok, 1965, 59–64, 1 fig.

FRIESE, FRANZ
1971A   Der Fels der Pferde. Kosmos,67:1, 26–29, 5 figs. (German).
1972A   Höhlenmalerei nach Plan. Kosmos, 68:10, 408–412, illustr. (German).

FRISCH, J.
1969A   Role of the study of dental variability in understanding primate evolution. Int. Congr. Anthropol.
           Ethnol. Sci., 8th, Tokyo, 1968, Proc., Vol. I. Anthropology, 312–315, 6 figs.

FRITH, H. J. and CALABY, J. H.
1969A   Kangaroos. Melbourne: F. W. Cheshire, xvi + 209 pp., frontispiece, 26 figs., 26 pls.
           Rev.: Sharman in Austral. J. Sci., 32:7, 300.

FROLOV, B. A.
1969A   Konstanty v psikhike *Homo sapiens*. [Constants in the psychism of *Homo sapiens*.] Vop. Antropol.,
           32, 187–194, 5 figs. (Russian).

FROST, DAVID
1970A   The re-excavation of Rancho La Brea. Rocks Miner., 45:3, 162–163, 2 figs.

FROST, H. M. and WU, KENT
1967A   Histological measurement of bone formation rates in unlabelled contemporary, archeological and
           paleontological compact bone. In: Wade, W. (ed.), 1967A, 9–22, 6 figs., 3 tables.

FRY, GARY F. and MOORE, JOHN G.
1969A   *Enterobius vermicularis*: 10,000-year-old human infection. Science (AAAS), 166:3913, 1620, 1 fig.

FRY, WILLIS E.
1969A   A paleontological site survey conducted in the Horse Heaven Hills of south-central Washington.
           Northwest Sci., 43:4, 156–161, 2 figs., 2 tables.

FRY, WILLIS E. and GUSTAFSON, ERIC PAUL
1972A   Cervids from the Pliocene and Pleistocene of Washington. Soc. Vert. Paleontol., Ann. Meeting, 32nd,
           1972, Abstr. (abs.).

FRYXELL, R., BIELICKI, T., DAUGHERTY, R. D., GUSTAFSON, C. E., IRWIN, H. T. and KEEL, B. C.
1968A   A human skeleton from sediments of mid-Pinedale age in southeastern Washington. Amer. Antiquity,
           33, 511–515, 2 figs.

FRYXELL, R., BIELICKI, T., DAUGHERTY, R. D., GUSTAFSON, C. E., IRWIN, H. T., KEEL, B. C. and
KRANTZ, G. S.
1968A   Human skeletal material and artifacts from sediments of Pinedale (Wisconsin) glacial age in south-
           eastern Washington, United States. Int. Congr. Anthropol. Ethnol. Sci., 8th, Tokyo, 1968,
           Proc., 3, 176–181, 5 figs.

FUCHS, GERHARD and MOSTLER, HELFRIED
1969A   Microfaunen aus der Tibet-Zone, Himalaya. Austr., Geol. Bundesanst., Verh., 1969:2, 133–143,
         2 figs. (German; English summary).

FUCHS, HERMAN
1963A   Asupra prezenţei genului *Myliobatis* în eocenul Clujului. [On the presence of the genus *Myliobatis*
         in the Eocene of Cluj.] Cluj, Univ., Stud., Ser. Geol.-Geogr., 8:1, 57–60, 1 fig. (Rumanian;
         Russian and French summaries).
1970A   Schädelfragment einer Sirene aus dem Eozän von Cluj, SR Rumänien. Geologie (Berlin), 19:10, 1185–
         1191, 3 figs., 1 pl. (German; Rumanian, English and Russian summaries).

FUENTES VIDARTE, C.   See: Pérez González, A., Fuentes Vidarte, C. and Aguirre, E., 1970A; Vidarte, Carolina
                       Fuentes, 1966A.

FUJII, SHOJI
1970A   Miocene *Stegolophodon* from Nakaniikawa district, Toyama Pref. In: Minato, M. *et al.* (eds.), 1968A,
         43, 4 figs. (Japanese).

FUJIKI, H.   See: Braunitzer, G. and Fujiki, H., 1969A.

FUJISHIMA, YASUTAKA   See: Hasegawa, Y., Obata, I., Honda, H. and Fujishima, Y., 1972A.

FUJIWARA, TAKAYO
1967A   Mineralogical comparison of animal remains excavated at Shansi, China. Res. Inst. Natur. Resour.
         (Tokyo), Misc. Rep., 68:2, 133–138, 1 fig., 1 table (Japanese; English summary).

FÜLÖP, JÓZSEF
1968A   Geology of the Transdanubian Central Mountains. Guide to Excursion 39C, Hungary. Int. Geol.
         Congr., 23rd, Czech., Guidebk., 50 pp., 27 figs., map.

FÜLÖP, JÓZSEF and TASNÁDI-KUBACSKA, ANDRÁS
1969A   One hundred years of the Hungarian Geological Institute. Budapest: Müszaki Könyvkiadó, 253 pp.,
         5 figs., portrs.

FULTON, ELISABETH   See: Camp, C. L., Nichols, R. H., Brajnikov, B., Fulton, E. and Bacskai, J. A.
                     (eds.), 1972A.

FUNK, R. E., FISHER, D. W. and REILLY, E. M., JR.
1970A   Caribou and Paleo-Indian in New York State: a presumed association. Amer. J. Sci., 268:2, 181–186,
         1 fig., 1 pl.

FURON, RAYMOND
1970A   Origine et évolution de quelques éléments des faunes africaines. Soc. Biogéogr., C.R., 398 (1969),
         104–111 (French).

G., T. N.
1969A   Henry Hurd Swinnerton. Geol. Ass. (London), Proc., 80, 124–126.

GABASHVILI, E. G.
1970A   Istoriiá izucheniiá gipparionovoĭ fauny Gruzii. The history of research on *Hipparion* fauna of
         Georgia.] Geol. Obshchest. Gruz., Izv., 6:1–2, 88–89 (Russian).

GABELAĬA, TS. D.
1970A   Novye dannye ob iskopaemykh rybakh Kisatibi. [New data on fossil fishes of Kisatibi.] Akad. Nauk
         Gruz. SSR, Soobshch., 59:1, 233–236, 2 figs. (Russian; Georgian and English summaries).
1971A   Aterina (Teleostei) iz Pliofśena Abkhazii. [*Atherina* (Teleostei) from the Pliocene of Abkhaziiá.]
         Paleontol. Zh., 1971:2, 130–131, 1 fig. (Russian).
1971B   Pliofśenovaiá ikhtiofauna s. Gvada. [Pliocene ichthyofauna of Gvada village.] Akad. Nauk Gruz. SSR,
         Soobshch., 62:2, 493–494 (Russian; Georgian and English summaries).
1971C   A new species of *Atherina* (Teleostei) from the Pliocene of Abkhazia. Paleontol. J., 5:2, 263–264,
         1 fig.

GABELAĬA, TS. D., RAMISHVILI, I. SH. and MAĬSURADZE, L. S.
1970A   K stratigrafii rybnykh sloev Gvada (Abkhaziiá). [On the stratigraphy of fish beds at Gvada
         (Abkhazia).] Akad. Nauk Gruz. SSR, Soobshch., 60:2, 385–388 (Russian; Georgian and
         English summaries).

GÁBORI, MIKLÓS
1969A   László Vértes. 1914–1968. Acta Archaeol. Hung., 21:3–4, 333–337, portr.

GÁBORI-CSÁNK, VERA (= GÁBORINÉ CSÁNK, VERONIKA)
1967A   Un nouveau site moustérien en Hongrie. Acta Archaeol. Hung., 19:3–4, 200–228, 4 figs., 6 pls.,
         3 tables (French).
1968A   La station du Paléolithique moyen d'Érd, Hongrie. Budapest: Akadémiai Kiadó; Monumenta Historica
         Budapestinensia III, 277 pp., 46 figs., 46 pls., tables (French).
         Rev.: Bosinski in Bonner Jahrb., 169, 539–541; Broglio in Riv. Sci. Preist., 24:1, 191–192; Fridrich
                in Archeol. Roz., 22:2, 220; Haltenorth in Säugetierkundl. Mitt., 17:3, 275; Klein in Amer.
                Anthropol., 71, 1119–1223, 1 table; Naber in Quartär, 20, 242–245; Pittioni in Archaeol.
                Austriaca, 46, 121–122.

GÁBORI-CSÁNK, V. and KRETZOI, MIKLÓS
1968A   Zoologie archéologique. In: Gábori-Csánk, V., 1968A, 223–244, 1 fig., tables (French).

GABUNIĬA, LEO KALLISTRATOVICH (= GABUNIA, L. C.)
1966D   Nekotorye obshchie cherty ekogeneza mezozoĭskikh mlekopitaĭushchikh. [Some general traits of the
         ecogenesis of Mesozoic mammals.] Akad. Nauk Gruz. SSR, Inst. Paleobiol., Nauchn. Sess.,
         12, 39–40 (Russian and Georgian).
1967B   Evoliŭtsionnyĭ progress v filogenese mlekopitaĭushchikh. [Evolutionary progress in the phylogenesis of
         mammals.] Akad. Nauk Gruz. SSR, Inst. Paleobiol., Obshch. Vop. Evoliŭts. Paleobiol., 3,
         59–91, 26 figs. (Georgian; Russian and French summaries).
1968A   O sootnoshenii mezhdu ontogenezom i filogenezom u loshadinykh. [On the relationship between
         ontogenesis and phylogenesis in equids.] Akad. Nauk Gruz. SSR, Inst. Paleobiol., Nauchn.
         Sess., 14, 7–9 (Russian).
1969A   Vymiranie drevnikh reptiliĭ i mlekopitaĭushchikh. [Extinction of ancient reptiles and mammals.]
         Tbilisi: "Meĭsniereba" Press, 234 pp., 19 figs., 7 tables (Russian; French summary).
1970A   O drevneĭshem predstavitele brontoteriid Evrazii. [On the oldest representative of brontotheriids of
         Eurasia.] Akad. Nauk Gruz. SSR, Soobshch., 58:3, 737–739, 1 fig. (Georgian; Russian and
         English summaries).
1970B   Sur la signification des faunes de mammifères du Miocène supérieur et du Pliocène de la région Ponto-
         Caspienne. G. Geol., 35:1, 161–170, 1 fig. (French).
1970C   Kontinental'nyĭ neogen Kartliĭskoĭ depressii. [Continental Neogene of Kartli depression.] In: Voprosy
         geologii Kartliĭskoĭ depressii, 30–31 (Russian).
1971A   O novom predstavitele kondiliărtr (Condylarthra) iz eotsena Zaĭsanskoĭ kotloviny. [On a new
         representative of the Condylarthra from Eocene of Zaĭsan Basin.] Akad. Nauk Gruz. SSR,
         Soobshch., 61:1, 233–235, 1 fig. (Russian; Georgian and English summaries).
1971B   Inadaptivnaĭa evoliŭtsiĭa kak odno iz vazhneĭshikh obshchikh usloviĭ vymiraniĭa mlekopitaĭushchikh.
         [Inadaptive evolution as one of the chief general causes of extinction of mammals.] Akad.
         Nauk SSSR, Paleontol. Inst., Tr., 130, 32–38 (Russian).

GABUNIĬA, L. K. and BUACHIDZE, TSISANA IOSIFOVNA
1970A   O pervoĭ nakhodke pozdnemiotsenovoĭ zhirafy v SSSR. [On the first discovery of late Pliocene giraffe
         in the USSR.] Akad. Nauk Gruz. SSR, Soobshch., 57:1, 241–244, 1 fig. (Georgian; Russian
         and English summaries).

GABUNIĬA, L. K. and RUBINSHTEĬN, M. M.
1965A   Biostratigraficheskaĭa parallelizatsiĭa kaĭnozoĭskikh otlozheniĭ Evrazii i Severnoĭ Ameriki v svete
         dannykh absoliŭtnoĭ geokhronologii. [Biostratigraphical parallelization of Cenozoic deposits of
         Eurasia and North America in the light of absolute geochronology data.] Geol. Obshchest.
         Gruz., Izv., 4:1, 7–27, 1 chart (Russian).
1967A   Biostratigraficheskaĭa parallelizatsiĭa kaĭnozoĭskikh otlozheniĭ Evrazii i Severnoĭ Ameriki v svete dannykh
         absoliŭtnoĭ geokhronologii. [Biostratigraphic parallelization of Cenozoic deposits of Eurasia and
         North America in the light of absolute geochronology data.] Akad. Nauk Gruz. SSR, Inst.
         Paleobiol., Nauchn. Sess., 5–6 (Russian).
1968A   Correlation of the Cenozoic deposits of Eurasia and North America based on the fossil mammals and
         absolute age. Int. Geol. Congr., 23rd, Czech., Rep., Abstr., sec. 10, 273–274 (abs.).
1968B   O sopostavlenii kaĭnozoĭskikh otlozheniĭ Evrazii i Severnoĭ Ameriki na osnovanii iskopaemykh
         mlekopitaĭushchikh i absoliŭtnogo vozrasta. [On the correlation of the Cenozoic deposits of
         Eurasia and North America based on the fossil mammals and absolute age data.] In: Granitsa
         tretichnogo i chetvertichnogo periodov, 90–101, 1 table (Russian; English summary).
1968C   On the correlation of the Cenozoic deposits of Eurasia and North America based on the fossil mammals
         and absolute age data. Int. Geol. Congr., 23rd, Czech., Rep., Proc., 10, 9–17, 1 table.

GABUNIĨĀ, L. K. and VEKUA, A. K.
1966D   K voprosu o svĩaziãkh tretichnykh mlekopitaĩushchikh Ēvrazii i Afriki i formirovanie nekotorykh sovremennykh grupp mlekopitaĩushchikh afrikanskikh savann. [On the question of relationships between the Tertiary mammals of Eurasia and Africa and the formation of some modern groups of mammals of African savannas.] In: II Vsesoĩuznoe soveshchanie po paleontologii mlekopitaĩushchikh kaĩnozoĩa (Russian).
1968A   Kvabebskaĩa fauna akchagyl'skikh mlekopitaĩushchikh. [Kvabebi fauna of Akchagyl mammals.] In: Granĩŝa tretichnogo i chetvertichnogo periodov, 42—47, 4 figs. (Russian; English summary).
1968B   Mammals of the Akchaghylian stage. Int. Geol. Congr., 23rd, Czech., Rep., Abstr., sec. 10, 274.
1968C   Kvabebi fauna of the Akchaghylian mammals. Int. Geol. Congr., 23rd, Czech., Rep., Proc., 10, 49—55, 4 figs.

GABUNIĨĀ, LEO KALLISTRATOVICH   See also: Rubinshteĩn, M. M. and Gabuniĩā, L. K., 1972A.

GADZHIEV, DEMIR VAGIDOVICH and ALIEV, S. D.
1966B   Nekotorye predstaviteli khishchnykh mlekopitaĩushchikh (Mammalia, Carnivora) iz paleoliticheskikh otlozhenĩĭ Azykhskoĩ peshchery. [Some representatives of carnivorous mammals (Mammalia, Carnivora) from Paleolithic deposits of Azykh cave.] Baku, Azerbaĩdzh. Gos. Med. Inst., Uch. Zap., 23, 7—13 (Russian).
1969A   Paleontologicheskoe obosnovanie stratigrafii Azykhskoĩ paleoliticheskoĩ stoĩanki. [Paleontological evidence in Azykh paleolithic locality stratigraphy.] Baku, Azerbaĩdzh. Gos. Med. Inst., Uch. Zap., 30, 232—236 (Russian).
1971A   Iskopaemye letuchie myshi iz paleoliticheskikh otlozhenĩĭ Azykhskoĩ peshchery. [Fossil bats from the Paleolithic deposits of Azykh cave.] Baku, Azerbaĩdzh. Univ., Uch. Zap., Ser. Biol., 1971:2, 45—50 (Russian).

GADZHIEV, DEMIR VAGIDOVICH   See also: Alizade, K. A. and Gadzhiev, D. V., 1970A.

GAEMERS, P. A. M.
1968A   Wat zijn Otolieten? Werkgroep Tert. Kwart. Geol., Meded., 5 (1), 2 figs. (Dutch).
         Rev.: Weiler in Zentralbl. Geol. Paläontol., Teil 2, 1968:6, 645—646.
1969A   Otolieten uit het Anversien van Antwerpen. Werkgroep Tert. Kwart. Geol., Meded., 6:1—2, 3—21, 3 pls. (Dutch).
         Rev.: Weiler in Zentralbl. Geol. Paläontol., Teil 2, 1970:3/4, 223—224; Weiler in Zentralbl. Geol. Paläontol., Teil 2, 1970:5, 426—427.
1971A   Bonefish-otoliths from the Aversian (middle Miocene) of Antwerp. Leidse Geol. Meded., 46:2, 237—267, 9 pls., 3 tables.
         Rev.: Weiler in Zentralbl. Geol. Paläontol., Teil 2, 1971:5, 400.

GAFFNEY, EUGENE S.
1970A   The north American baenoid turtles and the cryptodire-pleurodire dichotomy. Diss. Abstr., 31:4, 2155B (abs.).
1971A   Inadequacy of lower tetrapod fossils for determination of past continental relationships. Geol. Soc. Amer., Abstr., 3:7, 576 (abs.).
1971B   Chelonia. McGraw-Hill Yearbook Sci. Tech., 1971, 140—142, 3 figs.
1972A   The systematics of the North American family Baenidae (Reptilia, Cryptodira). Amer. Mus. Natur. Hist., Bull., 147:5, 241—320, 58 figs., 4 tables.

GAFFNEY, EUGENE S. and HIATT, ROBERT
1971A   A new baenid turtle from the upper Cretaceous of Montana. Amer. Mus. Nov., 2443, 9 pp., 6 figs., 1 table.

GAGNIÈRE, SYLVAIN
1970A   Informations archéologiques. Circonscription de Provence-Côte d'Azur-Corse. Gallia Préhist., 13:2, 551—583, 52 figs. (French).

GAGNIÈRE, S.   See also: Lumley, H. de, Gagnière, S. and Fournier, A., 1969A.

GAHERTY, G., KETTEL, D., MACDONALD, J., NIEMANN, L., VON GRAEVE, B. and ARIMA, E.
1969A   Notes on the physical anthropology of Lawrence Oschinsky. Anthropologica, 11:2, 275—292 (French summary).

GAI, PEI   See: Tszia, L.-p., Gai, P. and Li, Y.-s., 1964A.

GAĬDUK, I. M.
    1967A   Znachenie arkheologicheskikh pamîatnikov v opredelenii vozrasta chetvertichnykh otlozheniĭ.
                  [Significance of archeological relics for the determination of the age of Quaternary deposits.]
                  Geogr. Obshchest. SSSR, Altaĭsk. Otd., Izv., 8, 17–23 (Russian).
    1969A   Itogi issledovaniîa paleolita Altaĭskogo kraîa za gody Sovetskoĭ vlasti. [Results of the research on
                  Paleolithic of Altaĭ region during the Soviet government.] Geogr. Obshchest. SSSR, Altaĭsk. Otd.,
                  Izv., 10, 99–107 (Russian).

GAILLI, R., NOUGIER, L.-R. and ROBERT, R.
    1969A   L'art de la caverne de Niaux. (Compléments iconographiques). Préhist. Spéléol. Ariége., 24, 11–37,
                  17 figs. (French).

GAILLI, R.   See also: Beltrán, A., Robert, R. and Gailli, R., 1967A.

GALBREATH, EDWIN C.
    1969A   Cylindrodont rodents from the lower Oligocene of northeastern Colorado. Ill. Acad. Sci., Trans.,
                  62:1, 94–97, 2 figs., 2 tables.

GALBRAITH, HOWARD
    1963A   Evolution – Galbraith's view. Screenings, 12:3, 4.

GALITŠKIĬ, V. V., GEKKER, R. F., KOSTENKO, N. N. and SAKULINA, G. V.
    1968A   Karatauskoe îurskoe ozero. Putevoditel' ekskursii piatoĭ paleoekologo-litologicheskoĭ sessii. [Karatau
                  Jurassic lake. Guide to excursion of the fifth paleoecologic-lithologic session.] Alma-Ata:
                  Paleontol. Inst. Akad. Nauk SSSR, Minister. Geol. Kaz. SSR, 38 pp., illustr. (Russian).

GALL, HORST
    1971A   Obere Süsswassermolasse (Hangendserie) über Riestrümmermassen bei Graisbach (südöstliches Vorries)
                  und ihre Bedeutung für die Landschaftsgeschichte der Schwäbisch-Fränkischen Alb. Bayer.
                  Staatssamml. Paläontol. Hist. Geol., Mitt., 11, 295–327, 6 figs. (French; English summary).

GALL, HORST and MÜLLER, DIETER
    1970A   Die Monheimer Höhensande. Oberrhein. Geol. Ver., Jahresb. Mitt., 52, 113–131, 2 figs., 1 pl.,
                  1 table (German).

GALL, H.   See also: Fahlbusch, V. and Gall, H., 1970A; Fahlbusch, V., Gall, H. and Schmidt-Kittler, N.,
                  1972A.

GALL, JEAN-CLAUDE
    1971A   Faunes et paysages du Grès à Voltzia du Nord des Vosges. Essai paléoécologique sur le Buntsandstein
                  supérieur. Alsace-Lorraine, Serv. Carte Géol., Mém., 34, 318 pp., 39 figs., 36 pls., 20 tables
                  (French; English and German summaries).

GALL, J.-C. and GRAUVOGEL, L.
    1968A   Présentation d'un profil paléoécologique du grès à Voltzia (Buntsandstein supérieur) des Vosges.
                  Alsace-Lorraine, Serv. Carte Géol., Bull., 21:4, 305–312, 1 chart (French; English, German,
                  and Russian summaries).

GALLI, C.   See: Dingman, R. J. and Galli, C., 1965A.

GALLUS, ALEXANDER
    1968A   Archaeological excavations at Koonalda, Nullarbor plain, 1957–1967. J. Anthropol. Soc. S. Austral.,
                  6:7, 4–8.

GALTON, PETER M.
    1969A   The pelvic musculature of the dinosaur Hypsilophodon (Reptilia: Ornithischia). Postilla, 131, 64 pp.,
                  17 figs.
                  Rev.: Chrulew in Zentralbl. Geol. Paläontol., Teil 2, 1970:1, 69–70.
    1970A   The posture of hadrosaurian dinosaurs. J. Paleontol., 44:3, 464–473, 5 figs., 2 tables.
                  Rev.: Chrulew in Zentralbl. Geol. Paläontol., Teil 2, 1970:6, 515; 1971:1, 54.
    1970B   Ornithischian dinosaurs and the origin of birds. Evolution, 24:2, 448–462, 6 figs.
                  Rev.: Kuhn in Zentralbl. Geol. Paläontol., Teil 2, 1971:5, 412.
                  Abs.: L.L.S. in Auk, 88:1, 211–212.
    1970C   Pachycephalosaurids-dinosaurian battering rams. Discovery, Yale, 6:1, 23–32, 11 figs.
    1971A   A primitive dome-headed dinosaur (Ornithischia: Pachycephalosauridae) from the lower Cretaceous
                  of England and the function of the dome of pachycephalosaurids. J. Paleontol., 45:1, 40–47,
                  7 figs.

1971B   *Hypsilophodon*, the cursorial non-arboreal dinosaur. Nature, 231:5299, 159—161, 2 figs., 1 table.

1971C   The prosauropod dinosaur *Ammosaurus*, the crocodile *Protosuchus*, and their bearing on the age of the Navajo sandstone of northeastern Arizona. J. Paleontol., 45:5, 781—795, 13 figs., 2 tables.

1971D   The mode of life of *Hypsilophodon*, the supposedly arboreal ornithopod dinosaur. Lethaia, 4:4, 453—465, 5 figs., 1 table.

1971E   Manus movements of the coelurosaurian dinosaur *Syntarsus* and opposability of the theropod hallux. Arnoldia, 5:15, 8 pp., 5 figs.

1972A   Classification and evolution of ornithopod dinosaurs. Nature, 239:5373, 464—466.

GALUSHA, TED and BLICK, JOHN C.
1971A   Stratigraphy of the Santa Fe group, New Mexico. Amer. Mus. Natur. Hist., Bull., 144:1, 127 pp., 38 figs., 3 tables.

GAMA, A.   See: Théobald, N. and Gama, A., 1969A.

GAMBARIAN, P. P.
1967A   Proiskhozhdenie mnogoobraziia alliurov u mlekopitaiushchikh. [The origin of the diversity of gait in mammals.] Zh. Obshch. Biol., 28:3, 289—305, 17 figs. (Russian; English summary).
     Rev.: Anon. in Priroda, 1968:7, 110—112, 2 figs. (Russian).

GAMERO, MARÍA L. D., DE   See: Díaz de Gamero, M. L.

GAND, G.
1971A   Découverte de documents ichnologiques nouveaux dans les carrières de la Pissoire (plateau d'Antully-Saône-et-Loire). Soc. Hist. Natur. Amis Mus. Autun, Bull. Trim., 58, 3—14 (French).

GANIA, I. M. (= GANEA, I. M.)
1965A   Materialy po izucheniiu pleistotsenovykh ptits Moldavii. [Materials of the research on Pleistocene birds of Moldavia.] In: Novosti ornitologii. Materialy chetvertoĭ vsesoiuznoĭ ornitologicheskoĭ konferentsii, Alma-Ata, 1965, 88—90, 1 table (Russian).
1969A   [Fossil birds of prey from Moldavia.] Akad. Nauk Moldav. SSR, Izv., Ser. Biol. Khim. Nauk, 1969:1, 24—28, 4 tables (Russian).
1969B   Iskopaemye kurinye ptitsy Moldavii. [Fossil gallinaceous birds of Moldavia.] Akad. Nauk Moldav. SSR, Okh. Prir. Moldav., 7, 125—134 (Russian).

GANIA, I. M.   See also: Kurochkin, E. N. and Gania, I. M., 1972A.

GANS, CARL
1969A*   Biology of the Reptilia. Vol. 1. Morphology A. Edited by Angus d'A. Bellairs and Thomas S. Parsons. London and New York: Academic Press, xv + 373 pp., illustr.
     Rev.: Anon. in La Recherche, 1:7, 698—699; Arnold in New Sci., 42:647, 256—257; Cave in J. Anat., 105:3, 585; Estes in Copeia, 1970:4, 789—790; Gabe in L'Ann. Biol., 10:5—6, 347—348; Kuhn-Schnyder in Naturwiss., 57:5, 260; Liem in Nature, 224:5223, 994; Mertens in Salamandra, 5:3—4, 157; Peters in Biol. Zentralbl., 88:6, 796—797; Romer in Amer. Sci., 57:3, 240A; Salvador in Soc. Españ. Hist. Natur., Bol., Secc. Biol., 69:2, 174; Wake in Quart. Rev. Biol., 45:2, 210—211; Westphal in Zentralbl. Geol. Paläontol., Teil 2, 1969:6, 512—513.
1970A*   Biology of the reptilia. Vol. 2. Morphology B. Coeditor Thomas S. Parsons. London and New York: Academic Press, xiii + 374 pp., illustr.
     Rev.: Cruickshank in S. Afr. J. Sci., 67:7, 399; Gabe in L'Ann. Biol., 10:5—6, 347—348.

GARCÍA, JULIO and ALBERDI, M. TERESA
1968A   Nueva tortuga fósil en el Mioceno de Arévalo. Soc. Españ. Hist. Natur., Bol., Secc. Biol., 66:3—4, 141—149, 6 figs. (Spanish; English summary).

GARCÍA GUINEA, MIGUEL A.
1968A   Rev.: Ripoll Perelló in Ampurias, 31—32, 383—384.
1969A   Los problemas del arte paleolítico. Atlántida, 7:39, 354—357 (Spanish).

GARCÍA GUINEA, M. A.   See also: González Echegaray, P. J., García Guinea, M. A. and Begines Ramírez, A., 1963A; González Echegaray, J., García Guinea, M. A., Begines, A., Madariaga de la Campa, B. and Leroi-Gourhan, Arl., 1966A.

GARCÍA-RODRÍGUEZ, J.
1967A   Bioquímica y paleontología. Col-Pa (Madrid, Univ., Fac. Cienc.), 1967:12, 6—7 (Spanish).

GARD, L. M., LEWIS, G. E. and WHITMORE, F. C., JR.
    1972A   Steller's sea cow in Pleistocene interglacial beach deposits on Amchitka, Aleutian Islands. Geol. Soc.
                   Amer., Bull., 83:3, 867–869.

GARD, L. M. and SZABO, B. J.
    1971A   Age of the Pleistocene deposits at South Bight, Amchitka Island, Alaska. Geol. Soc. Amer., Abstr.,
                   3:7, 577 (abs.).

GARDINER, B. G.
    1969A   New palaeoniscoid fish from the Witteberg series of South Africa. Linn. Soc., Zool. J., 48:4, 423–452,
                   18 figs., 2 pls.

GAREVSKI, RISTO
    1969A   Stratigrafsko i paleontološko značenje na pleistocenskata fauna od pešterata Makarovec vo klisurata na
                   rekata Babuna vo okolinata na Titov Veles. [Stratigraphical and paleontological significance
                   of the Pleistocene fauna from the Makarovec cave in the Babuna River gorge in the vicinity of
                   Titov Veles.] Skopje, Prirodonauč. Muz., Posebno Izd., 6, 94 pp., 10 pls., 2 maps, 13 tables
                   (Macedonian; German summary).
           Rev.:   Thenius in Zentralbl. Geol. Paläontol., Teil 2, 1971:1, 62.

GARKUSHA, M. P., ENGOĬAN, M. A., OGANESĬAN, D. A. and SUKIASĬAN, S. S.
    1971A   O nakhodke ostatkov ryb v verkhnem devone Armĭanskoĭ SSR. [On the finding of fish remains in the
                   upper Devonian of the Armenian SSR.] Akad. Nauk SSSR, Dokl., 196:4, 903–904, 1 fig.
                   (Russian).

GARN, STANLEY M.
    1971A   The improper use of fossil nomenclature. Amer. J. Phys. Anthropol., 35:2, 217–218.

GARN, S. M., LEWIS, A. B. and WALENGA, A. J.
    1969A   Crown size profile patterns and presumed evolutionary "trends". Amer. Anthropol., 71, 79–84,
                   2 figs., 1 table.

GARROD, DOROTHY A. E., et al.
    1971A   Excerpts from "The stone age of Mount Carmel". In: Leakey, L. S. B., Prost, J. and Prost, S. (eds.),
                   1971A, 257–292 (reprinted from Garrod, D. A. E., et al., 1937).

GARUTT, VADIM EVGEN'EVICH
    1971A   K istorii vyĭavleniĭa promezhutochnykh zven'ev v filogeneticheskoĭ linii slonov Archidiskodon-
                   Mammuthus. [Concerning the history of the elucidation of intermediate links in the
                   phylogenetic line of elephants Archidiskodon-Mammuthus.] In: Khronologiĭa lednikovogo
                   veka. Materialy k simposiumu, Leningrad, mart 1972g., 78–88 (Russian).

GARUTT, V. E. and ALEKSEEVA, LĬUDMILA IVANOVNA
    1964A   Novye dannye ob evolĭutsii slonov roda Archidiskodon. [New data on the evolution of elephants of
                   the genus Archidiskodon.] In: Vsesoĭuznoe Soveshchanie po Izucheniĭu Chetvertichnogo
                   perioda, Novosibirsk, 1964, Tezisy Dokladov, Sekfsiĭa Istorii Flory, Fauny i Drevnego
                   Cheloveka, 7–8 (Russian).

GARUTT, V. E., METEL'TSEVA, E. P. and TIKHOMIROV, B. A.
    1970A   Novye dannye o pishche sherstistogo nosoroga v Sibiri. [New data on the food of woolly rhinoceros
                   in Siberia.] In: Severnyĭ Ledovityĭ Okean i ego poberezh'e v kaĭnozoe, 113–125, 3 figs.,
                   1 table (Russian).

GARWOOD, ROBERT A.   See: Gould, S. J. and Garwood, R. A., 1969A.

GARYAINOV, V. A. (= GARĬAINOV, V. A.)   See: Ochev, V. G., Shishkin, M. A., Garyainov, V. A. and
                   Tverdokhlebov, V. P., 1964A, 1965A.

GASC, JEAN-PIERRE
    1971A   Les variations columnaires dans la région présacrée des sauriens: application à la reconstitution de
                   Lacerta goliath Mertens. Ann. Paléontol., Vertébrés, 57:1, 133–155, 18 figs., 2 tables (French).

GASC, JEAN-PIERRE   See also: Castanet, J., Gasc, J.-P., Meunier, F. and Ricqlès, A. de, 1970A; Hoffstetter, R.
                   and Gasc, J.-P., 1969A.

GASHEV, N. S. and BAKHMUTOV, V. A.
  1968A   Prigotovlenie zamorozhennykh srezov kostnoĭ tkani na sannom mikrotome. [The preparation of frozen sections of bone tissue with a sledge microtome.] Mosk. Obshchest. Ispyt. Prir., Bĭull., Otd. Biol., 73:6, 146–148, 2 figs. (Russian).

GASKILL, PAMELA   See: Carroll, R. L. and Gaskill, P., 1971A.

GASPARINI, ZULMA B. DE
  1971A   Los Notosuchia del Cretacico de America del sur como un nuevo infraorden de los Mesosuchia (Crocodilia). Ameghiniana, 8:2, 83–103, 1 fig., 4 pls. (Spanish; English summary).
  1972A   Los Sebecosuchia (Crocodilia) del territorio Argentino. Consideraciones sobre su "status" taxonómico. Ameghiniana, 9:1, 23–34, 2 figs., 1 pl. (Spanish; English summary).

GATINSKIĬ, ĬU. G., GERUS, E. A., KLOCHKO, V. P., and TROFIMOV, D. M.
  1967A   Novye dannye po stratigrafii i tektonike severo-zapadnoĭ chasti Mali-Nigerskoĭ vpadiny. [New data on the stratigraphy and tectonics of the north-western part of Mali-Nigerian basin.] Nauch.-Issled. Lab. Geol. Zarubezh. Stran, Tr., 17, 27–37, 3 figs. (Russian).

GATINSKIĬ, ĬURIĬ GEORGIEVICH   See also: Kudriàvt̂sev, G. A., Agentov, V. B., Gatinskiĭ, Ĭu. G. and Mishina, A. V., 1969A.

GAUDANT, JEAN
  1967B   Rechereches sur l'anatomie et la position systématique du genre Lycoptera (poisson téléostéen). Soc. Géol. Fr., C.R., 1967:4, 164 (French).
  1968B   Contribution à une révision des Anaethalion de Cérin (Ain). Fr., Bur. Rech. Géol. Minières, Bull. (Sér. 2), Sect. 4, 1968:1, 95–115, 6 figs., 3 pls. (French).

GAUDANT, JEAN and MAUBEUGE, PIERRE
  1971A   Sur la découverte d'un nouvel Anaethalionidae (poisson téléostéen) dans l'Oxfordien des environs de Verdun (Meuse). Soc. Géol. Fr., C.R., 1971:2, 75 (French).

GAUDANT, JEAN   See also: Gaudant, M. and Gaudant, J., 1969A, 1971A.

GAUDANT, MIREILLE
  1969A   Sur quelques nouveaux poissons bérycoïdes crétacés du mont Liban. Notice préliminaire. Notes Mém. Moyen-Orient, 10, 273–283 (French).

GAUDANT, MIREILLE and GAUDANT, JEAN
  1969A   Note sur un Pleuronectiforme nouveau conservé au Service géologique de Tunisie: Numidiopleura enigmatica nov. gen., nov. sp. Soc. Géol. Fr., Bull., 11:5, 660–665, 2 figs., 1 pl. (French).
  1971A   Une nouvelle espèce de Diplomystus (poisson téléostéen) dans le Crétacé supérieur du Sud tunisien. Soc. Géol. Fr., C.R., 1971:2, 75 (French).

GAUSSEN, J.
  1964A   Rev.: R. P. in Ampurias, 31–32, 384–385.

GAUTIER, ACHILLES
  1964A   Kanttekeningen bij "Olduvai Gorge 1951–1961" en de kwartaire klimatologische tijdsindelingen in Oost-Afrika. Natuurwet. Tijdschr., 46:7, 205–210 (Dutch; English summary).
  1965B   Geological investigation in the Sinda-Mohari (Ituri, Ne-Congo). A monograph on the geological history of a region in the Lake Albert rift. Gent: University Press, 161 pp., 31 figs., 8 pls., 11 tables.
  1968A   Mammalian remains of the northern Sudan and southern Egypt. In: Wendorf, Fred (ed.), 1968A, 80–99, 2 figs., 6 tables.
  1970A   The fauna of Masloukh. Beirut, Mus. Nat. Lib., Bull., 23, 135.

GAVELA, BRANKO
  1955A   Nouvelles recherches et découvertes dans le domaine du Paléolithique en Yougoslavie. Les Eyzies, 5, 50–52 (French).
  1957A   Premières stations Paléolithiques en Serbie. Les Eyzies, 7, 47–50 (French).

GAZIN, C. LEWIS
  1969A   A new occurrence of Paleocene mammals in Evanston formation, southwestern Wyoming. Smithson. Contrib. Paleobiol., 2, 17 pp., 1 map, 3 pls.
  1971A   Paleocene primates from the Shotgun member of the Fort Union formation in the Wind River basin, Wyoming. Biol. Soc. Wash., Proc., 84:3, 13–37, 6 figs.

GEER, KLAUS
  1969A   Die 12. Tagung der Hugo-Obermaier-Gesellschaft 1968 in Marbach am Neckar mit Exkursionen nach Steinheim a.d. Murr, Mauer und Heidelberg. Quartär, 20, 203–221, 1 pl. (German).

GEIST, VALERIUS
1971A   The relation of social evolution and dispersal in ungulates during the Pleistocene, with emphasis on the Old World deer and the genus *Bison*. Quaternary Res., 1:3, 283–315, 7 figs., 1 table.
1972A   An ecological and behavioural explanation of mammalian characteristics, and their implication to therapsid evolution. Z. Säugetierkunde, 37:1, 1–15, 2 figs. (German summary).

GEKKER, ROMAN FEDOROVICH (= HECKER, R. F.)
1968A   Ekologicheskii aspekt v paleontologii i ekologicheskaia sistematika. [Ecological aspect in paleontology and ecological taxonomy.] In: Problemy paleontologii, 7–17 (Russian; English summary).
1969A   Pamiati Iozefa Augusty (1903–1968). [Memorial to Jozef Augusta (1903–1968).] Paleontol. Zh., 1969:3, 164–165 (Russian).

GEKKER, R. F., SHISHKIN, M. A. and IAKOVLEV, V. N.
1971A   Dmitrii Vladimirovich Obruchev (1900–1970). Paleontol. Zh., 1971:2, 145–146, portr. (Russian).

GEKKER, R. F.   See also: Galifskii, V. V., Gekker, R. F., Kostenko, N. N. and Sakulina, G. V., 1968A.

GENERALOV, P. P., KUZIN, I. L., ZAIONTS, I. L. and KRAPIVNER, R. B.
1970A   Osnovnye cherty paleogeografii Pechorskoi nizmennosti i basseina nizhnei Obi v noveishee vremia. [Fundamental traits of the paleogeography of Pechora lowlands and of lower Ob' in latest time.] In: Severnyi Ledovityi Okean i ego poberezh'e v kainozoe, 374–387 (Russian).

GENET-VARCIN, EMILIENNE
1969A   Structure et comportement des australopithéques d'après certains os post-craniens. Ann. Paléontol., Vertébrés, 55:1, 139–148, 1 fig. (French).
1969B   A la recherche du primate ancêtre de l'homme. Paris: Boubée et Cie., Ed., Coll. "L'homme et ses origines", 336 pp., 181 figs., tables (French).
        Rev.: Bilsborough in Endeavor, 29:108, 158; Bilsborough in Prehist. Soc., Proc., 36, 382–385; D.C.V. in Ampurias, 31–32, 395–397; Dorst in Mammalia, 34:2, 328–329; Furon in Cah. Géol., 86, 1130; Hunt in Amer. J. Phys. Anthropol., 36:2, 299–300; MacConaill in Man (J. Roy. Anthropol. Inst.), 5:3, 523; Segre Naldini in Quaternaria, 13, 438–439.
1972A   Étude de molaires inférieures humaines découvertes dans le gisement du Placard (Charente). Ann. Paléontol., Vertébrés, 58:1, 133–147, 1 fig. (French; English summary).

GENET-VARCIN, E. and RABISCHONG, P.
1965A   Remarques sur l'âge présumé de l'adolescent du type négroïde de Grimaldi. Congr. Préhist. France, 16e Sess., Monaco 1959, C.R., 573–577, 3 figs. (French).

GENING, V. F.
1969A   Izuchenie kompleksa stoianok pri d. Chernoozer'e na Irtyshe. [Studies on a complex of sites near Chernoozer'e village on Irtysh R.] In: Rybakov, B. A. (ed.), 1969A, 198–200 (Russian).

GENOVÉS TARAZAGA, SANTIAGO, et al.
1968A*   Yearbook of physical anthropology. 1966. Mexico: Amer. Assoc. of Physical Anthropologists, Yearbook Ser., 14, v + 320 pp., illustr.
        Rev.: Benfer in Amer. Anthropol., 71, 982–988; Brace in Amer. J. Phys. Anthropol., 31, 120–122; Schwidetzky in Homo, 20:3, 197; Vallois in L'Anthropologie, 73:3–4, 286.

GENOWAYS, HUGH H.   See: Jones, J. Knox, Jr. and Genoways, H. H., 1970A.

GENTRY, A.   See: Gentry, A. W. and Gentry, A., 1969A.

GENTRY, ALAN WILLIAM
1968B   The extinct bovid genus *Qurliqnoria* Bohlin. J. Mammal., 49, 769.
        Rev.: Thenius in Zentralbl. Geol. Paläontol., Teil 2, 1971:1, 67–68.
1970A   The Bovidae (Mammalia) of the Fort Ternan fossil fauna. In: Leakey, L. S. B., and Savage, R. J. G. (eds.), 1970A, 243–323, 22 figs., 17 pls., 5 tables.
        Rev.: Thenius in Zentralbl. Geol. Paläontol., Teil 2, 1971:4, 342–344.
1970B   Revised classification for *Makapania broomi* Wells and Cooke (Bovidae, Mammalia). Palaeontol. Afr., 13, 63–67, 4 figs.
        Rev.: Thenius in Zentralbl. Geol. Paläontol., Teil 2, 1972:3, 177–178.
1971A   The earliest goats and other antelopes from the Samos *Hipparion* fauna. Brit. Mus. (Natur. Hist.), Bull., Geol., 20:6, 231–296, 16 figs., 6 pls., 3 tables.
        Rev.: Thenius in Zentralbl. Geol. Paläontol., Teil 2, 1971:6, 520–521.

GENTRY, A. W. and GENTRY, A.
1969A   Fossil camels in Kenya and Tanzania. Nature, 222:5196, 898, 1 fig.

Rev.: Thenius in Zentralbl. Geol. Paläontol., Teil 2, 1971:1, 68.

GENTRY, A. W.   See also: Coryndon, S. C., Gentry, A. W., Harris, J. M., Hooijer, D. A., Maglio, V. J. and Howell, F. C., 1972A.

GEORGE, THOMAS N.
1971A   Systematics in palaeontology. Geol. Soc. London, J., 127:3, 197—245, 19 figs.

GEPTNER, V. G.   See: Heptner, W. G.

GERAGHTY, PAUL
1969A   Horns and antlers — not just weapons. Can. Audubon, 31:4—5, 151—157, 9 figs.

GERASIMOV, I. P.   See: Zimina, R. P. and Gerasimov, I. P., 1971A.

GERASIMOV, MIKHAIL MIKHAĬLOVICH
1968A   Ich suchte Gesichter. Gütersloh: C. Bertelsmann Verlag, 240 pp., illustr. (German).
          Rev.: Rieth in Anthropol. Anz., 31:3, 217—218.
1971A   The face finder. Translated from the German edition by Alan Houghton Broderick. Philadelphia: Lippincott, xxiv + 255 pp., illustr.
          Rev.: Angel in Science, 173:3998, 712; Morrison in Sci. Amer., 225:3, 234, 237—238.

GERBOVA, V. G.   See: Ravskiĭ, E. I. and Gerbova, V. G., 1970A.

GERETA, I. P.
1969A   Novye paleoliticheskie stoĭanki v Ternopol'e. [New Paleolithic sites in Ternopol' region.] In: Rybakov, B. A. (ed.), 1969A, 265—266.

GERITY, TOM
1961A   Tusk found in old gravels. Screenings, 10:9, 4, 1 fig.
1967A   Pre-projectile point cultures — evidence needed. Screenings, 16:8, 4, 1 fig.

GERMAN, R., FILZER, P., DEHM, R., FREUDE, H., JUNG, W. and WITT, W.
1968A   Ergebnisse der wissenschaftlichen Kern-Bohrung Wurzacher Becken 1 (DFG). Ver. Vaterländ. Naturk. Württemberg, Jahresh., 123, 33—68, 6 figs., 3 tables (German).

GERSTER, GEORG
1971A   Tiere versanken im Teer. Kosmos (Stuttgart), 67:11, 470—475, 5 figs. (German).

GERSTNER, PATSY A.
1970A   Vertebrate paleontology, an early nineteenth century transatlantic science. J. Hist. Biol., 3:1, 137—148.

GERUS, E. A.   See: Gatinskiĭ, Iu. G., Gerus, E. A., Klochko, V. P. and Trofimov, D. M., 1967A.

GÉRY, J.
1968A   Évolution régressive et évolution créatrice. Zool. Anz., 181:3/4, 161—168 (French; German summary).

GESS, W. H. R.
1969A   Excavation of a Pleistocene bone deposit at Aloes near Port Elizabeth. S. Afr. Archaeol. Bull., 24:93, 31—32.

GEYH, MEBUS A.
1971A   Die Anwendung der 14C-Methode und anderer radiometrischer Datierungsverfahren für das Quartär. Clausthaler Tekton. Hefte, 11, 118 pp., 12 figs. (German).

GHENEA, CONSTANTIN
1968A   Studiul depozitelor pliocene dintre valea Prutului şi valea Bîrladului. [Study of Pliocene deposits between the Prut and Bîrlad valleys.] Rom., Inst. Geol., Stud. Teh. Econ., Ser. J, 6, 137 pp., 16 figs., 9 pls., 3 maps, 4 tables (Rumanian; French and English summaries).
1969A   Les faciès de l'intervalle Pliocène supérieur-Pleistocène inférieur du bassin Dacique (Roumanie). In: Mezhdunarodnyĭ kollokvium po geologii i faune nizhnego i srednego pleĭstotsena Evropy. Tezisy dokladov, 52—54 (French).
1970A   Stratigraphy of the upper Pliocene-lower Pleistocene interval in the Dacic basin (Romania). Palaeogeogr., Palaeoclimatol., Palaeoecol., 8:2—3, 165—174, 1 fig., 2 tables.
1972A   Stratigrafiia intervala verkhniĭ pliotsen-nizhniĭ pleĭstotsen Dakiĭskogo basseĭna (Rumyniia). [Stratigraphy of the interval upper Pliocene-lower Pleistocene of the Dacian basin (Rumania).] In: Geologiia i fauna nizhnego i srednego pleĭstotsena Evropy, 143—153 (Russian).

GHENEA, C., BANDRABUR, T. and MIHĂILĂ, N.
    1967A   Considérations géologiques sur les dépôts à faune villafranchienne de Roumanie. Ass. Géol. Carpato-
                Balkanique, 8e Congr., Belgrade, 1967, Rapp., T.1, 375–381, 1 fig. (French; Russian summary).

GHEORGHIAN, M. D.   See: Stancu, J., Gheorghian, M. D. and Popescu, A., 1971A.

GHEȚIE, V.
    1964A   Evoluția aparatului locomotor. [Evolution of locomotor apparatus.] Natura, Ser. Biol., 16:1, 23–32,
                1 pl. (Rumanian).

GHICA, M.   See: Dumitrescu, M., Samson, P., Terzea, E., Rădulescu, C. and Ghica, M., 1963A.

GHISELIN, MICHAEL T.
    1969A   The triumph of the Darwinian method. Berkeley, Los Angeles and London: Univ. Calif. Press,
                x + 287 pp., 7 figs.
                Rev.: Hardin in BioScience, 20:9, 575; Hull in Syst. Zool., 18:4, 447–450; Lehman in Isis, 61,
                144–145; Simpson in Science (AAAS), 167:3923, 1362–1363; Smith in Nature, 225:5230,
                390.
    1969B   The principles and concepts of systematic biology. Discussions. In: Sibley, Ch. G. (ed.), 1969A,
                45–66.
    1972A   Models in phylogeny. In: Schopf, T. J. M. (ed.), 1972A, 130–145.

GIBERT, J.   See: Crusafont, M., Golpe, J.-M., Gibert, J. and Thaler, L., 1971A.

GIBSON, GORDON D.
    1969A   A bibliography of anthropological bibliographies: Africa. Current Anthropol., 10:5, 527–566.

GIEDION, SIEGFRIED
    1964C   Die Entstehung der Kunst. Köln: 433 pp., 350 figs., 20 col. pls., 5 maps (German).
                Rev.: Bandi in Schweiz. Ges. Urgesch., Jahrb., 52, 126–127; Zotz in Quartär, 17, 197–203.

GIGLIO, A.   See: Charrier, G. and Giglio, A., 1969A.

GILBERT-TOMLINSON, JOYCE
    1968A   A new record of Bothriolepis in the Northern Territory of Australia. Austral. Bur. Miner. Resour.,
                Geol. Geophys., Bull., 80, 189–226, 8 figs., 1 pl.

GILIĂROV, M. S.
    1970A   Zakonomernosti i napravleniĭā filogeneza. [Laws and trends in phylogenesis.] Zh. Obshch. Biol.,
                31:2, 179–188 (Russian; English summary).

GILL, DON
    1970A   The coyote and the sequential occupants of the Los Angeles Basin. Amer. Anthropol., 72:4, 821–826.

GILL, EDMUND D.
    1968A   Palaeoecology of fossil human skeletons. Palaeogeogr., Palaeoclimatol., Palaeoecol., 4:3, 211–217.
    1968B   Fossil sea lion as a palaeoclimatologic indicator. Palaeogeogr., Palaeoclimatol., Palaeoecol., 5, 235–
                239, 1 fig.
                Rev.: Thenius in Zentralbl. Geol. Paläontol., Teil 2, 1970:3/4, 239.
    1970A   The life of the present and the life of the past. T. S. Hall memorial lecture. Victorian Natur., 87:2,
                32–35.
    1971A   Applications of radiocarbon dating in Victoria, Australia. Roy. Soc. Victoria, Proc., 84:1, 71–85.
    1972A   The Dunolly fossil wombat. Victorian Natur., 89:3, 64–66, 1 fig.

GILL, JAMES R. and COBBAN, WILLIAM A.
    1966A   The Red Bird section of the upper Cretaceous Pierre shale in Wyoming. U.S. Geol. Surv., Prof.
                Paper, 393–A, iv + 73 pp., 17 figs., 12 pls., 3 tables.

GILLESPIE, J. M.
    1970A   Mammoth hair: stability of oc-Keratin structure and constituent proteins. Science (AAAS), 170:3962,
                1100–1102, 2 figs., 1 table.

GILLETTE, DAVID D.
    1972A   Coelomic cavity casts of upper Cretaceous fishes in Texas. J. Paleontol., 46:1, 50–54, 5 figs.
    1972B   Comments on North American glyptodonts. Soc. Vert. Paleontol. Ann. Meeting, 32nd, 1972, Abstr.
                (abs.).

GILLULY, J., WATERS, A. C. and WOODFORD, A. O.
  1968A   Rev.: Anon. in Calif., Div. Mines Geol., Miner. Inform. Serv., 21:10, 155; Baksi and Chanda in Sci.
                 Culture, 37:2, 93—94; Müller in Naturwiss., 58:6, 332.

GINGERICH, PHILIP D.
  1971A   Cranium of *Plesiadapis*. Nature, 232:5312, 566, 1 fig.
  1972A   Evolution of *Plesiadapis* and *Platychaerops* in Europe. Soc. Vert. Paleontol. Ann. Meeting, 32nd,
                 1972, Abstr. (abs.).
  1972B   Molar occlusion and jaw mechanics of the Eocene primate *Adapis*. Amer. J. Phys. Anthropol., 36:3,
                 359—368, 8 figs., 1 table.

GINGERICH, PHILIP D.   See also: Bown, T. M. and Gingerich, P. D., 1972A.

GINSBURG, LÉONARD
  1968C   Les mustelidés piscivores du Miocène français. Mus. Nat. Hist. Natur., Paris, Bull., 40:1, 228—238,
                 6 figs. (French).
                 Rev.: Thenius in Zentralbl. Geol. Paläontol., Teil 2, 1970:3/4, 239.
  1969A   Le plus ancien morse du monde. Mus. Nat. Hist. Natur., Paris, Bull., 41:4, 995—998, 1 fig. (French).
  1969B   Une faune de mammifères terrestres dans le Stampien marin d'Etampes (Essonne). Acad. Sci., C.R.,
                 Sér. D, 268:9, 1266—1268 (French).
  1969C   Sur un Amphicyoninae de l'Oligocène de l'Europe. Soc. Géol. Fr., C.R., 1969:3, 72—73 (French).
                 Rev.: Thenius in Zentralbl. Geol. Paläontol., Teil 2, 1970:3/4, 239.
  1970A   Les mammifères des faluns helvétiens du Nord de la Loire. Soc. Géol. Fr., C.R., 1970:6, 189—190
                 (French).
  1970B   Un ruminant nouveau des faluns miocènes de la Touraine et de l'Anjou. Mus. Nat. Hist. Natur., Paris,
                 Bull., 42:5, 996—1002, 1 fig. (French).
  1970C   Les reptiles fossiles. In: Grassé, P.-P. (ed.), 1970A, 1161—1332, 140 figs. (French).
  1971A   Sur l'évolution des *Steneofiber* (Mammalia, Rodentia) en France. Acad. Sci., C.R., Sér. D, 272:17,
                 2159—2161, 2 figs., 1 table (French).
  1972A   Sur l'âge des mammifères des faluns miocènes au Nord de la Loire. Acad. Sci., C.R., Sér. D, 274:25,
                 3345—3347 (French).

GINSBURG, L. and HEINTZ, E.
  1968A   La plus ancienne antilope d'Europe, *Eotragus artenensis*, du Burdigalien d'Artenay. Mus. Nat. Hist.
                 Natur., Paris, Bull., 40:4, 837—842, 1 pl., 1 table (French).
                 Rev.: Thenius in Zentralbl. Geol. Paläontol., Teil 2, 1971:1, 68.

GINSBURG, L., HILLY, J. and TAQUET, P.
  1968A   Une faune würmienne dans un remplissage de fente du massif du Filfila (littoral nord-constantinois,
                 Algérie). Soc. Géol. Fr., C.R., 1968:5, 157—158 (French).

GINSBURG, L. and JANVIER, PH.
  1970A   Présence de sables helvétiens d'origine fluviatile sous les faluns du bassin de Noyant-sous-le-Lude
                 (Maine-et-Loire). Mus. Nat. Hist. Natur., Paris, Bull., 42:2, 435—439, 1 fig. (French).

GINSBURG, L., LAPIERRE, F. and MONTENAT, C.
  1967A   Une faunule de mammifères principalement remaniée dans le Lutétien de Damery (Marne). Mus. Nat.
                 Hist. Natur., Paris, Bull., 39:5, 1003—1006 (French).

GINSBURG, L. and MENNESSIER, GUY
  1970A   Découverte d'un important gisement de vertébrés dans le Jurassique supérieur du Petit Plan de
                 Canjuers (Var). Acad. Sci., C.R., Sér. D, 271:6, 570—571 (French).

GINSBURG, L., MENNESSIER, G. and RUSSELL, D.
  1967A   Sur l'âge éocène inférieur des sables bleutés du Haut-Var et sur ses conséquences. Discussion. Soc.
                 Géol. Fr., C.R., 1967:7, 272—273 (French).

GINSBURG, LÉONARD   See also: Ellenberger, F., Ellenberger, P. and Ginsburg, L., 1969A, 1970A, 1970B.

GINTER, BOLESŁAW
  1967B   Résultats des recherches archéologiques de reconnaissance effectuées sur la Warta supérieure en 1965.
                 Łódź, Archeol. Etnogr. Mus., Prace Mat., Ser. Archeol., 14, 55—77, 17 figs. (Polish; French
                 summary).

GINTSINGER, A. V.
  1967A   Devonskaiâ sistema. Gornyĭ Altaĭ. [Devonian system. Gornyĭ Altaĭ.] Geologiiâ SSSR, 14, Western
                 Siberia (southern part), 178—195, 1 fig., 1 table (Russian).

GIOT, P.-R.
    1969A   Informations archéologiques. Circonscription de Bretagne et des Pays de la Loire. Gallia Préhist.,
                 12:2, 439–463, 56 figs. (French).

GITERMAN, ROZA EVSEEVNA   See: Alekseev, M. N., Giterman, R. E. and Dubrovo, I. A., 1972A.

GIVENS, R. DALE
    1970A   Comments. Curr. Anthropol., 11:1, 32–33.

GJESSING, GUTORM
    1969A   De aller eldste kulturformer. Ymer, 1969, 109–119, 2 figs. (Swedish).

GLADENKOV, ÎURIĬ BORISOVICH   See: Menner, V. V., Nikiforova, K. V., Pevzner, M. A., Alekseev, M. N.,
                 Gladenkov, Îu. B., Gurariĭ, G. Z. and Trubikhin, V. M., 1972A.

GLASS, BENTLEY   See: Keast, A., Erk, F. C. and Glass, B. (eds.), 1972A.

GŁAZEK, J., OBERC, J. and SULIMSKI, A.
    1971A   Miocene vertebrate faunas from Przeworno (lower Silesia) and their geological setting. Acta Geol. Pol.,
                 21:3, 473–516, 17 figs., 4 pls., 4 tables (Polish summary).
                 Rev.: Thenius in Zentralbl. Geol. Paläontol., Teil 2, 1971:6, 510–511.
    1972A   Odkrycie mioceńskich faun kręgowców w Przewornie (Dolny Ślask). [Discovery of Miocene vertebrate
                 faunas at Przeworno (lower Silesia).] Przegl. Geol., 20:2, 65–71, 7 figs. (Polish; Russian and
                 English summaries).

GLAZYRINA, N. S. and TOPORKOV, V. ÎA.
    1971A   K biostratigrafii nizhnechetvertichnykh otlozheniĭ vostochnogo sklona Srednego i Severnogo Urala.
                 [On the biostratigraphy of the lower Cretaceous deposits of the eastern slope of middle and
                 north Urals.] In: Geologiîa i poleznye iskopaemye Urala, 11–13 (Russian).

GLIESE, J. and STRAUCH, F.
    1969A   Eine Pliozän-Fauna in den Deckschichten der rheinischen Braunkohle. Eine vorläufige Mitteilung. Neues
                 Jahrb. Geol. Paläontol., Monatsh., 1969:7, 446–448 (German).

GLIKMAN, LEONID SERGEEVICH (= GLICKMAN, L. S.)
    1965A   Akuly i stratigrafiîa tretichnykh otlozheniĭ. [Sharks and the stratigraphy of Tertiary deposits.] In:
                 Problemy stratigrafii kaĭnozoîa, 30–36 (Russian; English summary).

GLIKMAN, L. S. and ISHCHENKO, V. V.
    1968A   Marine Miocene sediments in central Asia. Akad. Nauk SSSR, Dokl., Earth Sci. Sec., 177, 78–81,
                 1 fig. (Translated from Russian: Akad. Nauk SSSR, Dokl., 1967, 177:3, 662–665.)

GLIKMAN, L. S. and SHVAZHAĬTE, R. A.
    1971A   Akuly semeĭstva Anacoracidae iz senomana i turona Litvy, Povolzh'îa i Sredneĭ Azii. [Sharks of the
                 family Anacoracidae from the Cenomanian and Turonian of Lithuania, Volga region, and middle
                 Asia.] Paleontol. Stratigr. Pribalt. Belorus., 3, 185–192, 1 pl. (Russian; English summary).

GLIKMAN, LEONID SERGEEVICH   See also: Beliaev, G. M. and Glikman, L. S., 1965A, 1970A, 1970B;
                 Zhelezko, V. I., and Glikman, L. S., 1971A.

GLORY, ANDRÉ
    1965B   L'énigme de Lascaux. Congr. Préhist. France, 16e Sess., Monaco 1959, C.R., 586–595, 4 figs. (French).
    1965C   L'oiseau de la Pasiega (Espagne). Congr. Préhist. France, 16e Sess., Monaco 1959, C.R., 596–607,
                 4 figs., 1 table (French).
    1965D   Nouvelle galerie ornée de la caverne de la Mouthe. Congr. Préhist. France, 16e Sess., Monaco 1959,
                 C.R., 608–612, 2 figs. (French).

GLORY, ANDRÉ and VILLEVEYGOUX, ABBÉ
    1966A   L'émergence de l'homme et la genèse de l'intelligence, Homo noscens. Les Eyzies, 15, 75–91, 1 fig.,
                 1 table (French).

GLUSHNITSKIĬ, O. T. and MENNER, V. V.
    1970A   K detal'noĭ korrelîatsii razrezov srednego i verkhnego devona Noril'skogo raĭona. [On detailed
                 correlation of cross-sections in middle and upper Devonian of Noril'sk region.] Mosk. Obshchest.
                 Ispyt. Prir., Biull., Otd. Geol., 45:1, 71–83, 2 figs. (Russian).

GLUT, DONALD F.
1972A   The dinosaur dictionary. Secaucus, New Jersey: Citadel Press, Inc., 218 pp., illustr.

GODINA, ANNA ĪAKOVLEVNA
1968B   O proiskhozhdenii, istorii i nekotorykh zakonomernostĭakh evolĭutsii Giraffidae. [On the origin, history and some laws in the evolution of Giraffidae.] In: Zakonomernosti razvitiĭa organicheskogo mira po dannym paleontologii, 125–132, 1 fig. (Russian).
1971A   Novye dannye o neogenovykh zhirafakh Kazakhstana i Kirgizii. [New data on Neogene giraffes of Kazakhstan and Kirgisia.] Mosk. Obshchest. Ispyt. Prir., Biull., Otd. Geol., 46:2, 148–149 (Russian).
1971B   Novye dannye o zhirafakh roda Palaeotragus iz neogenovykh otlozhenĭĭ Zapadnoĭ Mongolii. [New data on giraffes of the genus Palaeotragus from the Neogene deposits of western Mongolia.] Sovm. Sovet.-Mongol. Nauch.-Issled. Geol. Eksped., Tr., 3, 120–123, 1 table (Russian).
1971C   O parallelizme v razvitii Palaeotragus i Giraffa i ego znachenii dlĭa rassmotreniĭa nekotorykh voprosov evolĭutsii. [On the parallelism in the evolution of Palaeotragus and Giraffa, and its importance in some evolutionary studies.] Akad. Nauk SSSR, Paleontol. Inst., Tr., 130, 62–69, 3 figs. (Russian).

GOGOLEV, Z. V.   See: Okladnikov, A. P., Vasil'evskiĭ, R. S.. Larichev, V. E., Derevĭanko, A. P., Gogolev, Z. V. and Toshchakova, E. M., 1969A.

GOIN, COLEMAN J.   See: Goin, O. B. and Goin, C. J., 1968A.

GOIN, OLIVE B. and GOIN, COLEMAN J.
1968A   DNA and the evolution of the vertebrates. Amer. Midland Natur., 80, 289–298, 1 table.

GOKHMAN, I. I.
1967A   Methods of studying average contours of craniological series. Discussion. Int. Congr. Anthropol. Ethnol. Sci., 7th, Moscow, 1964, 2, 36–39.

GOLDBERG, LEONARD   See: Boreske, J. R., Goldberg, L. and Cameron, B., 1972A.

GOLDBRANDSEN, JEAN   See: Davenport, L. C. and Goldbrandsen, J., 1963A.

GOLDIN, G. K.   See: Pidoplichko, I. G. and Goldin, G. K., 1964A.

GOLDSTEIN, MARCUS S.
1969A   Human paleopathology and some diseases in living primitive societies: A review of the recent literature. Amer. J. Phys. Anthropol., 31, 285–294, bibliogr.

GOLOVKO, VALENTINA PETROVNA
1962A   Novye dannye o sistematike i filogenii slonov r. Mammonteus. [New data on systematics and phylogeny of elephants of the genus Mammonteus.] In: Materialy po arkheologii Severnogo Prichernomor'ĭa, 4, 181–186 (Russian).

GOLPE POSSE, JUANA-MARIA
1971A   Datos sobre el yacimiento estampiense de "El Talladell" cerca de Tárrega. Barcelona (Prov.), Inst. Prov. Paleontol., Paleontol. Evol., 3, 59–62 (Spanish).
1971B   La medalla de oro de Sabadell para su ilustre ciudadano Miguel Crusafont-Pairó. Barcelona (Prov.), Inst. Prov. Paleontol., Bol. Inform., 3:1, 1–9 (Spanish).
1971C   Los Suiformes del Terciario español y sus yacimientos. Barcelona (Prov.), Inst. Prov. Paleontol., Bol. Inform., 3:2–3, 17–20 (Spanish).
1971D*   Boletin Informativo. Barcelona (Prov.), Inst. Prov. Paleontol., Bol. Inform., 3:6, 29 pp. (Spanish).
1972A   Suiformes del Terciario español y sus yacimientos. (Resumen). Acta Geol. Hisp., 7:1, 18–21 (Spanish).
1972B*   Boletin Informativo. Barcelona (Prov.), Inst. Prov. Paleontol., Bol. Inform., 4:1, 1–23; 4:2–3, 1–19 (Spanish).

GOLPE POSSE, JUANA-MARIA   See also: Crusafont Pairó, M. and Golpe Posse, J.-M., 1964A, 1968A, 1968B, 1969A, 1972A; Crusafont Pairó, M., Golpe, J.-M., Gibert, J. and Thaler, L., 1971A.

GOLSON, J.   See: Mulvaney, D. J. and Golson, J. (eds.), 1971A; Polach, H. A. and Golson, J., 1968A.

GOLZ, DAVID J. and KENNEDY, MICHAEL P.
1971A   Comparison of mammalian and invertebrate chronologies in the Eocene of southern California. Geol. Soc. Amer., Abstr., 3:2, 125 (abs.).

GOLZ, DAVID J.   See also: Woodburne, M. O. and Golz, D. J., 1972A.

GOMES DE MELO, SHEILA MARIS   See: Moreira, L. E. and Gomes de Melo, S. M., 1971A.

GOMES VALENCA, JOEL   See: Silva Santos, R. da and Gomes Valenca, J., 1968A.

GONCHAROV, VALENTIN FEDOROVICH
     1968A   Fauna chetvertichnykh mlekopitaŭshchikh basseĭna Iany i Omoloĭa i ee stratigraficheskoe znachenie.
               [Quaternary mammalian fauna of Iana and Omoloĭ basin and its stratigraphic significance.]
               In: Problemy izucheniiā chetvertichnogo perioda. Tezisy, 107–109 (Russian).

GONCHAROV, V. F.   See also: Baranova, Iu. P. et al., 1968A.

GONZÁLEZ ECHEGARAY, JOAQUÍN
     1962A   Cueva de las Chimeneas. Exc. Arqueol. Españ., 21, 35 pp., 5 figs., 25 pls., 2 maps (Spanish).

GONZÁLEZ ECHEGARAY, P. J., GARCÍA GUINEA, M. A. and BEGINES RAMÍREZ, A.
     1963A   Cueva de la Chora (Santander). Exc. Arqueol. Españ., 26, 5–50, 30 figs., 4 pls. (Spanish; French and
               English summaries).

GONZÁLEZ ECHEGARAY, J., GARCÍA GUINEA, M. A., BEGINES, A., MADARIAGA DE LA CAMPA, B. and
LEROI-GOURHAN, A.
     1966A   Cueva del Otero. Exc. Arqueol. Españ., 53 (Spanish).
               Rev.: Jordá Cerdá in Zephyrus, 18, 152–153.

GOODALL, VANNE MORRIS   See: Leakey, L. S. B. and Goodall, V. M., 1969A.

GOODMAN, M., BARNABAS, J., MATSUDA, G. and MOORE, G. W.
     1971A   Molecular evolution in the descent of man. Nature, 233:5322, 604–613, 4 figs., 4 tables.

GOODY, PETER C.
     1969A   Sedenhorstia dayi (Hay), a new elopoid from the Cenomian of Hajula in Lebanon. Amer. Mus. Nov.,
               2358, 1–23, 9 figs.
     1969B   The relationships of certain upper Cretaceous teleosts with special reference to the myctophoids.
               Brit. Mus. (Nat. Hist.), Bull., Geol., 1969, Suppl. 7, 255 pp., 102 figs., 1 table.
               Rev.: Gosline in Quart. Rev. Biol., 45:2, 180–181.
     1970A   Comments on enchodontid paper by McNulty and Kienzlen. Tex. J. Sci., 21:4, 455–457.
     1970B   The Cretaceous teleostean fish Cimolichthys from the Niobrara formation of Kansas and the Pierre
               shale of Wyoming. Amer. Mus. Nov., 2434, 29 pp., 9 figs.

GORBATKINA, T. E., LOZOVSKIĬ, V. R. and STROK, N. I.
     1971A   Triasovaiā sistema. [Triassic system.] Geologiiā SSSR, 4, Center of the European part of the USSR,
               348–373, 3 figs. (Russian).

GORDON, BYRAN C.
     1970A   Bison antiquus from the Northwest Territories. Arctic, 23, 132–133, 3 figs., 1 table.

GORDON, WESLEY D.
     1969A   A Pleistocene ecosystem. Chicago: Rand McNally and Co., Rand McNally Patterns of Life Series,
               79 pp., 45 figs.

GORSKIĬ, V. P.
     1963A   Triasovaiā sistema. Pechorskiĭ basseĭn. [Triassic system. Pechora basin.] Geologiiā SSSR, 2,
               Arkhangel'sk and Vologda Provinces, and Komi ASSR, 625–631 (Russian).

GORTON, M. P.   See: McKelvey, B. C., Webb, P. N., Gorton, M. P. and Kohn, B. P., 1970A.

GOSH, P. K. and SASTRY, M. V. A.
     1967A   A review of the lower Gondwanas of India. Int. Union Geol. Sci., 1st. Symp. Gondwana Stratigr.,
               Rev., 1967, 269–304, 1 table, 1 map.

GOSLINE, WILLIAM A.
     1971A   Functional morphology and classification of teleostean fishes. Honolulu: University of Hawaii Press,
               x + 208 pp., illustr.
               Rev.: Patterson in Science (AAAS), 176:4033, 399.

GOSZTONYI, A.
     1968A   Der Mensch und die Evolution. Teilhard de Chardins philosophische Anthropologie. München:
               Beck Publ., 264 pp. (German).

Rev.: Spindler in Anthropol. Anz., 31:3, 226—227.

GOTTIS, M.
1967A Sur la présence de sélaciens dans les eaux douces du lac éocène supérieur de Carcassonne. Soc. Linn.
       Bordeaux, Actes, Sér. B, 104:26, 3—5, 1 pl. (French).
1971A Pistes de quadrupèdes sur une plage d'un lac oligocène de l'Entre-Deux-Mers. Soc. Linn. Bordeaux,
       Bull., 1:2, 23—24, 2 figs. (French).

GOUJET, DANIEL
1972A Nouvelles observations sur la joue d'*Arctolepis* (Eastman) et d'autres Dolichothoraci. Ann. Paléontol.,
       Vertébrés, 58:1, 3—12, 4 figs., 1 pl. (French; English summary).

GOULD, STEPHEN JAY and GARWOOD, ROBERT A.
1969A Levels of integration in mammalian dentitions: an analysis of correlations in *Nesophontes micrus*
       (Insectivora) and *Oryzomys couesi* (Rodentia). Evolution, 23:2, 276—300, 7 figs., 6 tables.

GOULD, STEPHEN JAY   See also: Eldredge, N. and Gould, S. J., 1972A.

GOUZES, R.   See: Coppens, Y., Gouzes, R., Le Floch, R. and Paquet, M., s.d.

GOW, C. E.
1970A The anterior of the palate in *Euparkeria*. Palaeontol. Afr., 13, 61—62, 1 fig.
1972A The osteology and relationships of the Millerettidae (Reptilia: Cotylosauria). J. Zool., 167:2,
       219—264, 2 figs., 2 pls., 1 table.

GOŹDŹIEWSKI, STANISŁAW
1967A Zusammenhänge der Kephalo- mit Kraniometrischen Merkmalen beim Menschen. Discussion. Int.
       Congr. Anthropol. Ethnol. Sci., 7th, Moscow, 1964, 2, 235—241 (German).

GOZHIK, P. F.
1969A O vozraste medzhibozhskoĭ fauny. [On the age of Medzhibozh fauna.] In: Materialy po
       chetvertichnomu periodu Ukrainy, 138—143 (Russian; English summary).

GRADZIŃSKI, RYSZARD
1970A Sedimentation of dinosaur-bearing upper Cretaceous deposits of the Nemegt basin, Gobi Desert. In:
       Kielan-Jaworowska, Z. (ed.), 1970B, 147—229, 35 figs., 8 pls., 8 tables.
       Rev.: Chrulew in Zentralbl. Geol. Paläontol., Teil 2, 1971:1, 54—55.

GRADZIŃSKI, R., KAŹMIERCZAK, J. and LEFELD, J.
1968A Geographical and geological data from the Polish-Mongolian palaeontological expeditions. Palaeontol.
       Polonica, 19, 33—82, 35 figs., 3 pls.

GRADZIŃSKI, R. and WÓJCIK, Z.
1966A O krasie kopalnym w Polsce. [Fossil karst in Poland.] Warsaw, Muz. Ziemi, Pr., 9, 151—222, 7 figs.,
       7 tables (Polish and English).

GRAHAM, JOHN A.
1966A* Ancient Mesoamerica. Selected readings. Palo Alto, Calif.: Peek Pub., 300 pp., illustr.
       Rev.: Goldfried in Amer. Anthropol., 71, 348—349.

GRAHAM, JOHN A. and HEIZER, ROBERT F.
1967A Man's antiquity in North America: views and facts. Quaternaria, 9, 225—235 (Spanish and German
       summaries).

GRAHAM, JOHN A.   See also: Heizer, R. F. and Graham, J. A., 1967A.

GRAHAM, RICHARD E.
1960B A fossil *Bassariscus* from Hanging Gardens Cave, California. Speleo Digest, 1960, 2—118 — 2—119
       (reprinted from Cave Notes, 2:3, 20—21).

GRAHAM, RUSSELL W.
1972A Paleoecological significance of *Blarina brevicauda*, the short-tailed shrew. Soc. Vert. Paleontol. Ann.
       Meeting, 32nd, 1972, Abstr. (abs.).

GRAINDOR, M. and MARTIN, Y.
1971A La grotte de Gouy trésor artistique du Paléolithique supérieur. Présence Normande, 22:8, 20—28
       (French).

GRAĬZER, MIKHAIL IOSIFOVICH
1967A   Nizhnekamennougol'nye otlozheniĭâ Saĭâno-Altaĭskoĭ skladchatoĭ oblasti. [Lower Carboniferous depos
                of Saĭân-Altaĭ folded region.] Moscow: "Nauka" Press, 147 pp., 19 figs., 15 tables (Russian).

GRAMANN, FRANZ and KOCKEL, FRANZ
1969A   Das Neogen im Strimonbecken (Griechisch-Ostmazedonien). Geol. Jahrb., 87, 445—484, 7 figs.,
                2 pls., 4 tables (German; English and French summaries).

GRAND, P. M.
1967A   Rev.: Anati in Archeology, 24:1, 68—69.

GRANIER, JACKY
1969A   Les poissons découverts sur le sol de la cabane acheuléenne du Lazaret. In: Lumley, H. de (ed.),
                1969B, 111, 1 table (French).

GRANT, CHAPMAN
1972A   Disproof of continental drift. Environ. Southwest, 443, 3—7.

GRASSÉ, P.-P.
1970A*   Traité de Zoologie. Tome XIV, Fasc. 3. Reptiles — glandes endocrines — embryologie —
                systématique — paléontologie. Paris: Masson, 681—1428, illustr. (French).
                Rev.: Elkan in Brit. J. Herpetol., 4:9, 241; J. F. in Soc. Linn. Lyon, Bull., 40:5, LXXV; Underwood
                in Nature, 231:5301, 336—337.

GRAUVOGEL, L.   See: Gall, J.-C. and Grauvogel, L., 1968A.

GRAVEL, PIERRE B.
1969A   Hoebel's Anthropology: the study of man: a comment. Amer. Anthropol., 71, 302—305.

GRAY, JAMES
1968   Rev.: Hazen in Amer. Sci., 57:3, 264A.

GRAY, P. H. K.   See: Brothwell, D. R., Sandison, A. T. and Gray, P. H. K., 1969A.

GRAY, ROBERT
1969A   The great apes. New York: Grosset and Dunlap, Inc., xiv + 144 pp., frontispiece, illustr.

GRAZIOSI, PAOLO
1964C   L'art paléolithique de la "province méditerranéenne" et ses influences dans les temps postpaléolithiques
                In: Pericot García, L., and Ripoll Perelló, E. (eds.), 1964A, 35—46, 3 figs. (French; English
                summary).
1968A   Découverte d'outils du Paléolithique inférieur en Sicile. L'Anthropologie, 72:3—4, 399—408, 8 figs.
                (French).

GREAVES, WALTER STALKER
1972A   Spatial orientation of the temporal fossa in oreodonts. Soc. Vert. Paleontol. Ann. Meeting, 32nd,
                1972, Abstr. (abs.).
1972B   Evolution of the merycoidodont masticatory apparatus (Mammalia, Artiodactyla). Evolution, 26:4,
                659—667, 6 figs.

GRECHINA, N. I.
1971A   Rod Coryphaenoides (sem. Macruridae) iz oligoŝena Kamchatki. [Genus Coryphaenoides (fam.
                Macrouridae) from the Oligocene of Kamchatka.] Mosk. Obshchest. Ispyt. Prir., Bĭull., Otd.
                Geol., 46:2, 150 (Russian).
1971B   Mioŝenovaĭâ ikhtiofauna Sakhalina. [Miocene ichthyofauna of Sakhalin.] Mosk. Obshchest. Ispyt.
                Prir., Bĭull., Otd. Geol., 46:6, 143 (Russian).

GREEN, AMOS R.
1967A   Paleo-Indian and mammoth were contemporaneous in Berrien County, Michigan. Mich. Archaeol.,
                13:1, 1—10, 3 figs.

GREEN, MORTON
1970A   Recovering microvertebrates with acetic acid. S. Dakota Geol. Surv., Circ., 40, 11 pp., 5 figs.
1970B   Functions of a university museum. J. Geol. Educ., 18:4, 161—162, portr.
1971A   Additions to the Mission vertebrate fauna, lower Pliocene of South Dakota. J. Paleontol., 45:3,
                486—490, 3 figs.

1972A   Lagomorpha from the Rosebud formation, South Dakota. J. Paleontol., 46:3, 377—385, 1 fig., 7 tables.

GREEN, MORTON   See also: Harksen, J. C. and Green, M., 1971A; Parris, D. C. and Green, M., 1969A.

GREENE, DAVID L.
1970A   Environmental influences on Pleistocene hominid dental evolution. BioScience, 20:5, 276—279.
1970B   Comments. Curr. Anthropol., 11:1, 33.

GREENFIELD, LEONARD O.
1971A   Is *Kenyapithecus africanus* a valid species? Amer. J. Phys. Anthropol., 35:2, 281 (abs.).

GREENWOOD, P. H.
1968B   Fish remains. In: Wendorf, F. (ed.), 1968A, 100—109, 1 fig., 1 table.

GREENWOOD, P. H. and TODD, ELIZABETH J.
1970A   Fish remains from Olduvai. In: Leakey, L. S. B. and Savage, R. J. G. (eds.), 1970A, 225—241, 1 fig.

GREGG, D. R.   See: Fleming, C. A., Gregg, D. R. and Welles, S. P., 1971A; Welles, S. P. and Gregg, D. R., 1971A.

GREGORY, JOSEPH T.
1969A   Tertiary freshwater lakes of western America — an ephemeral theory. J. West, 8, 247—262, 1 fig.
1969B   Evolution und interkontinentale Beziehungen der Phytosauria (Reptilia). Palaeontol. Z., 43:1/2, 37—51, 6 figs., 1 table (German; English summary).
1971A   Speculations on the significance of fossil vertebrates for the antiquity of the Great Plains of North America. Hess. Landesamt Bodenforsch., Abh., 60, 64—72, 1 fig., 1 table.
1972A   Vertebrate faunas of the Dockum group, Triassic, eastern New Mexico and west Texas. N. Mex. Geol. Soc., Guidebk., Field Conf., 23, 120—123.

GREGORY, JOSEPH T. and WESTPHAL, FRANK
1969A   Remarks on the phytosaur genera of the European Trias. J. Paleontol., 43:5, 1296—1298.

GREGORY, WILLIAM KING
1972A   Studies on the evolution of the primates. In: McCown, T. D. and Kennedy, K. A. R. (eds.), 1972A, 209—218, 1 fig. (reprinted from Amer. Mus. Natur. Hist., Bull., 35:19, 336—44).

GRENOT, CLAUDE   See: Broin, F. de, Grenot, C. and Vernet, R., 1971A.

GRICHUK, V. P., HEY, R. W. and VENZO, S.
1964A   Otchet podkomissii INQUA po pliofsen-pleĭstofsenovoĭ granitše. [Report of the sub-committee of the INQUA on the Pliocene-Pleistocene boundary.] In: Nauchnye itogi VI kongressa mezhdunarodnoĭ assofsiafsii po izuchenifu chetvertichnogo perioda (INQUA). (Varshava, 1961), 100—112, 1 fig., 3 tables (Russian).

GRICHUK, V. P.   See also: Gromov, V. I., Vangengeĭm, E. A., Grichuk, V. P., Ivanova, I. K. and Nikiforova, K. V. (eds.), 1968A.

GRIFFIN, JAMES B.
1966A   Mesoamerica and the eastern United States in prehistoric times. Handbk. Mid. Amer. Ind., 4, 111—131.
1968A   Observation on Illinois prehistory in late Pleistocene and early Recent times. In: Bergstrom, R. E. (ed.), 1968A, 123—137, 3 figs.

GRIFFITHS, MERVYN
1968A   Echidnas. Oxford and New York: Pergamon Press, ix + 282 pp., 94 figs. Rev.: Manville in BioScience, 19:8, 754; Moss in Endeavor, 28:104, 103.

GRIGORESCU, DAN
1967A   Asupra prezenței unor fragmente scheletice de sirenide din paleogenul de la Albești-Muscel. [On the presence of some skeletal fragments of sirenians in the Paleogene of Albești-Muscel.] Bucharest, Univ., An., Ser. Științ. Natur. Geol.-Geogr., 16:1, 73—78, 2 pls. (Rumanian; Russian and French summaries).

GRIGORESCU, DAN and MARIN, ION
1971A   *Osmeroides dobrogensis* d'un nouvel Elopide fossile du Turonien du bassin de Babadag (Roumanie). Ann. Paléontol., Vertébrés, 57:2, 189—205, 3 figs., 3 pls. (French).

GRIGOR'EV, GENNADIĬ PAVLOVICH
  1968A   Nachalo verkhnego paleolita i proiskhozdenie *Homo sapiens.* [The beginning of the upper Paleolithic
             and the origin of *Homo sapiens.*] Leningrad: "Nauka" Press, 225 pp., illustr. (Russian).
  1970A   Novye aspekty problemy proiskhozhdeniĭa *Homo sapiens.* [New aspects of the problem of origin of
             Homo sapiens.] Vop. Antropol., 34, 40–50 (Russian).
  1970B   Chto my dumaem o proiskhozhdenii cheloveka. Nashi predki — neandertal'fsy. [What do we think
             about the origin of man. Our ancestors — the neanderthals.] Priroda, 1970:10, 43–45, portr.
             (Russian).
  1972A   Vzaimootnosheniĭa evoliŭtsii fizicheskogo tipa cheloveka s progressom ego material'noĭ kul'tury.
             [Mutual relationships between the physical type of man and the progress of his material
             culture.] Vop. Antropol., 41, 152–153 (Russian).
  1972B   [Discussion.] Vop. Antropol., 41, 157 (Russian).

GRIGOR'EVA, ALEKSANDRA DMITRIEVNA
  1966A   Napravleniĭa i metody sovremennoĭ paleobiogeografii. [Directions and methods in contemporaneous
             paleobiogeography.] Itogi Nauki, Ser. Geol., 10, Stratigr. Paleontol., 36–53 (Russian).

GRIGOR'EVA, E. N.
  1971A   O vozmozhnykh prichinakh smeny flor i faun. [On possible causes of the replacement of floras and
             faunas.] Vyssh. Ucheb. Zaved., Izv., Geol. Razved., 14:5, 14–16 (Russian).

GRIGOR'EVA, G. B., MARKEVICH, V. I., POPOVA, T. A. and CHERNYSH, E. K.
  1969A   Raboty Moldavskoĭ Ekspedifsii. [Works of the Moldavian expedition.] In: Rybakov, B. A. (ed.),
             1969A, 387–389.

GRIMM, HANS
  1970A   Vögel in der Begleitfauna des vor- und frühgeschichtlichen Menschen. Beitr. Vogelk., 16, 125–144
             (German).
             Rev.: Kuhn in Zentralbl. Geol. Paläontol., Teil 2, 1971:2–3, 180.
  1972A   Vögel in der Begleitfauna des vor- und frühgeschichtlichen Menschen. Beitr. Vogelk., 18:1, 51–60
             (German).

GRINDER, ROBERT E.
  1967A   A history of genetic psychology. The first science of human development. New York, London, Sydney:
             John Wiley and Sons, Inc., xii + 247 pp., illustr.
             Rev.: Chamla in L'Anthropologie, 73:1–2, 117–118.

GRIPP, KARL, SCHÜTRUMPF, R. and SCHWABEDISSEN, H.
  1967A*   Frühe Menschheit und Umwelt, Teil II. Naturwissenschaftliche Beiträge. Fundamenta, Reihe B, 2,
             330 pp., 28 figs., 61 pls., 42 tables (German).
             Rev.: Felgenhauer in Archaeol. Austriaca, 45, 80–81; Guenther in Quartär, 20, 228–231, 1 fig.;
             Heinzelin de Braucourt in Helinium, 10:1, 83–87; Mandera in Germania, 48, 135–137.

GRISHCHENKO, MIKHAIL NIKOLAEVICH
  1969A   Materialy po geologicheskoĭ kharakteristike nekotorykh arkheologicheskikh pamiĭatnikov v peshcherakh
             i grotakh severo-zapadnoĭ Moldavii. [Materials for geological characterization of some
             archeological sites in caves and grottoes of northwestern Moldavia.] Akad. Nauk Moldav. SSR,
             Okh. Prir. Moldav., 7, 135–146 (Russian).

GRISHCHENKO, V. A.
  1968B   A find of placoderms in the northern Tien Shan. Akad. Nauk SSSR, Dokl., Earth Sci. Sec., 179,
             53–54. (Translated from Russian: Akad. Nauk SSSR, Dokl., 1968, 179:3 666–667.)

GRISON, M.
  1960B   Rev.: Kurth in Homo, 19:2, 121.

GROMOV, VALERIAN INNOKENT'EVICH
  1969A   Antropogen ili kvarter? [Anthropogene or Quaternary?] In: Osnovnye problemy geologii antropogena
             Evrazii. K VIII kongressu INQUA, Parizh, 1969, 16–20 (Russian; English summary).
  1969B   Tiraspol'skiĭ faunisticheskiĭ kompleks. [Tiraspol'ian faunal complex.] In: Mezhdunarodnyĭ kollokvium
             po geologii i faune nizhnego i srednego pleĭstofsena Evropy. Tizisy dokladov, 1–3 (Russian).
  1970A   The Tiraspol faunal complex. Palaeogeogr., Palaeoclimatol., Palaeoecol., 8:2–3, 187–195, 3 tables.
  1972A   Tiraspol'skiĭ faunisticheskiĭ kompleks. [Tiraspol' faunal complex.] In: Geologiĭa i fauna nizhnego i
             srednego pleĭstofsena Evropy, 168–177 (Russian).

GROMOV, V. I., et al.
  1968A*   Rev.: Kosmowska-Ceranowicz in Przegl. Geol., 1970:1, 44–45 (Polish).

GROMOV, V. I., KRASNOV, I. I., NIKIFOROVA, K. V. and SHANTSER, E. V.
  1969A   Skhema podrazdeleniĭ antropogena. [A scheme of Antropogene subdivisions.] Akad. Nauk SSSR, Kom.
           Izuch. Chetvertich. Perioda, Biull., 36, 41–55, 1 fig., 1 chart (Russian).

GROMOV, V. I. and NIKIFOROVA, KSENIIA VLADIMIROVNA
  1968A   Granitsa mezhdu neogenom i antropogenom (chetvertichnym periodom). [The Neogene-Anthropogene
           (Quaternary) boundary.] In: Granitsa tretichnogo i chetvertichnogo periodov, 9–16 (Russian;
           English summary).
  1968B   The Neogene-Anthropogene (Quaternary period) boundary. Int. Geol. Congr., 23rd, Czech., Rep.,
           Abstr., sec. 10, 275–276 (abs.).
  1968C   The boundary between the Neogene and Anthropogene (Quaternary period). Int. Geol. Congr., 23rd,
           Czech., Rep., Proc., 10, 57–63.
  1969A   Riss-Würm auf dem Gebiet der Ud SSR. Deut. Ges. Geol. Wiss., Ber., Reiche A, Geol. Paläontol.,
           14:4, 471–475, 1 fig. (German).

GROMOV, V. I., VANGENGEĬM, E. A., GRICHUK, V. P., IVANOVA, I. K. and NIKIFOROVA, K. V.
  1968A*   Granitsa tretichnogo i chetvertichnogo periodov. [Tertiary-Quaternary boundary.] Moscow: "Nauka"
           Press, Reports of Soviet Geologists at the 23rd. Internat. Geol. Congr., Problem 10, 118 pp.
           (Russian; English summaries).

GROMOV, V. I., VANGENGEĬM, E. A. and NIKIFOROVA, K. V.
  1965B   Biostratigraficheskoe obosnovanie nizhneĭ granitsy i podrazdeleniia antropogenovoĭ sistemy.
           [Biostratigraphic substantiation of the lower limit and subdivision of the Anthropogene system.]
           In: Problemy stratigrafii kaĭnozoia, 100–118, 2 figs. (Russian; English summary).

GROMOVA, VERA ISAAKOVNA
  1972A   Novoe v sistematike i nomenklature drevneĭshikh loshadeĭ Evropy. [New in the systematics and
           nomenclature of the most ancient horses of Europe.] Akad. Nauk SSSR, Kom. Izuch.
           Chetvertich. Perioda, Biull., 38, 126–129 (Russian).

GROMOVA, VERA ISAAKOVNA and DUBROVO, IRINA ALEKSANDROVNA
  1969A   Ostatki iskopaemykh loshadeĭ iz tiraspol'skogo graviia. Die fossilen Pferde aus den Kiesen von Tiraspol.
           In: Mezhdunarodnyĭ kollokvium po geologii i faune nizhnego i srednego pleĭstotsena Evropy.
           Tezisy dokladov, 9–10, and 65–66 (Russian and German).

GROSS, WALTER
  1968E   Die Agnathen-Fauna der silurischen Halla-Schichten Gotlands. Geol. Fören. Stockholm, Förh., 90:3,
           369–400, 14 figs. (German; English summary).
  1969A   Lophosteus superbus Pander, ein Teleostome aus dem Silur Oesels. Lethaia, 2:1, 15–47, 17 figs.
           (German; English summary).
  1969B   Friedrich Freiherr von Huene 22.3.1875–4.4.1969. Palaeontol. Z., 43:3/4, 111–112 (German).
  1970A   Werner Janensch. 10.11.1878–29.10.1969. Palaeontol. Z., 44:1/2, 1–2 (German).
  1971A   Downtonische und dittonische Acanthodier-Reste des Ostseegebietes. [Downtonian and Dittonian
           acanthodian remains from the Baltic Sea area.] Palaeontographica, Abt. A, 136, 1–82, 28 figs.,
           10 pls. (English summary).
  1971B   Lophosteus superbus Pander: Zähne, Zahnknochen und besondere Schuppenformen. Lethaia, 4:2,
           131–152, 10 figs. (German; English summary).
  1971C   Unterdevonische Thelodontier- und Acanthodier-Schuppen aus Westaustralien. Paläontol. Z., 45:3/4,
           97–106, 3 figs., 1 pl. (German; English summary).

GROSS, WALTER   See also: Siegfried, P. and Gross, W., 1971A.

GROSSU, AL. V. and VOICU, GH.
  1971A   Ciprinidele fosile, reper geologo-economic în Bazinul de cărbuni Mehadia, zona Bolvaşniţa. [Fossil
           cyprinids, geological-economic marker in the coal basin Mehadia, Bolvaşniţa zone.] Stud. Cercet.
           Geol., Geofiz., Geogr., Ser. Geol., 16:1, 189–201, 7 pls. (Rumanian; French summary).

GROSSU, AL. V.   See also: Protopopesco-Pake, Em., Mateesco, C. N. and Grossu, Al. V., 1969A.

GROVES, COLIN P.
  1968A   The classification of the gibbons (Primates, Pongidae). Z. Säugetierkunde, 33:4, 239–246, 2 tables
           (German summary).
  1969A   Systematics of the anoa (Mammalia, Bovidae). Beaufortia, 17:223, 1–12, 4 figs., 2 tables.
  1970A   Gigantopithecus and the mountain gorilla. Nature, 226:5249, 973–974, 2 figs., 1 table.

GROVES, COLIN P. and NAPIER, J. R.
1968A   Dental dimensions and diet in australopithecines. Int. Congr. Anthropol. Ethnol. Sci., 8th, Tokyo, 1968, Proc., 3, 273–276, 3 tables.

GRUBER, ABRAHAM
1969A   A functional definition of primate tool-making. Man (J. Roy. Anthropol. Inst.), 4:4, 573–579, 2 figs.

GRUBER, JACOB W.
1967A*   The Philadelphia Anthropological Society. Papers presented on its Golden Anniversary. New York and London: Temple University Publications, ix + 162 pp.
          Rev.: Glick in Amer. Anthropol., 70, 1191–1192.

GRUCHY, C. G.
1971A   Reidentification of a Pleistocene *Salmo* as the first fossil *Gadus* from Canada. Can. J. Zool., 49:4, 427–430, 2 pls.

GUDILIN, I. S.
1966A   Kaĭnozoĭskaîa gruppa. [Cenozoic group.] Geologiîa SSSR, 29, Tuvinskaîa ASSR, 223–247, 3 figs., 1 table (Russian).

GUENSBURG, T. E.   See: Clark, J. and Guensburg, T. E., 1970A, 1972A.

GUENTHER, EKKE W.
1967B   Hornscheiden nacheiszeitlicher Boviden aus Schleswig-Holstein. Fundamenta, Reihe B, 2, 261–270, 2 pls., 1 table (German).
1968A   Ist die Rentierjägerstation von Munzingen ein "Lössmagdalénien"? Quartär, 19, 93–124, 6 figs., 1 pl., 3 tables (German).
1969A   Das Pleistozän von Süssenborn. Die Elefantenmolaren aus den Kiesen von Süssenborn bei Weimar. Paläontol. Abh., Abt. A, 3:3–4, 711–734, 8 figs., 12 pls., 7 tables. II Internat. Paläont. Kolloquium 1966 in Weimar (German; Russian and English summaries).
1969B   Der Fund eines Elefantenzahn-Auswurfstückes am Kliff bei Lindhöft. Naturwiss. Ver. Schleswig-Holstein, Schr., 39, 59–62, 1 map (German).
1969C   Elefantenbackenzähne aus den Mosbacher Sanden. II. Die Funde des Naturhistorischen Museums der Stadt Mainz. Mainz. Naturwiss. Arch., 8, 77–89, 3 pls. (German).

GUENTHER, EKKE W.   See also: Freund, G. and Guenther, E. W., 1968A.

GUÉRIN, CLAUDE
1970A   Le rhinocéros du gisement pléistocène de Villereversure (Ain). Lyons, Fac. Sci., Lab. Géol., Doc., 37, 27–53, 6 figs., 4 tables (French; English summary).
1971A   Découverte d'un gisement de mammifères du Pleistocène supérieur dans une rivière souterraine à la Balme-d'Épy (Jura). Soc. Géol. Fr., C.R., 1971:2, 110–111, 2 figs. (French).

GUÉRIN, C., BALLÉSIO, R. and MÉON-VILAIN, H.
1969A   Le *Dicerorhinus megarhinus* (Mammalia, Rhinocerotidae) du Pliocène de Saint-Laurent-des-Arbres (Gard). Lyons, Fac. Sci., Lab. Géol., Doc., 31, 55–145, 19 figs., 6 tables (French; English summary).
          Rev.: Thenius in Zentralbl. Geol. Paläontol., Teil 2, 1970:5, 439–440.

GUÉRIN, C. and MEIN, PIERRE
1971A   Les principaux gisements de mammifères miocènes et pliocènes du domaine Rhodanien. Lyons, Fac. Sci., Lab. Géol., Doc., 49, 131–170 (French).
          Rev.: Thenius in Zentralbl. Geol. Paläontol., Teil 2, 1971:6, 511.

GUÉRIN, C., MEIN, P., PHILIPPE, M. and TRUC, G.
1972A   Découverte d'hipparions anté-tortoniens dans le bassin de Vaison-la-Romaine (Vaucluse, Sud-Est de la France). Acad. Sci., C.R., Sér. D, 274:9, 1276–1279, 2 figs., 1 table (French).

GUÉRIN, C., MEIN, P. and TRUC, G.
1970A   Nouveaux mammifères et mollusques continentaux d'âge Pliocène terminal au toit du plateau de Valensole (Alpes de Haute-Provence). Acad. Sci., C.R., Sér. D, 271:23, 2094–2097 (French).
          Rev.: Thenius in Zentralbl. Geol. Paläontol., Teil 2, 1971:6, 511–512.

GUÉRIN, C.   See also: Catzigras, F., Guérin, C. and Onoratini, G., 1971A; Combémorel, R., Guérin, C. and Méon-Vilain, H., 1970A; David, L., Evin, J., Guérin, C., Mongereau, N. and Walter, B., 1972A.

GUERNET, CLAUDE and SAUVAGE, JACQUELINE
    1971A   Observations nouvelles sur le Néogène de la région de Pikermi et Raphina (Attique, Grèce). Soc. Géol.
                Fr., Bull. (1970), 12:2, 241–245, 1 fig. (French).

GUERRI, M.
    1970A   Grotta Spagnoli (Rignano Garganico, Prov. di Foggia). Riv. Sci. Preist., 25:2, 406 (Italian).

GUGGISBERG, C.A.W.
    1972A   Crocodiles: their natural history. New York: David and Charles, x + 195 pp., illustr.
                Rev.: Underwood in Nature, 238:5364, 417.

GUIDO, MARGARET
    1967A   Sicily: an archaeological guide. London: Faber & Faber, 219 pp., 14 figs., 11 pls., 27 maps.
                Rev.: Low in Amer. J. Archaeol., 72:2, 190; Small in Antiquaries J., 48:2, 318–319.

GUILDAY, JOHN E.
    1956A   Fossils and New Paris. Speleo Digest, 1956, 2–19 – 2–20 (reprinted from Netherworld News, 4:10).
    1959A   Cleaning and cataloguing of fossil material from New Paris (Pa.). Speleo Digest, 1959, 2–129 –
                2–131 (reprinted from Netherworld News, 7:5, 96–98).
    1961E   The lemming - New Paris. Speleo Digest, 1961, 2–72 – 2–73 (reprinted from Netherworld News,
                9:8, 142–144).
    1961F   Jaguar (old style). Speleo Digest, 1961, 2–74 – 2–77, 1 fig. (reprinted from Netherworld News, 9:3,
                41–43).
    1968B   Rev.: Thenius in Zentralbl. Geol. Paläontol., Teil 2, 1970:6, 517–518.
    1968C   Grizzly bears from eastern North America. Amer. Midland Natur., 79, 247–250, 1 fig., 1 table.
                Rev.: Ehrenberg in Zentralbl. Geol. Paläontol., Teil 2, 1969:3, 292.
    1970A   Ask the experts... Explorer (Cleveland Mus. Natur. Hist.), 12:4, 20–21, 2 figs.

GUILDAY, J. E. and ADAM, ELEANOR K.
    1972A   Small mammal remains from Jaguar Cave, Lemhi County, Idaho. Int. J. Speleol., 4:2, 200–201 (abs.).

GUILDAY, J. E. and DAWSON, MARY
    1969A   Evolution or not. Science (AAAS), 165:3892, 443.
    1971A   Obituary. J. LeRoy Kay, 1892–1971. Soc. Vert. Paleontol., News Bull., 93, 24.

GUILDAY, J. E., HAMILTON, H. W. and MC CRADY, A. D.
    1969A   The Pleistocene vertebrate fauna of Robinson Cave, Overton County, Tennessee. Palaeovertebrata
                (Montpellier), 2:2, 25–75, 15 figs., 28 tables (German and French summaries).
                Rev.: Thenius in Zentralbl. Geol. Paläontol., Teil 2, 1971:2–3, 188–189.
    1971A   The Welsh Cave peccaries (Platygonus) and associated fauna, Kentucky Pleistocene. Carnegie Mus.,
                Ann., 43:9, 249–320, 31 figs., 8 tables.

GUILDAY, J. E. and MC GINNES, HELEN
    1972A   Jaguar (Panthera onca) remains from Big Bone Cave, Tennessee and east central North America. Nat.
                Speleo. Soc., Bull., 34:1, 1–14, 7 figs., 1 table.

GUILDAY, J. E. and PARMALEE, PAUL W.
    1972A   Quaternary periglacial records of voles of the genus Phenacomys Merriam (Cricetidae: Rodentia).
                Quaternary Res., 2:2, 170–175, 2 figs.

GUILDAY, JOHN E.   See: Mills, R. S. and Guilday, J. E., 1972A; Parmalee, P. W., Oesch, R. D. and
                Guilday, J. E., 1969A.

GUILLEMOT, JACQUES and ÜNALAN, GÜNER
    1970A   Précisions sur l'âge pliocène terminal des couches de Puimoisson (plateau de Valensole, Alpes de
                Haute-Provence) à l'aide de faunes continentales nouvelles. Acad. Sci., C.R., Sér. D, 271:23,
                2084–2086 (French).

GUILLIEN, YVES
    1970A   Informations archéologiques. Circonscription de Poitou-Charentes. Gallia Préhist., 13:2, 365–379,
                23 figs. (French).

GUILLIEN, YVES and HENRY-MARTIN, G.
    1968A   Dentures de Rennes et saisons de chasse: L'abri Aurignacien de La Quina. L'Anthropologie, 72:3–4,
                337–348, 4 figs., 2 tables (French).

GUMERMAN, GEORGE J. and SKINNER, S. A.
   1968A   A synthesis of the prehistory of the central Little Colorado valley, Arizona. Amer. Antiquity, 33,
             185–199, 9 figs., 1 table.

GUNDERSON, HARVEY L.
   1969A   The bison. A history of destruction. Nebr., Univ., State Mus., Univ. Nebr. News, Mus. Notes, 48:22,
             3 figs.

GUNDERSON, HARVEY L.   See also: Schultz, C. B. and Gunderson, H. L., 1972A, 1972B.

GUPTA, V. J.
   1969A   Fossil primates from the lower Siwaliks of Kangra district, H.P. Punjab Univ., Res. Bull., Sci., 20:
             3–4, 577–578, 2 figs.
   1969B   Silurian-Devonian boundary in the Kashmir Himalayas. Geol. Soc. India, Bull., 6:1, 26–27.
   1969C   Palaeozoic stratigraphy of the area south-east of Srinagar, Kashmir. Punjab Univ., Res. Bull., Sci.,
             20:1–2, 1–14.

GUPTA, V. J. and CHAUDHURY, R. S.
   1969A   Vertebrates from Pinjor stage of Chakrana, Bilaspur (H.P.). Indian Sci. Congr., Proc., 56, 220–221.

GURARI, F. G., ZAL'TSMAN, I. G., TESLENKO, IU. V. and SHATSKII, S. B.
   1968A   Neogen Zapadnoi Sibiri i ego granitsa s pleistotsenom. [Neogene of western Siberia and its boundary
             with Pleistocene.] In: Granitsa tretichnogo i chetvertichnogo periodov, 48–51 (Russian;
             English summary).
   1968B   The Neogene of western Siberia and its boundary with the Pleistocene. Int. Geol. Congr., 23rd,
             Czech., Rep., Abstr., sec. 10, 276.

GURARII, G. Z.   See: Menner, V. V., Nikiforova, K. V., Pevzner, M. A., Alekseev, M. N., Gladenkov, IU. B.,
             Gurarii, G. Z. and Trubikhin, V. M., 1972A.

GUREEV, ALEKSEI ALEKSANDROVICH
   1971A   Zemleroiki (Soricidae) fauny mira. [Shrews (Soricidae) of the world fauna.] Leningrad: "Nauka"
             Press, 254 pp., 157 figs. (Russian).

GURULEV, S. A.   See: Bazarov, D. B., Antoshchenko-Olenev, I. V. and Gurulev, S. A., 1969A.

GURVICH, I. S.
   1969A   K60-letiiu Alekseia Pavlovicha Okladnikova. [Aleksei Pavlovich Okladnikov 60th anniversary.] Sov.
             Etnogr., 1969:2, 131–132 (Russian).

GUSEVA, I. S.
   1969A   Eshche raz ob uglakh gorizontal'nogo profilia litsevogo skeleta cheloveka. [Again on the angles of
             horizontal profile of human face skeleton.] Vop. Antropol., 32, 70–82 (Russian).

GUS'KOVA, A. I., DUISEBAEV, ZH. D., ZHYLKIBAEV, K. ZH. and VARNAVSKIKH, B. E.
   1971A   Verkhnii pliotsen Amangel'dinskogo boksitorudnogo raiona. [Upper Pliocene of Amangel'dy
             bauxite-ore district.] Akad. Nauk Kaz. SSR, Izv., Ser. Geol., 1971:2, 76–79 (Russian).

GUSTAFSON, CARL E.   See: Fryxell, R., Bielicki, T., Daugherty, R. D., Gustafson, C. E., Irwin, H. T. and
             Keel, B. C., 1968A; Fryxell, R., Bielicki, T., Daugherty, R. D., Gustafson, C. E., Irwin, H. T.,
             Keel, B. C. and Krantz, G. S., 1968A.

GUSTAFSON, ERIC PAUL
   1972A   An early Blancan fauna from the White Bluffs, south-central Washington. Soc. Vert. Paleontol. Ann.
             Meeting, 32nd, 1972, Abstr. (abs.).

GUSTAFSON, ERIC PAUL   See also: Fry, Willis E. and Gustafson, E. P., 1972A.

GUTGESELL, VICKI J.
   1970A   "Telanthropus" and the single species hypothesis: a reexamination. Amer. Anthropol., 72:3, 565–576,
             2 figs.

GUTH, CHRISTIAN   See: Beden, M. and Guth, C., 1970B.

GUTHRIE, DANIEL A.
   1969A   The carotid circulation in Aplodontia. J. Mammal., 50:1, 1–7, 2 figs.

1971A   A titanothere (Mammalia, Perissodactyla) from the early Eocene of Wyoming. J. Mammal., 52:2, 474–475, 1 fig.

1971B   The mammalian fauna of the Lost Cabin member, Wind River formation (lower Eocene) of Wyoming. Carnegie Mus., Ann., 43:4, 47–113, 22 figs., 39 tables.

1972A   "Chadron" ant hill faunas from Nebraska. Soc. Vert. Paleontol. Ann. Meeting, 32nd, 1972, Abstr. (abs.).

GUTHRIE, R. DALE

1968A   Paleoecology of a late Pleistocene small mammal community from interior Alaska. Arctic, 21, 223–244, 6 figs. (French and Russian summaries).

1968B   Paleoecology of the large-mammal community in interior Alaska during the late Pleistocene. Amer. Midland Natur., 79, 346–363, 5 figs., 1 table.

1970A   Bison evolution and zoogeography in North America during the Pleistocene. Quart. Rev. Biol., 45:1, 1–15, 3 figs.

1971A   Factors regulating the evolution of microtine tooth complexity. Z. Säugetierkunde, 36:1, 37–54, 4 figs. (German summary).

GUTHRIE, R. D. and MATTHEWS, JOHN V. JR.

1971A   The Cape Deceit fauna — early Pleistocene mammalian assemblage from the Alaskan Arctic. Quaternary Res., 1:4, 474–510, 12 figs., 3 tables.

GUTHRIE, R. DALE   See also: Hoskin, C. M., Guthrie, R. D. and Hoffman, B. L. P., 1970A.

GUTHRIE, RUSSELL D.

1972A   Re-creating a vanished world. Nat. Geogr. Mag., 141:3, 294–301, illustr.

GUTMANN, WOLFGANG F.

1968A   Die Embryonal-Entwicklung des Menschen und die Stammungsgeschichte der Wirbeltiere. Natur Mus., 98:2, 64–70, 2 figs. (German).

1969A   Zu Bau und Leistung von Tierkonstruktionen. Natur Mus., 99:2, 45–55, 6 figs. (German).

1971A   Die Verfestigung des Gefüges und die zunehmend direktere Kraftübertragung im Bewegungsapparat der Cranioten. Senckenbergiana Biol., 52:1/2, 151–169, 3 figs. (German).

GUTMANN, W. F.   See also: Peters, D. S., Mollenhauer, D. and Gutmann, W. F., 1971A.

GUTSCHICK, R. C.   See: McKee, E. D. and Gutschick, R. C., 1969A, 1969B.

HAAG, WILLIAM G.

1972A   The Bering Straight land bridge. In: Jennings, J. D. and Hoebel, E. A. (eds.), 1972A, 65–68, 1 fig. (reprinted from Sci. Amer., 206:1, 112–123).

HAAS, A.

1963A   Rev.: Alvarado in Soc. Españ. Hist. Natur., Bol., Secc. Biol., 61, 359–360.

HAAS, GEORG

1966A   On the vertebrate fauna of the lower Pleistocene site 'Ubeidiya. Isr. Acad. Sci. Hum., Publ., 1966, 68 pp., 14 pls.
Rev.: Czarnetzki in Anthropol. Anz., 30, 313.

1967B   Bemerkungen ueber die Fauna der Geula-Hoehle, Carmel. Quaternaria, 9, 97–104 (German).

1969A   The armour of placodonts from the muschelkalk of Wadi Ramon (Israel). Isr. J. Zool., 18:2–3, 135–147, 2 figs., 3 pls.

1969B   On the jaw muscles of *Ankylosaurus*. Amer. Mus. Nov., 2399, 11 pp., 7 figs.

1970A   Eine bemerkenswerte Interclavicula von (?) *Tanystropheus* aus dem Muschelkalk des Wadi Ramon, Israel. Paläontol. Z., 44:3–4, 207–214, 3 figs. (German; English summary).

1970B   *Metridiochoerus euronensis* n. sp., a new middle Pleistocene phacochoerid from Israel. Isr. J. Zool., 19:3, 179–181, 1 pl.

1972A   The microfauna of the Djebel Qafze Cave. Palaeovertebrata (Montpellier), 5:5, 261–270, 1 pl., 2 tables.

HAAS, NICU   See: Anati, E. and Haas, N., 1967B.

HAECKEL, ERNST HEINRICH

1972A   Origin and pedigree of man. Migration distribution of mankind. Human species and human races. In: McCown, T. D. and Kennedy, K. A. R. (eds.), 1972A, 133–148 (reprinted from Haeckel, 1868).

HAENSCH, W.-G.
1968A   Die paläolithischen Menschendarstellungen aus der Sicht der somatischen Anthropologie. Antiquitas,
            Reihe 2, 8, 148 pp., 93 figs. (German).
            Rev.: Bosinski in Bonner Jahrb., 169, 541; KV in Archeol. Roz., 21:2, 261 (Czech); Kühn in IPEK,
            22, 161; Züchner in Quartär, 20, 227–228.

HAFFER, JÜRGEN
1970A   Art-Entstehung bei einigen Waldvögeln Amazoniens. [Speciation in some Amazonian forest birds.]
            J. Ornithol., 111:3–4, 285–331, 17 figs., 5 tables (German; English summary).
1971A   Artentstehung bei Waldvögeln Amazoniens. Umschau, 71:4, 135–136, 1 fig. (German).

HAGER, MICHAEL W.
1972A   A late Pleistocene-Recent animal trap fauna from northeast Colorado. Geol. Soc. Amer., Abstr., 4:6,
            379 (abs.).
1972B   A Pleistocene deposit from southeastern Colorado. Soc. Vert. Paleontol. Ann. Meeting, 32nd, 1972,
            Abstr. (abs.).

HAGHIPOUR, A. and BRANTS, A.
1971A   Eocene fish remains from the Pabdeh formation north of Ilam. Iran, Geol. Surv., Rep., 19, 81–107,
            2 figs., 6 pls., 2 tables.

HAHN, GERHARD
1969A   Beiträge zur Fauna der Grube Guimarota Nr. 3. Die Multituberculata. Palaeontographica, Abt. A,
            133:1–3, 100 pp., 85 figs., 10 pls., 20 tables (German; English summary).
            Rev.: Krebs in Zentralbl. Geol. Paläontol., Teil 2, 1971:2–3, 181–182.
1971A   The dentition of the Paulchoffatiidae (Multituberculata, upper Jurassic). Port., Serv. Geol., Mem., 17,
            7–39, 23 figs., 4 tables.

HAHN, JOACHIM
1969A   Gravettien-Freilandstationen im Rheinland: Mainz-Linsenberg, Koblenz-Metternich und Rhens. Bonner
            Jahrb., 169, 44–87, 20 figs. (German).
1970A   Der Schatz aus dem Hohlenstein. Kosmos (Stuttgart), 1970:8, 362–364, 1 fig. (German).
1970B   Sondierung einer jungpaläolithischen Freilandstation bei Lommersum, Kreis Euskirchen. Bonner Jahrb.,
            170, 1–18, 14 figs. (German).
1971A   Verkhnepaleoliticheskaiă statuetka iz bivniă so stoiănki Hohlenstein-Stadel. [Upper Paleolithic ivory
            statuette from Hohlenstein-Stadel locality.] Sov. Arkheol., 1971:3, 211–217, 1 fig. (Russian).

HAHNE, C.
1966A   Wirbeltierfährten im Geologischen Museum des Ruhrbergbaues zu Bohum. Glückauf, 102:16, 843–
            844, 1 fig. (German).

HAINES, FRANCIS
1971A   Horses in America. New York: Thomas Y. Corwell Co., 213 pp., illustr.
            Rev.: Borland in Natur. Hist., 80:9, 89–90.

HAINES, R. WHEELER
1969A   Epiphyses and sesamoids. In: Gans, C. (ed.), 1969A, 81–115, 39 figs.

HAKENBERG, MACIEJ
1969A   Alb i cenoman między Małogoszczem a Staniewicami w południowo-zachodnim obrzeżeniu gor
            Świętokrzyskich. [Albian and Cenomanian between Małogoszcz and Staniewice, SW border of
            the Holy Cross mountains.] Stud. Geol. Pol., 26, 7–126, 7 figs., 5 pls., 1 map, 2 charts,
            1 table (Polish; English summary).

HALE, DAN
1970A   Archaeological and paleontological finds in the New Fern system (Jackson Co., Ala.). NSS News, 28,
            105–106.

HALL, I. H. S. and SQUIRRELL, H. C.
1972A   New sections in the basal Westphalian and uppermost Namurian strata at Risca and Abersychan,
            Monmouthshire. Gt. Brit., Geol. Surv., Bull., 38, 15–41, 7 figs., 1 pl.

HALL, L. R.   See: Conolly, J. R., Hall, L. R. and Rose, G., 1969A.

HALLAM, ANTHONY
1972A   Continental drift and the fossil record. Sci. Amer., 227:5, 56–66, illustr.

1972B   Models involving population dynamics. In: Schopf, T. J. M. (ed.), 1972A, 62–80, 8 figs.
1972C*   Atlas of palaeobiogeography. New York: Elsevier Publishing Co., xii + 500 pp., illustr.

HALLAM, A.   See also: Smith, A. G. and Hallam, A., 1970A.

HALLAM, J. S.   See: Barnes, B., Edwards, B. J. N., Hallam, J. S. and Stuart, A. J., 1971A.

HALLIDAY, WILLIAM R.
1969A   Britain's Pengelly Cave Studies Center. NSS News, 27, 151, 3 figs.

HALOUZKA, RUDOLF
1969A   Vývoj a st'ahovanie chobotnatcov. [Evolution and decline of proboscideans.] Svet Vedy, 16:7
            (Czechoslovakian).

HALOUZKA, R.   See also: Schmidt, Z. and Halouzka, R., 1970A.

HALSTEAD, LAMBERT BEVERLY (= TARLO, L. B. HALSTEAD)
1969A   The pattern of vertebrate evolution. Edinburgh: Oliver and Boyd, 209 pp., 46 figs., 2 ch., 2 tables.
            Rev.: Anon. in Biologist, 52:2, 74; Anon. in La Recherche, 1:2, 193; Bellairs in J. Anat., 105:3,
            587; Brough in New Sci., 42:652, 542; Chrulew in Zentralbl. Geol. Paläontol., Teil 2, 1970:6,
            512–513; Erdbrink in Geol. Mijnbouw, 48:5, 503; Gregory in J. Paleontol., 44:4, 789–790;
            Heintz in Nor. Geol. Tidsskr., 49, 439; Johnston in Human Biol., 42:2, 345; Martinsson in Geol.
            Fören. Stockholm, Förh., 91:2, 295–296; Moment in Quart. Rev. Biol., 45, 295–296; Müller in
            Biol. Zentralbl., 88:6, 799; Parrington in Nature, 222:5200, 1307; R.M.C.E. in Geol. J., 7:2, x;
            Roth-Lutra in Anat. Anz., 130:3–4, 454–455.
1971A   The presence of a spiracle in the Heterostraci (Agnatha). Linn. Soc., Zool. J., 50:2, 195–197, 1 fig.
1971B   Liopleurodon rossicus (Novozhilov) – a pliosaur from the lower Volgian of the Moscow basin.
            Palaeontology, 14:4, 566–570, 4 figs.

HALSTEAD, L. B. and MIDDLETON, JENNIFER
1972A   Notes on fossil whales from the upper Eocene of Barton, Hampshire. Geol. Ass. (London), Proc.,
            83:2, 185–190, 3 figs.

HALSTEAD, L. B. and NICOLL, PETER G.
1971A   Fossilized caves of Mendip. Stud. Speleol., 2:3–4, 93–102, 6 figs., 3 pls., 3 tables.

HALSTEAD, L. B. and STEWART, ALEXANDER DONALD
1970A   Middle Triassic reptiles from southern Tunisia. Geol. Soc. London, Proc., 1662, 19–25.

HALSTEAD, L. B. and TURNER, SUSAN
1970A   Thelodonts from upper Silurian erratic boulder 0.410. Geol. Soc. London, Proc., 1660, 335–340,
            4 figs., 2 pls.

HAMADA, TATSUJI
1970A   Comments on the reliability of bone radiocarbon. In: Suzuki, H. and Takai, F. (eds.), 1970A, 423–
            424, 2 tables.

HAMADA, T. and CHINZEI, K.
1971A   On the radiocarbon dating of fossil bone samples. Kaseki, 21, 28–37, 4 figs. (Japanese).

HAMAGUCHI, HIROSHI
1970A   Manganese content of skeleton of the Amud man. In: Suzuki, H. and Takai, F. (eds.), 1970A, 430–
            431.

HAMILTON, H. W.   See: Guilday, J. E., Hamilton, H. W. and McCrady, A. D., 1969A, 1971A.

HAMILTON, MARGARET E.
1972A   Australopithecine limb proportions. Amer. J. Phys. Anthropol., 37:3, 439 (abs.).

HAMILTON, W. ROGER
1972A   The history of mammals. London: Trustees of the British Museum (Natural History), 41 pp., illustr.

HAMMEL, E. A.
1969A   Theodore Doney McCown. June 18, 1908 – August 17, 1969. Kroeber Anthropol. Soc., Pap., 41,
            1–7, portr.
1970A   Theodore D. McCown (1908–1969). Calif., Univ., Lowie Mus. Anthropol., Ann. Rep., 1970, 45–46,
            portr.

HAMMOND, ALLEN L.
    1971A   Tools for archeology: aids to studying the past. Science (AAAS), 173:3996, 511–512.

HÁMOR, GÉZA
    1970A   Das Miozän des östlichen Mecsek-Gebirges. Hung., Magy. Áll. Földt. Intéz., Évk., 53:1, 483 pp.,
                62 figs., 14 folding inserts (Hungarian and German).

HANDBY, PETER L.   See: Talent, J. A., Duncan, P. M. and Handby, P. L., 1966A.

HANKINS, LELA RUTH
    1970A   Lamarck's evolutionary views: origin and development. Biologist, 52:4, 152–166, 1 fig.

HANSEN, CARL L.   See: Butzer, K. W. and Hansen, C. L., 1968A.

HANSEN, R. O. and BEGG, E. L.
    1970A   Age of Quaternary sediments and soils in the Sacramento area, California, by uranium and actinium
                series dating of vertebrate fossils. Earth Planet. Sci. Lett., 8, 411–419, 3 figs., 2 tables.

HANSEN, WALLACE R.
    1969A   The geologic story of the Uinta Mountains. U.S. Geol. Surv., Bull., 1291, xii + 144 pp., illustr.

HANSON, C. BRUCE
    1969A   Individual variation and evolutionary change in the dentiton of Hyracodon. Geol. Soc. Amer., Abstr.,
                Part 3, 22 (abs.).

HÄNTZSCHEL, W., EL-BAZ, F. and AMSTUTZ, G. C.
    1968A   Coprolites. An annotated bibliography. Geol. Soc. Amer., Mem., 108, 132 pp., 6 figs., 11 pls.
                Rev.: Allasinaz in Riv. Ital. Paleontol. Stratigr., 75:4, 885–886; Häntzschel in Zentralbl. Geol.
                Paläontol., Teil 2, 1970:1, 8–9; Kaszap in Földt. Közl., 100:2, 233 (Hungarian).

HARBAUGH, JOHN W.
    1967A   Computer simulation as an experimental tool in geology and paleontology. Kans., Univ., Dept. Geol.,
                Spec. Publ., 2, 368–389, 17 figs.

HARCOURT, R. A.
    1971A   The paleopathology of animal skeletal remains. Vet. Rec., 89:10, 267–272, 4 figs. (French and
                German summaries).

HARDING, R. S.   See: Washburn, S. L. and Harding, R. S., 1972A.

HARDISTY, M. W. and POTTER, I. C.
    1971A*   The biology of lampreys. New York and London: Academic Press, xiv + 423 pp., illustr.
                Rev.: Herre in Z. Zool. Syst. Evolut.-Forsch., 10:2, 160; Pickering in Nature, 237:5356, 466–467;
                Pickering in Nature, 240:5379, 286–287.

HARINGTON, C. R.
    1968A   A Pleistocene muskox (Symbos) from Dease Lake, British Columbia. Can. J. Earth Sci., 5:5, 1161–
                1165, 3 pls., 1 map, 1 table.
    1969A   Pleistocene remains of the lion-like cat (Panthera atrox) from the Yukon Territory and northern
                Alaska. Can. J. Earth Sci., 6:5, 1277–1288, 10 figs., 4 tables.
    1970A   A Pleistocene muskox (Ovibos moschatus) from gravels of Illinoian age near Nome, Alaska. Can. J.
                Earth Sci., 7:5, 1326–1331, 2 pls., 1 map, 1 table.
    1970B   A postglacial muskox (Ovibos moschatus) from Grandview, Manitoba, and comments on the
                zoogeography of Ovibos. Can. Nat. Mus., Publ. Pal., 2, 13 pp., 3 pls., 1 map, 1 table.
    1971A   A Pleistocene lion-like cat (Panthera atrox) from Alberta. Can. J. Earth Sci., 8:1, 170–174, 3 figs.,
                1 table.
    1971B   A Pleistocene mountain goat from British Columbia and comments on the dispersal history of
                Oreamnos. Can. J. Earth Sci., 8:9, 1081–1093, 6 figs., 3 tables (French summary).
    1971C   A postglacial freshwater drum (Aplodinotus grunniens) from Ontario, and comments on the
                zoogeography of the species. Can. J. Earth Sci., 8:9, 1137–1144, 5 figs.
    1972A   Extinct animals of Rampart Cave. Can. Geogr. J., 85:5, 178–183, illustr.

HARINGTON, C. R. and SERGEANT, D. E.
    1972A   Pleistocene ringed seal skeleton from Champlain Sea deposits near Hull, Quebec — a reidentification.
                Can. J. Earth Sci., 9:8, 1039–1051, 5 figs., 3 tables (French summary).

HARINGTON, C. R.   See also: Crossman, E. J. and Harington, C. R., 1970A; McAllister, D. E. and
                Harington, C. R., 1969A.

HARKSEN, J. C.
    1968A   *Ondatra* from the Pleistocene of South Dakota. S. Dak. Acad. Sci., Proc., 47, 46—48, 1 fig.

HARKSEN, J. C. and GREEN, M.
    1971A   Thin Elk formation, lower Pliocene, South Dakota. S. Dak. Geol. Surv., Rep., 100, 1—5, 5 figs.,
            1 table, map 2.

HARKSEN, J. C. and MACDONALD, J. R.
    1967A   Miocene Batesland formation named in southwestern South Dakota. S. Dak. Geol. Surv., Rep., 96,
            10 pp., 3 figs.
    1969A   Guidebook to the major Cenozoic deposits of southwestern South Dakota. S. Dak. Geol. Surv.,
            Guidebk., 2, 103 pp., 70 figs., 3 tables.
    1969B   Type sections for the Chadron and Brule formations of the White River Oligocene in the Big Badlands,
            South Dakota. S. Dak. Geol. Surv., Rep., 99, 10 figs., 1 table.

HARKSEN, J. C.   See also: Macdonald, J. R. and Harksen, J. C., 1968A.

HARPENDING, HENRY   See: Schanfield, M. and Harpending, H., 1968A.

HARRIS, ARTHUR H.
    1970A   The Dry Cave mammalian fauna and late pluvial conditions in southeastern New Mexico. Tex. J. Sci.,
            22, 3—27, 4 figs., 4 tables.

HARRIS, JOHN M.
    1971A   Chemical preparation of gypsum encrusted vertebrate material. J. Paleontol., 45:2, 350.

HARRIS, JOHN M. and WOOD, ALBERT E.
    1969A   A new genus of eomyid rodent from the Oligocene Ash Spring local fauna of trans-Pecos Texas.
            Pearce-Sellards Ser., Texas Mem. Mus., 14, 7 pp., 1 fig., 1 table.

HARRIS, JOHN M.   See also: Coryndon, S. C., Gentry, A. W., Harris, J. M., Hooijer, D. A., Maglio, V. J. and
            Howell, F. C., 1972A.

HARRIS, MARVIN
    1971A   Race. In: Holmes, L. D. (ed.), 1971A, 123—135 (reprinted from the Measure of Mankind, 1963).
    1972A   You are what they ate. Natur. Hist., 81:7, 24—25, 1 fig.

HARRISON, C. J. O.
    1971A   Flamingo (Phoenicopteridae) remains from the British upper Eocene. Brit. Ornithol. Club, Bull.,
            91:2, 36—39, 1 fig.

HARRISON, C. J. O. and WALKER, C. A.
    1970A   The extinct musk duck *(Biziura)* of New Zealand: a re-appraisal of *B. lautouri*. Brit. Ornithol. Club,
            Bull., 90:1, 6—10, 1 pl.
            Abs.: F.B.G. in Auk, 88:1, 222.
    1971A   A new ibis from the lower Eocene of Britain. Ibis, 113:3, 367—368, 1 pl.
    1972A   The affinities of *Halcyornis* from the lower Eocene. Brit. Mus. (Natur. Hist.), Bull., Geol., 21:4,
            153—169, 9 figs., 3 pls.

HARRISON, RICHARD J. and MONTAGNA, WILLIAM
    1969A   Man. New York: Appleton-Century-Crofts, viii + 387 pp., illustr.
            Rev.: Zihlman in Amer. J. Phys. Anthropol., 34:3, 457—458.

HARRISSON, TOM
    1967A   Revised Niah area phaseology. In: Solheim, W. G. (ed.), 1967A, 77—78.

HART, CYRIL
    1967A   Archaeology in Dean. Gloucester: John Bellows Ltd., xvii + 68 pp., 22 figs., 27 pls.
            Rev.: O'Neil in Antiquaries J., 48:1, 124.

HART, HOWARD R., JR.   See: Fleischer, R. L. and Hart, H. R., Jr., 1972A.

HARTENBERGER, JEAN-LOUIS
    1969A   Les Pseudosciuridae (Mammalia, Rodentia) de l'Éocène moyen de Bouxwiller, Egerkingen et Lissieu.
            Palaeovertebrata (Montpellier), 3:2, 28—61, 6 figs., 4 pls., 1 table (French; German and English
            summaries).

1970A   Les mammifères d'Egerkingen et l'histoire des faunes de l'Éocène d'Europe. Soc. Géol. Fr., C.R., 1970:7, 257 (French).

1970B   Les mammifères d'Egerkingen et l'histoire des faunes de l'Éocène d'Europe. Soc. Géol. Fr., Bull., (7), 12:5, 886–893, 1 fig., 2 tables (French).

1971A   Contribution à l'étude des genres *Gliravus* et *Microparamys* (Rodentia) de l'Éocène d'Europe. Palaeovertebrata (Montpellier), 4:4, 97–135, 18 figs., 5 pls., 2 tables (French; English and German summaries).

1971B   La systématique des Theridomyoidea (Rodentia). Acad. Sci., C.R., Sér. D, 273:21, 1917–1920, 1 fig., 2 pls. (French).

1972A   Les rongeurs d l'Éocène d'Europe et la biogéographie. Int. Geol. Congr., 24th, Canada, Abstr., 225 (French abs.).

1972B   Les rongeurs de l'Éocène d'Europe et la biogéographie. Int. Geol. Congr., 24th, Canada, Proc., Sec. 7, 155–162, 1 fig., 1 table (French).

HARTENBERGER, J.-L., SIGÉ, B. and SUDRE, J.
1969A   Les gisements de vertébrés de la région montpelliéraine. 1. Gisements éocènes. Fr., Bur. Rech. Géol. Minières, Bull. (Ser. 2), sec. 1, 1969:1, 7–18, 2 tables (French; English summary).

HARTENBERGER, J.-L., SIGÉ, B., SUDRE, J. and VIANEY-LIAUD, M.
1970A   Nouveaux gisements de vertébrés dans le bassin tertiaire d'Alès (Gard). Soc. Géol. Fr., C.R., 1970:7, 259 (French).

1970B   Nouveaux gisements de vertébrés dans le bassin tertiaire d'Alès (Gard). Soc. Géol. Fr., Bull. (7), 12:5, 879–885, 1 map, 4 tables (French).

HARTENBERGER, J. L.   See also: Cappetta, H., Hartenberger, J. L., Sigé, B. and Sudre, J., 1968A.

HASEGAWA, YOSHIKAZU
1964C   Discovery of the remains of the common otter from Ojika-do (limestone cave), Hiraodai (karst plateau), Kyushu, Japan. J. Mammal. Soc. Jap., 2:3, 82–84, 1 fig. (Japanese).

1968C   On the fossil elk deer from Japan. Natur. Sci. and Mus., 35:1–2, 8–20, 13 figs. (Japanese).

1972A   The Naumann's elephant, *Palaeoloxodon naumanni* (Makiyama) from the late Pleistocene off Shakagahana, Shodoshima Is. in Seto Inland Sea, Japan. Nat. Sci. Mus., Tokyo, Bull., 15:3, 513–591, 16 figs., 22 pls., 13 tables.

HASEGAWA, Y. and HOJO, Y.
1965A   Vertebral bone of Cetacea from upper Oligocene at Iwaya coast, Kita-kyushu City. Natur. Sci. and Mus., 32:11–12, 155–160, 2 figs. (Japanese).

HASEGAWA, Y. and KANIE, Y.
1971A   [Preliminary notes on a Pleistocene Nauman's elephant from Miyata formation, Ōkine, Yokosuka City.] Yokosuka City Mus., Sci. Rep., 18, 36–42, 5 figs. (Japanese; English summary).

HASEGAWA, Y. and OBATA, IKUWO
1972A   Notes on the excavation of a new Plesiosaur. Natur. Sci. and Mus., 39:7–8, 107–121, 20 figs. (Japanese).

HASEGAWA, Y., OBATA, I., HONDA, H. and FUJISHIMA, Y.
1972A   [Notes on two newly found mammalian fossils from the Urakawa District, Hokkaido.] Nat. Sci. Mus., Tokyo, Mem., 5, 239–243, 3 figs. (Japanese; English summary).

HASEGAWA, Y. and UENO, T.
1967A   [Shark teeth from Tomigusa formation.] In: [Fossils of Aman-cho], published by the meeting of the educational committee, Aman-cho, Shimoina-gun, Nagano Prefecture, Japan, 237 pp., illustr. (Japanese).

HASEGAWA, YOSHIKAZU   See also: Obata, I., Hasegawa, Y. and Otsuka, H., 1972A; Iwamoto, M. and Hasegawa, Y., 1972A; Obata, I., Hasegawa, Y. and Suzuki, T., 1970A; Ozaki, H. and Hasegawa, Y., 1969A.

HATAI, KOTORA
1965C   Some fossil stingrays from northeast Japan. Saito Ho-on Kai Mus., Res. Bull., 34, 15–18, 1 pl.

1969A   A memorial to Hisakatsu Yabe. Tohoku Univ., Sci. Rep., Ser. 2, 41:2, 109–128, portr., bibliog.

1969B   Hisakatsu Yabe (1878–1969). Geol. Soc. India, Bull., 6:4, 138–139, portr.

HATAI, K., HAYASAKA, S. and MASUDA, K.
1963A   Some fossil tympanics from the Mizuho period of northern Japan. Saito Ho-on Kai Mus., Res. Bull., no. 32, 5–17, pls. 1–2, 1 table.

HATAI, K. and KOTAKA, TAMIO
1971A   Some coprolites from Wakayama prefecture. Palaeontol. Soc. Jap., Trans. Proc., 81, 52—58, 10 figs.,
         1 table (Japanese summary).
         Rev.: Häntzschel in Zentralbl. Geol. Paläontol., Teil 2, 1971:6, 435.

HATAI, K. and MASUDA, K.
1966A   The stratigraphic position of *Trilophodon sendaicus* Matsumoto in the Mizuho-tô of Sendai City,
         Miyagi prefecture. Saito Ho-on Kai Mus., Res. Bull., 35, 1—10, 1 pl., 1 table.

HAUBOLD, HARTMUT
1969A   Parallelisierung terrestrischer Ablagerungen der tieferen Trias mit Pseudosuchier-Fährten. Geologie,
         18:7, 836—843, 4 figs., 2 tables (German; English and Russian summaries).
1969B   Die Evolution der Archosaurier in der Trias aus der Sicht ihrer Fährten. Hercynia, 6:1, 90—106,
         10 figs. (German; English summary).
1969C   *Chirotherium*-Fährten aus dem Buntsandstein im "Mauritanium" in Altenburg. Altenburg, Naturk.
         Mus. "Mauritanium", Abhandl. Ber., 6:1, 21—36 (German).
1970A   Versuch einer Revision der Amphibien-Fährten des Karbon und Perm. Freiberg. Forschungsh., Reihe
         C, 260, 83—117, 23 figs., 6 tables (German; English and Russian summaries).
1971A   Die Tetrapodenfährten des Buntsandsteins in der Deutschen Demokratischen Republik und in
         Westdeutschland und ihre Äquivalente in der gesamten Trias. Paläontol. Abh., Abt. A, 4:3,
         397—548, 34 figs., 35 pls., 22 tables (German; Russian and English summaries).
1971B   Ichnia amphibiorum et reptiliorum fossilium. Handb. Paläoherp., 18, 124 pp., 65 figs., 7 tables.
         Rev.: Fantini Sestini in Riv. Ital. Paleontol. Stratigr., 77:1, 135—136; Haltenorth in Säugetierkundl.
         Mitt., 20:1—2, 177—178; Mertens in Natur Mus., 101:5, 227; Thenius in Geol. Ges. Wien, Mitt.,
         63, 252; Westphal in Zentralbl. Geol. Paläontol., Teil 2, 1971:2—3, 177.

HAUGHTON, SIDNEY H.
1969A   Geological history of Southern Africa. Johannesburg: Geol. Soc. S. Afr., 535 pp., 16 pls.
         Rev.: Shackleton in Nature, 225:5236, 975.
1969B   Report of the honorary director for the year 1968. Palaeontol. Afr., 12, i—iv.
1970A   What is palaeontology? S. Afr. J. Sci., 66, 4—8, 1 fig.

HAUGHTON, S. H.   See also: Brink, A. S. and Haughton, S. H., 1967A.

HAYAMI, I. and OBATA, I.
1966A   Notes on the techniques of megafossil study (I). Natur. Sci. and Mus., 33:7—8, 118—134, 4 figs.,
         3 tables (Japanese).
1966B   Notes on the techniques of megafossil study (II). Natur. Sci. and Mus., 33:9—10, 151—163, 5 figs.
         (Japanese).

HAYASAKA, S.   See: Hatai, K., Hayasaka, S. and Masuda, K., 1963A.

HAYES, WILLIAM C.
1965A   Most ancient Egypt. Chicago, London: University of Chicago Press, 160 pp.
         Rev.: Trigger in Asian Perspectives, 9, 172.

HAYMAN, D. L., KIRSCH, J. A. W., MARTIN, P. G. and WALLER, P. F.
1971A   Chromosomal and serological studies of the Caenolestidae and their implications for marsupial
         evolution. Nature, 231:5299, 194—195, 1 fig.

HAYNES, C. VANCE, JR.
1965B   Carbon—14 dates and early man in the New World. Ariz., Univ., Geochronol. Lab., Interim Res. Rep.,
         9, 24 pp., 10 figs., 1 table.
1968B   Geochronology of late-Quaternary alluvium. In: Morrison, R. B. and Wright, H. E. (eds.), 1968A,
         591—631, 4 figs., 2 pls., 2 tables.
1968C   Quaternary geochronology of the Nyasa-Rukwa rift area, Africa. Int. Geol. Congr., 23rd, Czech., Rep.,
         Abstr., sec. 10, 276—277.
1969A   The earliest Americans. Science (AAAS), 166:3906, 709—715, 2 charts.
1970A   Man's first route to America. Science (AAAS), 167:3926, 1670—1671.
1970B   Geochronology of man-mammoth sites and their bearing on the origin of the Llano complex. In:
         Dort, W., Jr. and Jones, J. K., Jr. (eds.), 1970, 77—92, 8 figs.
1972A   The earliest Americans. In: Jennings, J. D. and Hoebel, E. A. (eds.), 1972A, 69—77, 2 figs.
         (reprinted from Science, 166, 709—714).

HAYNES, C. VANCE, JR.   See also: Clark, J. D. and Haynes, C. V., Jr., 1970A.

HAYS, JAMES D.
1971A   Faunal extinctions and reversals of the earth's magnetic field. Geol. Soc. Amer., Bull., 82:9, 2433–
         2447, 11 figs., 4 tables.

HEATH, JAMES E.
1968A   The origins of thermoregulation. In: Drake, E. T. (ed.), 1968A, 259–278, 3 figs., 4 tables.

HEATH, ROBIN J.
1972A   Recent discovery of a mammoth molar in the middle Trent valley gravels near Egginton, Derbyshire.
         Mercian Geol., 4:2, 107–108.

HEATON, MALCOLM J.
1972A   The palatal structure of some Canadian Hadrosauridae (Reptilia: Ornithischia). Can. J. Earth Sci.,
         9:2, 185–205, 17 figs. (French summary).
1972B   Captorhinid origins. Soc. Vert. Paleontol., Ann. Meeting, 32nd, 1972, Abstr. (abs.).

HEBERER, GERHARD
1967A*   Rev.: G. T. in Anthropos, 63/64:3/4, 616; Herre in Z. Tierzücht. Züchtungsbiol., 84:3–4, 358;
         Herre in Z. Tierzücht. Züchtungsbiol., 86:2, 194; Stubbe in Biol. Zentralbl., 87:5, 661–662.
1967D   Wer war der tool-maker in Oldoway? Fundamenta, Reihe B, 2, 306–312, 2 figs., 3 pls. (German).
1968A   Rev.: Altehenger in Anthropos, 65:3–4, 657–661; Marzotko in Gegenbaurs Morph. Jahrb., 112:3,
         440–441; Weninger in Anthropol. Ges., Mitt., 99, 247–248.
1968B   Der gerechtfertigte Haeckel. Einblicke in seine Schriften aus Anlass des Erscheinens seines Hauptwerkes
         "Generelle morphologie der organismen" vor 100 Jahren. Stuttgart: Fischer Verlag, ix +
         588 pp. (German).
         Rev.: Altehenger in Anthropos, 65:5–6, 1016–1018; Bock in Science (AAAS), 164:3880, 684–685;
         Gutmann in Natur Mus., 101:10, 442; Knussmann in Homo, 20:2, 132; Riedl in Anthropol.
         Ges., Mitt., 99, 239; Schott in Ethnogr.-Archäol. Z., 12:2, 289–292; Uschmann in Biol.
         Zentralbl., 89:4, 524–525; Vallois in L'Anthropologie, 74:1–2, 106–107.
1968C   Das Mauer-Erinnerungstreffen am 21. Oktober 1967. Anthropol. Anz., 31:1–2, 101–104, 2 figs.
         (German).
1968D   Homo – unsere Ab- und Zukunft. Stuttgart: Deutsche Verlagsanstalt, "Bücher der öffentlichen
         Wissenschaft", 118 pp., 70 figs. (German).
         Rev.: Guenther-Peters in Naturwiss. Ver. Schleswig-Holstein, Schr., 40, 114; Herre in Z. Tierzücht.
         Züchtungsbiol., 86:2, 194; Knussman in Homo, 20:2, 132; Roth-Lutra in Anat. Anz., 129:3,
         341–343; Vogel in Naturwiss. Rundsch., 22:12, 548.
1969A   The site of Homo erectus heidelbergensis. Int. Congr. Anthropol. Ethnol. Sci., 8th, Tokyo, 1968, Proc.
         Vol. I. Anthropology, 101–102 (abs.).
1969B   Der Ursprung des Menschen. Unser gegenwärtiger Wissensstand. Second edition. Stuttgart: Gustav
         Fischer Verlag, 52 pp., 23 figs. (German).
1970A   Die Evolution des Menschen. Z. Zool. Syst. Evolut.-Forsch., 8:2, 126–139, 12 figs. (English and
         French summaries).
1970B   Über einige Probleme der prae-pleistozänen (tertiären) Evolutionsgeschichte der Hominiden. Krapina,
         189–199, 4 figs. (German; Serbocroatian and English summaries).
         Rev.: Kochansky-Devidé in Zentralbl. Geol. Paläontol., Teil 2, 1971:5, 417–418.
1971A*   Die Evolution der Organismen. Die Kausalität der Phylogenie II/2. Third edition. Stuttgart:
         G. Fischer, VII + 349 pp., 111 figs., 7 tables (German).
         Rev.: Roth-Lutra in Anat. Anz., 130:3–4, 479; Thenius in Geol. Ges. Wien, Mitt., 63, 245–246.

HEBRARD, L.   See: Tessier, F., Hebrard, L. and Lappartient, J.-R., 1971A.

HECHT, MAX K.
1970A   The morphology of Eodiscoglossus, a complete Jurassic frog. Amer. Mus. Nov., 2424, 1–17, 10 figs.
         Rev.: Westphal in Zentralbl. Geol. Paläontol., Teil 2, 1970:6, 514.

HECHT, M. K., SCHAEFFER, B., PATTERSON, B., FRANK, R. van and WOOD, F. D.
1972A   George Gaylord Simpson: his life and works to the present. In: Dobzhansky, Th., Hecht, M. K. and
         Steere, W. C. (eds.), 1972B, 1–29, 3 figs.

HECHT, MAX K. and STEERE, WILLIAM C.
1970A*   Essays in evolution and genetics in honor of Theodosius Dobzhansky. A supplement to evolutionary
         biology. New York: Appleton-Century-Crofts, xv + 594 pp., illustr.
         Rev.: Grebenščikov in Biol. Zentralbl., 90:3, 382–383; Sheppard in J. Animal Ecol., 40:1, 255–256;
         Williams in Quart. Rev. Biol., 45, 391–392.

HECHT, MAX K.   See also: Dobzhansky, Th., Hecht, M. K. and Steere, W. C., 1968A, 1969A, 1970A, 1972A,
         1972B; Schaeffer, B., Hecht, M. K. and Eldredge, N., 1972A.

HECKER, R. F., SHISHKIN, M. A. and YAKOVLEV, V. N.
1971A   Dmitriy Vladimirovich Obruchev (1900—1970). Paleontol. J., 5:2, 279—280.

HEFELE, GEORG
1959A   Der Zoologe und Palaeontologe J. J. Kaup (1803—1873). Sein Leben in und für Darmstadt.
             Darmstadt: Hessisches Landesmuseum, 37 pp. (German).

HEÍM, JEAN-LOUIS   See: Anthony, J. and Heim, J.-L., 1970A.

HEINRICH, WOLF-DIETER
1969A   Wirbeltierfunde aus dem jüngeren Quartär von Pisede bei Malchin (DDR). Deut. Ges. Geol. Wiss.,
             Ber., Reihe A, Geol. Paläontol., 14:4, 537—543, 3 figs. (German).
1969B   Fischotolithen aus dem Obermiozän von Hohen Woos. Geologie, Beiheft 67, 111 pp., 11 figs.,
             19 pls., 1 table (German; English, French and Russian summaries).
             Rev.: Matthes in Hall. Jahrb. Mitteldeut. Erdgesch., 11, 108; Weiler in Zentralbl. Geol. Paläontol.,
             Teil 2, 1970:5, 427—428.
1970A   Nachweis der Teleostiergattung Lepidorhombus Günther, 1862 im Chatt von Malliss. Geologie, 19:7,
             883—887, 1 pl. (German).

HEINRICH, W.-D.   See also: Diebel, K. and Heinrich, W.-D., 1970A.

HEINTZ, ANATOL
1968A   The spinal plate in Homostius and Dunkleosteus. Discussion: E. A. Stensiö. Nobel Symp., 4th,
             Stockholm, 1967, Proc., 1968, 145—151, 2 figs.
1968B   Nye funn av fossile urfisk fra Ringerike. Nor. Vidensk.-Akad. Oslo, Årbok, 1967, 19—20 (Norwegian).
1969A   Two new mammoth-fragments from Norway and age-determination of one of them. Nor. Geol.
             Tidsskr., 49, 437—438, 1 fig.
1969B   Vårt fjortende mammutiunn og ny aldersbestemmelse av en mammutrest fra Norge. Naturen, 93,
             337—342, 2 figs. (Norwegian).
1969C   New agnaths from Ringerike sandstone. Nor. Vidensk.-Akad. Oslo, Mat.-Natur. Kl., Skr., N. Ser., 26,
             28 pp., 8 figs., 7 pls.

HEINTZ, A.   See also: Barth, T. F. W. and Heintz, A., 1970A.

HEINTZ, EMILE
1969A   Signification stratigraphique du genre Gazella (Bovidae, Artiodactyla, Mammalia) dans les formations
             villafranchiennes de France. Soc. Géol. Fr., C.R., 1969:4, 127—129, 1 table (French).
             Rev.: Thenius in Zentralbl. Geol. Paläontol., Teil 2, 1971:1, 68.
1969B   Mise au point sur les Proboscidiens des gisements villafranchiens de Perrier-Etouaires (Puy-de-Dôme) et
             de Vialette (Haute-Loire). Soc. Géol. Fr., C.R., 1969:2, 56—58 (French).
1969C   Le dimorphisme sexuel des appendices frontaux chez Gazella deperdita Gervais (Bovidae, Artiodactyla,
             Mammalia) et sa signification phylogénique. Mammalia, 33:4, 626—629, 1 pl. (French; English
             summary).
             Rev.: Thenius in Zentralbl. Geol. Paläontol., Teil 2, 1971:1, 69.
1970A   Les cervidés villafranchiens de France et d'Espagne. Mus. Nat. Hist. Natur., Paris, Mém., Sér. C, 22,
             1—303, 319 figs., 40 pls., 131 tables (French).
             Rev.: Thenius in Zentralbl. Geol. Paläontol., Teil 2, 1971:4, 344—346.
1971A   A propos de Gazella schreuderae Hooijer 1945 (Bovidae, Artiodactyla, Mammalia) du Pliocène de
             Grubbenvorst, Limburg (Pays-Bas). Ned. Akad. Wetensch., Proc., Ser. B, 74:1, 33—34, 1 table
             (French).
1971B   Gazella deperdita (Gervais) 1847 (Bovidae, Artiodactyla, Mammalia) du Pontien du Mont Lubéron,
             Vaucluse, France. Ann. Paléontol., Vertébrés, 57:2, 209—239, 6 figs., 5 pls., 8 tables (French).

HEINTZ, E.   See also: Crochet, J. Y. and Heintz, E., 1970A; Ginsburg, L. and Heintz, E., 1968A; Petter, G.
                  and Heintz, E., 1969A.

HEINTZ, NATASCHA
1968A   The pteraspid Lyktaspis n.g. from the Devonian of Vestspitsbergen. Nobel Symp., 4th, Stockholm,
             1967, Proc., 1968, 73—80, 4 figs.
1972A   The thelodont Sigurdia lata n.g., n.sp. from the lower Devonian at Sigurdfjellet, Spitsbergen. Nor.
             Polarinst., Årbok, 1970, 112—116.

HEINTZ, NICOLE (= PETIT-MAIRE, N.; PETIT-MAIRE HEINTZ, N.)
1966C   Le crâne des anthropomorphes. Croissance relative, variabilité, évolution. Mus. Roy. Afr. Cent., Ann.,
             Nouv. Sér. in-4º, Sci. Zool., 6, 122 pp., 28 figs., 94 graphs, 35 tables (French).
             Rev.: Kussmann in Gegenbaurs Morph. Jahrb., 114:3, 455—456; Meiklejohn in Human Biol., 40:4,
             541—543; Olivier in L'Anthropologie, 72, 163—164.

1966D   Tentative de définition du genre *Homo* d'après les caractères biométriques crâniens. Soc. Anthropol.
         Paris, Bull. Mém., Sér. 11, 9:4, 393—407, 8 figs., 1 table (French).
1966E   Évolution de la courbure des os de la voûte du crâne étudiés individuellement. Discussion. (Summary).
         Soc. Anthropol. Paris, Bull. Mém., Sér. 11, 9:4, 474—475 (French).
1967C   Deux nouveaux indices crâniens: leur intérêt évolutif dans la série des Hominidés. (Summary).
         Discussion. Soc. Anthropol. Paris, Bull. Mém., Sér. 12, 1:4, 496—497 (French).
1967D   Existe-t-il une réversion évolutive depuis le Paléolithique supérieur? (Summary). Discussion. Soc.
         Anthropol. Paris, Bull. Mém., Sér. 12, 1:4, 500—502 (French).

HEINTZ, NICOLE and OAKLEY, KENNETH P.
1969A   Datation relative des ossements humains de la Denise. Acad. Sci., C.R., Sér. D, 268:24, 2873—2874,
         1 table (French).

HEINTZ, NICOLE   See also: Friend, P. F.. Heintz, N. and Moody-Stuart, M., 1966A.

HEINZELIN DE BRAUCOURT, JEAN DE (= HEINZELIN, J. DE)
1959A   De fossiele mensen in Afrika. Natuurwet. Tijdschr., 41:6—8, 205—214, 5 figs. (Dutch; French
         summary).
1966A   Observations on the absolute chronology of the upper Pleistocene. In: Howell, F. C. and
         Bourliere, F. (eds.), 1966A, 285—303, 5 figs., 4 tables.
1968A   Geological history of the Nile Valley in Nubia. In: Wendorf, F. (ed.), 1968A, 19—55, 5 text figs.,
         82 atlas figs., 1 table.
1969A   Le groupe de l'Omo et l'âge du Pleistocène. Soc. Belge Géol. Paléontol. Hydrol., Bull., 78:1, 1—5,
         1 fig. (French).
1970A   Op zoek naar fossiele hominiden in Africa. Biol. Jaarboek, 38, 57—63 (Dutch).

HEINZELIN DE BRAUCOURT, J. DE and BROWN, F. H.
1969A   Some early Pleistocene deposits of the lower Omo valley: the Usno Formation. Quaternaria, 11,
         31—46, 12 figs. (German and Italian summaries).

HEINZELIN DE BRAUCOURT, JEAN DE   See also: Brown, F. H., Heinzelin, J. de and Howell, F. C., 1970A.

HEIPLE, KINGSBURY G. and LOVEJOY, C. OWEN
1971A   The distal femoral anatomy of *Australopithecus*. Amer. J. Phys. Anthropol., 35:1, 75—84, 5 figs.

HEIPLE, KINGSBURY G.   See also: Lovejoy, C. O., Burnstein, A. H. and Heiple, K. G., 1972A; Lovejoy, C. O.
         and Heiple, K. G., 1970A, 1972A.

HEISSIG, KURT
1969A   Die Rhinocerotidae (Mammalia) aus der oberoligozänen Spaltenfüllung von Gaimersheim bei Ingolstadt
         in Bayern und ihre phylogenetische Stellung. Bayer. Akad. Wiss., Math.-Naturwiss., Kl., Abh.,
         138, 133 pp., 34 figs., 5 pls., 24 tables (German).
         Rev.: Thenius in Zentralbl. Geol. Paläontol., Teil 2, 1970:6, 522—523.
1970A   Neue Fundstellen oligozäner Spaltenfaunen im Schwäbisch-Fränkischen Jura. Bayer. Staatssamml.
         Paläontol. Hist. Geol., Mitt., 10, 331—350, 4 figs., 1 pl. (German; English summary).
1971A   *Brachypotherium* aus dem Miozän von Südwestafrika. Bayer. Staatssamml. Paläontol. Hist. Geol.,
         Mitt., 11, 125—128, 2 figs., 1 table (German; English summary).
1972A   Paläontologische und geologische Untersuchungen im Tertiär von Pakistan 5. Rhinocerotidae (Mamm.)
         aus den unteren und mittleren Siwalik-schichten. Bayer. Akad. Wiss., Math.-Naturwiss., Kl.,
         Sitz.-Ber., 1971, 15—17 (German; abs.).

HEIZER, ROBERT F. and BAUMHOF, MARTIN A.
1970A   Big game hunters in the Great Basin: a critical review of the evidence. Calif., Univ., Archaeol. Res.
         Fac., Contrib., 7, 1—12.

HEIZER, ROBERT F. and BERGER, RAINER
1970A   Radiocarbon age of the Gypsum Cave culture. Calif., Univ., Archaeol. Res. Fac., Contrib., 7, 13—18,
         1 table.

HEIZER, ROBERT F. and COOK, SHERBURNE F.
1966A   New evidence of antiquity of Tepexpan and other human remains from the Valley of Mexico. In:
         Graham, J. A. (ed.), 1966A, 32—38, 1 fig., 1 table.

HEIZER, R. F., ELSASSER, A. B. and CLEWLOW, C. W., JR.
1970A   A bibliography of California archaeology. Calif., Univ., Archaeol. Res. Fac., Contrib., 6 ii + 78 pp.

HEIZER, ROBERT F. and GRAHAM, JOHN A.
1967A   A guide to field methods in archaeology. Approaches to the anthropology of the dead. Palo Alto:
           National Press, ix + 274 pp., 30 figs., 4 maps.
           Rev.: Binford in Amer. Anthropol., 70, 806—808; Brew in Amer. Antiquity, 33, 516.

HEIZER, ROBERT F. and NAPTON, LEWIS K.
1969A   Biological and cultural evidence from prehistoric human coprolites. Science (AAAS), 165:3893, 563—
           568, 6 figs., 1 table.

HEIZER, ROBERT F.   See also: Graham, J. A. and Heizer, R. F., 1967A; Hole, F. and Heizer, R. F., 1969A;
                            Reichlen, P. and Heizer, R. F., 1966A.

HELBY, R. J.   See: Hind, M. C. and Helby, R. J., 1969A.

HELDMANN, GEORG
1955A   Johann Jakob Kaup. Leben und Wirken des ersten Inspektors am Naturalien-Cabinet des
           Grossherzoglichen Museums. 1803—1873. Darmstadt: Author's private Ed., 28 pp., portr.,
           1 pl., suppl. 8 pp. (German).

HELLER, FLORIAN
1960E   Rev.: E.F.B. in Emu, 61, 74.
1968A   Die Wühlmäuse (Mammalia, Rodentia, Arvicolidae) des Ältest- und Altpleistozäns Europas. Eine
           Übersicht über die bisher bekannten Gattungen und Arten. Quartär, 19, 23—53, 2 figs.
           (German).
1969A   Georges Cuvier und die klassischen Fossilfundstellen Nordbayerns. Geol. Bl. Nordost-Bayern, 19, 173—
           179 (German).
           Rev.: Häntzschel in Zentralbl. Geol. Paläontol., Teil 2, 1970:5, 339.
1969B   Ein geschichtlicher Überblick über die Gattung Mimomys (Mammalia, Rodentia, Arvicolidae Gray,
           1821), ihre Klassifizierung und stratigraphische Verbreitung in Europa. Verona, Mus. Civ. Stor.
           Natur., Mem., Fuori Ser., 3, 81—94, 1 fig. (German; English summary).

HELLER, J.
1970A   The small mammals of the Geula Cave. Isr. J. Zool., 19:1, 1—49, 14 figs., 24 tables.
           Rev.: Thenius in Zentralbl. Geol. Paläontol., Teil 2, 1971:2—3, 189.

HELLMAN, GEOFFREY
1969A   Bankers, bones and beetles: the first century of the American Museum of Natural History. Garden
           City: Natural History Press, 275 pp.
           Rev.: Collier in Amer. Anthrop., 71, 1229—1230.

HELMCKE, DIETRICH
1972A   Das Problem der Vergrösserungsangabe auf Raster-Elektronenmikroskop-Aufnahmen geologischer
           Objekte. Neues Jahrb. Geol. Paläontol., Monatsh., 1972:4, 206—214, 4 figs. (German; English
           summary).

HELMER, D. and VIANEY-LIAUD, M.
1970A   Nouveaux gisements de rongeurs dans l'Oligocène moyen de Provence. Soc. Géol. Fr., C.R., 1970:2,
           45—46 (French).

HELMUTH, HERMANN
1968B   Kannibalismus in Paläanthropologie und Ethnologie. Ethnogr.-Archäol. Z., 9:2, 101—119, 1 fig.,
           1 table (German).

HEMMER, HELMUT
1967A   Rev.: Weninger in Anthropol. Ges., Mitt., 99, 237—238.
1969A   A new view of the evolution of man. Curr. Anthropol., 10:2—3, 179—180, 2 figs.
1970A   Reply. Curr. Anthropol., 11:1, 79.
1971A   Zur Kenntnis pleistozäner mitteleuropäischer Leoparden. (Panthera pardus). Neues Jahrb. Geol.
           Paläontol., Abh., 138:1, 15—36, 4 figs., 5 tables (German; English summary).
           Rev.: Thenius in Zentralbl. Geol. Paläontol., Teil 2, 1971:5, 414.
1971B   Fossil mammals of Java. II. Zur Fossilgeschichte des Tigers (Panthera tigris (L.)) in Java. Ned. Akad.
           Wetensch., Proc., Ser. B, 74:1, 35—52, 2 figs., 2 pls., 6 tables (German; English summary).
           Rev.: Thenius in Zentralbl. Geol. Paläontol., Teil 2, 1971:4, 338.
1971C   Zur Charakterisierung und stratigraphischen Bedeutung von Panthera gombaszoegensis (Kretzoi, 1938).
           Neues Jahrb. Geol. Paläontol., Monatsh., 1971:12, 701—711, 3 figs. (German).

1971D   Fossil mammals of Java, III. Zur Kenntnis der Evolution Javanischer Kleinkatzen: *Prionailurus bengalensis koenigswaldi* ssp.n. und *Felis chaus* ssp. aus dem Neolithikum von Sampung., Mittel-Java. Ned. Akad. Wetensch., Proc., Ser. B, 74:4, 365–375, 2 pls., 3 tables (German; English summary).

1972A   Zur systematischen Stellung von "*Jansofelis vaufrayi*" Bonifay, 1971, und "*Felis lunellensis*" Bonifay, 1971, aus dem Pleistozän Südfrankreichs (Carnivora, Felidae). Neues Jahrb. Geol. Paläontol., Monatsh., 1972:4, 215–223, 2 figs., 2 tables (German; English summary).

HEMMER, HELMUT and JAEGER, RUDOLF
1969A   Ein Radius von *Asinus* cf. *hydruntinus* Regalia aus dem Jungpleistozän von Stammheim/Kreis Friedberg [Hessen]. Hess. Landesamt Bodenforsch., Notizbl., 97, 38–43, 1 pl., 1 table (German; English summary).
         Rev.: Thenius in Zentralbl. Geol. Paläontol., Teil 2, 1970:5, 440.

HEMMER, H. and SCHÜTT, G.
1969A   Ein Unterkiefer von *Panthera gombaszoegensis* (Kretzoi, 1938) aus den Mosbacher Sanden. Mainzer Naturwiss. Arch., 8, 90–101 (German).
         Rev.: Thenius in Zentralbl. Geol. Paläontol., Teil 2, 1970:6, 518–519.
1970A   Körpergrösse und Extremitätenmasse ältest- und altpleistozäner europäischer Pantherkatzen (Genus *Panthera*). Mainzer Naturwiss. Arch., 9, 132–146, 4 figs., 5 tables (German; English summary).
         Rev.: Thenius in Zentralbl. Geol. Paläontol., Teil 2, 1971:5, 415.

HEMMINGS, E. THOMAS
1969A   The Escapule mammoth and associated projectile points, San Pedro valley, Arizona. Ariz. Acad. Sci., J., 5:3, 184–188, 6 figs., 1 table.

HENCKEN, HUGH   See: Briggs, L. C. and Hencken, H. (eds.), 1967A.

HENDERSON, LAWRENCE A.
1962A   Stone Age man in America. Screenings, 11:10, 1–2.

HENDEY, H.   See: Hendey, Q. B. and Hendey, H., 1968A.

HENDEY, Q. B.
1968A   The Melkbos site: an upper Pleistocene fossil occurrence in the south-western Cape Province. S. Afr. Mus., Ann., 52:4, 89–119, 3 figs., 3 pls., 15 tables.
         Rev.: Thenius in Zentralbl. Geol. Paläontol., Teil 2, 1971:1, 62–63.
1969A   Quaternary vertebrate fossil sites in the south-western Cape Province. S. Afr. Archaeol. Bull., 24:95–96, 96–105, 1 fig., 3 tables.
1970A   A review of the geology and paleontology of the Plio/Pleistocene deposits at Langebaanweg, Cape Province. Appendix. The Langebaanweg Bovidae, by A. W. Gentry. S. Afr. Mus., Ann., 56:2, 75–117, 4 figs., 4 pls., 3 tables.
         Rev.: Thenius in Zentralbl. Geol. Paläontol., Teil 2, 1971:1, 62–63.
1970B   The age of the fossiliferous deposits at Langebaanweg, Cape Province. S. Afr. Mus., Ann., 56:3, 119–131, 4 figs., 1 table.
         Rev.: Thenius in Zentralbl. Geol. Paläontol., Teil 2, 1971:2–3, 189–190.
1972A   The evolution and dispersal of the Monachinae (Mammalia: Pinnipedia). S. Afr. Mus., Ann., 59:5, 99–113, 2 figs.
1972B   A Pliocene ursid from South Africa. S. Afr. Mus., Ann., 59:6, 115–132, 2 figs., 2 pls., 3 tables.

HENDEY, Q. B. and HENDEY, H.
1968A   New Quaternary fossil sites near Swartklip, Cape Province. S. Afr. Mus., Ann., 52:2, 43–73, 2 figs., 7 pls., 19 tables.
         Rev.: Thenius in Zentralbl. Geol. Paläontol., Teil 2, 1971:1, 62–63.

HENDEY, Q. B. and REPENNING, C. A.
1972A   A Pliocene phocid from South Africa. S. Afr. Mus., Ann., 59:4, 71–98, 2 figs., 17 pls., 7 tables.

HENDEY, Q. B.   See also: Maglio, V. J. and Hendey, Q. B., 1970A.

HENKEL, SIEGFRIED
1970A   Eine neue Fossillagerstätte in Ostspanien und ihre Bedeutung für die Stammesgeschichte der Wirbeltiere. Umschau, 70:8, 247–248, 2 figs. (German).

HENKEL, SIEGFRIED and KREBS, BERNARD
1969A   Zwei Säugetier-Unterkiefer aus der Unteren Kreide von Uña (Prov. Cuenca, Spanien). Neues Jahrb. Geol. Paläontol., Monatsh., 1969:8, 449–463, 2 figs., 1 table (German).
         Rev.: Krebs in Zentralbl. Geol. Paläontol., Teil 2, 1970: 1, 73.

HENRICHSEN, I. G. C.
1970A   A catalogue of fossil vertebrates in the Royal Scottish Museum, Edinburgh. Part 1. Actinopterygii.
           Roy. Scottish Mus., Inform. Ser., Geol., 1, 102 pp.
1971A   A catalogue of fossil vertebrates in the Royal Scottish Museum, Edinburgh. Part 2. Agnatha. Roy.
           Scottish Mus., Inform. Ser., Geol., 2, vi + 38 pp.
1972A   A catalogue of fossil vertebrates in the Royal Scottish Museum, Edinburgh. Part 3. Actinistia and
           Dipnoi. Roy. Scottish Mus., Inform. Ser., Geol., 3, v + 26 pp.

HENRIKSEN, HARRY C.
1968A   Cutting down the evolutionary tree. Curator, 11:4, 306—309, 2 figs.

HENRY-MARTIN, G.   See: Guillien, Y. and Henry-Martin, G., 1968A.

HENSCHEN, FOLKE
1965A   The human skull. A cultural history. Introduction by Kenneth Oakley. London: Thames and
           Hudson, 168 pp., 22 figs., 76 pls.
           Rev.: Don Brothwell in Antiquaries J., 49:1, 137.
1966A   Rev.: Brentjes in Z. Säugetierkunde, 33:4, 255.

HENTHORN, WILLIAM E.
1968A   Recent archaeological activity in North Korea (II). The shell mound at Sǒp 'ohang. Asian Perspectives,
           11, 1—17, 12 figs.

HEPTNER, W. G. and NASIMOWITSCH, A. A.
1967A   Der Elch (Alces alces L.). Wittenberg-Lutherstadt: A. Ziemsen Verlag, "Die Neue Brehm-Bücherei",
           386, 232 pp., 16 figs., 58 pls., 14 maps (German).
           Rev.: Dorst in Mammalia, 32:2, 311; Haltenorth in Säugetierkundl. Mitt., 18:1, 86; Steinbacher in
           Natur Mus., 99:11, 534.

HEPTONSTALL, W. B.
1970A   Quantitative assessment of the flight of Archaeopteryx. Nature, 228:5267, 185—186, 2 figs.
1971A   Flying ability of Archaeopteryx. Nature, 231:5298, 128.
1971B   Archaeopteryx again. Nature, 234:5330, 479.
1971C   An analysis of the flight of the Cretaceous pterodactyl Pteranodon ingens (March). Scot. J. Geol.,
           7:1, 61—78, 4 figs., 2 tables.

HERBERT, SANDRA
1971A   Darwin, Malthus, and selection. J. Hist. Biol., 4:1, 209—217.

HERBST, RAFAEL
1971A   Esquema estratigráfico de la provincia de Corrientes, República Argentina. Asoc. Geol. Argent., Rev.,
           26:2, 221—243, 1 fig., 1 table (Spanish; English summary).

HERIC, THOMAS M.
1969A   Rancho La Brea: its history and its fossils. J. West, 8, 209—230, 9 pls.

HERMANN, WILHELM   See: Rădulescu, C. and Hermann, W., 1969A; Samson, P. and Hermann, W., 1968A.

HERRE, WOLF
1968A   Erna Mohr [1894—1968]. Z. Säugetierkunde, 33:5, 257—261, portr. (German).

HERRE, WOLF and KAUP, LOTHAR
1969A   Über Reste fossiler Tylopoden aus Mexiko. Z. Zool. Syst. Evolut.-Forsch., 7:4, 243—254, 15 figs.,
           5 tables (German; English and French summaries).
           Rev.: Thenius in Zentralbl. Geol. Paläontol., Teil 2, 1971:1, 69.

HERRERO, STEPHEN
1970A   Man and the grizzly bear (present, past, but future?). BioScience, 20:21, 1148—1153, 2 figs., 2 tables.

HERSHKOVITZ, PHILIP
1962A   Evolution of neotropical rodents (Muridae) with special reference to the phyllotine group. Fieldiana:
           Zool., 46, 524 pp., 123 figs., 66 tables.
1967A   Dynamics of rodent molar evolution: New World Cricetinae, family Muridae. Jour. Dental Res., 46:5,
           829—842, 8 figs.
1970A   All primates have chins. Chicago, Field Mus. Natur. Hist., Bull., 41:5, 8—10, illustr.
1970B   Notes on Tertiary platyrrhine monkeys and description of a new genus from the late Miocene of
           Colombia. Folia Primatol., 12:1, 1—37, 4 figs., 12 pls., 2 tables.

1971A   Basic crown patterns and cusp homologies of mammalian teeth. In: Dahlberg, Albert A. (ed.), 1971A, 95–150, 17 figs.

HERVIEU, JEAN
1969A   Découverte de la Pebble-Culture au Nord de l'Adamaoua (Cameroun). Incidences géomorphologiques et pédogénétiques. Acad. Sci., C.R., Sér. D, 268:19, 2335–2338, 1 fig., 1 table (French).

HESEMANN, JULIUS
1970A   Versuch einer neuen Pleistozän-Gliederung. Eiszeitalter Gegenwart, 21, 97–107, 4 tables (German; English summary).

HEUVELMANS, B.
1969A   Note préliminaire sur un specimen conservé dans la glace d'une forme encore inconnue d'hominidé vivant Homo pongoides (sp. seu subsp. nov.). Inst. Royal Sci. Natur. Belg., Bull., 45:4, 24 pp., 1 fig., 5 pls. (French).

HEWES, GORDON W.
1968A   A new ecological model for hominization. Int. Congr. Anthropol. Ethnol. Sci., 8th, Tokyo, 1968, Proc., 3, 276–278.

HEY, R. W.
1968A   The Quaternary geology of the Jabal Al Akhdar coast. In: Geology and archaeology of northern Cyrenaica, Libya (Petrol. Explor. Soc. Libya, 10th Ann. Field Conf.), 159–165, 3 figs.

HEY, R. W.   See also: Grichuk, V. P., Hey, R. W. and Venzo, S.. 1964A.

HEYLER, DANIEL
1969A   Vertébrés de l'Autunien de France. Paris: Cah. Paléontol., Eds. C.N.R.S., 259 pp., 172 figs., 52 pls., 4 graphs, 5 tables (French).
1969B   Un nouveau stégocéphale du Trias inférieur des Vosges Stenotosaurus lehmani. Ann. Paléontol. Vertébrés, 55:1, 73–80, 2 figs., 2 pls. (French).
                    Rev.: Westphal in Zentralbl. Geol. Paläontol., Teil 2, 1969:6, 511.
1969C   Acanthodii. In: Piveteau, J. (ed.), Traité de Paléo., T. IV, vol. 2, 21–70, 31 figs. (French).
1971A   Sur des os de Paramblypterus du gisement de Surmoulin (Bassin d'Autun). Soc. Hist. Natur. Amis Mus. Autun, Bull. (L'Eduen), 57, 3–14, 4 pls. (French).

HIATT, ROBERT   See: Gaffney, E. S. and Hiatt, R., 1971A.

HIBBARD, CLAUDE W.
1968A   Palaeontology. In: King, J. A. (ed.), 1968A, 6–26, 2 figs.
1969A   The rabbits (Hypolagus and Pratilepus) from the upper Pliocene, Hagerman local fauna of Idaho. Mich. Acad., 1:1, 81–97, 5 figs., 2 tables.
1970A   The Pliocene rodent Microtoscoptes disjunctus (Wilson) from Idaho and Wyoming. Mich., Univ., Mus. Paleontol., Contrib., 23:6, 95–98.
1970B   A new microtine rodent from the upper Pliocene of Kansas. Mich., Univ., Mus. Paleontol., Contrib., 23:7, 99–103, 1 fig., 1 pl.
1970C   Pleistocene mammalian local faunas from the Great Plains and central lowland provinces of the United States. In: Dort, W. and Jones, J. K. (eds.), 1970A, 395–433, 1 fig., 8 tables.
1972A   Early Pleistocene pre-glacial and glacial rocks and faunas of north-central Nebraska. Class Mammalia. Amer. Mus. Natur. Hist., Bull., 148:1, 77–116, 30 figs., 14 tables.
1972B   Sand Draw local fauna. Correlation, age, and paleoecology. Amer. Mus. Natur. Hist., Bull., 148:1, 131–134, 2 figs., 2 tables.
1972C   Two near early Pleistocene faunas from Meade County, Kansas. Soc. Vert. Paleontol. Ann. Meeting, 32nd, 1972, Abstr. (abs.).

HIBBARD, C. W. and BJORK, P. R.
1971A   The insectivores of the Hagerman local fauna, upper Pliocene of Idaho. Mich., Univ., Mus. Paleontol., Contrib., 23:9, 171–180, 4 figs., 5 tables.

HIBBARD, C. W. and JAMMOT, DOMINIQUE
1971A   The shrews of the Wakeeney local fauna, lower Pliocene of Trego County, Kansas. Mich., Univ., Mus. Paleontol., Contrib., 23:24, 377–380, 2 figs.

HIBBARD, C. W. and ZAKRZEWSKI, RICHARD J.
1972A   A new species of microtine from the late Pliocene of Kansas. J. Mammal., 53:4, 834–839, 1 fig., 2 tables.

HIBBARD, C. W.   See also: Skinner, M. F. and Hibbard, C. W., 1972A.

HIGGS, E. S. and JARMAN, M. R.
    1969A   The origins of agriculture: a reconsideration. Antiquity, 43:169, 31—41.

HIGGS, E. S.   See also: Coles, J. M. and Higgs, E. S., 1969A.

HIIEMÄE, KAREN and JENKINS, FARISH A.
    1969A   The anatomy and internal architecture of the muscles of mastication in *Didelphis marsupialis*. Postilla,
                   140, 49 pp., 14 figs.

HIIEMÄE, KAREN   See also: Crompton, A. W. and Hiiemäe, K., 1969A.

HILL, ANDREW and WALKER, ALAN
    1972A   Procedures in vertebrate taphonomy; notes on a Uganda Miocene fossil locality. Geol. Soc. London, J.,
                   128:4, 399—406, 9 figs., 1 table.

HILL, A.   See also: Bishop, W. W., *et al.*, 1971A.

HILL, W. C. OSMAN
    1966A   Rev.: Roth-Lutra in Anat. Anz., 128:2, 205—206.
    1968A   The genera of Old World apes and monkeys. In: Chiarelli, B. (ed.), 1968C, 7—15.
    1970A   Primates. Comparative anatomy and taxonomy. VIII Cynopithecinae. Edinburgh: Edinburgh Univ.
                   Press, xix + 680 pp., frontispiece, 117 figs., 36 pls., 36 tables, 11 maps.
                   Rev.: Anon. in The Biologist, 53:1, 45; Ashton in J. Anat., 110:1, 127; Hall-Craggs in Endeavour,
                   30:109, 51—52; Napier in Nature, 227:5262, 1065; Schultz in Folia Primatol., 13, 316.

HILL, WILLIAM H.
    1971A   Pleistocene snakes from a cave in Kendall County, Texas. Texas J. Sci., 22:2—3, 209—216.

HILLABY, JOHN
    1967A   Evolution under the dragon lava. New Sci., 33:536, 534—535, 1 fig.
    1967B   Comments. New Sci., 34:541, 164.
    1967C   Apemen, artifacts and hyaena. New Sci., 34:542, 200—202, 4 photos.
    1968A   The red lady of Paviland. New Sci., 40:628, 678—679.

HILLERUD, JOHN M.
    1970A   A subfossil assemblage from Milburn, Custer County, Nebraska. Nebr. Acad. Sci., Proc., 80, 34—35
                   (abs.).
    1972A   Taxonomic variation in fossil bison samples from the high plains. Soc. Vert. Paleontol., Ann. Meeting,
                   32nd, 1972, Abstr. (abs.).

HILLY, JEAN   See: Ginsburg, L., Hilly, J. and Taquet, P., 1968A.

HIND, M. C. and HELBY, R. J.
    1969A   The great artesian basin in New South Wales. Geol. Soc. Austral., J., 16:1, 481—497, 4 figs., 2 tables.

HINDS, JIM S.   See: Fassett, James E. and Hinds, Jim S., 1971A.

HIRSCH, JERRY
    1967A*   Behavior-genetics analysis. New York, Toronto, London, Sydney: McGraw-Hill, xvii + 522 pp.,
                   56 figs., 33 tables.
                   Rev.: Roberts in Amer. Anthropol., 70, 1236—1238.

HIRSCHFELD, SUE E.
    1969A   Distribution of Nearctic Pliocene megalonychid ground sloths. Geol. Soc. Amer., Abstr., Part 3, 25
                   (abs.).

HIRSCHFELD, S. E. and WEBB, S. D.
    1968A   Rev.: Thenius in Zentralbl. Geol. Paläontol., Teil 2, 1971:1, 66—67.

HLADY, WALTER M.
    1966B   Further additions to the bibliography of Manitoba archaeology. Manitoba Archaeol. News., 3:3, 3—6.

HLAVIN, WILLIAM J.
    1972A   New associations of fossil sharks from the Cleveland shale, upper Devonian (Famenian). Geol. Soc.
                   Amer., Abstr., 4:1, 21 (abs.).

HO, JU-CH'ANG   See: Wang, Y-y., Hsueh, H-h., Ho, J-c., and Chang, K-w., 1969A.

HO, TONG-YUN
1967A   Relationship between imino acid contents of mammalian bone collagen and body temperature as a basis for estimation of body temperature of prehistoric animals. Comp. Biochem. Physiol., 22:1, 113–119, 2 figs., 1 table.

HO, T-Y., MARCUS, L. F. and BERGER, R.
1969A   Radiocarbon dating of petroleum-impregnated bone from tar pits at Rancho La Brea, California. Science (AAAS), 164:3883, 1051–1052, 1 table.

HOCKETT, CHARLES F. and ASCHER, ROBERT
1972A   The human revolution. In: Jennings, J. D. and Hoebel, E. A. (eds.), 1972A, 99–114 (reprinted from Curr. Anthropol., 5:3, 135–146).

HODÁNOVÁ, D.   See: Čižek, F. and Hodánová, D., 1971A.

HOEBEL, E. ADAMSON
1969A   Hoebel's reply to Gravel. Amer. Anthropol., 71, 305–307.
1972A   Anthropology. The study of man. Fourth edition. New York and London: McGraw-Hill Book Co., x + 756 pp., illustr.

HOEBEL, E. ADAMSON   See also: Jennings, J. D. and Hoebel, E. A., 1972A.

HOFER, HELMUT O.
1969A   In memoriam Tilly Edinger. Gegenbaurs Morph. Jahrb., 113:2, 303–317, portr.
1969B   The evolution of the brain of primates: its influence on the form of the skull. N.Y. Acad. Sci., Ann., 167:1, 341–356, 6 figs.

HOFER, H. O.   See also: Carpenter, C. R. and Hofer, H. O. (eds.), 1969A.

HOFF, DONALD
1971A   A new quarrying method. Soc. Vert. Paleontol., News Bull., 93, 25–27, 3 figs.

HOFFMAN, BARRY L. P.   See: Hoskin, C. M., Guthrie, R. D. and Hoffman, B. L. P., 1970A.

HOFFMAN, DALE S.
1972A   Tertiary vertebrate paleontology and paleoecology of a portion of the lower Beaverhead River basin, Madison and Beaverhead Counties, Montana. Diss. Abstr., 32:11, 6546B–6547B (abs.).

HOFFMANN, ROBERT S. and JONES, J. KNOX, JR.
1970A   Influence of late-glacial and post-glacial events on the distribution of Recent mammals on the northern Great Plains. In: Dort, W., Jr. and Jones, J. K., Jr. (eds.), 1970A, 355–394, 17 figs., 2 tables.

HOFFMANN, W.
1965A   Ausgewählte Fundmeldungen und Neuerwerbungen des Jahres 1962. Jahresschrift Mitteldeutsch. Vorgesch., 49, 235–258, 8 figs., 4 pls. (German).
1966A   Ausgewählte Neufunde aus den Jahren 1963–1964. Jahresschrift Mitteldeutsch. Vorgesch., 50, 325–344, 5 figs. (German).
1968A   Ausgewählte Neufunde aus dem Jahre 1966. Jahresschrift Mitteldeutsch. Vorgesch., 52, 337–355, 2 figs. (German).

HOFFMANN, W. and SCHMIDT, B.
1965A   Ausgewählte Fundmeldungen und Neuerwerbungen des Jahres 1961. Jahresschrift Mitteldeutsch. Vorgesch., 49, 219–234, 3 figs., 5 pls. (German).

HOFFSTETTER, ROBERT
1968C   Rev.: Thenius in Zentralbl. Geol. Paläontol., Teil 2, 1970:5, 443.
1968E   Ñuapua, un gisement de vertébrés pléistocènes dans le Chaco Bolivien. Mus. Nat. Hist. Natur., Paris, Bull., 40:4, 823–836, 2 figs. (French).
1968F   Présence de Varanidae (Reptilia, Sauria) dans le Miocène de Catalogne. Considérations sur l'histoire de la famille. Mus. Nat. Hist. Natur., Paris, Bull., 40:5, 1051–1064, 3 figs. (French).
1969A   Remarques sur la phylogénie et la classification des Édentés Xénarthres (Mammifères) actuels et fossiles. Mus. Nat. Hist. Natur., Paris, Bull., 41:1, 91–103 (French).
          Rev.: Thenius in Zentralbl. Geol. Paläontol., Teil 2, 1970:5, 438–439.
1969B   Un primate de l'Oligocène inférieur sud-américain: Branisella boliviana gen. et sp. nov. Acad. Sci., C.R., Sér. D, 269:4, 434–437, 1 fig., 1 pl. (French).

1970A   Radiation initiale des mammifères placentaires et biogéographie. Acad. Sci., C.R., Sér. D, 270:25, 3027–3030 (French).

1970B   L'histoire biogéographique des marsupiaux et la dichotomie marsupiaux-placentaires. Acad. Sci., C.R., Sér. D, 271:4, 388–391, 1 fig. (French).

1970C   Les paléomammalogistes français et l'Amérique Latine. Acad. Soc. Lorraines Sci., Bull., 9:1, 233–243 (French).

1970D   *Colombitherium tolimense* - Pyrothérien nouveau de la formation Gualanday (Colombie). Ann. Paléontol., Vertébrés, 56:2, 149–171, 7 figs., 1 pl. (French; English summary).
         Rev.: Thenius in Zentralbl. Geol. Paläontol., Teil 2, 1971:2–3, 200.

1971A   Le peuplement mammalien de l'Amérique du Sud. Rôle des continents austraux comme centres d'origine, de diversification et de dispersion pour certains groupes mammaliens. Acad. Brasil. Ciênc., An., 43 Suppl., 125–144, 1 fig. (French).

1972A   Données et hypothèses concernant l'origine et l'histoire biogéographique des marsupiaux. Acad. Sci., C.R., Sér. D, 274:19, 2635–2638, 1 fig. (French).

1972B   Origine et dispersion des rongeurs hystricognathes. Acad. Sci., C.R., Sér. D, 274:21, 2867–2870, 1 fig. (French).

1972C   Relationships, origins, and history of the ceboid monkeys and caviomorph rodents: a modern reinterpretation. In: Dobzhansky, Th., Hecht, M. K. and Steere, W. C. (eds.), 1972B, 323–347, 6 figs.

HOFFSTETTER, R. and GASC, JEAN-PIERRE
     1969A   Vertebrae and ribs of modern reptiles. In: Gans, C. (ed.), 1969A, 201–310, 82 figs.

HOFFSTETTER, R. and LAVOCAT, RENÉ
     1970A   Découverte dans le Déséadien de Bolivie de genres pentalophodontes appuyant les affinités africaines des rongeurs caviomorphes. Acad. Sci., C.R., Sér. D, 271:2, 172–175, 1 fig. (French).
         Rev.: Anon. in La Recherche, 1:5, 456.

HOFFSTETTER, R., MARTINEZ, C., MATTAUER, M. and TOMASI, P.
     1971A   Lacayani, un nouveau gisement bolivien de mammifères déséadiens (Oligocène inférieur). Acad. Sci., C.R., Sér. D, 273:23, 2215–2218, 1 fig. (French).

HOFFSTETTER, R., MARTINEZ, C., MUÑOZ-REYES, J. and TOMASI, P.
     1971A   Le gisement d'Ayo Ayo (Bolivie), une succession stratigraphique Pliocène-Pléistocène datée par des mammifères. Acad. Sci., C.R., Sér. D, 273:25, 2472–2475, 1 fig. (French).

HOFFSTETTER, R., MARTINEZ, C. and TOMASI, P.
     1972A   Nouveaux gisements de mammifères néogènes dans les couches rouges de l'Altiplano bolivien. Acad. Sci., C.R., Sér. D, 275:6, 739–742, 1 fig. (French).

HOFFSTETTER, R. and RAGE, J.-C.
     1972A   Les Erycinae fossiles de France (Serpentes, Boidae). Compréhension et histoire de la sous-famille. Ann. Paléontol., Vertébrés, 58:1, 81–129, 11 figs., 2 pls. (French; English summary).

HOFMAN, GEORGE   See: Minch, J. A., Schulte, K. C. and Hofman, G., 1970A.

HOHENEMSER, HERBERT
     1971A   Penicillin für die Felsbilder von Lascaux. Kosmos (Stuttgart), 67:4, 177–181, 1 fig. (German).

HOIJER, HARRY   See: Beals, R. L. and Hoijer, H., 1971A.

HOJO, Y.   See: Hasegawa, Y. and Hojo, Y., 1965A.

HÖLDER, HELMUT
     1968A   Naturgeschichte des Lebens von seinen Anfängen bis zum Menschen. Verständ. Wiss., 93, 136 pp., 47 figs. (German).
         Rev.: Guenther in Naturwiss. Ver. Schleswig-Holstein, Schr., 40, 112–113; Heller in Geol. Bl. Nordost-Bayern, 19, 87; Hemmer in Homo, 20:4, 255; Kaltenbach in Anthropol. Ges., Mitt., 99, 234; Sittig in Aufschluss, 20:2, 55–56; Struve in Natur Mus., 99:11, 535; Uschmann in Biol. Zentralbl., 89:5, 666.

HOLE, FRANK and HEIZER, ROBERT F.
     1969A   An introduction to prehistoric archeology. Second edition. New York: Holt, Rinehart and Winston, xiv + 497 pp., illustr.
         Rev.: Sharp in Tex. Archeol. Soc., Bull., 41, 311–315.

HOLLAUS, ERFRIED
    1969A   Kurze Übersicht der bisherigen Kenntnisse des Pleistozäns im Nördlinger Ries. Geol. Bavarica, 61,
            131–141, 1 fig. (German).

HÖLLEIN, K.   See: Behrens, M., Frank, H., Höllein, K., Spaeth, W. v. and Wurster, P., 1970A.

HOLLIDAY, KATE
    1972A   By tar preserved. Los Angeles Times, West Magazine, July 30, 1972, 11–14, illustr.

HOLLOWAY, RALPH L., JR.
    1968A   Reply to Professor Washburn. Amer. Anthropol., 70, 101–106.
    1969A   Culture: a human domain. Curr. Anthropol., 10:4, 395–407.
    1969B   Reply. Curr. Anthropol., 10:4, 410–411.
    1970A   New endocranial values for australopithecines. Nature, 227:5254, 199–200, 2 tables.
    1970B   The australopithecine endocasts – a progress report. Amer. J. Phys. Anthropol., 33:1, 133 (abs.).
    1970C   Hominid evolution. Man (J. Roy. Anthropol. Inst.), 5:3, 518.
    1970D   Neural parameters, hunting, and the evolution of the human brain. In: Noback, C. R. and
            Montagna, W. (eds.), 1970A, 299–310.
    1972A   New australopithecine endocast, SK 1585, from Swartkrans, South Africa. Amer. J. Phys. Anthropol.,
            37:2, 173–186, 8 figs., 2 tables.
    1972B   Australopithecine endocasts, brain evolution in the Hominoidea, and a model of hominid evolution.
            In: Tuttle, R. (ed.), 1972A, 185–203, 1 fig., 4 pls., 2 tables.

HOLM, RICHARD W.   See: Ehrlich, P. R., Holm, R. W. and Raven, P. H. (eds.), 1969A.

HOLMAN, J. ALAN
    1967B   A Pleistocene herpetofauna from Ladds, Georgia. Georgia Acad. Sci. Bull., 25:8, 154–166, 1 fig.,
            1 table.
    1968A   A Pleistocene herpetofauna from Kendall County, Texas. Fla. Acad. Sci., Quart. J., 31:3, 165–172.
    1968B   Lower Oligocene amphibians from Saskatchewan. Fla. Acad. Sci., Quart. J., 31:4, 273–289, 2 figs.,
            1 table.
    1969A   The Pleistocene amphibians and reptiles of Texas. Mich., State Univ., Mus., Publ., Biol. Ser., 4:5,
            163–192, 1 fig.
    1969B   A small Pleistocene herpetofauna from Tamaulipas. Fla. Acad. Sci., Quart. J., 32:2, 153–158.
    1969C   Predation and the origin of tetrapods. Science (AAAS), 164:3879, 588.
    1969D   Pleistocene amphibians from a cave in Edwards County, Texas. Tex. J. Sci., 21:1, 63–67, 1 table.
    1969E   Herpetofauna of the Pleistocene Slaton local fauna of Texas. Southwest. Natur., 14:2, 203–212.
    1969F   The ancestral turtle. Int. Turtle Tortoise Soc., J., 3:2, 16–19, 4 figs.
    1970A   Herpetofauna of the Wood Mountain formation (upper Miocene) of Saskatchewan. Can. J. Earth Sci.,
            7:5, 1317–1325, 2 figs.
            Rev.: Westphal in Zentralbl. Geol. Paläontol., Teil 2, 1971:1, 53.
    1970B   A Pleistocene herpetofauna from Eddy County, New Mexico. Tex. J. Sci., 22, 29–39, 2 figs.
    1970C   Possible habits of juvenile prototetrapods. Mich. Acad., 3:2, 101–103.
    1971A   Climatic significance of giant tortoises from the Wood Mountain formation (upper Miocene) of
            Saskatchewan. Can. J. Earth Sci., 8:9, 1148–1151, 2 figs.
    1971B   Herpetofauna of the Sandahl local fauna (Pleistocene: Illinoian) of Kansas. Mich., Univ., Mus.
            Paleontol., Contrib., 23:22, 349–355, 1 fig., 1 table.
    1972A   Early Pleistocene pre-glacial and glacial rocks and faunas of north-central Nebraska. Amphibians and
            reptiles. Amer. Mus. Natur. Hist., Bull., 148:1, 55–71, 7 figs., 4 tables.
    1972B   Small vertebrate fossils from the lower Pliocene Wakeeney local fauna in Trego County, Kansas. Amer.
            Phil. Soc., Yearb., 1971, 323–324.
    1972C   Herpetofauna of the Kanopolis local fauna (Pleistocene: Yarmouth) of Kansas. Mich. Acad., 5:1, 87–
            98, 2 figs., 2 tables.
    1972D   Snakes of the Egelhoff local fauna (lower part of the Valentine formation), Keya Paha County,
            Nebraska. Soc. Vert. Paleontol., Ann. Meeting, 32nd, 1972, Abstr. (abs.).
    1972E   The Pleistocene herpetofauna of Miller's Cave, Texas. Int. J. Speleol., 4:2, 203 (abs.).

HOLMES, LOWELL D.
    1971A*   Readings in general anthropology. New York: Ronald Press Co., viii + 604 pp.
    1971B   Anthropology, an introduction. New York: Ronald Press Co., vii + 450 pp., illustr.

HOLSINGER, JOHN R.
    1967A   Some bones and shields from a cave in SW Virginia. NSS News, 25, 198–200, 3 figs.

HOLST, H. K. H., SMIT, J. and VEENSTRA, E.
    1970A   Lacertoid footprints from the early middle Triassic at Haarmühle, near Alstätte, W. Germany. Ned.
            Akad. Wetensch., Proc., Ser. B, 73:2, 157–165, 8 figs., 2 pls.

HOLST, H. K. H.			See also: Clercq, S. W. G. de and Holst, H. K. H., 1971A.

HOLTON, CHARLOTTE P.
1969A			The Whitney geological survey: its conflict with the California legislature. J. West, 8, 200—208.

HOLYOAK, D. T.
1971A			The supposed fossil of *Conurus* from the Pleistocene of Buenos Aires. Ardea, 59:1—2, 51—52.

HOMANN, WOLFGANG
1968A			Eiszeitliche Knochenfunde aus dem Bensheimer Baggersee. Aufschluss, 19, 61—64, 2 figs. (German).

HONDA, HITOMARO			See: Hasegawa, Y., Obata, I., Honda, H. and Fujishima, Y., 1972A.

HONORÉ, PIERRE
1967A			Das Buch der Altsteinzeit oder der Streit um die Vorfahren. Düsseldorf, Wien: Econ-Verlag, 468 pp.,
			frontispiece, 102 figs., 49 pls. (German).
			Rev.: Kurth in Homo, 20:1, 76.

HOOIJER, D. A.
1967F			Mammalian remains from Liang Toge, Flores. Appendix II. In: Jacob, T., 1967B, 160—161, 1 table.
1968D			Rev.: Thenius in Zentralbl. Geol. Paläontol., Teil 2, 1970:5, 440.
1969A			Pleistocene vertebrates from Celebes. XIII. *Sus celebensis* Müller & Schlegel, 1845. Beaufortia, 16:
			222, 215—218, 1 fig., 1 table.
			Rev.: Thenius in Zentralbl. Geol. Paläontol., Teil 2, 1971:2—3, 200.
1969B			Pleistocene East African rhinoceroses. In: Leakey, L. S. B. (ed.), 1969C, 71—98, 6 pls., 28 tables.
			Rev.: Thenius in Zentralbl. Geol. Paläontol., Teil 2, 1970:5, 440—441.
1969C			The *Stegodon* from Timor. Ned. Akad. Wetensch., Proc., Ser. B, 72:3, 203—210, 3 pls., 4 tables.
1970A			Pleistocene south-east Asia pygmy stegodonts. Nature, 225:5231, 474—475, 3 figs., 2 tables.
1970B			Miocene Mammalia of Congo, a correction. Mus. Roy. Afr. Cent., Ann., Sér. in 8°, Sci. Géol., 67,
			163—167, 1 table.
1971A			A giant land tortoise, *Geochelone atlas* (Falconer & Cautley), from the Pleistocene of Timor. I.
			Ned. Akad. Wetensch., Proc., Ser. B, 74:5, 504—517, 2 pls., 9 tables.
1971B			A giant land tortoise, *Geochelone atlas* (Falconer & Cautley), from the Pleistocene of Timor. II.
			Ned. Akad. Wetensch., Proc., Ser. B, 74:5, 518—525, 2 pls., 2 tables.
1971C			A new rhinoceros from the late Miocene of Loperot, Turkana district, Kenya. Harvard Univ., Mus.
			Comp. Zool., Bull., 142:3, 339—392, 1 fig., 11 pls., 36 tables, appendix.
1972A			*Stegodon trigonocephalus florensis* Hooijer and *Stegodon timorensis* Sartono from the Pleistocene of
			Flores and Timor. I. Ned. Akad. Wetensch., Proc., Ser. B, 75:1, 12—26, 3 pls., 12 tables.
1972B			*Stegodon trigonocephalus florensis* Hooijer and *Stegodon timorensis* Sartono from the Pleistocene of
			Flores and Timor. II. Ned. Akad. Wetensch., Proc., Ser. B, 75:1, 27—33, 5 tables.
1972C			Pleistocene vertebrates of the Netherlands Antilles. Int. J. Speleol., 4:2, 204.

HOOIJER, D. A. and PATTERSON, BRYAN
1972A			Rhinoceroses from the Pliocene of northwestern Kenya. Harvard Univ., Mus. Comp. Zool., Bull.,
			144:1, 1—26, 11 figs., 9 tables.

HOOIJER, D. A.			See also: Coryndon, S. C., Gentry, A. W., Harris, J. M., Hooijer, D. A., Maglio, V. J. and
			Howell, F. C. 1972A.

HOOKER, J. J.
1972A			The first land mammals from the marine Barton beds (upper Eocene) of Hampshire. Geol. Ass.
			(London), Proc., 83:2, 179—184, 1 table.

HOPKINS, DAVID M.
1961A			The Bering land bridge. Sci. of Man, 1, 168—169, 1 fig.
1967D*			Rev.: Anon. in Earth Sci. J., 2:2, 190; Schwidetzky in Homo, 20:2, 136.

HOPKINS, M. L., BONNICHSEN, R. and FORTSCH, D.
1969A			The stratigraphic position and faunal associates of *Bison (Gigantobison) latifrons* in southeastern Idaho,
			a progress report. Tebiwa, 12:1, 1—8, 1 fig.

HOPKINS, ROBERT S.
1969A			Darwin's South America. New York: John Day Co., 224 pp., illustr.

HOPKINS, W. S., JR.			See: Waldman, M. and Hopkins, W. S., Jr., 1970A.

HOPSON, JAMES A.
1969A   The origin and adaptive radiation of mammal-like reptiles and nontherian mammals. N.Y. Acad. Sci.,
              Ann., 167:1, 199–216, 10 figs.
1970A   The classification of nontherian mammals. J. Mammal., 51:1, 1–9.
              Rev.: Krebs in Zentralbl. Geol. Paläontol., Teil 2, 1971:2–3, 183–184.
1970B   Postcanine tooth replacement in the gomphodont cynodont Diademodon. Linn. Soc., Biol. J., 2:4,
              317–318 (abs.).
1971A   Postcanine replacement in the gomphodont cynodont Diademodon. Linn. Soc., Zool. J., 50:suppl. 1,
              1–21, 6 figs.
1972A   Endothermy, small body size, and the origin of mammalian reproduction. Soc. Vert. Paleontol., Ann.
              Meeting, 32nd, 1972, Abstr. (abs.).

HOPSON, JAMES A. and CROMPTON, A. W.
1969A   Origin of mammals. In: Dobzhansky, Th., Hecht, M. K. and Steere, W. C. (eds.), 1969A, 15–72,
              14 figs.
              Rev.: Krebs in Zentralbl. Geol. Paläontol., Teil 2, 1971:2–3, 182–183.

HOPSON, JAMES A. and KITCHING, JAMES W.
1972A   A revised classification of cynodonts (Reptilia: Therapsida). Palaeontol. Afr., 14, 71–85.

HORR, DAVID AGEE
1963A*   COWA surveys and bibliographies. Southeast Asia. COWA Surv. and Bibliog., Area 19, no. 2, 25 pp.

HOSKIN, C. M., GUTHRIE, R. D. and HOFFMAN, B. L. P.
1970A   Pleistocene, Holocene and Recent bird gastroliths from interior Alaska. Arctic, 23, 14–23, 9 figs.
              (French and Russian summaries).

HOSOKAWA, HIROSHI   See: Ogawa, T. and Hosokawa, H., 1969A; Ogawa, T., Kamiya, T., Sakai, S. and
              Hosokawa, H., 1970A.

HOTTA, SUSUMU
1968A   The structure of fossil proteins. Infra-red spectra of the proteins in the molar tooth dentine Elephas
              naumanni and Elephas maximus. Earth Sci. (Chikyu Kagaku), 22:4, 179–185, 3 figs., 1 table
              (Japanese; English summary).

HOTTON, NICHOLAS III
1969A   Vertebrate fossil collections – a fragmentary document. In: Cohen, D. M. and Cressey, R. F. (eds.),
              1969A, Biol. Soc. Wash., Proc., 82, 579–584.
1970A   Mauchchunkia bassa, gen. et sp. nov., an anthracosaur (Amphibia, Labyrintodontia) from the upper
              Mississipian. Kirtlandia, 12, 38 pp., 14 figs., 2 pls., 1 table.
              Rev.: Westphal in Zentralbl. Geol. Paläontol., Teil 2, 1971:2–3, 178–179.
1971A   Origins of vertebrate classes. N. Amer. Paleontol. Conv., Proc., Part H, 1146–1152.

HOURS, F.   See: Basançon, J., Copeland, L. and Hours, F., 1970A.

HOWARD, HILDEGARDE
1969A   A new avian fossil from Kern County, California. Condor, 71:1, 68–69, 1 fig.
              Rev.: Kuhn in Zentralbl. Geol. Paläontol., Teil 2, 1970:5, 434.
1969B   Avian fossils from three Pleistocene sites in central Mexico. Los Angeles Cty. Mus., Contrib. Sci., 172,
              11 pp., 1 map.
              Rev.: Kuhn in Zentralbl. Geol. Paläontol., Teil 2, 1970:3/4, 233.
1969C   Bibliography 1966–1969. Mimeograph, 1 p.
1970A   A review of the extinct avian genus, Mancalla. Los Angeles Cty. Mus., Contrib. Sci., 203, 1–12, 1 fig.,
              4 tables.
              Rev.: Kuhn in Zentralbl. Geol. Paläontol., Teil 2, 1971:5, 412–413.
1971A   In memoriam: Loye Holmes Miller [1874–1970]. Auk, 88:2, 276–285, portr., bibliog.
1971B   Quaternary avian remains from Dark Canyon Cave, New Mexico. Condor, 73:2, 237–240, 1 table.
              Rev.: Kuhn in Zentralbl. Geol. Paläontol., Teil 2, 1971:5, 413.
1971C   Pliocene avian remains from Baja California. Los Angeles Cty. Mus., Contrib. Sci., 217, 17 pp., 2 figs.,
              2 tables.
1972A   Type specimens of avian fossils in the collections of the Natural History Museum of Los Angeles County.
              Los Angeles Cty. Mus., Contrib. Sci., 228, 27 pp.
1972B   The incredible teratorn again. Condor, 74:3, 341–344, 1 fig.

HOWARD, HILDEGARDE and WARTER, STUART L.
1969A   A new species of bony-toothed bird (family Pseudodontornithidae) from the Tertiary of New Zealand.
              Canterbury Mus., Rec., 8:4, 345–357, 4 pls., 1 table.
              Rev.: Kuhn in Zentralbl. Geol. Paläontol., Teil 2, 1970:5, 434.

HOWE, BRUCE
1967A   The Palaeolithic of Tangier, Morocco. Excavations at Cape Ashakar, 1939–1947. In: Briggs, L. C.
          and Hencken, H. (eds.), 1967A, xi + 200 pp.
          Rev.: Butzer in Amer. Anthropol., 70, 809–810; Lacaille in Antiquaries J., 49:2, 399–400.

HOWE, JOHN A.
1970A   The range of variation in *Equus (Plesippus) simplicidens* Cope from the Broadwater quarries of
          Nebraska. J. Paleontol., 44:5, 958–968, 3 figs., 5 tables.

HOWELL, F. CLARK
1968A   Omo research expedition. Nature, 219:5154, 567–572, 4 figs.
1969A   Remains of Hominidae from Pliocene/Pleistocene formations in the lower Omo basin, Ethiopia. Nature,
          223:5212, 1234–1239, 10 figs., 1 table.
1969B   Hominid teeth from white sands and brown sands localities, lower Omo basin (Ethiopia). Quaternaria,
          11, 47–64, 2 figs., 5 tables (Italian and German summaries).
1969C   Remains of Hominidae from Pliocene/Pleistocene formations in the lower Omo basin (southwest
          Ethiopia). Amer. Anthropol. Ass., Bull., 2:3, 48 (abs.).
1971A   Review of man-apes or ape-men? In: Dolhinow, P. and Sarich, V. M. (eds.), 1971A, 156–165, 1 fig.,
          1 table (reprinted from Amer. J. Phys. Anthropol., 27).
1971B   Just who was Neanderthal? In: Holmes, L. D. (ed.), 1971A, 113–122 (reprinted from Early Man,
          1965).
1972A   Pliocene/Pleistocene Hominidae in eastern Africa: absolute and relative ages. In: Bishop, W. W. and
          Miller, J. A. (eds.), 1972A, 331–368, 8 figs.

HOWELL, F. C. and BOURLIERE, F.
1966A*   African ecology and human evolution. Second printing. Chicago: Aldine Publ. Co., 666 pp., illustr.
          Rev.: Maier in Z. Säugetierkunde, 36:2, 123.
1966B *   Transcript of discussions. In: Howell, F. C. and Bourliere, F. (eds.), 1966A, 547–654, 7 figs.,
          16 tables.

HOWELL, F. C. and BUTZER, K. W.
1968A   New field investigations in the lower Omo basin (Ethiopia), and their significance for human
          evolutionary studies. Amer. Anthropol. Ass., Bull., 1:3, 66 (abs.).

HOWELL, F. C., COLE, G. H., KLEINDIENST, M. R., SZABO, B. J. and OAKLEY, K. P.
1972A   Uranium-series dating of bone from the Isimila prehistoric site, Tanzania. Nature, 237:5349, 51–52,
          2 tables.

HOWELL, F. C., FICHTER, L. S. and ECK, G.
1969A   Vertebrate assemblages from the Usno formation, white sands and brown sands localities, lower Omo
          basin, Ethiopia. Quaternaria, 11, 65–88, 8 figs., 3 tables (German and Italian summaries).

HOWELL, F. C., FICHTER, L. S. and WOLFF, R.
1969A   Fossil camels in the Omo beds, southern Ethiopia. Nature, 223:5202, 150–152, 2 figs., 1 table.
          Rev.: Thenius in Zentralbl. Geol. Paläontol., Teil 2, 1971:1, 68.

HOWELL, F. C. and TATTERSALL, IAN M.
1971A   Hominidae. McGraw-Hill Yearbook Sci. Tech., 1971, 220–224, 2 figs.

HOWELL, F. C., TURNBULL, C., SHARP, L., CLARK, J. G. D. and DEVORE, I.
1968A   Discussion: the use of ethnography in reconstructing the past. In: Lee, R. B. and DeVore, I. (eds.),
          1968A, 287–289.

HOWELL, F. CLARK   See also: Brown, F. H., Heinzelin, J. de and Howell, F. C., 1970A; Clarke, R. J. and
          Howell, F. C., 1972A; Coryndon, S. C., Gentry, A. W., Harris, J. M., Hooijer, D. A., Maglio,
          V. J. and Howell, F. C., 1972A.

HOWELL, THOMAS R.
1969A   A Pleistocene vertebrate fauna from Nicaragua. Geol. Soc. Amer., Abstr., 121, 143–144 (abs.).

HOWELLS, WILLIAM W.
1966A   *Homo erectus.* Sci. Amer., 215:5, 46–53, illustr.
1968A   How to be human. In: Cohen, Y. A. (ed.), 1968A, 23–27 (reprinted from Howells, 1959).
1969A   The use of multivariate techniques in the study of skeletal populations. Amer. J. Phys. Anthropol., 31,
          311–314.
1969B   Mount Carmel man: morphological relationships. Int. Congr. Anthropol. Ethnol. Sci., 8th, Tokyo, 1968,
          Proc., Vol. I. Anthropology, 269–272, 5 figs., 1 table.

HOWIE, A. A.
1970A   A new capitosaurid labyrinthodont from East Africa. Palaeontology, 13:2, 210–253, 24 figs., 1 pl.
          Rev.: Westphal in Zentralbl. Geol. Paläontol., Teil 2, 1971:1, 53.
1972A   On a Queensland labyrinthodont. In: Joysey, K. A. and Kemp, T. S. (eds.), 1972A, 50–64, 6 figs.,
          1 pl.

HOWIE, ANNE   See: Bartholomai, A. and Howie, A., 1970A.

HOYANAGI, MUTSUMI
1969A   [Controversy about the recent discovery of Sinanthropus lantianensis in Shensi.] Chigaku Zasshi,
          78:4, 282–295, 6 figs., 2 tables (Japanese).

HRDLIČKA, ALEŠ
1971A   The Rhodesian find of 1921. In: Leakey, L. S. B., Prost, J. and Prost, S. (eds.), 1971A, 211–218,
          4 figs. (reprinted from Skeletal Remains of Early Man, 1930).
1972A   The Neanderthal phase of man. In: McCown, T. D. and Kennedy, K. A. R. (eds.), 1972A, 257–285,
          5 figs. (reprinted from J. Roy. Anthropol. Inst., 57, 249–273).

HSUEH, HSIANG-HSI   See: Wang, Y-y., Hsueh, H-h., Ho, J-c., and Chang, K-w., 1969A.

HU, CHANG-KANG
1962C   Abs.: Sci. Abstr. China, Earth Sci., 1:2, 11.
1963A   Abs.: Sci. Abstr. China, Earth Sci., 2:2, 5.
1964A   Abs.: Sci. Abstr. China, Earth Sci., 2:4, 9.

HU, SHOW-YUNG
1963A   Abs.: Sci. Abstr. China, Earth Sci., 2:1, 7.
1964A   Abs.: Sci. Abstr. China, Earth Sci., 2:2, 8–9.

HUANG, WAN-PO
1963A   Abs.: Sci. Abstr. China, Earth Sci., 1:4, 9.

HUANG, WAN-PO and CHI, HUNG-GIANG
1963A   Abs.: Sci. Abstr. China, Earth Sci., 2:1, 8.

HUANG, ZEN-WEI and MENG, ZI-KIANG
1964A   Abs.: Sci. Abstr. China, Earth Sci., 2:3, 8–9.

HUBBS, C. L. and POTTER, I. C.
1971A   Distribution, phylogeny and taxonomy. In: Hardisty, M. W. and Potter, I. C. (eds.), 1971A, 1–65,
          12 figs., 2 tables.

HÜBNER, J.
1966A   Theorie und biologische Entwicklungslehre. München: C. H. Beck Verlag, 324 pp. (German).
          Rev.: Schwidetzky in Homo, 19:2, 121.

HÜBNER, PAUL
1969A   Vom ersten Menschen wird erzählt in Mythen, Wissenschaft und Kunst. Düsseldorf-Wien: Econ Press,
          313 pp., 65 pls. (German).
          Rev.: Franzen in Natur Mus., 101:1, 40–41.

HUCHARD, P.   See: Combier, J., Drouot, E. and Huchard, P., 1959A.

HÜCKEL, ULRICH
1970A   Fossil-Lagerstätten, Nr. 7: Die Fischschiefer von Haqel und Hjoula in der Oberkreide des Libanon.
          Neues Jahrb. Geol. Paläontol., Abh., 135:2, 113–149, 17 figs., 5 tables (German; English
          summary).

HUEBER, FRANCIS M. and OLSON, EVERETT C.
1972A   Presentation of the Paleontological Society medal to Preston E. Cloud, Jr. J. Paleontol., 46:3, 470–
          472, 1 fig.

HUGHES, A. R.   See: Tobias, P. V. and Hughes, A. R., 1969A.

HUGHES, B.
1968A   The tarsus of rhynchocephalian reptiles. J. Zool., 156, 457–481, 11 figs., 2 tables.

HUGHES, DAVID R.
1967A   Osteological evidence suggestive of the origin of the Mongoloid peoples. In: Solheim, W. G. (ed.),
          1967A, 1–10.
1968A   Skeletal plasticity and its relevance in the study of earlier populations. In: Brothwell, D. R. (ed.),
          1968A, 31–55, 1 table.

HUGHES, N. F.
1972A   Organisms and continents through time. Spec. Pap. Paleontol., 12, illustr.

HUGUENEY, MARGUERITE
1968A   Les gliridés (Rodentia) de l'Oligocène supérieur de Saint-Victor-la-Coste (Gard). Palaeovertebrata
          (Montpellier), 2:1, 1–23, 3 pls. (French; English and German summary).
1969A   Les rongeurs (Mammalia) de l'Oligocène supérieur de Coderet-Bransat (Allier). Lyons, Fac. Sci., Lab.
          Géol., Doc., 34, 227 pp., 116 figs., 5 pls., 32 tables (French; English summary).
          Rev.: David et al. in Lyons, Fac. Sci., Lab. Géol., Doc., 36, 31–32.
1971A   *Pseudocricetodon philippi,* nouvelle espèce de Cricétidé (Rodentia, Mammalia) de l'Oligocène moyen
          de Saint-Martin-de-Castillon (Vaucluse). Acad. Sci., C.R., Sér. D, 272:20, 2533–2535, 6 figs.
          (French).
1972A   Les talpidés (Mammalia, Insectivora) de Coderet-Bransat (Allier) et l'évolution de cette famille au cours
          de l'Oligocène supérieur et du Miocène inférieur d'Europe. Lyons, Fac. Sci., Lab. Géol., Doc.,
          50, 81 pp., 43 figs., 10 tables (French).

HUGUENEY, MARGUERITE and KISSLING, DANIEL
1972A   Nouveaux gisements de mammifères de l'Oligocène supérieur de Suisse occidentale. Géobios, 5:1, 55–
          66, 3 figs. (French; English summary).

HUGUENEY, MARGUERITE and MEIN, PIERRE
1968A   Les Eomyidés (Mammalia, Rodentia) néogènes de la région Lyonnaise. Géobios, 1, 187–204, 30 figs.,
          1 table (French; English abstract).

HUGUENEY, M., TRUC, G. and PHILIPPE, M.
1971A   Nouveaux gisements à micromammifères et mollusques continentaux dans l'Oligocène moyen du
          synclinal d'Apt (Vaucluse, Sud-Est de la France). Acad. Sci., C.R., Sér. D, 272:19, 2430–2433,
          1 table (French).

HUGUENEY, MARGUERITE   See also: Triat, J.-M., Truc, G. and Hugueney, M., 1971A.

HUGUES, C., LORBLANCHET, M. and RAVOUX, G.
1969A   Sur le Paléolithique ancien et moyen des Cévennes et des Garrigues du Gard. Quartär, 20, 47–68,
          14 figs. (French).

HULSE, FREDERICK S.
1965A   The human species. An introduction to physical anthropology. New edition. New York: Random
          House, xxii + 504 pp., illustr.
          Rev.: Abbie in Mankind, 7:3, 243.

HÜNERMANN, KARL ALBAN
1968A   Die Suidae (Mammalia, Artiodactyla) aus den Dinotheriensanden (Unterpliozän = Pont) Rheinhessens
          (Südwestdeutschland). Schweiz. Pal. Abh., 86, 96 pp., 68 figs., 1 pl., 19 tables (German).
1969A   Über den Leitwert der Suidae im europäischen Neogen. Eclogae Geol. Helv., 62:2, 715–730, 7 figs.,
          2 tables (German; English summary).
          Rev.: Thenius in Zentralbl. Geol. Paläontol., Teil 2, 1971:1, 69–70.
1969B   Das Pleistozän von Süssenborn. *Sus scrofa priscus* Goldfuss im Pleistozän von Süssenborn bei Weimar.
          Paläontol. Abh., Abt. A, 3:3–4, 611–616, 3 figs. II Internat. Paläont. Kolloquium 1966 in
          Weimar (German; Russian and English summaries).
1971A   Die plio-pleistozänen Wirbeltierfaunen von Hajnáčka und Ivanovce (Slowakei), ČSR. VII. *Sus minor*
          (Depéret, 1890). [The Plio-Pleistocene vertebrate faunas from Hajnácka and Ivanovce (Slovakia),
          Czech. SSR. VII. *Sus minor* (Depéret, 1890)] Neues Jahrb. Geol. Paläontol., Monatsh., 1971:4,
          213–230, 9 figs., 2 tables (German; English summary).
          Rev.: Thenius in Zentralbl. Geol. Paläontol., Teil 2, 1971:5, 415–416.
1971B   *Potamotherium miocenicum* (Peters) (Carnivora, Mammalia) von Elgg, Kanton Zürich. Hess. Landesamt
          Bodenforsch., Abh., 60, 73–82, 4 figs., 1 pl., 1 table (German).

HUNT, JOHN
1969A   A world full of animals. New York: David McKay, vi + 378 pp., 16 pls.

HUNT, ROBERT M., JR.
1971A   North American amphicyonids (Mammalia: Carnivora). Diss. Abstr., 32:6, 3540B (abs.).
1972A   Miocene amphicyonids (Mammalia, Carnivora) from the Agate Springs quarries, Sioux County,
               Nebraska. Amer. Mus. Nov., 2506, 39 pp., 16 figs., 5 tables.

HURNÍK, STANISLAV and KNOBLOCH, ERWIN
1966A   Einige Ergebnisse paläontologischer und stratigraphischer Untersuchungen im Tertiär Böhmens.
               Dresden, Staatl. Mus. Mineral. Geol., Abh., 11, 17–161, 57 figs., 8 pls., 13 maps, 3 tables
               (German).

HÜRZELER, J.   See: Crusafont Pairó, M. and Hürzeler, J., 1969A.

HUSSAIN, S. TASEER
1971A   Revision of Hipparion (Equidae, Mammalia) from the Siwalik Hills of Pakistan and India. Bayer.
               Akad. Wiss., Math.-Naturwiss. Kl., Abh., 147, 68 pp., 17 figs., 5 pls., 19 tables, 1 map (German
               summary).
               Rev.: Thenius in Zentralbl. Geol. Paläontol., Teil 2, 1971:6, 521–522.
1971B   Revision of Hipparion (Equidae, Mammalia) from the Siwalik Hills of Pakistan and India. Bayer.
               Akad. Wiss., Math.-Naturwiss. Kl., Sitz.-Ber., 1970, 7–9 (German; abs.).

HUSSAIN, S. T. and SONDAAR, P. Y.
1968A   Rev.: Adrover in Teruel, 40, 244.

HUTCHISON, J. HOWARD
1969A   Insectivores from the type Villafranchian stage of Italy. Geol. Soc. Amer., Abstr., Part 3, 28–29
               (abs.).
1971A   Cf. Uintatherium (Dinocerata, Mammalia) from the Uintan (middle to late Eocene) of southern
               California. PaleoBios, 12, 8 pp., 2 figs., 2 tables.
               Rev.: Thenius in Zentralbl. Geol. Paläontol., Teil 2, 1971:5, 416–417.
1972A   Review of the Insectivora from the early Miocene Sharps formation of South Dakota. Los Angeles
               Cty. Mus., Contrib. Sci., 235, 16 pp., 5 figs., 2 tables.

HUTCHISON, J. H.   See also: Berzi, A., Michaux, J., Hutchison, J. H. and Lindsay, E., 1970A; Bramble, D. M.
               and Hutchison, J. H., 1971A; Savage, D. E., Waters, B. T. and Hutchison, J. H., 1972A, 1972B;
               Savage, D., Whistler, D. and Hutchison, H., 1969A; Waters, B. T., Hutchison, J. H., and
               Savage, D. E., 1972A.

HUXLEY, JULIAN
1969A   The wonderful world of evolution. London: Macdonald, 96 pp., illustr.
               Rev.: George in Nature, 222:5200, 1307.
1970A   Memories. London: George Allen and Unwin Ltd., 296 pp., frontispiece, 22 photos.
               Rev.: G. G. Simpson in Science, 173:3992, 135.
1971A   Udivitel'nyǐ mir evoliutsii. Translated from "the wonderful world of evolution" by Dm. Sukharev.
               Moscow: "Mir" Press, 112 pp., illustr. (Russian).
               Rev.: Iablokov in Priroda, 1972:2, 120–121 (Russian).

HUXLEY, JULIAN S.   See also: Wells, H. G., Huxley, J. S. and Wells, G. P., 1970A.

HUXLEY, THOMAS HENRY
1972A   On some fossil remains of man. In: McCown, T. D. and Kennedy, K. A. R. (eds.), 1972A, 101–107,
               2 figs. (reprinted from Huxley, 1863).

IABLOKOV, ALEKSEǏ VLADIMIROVICH (= YABLOKOV, A. V.)
1963A   O probleme rudimentarnykh organov (na primere izucheniia morskikh mlekopitaiushchikh). [On the
               problem of rudimentary organs (exemplified by a study of marine mammals).] Zool. Zh., 42:3,
               441–450, 4 figs., 1 table (Russian; English summary).
1966A   Is there a convergence or a parallelism in the evolution of Cetacea. Natur. Sci. and Mus., 33:9–10,
               164–175, 2 figs., 1 table (Japanese).
1968A   O raznykh formakh progressivnogo razvitiia v organicheskoǐ prirode. [On different forms of progressive
               evolution in the organic nature.] In: Problemy evoliutsii, 1, 98–115 (Russian; English summary)

IABLOKOV, A. V.   See also: Timofeev-Resovskiǐ, N. V., Vorontsov, N. N. and Iablokov, A. V., 1969A.

ĪABLOKOV-KHNZORIĀN, S. M.
    1968A   O vide. [On the species.] Zh. Obshch. Biol., 29:6, 645–657 (Russian; English summary).

ĪAKHIMOVICH, N. N.
    1965A   Kaĭnozoĭskie otlozheniiā vostochnogo sklona Ĩuzhnogo Urala i problemy ikh izucheniiā. [Cenozoic deposits of the eastern slope of south Urals and the problems of their study.] In: Materialy po geologii i poleznym iskopaemym Ĩuzhnogo Urala,4, 108–117 (Russian).
    1965B   Opornye razrezy plioĩsenovykh i cheˌvertichnykh otlozheniĭ na vostochnom sklone Ĩuzhnogo Urala. [Key sections of Pliocene and Quaternary deposits on the eastern slopes of south Urals.] In: Materialy po geologii i poleznym iskopaemym Ĩuzhnogo Urala, 4, 118–134 (Russian).

ĪAKHIMOVICH, V. L.
    1970A   K plioĩsen-pleĭstoĩsenovoĭ istorii Pechorskogo basseĭna. [On the Pliocene-Pleistocene history of the Pechora basin.] In: Severnyĭ Ledovityĭ Okean i ego poberezh'e v kaĭnozoe, 293–300, 2 figs., 1 table (Russian).

ĪAKHIMOVICH, V. L. and NEMKOVA, V. K.
    1969A   Ob usloviiākh zaleganiiā ostatkov elasmoteriiā, naĭdennogo u pos. Buruktal Svetlinskogo raĭona Orenburgskoĭ oblasti. [On the conditions of occurrence of *Elasmotherium* remains, found near Buruktal settlement, Svetlyĭ district, Orenburg province.] In: Voprosy geologii vostochnoĭ okrainy Russkoĭ Platformy i Ĩuzhnogo Urala, 9, 146–153, 3 figs., 1 table (Russian).

ĪAKIMOV, V. P. (= YAKIMOV, V. P.)
    1964B   Blizhaĭshie predshestvenniki cheloveka. [The nearest predecessors of man.] In: U istokov chelovechestva. (Osnovnye problemy antropogeneza), 52–82, 5 figs., 7 tables (Russian).
    1965A   Races and time. UNESCO (Int. Soc. Sci. J.), 17:1, 153–156.
    1968A*   Simposium. Problema grani mezhdu zhivotnym i chelovekom. Diskussiiā. [Symposium. The problem of transition between animal and man. Introductory allocution. Discussion.] Int. Congr. Anthropol. Ethnol. Sci., 7th, Moscow, 1964, Proc., 3, 581–616 (Russian).
    1969A   Otkrytie nizhneĭ cheliùsti gigantopiteka v Indii. [The discovery of *Gigantopithecus* mandible in India.] Vop. Antropol., 33, 173–174, 1 fig. (Russian).
    1969B   Finds of the Mousterian men on the territory of the USSR and their significance for the problem of the origin of *Homo sapiens.* Int. Congr. Anthropol. Ethnol. Sci., 8th, Tokyo, 1968, Proc., Vol. I. Anthropology, 266–268, 1 table.

ĪAKIMOV, V. P.   See also: Roginskiĭ, Ĩa. Ĩa. and Ĩakimov, V. P., 1968A.

ĪAKOVLEV, VLADIMIR NIKOLAEVICH (= JAKOVLEV, V. N. = YAKOVLEV, V. N.)
    1964A   Istoriiā formirovaniiā faunisticheskikh kompleksov presnovodnykh ryb. [History of formation of faunal complexes of fresh-water fishes.] Vop. Ikhtiol., 4:30, 10–22 (Russian).
    1968A   Ikhtiofauna mezozoĭskikh ozer Sibiri. [Ichthyofauna of Siberian Mesozoic lakes.] In: Mezozoĭskie i kaĭnozoĭskie ozera Sibiri, 189–202, 4 pls., 2 tables (Russian).
    1968B   O funkĩsional'nom znachenii geteroĩserkii. [On the functional significance of heterocercality.] In: Ocherki po filogenii i sistematike iskopaemykh ryb i bezcheliùstnykh, 10–20, 6 figs. (Russian).

ĪAKOVLEV, V. N.   See also: Gekker, R. F., Shishkin, M. A. and Ĩakovlev, V. N., 1971A.

ĪANOVSKAĪA, NATAL'ĪA MIKHAĬLOVNA (= JANOVSKAJA, N. M. = YANOVSKAYA, N. M.)
    1970A   Novye ĩsinodiktisy iz srednego oligoĩsena Mongolii i Kazakhstana i evoliùtsiiā khishchnykh podsemeĭstva Caninae. [New cynodictises from the middle Oligocene of Mongolia and Kazakhstan and the evolution of carnivora of the subfamily Caninae.] In: Materialy po evoliùtsii nazemnykh pozvonochnykh, 71–84, 8 figs., 2 tables (Russian).
    Rev.: Thenius in Zentralbl. Geol. Paläontol., Teil 2, 1971:2–3, 196.

ĪANOVSKAĪA, NATAL'ĪA MIKHAĬLOVNA   See also: Flerov, K. K. and Ĩanovskaiā, N. M., 1971A.

ĪAĨSKO, IVAN ĪAKOVLEVICH (= YATZKO, I. YA.)
    1969A   O priznakakh zabolevaniĭ i drugikh neobychnykh sledakh na kostiakh plioĩsenovykh mlekopitaiùshchikh. [On symptoms of disease and other unusual traces on bones of Pliocene mammals.] In: Mezhdunarodnyĭ kollokvium po geologii i faune nizhnego i srednego pleĭstoĩsena Evropy. Tezisy dokladov, 34–35 (Russian).

ĪAVORSKIĬ, VASILIĬ IVANOVICH, *et al.*
    1970A   K 100-letiiù so dnia rozhdeniiā N. N. Ĩakovleva. [1870–1966]. [To the 100th birthday of N. N. Iakovlev.] Sov. Geol., 13:9, 117–119, portr. (Russian).

IAVORSKIĬ, V. I. and RZHONSNITSKAIA, M. A.
     1967A   Devonskaia sistema. Okrainy Kuznetskogo basseĭna. [Devonian system. Borders of Kuznetsk basin.]
                 Geologiia SSSR, 14, Western Siberia (southern part), 210–221, 2 figs. (Russian).

IAWORSKY, G.
     1965A   La grotte du Vallonnet (Roquebrune – Cap Martin, A.-M.). Congr. Préhist. France, 16e Sess., Monaco
                 1959, C.R., 132–134, 1 fig. (French).
     1967A   Les grottes du gîte des Moulins, à Monaco. Présence du Rhinocéros de Merck. Monaco, Mus.
                 Anthropol. Préhist., Bull., 13, 61–89, 16 figs. (French).

IBRAGIMOV, I. M.   See: Kuznetsov, V. V., Karabalaev, K. K. and Ibragimov, I. M., 1964A.

IGNAT'EV, V. I.
     1967A   Permskaia sistema. Tatarskiĭ iarus. [Permian system. Tatarian stage.] Geologiia SSSR, 11, Povolzh'e
                 and Prikam'e, 395–427, 6 figs. (Russian).

IKEBE, N., CHIJI, M. and NAKASEKO, K.
     1969A   Problems on the terminal Miocene in Japan. G. Geol., 35:4, 11–25, 1 fig., 6 tables (French summary).

ILLIES, J.   See: Fittkau, E. J., Illies, J., Klinge, H., Schwabe, G. H. and Sioli, H. (eds.), 1969A.

ILVES, E., PUNNING, J.-M. and LIIVA, A.
     1968A   Radiouglerodnoe datirovanie subfossil'nykh kosteĭ. [Radiocarbon dating of subfossil bones.]
                 Toimetised Eesti NSV Tead. Akad., Ser. Biol., 17:4, 431–433 (Russian; Esthonian and
                 German summaries).
     1969A   Spisok radiouglerodnykh datirovok Instituta zoologii i botaniki Akademii nauk Estonskoĭ SSR.
                 Soobshchenie IV. [List of radiocarbon datings from the Institute of Zoology and Botanics of
                 the Academy of Sciences of the Esthonian SSR. Communication IV.] Toimetised Eesti NSV
                 Tead. Akad., Ser. Biol., 18:4, 417–426 (Russian; Esthonian and German summaries).

ILVES, E.   See also: Punning, J.-M., Liiva, A. and Ilves, E., 1968A.

IMAI, YOSHIKAZU
     1969A   An electron microscope study on antique human bones and Pleistocene fossil bones. Int. Congr.
                 Anthropol. Ethnol. Sci., 8th, Tokyo, 1968, Proc., Vol. I. Anthropology, 118, 1 fig.

IMAIZUMI, YOSHINORI
     1968A   Burramys only known from fossils. Natur. Sci. and Mus., 35:3–4, 54, 1 fig. (Japanese).

IMPERATORI, LEO
     1967A   Método fotográfico para obtener las curvas de nivel en los fósiles. Soc. Españ. Hist. Natur., Bol.,
                 Secc. Biol., 65:1–2, 145–155, 15 figs. (Spanish; English summary).
     1971A   Coprolitos en el Cuaternario de Ambrona. Soc. Españ. Hist. Natur., Bol., Secc. Geol., 69:2, 187–190,
                 5 figs. (Spanish).

INNES, HAMMOND
     1971A   Levkas man. New York: Alfred A. Knopf, 322 pp.
                 Rev.: Picard in J. Paleontol., 46:4, 603.

INSKEEP, R. R.
     1969A   Health hazards and healing in antiquity. S. Afr. Archaeol. Bull., 24:93, 21–29.
     1969B   Some problems relating to the early Stone Age in South Africa. S. Afr. Archaeol. Bull., 24:95–96,
                 174–181.

INSOLE, A. N.   See: Bosma, A. and Insole, A. N., 1972A.

IONETE, L.
     1964A   Pe unde au traĭt zimbrii. [Where bison lived.] Natura, Ser. Biol., 16:3, 88–90, 2 figs. (Rumanian;
                 Russian and English summaries).

IORDAN, MAGDALENA   See: Patrulius, D. and Iordan, M., 1969A, 1970A.

IORDANSKIĬ, N. N.
     1970A   Podvizhnost' kosteĭ cherepa: v chem ee biologicheskiĭ smysl? [Mobility of skull bones: its biological
                 interpretation.] Priroda, 1970:8, 56–60, 6 figs., portr. (Russian).

1971A   K funktsional'nomu analizu cherepa iashcheritŝ (Lacertilia). Osobennosti stroeniia, sviazannye s kinetizmom. [A contribution to the functional analysis of skull in lizards (Lacertilia). The skull peculiarities related to cranial kinesis.] Zool. Zh., 50:5, 724–733, 3 figs. (Russian; English summary).

1971B   Kinetizm cherepa v evoliutsii reptiliĭ. [Cranial kinesis in the evolution of reptiles.] Zh. Obshch. Biol., 32:3, 348–365, 7 figs. (Russian; English summary).

IOSIFOVA, IŪ. I.
1971A   Paleogenovaia i neogenovaia sistemy. [Paleogene and Neogene systems.] Geologiia SSSR, 4, center of the European part of the USSR, 458–489, 11 figs., 1 table (Russian).

IOSIFOVA, IŪ. I. and DANIL'CHENKO, P. G.
1970A   Nakhodka morskikh miotsenovykh ryb v okrestnostiakh Tambova. [The discovery of marine Miocene fishes in the vicinity of Tambov.] Akad. Nauk SSSR, Dokl., 190:1, 162–165, 2 figs., 1 pl. (Russian).
1970B   A find of Miocene marine fish near Tambov. Akad. Nauk SSSR, Dokl., Earth Sci. Sec., 190, 25–28, 3 figs. (Translated from Russian: Akad. Nauk SSSR, Dokl., 1970, 190:1, 162–165.)

IRWIN, HENRY T.
1970A   Archeological investigations at the Union Pacific mammoth kill site, Wyoming, 1961. Nat. Geogr. Soc., Res. Reps., 1961–1962, 123–125.

IRWIN, HENRY T.   See also: Fryxell, R., Bielicki, T., Daugherty, R. D., Gustafson, C. E., Irwin, H. T. and Keel, B. C., 1968A; Fryxell, R., Bielicki, T., Daugherty, R. D., Gustafson, C. E., Irwin, H. T., Keel, B. C. and Krantz, G. S., 1968A.

IRWIN-WILLIAMS, CYNTHIA
1969A   Comments on the associations of archaeological materials and extinct fauna in the Valsequillo region, Puebla, Mexico. Amer. Antiquity, 34, 82–83.

ISĂ, GH. I.
1967A   Contribuţii privitoare la răspîndirea mamutului (*Elephas (Mammutus) primigenius* Blum.) in Republica Socialista România. [Concerning the distribution of mammoth (*Elephas (Mammutus) primigenius* Blum.) in the Rumanian Socialist Republic.] Natura, Ser. Biol., 19:3, 79–81, 7 figs. (Rumanian).

ISAAC, A. BARBARA   See: Isaac, G. L. and Isaac, A. B. (eds.), 1969A, 1969B.

ISAAC, GLYNN L.
1968A   Traces of Pleistocene hunters: an East African example. In: Lee, R. B. and DeVore, I. (eds.), 1968A, 253–261, 2 tables.
1969A   Studies of early culture in East Africa. World Archaeol., 1:1, 1–28, 5 figs., 2 tables.

ISAAC, GLYNN L. and ISAAC, A. BARBARA
1969A*   East Africa. COWA, Surv. Bibliogr., Area 14, 4, 1–26.
1969B*   Equatorial Africa. COWA, Surv. Bibliogr., Area 12, 4, 1–11.

ISAAC, G. L., LEAKEY, R. E. F. and BEHRENSMEYER, A. K.
1971A   Archeological traces of early hominid, east of Lake Rudolf, Kenya. Science, 173:4002, 1129–1134, 4 figs., 3 tables.

ISHCHENKO, VALERIĬ VASIL'EVICH   See: Glikman, L. S. and Ishchenko, V. V., 1968A.

ISHIBASHI, ICHIRO   See: Tezuka, H. and Ishibashi, I., 1971A.

ISKAKOVA, K. I.
1969A   Iskopaemye zemnovodnye Priirtysh'ia. [Fossil amphibians of Irtysh region.] Akad. Nauk Kaz. SSR, Izv., Ser. Biol., 1969:1, 48–52, 1 table (Russian; Kazakh summary).

ISLAMOV, A. I. and TETIŪKHIN, G. F.
1969A   Stratigrafiia chetvertichnykh otlozheniĭ Syrdar'inskogo artezianskogo basseĭna. [Stratigraphy of the Quaternary deposits of Syr-Darya artesian basin.] In: Gidrogeologiia i inzhenernaia geologiia aridnoĭ zony SSSR, 5, 3–11 (Russian).

ISPHORDING, WAYNE C. and LAMB, GEORGE M.
1970A   Age of the Citronelle formation, an end to a controversy. Geol. Soc. Amer., Abstr., 2:7, 584–585 (abs.).

1971A   Age and origin of the Citronelle formation in Alabama. Geol. Soc. Amer., Bull., 82:3, 775–779, 1 fig., 1 table.

ISSAR, A. and KAFRI, U.
1969A   The discovery of a Pleistocene mammalian fauna and artifacts at 'Evron, western Galilee. Isr. J. Earth-Sci., 18 :3/4, 147.

IUDIN, K. A. (= YUDIN, K. A.)
1970A   O nekotorykh printsipial'nykh i metodicheskikh voprosakh nadvidovoĭ sistematiki ptits. [Questions of principle and method in bird systematics above the species level.] Zool. Zh., 49:4, 588–600 (Russian; English summary).
1970B   Biologicheskoe znachenie i evoliutsiia kinetichnosti cherepa ptits. [The biological significance and evolution of cranial kinesis in birds.] Akad. Nauk SSSR, Zool. Inst., Trudy, 47, 32–66, 12 figs. (Russian).

IUROVSKAIA, V. Z.
1972A   Problema brakhiatsii v svete nekotorykh dannykh po paleontologii primatov. [The problem of brachiation in the light of some data on the paleontology of primates.] Vop. Antropol., 41, 48–59 (Russian).

IVAKHNENKO, M. F. (= IVACHNENKO, M. F.)
1971A   Novye dannye po rannetriasovym labirintodontam Russkoĭ platformy (o vidovom sostave roda Thoosuchus). [New data on early Triassic labyrinthodonts of the Russian platform (on the specific composition of the genus Thoosuchus).] Mosk. Obshchest. Ispyt. Prir., Biull., Otd. Geol., 46:6, 145–146 (Russian).
1972A   Novyĭ bentozukhid iz nizhnego triasa Verkhnego Povolzh'ia. [A new benthosuchid from the lower Triassic of the upper Volga region.] Paleontol. Zh., 1972:4, 93–99, 2 figs. (Russian).

IVANCHENKO, V. I.
1969A   Ob iskopaemykh rybakh iz sarmatskikh otlozheniĭ MSSR. [On fossil fishes from Sarmatian deposits of the MSSR.] In: Stratigrafiia neogena Moldavii i Iuga Ukrainy, 84–88, 1 pl. (Russian).

IVAN'EV, LEONID NIKIFOROVICH (= IVANJEV, L. N. = IVAN'YEV, L. N.)
1969A   Zub Palaeoloxodon cf. namadicus (Falconer et Cautley) iz Irkutskoĭ oblasti. [Tooth of Palaeoloxodon cf. namadicus (Falconer et Cautley) from Irkutsk province.] Geogr. Obshchest. SSSR, Vost.- Sibirsk. Otd., Izv., 66, 83–88 (Russian).
1971A   K voprosu o rode Hypsohipparion (Equidae). [On the genus Hypsohipparion (Equidae).] Paleontol. Zh., 1971:3, 125–126, 1 fig., 1 table (Russian).
1971B   Concerning the genus Hypsohipparion (Equidae). Paleontol. J., 5:3, 396–398, 1 fig., 1 table.

IVAN'EV, LEONID NIKIFOROVICH and KHOZATSKIĬ, LEV ISAAKOVICH
1970A   Ostatki neogenovykh presmykaiushchikhsia i zemnovodnykh ostrova Ol'khon na ozere Baĭkal. [Remains of Neogene reptiles and amphibians from Ol'khon Is. in the Baĭkal lake.] Geogr. Obshchest. SSSR, Vost.-Sibirsk. Otd., Izv., 67, 153–158 (Russian).

IVANHOE, FRANCIS
1970A   Was Virchow right about Neanderthal? Nature, 227:5258, 577–579.

IVANOV, A. I.
1970A   Pamiati Petra Petrovicha Sushkina. [1868–1928]. [In memoriam: Petr Petrovich Sushkin. [1868–1928].] Akad. Nauk SSSR, Zool. Inst., Trudy, 47, 5–8 (Russian).

IVANOV, S. G.
1972A   Ob osnovnykh faktorakh i zakonomernostiakh antropogeneza v trudakh Ch. Darvina. [Basic factors and regularities in the anthropogenesis in Ch. Darwin's works.] Vop. Antropol., 40, 15–31 (Russian).

IVANOVA, IRINA KONSTANTINOVNA
1964A   Ekskursiia po paleoliticheskim mestonakhozhdeniiam na VI kongresse INQUA v Pol'she. [Excursion to Paleolithic sites at the VI INQUA Congress in Poland.] In: Nauchnye itogi VI kongressa mezhdunarodnoĭ assotsiatsii po izucheniiu chetvertichnogo perioda (INQUA). (Varshava, 1961), 88–99, 7 figs. (Russian).
1968A   On Eopleistocene and the boundary between the Tertiary and Quaternary periods based on paleoanthropological data. Int. Geol. Congr., 23rd, Czech., Rep., Abstr., sec. 10, 278 (abs.).
1968B   Ob eopleistotsene i granitse mezhdu tretichnym i chetvertichnym periodami po paleoantropologicheskim dannym. [On Eopleistocene and the boundary between Tertiary and Quaternary periods based on paleoanthropological data.] In: Granitsa tretichnogo i chetvertichnogo periodov, 32–41, 2 tables (Russian; English summary).

1969A   Geologicheskoe stroenie doliny r. Dnestr v raĭone must'erskogo mestonakhozhdeniĩa Stinka.
         [Geological structure of Dnestr R. valley in the area of the Mousterian site Stinka.] Akad.
         Nauk SSSR, Kom. Izuch. Chetvertich. Perioda, Bĭull., 36, 129—136, 4 figs. (Russian).
1969B   Geologicheskie uslovĩiã nakhozhdeniĩa paleolita na territorii SSSR. [Geological conditions of
         occurrence of Paleolithic on the territory of USSR.] Mosk. Obshchest. Ispyt. Prir., Bĭull., Otd.
         Geol., 44:3, 18—41, 4 figs. (Russian).
1969C   Geologicheskiĭ vozrast iskopaemykh lĩudeĭ Severnoĭ Evrazii. [Geological age of fossil men of north
         Eurasia.] In: Osnovnye problemy geologii antropogena Evrazii. K VIII kongressu INQUA,
         Parizh, 1969, 60—70 (Russian; English summary).
1969D   Étude géologique des gisements paléolithiques de l'U.R.S.S. L'Anthropologie, 73, 5—48, 18 figs.,
         1 table, 2 maps (French).

IVANOVA, IRINA KONSTANTINOVNA   See also: Gromov, V. I., Vangengeĭm, E. A., Grichuk, V. P.,
         Ivanova, I. K. and Nikiforova, K. V. (eds.), 1968A; Nikiforova, K. V., Ivanova, I. K. and
         Konstantinova, N. A., 1969A, 1970A, 1971A; Vereĭskiĭ, N. G., Ivanova, I. K. and
         Neĭshtadt, M. I., 1964A.

IWAMOTO, MITSUO and HASEGAWA, YOSHIKAZU
    1972A   Two macaque fossil teeth from the Japanese Pleistocene. Primates, 13(1), 77—81, 3 figs.

IZETT, GLENN A.
    1968A   The Miocene Troublesome formation in Middle Park, northwestern Colorado. Colorado, Univ. Mus.,
             Field Confer. Guidebk., 147—189, 7 figs., 4 tables.

JACKSON, KATHRYN
    1972A   Dinosaurs. Illustrated by Jay H. Matternes. Washington, D. C.: National Geographic Society, 31 pp.,
             illustr.

JACOB, HELGA   See: Feustel, R., et al., 1971A; 1971B.

JACOB, TEUKU
    1965A   The paramastoid crest in Indonesian skulls. Anthropologica, 7:2, 239—247, 5 tables, 2 pls.
    1967B   Some problems pertaining to the racial history of the Indonesian region. Utrecht: Drukkerij
             Neerlandia, xiv + 162 pp., illustr.
             Rev.: Vallois in L'Anthropologie, 73:3—4, 289—291.

JACOB, TEUKU and CURTISS, GARNISS H.
    1971A   Preliminary potassium-argon dating of early man in Java. Calif., Univ., Archaeol. Res. Fac., Contrib.,
             12, 50.

JAEGER, HERMANN
    1971A   Werner Janensch (1878—1969). Deut. Ges. Geol. Wiss., Ber., Reihe A, Geol. Paläontol., 16:2, 149—154,
             1 fig., portr. (German).

JAEGER, JEAN-JACQUES
    1969A   Les rongeurs du Pléistocène moyen de Ternifine (Algérie). Acad. Sci., C.R., Sér. D, 269:16, 1492—
             1495 (French).
    1970A   Découverte au Jebel Irhoud des premières faunes de rongeurs du Pléistocène inférieur et moyen du
             Maroc. Acad. Sci., C.R., Sér. D, 270:7, 920—923, 1 table (French).
    1970B   Pantolestidae nouveaux (Mammalia, Insectivora) de l'Éocène moyen de Bouxwiller (Alsace). Palaeo-
             vertebrata (Montpellier), 3:3, 63—82, 7 figs., 3 pls., 5 tables (French; English and German
             summaries).
    1971A   Les micromammifères du "Villafranchien" inférieur du lac Ichkeul (Tunisie): données stratigraphiques
             et biogéographiques nouvelles. Acad. Sci., C.R., Sér. D, 273:5, 562—565, 1 fig. (French).
    1971B   La faune de mammifères du Lutétien de Bouxwiller (Bas-Rhin) et sa contribution à l'élaboration de
             l'échelle des zones biochronologiques de l'Éocène européen. Alsace-Lorraine, Serv. Carte Géol.,
             Bull., 24:2—3, 93—105, 3 tables (French; English, German and Russian summaries).

JAEGER, J.-J. and MARTIN, J.
    1971A   Découverte au Maroc des premiers micromammifères du Pontien d'Afrique. Acad. Sci., C.R., Sér. D,
             272:17, 2155—2158, 2 figs. (French).
             Rev.: Thenius in Zentralbl. Geol. Paläontol., Teil 2, 1971:6, 512.

JAEGER, RUDOLF   See: Hemmer, H. and Jaeger, R., 1969A.

JAHN, MELVIN E.
1969A   Some notes on Dr. Scheuchzer and on *Homo diluvii testis*. In: Schneer, C. J. (ed.), 1969A, 192–
213, 3 figs.

JAIN, SOHAN LALL   See: Chatterjee, S., Jain, S. L., Kutty, T. S. and Chowdhury, T. K. R., 1969A;
Souza, C., Fausto, L. de and Jain, S. L., 1968A.

JAKOVLEV, V. N.   See: Íakovlev, V. N.

JAKUBOWSKI, GWIDON
1971A   Nowe znalezisko szczątków leśnego nosorożca. [New find of fossils of *Dicerorhinus mercki* (Jäg.)].
Przegl. Geol., 19, 99–101, 3 figs. (Polish).

JAKUBOWSKI, G., KRYSIAK, K. and ROSKOSZ, T.
1968A   The forest elephant – *Palaeoloxodon antiquus* (Falc. et Caut., 1847) from Warsaw. Warsaw, Muz.
Ziemi, Pr., 12, 187–215, 3 figs., 10 pls., 11 tables (Polish summary).

JÁMBOR, A., KORPÁS, L., KRETZOI, M., PÁLFALVY, I. and RÁKOSI, L.
1971A   A dunántúli oligocén képződmények rétegtani problémái. [Stratigraphische Probleme des
transdanubischen Oligozäns]. Hung., Magy. Áll. Földt. Intéz., Évi Jelent. (1969), 141–154
(Hungarian; German summary).

JAMES, EDWIN OLIVER
1965B   From cave to cathedral. Temples and shrines of prehistoric, classical and early Christian times.
London: Thames and Hudson, 404 pp., 48 figs., 152 pls.
Rev.: Goldman in Natur. Hist., 74:10, 9.

JAMMOT, DOMINIQUE   See: Hibbard, C. W. and Jammot, D., 1971A.

JANICKE, VOLKMAR
1970A   Ein *Strobilodus* als Speiballen im Solnhofener Plattenkalk (Tiefes Untertithon, Bayern). Neues Jahrb.
Geol. Paläontol., Monatsh., 1970:1, 61–64, 1 fig. (German; English summary).

JANICKE, V. and SCHAIRER, GERHARD
1970A   Fossilerhaltung und Problematica aus den Solnhofener Plattenkalken. Neues Jahrb. Geol. Paläontol.,
Monatsh., 1970:8, 452–464, 14 figs. (German).
Rev.: Häntzschel in Zentralbl. Geol. Paläontol., Teil 2, 1971:4, 250.

JANICKE, V.   See also: Barthel, K. W. and Janicke, V., 1970A.

JÁNOSSY, DÉNES
1960A   Wirbeltierkleinfauna aus den Moustérien-Schichten der Subalyuk-Höhle (Nordostungarn). Anthropos,
Brno, 1960 Suppl., 71–76, 1 fig. (German; Russian summary).
1969A   Stratigraphische Auswertung der europäischen mittelpleistozänen Wirbeltierfauna. Teil I. Deut. Ges.
Geol. Wiss., Ber., Reihe A, Geol. Paläontol., 14:4, 367–438, 8 figs., 3 tables (German).
Rev.: Thenius in Zentralbl. Geol. Paläontol., Teil 2, 1971:2–3, 190–191.
1969B   Stratigraphische Auswertung der europäischen mittelpleistozänen Wirbeltierfauna. Teil II. Deut. Ges.
Geol. Wiss., Ber., Reihe A, Geol. Paläontol., 14:5, 573–643, 20 figs., 7 pls., 34 tables
(German).
Rev.: Thenius in Zentralbl. Geol. Paläontol., Teil 2, 1971:2–3, 190–191.
1969C   A new eomyid (Rodentia, Mammalia) from the lowest Pleistocene of Hungary. Öslénytani Viták,
13, 5–40 (Hungarian; detailed English abstract).
1969D   Die Grenze Altpleistozän-Mittelpleistozän auf Grund von Kleinvertebratenresten in Ungarn.
In: Mezhdunarodnyĭ kollokvium po geologii i faune nizhnego i srednego pleĭstotsena Evropy.
Tezisy dokladov, 54–56 (German).
1970A   The boundary of lower-middle Pleistocene on the basis of microvertebrates in Hungary.
Palaeogeogr., Palaeoclimatol., Palaeoecol., 8:2–3, 147–152, 1 fig.
1970B   Ein neuer Eomyidae (Rodentia, Mammalia) aus dem Ältestpleistozän ("Oberes Villafrankium",
Villányium) des Osztramos (Nordostungarn). Budapest, Hist.-Natur. Mus. Nat. Hungarica,
Ann., 62, 99–113, 4 figs., 1 pl. (German).
1970-71A   Der erste Nachweis einer kalt-Moustérien Vertebratenfauna in Ungarn (Tokod-Nagyberek, Kom.
Komárom). Vert. Hungarica, 12, 103–110 (German; Hungarian summary).
1972A   Die mittelpleistozäne Vogelfauna der Stránská Skála. In: Musil, R. (ed.), 1972A, 35–64, 6 figs.,
2 pls., 1 table (German).
1972B   Granitsa mezhdu nizhnim i srednim pleĭstotsenom, ustanovlennaiă na osnovanii izucheniiă ostatkov
melkikh pozvonochnykh v Vengrii. [The limit between the lower and middle Pleistocene,
established on the basis of small vertebrate remains study in Hungary.] In: Geologiiă i
fauna nizhnego i srednego pleĭstotsena Evropy, 117–123 (Russian).

JÁNOSSY, D., KROLOPP, E. and BRUNNACKER, K.
    1968A   Die Felsnische Uppony I (Nordungarn). Eiszeitalter Gegenwart, 19, 31–47, 5 figs., 4 tables (German; English summary).
           Rev.: Thenius in Zentralbl. Geol. Paläontol., Teil 2, 1971:2–3, 191–192.

JANOVSKAJA, N. M.   See: Ianovskaia, N. M.

JANSSENS, PAUL A.
    1970A   Palaeopathology. Diseases and injuries of prehistoric man. London: John Baker, xiii + 170 pp., 75 pls.
           Rev.: Ackerman in Quart. Rev. Biol., 46:3, 328; Armelagos in Amer. J. Phys. Anthropol., 35:2, 263–264; Hughes in Nature, 226:5242, 380–381; Merbs in Amer. Anthropol., 73:6, 1425–1426; Roth-Lutra in Anat. Anz., 131:1–2, 163; Sandison in Man (J. Roy. Anthropol. Inst.), 5:4, 707–708; Stewart in Science (AAAS), 168:3938, 1565–1566; Wells in Antiquity, 45:177, 63–64; Wells in Helinium, 10:2, 201–202.

JANTSKY, ZS.   See: Kilényi, I. and Jantsky, Zs. (eds.), 1970A.

JANVIER, PHILIPPE
    1969A   Découverte d'*Amphilagus ulmensis* Tobien dans les Faluns de l'Anjou. Mus. Nat. Hist. Natur., Paris, Bull., 41:4, 999–1003, 2 figs. (French).
    1971A   La position et la forme du sac nasal chez les Osteostraci. Acad. Sci., C.R., Sér. D, 272:19, 2434–2436, 2 figs. (French).
    1971B   Nouveau matériel d'*Andreolepis hedei* Gross, Actinoptérygien énigmatique du Silurien de Gotland (Suède). Acad. Sci., C.R., Sér. D, 273:23, 2223–2224, 1 fig., 1 table (French).
    1971C   Notes sur la géologie et la paléontologie du Miocène de Lisbonne. VIII. Lagomorphes (Lagomorpha, Mammalia). Lisbon, Univ., Fac. Ciênc., Rev., Sér. 2, C (Ciênc. Natur.), 16:2, 311–321, 4 figs. (French).

JANVIER, PHILIPPE and MONTENAT, CHRISTIAN
    1970A   Le plus ancien Léporidé d'Europe Occidentale, *Hispanolagus crusafonti* nov. gen. nov. sp., du Miocène supérieur de Murcia (Espagne). Mus. Nat. Hist. Natur., Paris, Bull., 42:4, 780–788, 5 figs. (French).

JANVIER, PHILIPPE and WELCOMME, J.-L.
    1969A   Affinités et paléobiologie de l'espèce *Carcharodon megalodon* Ag. Squale géant des faluns de la Touraine et de l'Anjou. Faune de France, 8:34, 1–6 (French).

JANVIER, PHILIPPE   See also: Ginsburg, L. and Janvier, Ph., 1970A.

JARCHO, SAUL
    1966A*   Rev.: Hughes in New Sci., 32:522, 471.

JARDINE, N.
    1969A   The observational and theoretical components of homology: a study based on the morphology of the dermal skull-roofs of rhipidistian fishes. Linn. Soc., Biol. J., 1:4, 327–361, 5 figs., 2 tables.
    1971A   The application of Simpson's criterion of consistency to phenetic classifications. Syst. Zool., 20, 70–72, 1 fig.

JARDINE, N. and MCKENZIE, DAN
    1972A   Continental drift and the dispersal and evolution of organisms. Nature, 235:5332, 20–24, 5 figs.

JARMAN, M. R.
    1969A   The prehistory of upper Pleistocene and recent cattle. Part I: east Mediterranean, with reference to north-west Europe. Prehist. Soc., Proc., 35:11, 236–266, 10 figs.

JARMAN, M. R.   See also: Higgs, E. S. and Jarman, M. R., 1969A.

JARVIK, ERIK
    1968A   The systematic position of the Dipnoi. Nobel Symp., 4th, Stockholm, 1967, Proc., 1968, 223–245, 6 figs.
    1968B   Aspects of vertebrate phylogeny. Nobel Symp., 4th, Stockholm, 1967, Proc., 1968, 497–527, 4 figs.

JASCHKE, ADOLF
    1970A   Ein 190 Millionen Jahre altes Reptilienei? Aufschluss, 21:6, 214, 1 fig. (German).

JASTROW, ROBERT
  1968A   Cosmic evolution. Natur. Hist., 77:1, 32–39, illustr.

JAUHARI, ANIL KUMAR   See: Sahni, A., Mehrotra, D. K. and Jauhari, A. K., 1971A.

JAY, PHYLLIS C.
  1968A*   Primates. Studies in adaptation and variability. New York, London: Holt, Rhinehart and Winston,
                  xii + 529 pp., illustr.
                  Rev.: Menzel in Amer. J. Phys. Anthropol., 31, 117–120; Vogel in Z. Morphol. Anthropol., 62:3,
                  342–345.
  1968B   Primate field studies and human evolution. In: Jay, P. C. (ed.), 1968A, 487–503.

JAY, P. C.   See also: Washburn, S. L. and Jay, P. C. (eds.), 1968A.

JEANNET, MARCEL
  1971A   Découverte d'une dent de mammouth à Vaulx-en-Velin (Rhône). Soc. Linn. Lyon, Bull., 40:5, LXV–
                  LXVIII, 2 figs. (French).

JEANRENAUD, P.   See: Macarovici, N. and Jeanrenaud, P., 1968A.

JEFFERIES, R. P. S.
  1969A   L'origine des Vertébrés révélée par l'étude de fossiles étranges jusqu'ici classés dans les Echinodermes.
                  Sci. Progrès La Nature, 3405, 7–10, 6 figs. (French).
  1971A   Some comments on the origin of chordates. J. Paleontol., 45:5, 910–912.

JEFFERSON, GEORGE T.
  1969A   Late Pleistocene mammals from a cave in southern Nevada. Geol. Soc. Amer., Abstr., Part 3, 30 (abs.).
  1971A   New Pleistocene vertebrate sites on the Mojave Desert: a reconnaissance report. Geol. Soc. Amer.,
                  Abstr., 3:2, 140–141 (abs.).

JEFFERSON, G. T.   See also: Reynolds, R. E. and Jefferson, G. T., 1971A, 1971B.

JEHENNE, Y.
  1969A   Étude du gisement de Saint-Capraise d'Eymet en Dordogne. Poitiers, Univ., Inst. Géol. Anthropol.
                  Préhist., Trav., 10, 1–42, 9 figs., 4 pls., 6 tables (French; German and English summaries).
  1970A   Étude de restes de crocodiliens stampiens du Bassin d'Aquitaine. Poitiers, Univ., Inst. Géol. Anthropol.
                  Préhist., Trav., 11, 11 pp., 4 figs., 4 pls., 1 table (French; German summary).

JEHL, JOSEPH R., JR.
  1969A   Fossil grouse of the genus Dendragapus. San Diego Soc. Natur. Hist., Trans., 15:12, 165–174, 2 figs.,
                  7 tables.

JELÍNEK, JAN
  1966A*   Symposium de taxinomie et nomenclature des Hominidés fossiles. Anthropologie, Brno, 3:3, 88 pp.,
                  illustr. (French).
                  Rev.: Vallois in L'Anthropologie, 72:3–4, 361–363.
  1967A   A new discovery of the jaw of an intermediate type of Neanderthal man in Czechoslovakia. Akten des
                  Anthropologischen Kongresses, Brno, 1965. Anthropos, Brno, 19, 148–149, 2 figs.
  1969A   Neanderthal man and Homo sapiens in central and eastern Europe. With comments and reply. Current
                  Anthropol., 10:5, 475–503, 17 figs., 2 tables.
                  Rev.: Anon. in Interamer., 17:3, 8.
  1969B   The Anthropos Institute, Moravian Museum, Brno. Mus., UNESCO, 22:1, 1–9, 11 photos (French and
                  English).

JENKINS, FARISH A., JR.
  1969A   Occlusion in Docodon (Mammalia, Docodonta). Postilla, 139, 24 pp., 15 figs., 1 table.
                  Rev.: Krebs in Zentralbl. Geol. Paläontol., Teil 2, 1971:2–3, 184.
  1970A   Cynodont postcranial anatomy and the "prototherian" level of mammalian organization. Evolution,
                  24:1, 230–252, 3 figs.
  1970B   The Chañares (Argentina) Triassic reptile fauna VII. The postcranial skeleton of the traversodontid
                  Massetognathus pascuali (Therapsida, Cynodontia). Breviora, 352, 1–28, 10 figs.
  1971A   The postcranial skeleton of African cynodonts. Yale Univ., Peabody Mus. Natur. Hist., Bull., 36,
                  x + 216 pp., frontispiece, 62 figs. (German and Russian abstracts).
  1972A   Chimpanzee bipedalism: cineradiographic analysis and implications for the evolution of gait. Science,
                  178:4063, 877–879, 2 figs.

JENKINS, FARISH A.   See also: Hiiemäe, K. and Jenkins, F. A., 1969A.

JENNINGS, JESSE D.
    1969A   Prehistory of North America. New York: McGraw-Hill, xi + 391 pp., illustr.
        Rev.: E. B. in Archeol. Soc. N. J., News., 82, 8; Baerreis in Amer. Anthropol., 71, 558–559; Bass in
        Amer. J. Phys. Anthropol., 29, 452–453; Grange in Science (AAAS), 165:3899, 1248; Longacre
        in Amer. J. Archaeol., 73:2, 259–260.

JENNINGS, JESSE DAVID and HOEBEL, E. ADAMSON
    1972A   Readings in anthropology. Third edition. New York: McGraw-Hill, 489 pp.

JENSEN, JAMES A.
    1966A   Dinosaur eggs from the upper Cretaceous North Horn formation of central Utah. Brigham Young
        Univ. Geol. Studies, 13, 55–67, 2 figs., 4 pls.
    1969A   Discovery of extensive dinosaur egg materials in the upper and lower Cretaceous of Utah. Geol. Soc.
        Amer., Abstr., 121, 607–608 (abs.).
    1969B   Fossil eggs from Utah and a concept of surviving feathered reptiles. Utah Acad. Sci., Proc., 46:1,
        125–133.
    1970A   Fossil eggs in the lower Cretaceous of Utah. Brigham Young Univ. Geol. Studies, 17:1, 51–65, 5 figs.,
        3 pls.
    1972A   Discovery of the one-toothed jaw of Coalsack Bluff. Explorer (Cleveland Mus. Natur. Hist.), 14:2,
        5–8, 5 figs.

JENSEN, JAMES A.   See also: Elliot, D. H., Colbert, E. H., Breed, W. J., Jensen, J. A. and Powell, J. S., 1970A.

JEPSEN, GLENN L.
    1970A   Bat origins and evolution. In: Wimsatt, Wm. (ed.), 1970A, 1–64, 19 figs., 1 table.

JEPSEN, GLENN L. and WOODBURNE, MICHAEL O.
    1969A   Paleocene hyracothere from Polecat Bench formation, Wyoming. Science (AAAS), 164:3879, 543–
        547, 1 fig., 2 tables.

JERISON, HARRY J.
    1969A   Brain evolution and dinosaur brains. Amer. Natur., 103, 575–588, 4 figs.
    1970A   Gross brain indices and the analysis of fossil endocasts. In: Noback, C. R. and Montagna, W. (eds.),
        1970A, 225–244, 5 figs., 1 table.
    1971A   Quantitative analysis of the evolution of the camelid brain. Amer. Natur., 105:943, 227–239,
        4 figs., 2 tables.

JERZMAŃSKA, ANNA
    1968A   Ichtyofaune des couches à ménilite (flysch des Karpathes). Acta Palaeontol. Pol., 13:3, 379–496,
        23 figs., 7 pls., 9 tables (French; Polish and Russian summaries).
        Rev.: Weiler in Zentralbl. Geol. Paläontol., Teil 2, 1969:3, 284–285.

JESSEN, HANS
    1968A   A Devonian osteolepidid fish from British Columbia. Can., Geol. Surv., Bull., 165, 65–70, 1 fig., 1 pl.
    1968B   *Moythomasia nitida* Gross und *M.* cf. *striata* Gross, devonische Palaeonisciden aus dem oberen
        Plattenkalk der Bergisch-Gladbach-Paffrather Mulde (Rheinisches Schiefergebirge).
        Palaeontographica, Abt. A, 128:4–6, 87–114, 8 figs., 7 pls. (German; English summary).
    1972A   Schultergürtel und Pectoralflosse bei Actinopterygiern. Fossils and Strata, 1, 101 pp., 13 figs., 25 pls.
        (German; Russian and English summaries).

JIMÉNEZ FUENTES, EMILIANO
    1968A   *Stereogenys salmanticensis* nov. sp., quelonio eocénico del valle del Duero. Estud. Geol. (Inst. Invest.
        "Lucas Mallada"), 24:3/4, 191–203, 8 figs., 4 tables (Spanish).
    1970A   Los reptiles fósiles del valle del Duero. Sobre un cuarto paratipo casi completo de *Stereogenys*
        salmanticensis, Jim. Estud. Geol. (Inst. Invest. Geol. "Lucas Mallada"), 26:3, 245–259, 7 figs.,
        3 tables (Spanish).
    1971A   Los reptiles fósiles del valle del Duero: *Podocnemis carbajosai,* nov. sp., del Eoceno de Salamanca.
        Estud. Geol. (Inst. Invest. Geol. "Lucas Mallada"), 27:1, 85–93, 6 figs. (Spanish; English
        summary).
    1971B   Primer pseudotrionyx español: *Allaeochelys casasecai,* nov. sp. del Luteciense de Corrales (Zamora).
        Estud. Geol. (Inst. Invest. Geol. "Lucas Mallada"), 27:2, 153–166, 10 figs., 3 tables (Spanish).

JOHANSON, D. CARL   See: Taieb, M., Coppens, Y., Johanson, D. C. and Kalb, J., 1972A.

JOHN, B. S.
    1971A   The 'Red Lady' of Paviland: a comment. Antiquity, 45:178, 141–144, 1 fig.

JOHNSON, ALFRED E.
     1966A   Archaeology of Sonora, Mexico. Handbk. Mid. Amer. Ind., 4, 26–37, 4 figs.

JOHNSON, GARY D.
     1972A   Phyllodont tooth plate from the lower Cretaceous of Texas. Tex. J. Sci., 24:1, 67–74, 3 figs.

JOHNSON, GARY D.   See also: Vondra, C. F., Johnson, G. D., Bowen, B. E. and Behrensmeyer, A. K., 1971A.

JOHNSON, HOPE
     1969A   A paleontological holiday: a visit to the Hunter quarry near Eastend. Blue Jay, 27:1, 7–11, 4 figs.

JOHNSON, RALPH G.
     1969A   The amazing fossils of Mazon Creek. Geol. Soc. Amer., Abstr., 121, 151–152 (abs.).

JOHNSON, RALPH G.   See also: Richardson, E. S., Jr. and Johnson, R. G., 1971A.

JOHNSTON, BERNICE
     1969A   I'll take the low road. Desert Mag., 32:5, 6–11, 8 figs.

JOLLIE, MALCOLM
     1968A   Some implications of the acceptance of a delamination principle. Nobel Symp., 4th, Stockholm, 1967,
                    Proc., 1968, 89–107, 12 figs.
     1968B   The head skeleton of a new-born *Manis javanica* with comments on the ontogeny and phylogeny of
                    the mammal head skeleton. Acta Zool., 49:3, 227–305, 15 figs., 1 table.
     1971A   A theory concerning the early evolution of the visceral arches. Acta Zool., 52:1, 85–96, 9 figs.

JOLLY, CLIFFORD J.
     1970A   The seedeaters: a new model of hominid differentiation based on a baboon analogy. Man (J. Roy.
                    Anthropol. Inst.), 5:1, 5–26, 1 fig., 1 table.
     1970B   Hominid evolution. Man (J. Roy. Anthropol. Inst.), 5:3, 518–519.
     1970C   *Hadropithecus:* a lemuroid small-object feeder. Man (J. Roy. Anthropol. Inst.), 5:4, 619–626, 3 figs.,
                    1 plate.
     1970D   The large African monkeys as an adaptive array. In: Napier, J. R. and Napier, P. H. (eds.), 1970A,
                    139–174, 7 figs.

JOLY, J.
     1970A   Informations archéologiques. Circonscription de Bourgogne. Gallia Préhist., 13:2, 411–458, 37 figs.
                    (French).

JONES, FREDERIC WOOD
     1972A   Man's relationship to the anthropoid apes. Conclusion. In: McCown, T. D. and Kennedy, K. A. R.
                    (eds.), 1972A, 302–321, 1 fig. (reprinted from Jones, 1929).

JONES, J. KNOX, JR.
     1969A*   Contributions in mammalogy. A volume honoring professor E. Raymond Hall. Kans., Univ., Mus.
                    Natur. Hist., Misc. Publ., 51, 428 pp., 122 figs.

JONES, J. KNOX, JR. and GENOWAYS, HUGH H.
     1970A   Chiropteran systematics. In: Slaughter, B. H. and Walton, D. W. (eds.), 1970A, 3–21, 9 figs., 1 table.

JONES, J. KNOX, JR.   See also: Dort, W., Jr. and Jones, J. K., Jr. (eds.), 1970A; Hoffmann, R. S. and
                    Jones, J. K., Jr., 1970A; Koopman, K. F. and Jones, J. K., Jr., 1970A.

JONES, R. D.   See: Vlademar, A. E. and Jones, R. D., 1970A.

JONES, RHYS
     1968A   The geographical background to the arrival of man in Australia and Tasmania. Archaeol., Phys.
                    Anthropol. Oceania, 3:3, 186–215, 6 figs., 1 table.

JONES, RHYS   See also: Bowler, J. M., Jones, R., Allen, H. and Thorne, A. G., 1970A.

JONES, ROBERT W. and BOWERS, ALFRED W.
     1968A   Mammoth from Pleistocene spring deposits, Soda Springs, Idaho. Northwest Sci., 42:1, 35 (abs.).

JONET, SIMON
     1968A   Notes d'ichthyologie miocène portugaise. IV. Les Labridae. Soc. Geol. Port., Bol., 16:3, 209–220,
                    1 pl. (French).

Rev.: Weiler in Zentralbl. Geol. Paläontol., Teil 2, 1969:3, 285.

1968B Notes d'ichthyologie miocène Portugaise. V. — Quelques batoïdes. Lisbon, Univ., Fac. Sci., Rev., Sér. 2, C (Ciênc. Natur.), 15:2, 233—258, 3 figs., 1 pl., 1 table (French).

Rev.: Weiler in Zentralbl. Geol. Paläontol., Teil 2, 1970:3/4, 225.

1971A Considérations préliminaires sur des vertébrés cénomaniens des environs de Lisbonne. Soc. Geol. Port., Bol., 17:2—3, 177—180 (French).

JONET, S. See also: Telles Antunes, M. and Jonet, S., 1970A.

JONG, C. G. VAN ZYLL DE
1972A A systematic review of the Nearctic and Neotropical river otters (Genus Lutra, Mustelidae, Carnivora). Toronto, Roy. Ont. Mus., Life Sci., Contrib., 80, 104 pp., 38 figs., 3 tables.

JORDÁ CERDÁ, FRANCISCO
1964D El arte rupestre paleolítico de la región cantábrica: nueva secuencia cronológico-cultural. In: Pericot García, L. and Ripoll Perelló, E. (eds.), 1964A, 47—81, 3 tables (Spanish; English summary).

JORDÁ CERDÁ, F., MALLO, M. and PEREZ, M.
1970A Les grottes du Pozo del Ramu et de la Lloseta (Asturies, Espagne) et ses représentations rupestres paléolithiques. Préhist. Spéléol. Ariége., 25, 95—139, 30 figs. (French).

JÖRG, ERWIN
1969A Eine Fischfauna aus dem Oberen Buntsandstein (Unter-Trias) von Karlsruhe-Durlach (Nordbaden). Naturk. Forsch. Südwestdeutschland, Beitr., 28:2, 87—102, 4 pls. (German).
1970A Fischfunde im oberen Buntsandstein (Untertrias) von Karlsruhe-Durlach. Deut. Geol. Ges., Z., 121, 105—110, 3 figs. (German).
1971A Ein Cranium von Coelodonta antiquitatis (Blumenb.) (Perissodactyla, Mamm.) aus pleistozänen Neckarkiesen von Mannheim-Käfertal. Hess. Landesamt Bodenforsch., Abh., 60, 83—88, 1 pl. (German).

JOSHI, R. V. and SALI, S. A.
1971A Fossils and middle Stone Age tools from Nandur-Madhmeshwar on the Godavari River (Nasik district, Maharashtra state). Curr. Sci., 40:1, 13—14, 4 figs.

JOSSELYN, DANIEL W.
1968A Progress in archaeological dating. Anthropol. J. Can., 6:3, 32.
1969A More on an "ice bridge" entry into America. Anthropol. J. Can., 7:3, 32.
1969B Life on the Arctic ice floes. Anthropol. J. Can., 7:1, 32.

JOYSEY, K. A.
1972A The fossil species in time and space: some problems of evolutionary interpretation among Pleistocene mammals. In: Joysey, K. A. and Kemp, T. S. (eds.), 1972A, 267—280, 7 figs.

JOYSEY, K. A. and KEMP, T. S.
1972A* Studies in vertebrate evolution. Edinburgh: Oliver and Boyd, 284 pp., illustr.
Rev.: Kermack in Nature, 239:5368, 176.

JUDD, FRANK See: Dalquest, W. W., Roth, E. and Judd, F., 1969A.

JUDE, P. E.
1961A La vie et les menus des Paléolithiques. Les Eyzies, 10, 98—104 (French).
1962A Le déclin du Würmien et ses conséquences. Les Eyzies, 11, 50—56 (French).

JUKES, THOMAS H. See: King, J. L. and Jukes, T. H., 1969A.

JULLIEN, ROBERT
1965B Rev.: Sauter in Schweiz. Ges. Urgesch., Jahrb., 53, 190.
1966A Considérations sur l'origine de l'homme et l'apparition de l'Homo sapiens. Lisbon, Univ., Fac. Letr., Rev., Sér. 3, 10, 27—33 (French).

JULLIEN, R. and PILLARD, BRIGITTE
1969A Les lagomorphes découverts sur le sol de la cabane acheuléenne du Lazaret. In: Lumley, H. de (ed.), 1969B, 75—83, 4 figs., 2 tables (French).
1969B Les insectivores et les chiroptères découverts sur le sol de la cabane acheuléenne du Lazaret. In: Lumley, H. de (ed.), 1969B, 95, 1 fig. (French).

JULLIEN, R. See also: Beaufort, F. de and Jullien, R., 1968A.

JUNG, W.   See: German, R., Filzer, P., Dehm, R., Freude, H., Jung, W. and Witt, W., 1968A.

JURCSÁK, T.   See: Macarovici, N. and Jurcsák, T., 1968A; Terzea, E. and Jurcsák, T., 1967A, 1968A, 1969A.

JUX, U.   See: Ahorner, L. and Jux, U. (eds.), 1967A.

KABO, V. R.
    1969A   Proiskhozhdenie i ranniaĩa istoriiã aborigenov Avstralii. [The origin and early history of Australian
                 aborigines.] Moscow: "Nauka" Press, 408 pp., illustr. (Russian).
                 Rev.: Alekseev in Sov. Etnogr., 1970:2, 195–197 (Russian).

KACHROO, R. K.   See: Dixit, P. C., Kachroo, R. K., Rai, H. and Sharma, N. L., 1971A.

KADYROV, M. KH.   See: Kambariddinov, R. K., Kadyrov, M. Kh., Aripov, A. A. and Sharakhmedov, Sh. Sh., 1971A.

KAFRI, U.   See: Issar, A. and Kafri, U., 1969A.

KAHANE, P. P.
    1967A   The Samuel Bronfman Biblical and Archaeological Museum. Mus., UNESCO, 20:1, 16–24, illustr.
                 (French and English; Spanish and Russian summaries).

KAHLER, MARIE-LUISE
    1969A   Das Pleistozän von Süssenborn. Fossile Backenzahnfunde aus Süssenborn in Goethes Mineraliensammlung
                 und deren Bedeutung für Goethe. Paläontol. Abh., Abt. A, 3:3–4, 385–389, 5 figs. II Internat.
                 Kolloquium 1966 in Weimar (German).

KAHLKE, HANS-DIETRICH
    1960B   The early middle Pleistocene mammalian fauna of Süssenborn. Anthropos, Brno, 1960 Suppl., 77–99,
                 5 figs., 11 pls. (Russian summary).
    1967A   Ausgrabungen auf vier Kontinenten. Leipzig-Jena-Berlin: Urania Verlag, 218 pp., 48 pls. (German).
                 Rev.: KV in Archeol. Roz., 21:5, 687.
    1968A   Vertebratenstratigraphie zur Pliozän/Pleistozän-Grenze. Int. Geol. Congr., 23rd, Czech., Rep., Abstr.,
                 sec. 10, 278–279 (German).
    1968B   Vertebratenstratigraphie zur Plio/Pleistozän-Grenze. Int. Geol. Congr., 23rd, Czech., Rep., Proc., 10,
                 27–39 (German).
    1969A*   Das Pleistozän von Süssenborn. II. Internationales Paläontologisches Kolloquium 1966. Paläontol.
                 Abh., Abt. A, 3:3–4, 367–788, 190 figs., 46 pls. (German).
                 Rev.: Thenius in Zentralbl. Geol. Paläontol., Teil 2, 1970:3/4, 233–234.
    1969B   Das Pleistozän von Süssenborn. Die Ovibos - Reste aus den Kiesen von Süssenborn bei Weimar.
                 Paläontol. Abh., Abt. A, 3:3–4, 521–529, 3 figs., 2 pls. II Internat. Paläont. Kolloquium 1966
                 in Weimar (German; Russian and English summaries).
                 Rev.: Thenius in Zentralbl. Geol. Paläontol., Teil 2, 1971:1, 70.
    1969C   Das Pleistozän von Süssenborn. Die Soergelia - Reste aus den Kiesen von Süssenborn bei Weimar.
                 Paläontol. Abh., Abt. A, 3:3–4, 531–545, 8 figs., 4 pls. II Internat. Paläont. Kolloquium 1966
                 in Weimar (German; Russian and English summaries).
                 Rev.: Thenius in Zentralbl. Geol. Paläontol., Teil 2, 1971:1, 70.
    1969D   Das Pleistozän von Süssenborn. Die Cerviden - Reste aus den Kiesen von Süssenborn bei Weimar.
                 Paläontol. Abh., Abt. A, 3:3–4, 547–610, 36 figs., 10 pls. II Internat. Paläont. Kolloquium
                 1966 in Weimar (German; Russian and English summaries).
    1969E   Das Pleistozän von Süssenborn. Die Rhinocerotiden - Reste aus den Kiesen von Süssenborn bei
                 Weimar. Paläontol. Abh., Abt. A, 3:3–4, 667–709, 30 figs., 4 pls. II Internat. Paläont.
                 Kolloquium 1966 in Weimar (German; Russian and English summaries).
    1969F   Das Pleistozän von Süssenborn. Die stratigraphische Stellung der Kiese von Süssenborn bei Weimar.
                 Paläontol. Abh., Abt. A, 3:3–4, 787–788. II Internat. Paläont. Kolloquium 1966 in Weimar
                 (German).
    1971A   Nakhodka iskopaemogo slona v Orlishausene. [The find of a fossil elephant in Orlishausen.] Priroda,
                 1971:2, 63–65, 3 figs., portr. (Russian).

KAHLKE, H-D.   See also: David, A. I. and Kahlke, H.-D., 1969A.

KAHN, THEODORE C.
    1972A   An introduction to hominology, the study of the whole man. Second edition. Springfield, Ill.:
                 Charles C. Thomas, xvii + 384 pp., 23 figs., 8 tables.

KAĬIALAĬNEN, V. I. and KULAKOV, IŪ. N.

1965A   Osnovnye cherty istorii geologicheskogo razvitiĭa Ĭano-Indigirskoĭ (Primorskoĭ) nizmennosti v neogen-chetvertichnoe vremĭa. [Main features of the history of geological development of Ĭana-Indigirka (Maritime) lowlands in Neogene-Quaternary time.] Nauch.-Issled. Inst. Geol. Arktiki, Tr., 143, 56—64, 1 fig. (Russian; English summary).

KAISER, HANS E.

1970A   Vergleichende Untersuchungen über die Knochenstruktur der Pinnipedia: Über die Knochenstruktur des Schädels vom Walross, *Odobenus rosmarus* L. Anat. Anz., 127:1, 1—21, 12 figs. (German; English summary).

1970B   Das Abnorme in der Evolution. Acta Biotheoret., 17 suppl. 1, 623 pp., 328 figs., 2 pls. (German). Rev.: Roth-Lutra in Anat. Anz., 131:1—2, 173—174.

KAISER, KARLHEINZ

1967A   Das Klima Europas im quartären Eiszeitalter. Fundamenta, Reihe B, 2, 1—27, 5 figs., 2 tables (German).

KALABIS, VLADIMÍR

1966A   Předběžná zpráva o rybí fauně v ždánicko-hustopečském souvrství na lokalitě Krumvíř. [Preliminary report on fish fauna from Ždanice-Hustopeč beds at Krumvíř locality.] Czech., Ustřed. Ústav Geol., Zprávy Geol. Výzk., 1964:1, 321—322 (Czech).

KALANDADZE, NIKOLAĬ NIKOLAEVICH

1969A   Triasovye kannemeĭeridy ĭuzhnogo Priural'ĭa. [Triassic kannemeyerids of southern Urals region.] Mosk. Obshchest. Ispyt. Prir., Biull., Otd. Geol., 44:6, 148 (Russian).

1970A   Novye triasovye kannemeĭeridy ĭuzhnogo Priural'ĭa. [New Triassic kannemeyerids from southern Cisuralia.] In: Materialy po evolĭutsii nazemnykh pozvonochnykh, 51—57, 6 figs. (Russian).

KALANDADZE, N. N., OCHEV, V. G., TATARINOV, L. P., CHUDINOV, P. K. and SHISHKIN, M. A.

1968A   Katalog permskikh i triasovykh tetrapod SSSR. [Catalogue of Permian and Triassic tetrapods of the USSR.] In: Verkhnepaleozoĭskie i mezozoĭskie zemnovodnye i presmykaĭushchiesĭa SSSR, 72—91 (Russian).

KALANDADZE, N. N. and RESHETOV, V. IŪ.

1971A   Nakhodki drevneĭshikh mlekopitaĭushchikh v Gobi. [Finds of the oldest mammals in Gobi.] Priroda, 1971:4, 106—107 (Russian).

1971B   Interesnye paleontologicheskie nakhodki v Mongolii. [Interesting paleontological finds in Mongolia.] Priroda, 1971:5, 83—84, 1 fig. (Russian).

KALANDADZE, N. N.   See also: Danilov, A. I. and Kalandadze, N. N., 1970A; Kurochkin, E. N., Kalandadze, N. N. and Reshetov, V. Ĭu., 1970A.

KALB, JON   See: Taieb, M., Coppens, Y., Johanson, D. C. and Kalb, J., 1972A.

KALECHITS, E. G.   See: Voznĭachuk, L. N., Shcheglova, V. V. and Kalechits, E. G., 1972A.

KALLAY, J.

1969A   Two sets of upper incisors of two neanderthalers from Krapina. Akad. savet FNRJ., Bull. Sci., Sec. A, 14:3—4, 71—73, 3 figs., 1 table.

1970A   A new classification of the taurodont teeth of the Krapina Neanderthal man. Akad. savet FNRJ., Bull. Sci., Sec. A, 15:1—2, 2—3, 3 figs.

1970B   Anthropologische Betrachtungen über die Lage des Unterkieferastes. Akad. savet FNRJ., Bull. Sci., Sec. A, 15:3—4, 75—76, 1 fig. (German).

1970C   Komparative Bemerkungen über die Kiefer der Urmenschen von Krapina mit Berücksichtigung auf ihre Stellung unter den Hominiden. Krapina, 153—164, 20 figs. (Serbocroatian; English summary). Rev.: Kochansky-Devidé in Zentralbl. Geol. Paläontol., Teil 2, 1971:5, 418.

1970D   Die Eigentümlichkeiten der Zähne der Neandertaler von Krapina. Krapina, 165—176, 2 pls. (Serbocroatian; English summary). Rev.: Kochansky-Devidé in Zentralbl. Geol. Paläontol., Teil 2, 1971:5, 418.

1970E   Paläostomatologische Eigentümlichkeiten der Neandertaler aus Krapina. Krapina, 201—206, 2 pls. (Serbocroatian; German and English summaries). Rev.: Kochansky-Devidé in Zentralbl. Geol. Paläontol., Teil 2, 1971:5, 418—419.

KAMBARIDDINOV, R. K.

1969A   Iskopaemaĭa kost' loshadi iz Tadzhikistana. [Fossil bone of horse from Tadzhikistan.] Akad. Nauk Uzb. SSR, Dokl., 1969:5, 43—45, 1 fig., 1 table (Russian; Uzbek summary).

1969B   Poslednie nakhodki iskopaemykh mlekopitaiushchikh antropogena Pavlodarskogo Priirtysh'ia i ikh
stratigraficheskoe polozhenie. [Recent findings of fossil mammals of Anthropogene age of
Pavlodar Priirtysh'e and their stratigraphic position.] In: Gidrogeologiia i inzhenernaia
geologiia aridnoi zony SSSR, 5, 173—180 (Russian).

KAMBARIDDINOV, R. K., KADYROV, M. KH., ARIPOV, A. A. and SHARAKHMEDOV, SH. SH.
1971A   O nakhodke kostnykh ostatkov drevnechetvertichnogo vozrasta v iuzhnoi Fergane. [On the find of
early Quaternary bone remains in southern Fergana.] Akad. Nauk Uzb. SSR, Dokl., 1971:5,
43—44, 1 fig. (Russian).

KAMBARIDDINOV, R. K. and KAMBARIDDINOVA, T. K.
1969A   O faune i stratigrafii kainozoiskikh molass Pritashkentskogo raiona. [On the fauna and stratigraphy of
Cenozoic molass of Tashkent region.] Uzbek. Geol. Zh., 1969:6, 25—28, 2 figs. (Russian;
Uzbek summary).
1970A   O nizhnei granitse antropogena i stratigrafii lessovykh porod Srednei Azii s faunisticheskim
obosnovaniem. [On the lower boundary of the Anthropogene and the stratigraphy of loess of
middle Asia on faunistic basis.] Mezhdunar. Simp. Litol. Genez. Less. Porod, T. 1, 224—232
(Russian).

KAMBARIDDINOV, R. K. and SHARAKHMEDOV, SH. SH.
1971A   Novye dannye o vozraste mirzarabatskoi serii v Pritashkentskom raione. [New data on the age of
Mirzarabat series in Tashkent region.] Tashkent, Univ., Nauch. Tr., 405, 191—192 (Russian).

KAMBARIDDINOV, R. K.   See also: Mavlianov, G. A., Kambariddinov, R. K. and Mirzabaev, Kh., 1968A.

KAMBARIDDINOVA, T. K. and TALIPOV, M. A.
1969A   Faunisticheskie i sporovo-pyl'tsevye kompleksy chetvertichnykh (antropogenovykh) otlozhenii
vostochnoi chasti Issykkul'skoi vpadiny. [Faunistic and spore-pollen complexes of Quaternary
(Anthropogene) deposits of the eastern part of Issyk-kul' basin.] In: Gidrogeologiia i
inzhenernaia geologiia aridnoi zony SSSR, 5, 169—172 (Russian).

KAMBARIDDINOVA, T. K.   See also: Kambariddinov, R. K. and Kambariddinova, T. K., 1969A, 1970A.

KAMEI, TADAO
1962A   Some problems on the succession of the Quaternary mammalian faunas in Japan. Earth Sci.
(Chikyū Kagaku), 61, 23—34, 5 figs. (Japanese; English summary).
1971A   Pleistocene crocodile from Kinki district, central Japan. In: Minato, M., et al. (eds.), 1968A, 97, 7 figs.

KAMIYA, TOSHIRO   See: Ogawa, T., Kamiya, T., Sakai, S. and Hosokawa, H., 1970A.

KAMPA, ENGELBERT
1971A   "Fossilien" aus Kunststoff. Kosmos (Stuttgart), 67:6, 245—246, 3 figs. (German).

KAMSHILOV, M. M.
1970A   Organizovannost' i evoliutsiia. [Organization and evolution.] Zh. Obshch. Biol., 31:2, 157—178
(Russian; English summary).

KANIE, Y.   See: Hasegawa, Y. and Kanie, Y., 1971A.

KANIVETS, V. I.
1969A   Issledovaniia v Pechorskom pripoliarnom raione. [Research in Pechora sub-polar region.] In:
Rybakov, B. A. (ed.), 1969A, 3—4 (Russian).

KANNO, SABURO   See: Shikama, T. and Kanno, S., 1970A.

KANTMAN, SÖNMEZ
1969A   Essai sur la formation de concept du "type" dans l'étude du Paléolithique. Quartär, 20, 69—77
(French).

KAPLAN, MARTIN M.   See: Moorhead, P. S. and Kaplan, M. M., 1967A.

KAPOOR, A. S.
1970A   Development of dermal bones related to sensory canals of the head in the fishes Ophicephalus punctatus
Bloch (Ophicephalidae) and Wallago attu Bl. & Schn. (Siluridae). Linn. Soc., Zool. J., 49:2,
69—97, 47 figs., 4 pls.

KAPOOR, HARI MOHAN
1965A   Habitat of Amblypterus kashmirensis Woodward and Amblypterus symmetricus Woodward.
J. Palaeontol. Soc. India, 10, 51.

KAPOOR, HARI MOHAN and SAHNI, ASHOK
    1971A   A shark tooth from Zewan series of Guryul Ravine, Kashmir. Kyoto, Univ., Fac. Sci., Mem., Ser.
           Geol. Mineral., 38:1, 163—166, 1 fig.

KAPP, RONALD O.
    1970A   A 24,000-year-old Jefferson mammoth from Midland County, Michigan. Mich. Acad., 3:2, 95—99,
           3 figs.
    1970B   Pollen analysis of pre-Wisconsin sediments from the Great Plains. In: Dort, W., Jr. and Jones,
           J. K., Jr. (eds.), 1970, 143—155, 3 figs.

KARABALAEV, K. K.   See: Kuznetsov, V. V., Karabalaev, K. K. and Ibragimov, I. M., 1964A.

KARASZEWSKI, WŁADYSŁAW
    1969A   [Tracks of Reptilia in the lower Liassic of the Świętokrzyskie Mountains, middle Poland.] Kwart.
           Geol. (Pol., Inst. Geol.), 13:1, 115—119, 4 figs. (Polish; Russian and English summaries).

KARATAJŪTÉ-TALIMAA, VALENTINA NIKOLAEVNA
    1968A   O stratigraficheskom polozhenii i korreliatsii dauntonskikh otlozhenii (miniiaskie i iuraskie sloi) iuzhnoi
           Pribaltiki. [On the stratigraphic position and correlation of Downtonian deposits (Minija and
           Jūra beds) of the southern Baltic area.] In: Stratigrafiia nizhnego paleozoia Pribaltiki i
           korreliatsiia s drugimi regionami, 273—285, 2 tables (Russian and English).
    1968B   Novye telodonty, geterostraki i artrodiry iz chortkovskogo gorizonta Podolii. [New thelodonts,
           heterostracans and arthrodires from Chortkov horizon of Podolia.] In: Ocherki po filogenii i
           sistematike iskopaemykh ryb i bezcheliustnykh, 33—42, 4 figs., 5 pls. (Russian).
    1968C   Smena ikhtiofauny na granitse silura i devona v Evrope (po materialam ludlova-dauntona-dittona
           Pribaltiki i Podolii). [Change of the ichthyofauna at the Silurian-Devonian boundary in Europe
           (according to the materials of the Ludlowian-Downtonian-Dittonian of the eastern Baltic area
           and Podolia).] In: Stratigrafiia nizhnego paleozoia Tsentral'noi Evropy, 149—152, 1 table
           (Russian; English summary).
    1970A   Ikhtiofauna dauntona Litvy, Estonii i Severnogo Timana. [Downtonian fish fauna of Lithuania,
           Estonia and North-Timan.] Paleontol. Stratigr. Pribalt. Beloruss., 2, 33—66, 14 figs., 2 pls.
           (Russian; English summary).

KARATAJŪTÉ-TALIMAA, V. N.   See also: Obruchev, D. V. and Karatajūté-Talimaa, V. N., 1968A, 1967A.

KARLOV, N. N.
    1968A   Ikhtiodorulit *Gyracanthus formosus* Agassiz iz Donetskogo karbona. [Ichthyodorulite of *Gyracanthus*
           formosus Agassiz from the Donets basin Carboniferous.] Paleontol. Sb., 5:1, 107—109, 1 fig.
           (Russian; English summary).
    1971A   Dokumenty pliotsenovoi pustyni na iuge SSSR. [Documents of a Pliocene desert in the south of the
           USSR.] In: Prirodnye i trudovye resursy Levoberezhnoi Ukrainy i ikh ispol'zovanie, 10, 138—
           142 (Russian).

KARP, WALTER
    1965A   The Smithsonian Institution. Washington: Smithsonian Institution, 125 pp., illustr.
    1968A   Charles Darwin and the origin of the species. New York: Harper and Row, 153 pp., illustr.
           (juvenile).
           Rev.: Hatch in Biologist, 51:4, 156; Neill in Audubon Mag., 70:3, 105.

KARRER, CHRISTINE
    1971A   Die Otolithen der Moridae (Teleostei, Gadiformes) und ihre systematische Bedeutung. Zool. Jahrb.,
           Abt. Syst. Ökol. Geogr. Tiere, 98:2, 153—204 (German; English summary).

KASHINA, T. I.   See: Larichev, V. E. and Kashina, T. I., 1969A.

KASYMOV, M. R.
    1969A   Issledovanie mnogosloinoi paleoliticheskoi stoianki Kul'bulak. [Research on the multi-layered
           Paleolithic site Kul'bulak.] In: Rybakov, B. A. (ed.), 1969A, 408—409 (Russian).

KASZAP, A.
    1968A   Rev.: Bogsch in Zentralbl. Geol. Paläontol., Teil 2, 1971:5, 395.

KATO, A.   See: Ozaki, H., Kato, A. and Obata, I., 1965A.

KAUP, LOTHAR   See: Herre, W. and Kaup, L., 1969A.

KAVANAUGH, DAVID H.
1972A   Hennig's principles and methods of phylogenetic systematics. Biologist, 54:3, 115—127, 1 fig.

KAYE, JOHN M.
1971A   A peccary from the Pleistocene or Holocene of Mississippi. Tulane Stud. Geol. Paleontol., 8:4, 219—
           220, 1 fig.

KAZANTSEVA, AL'VINA ALEKSANDROVNA
1968A   Paleonistsidy bystrianskoĭ svity Minusinskikh kotlovin. [Palaeoniscids of Bystraia formation of the
           Minusinsk troughs.] In: Ocherki po filogenii i sistematike iskopaemykh ryb i bezcheliustnykh,
           87—112, 22 figs., 10 pls. (Russian).
1971A   K sistematike Palaeonisciformes. [On the taxonomy of Palaeonisciformes.] Akad. Nauk SSSR,
           Paleontol. Inst., Tr., 130, 160—167, 7 figs. (Russian).
1971B   Pamiàti D. V. Obrucheva (26 iiulià 1900g.—21 dekabrià 1970g.) [In memoriam D. V. Obruchev
           (26 July 1900—21 December 1970]. Vop. Ikhtiol., 11:69, 728—732, portr. (Russian).

KAZARINOV, V. P.
1967A   Melovaià sistema. Chulymo-Eniseĭskaià vpadina. [Cretaceous system. Chulym-Eniseĭ depression.]
           Geologiià SSSR, 14, Western Siberia (southern part), 327—335, 1 table (Russian).

KAŹMIERCZAK, JÓZEF   See: Gradziński, R., Kaźmierczak, J. and Lefeld, J., 1968A.

KAZ'MINA, TAT'IÀNA ALEKSEEVNA
1969A   K stratigrafii neogen-chetvertichnykh otlozheniĭ Zapadno-Sibirskoĭ nizmennosti po faune ostrakod.
           [Stratigraphy of Neogene-Quaternary deposits of west Siberian lowlands based on ostracod
           fauna.] In: Problemy chetvertichnoĭ geologii Sibiri, 55—62, 1 table (Russian; English summary).

KEAST, ALLEN
1968A   Evolution of mammals on southern continents. I. Introduction: the southern continents as background
           for mammalian evolution. Quart. Rev. Biol., 43:3, 225—233, 1 fig.
1968B   Evolution of mammals on southern continents. IV. Australian mammals: zoogeography and evolution.
           Quart. Rev. Biol., 43:4, 373—408, 13 figs., 6 tables.
1971A   Continental drift and the evolution of the biota on southern continents. Quart. Rev. Biol., 46:4,
           335—378, 4 figs.
           Rev.: S. M. in Emu, 72:4, 187—189.
1972A   Introduction: the southern continents as backgrounds for mammalian evolution. In: Keast, A., Erk,
           F. C. and Glass, B. (eds.), 1972A, 19—22, 1 fig.
1972B   Continental drift and the evolution of the biota on southern continents. In: Keast, A., Erk, F. C. and
           Glass, B. (eds.), 1972A, 23—87, 4 figs.
1972C   Australian mammals: zoogeography and evolution. In: Keast, A., Erk, F. C. and Glass, B. (eds.),
           1972A, 195—246, 13 figs., 5 tables.

KEAST, A., ERK, F. C. and GLASS, B.
1972A*   Evolution, mammals, and southern continents. Albany, New York: State University of New York
           Press, illustr.

KEEL, BENNIE C.   See: Fryxell, R., Bielicki, T., Daugherty, R. D., Gustafson, C. E., Irwin, H. T. and
           Keel, B. C., 1968A; Fryxell, R., Bielicki, T., Daugherty, R. D., Gustafson, C. E., Irwin, H. T.,
           Keel, B. C. and Krantz, G. S., 1968A.

KEENE, HARRIS J.
1967A   Australopithecine dental dimensions in a contemporary population. Amer. J. Phys. Anthropol., 27,
           379—384, 1 plate, 4 tables.

KEIL, A.
1966A   Rev.: Keresztesi in Anthropol. Ges., Mitt., 98, 85—86.

KEITH, ARTHUR
1972A   A chapter of conclusions. In: McCown, T. D. and Kennedy, K. A. R. (eds.), 1972A, 198—209, 3 figs.
           (reprinted from Keith, 1915).

KEITH, ARTHUR   See also: McCown, T. D. and Keith, A., 1972A.

KELLER, BERTHOLD
1968A   Über die Präparation eiszeitlicher Säugetierreste. Aufschluss, 19, 15—16, 2 figs. (German).

KELLER, CHARLES M.   See: Isaac, G. L. and Keller, C. M., 1969A.

KELLER, ROLF
1971A Liebe Kosmos-Gesellschafter. Kosmos (Stuttgart), 67:11, 324–325, 2 figs. (German).

KELLOGG, REMINGTON
1969A Cetothere skeletons from the Miocene Choptank formation of Maryland and Virginia. U.S. Nat. Mus., Bull., 294, 40 pp., 2 figs., 22 tables, 25 plates.

KELSO, A. J.
1970A Physical anthropology. An introduction. New York: J. B. Lippincott Co., xxii + 355 pp., illustr. Rev.: McKern in Amer. J. Phys. Anthropol., 36:1, 143–144; Meiklejohn in J. Human Evol., 1:1, 125–127; Wolpoff in Amer. Anthropol., 73:6, 1432–1433.

KEMP, T. S.
1969A The atlas-axis complex of the mammal-like reptiles. J. Zool., 159:2, 223–248, 7 figs.
1969B On the functional morphology of the gorgonopsid skull. Roy. Soc. London, Phil. Trans., Ser. B, 256:801, 1–83, 25 figs., 1 pl., 3 tables.
1972A The jaw articulation and musculature of the whaitsiid Therocephalia. In: Joysey, K. A. and Kemp, T. S. (eds.), 1972A, 213–230, 6 figs.
1972B Whaitsiid Therocephalia and the origin of cynodonts. Roy. Soc. London, Phil. Trans., Ser. B, 264: 857, 1–54, 17 figs., 2 pls., 2 tables.

KEMP, T. S. See also: Joysey, K. A. and Kemp, T. S. (eds.), 1972A.

KENDALL, BRUCE D. See: Pierson, P. and Kendall, B. D., 1969A.

KENNEDY, KENNETH A. R.
1972A The paleontology of human populations. Biologist, 54:3, 97–114, 6 figs.

KENNEDY, KENNETH A. R. See also: Lynch, T. F. and Kennedy, K. A. R., 1970A; McCown, T. D. and Kennedy, K. A. R. (eds.), 1972A.

KENNEDY, LUCILLE
1970A Dinosaur bone found at La Jolla! S. Calif. Paleontol. Soc., Bull., 2:2, 2–3 (reprinted from the Fossileer, 4:8, 1969).

KENNEDY, MICHAEL P.
1971A Eocene shoreline facies in the San Diego coastal area, California. Geol. Soc. Amer., Abstr., 3:2, 142 (abs.).

KENNEDY, MICHAEL P. See also: Golz, D. J. and Kennedy, M. P., 1971A.

KERKMANN, KLAUS See: Feustel, R., et al., 1971A, 1971B.

KERMACK, DORIS M.
1970A True serial-sectioning of fossil material. Linn. Soc., Biol. J., 2:1, 47–53.

KERMACK, DORIS M. and KERMACK, KENNETH A.
1971A* Early mammals. Linn. Soc., Zool. J., 50:suppl. 1, xiv + 203 pp., illustr. Rev.: Butler in Nature, 234:5328, 366; Griffith in J. Natur. Hist., London, 6:3, 357; Krebs in Zentralbl. Geol. Paläontol., Teil 2, 1972:3, 168.

KERMACK, D. M., KERMACK, K. A. and MUSSETT, F.
1968A Rev.: Krebs in Zentralbl. Geol. Paläontol., Teil 2, 1970:1, 73–74.

KERMACK, KENNETH A.
1967D Clues to evolution. New Sci., 34:541, 163–164.
1972A The origin of mammals and the evolution of the temporomandibular joint. Roy. Soc. Med., Proc., 65:4, 389–392.

KERMACK, K. A. and KIELAN-JAWOROWSKA, ZOFIA
1971A Therian and non-therian mammals. Linn. Soc., Zool. J., 50:suppl. 1, 103–115, 3 figs., 2 pls. Rev.: Krebs in Zentralbl. Geol. Paläontol., Teil 2, 1972:3, 171–172.

KERMACK, KENNETH A. See also: Kermack, D. M. and Kermack, K. A. (eds.), 1971A; Kielan-Jaworowska, Z. and Kermack, K. A., 1970A.

KERN, J. P., STUMP, T. E. and DOWLEN, R. J.
1971A   An upper Pleistocene marine fauna from Mission Bay, San Diego, California. San Diego Soc. Natur.
          Hist., Trans., 16:15, 329–338, 3 figs., 3 tables

KETRARU, N. A.
1965C   Issledovaniia paleoliticheskikh grotov Severo-Zapada Moldavii. [Studies on Paleolithic caves of north-
          western Moldavia.] Akad. Nauk Moldav. SSR, Okh. Prir. Moldav., 3, 60–77, 14 figs. (Russian).

KETRARU, N. A.   See also: David, A. I. and Ketraru, N. A., 1966A, 1970A.

KETTEL, D.   See: Gaherty, G., Kettel, D., MacDonald, J., Niemann, L., Von Graeve, B. and Arima, E., 1969A.

KEYES, I. W.
1972A   New records of the elasmobranch C. megalodon (Agassiz) and a review of the genus Carcharodon in
          the New Zealand fossil record. N.Z. J. Geol. Geophys., 15:2, 228–242, 12 figs., 1 table.

KEYSER, A. W.
1972A   A re-evaluation of the systematics and morphology of certain anomodont Therapsida. Palaeontol.
          Afr., 14, 15–16.

KHALVADZHIEV, MIKHAIL
1969A   Tertsierna bozaina fauna v Rusensko. [Tertiary mammalian fauna in Ruse region.] Ruse, Bulg., Nar.
          Muz., Izv., 2, 191–220 (Bulgarian; German summary).

KHAN, EHSANULLAH
1970A   Biostratigraphy and palaeontology of a Sangamon deposit at Fort Qu'Appelle, Saskatchewan. Can.,
          Nat. Mus., Publ. Pal., 5, viii + 82 pp., 28 pls., 17 tables.
          Rev.: Thenius in Zentralbl. Geol. Paläontol., Teil 2, 1971:6, 516–517.
1971A   Pleistocene deposits around Ariyalur (Madras). Curr. Sci., 40:2, 37–38

KHAN, EHSANULLAH   See also: Sahni, M. R. and Khan, E., 1968A, 1968B.

KHARITONOV, V. M.
1971A   O sravnitel'no-sistematicheskom izuchenii iskopaemykh gominid. [On the comparative-systematic
          study of fossil hominids.] Vop. Antropol., 39, 95–100 (Russian).
1972A   [Discussion.] Vop. Antropol., 41, 162–163 (Russian).

KHATRI, A. PRAKASH
1966A   The Pleistocene mammalian fossils of the Narmada River valley and their horizons. Asian Perspectives
          9, 113–133, 17 figs., 8 pls., 1 table.

KHISAROVA, GIZZAT DZHANTIMIROVNA
1971A   Ryby iz kontinental'nykh otlozhenii pozdnego mela i kainozoia Tsentral'nogo i Vostochnogo
          Kazakhstana. [Fishes from continental deposits of late Cretaceous and Cenozoic of central and
          eastern Kazakhstan.] Akad. Nauk Kaz. SSR, Inst. Zool., Mater. Fauny i Flory, 5, 57–62,
          2 figs. (Russian).

KHMELEVSKII, V. V. (= CHMIELEWSKI, W.)
1969A   Vliianie perigliatsial'noi sredy na rasselenie cheloveka v verkhnem pleistotsene (Pol'shi). [Influence of
          periglacial environment on the dispersal of man in the upper Pleistocene (of Poland).] In:
          Less-Perigliatsial-Paleolit na territorii Srednei i Vostochnoi Evropy. (VIII Kongress INKVA,
          Parizh, 1969), 346–404 (Russian).

KHOMIZURI, N. I.
1972A   Sledy dinozavra v Tadzhikistane. [Dinosaur tracks in Tadzhikistan.] Priroda, 1972:6, 94–95, 1 fig.,
          1 pl. (Russian).

KHOREV, V. S.   See: Motuzko, A. N., Sudakova, N. G. and Khorev, V. S., 1969A.

KHOSATZKY, LEV I.   See: Khozatskii, L. I.

KHOZATSKII, LEV ISAAKOVICH (= KHOSATZKY, L. I.)
1967B   Nakhozhdenie iskopaemykh ostatkov zheltopuzika na Apsherone. [Fossil remains of Ophisaurus on
          Apsheron peninsula.] Baku, Azerbaidzh. Univ., Uch. Zap., Ser. Biol., 1967:4, 93–105, 13 figs.
          (Russian).
1968A   Oligomerizatsiia v evoliutsii pantsiria pozvonochnykh zhivotnykh. [Oligomerization and evolution of
          the armour of vertebrate animals.] Vses. Paleontol. Obshchest., Ezhegod., 18, 367–369
          (Russian).

KHOZATSKIĬ, L. I. and BORKIN, L. IA.
1971A   Rol' preadaptatsii v evoliutsii i rasselenii organizmov. [Role of preadaptation in the evolution and
             dispersal of organisms.] In: Tezisy dokladov XVII sessii Vsesoiuznogo paleontologicheskogo
             obshchestva, 25–29 ianv. 1971g., 98–100 (Russian).

KHOZATSKIĬ, L. I. and KUROCHKIN, EVGENIĬ NIKOLAEVICH
1966A   Nekotorye dannye o ptitsakh pliotsena Moldavii. [Some data on birds of Moldavian Pliocene.] Pribalt.
             Ornitol. Konf., 6th, Vil'nius, 1966, Mater., 153–155 (Russian).

KHOZATSKIĬ, L. I. and KUZNETSOV, VALENTIN VASIL'EVICH
1971A   Presnovodnaia cherepakha oligotsena Dzhungarskogo Alatau. [A freshwater turtle from the Oligocene
             of Dzhungarian Alatau.] Akad. Nauk Kaz. SSR, Inst. Zool., Mater. Fauny i Flory, 5, 34–51,
             5 figs. (Russian).

KHOZATSKIĬ, L. I. and MŁYNARSKI, MARIAN
1971A   Chelonians from the upper Cretaceous of the Gobi Desert, Mongolia. In: Kielan-Jaworowska, Z. (ed.),
             1971B, 131–144, 7 figs., 3 pls.

KHOZATSKIĬ, L. I. and TOFAN, V. E.
1970A   Proshloe i sovremennoe sostoianie gerpetofauny Moldavii. [Past and present state of the herpetofauna
             of Moldavia.] Tiraspol', Gos. Pedagog. Inst., Uch. Zap., 20, 157–181 (Russian).

KHOZATSKIĬ, L. I.   See also: Birman, A. S., Zhegallo, V. I., Rastsvetaev, L. M., Khozatskiĭ, L. I. and
             Shevyreva, N. S., 1971A; Ivan'ev, L. N. and Khozatskiĭ, L. I., 1970A; Verzilin, N. N.,
             Khozatskiĭ, L. I., Vu Din' Li and Nesov, L. A., 1970A; Verzilin, N. N., Martinson, G. G. and
             Khozatskiĭ, L. I., 1970A, 1971A.

KHRISANFOVA, ELENA NIKOLAEVNA
1967B   Analyse morphologique de la mutabilité du squelette postcranien de l'homme (squelette du tronc et os
             longs des membres) du point de vue des étapes de sa formation. Discussion. Int. Congr.
             Anthropol. Ethnol. Sci., 7th, Moscow, 1964, Proc., 2, 437–443 (French).
1967C   Evoliutsiia struktury dlinnykh kostei cheloveka. [Structural evolution of human long bones.] Moscow:
             "Nauka" Press, 102 pp., 26 figs. (Russian).
             Rev.: Bogdanov and Mazhuga in Vop. Antropol., 31, 178–179.
1969A   Znachenie morfologii postkranial'nogo skeleta (skelet tulovishcha i dlinnye kosti konechnostei) dlia
             taksonomii gominid. [Significance of the morphology of postcranial skeleton (skeleton of the
             trunk and long bones of extremities) for the taxonomy of hominids.] In: Noveishaia tektonika,
             noveishie otlozheniia i chelovek, 1, 201–210 (Russian).
1971A   Nekotorye aspekty gormonal'nykh issledovanii v antropologii. II. Znachenie izucheniia steroidnykh
             gormonov v funktsional'noi i evoliutsionnoi antropologii. [Some aspects of hormonal investi-
             gations in anthropology. Part II. The significance of studying the steroid hormones in
             functional and evolutionary anthropology.] Vop. Antropol., 38, 3–14, 5 tables (Russian).
1972A   [Discussion.] Vop. Antropol., 41, 157–159 (Russian).

KHRUSTOV, G. F.
1968A   Formation and highest frontier of the implemental activity of Anthropoids. Int. Congr. Anthropol.
             Ethnol. Sci., 7th, Moscow, 1964, Proc., 3, 503–509.

KHUBKA, A. N. and SHUSHPANOV, K. I.
1971A   Novye dannye o vozraste Chishmikioiskogo mestonakhozhdeniia fauny pozvonochnykh. [New data on
             the age of Chishmikioi vertebrate fauna locality.] Akad. Nauk Moldav. SSR, Izv., Ser. Biol.
             Khim. Nauk, 1971:4, 58–62.

KHUBKA, A. N.   See also: Negadaev-Nikonov, K. N., David, A. I. and Khubka, A. N., 1970A.

KHUDAĬBERDIEV, T. N.
1971A   O nakhodke cherepa iskopaemogo bizona (Bison priscus Bojanus) v Ferganskoi doline. [On the find
             of a skull of fossil bison (Bison priscus Bojanus) in the Fergana Valley.] Uzbek, Biol. Zh.,
             1971:6, 36–38, 2 figs., 1 table (Russian; Uzbek summary).

KHUKHIA, N. V.   See: Vekua, A. K. and Khukhia, N. V., 1972A.

KIELAN-JAWOROWSKA, ZOFIA
1963A*   Mały słownik paleontologiczny. [Little dictionary of paleontology.] Warsaw: "Wiedza Powszechna",
             216 pp., illustr. (Polish).
1968A*   Results of the Polish-Mongolian palaeontological expeditions — part I. Palaeontol. Polonica, 19, 191
             pp., 54 figs., 27 pls.

Rev.:   Morris in J. Paleontol., 44:1, 168–170.

1968B   Preliminary data on the upper Cretaceous Eutherian mammals from Bayn Dzak, Gobi desert.
            Palaeontol. Polonica, 19, 171–191, 4 figs., 6 pls., 2 tables.

1968C   Archaeolambdidae Flerov (Pantodonta) from the Paleocene of the Nemegt basin, Gobi desert.
            Palaeontol. Polonica, 19, 133–140, 1 fig., 2 pls.
            Rev.:   Thenius in Zentralbl. Geol. Paläontol., Teil 2, 1970:5, 444.

1969A   Hunting for dinosaurs. Translated from Polish. Cambridge, Mass., and London, England: MIT Press,
            177 pp., illustr.
            Rev.:   Colbert in Natur. Hist., 79:7, 122–123; Cox in Nature, 227:5265, 1375; Jerzmańska in Przegl.
            Zool., 13:4, 362 (Polish); Montalenti in Scientia, 106:7–8, 708; Ostrom in Quart. Rev. Biol.,
            46:3, 286; Sestini in Riv. Ital. Paleontol. Stratigr., 76:3, 485.

1969B   Discovery of a multituberculate marsupial bone. Nature, 222:5198, 1091–1092, 2 figs.
            Rev.:   Krebs in Zentralbl. Geol. Paläontol., Teil 2, 1971:4, 335.

1969C   Fossils from the Gobi Desert. Sci. J., 5A:1, 32–38, 12 figs.

1970A   Unknown structures in multituberculate skull. Nature, 226:5249, 974–976, 2 figs.
            Rev.:   Krebs in Zentralbl. Geol. Paläontol., Teil 2, 1971:2–3, 185.

1970B*   Results of the Polish-Mongolian palaeontological expeditions – part II. Palaeontol. Polonica, 21,
            229 pp., 59 figs., 42 pls.

1970C   New upper Cretaceous multituberculate genera from Bayn Dzak, Gobi Desert. In: Kielan-
            Jaworowska, Z. (ed.), 1970B, 37–49, 2 figs., 8 pls., 2 tables.
            Rev.:   Krebs in Zentralbl. Geol. Paläontol., Teil 2, 1971:2–3, 184–185.

1971A   Skull structure and affinities of the Multituberculata. In: Kielan-Jaworowska, Z. (ed.), 1971B, 5–41,
            14 figs., 5 pls.

1971B*   Results of the Polish-Mongolian palaeontological expeditions – part III. Palaeontol. Polonica, 25,
            158 pp., 50 figs., 28 pls.

1972A   Palaeozoological Institute of the Polish Academy of Sciences, Warsaw. Soc. Vert. Paleontol., News
            Bull., 94, 72–74.

1972B*   Results of the Polish-Mongolian palaeontological expeditions – part IV. Palaeontol. Polonica, 27,
            143 pp., 50 figs., 53 pls.

KIELAN-JAWOROWSKA, Z. and BARSBOLD, RINCHEN
    1972A   Narrative of the Polish-Mongolian palaeontological expeditions 1967–1971. In: Kielan-
                Jaworowska, Z. (ed.), 1972B, 5–13, 2 pls., 1 map.

KIELAN-JAWOROWSKA, Z. and DOVCHIN, NAYDIN
    1968A   Narrative of the Polish-Mongolian palaeontological expeditions 1963–1965. Palaeontol. Polonica, 19,
                7–30, 4 pls.

KIELAN-JAWOROWSKA, Z. and KERMACK, K. A.
    1970A   Therian and non-therian mammals. Linn. Soc., Biol. J., 2:4, 319–320 (abs.).

KIELAN-JAWOROWSKA, Z. and KOWALSKI, K.
    1965A   Polish-Mongolian palaeontological expeditions to the Gobi Desert in 1963 and 1964. Akad. Pol. Sci.,
                Bull., Sér. Sci. Biol., 13:3, 175–179, map.

KIELAN-JAWOROWSKA, Z. and SOCHAVA, ANDREY V.
    1969A   The first multituberculate from the uppermost Cretaceous of the Gobi desert (Mongolia). Acta
                Palaeontol. Pol., 14:3, 355–371, 3 figs., 2 pls. (Polish and Russian summaries).

KIELAN-JAWOROWSKA, Z.   See also: Kermack, K. A. and Kielan-Jaworowska, Z., 1971A.

KIENZLEN, GERALDINE   See: McNulty, C. L. and Kienzlen, G., 1970A.

KILÉNYI, ISTVÁNNÉ
    1969A*   A magyar földtani irodalom jegyzéke, 1968. [Bibliography of Hungarian earth science publications,
                1968.] Földt. Közl., 99:3, 267–284 (Hungarian).

KILÉNYI, ISTVÁNNÉ and JANTSKY, ZS.
    1970A*   A magyar földtani irodalom jegyzéke, 1969. [Bibliography of Hungarian earth science publications,
                1969.] Földt. Közl., 100:3, 315–329 (Hungarian).

KILFOYLE, CLINTON F.
    1969A   Catalog of type specimens of fossils in the New York State Museum. N.Y. State Mus. and Sci. Serv.,
                Bull., 413, v + 305 pp.

KIMURA, TASUKU   See: Endo, B. and Kimura, T., 1970A.

KING, JACK LESTER and JUKES, THOMAS H.
1969A   Non-Darwinian evolution. Science (AAAS), 164:3881, 788—798, 1 fig., 6 tables.

KING, JAMES R.   See: Farner, D. S., King, J. R. and Parkes, K. C. (eds.), 1971A; Mehringer, P. J., Jr.,
                King, J. E. and Lindsay, E. H., 1970A.

KING, JOHN A.
1968A*   Biology of *Peromyscus* (Rodentia). Amer. Soc. Mammal., Spec. Publ., 2, xiv + 593 pp., illustr.
                Rev.: Evans in Quart. Rev. Biol., 45:2, 211—212; Kavanau in Science (AAAS), 165:3895, 782—783;
                Mac Arthur in Amer. Sci., 57:3, 244A.

KING, JUDITH E.   See: Berry, J. A. and King, J. E., 1970A.

KING, THOMAS F.
1968A   County antiquities legislation new hope for archaeological preservation. Amer. Antiquity, 33, 505—506.

KINGDON, JONATHAN
1971A   East African mammals: an atlas of evolution in Africa. Vol. I. New York and London: Academic
                Press, x + 446 pp., illustr.
                Rev.: Corbet in Nature, 235:5338, 403; Haltenorth in Säugetierkundl. Mitt., 20:3, 262—263; Herre in
                Z. Zool. Syst. Evolut.-Forsch., 9:4, 320; Napier in J. Anat., 110:3, 478.

KINZEY, WARREN G.
1970A   Rates of evolutionary change in the hominid canine teeth. Nature, 225:5229, 296, 1 table.
1971A   Evolution of the human canine tooth. Amer. Anthropol., 73:3, 680—694, 1 fig., 2 tables.
1972A   Allometric transposition of brain/body size relationships in hominid evolution. Amer. J. Phys.
                Anthropol., 37:3, 442—443 (abs.).

KIPIANI, MARIĬA GEORGIEVNA and KOLBUTOV, A. D.
1970A   Paleogeografiĭa severa Zapadno-Sibirskoĭ nizmennosti i Russkoĭ ravniny v pozdnem pleĭstoĭsene i
                goloĭsene. [Paleogeography of the north of west-Siberian lowlands and of Russian plain during
                late Pleistocene and Holocene.] In: Severnyĭ Ledovityĭ Okean i ego poberezh'e v kaĭnozoe,
                356—362 (Russian).

KIPP, FRIEDRICH A.
1966A   Indizien für die Sprachfähigkeit fossiler Menschen. Stuttgarter Beitr. z. Naturk., 170, 5 pp., 1 fig.
                (German).

KIRIAKOFF, S. G.
1959A   Aspecten van de moderne Biogeografie. VII. — Oorsprong en Evolutie der Floras en Faunas.
                Natuurwet. Tijdschr., 41:5, 137—147 (Dutch; French summary).
1961A   Kanttekeningen bij een recent werk over Taxonomie. Natuurwet. Tijdschr., 43:7—8, 162—165 (Dutch;
                French abstract).
1968A   De moderne dierkundige systematiek. Natuurwet. Tijdschr., 50:1—3, 3—43, 5 figs. (Dutch).

KIRINA, T. I.
1964A   K stratigrafii ĭurskikh otlozheniĭ Vilĭuĭskoĭ sineklizy. [The stratigraphy of the Jurassic deposits of the
                Vilĭuĭ syneclise.] Akad. Nauk SSSR, Dokl., 158:1, 98—101 (Russian).
1965A   Stratigraphy of Jurassic deposits of the Vilyuy syneclise. Akad. Nauk SSSR, Dokl., Earth Sci. Sec.,
                158, 13—15. (Translated from Russian: Akad. Nauk SSSR, Dokl., 1964, 158:1, 98—101.)

KIRK, R. L.
1969A   Biochemical polymorphism and the evolution of human races. Int. Congr. Anthropol. Ethnol. Sci.,
                8th, Tokyo, 1968, Proc., Vol. I. Anthropology, 371—376, 3 figs., 2 tables.

KIRK, RUTH
1969A   The rescue of Marmes man. Pac. Discovery, 22:4, 10—15, 16 figs.

KIRKALDY, J. F.
1967A   Fossils in colour. London: Blandford Press, 223 pp., illustr.
                Rev.: Anon. in Earth Sci. J., 2:2, 196.

KIRKLAND, DOUGLAS W.   See: Anderson, R. Y. and Kirkland, D. W., 1969A.

KIRKLAND, PEGGY L.
1963A   Permian stratigraphy and stratigraphic paleontology of a part of the Colorado Plateau. Symp. 4th
                Field Conf., 80—100, 8 figs.
                Abs.: Author in GeoSci. Abs., 5:12, 7—8.

KIRSANOV, N. V.
    1971A   Akchagyl Povolzh'ia. [Akchagylian of the Volga region.] In: Stratigrafiia neogena Vostoka
             Evropeiskoi chasti SSSR, 22—45, 7 figs., 1 table (Russian).

KIRSCH, J. A. W.   See: Hayman, D. L., Kirsch, J. A W., Martin, P. G. and Waller, P. F., 1971A.

KIRSHENBLAT, IA. D.
    1969A   Kainotropozy — odno iz glavnykh napravlenii evoliutsionnogo protsessa. [Cainotroposes — one of the
             principal directions of evolutionary process.] Akad. Nauk Ukr. SSR, Inst. Zool., Vestn. Zool.,
             1969:3, 24—28, 1 fig. (Russian; English summary).

KISGYÖRGY, Z.   See: Samson, P., Radulesco, C. and Kisgyörgy, Z., 1971A.

KISSLING, DANIEL   See: Hugueney, M. and Kissling, D., 1972A; Stinton, F. C. and Kissling, D., 1968A.

KISTIAKOVSKII, A. B.   See: Pidoplichko, I. G., Kistiakovskii, A. B., Korneev, A. P. and Vereshchagin,
             N. K., 1969A.

KITAHARA, J.
    1971A   Evolution of the siamang (Symphalangus syndactylus) in southeast Asia during Pleistocene. Int. Congr.
             Primat., 3rd, Zurich, 1970, Proc., 1, 67—73, 3 tables.

KITCHING, JAMES W.
    1971A   Paleontological investigations in the McGregor Glacier area. Antarctic J., 6:4, 118—119.

KITCHING, J. W., COLLINSON, J. W., ELLIOT, D. H. and COLBERT, E. H.
    1972A   Lystrosaurus zone (Triassic) fauna from Antarctica. Science, 175:4021, 524—527, 3 figs., 1 table.

KITCHING, JAMES W.   See also: Hopson, J. A. and Kitching, J. W., 1972A.

KLAITS, BARRIE G.
    1972A   The moving mesaxonic manus: a comparison of tapirs and rhinoceroses. Mammalia, 36:1, 126—145,
             1 fig., 4 pls. (French summary).

KLAPCHUK, M. N.   See: Liubin, V. P., Burchak-Abramovich, N. I. and Klapchuk, M. N., 1971A.

KLAUSEWITZ, W.
    1970A   Die Donnerechse ist wieder aufgestellt. Natur Mus., 100:3, 151—152, 1 fig. (German).

KLEBANOVA, N. I.
    1971A   Sel'devye iz khadumskikh otlozhenii (maikopskoi svity) Kavkaza. [Clupeidae from Khadum deposits
             (Maikop suite) of Caucasus.] Mosk. Obshchest. Ispyt. Prir., Biull., Otd. Geol., 46:6, 143—144
             (Russian).

KLEEMANN, GEORG
    1971A   Zwei Wege zum Vollmenschen? Kosmos (Stuttgart), 67:2, 34, 36 (German).
    1971B   Zwei neue Unterkiefer der Steinheimer-Gruppe. Naturwiss. Rundsch., 24:3, 119, 1 fig. (German).

KLEIMAN, G. P.   See: Borisov, B. A. and Kleiman, G. P., 1967A.

KLEIN, HENDRIK
    1971A   Pathologische Veränderungen an einem Elefanten-Oberkiefer aus pleistozänen Kiesen des Oberrheins
             (SW—Deutschland). Neues Jahrb. Geol. Paläontol., Monatsh., 1971:6, 355—362, 1 pl. (German;
             English summary).

KLEIN, RICHARD G.
    1967B   Open-air Mousterian sites of south Russia. Quaternaria, 9, 199—223, 4 figs., 6 tables (French and
             Italian summaries).
    1967C   El hombre del Pleistoceno en el litoral oriental del Mar Negro. Ampurias, 29, 93—115, 4 figs.,
             2 tables (Spanish).
    1968A   Early man in Slovenia. Amer. Anthropol. Ass., Bull., 1:3, 77 (abs.).
    1969A   Mousterian cultures in European Russia. Science (AAAS), 165:3890, 257—265, 5 figs., 1 table.
    1969B   The Mousterian of European Russia. Prehist. Soc., Proc., 35:4, 77—111, 7 figs., 4 tables, 1 map.
    1969C   Man and culture in the late Pleistocene: a case study. San Francisco: Chandler Publishing Co.,
             xxvi + 259 pp., 73 figs., 44 tables, 4 maps.
             Rev.: Solecki in Amer. Sci., 60:2, 264—265.

1970A   Der Neanderthaler in Russland. [The Neanderthal in Russia.] Naturwiss. Rundsch., 23, 71–72.
1970B   Problems in the study of the Middle Stone Age of South Africa. S. Afr. Archaeol. Bull., 25:99–100,
          127–135, 1 fig., 2 tables.
1971A   The Pleistocene prehistory of Siberia. Quaternary Res., 1:2, 133–161, 9 figs., 3 tables, 2 maps.
1972A   The late Quaternary mammalian fauna of Nelson Bay Cave (Cape Province, South Africa): its implica-
          tions for megafaunal extinctions and environmental and cultural change. Quaternary Res., 2:2,
          135–142, 2 tables.

KLEINDIENST, MAXINE R.   See: Howell, F. C., Cole, G. H., Kleindienst, M. R., Szabo, B. J. and
          Oakley, K. P., 1972A.

KLEINENBERG, S.   See: Klevezal, G. and Kleinenberg, S., 1969A.

KLEMMER, K.
1964A*   Rev.: Elkan in Brit. J. Herpetol., 3:10, 261–262.

KLEVEZAL, G. and KLEINENBERG, S.
1969A   Age determination of mammals by layered structure in teeth and bone. Translated from the Russian.
          Quebec: Fisheries Research Board of Canada, 142 pp., 67 figs.
          Rev.: Haltenorth in Säugetierkundl. Mitt., 17:3, 277.

KLÍMA, BOHUSLAV
1963B   Rev.: Wyss in Schweiz. Ges. Urgesch., Jahrb., 52, 128–129.
1966D   Le campement des chasseurs de mammouths près de Dolní Věstonice (Moravie). In: Filip, J. (ed.),
          1966B, 32, pl. I (French).
1966E   Nouvelle station des chasseurs de mammouths à Pavlov (Moravie). In: Filip, J. (ed.), 1966B, 33,
          1 fig., pl. I (French).
1966F   Exploration archéologique de la grotte de Pekárna (Mokrá) près de Brno (Moravie). In: Filip, J. (ed.),
          1966B, 34–35, 1 fig., pl. III (French).
1968A   Das Pavlovien in den Weinberghöhlen von Mauern. Quartär, 19, 263–273, 5 figs.
1969A   [Petřkovice II. – A new Paleolithic site in Ostrava.] Archeol. Rozhl., 21:5, 583–595, 10 figs. (Czech.;
          German summary).
1969B   Die grosse Anhäufung von Mammutknochen in Dolní Věstonice. Česk. Akad. Věd, Přirodověd. Ústav
          Brne, Prace, 3:6, 58 pp., illustr. (German; English summary).
1970A   Zum 65. Geburtstag von Zdeněk Burian. Quartär, 21, 105–106, 2 pls., portr. (German).

KLINGE, H.   See: Fittkau, E. J., Illies, J., Klinge, H., Schwabe, G. H. and Sioli, H. (eds.), 1969A.

KLINGENER, DAVID
1968A   Rodents of the Mio-Pliocene Norden Bridge local fauna, Nebraska. Amer. Midland Natur., 80, 65–74,
          3 figs.

KLIÚSHNIKOV, MIKHAIL NIKOLAEVICH
1958A   Paleogenovye otlozheniiá Dneprovsko-Donetskoǐ vpadiny. [Paleogene deposits of Dnepr-Donets
          depression.] Geologiiá SSSR, 5, Ukrainian SSR, Moldavian SSR, 642–658, 3 figs., 1 table
          (Russian).

KLOCHKO, V. P.   See: Gatinskiǐ, Iu. G., Gerus, E. A., Klochko, V. P. and Trofimov, D. M., 1967A.

KNOBLOCH, ERWIN   See: Hurník, S. and Knobloch, E., 1966A.

KNORRE, DIETRICH VON   See: Feustel, R., et al., 1971B.

KNUSSMANN, RAINER
1967B   Humerus, Ulna und Radius der Simiae. Vergleichend-morphologische Untersuchungen mit
          Berücksichtigung der Funktion. Bibl. Primatol., 5, 399 pp., 228 figs., 46 tables (German).
          Rev.: Kaufmann in Arch. Suiss. Anthropol. Gén., 32, 145–146; Krogman in Amer. J. Phys. Anthropol.,
          27, 399–401; Masali in Riv. Antropol., 53, 120–121; Niethammer in Bonner Zool. Beitr., 20:
          1–3, 313; Preuschoft in Zentralbl. Geol. Paläontol., Teil 2, 1968:6, 667–669; Roth-Lutra in
          Anat. Anz., 122:2, 188–189; Vallois in L'Anthropologie, 72, 159–161.

KOBAYASHI, IWAO
1971A   [Micro-structure of crown cement of a tooth of fossil elephant Elephas namadicus naumanni
          Makiyama.] Geol. Soc. Jap., J., 77:11, 723–729, 4 figs., 2 pls. (Japanese; English summary).

KOBAYASHI, IWAO and SUGA, SHŌICHI
1971A   [Alteration of the surface layer of fossil elephant molar from the sea-bottom in the Japan Sea.]
             Geol. Soc. Jap., J., 77:12, 765–769, 1 fig., 2 pls., 1 table (Japanese; English summary).

KOBAYASHI, KUNIO
1963B   Epitome of Quaternary history of Hamamatsu and its environs in central Japan. Shinshu Univ., Fac.
             Sci., J., 13, 21–46, 7 figs., 7 pls., 4 tables.

KOBELEV, M. V., PANOV, B. S. and PERMIAKOV, V. V.
1971A   Verkhniĭ devon ĭugo-zapadnoĭ okrainy Donetskogo basseĭna. [Upper Devonian of the southwestern
             margin of the Donets basin.] Geol. Zh., 31:4, 67–74, 8 figs. (Russian).

KOBY, FRÉDÉRIC-EDOUARD
1960B   Sur l'extension maxima vers le Sud-Ouest de quelques représentants de la faune froide würmienne.
             Anthropos, Brno, 1960 Suppl., 101–107, 1 map (French; Russian summary).
1960E   Canine d'Ursus spelaeus à couronne bifide. Chercheurs Wallonie, Bull., 17, 5–9 (French).
1965A   Remarques critiques sur les genres Mimomys et Arvicola. Eclogae Geol. Helv., 58:2, 1093–1106,
             6 figs. (French).
1968A   Oligodontie par retention des canines supérieures chez un ours des cavernes. Eclogae Geol. Helv.,
             61:2, 577–580, 2 figs. (French).
1968B   Les "rennes" de Tursac paraissent être plutôt des Daims. Préhist. Spéléol. Ariége., 23, 121–130,
             3 figs. (French).

KOCHANSKY-DEVIDÉ, V.
1970A   Prof. Dr. Gorjanović als Paläontologe. Krapina, 5–11, 1 fig. (Serbocroatian; German summary).
             Rev.: Kochansky-Devidé in Zentralbl. Geol. Paläontol., Teil 2, 1971:5, 359.

KOCHETKOVA, VERONIKA IVANOVNA (= KOTCHETKOVA, V. I.)
1960B   Faktory, opredeliaiushchie formu i rel'ef endokrana. [Factors determining the form and relief of
             endocranium.] Vop. Anthropol., 1, 15–30 (Russian).
1964B   Evoliutsiia mozga v sviazi s progressom material'noĭ kul'tury. [Brain evolution in connection with the
             progress of material culture.] In: U istokov chelovechestva. (Osnovnye problemy
             antropogeneza), 191–243, 13 figs., 4 tables (Russian).
1967B   Mozg paleoliticheskogo cheloveka Pavlov I. [The brain of the Paleolithic man Pavlov I.] Akten des
             Anthropologischen Kongresses, Brno, 1965. Anthropos, Brno, 19, 150–152, 5 figs., 3 tables
             (Russian).
1968A   Les relations: homme-culture-milieu au Paléolithique. Int. Congr. Anthropol. Ethnol. Sci., 8th, Tokyo,
             1968, Proc., 3, 270–273 (French).
1968B   Opyt rekonstruktsii endokrana atlantropa mavritanskogo. [An experiment of reconstruction of the
             endocranium of Atlanthropus mauritanicus.] Vop. Anthropol., 29, 3–19, 12 figs. (Russian).
1969A   Vozmozhnye varianty makrostruktury mozga Homo habilis. [Possible variants of brain macrostructure
             of Homo habilis.] Vop. Anthropol., 32, 29–42, 8 figs., 2 tables (Russian).
1969B   Reconstruction de l'endocrâne de l'Atlanthropus mauritanicus et de l'Homo habilis. Int. Congr.
             Anthropol. Ethnol. Sci., 8th, Tokyo, 1968, Proc., Vol. I. Anthropology, 102–104 (French).
1970A   Novye dannye o makrostrukture mozga gominid i ikh interpretatsiia. [New data on the macrostructure
             of the hominid brain and their interpretation.] Vop. Anthropol., 34, 3–19, 1 fig., 2 tables
             (Russian).
1970B   On brain size and behavior in early man. Curr. Anthropol., 11:2, 176.
1970C   Paleonevrologiia, ee sovremennoe sostoianie. [Paleoneurology, its present state.] Itogi Nauki, Ser.
             Biol., 1969 (Russian).

KOCKEL, FRANZ   See: Gramann, F. and Kockel, F., 1969A.

KOENIGSWALD, G. H. R. VON
1956H   Rev.: A. Hacquaert in Natuurwet. Tijdschr., 38:1, 32.
1964E   Potassium-argon dates and early man: Trinil. Int. Ass. Quaternary Res., 6th Congr. (1961), Rept., 4,
             325–327.
1967E   Evolutionary trends in the deciduous molars of the Hominidea. J. Dental Res., 46:5, 779–786,
             6 figs.
1967F   Incontro con l'uomo preistorico. Milan: Il Saggiatore, 286 pp., 50 figs., 39 tables (Italian).
             Rev.: Fedele in Riv. Antropol., 55, 306–307.
1968C   The phylogenetical position of the Hylobatinae. In: Chiarelli, B. (ed.), 1968C, 271–276.
1968D   Die Geschichte des Menschen. Second edition. Verständ. Wiss., 74, 160 pp., 91 figs. (German).
             Rev.: Angst in Natur. Mus., 100:4, 200; Hemmer in Homo, 20:1, 71; Henschen in Naturwiss., 56:1,
             46–47; Marinelli in Zool.-Bot. Ges. Wien, Verh., 108/109, 182; Niethammer in Bonner Zool.
             Beitr., 20:1–3, 313; Roth-Lutra in Anat. Anz., 128:3, 318–319; Vogel in Naturwiss. Rundsch.,

22, 273–274; Vogel in Z. Morphol. Anthropol., 61:1, 115–116; Weninger in Anthropol. Ges., Mitt., 99, 248; Zapfe in Naturhist. Mus. Wien, Ann., 73, 444.

1968E   Probleme der ältesten menschlichen Kulturen. In: Rensch, B. (ed.), 1968B, 149–173, 4 figs. (German).

1969A   Miocene Cercopithecoidea and Oreopithecoidea from the Miocene of East Africa. In: Leakey, L. S. B. (ed.), 1969C, 39–52, 1 pl., 1 table.

1969B   Java: Prae-Trinil man. Int. Congr. Anthropol. Ethnol. Sci., 8th, Tokyo, 1968, Proc., Vol. I. Anthropology, 104–105.

1970A   *Hipparion* as a guide-fossil. G. Geol., 35:1, 197–199.

1970B   *Hipparion* from the Pleistocene of Europe, especially from the Red Crag of East Anglia. Palaeogeogr., Palaeoclimat., Palaeoecol., 8:2–3, 261–264, 1 fig.

1972A   Gippariony pleïstotsena Evropy. [Hipparions of the European Pleistocene.] In: Geologiiâ i fauna nizhnego i srednego pleïstotsena Evropy, 72–76 (Russian).

1972B   Was ist *Ramapithecus*? Natur Mus., 102:5, 173–183, 3 figs., 1 table (German).

KOENIGSWALD, WIGHART VON
1969A   Die Maniden (Pholidota, Mamm.) des europäischen Tertiärs. Bayer. Staatssamml. Paläontol. Hist. Geol., Mitt. 9, 61–71, 9 figs. (German; English summary).
      Rev.: Thenius in Zentralbl. Geol. Paläontol., Teil 2, 1970:5, 439.

1970A   Mittelpleistozäne Kleinsäugerfauna aus der Spaltenfüllung Petersbuch bei Eichstätt. Bayer. Staatssamml. Paläontol. Hist. Geol., Mitt., 10, 407–432, 40 figs. (German; English summary).
      Rev.: Author's summary in Geol. Bl. Nordost-Bayern, 21:2/3, 152–153.

1970B   *Peratherium* (Marsupialia) im Ober-Oligozän und Miozän von Europa. Bayer. Akad. Wiss., Math.-Naturwiss. Kl., Abh., 144, 1–79, 63 figs., 1 pl. (German).
      Rev.: Groiss in Geol. Bl. Nordost-Bayern, 21:1, 62; Krebs in Zentralbl. Geol. Paläontol., Teil 2, 1971: 2–3, 185–186.

1971A   Die altpleistozäne Wirbeltierfaunula aus der Spaltenfüllung Weissenburg 7 (Bayern). Bayer. Staatssamml. Paläontol. Hist. Geol., Mitt., 11, 117–122, 3 figs. (German; English summary).

1972A   Sudmer-Berg-2, eine Fauna des frühen Mittelpleistozäns aus dem Harz. Neues Jahrb. Geol. Paläontol., Abh., 141:2, 194–221, 19 figs. (German).

KOHN, B. P.   See: McKelvey, B. C., Webb, P. N., Gorton, M. P. and Kohn, B. P., 1970A.

KOKURICHEV, P. I. and DOBIN, M. A.
1972A   Sostoïânie mîâgkikh tkaneï loshadi, prolezhavsheï v vechnoï merzlote bolee 30000 let. [State of the soft tissues of a horse, which remained in the permafrost for over 30,000 years.] Zool. Zh., 51:9, 1429–1431, 8 figs. (Russian; English summary).

KOLBUTOV, A. D.   See: Kipiani, M. G. and Kolbutov, A. D., 1970A.

KOLESNIKOV, CH. M. and SOCHAVA, A. V.
1972A   Paleobiokhimicheskoe issledovanie skorlupy ïaïts melovykh dinozavrov Gobi. [Paleobiochemical study of egg shells of the Cretaceous dinosaurs from Gobi.] Paleontol. Zh., 1972:2, 101–112, 5 figs., 1 table (Russian).

KOLESNIKOV, CH. M.   See also: Martinson, G. G., Sochava, A. V. and Kolesnikov, Ch. M., 1971A.

KOLINKO, VLADIMIR
1971A   Mammoth bone dwellings. Illustr. London News, 258:6866, 28–29, illustr.

KOLLMANN, HEINZ A.   See: Bachmayer, F., Kollmann, H. A., Schultz, O. and Summesberger, H., 1971A.

KOLLMANN, KURT
1964A   Jungtertiär im Steirischen Becken. Geol. Ges. Wien, Mitt., 57:2, 479–632, 2 figs., 2 maps, 4 charts (German).

KOLODEZNIKOV, K. E.   See: Menner, Vl. Vl., Krylova, A. K., Kolodeznikov, K. E. and Fradkin, G. S., 1970A.

KOLPAKOV, V. V.
1970A   Ob iskopaemykh pustynîâkh nizhnego techenîâ r. Leny. [On fossil deserts of the lower course of Lena R.] Akad. Nauk SSSR, Kom. Izuch. Chetvertich. Perioda, Bîull., 37, 75–82, 5 figs. (Russian).

KONSTANTINOVA, N. A. and CHEPALYGA, A. L.
1972A   Novoe mestonakhozhdenie tiraspol'skoï fauny bliz s. Malaeshty. [New Tiraspol' fauna locality near Malaeshty.] In: Geologiiâ i fauna nizhnego i srednego pleïstotsena Evropy, 177–183 (Russian).

KONSTANTINOVA, N. A.   See also: Nikiforova, K. V., Ivanova, I. K. and Konstantinova, N. A., 1969A, 1970A, 1971A.

KOOPMAN, KARL F.
1970A   Zoogeography of bats. In: Slaughter, B. H. and Walton, D. W. (eds.), 1970A, 29–50, 11 figs., 2 tables.

KOOPMAN, KARL F. and JONES, J. KNOX, JR.
1970A   Classification of bats. In: Slaughter, B. H. and Walton, D. W. (eds.), 1970A, 22–28, 1 table.

KOPECKÝ, LUBOMÍR   See: Šantrůček, P., Bůzek, Č., Kopecký, L., Malecha, A. and Václ, J., 1968A.

KOPP, K.-O., PAVONI, N. and SCHINDLER, C.
1969A   Geologie Thrakiens IV: Das Ergene-Becken. Geol. Jahrb., Suppl. 76, 136 pp., 15 figs., 7 pls., 1 table (German; English and French summaries).

KOPPER, JOHN S.   See: Waldren, W. and Kopper, J. S., 1968A.

KORN, NOEL   See: Brace, C. L., Nelson, H. and Korn, N., 1971A.

KORNEEV, A. P.   See: Pidoplichko, I. G., Kistiakovskiĭ, A. B., Korneev, A. P. and Vereshchagin, N. K., 1969A.

KORNIETS, NINEL' LEONIDOVNA
1962A   Pro prychyny vymyrannia mamonta na terytorii Ukrainy. [On the causes of extinction of mammoth on the territory of Ukraine.] In: Vykopni fauny Ukrainy i sumizhnykh terytoriĭ, 1, 91–169, 49 figs., 4 pls., 20 tables (Ukrainian; Russian summary).

KORNUTOVA, E. I.
1968A   Istoriia razvitiia Toreĭskikh ozer Vostochnogo Zabaĭkal'ia. [History of the development of Torei lakes in eastern Transbaĭkalia.] In: Mozozoĭskie i kaĭnozoĭskie ozera Sibiri, 74–88, 5 figs. (Russian).

KOROBKOV, ALEKSEĬ IL'ICH
1971A   Teoreticheskie problemy paleontologii v interpretatsii O. Shindevol'fa. [Theoretical problems of paleontology in O. Schindewolf's interpretation.] Vop. Paleontol., 6, 24–32, 2 figs. (Russian).

KOROBKOV, IL'IA ALEKSEEVICH
1968A   Sovremennoe sostoianie sistematiki organizmov. [Present state of the systematics of organisms.] Leningrad. Univ., Vestn., 1968:6, 31–40 (Russian; English summary).

KOROBKOV, I. I.
1970A   Zamechaniia v sviazi so stat'eĭ G. P. Grigor'eva "Novye aspekty problemy proiskhozhdeniia Homo sapiens". [Comments on the article by G. P. Grigor'ev "New aspects of the problem of origin of Homo sapiens".] Vop. Anthropol., 34, 51–54 (Russian).

KOROBKOVA, G. F.
1969A   K 70–letiiu Sergeia Aristarkhovicha Semenova. [Sergei Aristarkhovich Semenov 70th anniversary.] Sov. Arkheol., 1969:2, 130–133, portr. (Russian).
1969B   Resul'taty binokuliarnogo issledovaniia mergeliia iz verkhnepaleoliticheskoĭ stoianki Kostenki 1. [Results of binocular examination of marl from upper Paleolithic site Kostenki 1.] Sov. Etnogr., 1969:1, 142–143 (Russian).

KOROLEV, V. G.   See: Talipov, M. A. and Korolev, V. G., 1970A.

KOROLEVA, N. V.   See: Barskov, I. S. and Koroleva, N. V., 1969A.

KOROTKEVICH, ELENA LEONIDOVNA (= KOROTKEVYCH, O. L. = KOROTKEVITSCH)
1969A   Krupnyĭ predstavitel' koshach'ikh iz pliotsena iuga Ukrainy. [A large representative of Felidae from the Pliocene of southern Ukraine.] Akad. Nauk Ukr. SSR, Inst. Zool., Vestn. Zool., 1969:4, 43–48, 1 fig., 1 table (Russian; English summary).
1970A   Mlekopitaiushchie berislavskoĭ pozdnesarmatskoĭ gipparionovoĭ fauny. [Mammals of the Berislav late Sarmatian hipparion fauna.] Prirodn. Obstan. i Fauny Proshl., 5, 24–121, 31 figs., 35 tables (Russian).
1970B   Pozdneneogenovye oleni Severnogo Prichernomor'ia. [Late Neogene deer from northern Black Sea region.] Kiev: "Naukova Dumka" Press, 196 pp., illustr. (Russian).
1971A   Novaia forma olenia iz neogenovykh otlozheniĭ iuga Ukrainy. [A new form of deer from the Neogene deposits of the south of Ukraine.] Akad. Nauk Ukr. SSR, Inst. Zool., Vestn. Zool., 1971:1, 59–63, 1 fig. (Russian; English summary).
1971B   Novyĭ vyd tragotserusa z giparionovoĭ fauny s. Bilka. [A new species of Tragocerus from the Hipparion fauna of the village Belka.] Akad. Nauk URSR, Zool. Muz., Zb. Prats, 34, 127–137, 7 figs., 2 tables (Ukrainian; Russian and English summaries).

1971C   Do pytanni͡a pro vydovu nalezhnist' starokondakivs'kogo gipariona. [On the problem of the specific
             relationship of *Hipparion* from Starokondakovo.] Akad. Nauk URSR, Zool. Muz., Zb. Prats,
             34, 137–140, 1 fig. (Ukrainian; Russian and English summaries).

1972A   Ekologicheska͡ia kharakteristika gipparionovykh faun ͡iuga SSSR. [Ecological characteristics of the
             hipparion faunas of the south of USSR.] In: Pozvonochnye neogena i pleĭsto͡tsena Moldavii,
             37–45, 1 table (Russian).

1972B   Osnovnye etapy razviti͡ia pozdnemio͡tsenovoĭ fauny kopytnykh i khobotnykh Severnogo
             Prichernomor'͡ia. [Main stages in the development of late Miocene ungulate and proboscidian
             fauna in the northern Black Sea area.] Akad. Nauk Ukr. SSR, Inst. Zool., Vestn. Zool., 1972:4,
             7–13, 1 table (Russian; English summary).

1972C   Parnopalye gipparionovoĭ fauny s. Belka. Samoteriĭ. [Artiodactyla of the *Hipparion* fauna of Belka
             village. *Samotherium.*] Prirodn. Obstan. i Fauny Proshl., 6, 19–34, 6 figs., 6 tables (Russian).

KOROTKEVYCH, O. L.   See: Korotkevich, E. L.

KORPÁS, L.   See: Jámbor, A., Korpás, L., Kretzoi, M., Pálfalvy, I. and Rákosi, L., 1971A.

KORTLANDT, A.
1968A   Handgebrauch bei freilebenden Schimpansen. In: Rensch, B. (ed.), 1968B, 59–102, 12 figs. (German).

KORZHUEV, P. A.
1968A   Kostnyĭ mozg, gravita͡tsi͡ia i nevesomost'. [Bone marrow, gravitation and weightlessness.] Zh. Obshch.
             Biol., 29:5, 587–593, 2 tables (Russian; English summary).

KOSMINSKIĬ, V. V.
1970A   O landshaftakh i klimatakh paleogena i neogena Kazakhstana i Sredneĭ Azii. [Landscapes and climate
             of Kazakhstan and middle Asia during Paleogene and Neogene.] Vses. Geogr. Obshchest., Izv.,
             102:1, 39–48, 3 figs. (Russian).

KOSTENKO, N. N.
1971A   Chetvertichna͡ia sistema. Vostochnye Kyzylkumy, Bol'shoĭ Karatau, Otrogi Talasskogo Alatau.
             [Quaternary system. Eastern Kyzylkumy, Great Karatau, offshoots of Talas Alatau.] Geologi͡ia
             SSSR, 40:1, Southern Kazakhstan, 498–504, 1 fig. (Russian).

KOSTENKO, N. N. and KOZHAMKULOVA, B. S.
1964A   Paleontologicheskie kriterii v korrel͡ia͡tsii nizhneantropogenovykh otlozheniĭ Kazakhstana i
             Tadzhikistana. [Paleontological criteria for correlation of lower Quaternary deposits of
             Kazakhstan and Tadzhikistan.] Akad. Nauk Kaz. SSR, Vestn., 1964:6, 89–91 (Russian).

KOSTENKO, N. N., NIKITIN, E. A. and LI͡ADZHINA, K. A.
1971A   Paleogenova͡ia sistema. Betpak-Dala, Chuĭska͡ia vpadina, khrebty Karatau, Kirgizskiĭ, Kendyk-tas i
             Chu-Balkhashskiĭ vodorazdel. [Paleogene system. Betpak-Dala, Chu depression, Karatau, Kirgiz,
             Kendyk-tas ranges and Chu-Balkhash watershed.] Geologi͡ia SSSR, 40:1, Southern Kazakhstan,
             436–445 (Russian).

KOSTENKO, N. N., NIKITIN, E. A. and POLUMISKOVA, L. A.
1971A   Melova͡ia sistema. Betpak-Dala, Chuĭska͡ia vpadina, khrebty Karatau, Kirgizskiĭ, Kendyk-tas i Chu-
             Balkhashskiĭ vodorazdel. [Cretaceous system. Betpak-Dala, Chu depression, Karatau, Kirgiz,
             Kendyk-tas ranges and Chu-Balkhash watershed.] Geologi͡ia SSSR, 40:1, Southern Kazakhstan,
             410–414 (Russian).

KOSTENKO, N. N., NIKITIN, E. A., POLUMISKOVA, L. A. and FEDORENKO, O. A.
1971A   Melova͡ia sistema. Vostochnye Kyzylkumy, Bol'shoĭ Karatau, otrogi Talasskogo Alatau. [Cretaceous
             system. Eastern Kyzylkumy, Great Karatau, offshoots of Talas Alatau.] Geologi͡ia SSSR,
             40:1, Southern Kazakhstan, 390–403, 2 figs. (Russian).

KOSTENKO, N. N., NIKITIN, E. A. and SAVINOVA, A. P.
1971A   Neogenova͡ia sistema. Betpak-Dala, Chuĭska͡ia vpadina, khrebty Karatau, Kirgizskiĭ, Kendyk-tas i Chu-
             Balkhashskiĭ vodorazdel. [Neogene system. Betpak-Dala, Chu depression, Karatau, Kirgiz,
             Kendyk-tas ranges and Chu-Balkhash watershed.] Geologi͡ia SSSR, 40:1, Southern Kazakhstan,
             468–472, 1 fig. (Russian).

KOSTENKO, N. N. and SAVINOVA, A. P.
1971A   Neogenova͡ia sistema. Vostochnye Kyzylkumy, Bol'shoĭ Karatau, otrogi Talasskogo Alatau, Vostochnoe
             Priaral'e. [Neogene system. Eastern Kyzylkumy, Great Karatau, offshoots of Talas Alatau,
             Eastern Aral Sea region.] Geologi͡ia SSSR, 40:1, Southern Kazakhstan, 458–468, 1 fig.
             (Russian).

KOSTENKO, N. N.   See also: Bazhanov, O. V., Bocharova, N. I., Didenko-Kislitsina, L. K. and Kostenko,
          N. N., 1971A; Bazhanov, O. V., Didenko-Kislitsina, L. K. and Kostenko, N. N., 1971A;
          Bazhanov, V. S. and Kostenko, N. N., 1964A, 1971A; Galitskiĭ, V. V., Gekker, R. F.,
          Kostenko, N. N. and Sakulina, G. V., 1968A.

KOSTER, WILLIAM J.
     1969A   Fishes of the Rita Blanca lake deposit. In: Anderson, R. Y. and Kirkland, D. W. (eds.), 1969A,
               135—139, 1 pl.

KOTAKA, T.   See: Hatai, K. and Kotaka, T., 1971A.

KOTANI, YOSHINOBU
     1969A   Upper Pleistocene and Holocene environmental conditions in Japan. Arctic Anthropol., 5:2, 133—158,
               5 figs., 4 tables.

KOTCHETKOVA, V. I.   See: Kochetkova, V. I.

KOTTLOWSKI, FRANK E.
     1955A   Cenozoic sedimentary rocks in south-central New Mexico. N. Mex. Geol. Soc., Guidebk., Field Conf.
               6, 88—91, 4 figs.

KOTTLOWSKI, F. E.   See also: Summers, W. K. and Kottlowski, F. E. (eds.), 1969A.

KOTYK, V. A.
     1971A   O granitse nizhnego i srednego devona Volyno-Podolii. [On the limit between lower and middle
               Devonian of Volyno-Podolia.] Sov. Geol., 14:3, 113—120, 3 figs. (Russian).

KOVÁCS, ALEXANDRU   See: Rădulescu, C. and Kovács, A., 1968A.

KOVANDA, J.   See: Šibrava, V., Fejfar, O., Kovanda, J. and Valoch, K., 1969A; Valoch, K., Pelišek, J.,
          Musil, R., Kovanda, J. and Opravil, E., 1969A.

KOVRIZHNYKH, ĪŪ. B.
     1971A   Melovaĭa sistema. Vostochnoe Priaral'e. [Cretaceous system. Eastern Aral Sea region.] Geologiĭa
               SSSR, 40:1, Southern Kazakhstan, 403—410 (Russian).

KOWALSKI, KAZIMIERZ
     1960C   Prospalax priscus (Nehring) (Spalacidae, Rodentia) from the Pliocene of Poland. Anthropos, Brno,
               1960 Suppl., 109—114, 1 fig. 1 table (Russian summary).
     1964C   Pleistocene rodents from the Nietoperzowa Cave in Poland. Int. Ass. Quaternary Res., 6th Congr.
               (1961), Rept., 2, 527—533.
     1968A   Pararhizomys hipparionum Teilhard & Young, 1931 (Rodentia) from the Pliocene of Altan Teli,
               western Mongolia. Palaeontol. Polonica, 19, 163—168, 1 fig., 1 pl.
     1970A   Variation and speciation in fossil voles. In: Berry, R. J. and Southern, H. N. (eds.), 1970A, 149—161,
               7 figs., 1 table.
     1970B   Les mammifères fossiles des remplissages karstiques de Pologne. In: Orghidan, T. (ed.), 1970A
               (French).
     1971A   Qui a tué les grands mammifères? Sci. Progrès Découverte, 3432, 31—37, 5 figs. (French).
     1971B   The biostratigraphy and paleoecology of late Cenozoic mammals of Europe and Asia. In: Turekian,
               K. K. (ed.), 1971A, 465—477.
               Rev.: Thenius in Zentralbl. Geol. Paläontol., Teil 2, 1971:6, 512—513.

KOWALSKI, K. and LI, CHUAN-KUEI
     1963A   Abs.: Sci. Abstr. China, Earth Sci., 2:1, 5—6
     1963B   Abs.: Sci. Abstr. China, Earth Sci., 2:1, 6.

KOWALSKI, KAZIMIERZ   See also: Kielan-Jaworowska, Z. and Kowalski, K., 1965A.

KOZHAMKULOVA, BALDYRGAN SERALIEVNA
     1969A   Antropogenovaĭa iskopaemaĭa teriofauna Kazakhstana. [Fossil Anthropogene theriofauna of
               Kazakhstan.] Alma-Ata: "Nauka" Press, 185 pp., 18 figs., 34 pls., 85 tables (Russian).
     1970A   Ranneantropogenovye mlekopitaĭushchie Tadzhikistana (obzor nakhodok ostatkov). [Early
               Anthropogene mammals of Tadzhikistan (a review of the finds of remains).] In:
               Biostratigraficheskie i paleobiofatsial'nye issledovaniĭa i ikh prakticheskoe znachenie, 59—61
               (Russian).

KOZHAMKULOVA, B. S. and ORLOVSKAIÂ, E. R.
1971A   Fauna pozvonochnykh i flory îuzhnoï poloviny Kazakhstana v mezozoe i kaïnozoe. [Vertebrate fauna and floras of the southern half of Kazakhstan in Mesozoic and Cenozoic.] Akad. Nauk Kaz. SSR, Vestn., 1971:5, 25–29 (Russian; Kazakh summary).

KOZHAMKULOVA, B. S.   See also: Bazhanov, V. S., Birîukov, M. D., Vetrov, F. E., Kozhamkulova, B. S., Lychev, G. F., Musakulova, L. T. and Savinov, P. F., 1971A; Kostenko, N. N. and Kozhamkulova, B. S., 1964A.

KOZHEMÎAKINA, I. A.
1970A   Eïfel'skie otlozheniîa Roslavl'skogo progiba i vostochnogo sklona Belorusskoï anteklizy. [Eifelian sediments of the Roslavl' trough and the eastern slope of the Belorussian anteclise.] Sov. Geol., 13:10, 82–95, 5 figs. (Russian).

KOZŁOWSKI, JANUSZ K.
1969A   Problemy geochronologii paleolitu w dolinie Wisły pod Krakowem. [Problems of geochronology of the Paleolithic in the Cracow section of the Vistula valley.] Folia Quaternaria, 31, 67 pp., 29 figs., 1 chart, 5 tables (Polish; English and Russian summaries).
1970A   W sprawie wczesnych etapów antropogenezy. [Concerning the early stages of the anthropogenesis.] Archeol. Polski, 15:1, 253–254 (Polish).

KOZŁOWSKI, J. K. and KUBIAK, HENRYK
1972A   Late Palaeolithic dwellings made of mammoth bones in south Poland. Nature, 237:5356, 463–464, 2 figs.

KOZŁOWSKI, J. K., KUBIAK, H. and WELC, A.
1970A   A Paleolithic site with mammoth remains at Nowa Huta (Cracow, Poland). Folia Quaternaria, 36, 20 pp., 2 figs., 6 pls., 2 tables (Polish and Russian summaries).

KRAEGE, HERMAN
1970A   Large extinct animals practically unknown. Rocks Miner., 45:11, 687.

KRAGLIEVICH, JORGE LUCAS
1959C   Contribuciones al conocimiento de la geología cuartaria en la Argentina. IV. Nota acerca de la geología costera en la desembocadura del arroyo Malacara (Prov. de Buenos Aires). Mus. Argent. Cienc. Natur. "Bernardino Rivadavia" Comun. Geol., 1:17, 9 pp., 1 fig. (Spanish).

KRAMER, THOMAS L.
1972A   Paleoecology of the Mud Creek local biota. Soc. Vert. Paleontol., Ann. Meeting, 32nd, 1972, Abstr. (abs.).

KRANTZ, GROVER S.
1968A   A new method of counting mammal bones. Amer. J. Archaeol., 72:3, 286–288.
1968B   Brain size and hunting ability in earliest man. Current Anthropol., 9:5, 450–451.
1970A   Human activities and megafaunal extinctions. Amer. Sci., 58:2, 164–170, 4 figs.
1970B   Reply. Curr. Anthropol., 11:2, 176.

KRANTZ, GROVER S.   See also: Fryxell, R., Bielicki, T., Daugherty, R. D., Gustafson, C. E., Irwin, H. T., Keel, B. C. and Krantz, G. S., 1968A.

KRAPIVNER, R. B.   See: Generalov, P. P., Kuzin, I. L., Zaïonts, I. L. and Krapivner, R. B., 1970A.

KRASNENKOV, R. V. and ALEKSANDROVA, L. P.
1967A   O vozraste neogenovykh terras basseïna verkhnego i srednego Dona. [On the age of Neogene terraces of the middle and upper Don basin.] Mosk. Obshchest. Ispyt. Prir., Bîull., Otd. Geol., 42:6, 142–143 (Russian).

KRASNENKOV, R. V., ALEKSANDROVA, L. P., SHCHERBAKOVA, L. A. and CHEPALYGA, A. L.
1970A   Novye paleontologicheski okharakterizovannye razrezy antropogenovykh otlozheniï v basseïne Srednego i Verkhnego Dona. [New paleontologically characterized sections of Quaternary deposits in the basin of middle and upper Don.] In: Materialy po geologii i poleznym iskopaemym îsentral'nykh raïonov Evropeïskoï chasti SSSR, 6, 276–284 (Russian).

KRASNOV, I. I. and ZARRINA, E. P.
1964A   Chetvertichnaîa sistema. [Quaternary system.] Geologiîa SSSR, 44:1, West Siberian Lowlands, 192–243 (Russian).

KRASNOV, I. I.   See also: Antypko, B. E. and Krasnov, I. I., 1964A; Gromov, V. I., Krasnov, I. I., Nikiforova, K. V. and Shant̄ser, E. V., 1969A.

KRASNYĬ, L. I.
1966A   Melovai͡a sistema. Zei̯sko-Bureinskai͡a vpadina. [Cretaceous system. Zeia-Bureia depression.] Geologii͡a SSSR, 19, Khabarovsk area and Amur Province, 258–260 (Russian).

KRAUS, BERTRAM S.
1964A   Rev.: Dart in Sci. S. Afr., 2:9, 445–446; Miele in Mankind Quart., 10:2, 116–117.

KRÄUSEL, WOLFGANG
1968A   Wesen und Wandel der Fossilien. Aufschluss, 19:7–8, 177–184, 2 figs. (German).

KRÄUSEL, WOLFGANG and SIMON, WILHELM
1968A   Über Fossilien. Hundert Buchtitel ausgewählt. Aufschluss, 19, 227–234, 8 figs. (German).

KREBS, BERNARD
1968A   Contribuição para a fauna do Kimeridgiano da mina de lignito Guimarota (Leiria, Portugal). I Parte. II – Le crocodilien Machimosaurus. Portugal, Serv. Geol. Mem., 14, 21–53, 18 figs., 5 tables (French; Portuguese summary).
1969A   Ctenosauriscus koeneni (v. Huene), die Pseudosuchia und die Buntsandstein-Reptilien. Eclogae Geol. Helv., 62:2, 697–714, 2 figs., 2 pls. (German; English and French summaries).
1969B   Nachweis eines rudimentären Coronoids im Unterkiefer der Pantotheria (Mammalia). Palaeontol. Z., 43:1/2, 57–63, 4 figs., 1 pl. (German; English and French summaries).
         Rev.: Krebs in Zentralbl. Geol. Paläontol., Teil 2, 1970:1, 74.
1970A   Evolution of the dryolestid lower jaw and its dentition. Linn. Soc., Biol. J., 2:4, 319 (abs.).
1971A   Evolution of the mandible and lower dentition in dryolestids (Pantotheria, Mammalia). Linn. Soc., Zool. J., 50:suppl. 1, 89–102, 9 figs., 2 pls. (German summary).
         Rev.: Krebs in Zentralbl. Geol. Paläontol., Teil 2, 1972:3, 171.

KREBS, BERNARD   See also: Henkel, S. and Krebs, B., 1969A.

KRETZOI, MIKLÓS
1962D   Fauna und Faunenhorizont von Csarnóta. Hung., Magy. Áll. Földt. Intéz., Évi Jelent., 1959, 297–395, 10 figs., 5 pls. (Hungarian and German; Russian summary).
1967A   Tyrrhenicola und Allophaiomys. Vert. Hungarica, 9, 171–175 (German; Hungarian summary).
1967B   Mimomys – Fund aus dem Kuban-Gebiet. Vert. Hungarica, 9, 177–187 (German; Hungarian summary).
1968A   Vértes Lászlò. 1914–1968. Archaeol. Ért., 95:2, 262–264, portr.
1968B   New generic names for homonyms. Vert. Hungarica, 10, 163–166 (Hungarian summary).
1968C   Étude paléontologique. In: Gábori-Csánk, V., 1968A, 59–104, 1 table (French).
1968D   Die Entwicklung der Wirbeltiere. In: Tasnádi-Kubacska, A. (ed.), 1968A, 298–444 (German).
1969A   Das Pleistozän von Süssenborn. Die Castor- und Trogontherium-Reste aus den Kiesen von Süssenborn bei Weimar. Paläontol. Abh., Abt. A, 3:3–4, 771–783, 1 fig., 1 pl., 8 tables. II Internat. Paläont. Kolloquium 1966 in Weimar (German; Russian and English summaries).
1969B   Geschichte der Primaten und der Hominisation. Symp. Biol. Hungarica, 9, 23–31 (German).
1969C   Skizze einer Arvicoliden-Phylogenie-Stand 1969. Vert. Hungarica, 11:1–2, 155–193, 12 figs. (German; Hungarian summary).
1969D   Bemerkungen zur Primaten-Nomenklatur. Vert. Hungarica, 11:1–2, 195–199 (German; Hungarian summary).
1969E   Hundred years of paleontological research. In: Fülöp, J. and Tasnádi-Kubacska, A. (eds.), 1969A, 152–181.
1970-71A   Bemerkungen zur Spalaciden-Phylogenie. Vert. Hungarica, 12, 111–121, 1 pl. (German; Hungarian summary).
1970-71B   Kritische Bemerkungen zur Abstammung der Ursiden. Vert. Hungarica, 12, 123–134, 1 pl. (German; Hungarian summary).

KRETZOI, MIKLÓS and PÁLFALVY, ISTVÁN
1969A   Floren- und Wirbeltierfaunen-Angaben zur Stratigraphie der Diatomite von Szurdokpüspöki. Hung., Magy. Áll. Földt. Intéz., Évi Jelent., 1967, 273–279 (Hungarian; German summary).

KRETZOI, MIKLÓS   See also: Gábori-Csánk, V. and Kretzoi, M., 1968A; Jámbor, A., Korpás, L., Kretzoi, M., Pálfalvy, I. and Rákosi, L., 1971A.

KRIEGER, ALEX D.
1961B   [Letter to the editor.] Sci. of Man, 2, 33.

KRIVÁN, P.
1968A   Division paléoclimatique et stratigraphique de la station. In: Gábori-Csánk, V., 1968A, 33—38, 1 fig., 1 table (French).

KROEBER, THEODORA
1970A   Alfred Kroeber. A personal configuration. Berkeley: Univ. Calif. Press, xii + 292 pp., illustr. Rev.: Driver in Science (AAAS), 170:3965, 1391.

KROLOPP, ENDRE   See: Jánossy, D., Krolopp, E. and Brunnacker, K., 1968A.

KROMMENHOEK, W.   See: Bartheld, F. von, Erdbrink, D. P. and Krommenhoek, W., 1970A.

KRUCKOW, THORWALD
1964A   Haifisch-Zähne und Fisch-Reste in Tertiär-Geschieben. Aufschluss, Sonderheft, 14, 57—63, 13 figs. (German).

KRUEGER, HAROLD W.
1965A   The preservation and dating of collagen in ancient bones. Int. Radiocarb. Tritium Dating Confer., 6th, Proc., 332—337.

KRUKOFF, SERGE
1971A   Rotation de la face autour du nasion, par rapport à la base du crâne, chez les Pongidés et les Hominidés. Acad. Sci., C.R., Sér. D, 272:14, 1850—1853, 2 figs., 1 table (French).

KRUSAT, GEORG
1969A   Ein Pantotheria-Molar mit dreispitzigem Talonid aus dem Kimmeridge von Portugal. Palaeontol. Z., 43:1/2, 52—56, 1 fig. (German; English and French summaries). Rev.: Krebs in Zentralbl. Geol. Paläontol., Teil 2, 1970:1, 74.

KRUSAT, GEORG   See also: Kühne, W. G. and Krusat, G., 1972A.

KRYLOVA, ANNA KUZ'MINICHNA   See: Menner, Vl. Vl., Krylova, A. K., Kolodeznikov, K. E. and Fradkin, G. S., 1970A.

KRYSIAK, KAZIMIERZ   See: Jakubowski, G., Krysiak, K. and Roskosz, T., 1968A.

KUBIAK, HENRYK
1968A   Mastodont remains from the Miocene of Begger Noor, western Mongolia. Palaeontol. Polonica, 19, 143—149, 2 pls.
1969A   Über die Bedeutung der Kadaver des Wollhaarnashorns von Starunia. Deut. Ges. Geol. Wiss., Ber., Reihe A, Geol. Paläontol., 14:3, 345—347 (German). Rev.: Thenius in Zentralbl. Geol. Paläontol., Teil 2, 1970:6, 523.

KUBIAK, HENRYK   See also: Kozłowski, J. K. and Kubiak, H., 1972A; Kozłowski, J. K., Kubiak, H. and Welc, A., 1970A.

KUDRIAVTSEV, G. A., AGENTOV, V. B., GATINSKIĬ, IU. G. and MISHINA, A. V.
1969A   Geologiiâ Iugo-Vostochnoĭ Azii. Indokitaĭ. [Geology of southeastern Asia. Indochina.] Nauch.-Issled. Lab. Geol. Zarubezh. Stran, Tr., 19, 239 pp., 27 figs., 2 maps, 5 tables (Russian).

KUENZI, W. DAVID and FIELDS, ROBERT W.
1971A   Tertiary stratigraphy, structure, and geologic history, Jefferson Basin, Montana. Geol. Soc. Amer., Bull., 82:12, 3373—3393, 4 figs., 3 tables.

KÜHN, HERBERT
1965A   Rev.: L. R. N. in Préhist. Spéléol. Ariége., 25, 179—180.
1966A   Rev.: Kurth in Homo, 19:3—4, 242.
1966D   Henri Breuil. Lisbon, Univ., Fac. Letr., Rev., Sér. 3, 10, 57—59.
1969A   André Glory. Ipek, 22, 133.
1969B   Raymond Vaufray. Ipek, 22, 134.
1969C   Lothar F. Zotz. Ipek, 22, 135.
1971A   Neue Felsbilder der Eiszeit. Naturwiss., 58:5, 225—228, 4 figs. (German; English abstract).

KUHN, OSKAR
1966A   Rev.: Kuhn-Schnyder in Aufschluss, 18:11, 322—323.
1967A   Rev.: Mertens in Salamandra, 7, 42.
1967C   Rev.: Leonardi in Natura, 59:2, 144.

1967D   Die vorzeitlichen Fischartigen und Fische. Wittenberg Lutherstadt: A. Ziemsen Verlag, "Die Neue
          Brehm-Bücherei", 384, 127 pp., 97 figs. (German).
          Rev.: Klausewitz in Natur Mus., 101:1, 39—40; Rietschel in Natur Mus., 99:7, 356; Steininger in
          Geol. Ges. Wien, Mitt., 60, 164; Weiler in Zentralbl. Geol. Paläontol., Teil 2, 1968:6, 648–649.
1967E   Frankens Bedeutung für die Saurierforschung (Paläoherpetologie). Naturforsch. Ges. Bamberg, Ber.,
          42, 13—26 (German).
          Rev.: Westphal in Zentralbl. Geol. Paläontol., Teil 2, 1968:6, 639.
1968B   Weitere Beiträge zum System und zur Evolution der Amphibien und Reptilien. Naturforsch. Ges.
          Bamberg, Ber., 43, 1—8 (German).
          Rev.: Westphal in Zentralbl. Geol. Paläontol., Teil 2, 1969:6, 509.
1968C   Die vorzeitlichen Krokodile. Krailling bei München: Oeben, 124 pp., 68 figs. (German).
          Rev.: Berg in Zentralbl. Geol. Paläontol., Teil, 1969:3, 290; Bülow in Kosmos (Stuttgart), 66:1, 23;
          Haltenorth in Säugetierkundl. Mitt., 17:3, 278; Mertens in Natur Mus., 99:10, 482; Wermuth in
          Salamandra, 8:1, 50—51.
1968D   Die deutschen Saurier. Krailling: Oeben-Verlag, 107 pp., 50 figs. (German).
          Rev.: Bülow in Kosmos (Stuttgart), 66:1, 23; Haltenorth in Säugetierkundl. Mitt., 17:3, 278; Jörg in
          Aufschluss, 19, 276; Westphal in Zentralbl. Geol. Paläontol., Teil 2, 1968:6, 639.
1969A   Über die Abgrenzung der Anthracosauria und Cotylosauromorpha. Naturforsch. Ges. Bamberg, Ber.,
          44, 52—59, 2 figs. (German).
          Rev.: Westphal in Zentralbl. Geol. Paläontol., Teil 2, 1970:5, 430—431.
1969B*   Handbuch der Paläoherpetologie. Encyclopedia of Paleoherpetology. Stuttgart, Germany and Portland
          USA, 19 vols.
          Rev.: Fox in Brit. J. Herpetol., 4:9, 243—244; Scherf in Naturwiss. Rundsch., 24:11, 499.
1969C   Cotylosauria. Handb. Paläoherp., Teil 6, 89 pp., 47 figs. (German).
          Rev.: Chrulew in Zentralbl. Geol. Paläontol., Teil 2, 1970:3/4, 228—230; Fantini Sestini in Riv. Ital.
          Paleontol. Stratigr., 75:4, 890; Haltenorth in Säugetierkundl. Mitt., 18:1, 88; Krumbiegel in
          Deut. Ges. Geol. Wiss., Ber., Reihe A, Geol. Paläontol., 16:1, 71—72; Mertens in Natur Mus.,
          100:3, 145—146; Romer in Copeia, 3, 606; Scherf in Naturwiss. Rundsch., 23, 344; Swinton in
          J. Paleontol., 46:2, 321; Thenius in Geol. Ges. Wien, Mitt., 62, 212.
1969D   Proganosauria, Bolosauria, Placodontia, Araeoscelidia, Trilophosauria, Weigeltisauria, Millerosauria,
          Rhynchocephalia, Protosauria. Handb. Paläoherp., Teil 9, 74 pp., 27 figs. (German).
          Rev.: Fantini Sestini in Riv. Ital. Paleont. Stratigr., 75:3, 685; Halstead in Brit. J. Herpetol., 4:6, 159;
          Haltenorth in Säugetierkundl. Mitt., 17:3, 278; Krumbiegel in Deut. Ges. Geol. Wiss., Ber.,
          Reihe A, Geol. Paläontol., 15:1, 149—151; Mertens in Natur Mus., 100:3, 144—145; Romer in
          Copeia, 1970:1, 203; Scherf in Naturwiss. Rundsch., 23, 123, 303; Scherf in Naturwiss. Rundsch.
          24:3, 132; Swinton in J. Paleontol., 46:2, 321; Thenius in Geol. Ges. Wien, Mitt., 61, 207—208;
          Westphal in Zentralbl. Geol. Paläontol., Teil 2, 1969:6, 513—514.
1969E   Die Evolution der Fischartigen und Fische. Naturforsch. Ges. Bamberg, Ber., 44, 1—23, 13 figs.
          (German).
1970A   Über die Amphibien und Reptilien der deutschen Trias. Naturforsch. Ges. Bamberg, Ber., 45, 42—48
          (German).
1970B   Neue Fortschritte und Probleme der Paläoherpetologie. Naturforsch. Ges. Bamberg, Ber., 45, 1—41,
          20 figs. (German).
          Rev.: Westphal in Zentralbl. Geol. Paläontol., Teil 2, 1971:4, 333—334.
1970C   Die säugetierähnlichen Reptilien. Wittenberg Lutherstadt: A. Ziemsen Verlag, "Die Neue Brehm-
          Bücherei", 423, 80 pp., illustr. (German).
          Rev.: Haltenorth in Kosmos (Stuttgart), 67:6, 174; Haltenorth in Säugetierkundl. Mitt., 19, 190;
          Zapfe in Geol. Ges. Wien, Mitt., 63, 250.
1970D   Die Saurier des deutschen Rotliegenden (Unterperm). Altötting: Verlag Gebr. Geiselberger, 52 pp.,
          29 figs. (German).
          Rev.: Haltenorth in Säugetierkundl. Mitt., 18, 389; Haubold in Hercynia, 8:3, 239—240; Mertens in
          Salamandra, 7, 41; Trunko in Aufschluss, 22:1, 57—58; Westphal in Zentralbl. Geol. Paläontol.,
          Teil 2, 1970:6, 513.
1970E   Neue Fortschritte und Probleme der Paläoherpetologie. Naturforsch. Ges. Bamberg, Ber. (1970), 45,
          1—41, 20 figs. (German).
1970F   Über die Amphibien und Reptilien der deutschen Trias. Naturforsch. Ges. Bamberg, Ber. (1970), 45,
          42—48 (German).
          Rev.: Westphal in Zentralbl. Geol. Paläontol., Teil 2, 1971:4, 334.
1971A   Die vorzeitlichen Vögel. Wittenberg Lutherstadt: A. Ziemsen Verlag, "Die Neue Brehm-Bücherei,"
          435, 72 pp., 38 figs. (German).
          Rev.: Kleinschmidt in Kosmos, 68:2, 50; Kuhn in Zentralbl. Geol. Paläontol., Teil 2, 1971:2—3,
          180—181; Zapfe in Geol. Ges. Wien, Mitt., 63, 252.
1971B   Die Saurier der deutschen Trias. Altötting: Geiselberger Press, 105 pp., 52 figs. (German).
          Rev.: Groiss in Geol. Bl. Nordost-Bayern, 21:4, 229; Kleinschmidt in Kosmos, 68:3, 88—89; Mertens
          in Salamandra, 7:3—4, 157; Westphal in Zentralbl. Geol. Paläontol., Teil 2, 1971:5, 395.

1971C   Die Saurier des deutschen Jura. Altötting: Geiselberger Press, 71 pp., 39 figs. (German).
         Rev.: Mertens in Natur Mus., 102:5, 192; Westphal in Zentralbl. Geol. Paläontol., Teil 2, 1971:5,
         395.
1971D   Die Tierwelt des Solnhofener Schiefers. Third edition. Wittenberg Lutherstadt: A. Ziemsen Verlag,
         "Die Neue Brehm-Bücherei", 119 pp., 149 figs. (German).
         Rev.: Groiss in Geol. Bl. Nordost-Bayern, 21:4, 228−229; Kleinschmidt in Kosmos, 68:3, 88;
         Rietschel in Natur Mus., 102 :8, 317; Zapfe in Geol. Ges. Wien, Mitt., 63, 251.
1971E   Die Amphibien und Reptilien des deutschen Tertiärs und Diluviums. Altötting: Geiselberger Press,
         91 pp., 42 figs. (German).
         Rev.: Westphal in Zentralbl. Geol. Paläontol., Teil 2, 1971:6, 505; Wild in Kosmos, 68:4, 120.
1971F   Die Reptilien der deutschen Kreide. Naturforsch. Ges. Bamberg, Ber., 46, 1−4 (German).
1972A   Seymourida, usw. Handb. Paläoherp., 5B, 20−69, 35 figs. (German).

KUHN-SCHNYDER, EMIL
1969A   Georges Cuvier 1769−1832. Ver. Vaterländ. Naturk. Württemberg, Jahresh., 124, 65−105, 7 figs.
         (German).
         Rev.: Häntzschel in Zentralbl. Geol. Paläontol., Teil 2, 1970:5, 339.
1969B   Präparation von Fossilien mit dem Sandstrahlgerät. Naturwiss., 56:6, 293−295, 3 figs. (German).
         Rev.: Häntzschel in Zentralbl. Geol. Paläontol., Teil 2, 1970:5, 340−341; Weiler in Zentralbl. Geol.
         Paläontol., Teil 2, 1971:5, 401.
1969C   Das Paläontologische Institut und Museum der Universität Zürich. Naturforsch. Ges. Zürich,
         Vierteljahresschr., 114, 474−483, 5 figs. (German).
1971A   Über einen Schädel von Askeptosaurus italicus Nopcsa aus der mittleren Trias des Monte San Giorgio
         (Kt. Tessin, Schweiz). Hess. Landesamt Bodenforsch., Abh., 60, 89−98, 2 figs., 1 pl. (German).
1971B   Das Paläontologische Institut und Museum der Universität Zürich. Naturforsch. Ges. Zürich,
         Vierteljahresschr., 116, 484−492, 4 figs. (German).
1971C   Die Evolution des Menschen in paläontologischer Sicht. Zürich, Univ., Paläontol. Inst., Mitt., 80,
         11−39, 5 figs. (German).

KÜHNE, WALTER GEORG
1966A   Découverte de dents de mammifères dans le Wealdien de Galve (Province de Teruel, Espagne). Teruel,
         35, 159−161 (French).
1968B   Kimeridge mammals and their bearing on the phylogeny of the Mammalia. In: Drake, E. T. (ed.),
         1968A, 109−123, 8 figs.
1968C   Contribuição para a fauna do Kimeridgiano da mina de lignito Guimarota (Leiria, Portugal). I Parte.
         I − History of discovery, report on the work performed, procedure, technique and generalities.
         Port., Serv. Geol., Mem., 14, 7−20, 7 figs.
1969A   A multituberculate from the Eocene of the London Basin. Geol. Soc. London, Proc., 1658, 199−202,
         1 fig.
1969B   Säugetiere im Schatten der Dinosaurier. Umschau, 69:12, 373−377, 7 figs. (German).
1971A   Photoelectric separation of microfossils from gangue. Geol. Soc. London, Proc., 1664, 221−222.
1971B   Collecting vertebrate fossils by the Henkel process. Curator, 14:3, 175−179, 8 figs.
1972A   Progress in biological evolution. In: Joysey, K. A. and Kemp, T. S. (eds.), 1972A, 281−284.

KÜHNE, W. G. and CRUSAFONT-PAIRÓ, M.
1968A   Mamíferos del Wealdense de Uña, cerco de Cuenca. Acta Geol. Hisp., 3:5, 133−134 (Spanish; English
         summary).
         Rev.: H.-P. in Soc. Españ. Hist. Natur., Bol., Secc. Geol., 67:2, 220.

KÜHNE, W. G. and KRUSAT, G.
1972A   Legalisierung des Taxon Haldanodon (Mammalia, Docodonta). Neues Jahrb. Geol. Paläontol., Monatsh.,
         1972:5, 300−302 (German).

KÜHNE, WALTER G.   See also: Every, R. G. and Kühne, W. G., 1970A, 1970B, 1971A.

KUKALOVÁ, JARMILA
1968A   Profesor RNDr. Josef Augusta Dr. Sc. zemřel. Čas. Min. Geol., 13, 369, portr.

KULAKOV, ĨŪ. N.   See: Kařialainen, V. I. and Kulakov, Ĩu. N., 1965A.

KULEVA, GALINA VASIL'EVNA
1970A   K paleontologicheskoĭ kharakteristike tatarskikh otlozheniĭ basseĭnov rek B. i M. Kineleĭ, Kutuluka,
         Borovki (Srednee Povolzh'e). [On paleontological characters of Tatarian deposits in B. and M.
         Kinel', Kutuluk, Borovka river basins (middle Volga region).] In: Voprosy geologii ĩuzhnogo
         Urala i Povolzh'ĩa, 7:1, 42−51 (Russian).

KULIKOVA, VERA FROLOVNA
    1971A   XVII Sessiia Vsesoiuznogo Paleontologicheskogo Obshchestva. [The XVII-th session of the All-Union
               Paleontological Society.] Paleontol. Zh., 1971:4, 140–143 (Russian).

KUL'KOVA, INESSA ARSEN'EVNA   See: Baranova, Iu. P., Biske, S. F., Goncharov, V. F., Kul'kova, I. A.
               and Titkov, A. S., 1968A.

KULLING, OSKAR
    1970A   Notes on the first find of upper Devonian stegocephalian fossils in east Greenland in 1929. Geol.
               Fören. Stockholm, Förh., 92:4, 496–500.

KUMMEL, BERNHARD
    1970A   History of the earth. Second edition. San Francisco: W. H. Freeman & Co., 707 pp., 500 figs.
               Rev.: Cuffey in J. Paleontol., 46:2, 321–322; P. J. B. in Geol. J., 8:1, iii; Palmer in Quart. Rev.
               Biol., 46:4, 413; Schopf in J. Geol., 79:4, 504; T. L. B. in Calif. Geol., 25:1, 21.

KUMMEL, BERNARD and RAUP, DAVID
    1965A*   Rev.: Anon. in Calif., Div. Mines Geol., Miner. Inform. Serv., 18:6, 108; Chanda in Sci. Culture,
               35:12, 681–682.

KUMMEL, BERNARD and TEICHERT, CURT
    1970A*   Stratigraphic boundary problems: Permian and Triassic of west Pakistan. Kans., Univ., Dept. Geol.,
               Spec. Publ., 4, 474 pp., illustr.
    1970B   Stratigraphy and paleontology of the Permian-Triassic boundary beds, Salt Range and Trans-Indus
               ranges, west Pakistan. In: Kummel, B. and Teichert, C. (eds.), 1970A, 1–110, 38 figs.,
               3 tables.

KUMMER, B.
    1969A   General problems in biomechanics of the upright posture and gait. (An introduction). Int. Congr.
               Anthropol. Ethnol. Sci., 8th, Tokyo, 1968, Proc., Vol. I. Anthropology, 316–322, 23 figs.

KUMMER, G. and GEMEINHARDT, M.
    1964A   Rev.: Schwidetzky in Homo, 19:3–4, 233.

KÜMMERLE, EBERHARD
    1971A   Zur Geologie der nordwestlichen Stadtgebiete von Frankfurt a. M. Hess. Landesamt Bodenforsch.,
               Notizbl., 99, 214–231, 5 figs., 1 pl. (German).

KUNZ, MICHAEL
    1969A   The Paleo-Indian big game hunter: a misconception. Anthropol. J. Can., 7:1, 27–29.

KUPFAHL, HANS-GÜNTHER
    1961A   Der Buntsandstein auf Blatt Schlitz in Hessen mit besonderer Berücksichtigung des Fährtensandsteins.
               Hess. Landesamt Bodenforsch., Notizbl., 89, 266–275, 1 fig., 1 pl. (German).

KUPRINA, NINA PAVLOVNA
    1970A   Stratigrafiia i istoriia osadkonakopleniia pleistotsenovykh otlozhenii Tsentral'noi Kamchatki.
               [Stratigraphy and sedimentation history of Pleistocene deposits of central Kamchatka.] Akad.
               Nauk SSSR, Geol. Inst., Tr., 216, 148 pp., 43 figs., 18 tables (Russian).

KUPSCH, W. O.
    1969A   Elephant and Venus. Can. Geogr. J., 79:1, 34–38, 6 figs.

KUROCHKIN, EVGENII NIKOLAEVICH (= KUROTCHKIN, E. N.)
    1968C   Iskopaemye ostatki oligotsenovykh ptits iz Mongolii. [Fossil remains of Oligocene birds from
               Mongolia.] Ornitologiia, 9, 323–330, 4 figs. (Russian).
    1969A   Novoe nazvanie dlia roda Tutor Kurotchkin, 1968. [New name for the genus Tutor Kurotchkin,
               1968.] Paleontol. Zh., 1969:2, 122 (Russian).
    1969B   New name for the genus Tutor Kurotchkin, 1968. Paleontol. J., 3:2, 257.
    1971A   K avifaune pliotsena Mongolii. [Contribution to avifauna of the Pliocene of Mongolia.] Sovm. Sovet.-
               Mongol. Nauch.-Issled. Geol. Eksped., Tr., 3, 58–67, 1 table (Russian).
    1971B   Sostoianie i zadachi paleornitologii. [The state and objectives of palaeornithology.] Akad. Nauk SSSR
               Paleontol. Inst., Tr., 130, 347–355 (Russian).
               Rev.: Kuhn in Zentralbl. Geol. Paläontol., Teil 2, 1972:3, 167.
    1971C   Osnovnye voprosy izucheniia iskopaemykh ptits. [Fundamental problems in the study of fossil birds.]
               In: Zoologiia pozvonochnykh. Voprosy ornitologii, 116–151 (Russian).

KUROCHKIN, E. N. and GANIĂ, I. M.
1972A   Ptitsy srednego sarmata Moldavii. [Middle Sarmatian birds of Moldavia.] In: Pozvonochnye neogena i pleĭstotsena Moldavii, 45–70, 2 pls. (Russian).

KUROCHKIN, E. N., KALANDADZE, N. N. and RESHETOV, V. IŬ.
1970A   Pervye resul'taty Sovetsko-Mongol'skoĭ paleontologicheskoĭ ekspedifsii. [First results of Soviet-Mongolian paleontological expedition.] Priroda, 1970:4, 115, 1 fig. (Russian).

KUROCHKIN, E. N. and LUNGU, A. N.
1970A   Novyĭ straus iz srednego sarmata Moldavii. [A new ostrich from middle Sarmatian of Moldavia.] Paleontol. Zh., 1970:1, 118–126, 2 figs., 2 pls., 1 table (Russian).
          Rev.: Kuhn in Zentralbl. Geol. Paläontol., Teil 2, 1970:6, 516.
1970B   A new ostrich from the middle Sarmatian of Moldavia. Paleontol. J., 4:1, 103–111, 2 figs., 1 pl., 1 table.

KUROCHKIN, E. N.   See also: Flerov, K. K. and Kurochkin, E. N., 1971A; Khozatskiĭ, L. I. and Kurochkin, E. N., 1966A.

KURSALOVA, V. I.   See: Agadzhanîan, A. K., Dobredeev, O. P., Kursalova, V. I. and Motuzko, A. N., 1972A.

KURTÉN, BJÖRN
1967C   Continental drift and the paleogeography of reptiles and mammals. Comment. Biol., Soc. Sci. Fennica, 31:1, 1–8, 2 figs.
1967D   Some quantitative approaches to dental microevolution. J. Dental Res., 46:5, 817–828, 17 figs., 4 tables.
1968C   Pleistocene mammals and the Bering bridge. In: Genovés, T., et al. (eds.), 1968A, 34–41 (reprinted from Commentationes Biologicae, 1966).
1968D   Cave bears. Stud. Speleol., 2:1, 13–24, 9 figs., 3 pls.
          Rev.: Ehrenberg in Zentralbl. Geol. Paläontol., Teil 2, 1970:3/4, 240.
1968E   Introducción a la Paleontología. El mundo de los dinosáurios. Translated from English by F. Alférez Delgado. Madrid: "Biblioteca para el hombre actual"; Ed. Guadarrama, 256 pp., illust. (Spanish).
          Rev.: L. de A. in Spain, Inst. Geol. Minero, Bol. Geol. Minero, 80:3, 73.
1969A   Das Pleistozän von Süssenborn. Die Carnivoren-Reste aus den Kiesen von Süssenborn bei Weimar. Paläontol. Abh., Abt. A, 3:3–4, 735–756, 12 figs., 4 pls. II Internat. Paläont. Kolloquium 1966 in Weimar (German; Russian and English summaries).
          Rev.: Thenius in Zentralbl. Geol. Paläontol., Teil 2, 1970:3/4, 240–241.
1969B   Continental drift and evolution. Sci. Amer., 220:3, 54–64, illustr.
1969C   A radiocarbon date for the cave bear remains (Ursus spelaeus) from Odessa. Comment. Biol., Soc. Sci. Fennica, 31:6, 1–3.
1969D   Istiden. Stockholm: International Book Production, 179 pp., illustr. (Finnish).
1970A   The Neogene wolverine Plesiogulo and the origin of the Gulo (Carnivora, Mammalia). Acta Zool. Fennica, 131, 1–22, 8 figs., 2 tables.
          Rev.: Thenius in Zentralbl. Geol. Paläontol., Teil 2, 1971:6, 517–518.
1971A   The age of mammals. London: Weidenfeld and Nicolson Press, "The World Naturalist" series, 250 pp., 67 figs., 11 pls., 15 tables.
          Rev.: Butler in Nature, 234:5328, 366; Kermack in New Sci., 54:794, 291; Morrison in Sci. Amer., 226:4, 115–116; Thenius in Zentralbl. Geol. Paläontol., Teil 2, 1971:6, 505–506.
1971B   Time and hominid brain size. Soc. Sci. Fennica, Comment. Biol., 36, 8 pp., 1 fig.
1972A   Not from the apes. New York: Pantheon Books, viii + 183 pp., 6 figs.
          Rev.: Molleson in New Sci., 55:807, 259–260; Morrison in Sci. Amer., 226:4, 115–116.
1972B   The cave bear. Sci. Amer., 226:3, 60–72, illustr.
1972C   The 'half-life' concept in evolution illustrated from various mammalian groups. In: Bishop, W. W. and Miller, J. A. (eds.), 1972A, 187–194, 2 tables.
1972D   Early Tertiary land mammals. In: Hallam, A. (ed.), 1972C, illustr.
1972E   The genus Dinofelis (Carnivora, Mammalia) in the Blancan of North America. Pearce-Sellards Ser., Texas Mem. Mus., 19, 7 pp., 1 fig., 1 table.

KURTH, GOTTFRIED
1967A   Zur Gliederung des Genus Homo in Zeit und Raum. Akten des Anthropologischen Kongresses, Brno, 1965. Anthropos, Brno, 19, 155–163, 6 figs., 1 table (German).
1967B   Implications of primate paleontology for behavior. In: Spuhler, J. N. (ed.), 1967A, 199–216.
1968A*   Evolution und Hominisation. Beiträge zur Evolutionstheorie wie Datierung, Klassifizierung und Leistungsfähigkeit der humanen Hominiden. Second edition. Stuttgart: G. Fischer Verlag, XII + 299 pp., 60 figs. (German and English texts and summaries).
          Rev.: Angst in Natur Mus., 100:5, 241–242; Ankel in Homo, 20:2, 132; Comas in An. Antropol., Mexico, 7, 303–305; G. T. in Anthropos, 65:1–2, 344; H. V. V. in L'Anthropologie,

74:1–2, 108; Haltenorth in Säugetierkundl. Mitt., 18, 288; Howell in Science (AAAS), 165:
3890, 275–276; Kennedy in Amer. Anthropol., 72:4, 953–954; ms in Archeol. Roz., 22:2,
219–220; Marinelli in Zool.-Bot. Ges. Wien, Verh., 108/109, 183; Marzotko in Gegenbaurs
Morph. Jahrb., 113:3, 462–463; Müller in Biol. Zentralbl., 88:4, 530–531; Preuschoft in
Zentralbl. Geol. Paläontol., Teil 2, 1969:4, 301–303; Schindewolf in Zentralbl. Geol. Paläontol.,
Teil 2, 1969:4, 300–301; Swinton in Man (J. Roy. Anthropol. Inst.), 4:2, 294; Tillner in
Anthropol. Anz., 31:4, 298–299; Vogel in Z. Morphol. Anthropol., 61:3, 352–353.
1972A   Wichtiger Fossilfund datiert. Kosmos, 68:3, 68 (German).

KURZANOV, S. M.
1971A   Bystronogie giganty? [Fleet-footed giants?] Priroda, 1971:3, 122–124, 2 figs. (Russian).
1972A   O polovom dimorfizme proto023eratopsov. [On the sexual dimorphism in protoceratopsians.]
         Paleontol. Zh., 1972:1, 104–112, 5 figs. (Russian).

KUSS, SIEGFRIED E.
1967A   Pleistozäne Säugetierfunde auf den ostmediterranen Inseln Kythera und Karpathos. Naturforsch. Ges.
         Freiburg i. Br., Ber., 57, 207–216, 2 pls. (German).
         Rev.: Hünermann in Zentralbl. Geol. Paläontol., Teil 2, 1969:6, 515–516.
1969A   Die paläolitische osteokeratische "Kultur" der Insel Kreta (Griechenland). Naturforsch. Ges. Freiburg
         i. Br., Ber., 59:2, 137–168, 3 figs., 6 pls. (German; English and French summaries).
1969B   Die erste pleistozäne Säugetierfauna der Insel Kasos (Griechenland). Naturforsch. Ges. Freiburg i. Br.,
         Ber., 59:2, 169–177, 1 fig. (German).
         Rev.: Thenius in Zentralbl. Geol. Paläontol., Teil 2, 1971:2–3, 192.
1970A   Abfolge und Alter der pleistozänen Säugetierfaunen der Insel Kreta. Naturforsch. Ges. Freiburg i. Br.,
         Ber., 60:1, 35–83, 21 figs. (German, English abstract).

KUSTER-WENDENBURG, ELISABETH
1969A   Fossil-Grabungen in den mitteleozänen Süsswasserpeliten der "Grube Messel" bei Darmstadt (Hessen).
         Hess. Landesamt. Bodenforsch., Notizbl., 97, 65–75, 9 figs. (German; English and French
         summaries).

KUTSCHER, FRITZ
1971A   Ferdinand Broili, der bisher erfolgreichste Bearbeiter von Hunsrückschiefer-Fossilien. Hess. Landesamt.
         Bodenforsch., Notizbl., 99, 383–389 (German).

KUTSYBA, A. M.
1958A   Devon Dneprovsko-Donetskoĭ vpadiny. [The Devonian of the Dnepr-Donets depression.] Geologiĭa
         SSSR, 5, Ukrainian SSR, Moldavian SSR, 418–460, 7 figs., 1 table (Russian).

KUTTY, T. S.
1969A   Some contributions to the stratigraphy of the upper Gondwana formations of the Pranhita-Godavari
         Valley, central India. Geol. Soc. India, J., 10:1, 33–48, 1 fig., 2 tables.
1971A   Two faunal associations from the Maleri formation of the Pranhita-Godavari Valley. Geol. Soc. India,
         J., 12:1, 63–67.
1972A   Permian reptilian fauna from India. Nature, 237:5356, 462–463, 2 figs.

KUTTY, T. S.   See also: Chatterjee, S., Jain, S. L., Kutty, T. S. and Chowdhury, T. K. R., 1969A.

KUZIN, I. L.   See: Generalov, P. P., Kuzin, I. L., Zaĭonts, I. L. and Krapivner, R. B., 1970A.

KUZ'MINA, I. E.
1970A   Mlekopitaĭushchie i landshaft Severnogo Urala v pozdnem antropogene. [Mammals and landscape of
         the north Urals in the late Quaternary.] In: Severnyĭ Ledovityĭ Okean i ego poberezh'e v
         kaĭnozoe, 363–367 (Russian).
1971A   Formirovanie teriofauny Severnogo Urala v pozdnem antropogene. [Formation of theriofauna of the
         north Urals in the late Quaternary.] Akad. Nauk SSSR, Zool. Inst., Tr., 49, 44–122, 16 figs.,
         10 pls., 43 tables (Russian; English summary).

KUZNETSOV, VALENTIN VASIL'EVICH
1964A   Presnovodnye cherepakhi mezozoĭa i kaĭnozoĭa Kazakhstana. [Freshwater turtles from the Mesozoic
         and Cenozoic of Kazakhstan.] In: Voprosy gerpetologii (Russian).
1969A   Paleoekologicheskie osobennosti iskopaemykh cherepakh Kazakhstana i Sredneĭ Azii. [Paleoecological
         peculiarities of fossil turtles of Kazakhstan and central Asia.] In: Tezisy dokladov 1-go
         Vsesoĭuznogo soveshchaniĭa po paleobiogeokhimii i paleoekologii, 1969, 75–76 (Russian).
1970A   Kontinental'nye cherepakhi Tadzhikistana. [Continental turtles of Tadzhikistan.] Akad. Nauk Tadzh.
         SSR, Izv., Otd. Biol. Nauk, 1970:3, 79–81 (Russian; Tadzhik summary).

1972A   Novyĭ vid nazemnoĭ cherepakhi iz Severo-Zapadnogo Priaral'ĭa (Kazakhstan). [New species of a land turtle from northwestern Aral Sea region (Kazakhstan).] Akad. Nauk Kaz. SSR, Izv., Ser. Biol., 1972:1, 44–50, 3 figs. (Russian; Kazakh summary).

KUZNETSOV, V. V. and BIRĬUKOV, M. D.
1969A   Primenenie zuboproteznykh materialov dlĭa snĭatĭĭa kopiĭ s paleozoologicheskikh ob"ektov. [Use of dental materials for making copies of paleozoological objects.] Paleontol. Zh., 1969:3, 134–135 (Russian).
1969B   Use of dental materials for making copies of paleozoological objects. Paleontol. J., 3:3, 406–407.

KUZNETSOV, V. V., KARABALAEV, K. K. and IBRAGIMOV, I. M.
1964A   Iskopaemaĭa nazemnaĭa cherepakha iz Kirgizii. [Fossil land turtle from Kirgizia.] In: Materialy po geologii Tĭan'-Shanĭa, 4, 135–146, illustr. (Russian).

KUZNETSOV, VALENTIN VASIL'EVICH   See also: Khozatskiĭ, L. I. and Kuznetsov, V. V., 1971A.

LACHASTRE, J.   See: Delpech, F., Lachastre, J., Prat, F. and Suire, C., 1970A.

LACORRE, F.
1960A   Rev.: A. P. di C. in Riv. Sci. Preist., 20:1, 281–284.

LADDAGA FORMENTIN, ORNELLA   See: Piccoli, G., Laddaga Formentin, O., Winkler del Pup, G. and Zanferrari Visentin, M. E., 1970A.

LAET, SIGFRIED J. DE
1967A   La préhistoire de l'Europe. Bruxelles: Éditions Meddens, 212 pp., 36 figs., 83 pls., 8 maps (French).
          Rev.: Joachim in Bonner Jahrb., 170, 476–477; Kimmig in Helinium, 9, 180–185; Mandera in Germania, 47:1–2, 258–259; Piggott in Antiquaries J., 48:2, 314–315.

LAET, SIGFRIED J. DE and THOMAS, HOMER L.
1969A*   Western Europe: Part I. COWA, Surv., Bibliogr., Area 3, 4, 1–17.

LAGUTIN, P. K.   See: Aĭzenverg, D. E. and Lagutin, P. K., 1970A.

LAJOIE, K. R.   See: Brown, F. H. and Lajoie, K. R., 1971A.

LALIEV, A. G.
1964A   Oligofsen. [Oligocene.] Geologĭa SSSR, 10, Georgian SSR, 213–238, 3 tables (Russian).

LAMB, GEORGE M.   See: Isphording, W. C. and Lamb, G. M., 1970A, 1971A.

LAMB, SAMUEL H.
1970A   Trail to... oblivion. S. Calif. Paleontol. Soc., Bull., 2:5, 2–3 (reprinted from New Mexico Wildlife, Nov.–Dec., 1968).

LAMBERT, P. W.
1969A   Age of the Rio Grande Valley at Albuquerque, New Mexico. Geol. Soc. Amer., Spec. Pap., 121, 168–169 (abs.).
1970A   Quaternary stratigraphy of the Albuquerque area, New Mexico. N. Mex. Geol. Soc., Guidebk., Field Conf., 21, 160 (abs.).

LAMMERS, GEORGE E.
1968B   A note on the Saskatoon site, Saskatoon, Saskatchewan and its contained paleofauna. Na'pao, 1, 32–33.
1969A   The Plio-Pleistocene fauna from the San Pedro Valley, Cochise County, Arizona. Geol. Soc. Amer., Abstr., 121, 524 (abs.).
1970A   The late Cenozoic Benson and Curtis Ranch faunas from the San Pedro Valley, Cochise County, Arizona. Diss. Abstr., 31:5, 2862B (abs.).

LAMPEREIN R., CARLOS   See: Covacevich C., V. and Lamperein R., C., 1969A, 1970A.

LAMPRECHT, HERBERT
1965A   Die Entstehung der Arten. Ver. Verbreitung Naturwiss. Kenntnisse Wien, Schrift., 105, 61–77, 6 figs. (German).

LANCASTER, C. S.   See: Washburn, S. L. and Lancaster, C. S., 1968A, 1971A.

LANCASTER, JANE B.
   1968A   On the evolution of tool-using behavior. Amer. Anthropol., 70, 56–66, 2 tables.
   1971A   On the evolution of tool-using behavior. In: Dolhinow, P. and Sarich, V. M. (eds.), 1971A, 343–360,
             2 tables (reprinted from Amer. Anthropol., 70).

LANDRY, STUART O., JR.
   1970A   The Rodentia as omnivores. Quart. Rev. Biol., 45, 351–372, 2 figs.

LANDRY, S. O.   See also: Coats, D. R., Landry, S. O. and Lipe, W. D., 1971A.

LANE, N. GARY   See: Dunkle, D. H. and Lane, N. G., 1971A.

LANG, HANS DIETRICH
   1969A   Zum Alter eines Nashorn-Schädels aus Leine-Kiesen in Hannover. Naturhist. Ges. Hannover, Ber.,
             Beih., 113, 5–13, 1 fig., 2 tables (German).

LANG, W. D.
   1939A   Mary Anning (1799–1847) and the pioneer geologists of Lyme. Dorset Natur. Hist. Archaeol. Soc.,
             Proc., 60, 142–164, 4 portrs.

LANGE, BRIGITTE (= LANGE-BADRÉ, B.)
   1969A   Un nouveau mustéliné des Phosphorites du Quercy, Mustelictis piveteaui. Acad. Sci., C.R., Sér. D,
             268:24, 2870–2872, 1 fig. (French).
   1970A   Mustelictis piveteaui mustélidé nouveau des Phosphorites du Quercy. Ann. Paléontol., Vertébrés,
             56:1, 75–91, 3 figs., 1 pl., 1 table (French).
   1970B   Sur l'existence d'un gisement fossilifère d'âge oligocène inférieur dans les phosphorites du Quercy.
             Soc. Géol. Fr., C.R., 1970:5, 151–152 (French).

LANGE-BADRÉ, BRIGITTE (= LANGE, B.)
   1972A   A propos de l'origine des Hyaenodon européens. Acad. Sci., C.R., Sér. D, 275:20, 2215–2217,
             2 figs., 1 table (French).

LANGER, WOLFHART
   1970A   Der Naturhistoriker Georg August Goldfuss (1782–1848). Kurzbiographie und Verzeichnis seiner
             wissenschaftlichen Schriften. Decheniana, 122:2, 177–180 (German).
             Rev.: Häntzschel in Zentralbl. Geol. Paläontol., Teil 2, 1971:2–3, 98.
   1970B   Georg August Goldfuss. Ein biographischer Beitrag. Bonner Geschichtsblätter, 23, 229–243 (German).
             Rev.: Häntzschel in Zentralbl. Geol. Paläontol., Teil 2, 1971:2–3, 98.

LANGER, WOLFHART   See also: Müller, K. and Langer, W., 1970A.

LANGSTON, WANN, JR.
   1970A   A fossil ray, possibly Myledaphus (Elasmobranchii: Batoidea) from the late Cretaceous Oldman
             formation of western Canada. Can., Nat. Mus., Publ. Pal., no. 6, viii + 15 pp., 2 figs., 3 pls.
   1972A   The archaic eusuchian crocodilian, Leidyosuchus. Soc. Vert. Paleontol., Ann. Meeting, 32nd, 1972,
             Abstr. (abs.).

LANGSTON, WANN, JR., et al.
   1972A   Fossil vertebrates in the United States. A report of an ad hoc committee of the Society of Vertebrate
             Paleontology on the status of fossil vertebrate conservation in the United States. Society of
             Vertebrate Paleontology, 154 pp., 8 tables.

LANNING, EDWARD P.
   1970A   Pleistocene man in South America. World Archaeol., 2:1, 90–111, 10 figs.

LANNING, EDWARD P. and PATTERSON, THOMAS C.
   1967A   Early man in South America. Sci. Amer., 217:5, 44–50, illustr.

LANPHERE, MARVIN A.   See: Dalrymple, G. B. and Lanphere, M. A., 1969A.

LANTIER, RAYMOND
   1964A   Propos sur l'art rupestre de l'Espagne Orientale. In: Pericot García, L.and Ripoll Perelló, E. (eds.),
             1964A, 145–150, 2 figs. (French; English summary).

LAPIERRE, FRANCIS   See: Ginsburg, L., Lapierre, F. and Montenat, C., 1967A.

LAPLACE, GEORGES
  1961A   Alberto-Carlo Blanc. Les Eyzies, 10, 49–50 (French).
  1966A   Rev.: Merino in Munibe, 19, 107–117.

LAPORTE, GUY S.   See: Lefevre, M. and Laporte, G. S., 1968A.

LAPORTE, LEO F.
  1968A   Rev.: Anon. in Calif., Div. Mines Geol., Miner. Inform. Serv., 23:5, 95.

LAPPARENT, ALBERT F. DE
  1966A   Rev.: Esteras in Teruel, 37, 141.
  1967A   Les dinosaures de France. Sciences, Paris, 51, 4–19, 10 figs., 4 tables (French).

LAPPARENT, A. F. DE, CURNELLE, R., DEFAUT, B., MIROSCHEDJI, A. DE and PALLARD, B.
  1969A   Nouveaux gisements de dinosaurs en Espagne centrale. Estud. Geol. (Inst. Invest. Geol. "Lucas
             Mallada"), 25:3/4, 311–315, 3 figs. (French; Spanish and English summaries).

LAPPARENT, A. F. DE and DAVOUDZADEH, M.
  1972A   Jurassic dinosaur footprints of the Kerman area, central Iran. Iran, Geol. Surv., Rep., 26, 5–22,
             8 figs., 3 pls., 2 tables (French summary).

LAPPARENT, A. F. DE, LE JONCOUR, M., MATHIEU, A. and PLUS, B.
  1965A   Rev.: Adrover in Teruel, 36, 211.

LAPPARENT, A. F. DE and STÖCKLIN, JOVAN
  1971A   Sur le Jurassique et le Crétacé du Band-e-Turkestan (Afghanistan du Nord-Ouest). Soc. Géol. Fr.,
             C.R., 1971:7, 387–388 (French).

LAPPARENT, A. F. DE   See also: Dollé, P., Lapparent, A. F. de and Montenat, Ch., 1970A; Sarsonneur, C.
      and Lapparent, F. de, 1966A.

LAPPARTIENT, J.-R.   See: Tessier, F., Hebrard, L. and Lappartient, J.-R., 1971A.

LARICHEV, V. E.
  1964D   Drevnĕĭshie (nizhnepleĭstoĭsenovye) gominidy Afriki i Azii i problemy rannikh etapov stanovlenii͡a
             cheloveka (po dannym novykh otkrytiĭ v Vostochnoĭ Afrike i I͡ugo-Vostochnoĭ Azii). [The
             most ancient (lower Pleistocene) hominids of Africa and Asia and the problems of the early
             stages in the making of man (on the data of new finds in East Africa and South-East Asia).]
             In: Vsesoi͡uznoe Soveshchanie po Izuchenii͡u Chetvertichnogo perioda, Novosibirsk, 1964,
             Tezisy Dokladov, Sekt͡sii͡a Istorii Flory, Fauny i Drevnego Cheloveka, 87–90 (Russian).
  1970A   Otkrytii͡a v Lan'tĭane. [Discoveries in Lantian.] Akad. Nauk SSSR, Sib. Otd., Izv., Ser. Obshch. Nauk,
             1970:2:6, 39–48, 7 figs. (Russian).

LARICHEV, V. E. and KASHINA, T. I.
  1969A   Novye dannye o pami͡atnikakh nizhnego paleolita Vostochnoĭ Azii. [New data on lower Paleolitic of
             east Asia.] Akad. Nauk SSSR, Sibirsk. Otd., Izv., Ser. Obshch. Nauk, 1969:1, 83–93, 3 figs.
             (Russian).

LARICHEV, V. E.   See also: Okladnikov, A. P. and Larichev, V. E., 1969A, 1971A; Okladnikov, A. P.,
      Vasil'evskiĭ, R. S., Larichev, V. E., Derevi͡anko, A. P., Gogolev, Z. V. and Toshchakova, E. M.,
      1969A.

LARIONOVA, E. N.   See: Nalivkin, V. D., Larionova, E. N. and Shershnev, K. S., 1969A.

LARSEN, HELGE
  1968A   Trail Creek final report on the excavation of two caves on Seward Peninsula, Alaska. Acta Arctica,
             15, 90 pp., 42 figs., 10 pls.

LARSEN, KENNETH
  1970A   A fossil turtle from the Green River formation in Utah. Great Basin Natur., 30:1, 13–15, 1 fig.,
             2 tables.

LARSON, STEN
  1955A   Tertiär och Pleistocen artbildning inom underordningen Charadrii. Vår Fågelvärld, 14:2, 65–78,
             3 figs. (Swedish; English summary).

LASERON, CHARLES F.
  1969A   Ancient Australia. The story of its past geography and life. Revised by Rudolph Oskar
                 Brunnschweiler. Sydney: Angus and Robertson Ltd., 253 pp., 5 figs., 38 pls., 26 maps.
                 Rev.: Scrutarius in Walkabout, 35:10, 48; Simpson in New Sci., 44:672, 202.

LASKER, GABRIEL W.
  1963D   Teaching aids in physical anthropology. (With a listing prepared by Kenneth A. R. Kennedy.)
                 In: Mandelbaum, D. G., Lasker, G. W. and Albert, E. M. (eds.), 1963B, 63—68.

LASKER, GABRIEL W.   See also: Mandelbaum, D. G., Lasker, G. W. and Albert, E. M. (eds.), 1963B.

LASKOWSKI, WOLFGANG
  1968A*   Der Weg zum Menschen. Vom Urnebel zum Homo sapiens. Berlin: W. de Gruyter & Co., 194 pp.,
                 79 figs., 9 tables (German).
                 Rev.: G. T. in Anthropos, 65:1—2, 343—344; Glowatzki in Anthropol. Anz., 31:4, 283—284;
                 Helmuth in Z. Morphol. Anthropol., 61:1, 116—117; Knussmann in Homo, 20:4, 255;
                 MacConaill in Man (J. Roy. Anthropol. Inst.), 4:1, 138—139; Rieger in Biol. Zentralbl., 89:1,
                 120—121.

LASKOWSKA-WYSOCZAŃSKA, WANDA
  1971A   Stratygrafia czwartorzędu i paleogeomorfologia Niziny Sandomierskiej i Przedgórza Karpat rejonu
                 rzeszowskiego. [Quaternary stratigraphy and palaeogeomorphology of the Sandomierz
                 lowland and the foreland of the middle Carpathians, Poland.] Stud. Geol. Pol., 34, 109 pp.,
                 14 figs., 7 maps, 3 tables (Polish; English summary).

LASKOWSKA-WYSOCZAŃSKA, WANDA and NIKLEWSKI, J.
  1969A   Stratigraphical position of the skeleton of Mammuthus trogontherii from Rzochów near Mielec.
                 Pol. Akad. Nauk, Bull., Sér. Sci. Géol. Géogr., 17, 131—141, 5 figs., 1 table.

LASSARADE, L., ROUVREAU, M. and TEXIER, A.
  1969A   Le gisement paléolithique "du lycée", à Pons (Charente-Maritime). Soc. Préhist. Fr., Bull., Étud. Trav.,
                 66, 341—354, 11 figs., 2 tables (French).

LAUGHLIN, WILLIAM S.
  1968A   Hunting: an integrating biobehavior system and its evolutionary importance. In: Lee, R. B. and
                 DeVore, I. (eds.), 1968A, 304—320, 1 fig., 1 table.

LAUGHLIN, W. S. and OSBORNE, R. H.
  1967A*   Human variation and origins: an introduction to human biology and evolution. San Francisco:
                 W. H. Freeman and Co., 297 pp., illustr.
                 Rev.: Kelso in Amer. Jour. Phys. Anthropol., 29, 112—113; Molnar in Amer. Anthropol., 71, 1188—
                 1190; Schwidetzky in Homo, 20:4, 250.

LAVENBERG, ROBERT J.   See: Fitch, J. E. and Lavenberg, R. J., 1971A.

LAVILLE, HENRI
  1969A   L'interstade Würm II — Würm III et la position chronologique du Paléolithique supérieur ancien en
                 Périgord. Acad. Sci., C.R., Sér. D, 269:1, 10—12 (French).

LAVOCAT, RENÉ
  1966A*   Rev.: Kuhn-Schnyder in Schweiz. Ges. Urgesch., Jahrb., 53, 202—203.
  1967E   Histoire des mammifères. Paris: Éditions du Seuil, Série Le rayon de la science, vol. 28, 190 pp.,
                 illustr. (French).
  1969A   La systématique des rongeurs hystricomorphes et la dérive des continents. Acad. Sci., C.R., Sér. D,
                 269:16, 1496—1497 (French).
  1971A   Essai sur les relations du maxillaire et du palatin dans la région orbito-temporale des Rongeurs. Hess.
                 Landesamt Bodenforsch., Abh., 60, 117—120 (French).
  1971B   Affinités systématiques des Caviomorphes et des Phiomorphes et origine africaine des Caviomorphes.
                 Acad. Brasil. Ciênc., An., 43 Suppl., 515—522 (French).

LAVOCAT, RENÉ   See also: Hoffstetter, R. and Lavocat, R., 1970A.

LAVRENT'EV, A. I.
  1968A   Îuzhnyĭ slon iz galechnika molodoĭ terrasy Eniseîa. [Southern elephant from the gravel of the young
                 terrace of Eniseĭ R.] In: Kaĭnozoĭ Zapadnoĭ Sibiri, 153—155, 1 fig. (Russian).

LAWLOR, FLORINE
    1970A   Exploring Nevada's Gypsum Cavern. Desert Mag., 33:1, 28—29, 38, illustr.

LAWRENCE, DAVID R.
    1971A   The nature and structure of paleoecology. J. Paleontol., 45, 593—607, 7 figs.

LAZA, A.
    1966A   Vîrsta hominidelor. [The age of hominids.] Natura, Ser. Biol., 18:2, 80—82 (Rumanian).

LAZAREV, PETR ALEKSEEVICH
    1968A   K voprosu o sistematike pleĭstotsenovoĭ loshadi Iakutii. [On the systematic position of the Pleistocene horse from Iakutia.] In: Problemy izucheniĭa chetvertichnogo perioda. Tezisy, 115—116 (Russian).
    1971A   Nizhnepleĭstotsenovaĭa loshad' na Severo-Vostoke SSSR. [Lower Pleistocene horse in the northeast of the USSR.] Kolyma, 1971:6, 45, 1 table (Russian).

LAZUKOV, G. I.
    1970A   Antropogen severnoĭ poloviny Zapadnoĭ Sibiri. (Stratigrafiĭa). [Anthropogene of the northern half of west Siberia. (Stratigraphy).] Moscow: Moscow Univ. Press, 322 pp., illustr. (Russian).

LAZUKOV, G. I.   See also: Markov, K. K., Velichko, A. A., Lazukov, G. I. and Nikolaev, V. A., 1968A.

LE MINH VIEN   See: Lindberg, G. V. and Le Minh Vien, 1970A.

LEACH, GERALD
    1972A   Why those dinosaurs really died. San Francisco Chron., July 22, 1972, 9.

LEAKEY, L. S. B.
    1960F   Finding the world's earliest man. Photographs by Des Bartlett. Nat. Geogr. Mag., 118:3, 420—435, illustr.
    1965A   Rev.: Martí Jusmet in Ampurias, 29, 355—358.
    1966D   Very early East African Hominidae and their ecological setting. In: Howell, F. C. and Bourliere, F. (eds.), 1966A, 448—457.
    1967A   Rev.: Martí Jusmet in Ampurias, 29, 355—358.
    1967G   The search for man's ancestors. In: Rapport, S. and Wright, H. (eds.), 1967A, 4—18 (reprinted from Leakey, L. S. B., 1960D, Adam's ancestors).
    1967H   The discovery of Zinjanthropus. In: Rapport, S. and Wright, H. (eds.), 1967A, 32—44 (reprinted with revisions from Nat. Geogr. Mag., 118:3, 420—435).
    1969A   Fort Ternan hominid. Nature, 222:5199, 1202.
    1969B   Ecology of north Indian Ramapithecus. Nature, 223:5210, 1075—1076.
    1969C*   Fossil vertebrates of Africa. Vol. 1. New York and London: Academic Press, ix + 102 pp., illustr. Rev.: Albanesi in Riv. Ital. Paleontol. Stratigr., 75:4, 890; Anon. in La Recherche, 1:2, 193; Clark in Man (J. Roy. Anthropol. Inst.), 5:4, 708—709; Cooke in Quart. Rev. Biol., 45:2, 181—182; Fedele in J. Human Evol., 1:1, 123—124; Haltenorth in Säugetierkundl. Mitt., 18:1, 88; Preuschoft in Zentralbl. Geol. Paläontol., Teil 2, 1970:3/4, 247—248; Savage in Nature, 224: 5225, 1235—1236; Shotwell in Palaeogeogr., Palaeoclimatol., Palaeoecol., 8:4, 346—347.
    1969D   Archeological and paleontological investigations at Olduvai Gorge and Lake Natron, Tanzania, and Fort Ternan, Kenya, 1964. Nat. Geogr. Soc., Res. Reps., 1964, 119—121.
    1970A   "Newly" recognized mandible of Ramapithecus. Nature, 225:5228, 199—200, 1 fig.
    1970B   The relationship of African apes, man, and Old World monkeys. Nat. Acad. Sci. , Proc., 67, 746—748.
    1970C   Additional information on the status of Giraffa jumae from East Africa. In: Leakey, L. S. B. and Savage, R. J. G. (eds.), 1970A, 325—330, 4 pls., 1 table. Rev.: Thenius in Zentralbl. Geol. Paläontol., Teil 2, 1971:4, 346.
    1970D   Archeological research at Olduvai Gorge, Tanzania, and Fort Ternan, Kenya, 1961—1962. Nat. Geogr. Soc., Res. Reps., 1961—1962, 131—134.
    1970E   The stone age races of Kenya. London: Oxford University Press, xvii + 150 pp., 52 figs., 37 pls. Rev.: Roth-Lutra in Anat. Anz., 130:3—4, 478—479.
    1971A   Basic rectangle of the mandible in the Hominoidae. Nature, 231:5297, 60.
    1971B   History of the national museums of Kenya. Kenya Past and Present, 1:1, 1—2.
    1971C   A new fossil skull from Olduvai. In: Leakey, L. S. B., Prost, J. and Prost, S. (eds.), 1971A, 353—359, 2 figs. (reprinted from Nature, Aug. 1959).
    1971D   New finds at Olduvai Gorge. In: Leakey, L. S. B., Prost, J. and Prost, S. (eds.), 1971A, 365—369, 4 figs. (reprinted from Nature, Feb. 1961).
    1971E   A new lower Pliocene primate from Kenya. In: Leakey, L. S. B., Prost, J. and Prost, S. (eds.), 1971A, 377—384 (reprinted from Annals and Mag. of Natur. Hist., Nov. 1961).
    1971F   Bone smashing by late Miocene Hominidae. In: Leakey, L. S. B., Prost, J. and Prost, S. (eds.), 1971A, 443—447, 5 figs. (reprinted from Nature, May 1968).

1972A   Facts instead of dogmas on man's origin. In: McCown, T. D. and Kennedy, K. A. R. (eds.), 1972A, 386–399 (reprinted from Origin of Man, 1965).

LEAKEY, L. S. B. and GOODALL, VANNE MORRIS
1969A   Unveiling man's origins. Cambridge, Mass.: Schenkman Pub. Co., xvii + 220 pp., frontispiece, illustr. Rev.: Harrison in New Sci., 49:736, 212; Humphrey in S. Afr. Archaeol. Bull., 26:103–104, 184; Johnston in Human Biol., 42:3, 527; Kurth in Homo, 21:1, 65; Turner in Amer. J. Phys. Anthropol., 36:3, 446–447.

LEAKEY, L. S. B. and LEAKEY, MARY D.
1968A   Archeological excavations at Olduvai Gorge, Tanzania. Nat. Geogr. Soc., Res. Reps., 1963, 179–182.
1971A   Recent discoveries of fossil hominids in Tanganika: at Olduvai and near Lake Natron. In: Leakey, L. S. B., Prost, J. and Prost, S. (eds.), 1971A, 425–429, 7 figs. (reprinted from Nature, April 1969).

LEAKEY, L. S. B., PROST, J. and PROST, S.
1971A*   Adam, or ape. A sourcebook of discoveries about early man. Cambridge, Mass. and London: Schenkman Publishing Co., xiii + 452 pp., illustr.

LEAKEY, L. S. B. and SAVAGE, R. J. G.
1970A*   Fossil vertebrates of Africa. Vol. 2. New York and London: Academic Press, ix + 333 pp., illustr. Rev.: Albanesi in Riv. Ital. Paleontol. Stratigr., 77:2, 299; Black in J. Mammal., 52:4, 859–860; Fedele in J. Human Evol., 1:1, 123–124; Haltenorth in Säugetierkundl., Mitt., 20:1–2, 181; Herre in Z. Zool. Syst. Evolut.-Forsch., 9:2, 159.

LEAKEY, L. S. B., TOBIAS, P. V. and NAPIER, J. R.
1971A   A new species of the genus Homo from Olduvai Gorge. In: Leakey, L. S. B., Prost, J. and Prost, S. (eds.), 1971A, 431–438 (reprinted from Nature, April 1964).

LEAKEY, L. S. B.   See also: Leakey, M. D., Clarke, R. J. and Leakey, L. S. B., 1971A.

LEAKEY, M., TOBIAS, P. V., MARTYN, J. E. and LEAKEY, R. E. F.
1969A   An Acheulean industry with prepared core technique and the discovery of a contemporary hominid mandible at Lake Baringo, Kenya. Prehist. Soc., Proc., 35:3, 48–76, 12 figs., 2 pls., 2 tables.

LEAKEY, MARY D.
1968A   Centre for prehistory and palaeontology. Honorary director's report. Nairobi Nat. Mus., Rep., 1967–68, 27–38.
1969A   Recent discoveries of hominid remains at Olduvai Gorge, Tanzania. Nature, 223:5207, 756.
1970A   Early artefacts from the Koobi Fora area. Nature, 226:5242, 228–230, 1 fig., 1 table.
1971A   Discovery of postcranial remains of Homo erectus and associated artefacts in Bed IV at Olduvai Gorge, Tanzania. Nature, 232:5310, 380–383, 4 figs., 2 tables.
1971B   Olduvai Gorge, Volume 3: excavations in Beds I and II, 1960–1963. Cambridge: Cambridge University Press, xix + 306 pp., frontispiece, 121 figs., 41 pls., 10 tables, 1 map. Rev.: Keller in Amer. Sci., 60:5, 640; Patterson in Human Biol., 44:3, 587–588.

LEAKEY, M. D., CLARKE, R. J. and LEAKEY, L. S. B.
1971A   New hominid skull from Bed I, Olduvai Gorge, Tanzania. Nature, 232:5318, 308–312, 3 figs., 2 tables, cover.

LEAKEY, MARY D.   See also: Leakey, L. S. B. and Leakey, M. D., 1968A, 1971A.

LEAKEY, RICHARD E. F.
1969A   New Cercopithecidae from the Chemeron beds of Lake Baringo, Kenya. In: Leakey, L. S. B. (ed.), 1969C, 53–69, 5 pls., 14 tables.
1969B   Early Homo sapiens remains from the Omo River region of south-west Ethiopia. Nature, 222:5199, 1132–1133.
1970A   Fauna and artefacts from a new Plio-Pleistocene locality near Lake Rudolf in Kenya. Nature, 226:5242, 223–224, 3 figs.
1970B   In search of man's past at Lake Rudolf. Illustrated by Gordon W. Gahan. Nat. Geogr. Mag., 137:5, 712–733, illustr.
1971A   Further evidence of lower Pleistocene hominids from East Rudolf, North Kenya. Nature, 231:5300, 241–245, 4 figs., 6 tables.
1971B   New perspectives on man's origin: current research in East Africa. Kenya Past and Present, 1:1, 3–10, illustr.
1972A   Further evidence of lower Pleistocene hominids from East Rudolf, North Kenya, 1971. Nature, 237:5353, 264–269, 9 figs., 5 tables.

LEAKEY, R. E. F., MUNGAI, J. M. and WALKER, A. C.
1971A   New australopithecines from East Rudolf, Kenya. Amer. J. Phys. Anthropol., 35:2, 175—186, 2 pls.
1972A   New australopithecines from East Rudolf, Kenya (II). Amer. J. Phys. Anthropol., 36:2, 235—252,
          3 pls., 2 tables.

LEAKEY, R. E. F.   See also: Isaac, G. L., Leakey, R. E. F. and Behrensmeyer, A. K., 1971A; Leakey, M.,
          Tobias, P. V., Martyn, J. E. and Leakey, R. E. F., 1969A.

LEANZA, ARMANDO F.
1969A   Sistema de salta. Su edad, sus peces voladores, su asincronismo con el horizonte calcareo-dolomitico
          y con las calizas de miraflores y la hibridez del sistema subandino. Asoc. Geol. Argent., Rev.,
          24:4, 393—407, 3 figs. (Spanish; English summary).

LEAR, JOHN
1970A   The bones on Coalsack Bluff. A story of drifting continents. Saturday Review, 1970, Feb. 7, 46—51,
          7 figs.

LEARY, RICHARD L.
1971A   Catalog of paleozoic paleozoological type and figured specimens at the Illinois State Museum. Ill.
          Acad. Sci., Trans., 64:3, 254—259.

LEBEAU, MARIE-ODILE   See: Bonis, L. de, Lebeau, M.-O. and Ricqlès, A. de, 1972A.

LEBEDEV, V. D. and FEDOTOV, V. F.
1969A   Okun' iz likhvinskikh drevneozernykh chetvertichnykh otlozhenii. [Perch from Likhvin ancient
          lacustrine Quaternary deposits.] Mosk. Obshch. Ispyt. Prir., Biull., Otd. Geol., 44:6, 148
          (Russian).

LEBEDEV, V. D.   See also: Sychevskaîa, E. K. and Lebedev, V. D., 1971A.

LEBEDEVA, NATAL'IA ALEKSEEVNA
1968A   Korrelîatsiîa antropogenovykh otlozhenii Predkavkaz'îa, Priazov'îa i lednikovykh otlozhenii doliny
          Dnepra. [Correlation of Anthropogene deposits of north Caucasian and north Azovian regions
          with glacial deposits of Dnepr Valley.] In: Granitsa tretichnogo i chetvertichnogo periodov,
          82—85, 1 fig. (Russian; English summary).
1971A   O polozhenii ostatkov mlekopitaiushchikh khaprovskogo i tamanskogo faunisticheskogo kompleksov v
          razreze morskikh sloev Akchagyla i Apsherona Vostochnogo Zakavkaz'îa. [On the position of
          mammalian remains of the Khapry and Taman' faunal associations within the section of marine
          Akchagylian and Apsheronian strata of eastern Transcaucasia.] Vses. Nauch.-Issled. Inst.
          Prirodn. Gazov, Tr., 31 (39—32) 40, 248—275 (Russian).
1972A   O geologicheskom polozhenii ostatkov nazemnykh mlekopitaiushchikh khaprovskogo, tamanskogo i
          tiraspol'skogo faunisticheskikh kompleksov v razreze morskikh sloev akchagyla i apsherona
          Vostochnogo Zakavkaz'îa. [On the geologic position of land mammals remains of the Khapry,
          Taman' and Tiraspol' faunal associations in the section of Akchagyl and Apsheron marine strata
          of eastern Transcaucasia.] Akad. Nauk SSSR, Kom. Izuch. Chetvertich. Perioda, Biull., 38, 99—
          115, 6 figs., 1 chart (Russian).

LEBEDEVA, N. A.   See also: Safronov, I. N. and Lebedeva, N. A., 1968A.

LEBEDKINA, NATALIE S.
1968A   The development of bones in the skull roof of Amphibia. Nobel Symp., 4th, Stockholm, 1967, Proc.,
          1968, 317—329, 9 figs.
          Rev.: Westphal in Zentralbl. Geol. Paläontol., Teil 2, 1969:2, 209.
1968B   Razvitie kostei kryshi cherepa khvostatykh amfibii. [The development of the skull roof's bones in
          Urodela.] Akad. Nauk SSSR, Zool. Inst., Trudy, 46, 86—124, 27 figs. (Russian).

LEBEN, FRANCE
1967A   Stratigrafija in časovna uvrstitev jamskih najdb na Tražeškem Krasu. [Stratigraphy and age of cave
          sites on the Triestine Karst. (A contribution to the knowledge of cave archeology on Slovenian
          territory.)] Arheol. Vestn., 18, 43—86, 7 figs., 23 pls., 1 chart (Slovenian; German summary).

LECACHEUX, B.
1967A   Prise d'empreinte et reproduction de la table interne d'un crâne non scié grâce aux élastomères et à
          la galvanoplastie. Soc. Anthropol. Paris, Bull. Mém., Sér. 12, 1:2, 193—197, 3 figs. (French).

LEE, D. N. and WOODHOUSE, H. C.
1970A   Art on the rocks of southern Africa. Cape Town: Purnell and Sons Ltd., 165 pp., 248 photos, 38 drawings.

LEE, RICHARD B. and DeVORE, IRVEN
1968A*   Man the hunter. Chicago: Aldine Publishing Co., xvi + 415 pp., illustr.
    Rev.: Anon. in Explorer (Cleveland Mus. Natur. Hist.), 12:4, 30; ms in Archeol. Roz., 22:2, 226–227; Marks in Amer. J. Phys. Anthropol., 32:1, 161–162; Reynolds in Man, 4:4, 658–660; Rutherford in Asian Perspectives, 11, 203–204.
1968B   Problems in the study of hunters and gatherers. In: Lee, R. B. and DeVore, I. (eds.), 1968A, 3–12.

LEE, THOMAS E.
1961C   The question of Indian origins. Sci. of Man, 1, 159–167, 1 map.
1968A   The question of Indian origins, again. Anthropol. J. Can., 6:4, 22–32.

LEE, YU-CHING
1963A   Abs.: Sci. Abstr. China, Earth Sci., 2:1, 7.

LEES, PATRICIA M.   See: Clemens, W. A., Jr. and Lees, P. M., 1971A.

LEFELD, JERZY
1971A   Geology of the Djadokhta formation at Bayn Dzak (Mongolia). In: Kielan-Jaworowska, Z. (ed.), 1971B, 101–130, 16 figs., 3 pls., 9 tables.

LEFELD, JERZY   See also: Gradziński, R., Kaźmierczak, J. and Lefeld, J., 1968A.

LEFEVRE, MARCEL and LAPORTE, GUY S.
1968A   The "Maladie Verte" of Lascaux. Diagnosis and treatment. Stud. Speleol., 2:1, 35–44, 2 figs., 4 pls.

LE FLOCH, R.   See: Coppens, Y., Gouzes, R., Le Floch, R. and Paquet, M., s.d.

LEGAULT, J. A.
1968A   Conodonts and fish remains from the Stonehouse formation, Arisaig, Nova Scotia. Can., Geol. Surv., Bull., 165, 1–45, 3 pls., 1 map, 3 tables.

LEGIGAN, PHILIPPE
1970A   Quelques précisions à propos du "sable des Landes". Soc. Géol. Fr., C.R., 1970:4, 116–117 (French).

LEGOUX, PIERRE ROGER
1969A   Détermination de l'âge dentaire de l'enfant néandertalien du Pech-de-l'Azé (Dordogne). Acad. Sci., C.R., Sér. D, 268:24, 2875–2878, 2 figs. (French).
1970A   Étude odontologique de l'enfant néandertalien du Pech-de-l'Azé. Arch. Inst. Paléontol. Hum., Mém., 33, 53–87, 5 pls., 2 tables (French).

LEHMAN, JEAN-PIERRE
1964D   Notice sur Marcellin Boule. Mus. Nat. Hist. Natur., Paris, Arch., 7 Sér., 8, X-XVIII, portr. (French).
1967D   Paléontologie. In: Aubouin, J., Brousse, R. and Lehman, J.-P., 1967A, v. 2, Part 2, 3–223, 326 figs., 8 pls. (French).
    Rev.: Furon in Rev. Gén. Sci., 75, 181.
1968B   Remarques concernant la phylogénie des Amphibiens. Nobel Symp., 4th, Stockholm, 1967, Proc., 1968, 307–315, 6 figs. (French).
    Rev.: Westphal in Zentralbl. Geol. Paläontol., Teil 2, 1969:2, 209.
1969A   Incertae sedis. Palaeospondylus gunni Traquair. In: Piveteau, J. (ed.), 1969A, Traité de Paléo., T. IV, vol. 2, 777–781, 3 figs. (French).
1970A   Camille Arambourg. Soc. Vert. Paleontol., News Bull., 88, 76, portr.
1970B   L'expédition paléontologique française de 1969 au Spitzberg. Atomes, 25:274, 193–198, 8 figs. (French).
1970C   Les expéditions et les fouilles paléontologiques (vertébrés) organisées par la France à l'étranger. Acad. Soc. Lorraines Sci., Bull., 9:1, 244–252 (French).
1971A   Nouveaux vertébrés fossiles du Trias de la série de Zarzaïtine. Ann. Paléontol., Vertébrés, 57:1, 71–113, 11 figs., 10 pls. (French; English summary).
    Rev.: Westphal in Zentralbl. Geol. Paläontol., Teil 2, 1971:5, 409.

LEHMAN, J.-P.   See also: Auboin, J., Brousse, R. and Lehman, J.-P., 1967A.

LEHMANN, ERNST VON
1968A   Ein neuer Nachweis des Moschusochsen (Ovibos moschatus Zimmermann, 1780) im Rheinland. Decheniana, 121:1–2, 197–198, 1 pl. (German).

LEHMANN, ERNST VON   See also: Boecker, M., Lehmann, E. v. and Remy, H., 1972A.

LEHMANN, ULRICH
  1964A   Rev.: Gautier in Natuurwet. Tijdschr., 46:2–6, 181.
  1966B   Die Teufels- oder Fuchslucken bei Eggenburg (NÖ.). 6. Die Boviden. Österreich. Akad. Wiss., Denk.,
               112, 83–88, pl. 10 (German).
  1969A   Die Bocksteinschmiede im Lonetal. Die Fauna. In: Wetzel, R. and Bosinski, G., 1969A, 133–167,
               11 figs., 3 pls. (German).

LEHRMAN, ROBERT L.
  1966A   Race, evolution, and mankind. New York: Basic Books, Inc., vi + 200 pp., 23 figs.
               Rev.: Binford in Amer. Anthropol., 70, 169.

LEICH, HELMUT
  1968A   Nach Millionen Jahren ans Licht. Versteinerungen der Jurazeit. Ein Bildband. Thun and Munich:
               Ott Verlag, 164 pp., 71 pls. (German).
               Rev.: Westphal in Naturwiss. Rundsch., 22:5, 278–279.

LEINDERS, JOSEPH and MICHAUX, JACQUES
  1969A   Complément à la connaissance de la faune de mammifères du Pliocène de Roussillon. Précision sur
               l'extension chronologique du genre Canis en Europe. Soc. Géol. Fr., C.R., 1969:8, 322–324,
               2 tables (French).
               Rev.: Thenius in Zentralbl. Geol. Paläontol., Teil 2, 1971:5, 415.

LEISMAN, GILBERT A.   See: Bridge, T. E., Leisman, G. A. and Lockard, W., 1972A.

LEMLEY, RAY E.
  1971A   Notice of new finds in the Badlands. S. Dak. Acad. Sci., Proc., 50, 70–74.

LEMOZI, A.
  1965A   La grotte Marcenac, station du Paléolithique supérieur. (Étude comparative). Congr. Préhist. France,
               16e Sess., Monaco 1959, C.R., 778–807, 31 figs. (French).

LENGYEL, IMRE
  1968A   Biochemical aspects of early skeletons. In: Brothwell, D. R. (ed.), 1968A, 271–288, 11 figs., 1 table.
  1969A   A comparative electrophoretic examination of Recent and fossil human bone proteins. Symp. Biol.
               Hungarica, 9, 117–123, 4 figs.

LENZ, A. C.   See: Broad, D. S. and Lenz, A. C., 1972A.

LEOKUM, A.
  1970A   How is carbon-14 used to date objects? Rocks Miner., 45:9, 585.

LEONARDI, PIERO
  1961C   Carlos Darwin y el evolucionismo. Madrid: Ediciones Fax, 224 pp., 67 figs. (Spanish).
  1969A   Angelo Pasa. Verona, Mus. Civ. Stor. Natur., Mem., Fuori Ser., 3, 3–14, 1 photo (Italian).

LEONARDI, PIERO, et al.
  1967A   Le Dolomiti. Geologia dei monti tra Isarco e Piave. 2 vols. Trento: A cura del Consiglio nazionale
               delle ricerche e della Guinta provinciale di Trento, 1019 pp., 519 figs., maps, bibliog. (Italian;
               English summary).
               Rev.: Rosenberg in Austr. Geol. Bundesanst., Verh. 1969:1, 98–109 (essay review).

LEONARDI, P. and ALLEGRANZI, A.
  1965A   Grotta del Broion (Colli Berici, prov. di Vicenza). Riv. Sci. Preist., 20, 363 (Italian).

LEONARDI, P. and RUFFO, S.
  1969A   Riparo Tagliente (Prov. di Verona). Riv. Sci. Preist., 24:2, 351–352 (Italian).

LEONHARDY, FRANK C.
  1966A   Rev.: Frison in Mich. Archaeol., 13:4, 206–207.

LEONOV, GEORGIĬ PAVLOVICH
  1967A   Paleogenovaiă sistema. [Paleogene system.] Geologiiă SSSR, 11, Povolzh'e and Prikam'e, 579–603,
               1 fig., 2 tables (Russian).

LEOPOLD, CARL A. and ARDREY, ROBERT
    1972A   Toxic substances in plants and the food habits of early man. Science (AAAS), 176:3034, 512–514.

LEPERSONNE, JACQUES
    1970A   Revision of the fauna and the stratigraphy of the fossiliferous localities of the Lake Albert - Lake
               Edward Rift (Congo). Mus. Roy. Afr. Cent., Ann., Sér. in 8º, Sci. Géol., 67, 171–207,
               5 tables.

LEPPER, JOCHEN
    1969A   Zur Deutung eines Fährten-Fundes aus dem Buntsandstein der Rhön. Geol. Bl. Nordost-Bayern, 19:3,
               128–132, 2 figs., 1 table (German).

LEQUATRE, PAUL
    1966A   La grotte de Prélétang (commune de Presles, Isère). I. Le repaire d'ours des cavernes et son industrie
               moustérienne. Gallia Préhist., 9:1, 1–83, 49 figs., tables (French).

LEQUATRE, PAUL   See also: Bocquet, A. and Lequatre, P., 1968A.

LERNER, I. MICHAEL
    1968A   Heredity, evolution, and society. San Francisco: W. H. Freeman and Co., xvi + 307 pp., illustr.
               Rev.: Darlington in Endeavor, 28:104, 102; Montalenti in Scientia, 106:1–2, 120–121; Schwidetzky
               in Homo, 20:4, 250.

LEROI-GOURHAN, ANDRÉ
    1965C   Rev.: Ripoll Perelló in Ampurias, 29, 346–348.
    1967A   Rev.: Blum in Amer. Sci., 57:1, 58A–59A.
    1968B   Rev.: Baz-Dresch in NSS News, 27, 79.
    1968C   Prehistoria del arte occidental. Translated from French. Barcelona: Gustavo Gili, 480 pp., illustr.
               (Spanish).

LEROI-GOURHAN, ARLETTE
    1968A   Le Néanderthalien IV de Shanidar. Soc. Préhist. Fr., Bull., C.R., 65:3, 79–82, 1 fig. (French).

LEROI-GOURHAN, ARLETTE   See also: González Echegaray, J., García Guinea, M. A., Begines, A.,
               Madariaga de la Campa, B. and Leroi-Gourhan, Arl., 1966A.

LEROY, PIERRE
    1971A*   Dans le sillage des Sinanthropes. Paris: Fayard, 99 pp. (French).
               Rev.: Piront in Rev. Quest. Sci., 32:4, 558.

LEROY, PIERRE   See also : Barjon, L. and Leroy, P., 1964A.

LESSERTISSEUR, JACQUES
    1968A   Du bipède animal au bipède humain. Soc. Zool. Fr., Bull., 93:4, 505–534, 22 figs. (French).

LESSERTISSEUR, J. and ROBINEAU, D.
    1969A   Le mode d'alimentation des premiers vertébrés et l'origine des mâchoires. I. Les faits et les theories.
               Mus. Nat. Hist. Natur., Paris, Bull., 41:6, 1321–1347, 21 figs., 2 tables (French).
    1970A   Le mode d'alimentation des premiers vertébrés et l'origine des mâchoires. II. Les correlations et les
               conséquences. Mus. Nat. Hist. Natur., Paris, Bull., 42:1, 102–121, 6 figs. (French; English
               and German summaries).

LESTREL, PETER   See: Read, D. W. and Lestrel, P., 1972A.

LEV, D. N.
    1965A   Samarkandskaia paleoliticheskaia stoianka. (Predvaritel'noe soobshchenie). [Paleolithic site in
               Samarkand. (Preliminary report).] Akad. Nauk Uzbek. SSR, Inst. Ist. Arkheol., Ist. Mater.
               Kul't. Uzbekist., 6, 22–29 (Russian).

LEVENE, H., EHRMAN, L. and RICHMOND, R.
    1970A   Theodosius Dobzhansky up to now. In: Hecht, M. K. and Steere, W. C. (eds.), 1970A, 1–41, illustr.

LEVINE, WILLIAM E.
    1971A   A specimen of Dinictis (Felidae) from the lower Oligocene near Chadron, Nebraska. Nebr. Acad. Sci.,
               Proc., 81, 49.

LEVINS, RICHARD
1968A   Evolution in changing environments. Some theoretical explorations. Princeton: University Press, 120 pp., 39 figs., 10 tables.
        Rev.: Denniston in Amer. Anthropol., 71, 1194—1195; Schöneich in Biol. Zentralbl., 89:1, 122.

LEWIS, ARTHUR B.   See: Garn, S. M., Lewis, A. B. and Walenga, A. J., 1969A.

LEWIS, G. EDWARD
1968A   Stratigraphic paleontology of the Barstow formation in the Alvord Mountain area, San Bernardino County, California. U.S. Geol. Surv. Prof. Pap., 600—C, 75—79, 1 fig., 1 table.
1969A   Larger fossil mammals and mylagaulid rodents from the Troublesome formation (Miocene) of Colorado. U.S. Geol. Surv., Prof. Paper, 650—B, 53—56, 2 figs.
1970A   New discoveries of Pleistocene bisons and peccaries in Colorado. U.S. Geol. Surv., Prof. Paper, 700—B, 137—140, 1 fig.
1971A   Preliminary notice of new man-like apes from India. In: Leakey, L. S. B., Prost, J. and Prost, S. (eds.), 1971A, 225—227, 1 fig. (reprinted from Amer. J. Sci., 27, 1934).

LEWIS, G. E.   See also: Gard, L. M., Lewis, G. E. and Whitmore, F. C., Jr., 1972A.

LEWIS, JOHN and TOWERS, BERNARD
1969A   Naked ape or *Homo sapiens?* New York: Humanities Press, 134 pp., 5 figs.
        Rev.: Chatterjee in Man in India, 50:3, 310—311; Dixon in New Sci., 44:662, 345.

LEWIS, K. B.
1968A   Size of fossil animals as an indicator of paleotemperatures. Tuatara, 16:1, 62—68, 1 fig.

LEWIS, OWEN J.
1969A   The hominoid wrist joint. Amer. J. Phys. Anthropol., 30, 251—268, 10 figs.
1971A   Brachiation and the early evolution of the Hominoidea. Nature, 230:5296, 577—578, 3 figs.
1972A   Evolution of the hominoid wrist. In: Tuttle, R. (ed.), 1972A, 207—222, 3 figs., 2 pls.
1972B   The evolution of the hallucial tarsometatarsal joint in the Anthropoidea. Amer. J. Phys. Anthropol., 37:1, 13—34, 3 figs., 3 pls.

LEWONTIN, R. C.
1968A*   Population biology and evolution. Proceedings International Symposium, June 7—9, 1967 Syracuse, N.Y. Syracuse, N.Y.: Syracuse Univ. Press, 205 pp., illustr.
        Rev.: Williams in Quart. Rev. Biol., 45:1, 103—104.

LHOTE, HENRI
1964A   Faits nouveaux concernant la chronologie relative et absolue des gravures et peintures pariétales du Sud Oranais et du Sahara. In: Pericot García, L. and Ripoll Perelló, E. (eds.), 1964A, 191—214, 1 table (French; English summary).
1964B   Sur les rapports entre les centres d'art préhistoriques d'Europe (province franco-cantabrique et Levant espagnol) et celui du Sahara. In: Pericot García, L. and Ripoll Perelló, E. (eds.), 1964A, 215—223 (French; English summary).
1966A   Le mammouth et l'éléphant dans l'art pariétal. Lisbon, Univ., Fac. Letr., Rev., Sér. 3, 10, 125—149, 35 figs. (French).
1967A   Nouvelle lecture de la plaquette dite de "la femme au renne". Soc. Préhist. Fr., Bull., Étud. Trav., 64:1, 123—130, 2 figs. (French).

LI, CHUAN-KUEI
1962A   Abs.: Sci. Abstr. China, Earth Sci., 2:1, 1—2.
1963A   Abs.: Sci. Abstr. China, Earth Sci., 2:1, 6—7.
1963B   Abs.: Sci. Abstr. China, Earth Sci., 2:1, 2.
1965A   Abs.: Sci. Abstr. China, Earth Sci., 3:2, 7.

LI, CHUAN-KUEI   See also: Chow, M. and Li, C., 1965A, 1965B.

LI, YAN-SIAN   See: Tszia, L.-p., Gai, P. and Li, Y.-s., 1964A.

LIADZHINA, KARINA ALEKSEEVNA   See: Kostenko, N. N., Nikitin, E. A. and Liadzhina, K. A., 1971A.

LIARSKAIA, LIUBOV' ANATOL'EVNA (= LYARSKAYA, L.)
1970A   O biofatsial'noi zonal'nosti rannefranskogo basseina na territorii Latvii. [On the biofacies zonality of the early Frasnian basin on the territory of Latvia.] Paleontol. Stratigr. Pribalt. Beloruss., 2, 353—360, 2 figs. (Russian; English summary).

1971A   Novye nakhodki ostatkov psammosteid iz Shvïantoïskogo gorizonta Latvii. [New finds of psammosteid remains from Šventoji horizon of Latvia.] Paleontol. Stratigr. Pribalt. Belorus., 3, 97–104, 9 figs. (Russian; English summary).

LIÄRSKAÏA, L. A.   See also: Vorob'eva, E. I. and Lïarskaïa, L. A., 1968A.

LÏASHENKO, ALEKSEĬ IVANOVICH   See: Sereda, T. T., Ellern, S. S. and Lïashenko, A. I., 1967A.

LIDER, V. A.
1968A   Znachenie fauny mlekopitaïushchikh i periodichnosti tektonicheskikh dvizheniĭ dlïa stratigrafii chetvertichnykh otlozheniĭ. [Significance of mammalian fauna and of periodicity of tectonic movements for the stratigraphy of Quaternary deposits.] In: Problemy izucheniïa chetvertichnogo perioda. Tezisy, 116–118 (Russian).
1969A   Chetvertichnaïa sistema. [Quaternary system.] Geologiïa SSSR, 12:1, Perm, Sverdlovsk, Chelïabinsk, and Kurgan Provinces, 425–454, 2 figs., 1 table (Russian).

LIDICKER, WILLIAM Z., JR.   See: Martinez R., C. and Lidicker, W. Z., Jr., 1971A.

LIGERON, J.-MICHEL
1971A   Excursion géologique (du 24 mai 1970). Étude des terrains tertiaires dans la région Nord-Ouest de Reims. Bull. Soc. Hist. Nat. Ardennes, 60:108, 11–26, 5 figs. (French).

LIGHTHILL, M. JAMES
1970A   How do fishes swim? Endeavor, 29:107, 77–83, 13 figs., 3 tables.

LIIVA, A.   See: Ilves, E., Punning, J.-M. and Liiva, A., 1968A, 1969A; Punning, J.-M., Liiva, A. and Ilves, E., 1968A.

LILLEGRAVEN, JASON A.
1968A   The latest Cretaceous mammals of the upper part of the Edmonton formation of Alberta, Canada, and a review of the marsupial-placental dichotomy in mammalian evolution. Diss. Abstr., 29:6, 2241B–2242B (abs.).
1969A   The stratigraphy and vertebrate fossils of the Oligocene Brule formation, Slim Buttes, northwestern South Dakota. Geol. Soc. Amer., Abstr., Part 3, 34 (abs.).
1969B   Latest Cretaceous mammals of upper part of Edmonton formation of Alberta, Canada, and review of marsupial-placental dichotomy in mammalian evolution. Kans., Univ., Pal. Contrib., 50, 122 pp., 53 figs., 21 tables.
     Rev.: Krebs in Zentralbl. Geol. Paläontol., Teil 2, 1971:2–3, 186–187.
1970A   Stratigraphy, structure, and vertebrate fossils of the Oligocene Brule formation, Slim Buttes, northwestern South Dakota. Geol. Soc. Amer., Bull., 81:3, 831–850, 10 figs., 1 table.
1972A   Ordinal and familial diversity of Cenozoic mammals. Taxon, 21:2–3, 261–274, 6 figs., 1 table.
1972B   Preliminary report on late Cretaceous mammals from the El Gallo formation, Baja California Del Norte, Mexico. Los Angeles Cty. Mus., Contrib. Sci., 232, 11 pp., 5 figs. (Spanish summary).

LIMOGES, CAMILLE
1969A   Une lecture de Darwin. Sciences, 58/59, 70–73, illustr. (French).
1970A   La sélection naturelle. Étude sur la première constitution d'un concept (1837–1859). Paris: Presses Univ. de France, 184 pp. (French).
     Rev.: Ghiselin in Science (AAAS), 170:3957, 523–524.
1970B   Darwinisme et adaptation. [Darwinism and adaptation.] Rev. Quest. Sci., 31, 353–374 (French).

LINARES, OMAR J.   See: Reig, O. A. and Linares. O. J., 1969A.

LINDBERG, G. U.
1971A   Rol' krupnykh kolebaniĭ urovnïa okeana v rasselenii i evolïuïsii organizmov. [Role of large-scale ocean level fluctuations in the dispersal and evolution of organisms.] In: Tezisy dokladov XVII sessii Vsesoïuznogo paleontologicheskogo obshchestva, 25–29 ïanv. 1971g., 49–51 (Russian).

LINDBERG, G. U. and LE MINH VIEN
1970A   Ubezhishche dlïa ryb Paleomekonga. [Refuge for the Paleomekong fishes.] Vop. Ikhtiol., 10:3(62), 577 (Russian).

LINDER, ALLAN D.
1970A   Fossil sculpins (Cottidae) from Idaho. Copeia, 1970:2, 755–756, 1 fig.

LINDIG, WOLFGANG
1970A   On evidence of early man in America. Curr. Anthropol., 11:2, 168.

LINDSAY, EVERETT
1969A   Rodents from the Hartman Ranch local fauna, California. Geol. Soc. Amer., Abstr., 121, 525 (abs.).
1971A   Middle Miocene rodents from the Cuyama Badlands, Southern California. Geol. Soc. Amer., Abstr., 3:2, 148 (abs.).
1972A   Late Cenozoic vertebrate faunas, San Pedro Valley, Arizona. Soc. Vert. Paleontol., Ann. Meeting, 32nd, 1972, Abstr. (abs.).
1972B   Small mammal fossils from the Barstow formation, California. Calif., Univ., Publ. Geol. Sci., 93, 104 pp., 55 figs., 12 tables.

LINDSAY, EVERETT H. and LUNDIN, ROBERT F.
1972A   An Oligocene oreodont (Mammalia: Artiodactyla) from central Arizona. J. Paleontol., 46:1, 115–119, 1 fig., 1 pl., 1 table.

LINDSAY, EVERETT H.   See also: Berzi, A., Michaux, J., Hutchison, J. H. and Lindsay, E., 1970A; Mehringer, P. J., Jr., King, J. E. and Lindsay, E. H., 1970A.

LINDSEY, K. DON
1972A   Paleontology division. Denver Mus. Natur. Hist., Ann. Rep., 1971, 32, 1 photo.

LINEAWEAVER, THOMAS H. and BACKUS, RICHARD H.
1970A   The natural history of sharks. Philadelphia and New York: J. B. Lippincott Co., 256 pp., frontispiece, illustr.
     Rev.: Anon. in Frontiers, 351, 31, 2 figs.

LINS ROLIM, JOSÉ
1971A   Sôbre alguns mamíferos fósseis de Lagoa da Pedra - Município de Santa Cruz do Capibaribe - Pernambuco. Pernambuco, Univ. Fed., Inst. Geociênc., Sér. B, 1:3, 19 pp., 9 figs. (Portuguese).

LIPATOVA, V. V., LOPATO, A. ĨU., MAKAROVA, I. S., OCHEV, V. G., PODGORNYĬ, ĨU. I., STAROZHILOVA, N. N., SAĬDAKOVSKIĬ, L. ÍA. and SHISHKIN, M. A.
1972A   Novye dannye po paleontologicheskomu obosnovaniĩu srednego triasa Prikaspiĭskoĭ vpadiny. [New data concerning paleontological evidence for middle Triassic deposits in the pre-Caspian depression.] Akad. Nauk SSSR, Dokl., 204:4, 927–930 (Russian).

LIPE, W. D.   See: Coats, D. R., Landry, S. O. and Lipe, W. D., 1971A.

LIPPS, JERE H.
1969A   Climatic regulation of factors controlling otariid pinniped origins and diversification. Geol. Soc. Amer., Spec. Pap., 121, 176 (abs.).

LIPPS, JERE H.   See also: Valentine, J. W. and Lipps, J. H., 1970A.

LIPPS, LEWIS   See: Ray, C. E. and Lipps, L., 1970A.

LIPTÁK, P.
1969A   On the evolutionary systematics of Hominidae. Symp. Biol. Hungarica, 9, 107–111.

LISKUN, I. G. and DEVIÂTKIN, E. V.
1964A   O pervichnykh dolomitakh iz kontinental'nykh neogenovykh otlozheniĭ Chuĭskoĭ kotloviny Gornogo Altaĩa. [Primary dolomites from the continental Neogene deposits of the Chuĩa basin of the Altaĩ upland.] Akad. Nauk SSSR, Dokl., 158:2, 359–362, 1 fig., 1 table (Russian).
1965A   Primary dolomite from continental Neogene deposits of the Chuya basin, Gornyy Altai. Akad. Nauk SSSR, Dokl., Earth Sci. Sec., 158, 44–47, 1 fig., 1 table. (Translated from Russian: Akad. Nauk SSSR, Dokl., 1964A, 158:2, 359–362).

LISOWSKI, F. P.
1965A   Human fossil remains recently discovered in Shensi province, China. Man (J. Roy. Anthropol. Inst.), 65, 119–120.

LISZKOWSKI, JERZY
1970A   Biostratygrafia danu i paleocenu z Nasiłowa i Bochotnicy w świetle analizy ichtiofauny. [Biostratigraphy of Danian and Paleocene from Nasiłow and Bochotnica in the light of ichthyofauna analysis.] Przegl. Geol., 1970:8–9, 391–397, 2 figs., 1 table (Polish; English and Russian summaries).

LITOVCHENKO, L. M.
    1969A   Tel'manskaĭa paleoliticheskaĭa stoĭanka (II kul'turnyĭ sloĭ). [Tel'manskaĭa Paleolithic settlement
                (second cultural layer).] Sov. Arkheol., 1969:3, 110–123, 2 figs., 3 tables (Russian; French
                summary).

LITTLEJOHN, MURRAY J.
    1969A   The systematic significance of isolating mechanisms. In: Sibley, Ch. G. (ed.), 1969A, 459–493,
                3 figs., 7 tables.

LIU, HOU-YI
    1963A   Abs.: Sci. Abstr. China, Earth Sci., 2:2, 5–6.

LIU, HSIEN-T'ING
    1962A   Abs.: Sci. Abstr. China, Earth Sci., 1:2, 10.
    1963A   Abs.: Sci. Abstr. China, Earth Sci., 1:2, 11–12.

LIU, HSIEN-T'ING and CHANG, MI-MAN
    1963A   Abs.: Sci. Abstr. China, Earth Sci., 2:1, 4.

LIU, HSIEN-T'ING and HSIEH, HSIANG-HSU
    1965A   Abs.: Sci. Abstr. China, Earth Sci., 3:4, 9.

LIU, HSIEN-T'ING and ZHOU, JIA-JIAN
    1965A   Abs.: Sci. Abstr. China, Earth Sci., 3:4, 8–9.

LIU, TUNG-SEN and LEE, YU-CHING
    1963A   Abs.: Sci. Abstr. China, Earth Sci., 2:2, 5.
    1963B   Abs.: Sci. Abstr. China, Earth Sci., 2:2, 6.

LIU, TUNG-SEN, LIU, HSIEN-T'ING and SU, TE-TSAO
    1963A   Abs.: Sci. Abstr. China, Earth Sci., 2:1, 2–3.

LIU, TUNG-SEN, LIU, HSIEN-T'ING and TANG, HSIN
    1962A   Abs.: Sci. Abstr. China, Earth Sci., 1:4, 5.

LIU, YUHAI
    1963A   Abs.: Sci. Abstr. China, 1:4, 6.

LIUBIN, V. P.
    1969A   O veroĭatnosti iskustvennykh sooruzheniĭ v grote Kiik-Koba. [On the probability of artificial
                constructions in the Kiik-Koba cave.] Sov. Arkheol., 1969:2, 244–246, 1 fig. (Russian).
    1972A   Pervobytnyĭ chelovek v gorakh Bol'shogo Kavkaza. [Primitive man in the mountains of the Great
                Caucasus.] Akad. Nauk SSSR, Inst. Arkheol., Krat. Soobshch., 131, 25–30, 2 figs. (Russian).

LIUBIN, V. P., BURCHAK-ABRAMOVICH, N. I. and KLAPCHUK, M. N.
    1971A   Kepshinskaĭa peshchera i voprosy paleogeografii pleĭstotsena Sochinskogo Prichernomor'ĭa. [Kepsha
                cave and the problems of Pleistocene paleogeography of the Sochi Black Sea area.] Akad.
                Nauk SSSR, Inst. Arkheol., Krat. Soobshch., 126, 40–48, 4 figs., 3 tables (Russian).

LIUBIN, V. P.   See also: Burchak-Abramovich, N. I. and Liubin, V. P., 1972A.

LIUBISHCHEV, ALEKSANDR ALEKSANDROVICH
    1968A   Problemy sistematiki. [Problems of systematics.] In: Problemy evoliutsii, 1, 7–29, 6 figs. (Russian;
                English summary).

LIUTKEVICH, EVGENII MIKHAĬLOVICH
    1969A   O priurochennosti permskikh Tetrapoda preimushchestvenno k tatarskomu ĭarusu Russkoĭ platformy i
                Priural'ĭa. [On the localization of Permian Tetrapoda mainly in the Tatarian stage of Russian
                Platform and Priural'e.] In: Voprosy geologii ĭuzhnogo Urala i Povolzh'ĭa, 6:1, 106–121
                (Russian).

LIVINGSTONE, DANIEL A.
    1971A   Speculations on the climatic history of mankind. Amer. Sci., 59:3, 332–337.

LLINÁS, R.
    1969A*   Neurobiology of cerebellar evolution and development. (Proc. 1st Intern. Symp. Inst. Biomed. Research).
                Chicago: American Medical Association, 931 pp., illustr.
                Rev.: Webster in Nature, 226:5251, 1176.

LOCKARD, WALTER   See: Bridge, T. E., Leisman, G. A. and Lockard, W., 1972A.

LOCKE, STEPHEN
1971A   A late Pleistocene mammal fauna from Caerwent quarry, Monmouthshire. Bristol Natur. Soc., Proc. (1970), 32:1, 84–87.

LOMMEL, ANDREAS
1967A   Shamanism: the beginnings of art. New York, Toronto: McGraw-Hill, 175 pp., frontispiece, 52 illustr., 44 pls.
          Rev.: Anati in Caesaraugusta, 31–32, 271–272; Cranstone in Mus. J., 68:4, 179–180; Hammond in Amer. Anthropol., 71, 533–534.

LONG, CHARLES A.
1969A   An analysis of patterns of variation in some representative mammalia. Part II. Studies on the nature and correlation of measures of variation. Kans., Univ., Mus. Natur. Hist., Misc. Publ., 51, 289–302, 1 fig., 3 tables.
1971A   Significance of the late Pleistocene fauna from the Little Box Elder Cave, Wyoming, to studies of zoogeography of Recent mammals. Great Basin Natur., 31, 93–105, 4 figs., 1 table.

LONGIN, R.
1970A   Extraction du collagène des os fossiles pour leur datation par la méthode du Carbone 14. Lyon: 1 vol. in 4⁰, 70 pp., 13 figs., 12 tables (French).
          Rev.: Flandrin in Soc. Géol. Fr., C.R., 1971:5, 288.
1971A   New method of collagen extraction for radiocarbon dating. Nature, 230:5291, 241–242, 2 figs., 2 tables.

LOPATO, A. ÎU.   See: Lipatova, V. V., Lopato, A. ÎU., Makarova, I. S., Ochev, V. G., Podgornyĭ, ÎU. I., Starozhilova, N. N., Saĭdakovskiĭ, L. Îa. and Shishkin, M. A., 1972A.

LORBLANCHET, MICHEL
1967B   Découverte de gravures pariétales paléolithiques dans la grotte de la Roque (Hérault). Soc. Préhist. Fr., Bull., Étud. Trav., 64:1, 143–154, 8 figs. (French).
1970A   Le chanoine Lemozi (1882–1970). Soc. Préhist. Fr., Bull., C.R., 67:9, 265–266 (French).
1971A   Nouvelles figures pariétales paléolithiques en Quercy. Soc. Préhist. Fr., Bull., Étud. Trav., 68:1, 293–310, 15 figs. (French).

LORBLANCHET, MICHEL   See also: Hugues, C., Lorblanchet, M. and Ravoux, G., 1969A.

LORENZ-ROMER, HELGA
1956B   Einige Ergebnisse von Zahn- und Kieferstudien an prähistorischen Kinderschädeln aus Mitteldeutschland. Jahresschrift Mitteldeutsch. Vorgesch., 40, 261–269, 4 figs., 2 pls. (German).

LORING, STEPHEN H. and WOOD, ALBERT E.
1969A   Deciduous premolars of some North American Tertiary camels (family Camelidae). J. Paleontol., 43:5, 1199–1209, 6 figs.
          Rev.: Thenius in Zentralbl. Geol. Paläontol., Teil 2, 1971:1, 70.

LORRAIN, DESSAMAE   See: Dibble, D. S. and Lorrain, D., 1968A.

LOSOS, LUDVIK   See: Březinová, D., Losos, L. and Majzner, Z., 1968A.

LOVE, J. D.
1970A   Cenozoic geology of the Granite Mountains area, central Wyoming. U.S. Geol. Surv., Prof. Paper, 495–C, viii + 154 pp., frontispiece, 61 figs., 10 pls., 13 tables.

LOVE, J. D.   See also: McKenna, M. C. and Love, J. D., 1970A, 1972A.

LOVEJOY, C. OWEN
1970A   The taxonomic status of the 'Meganthropus' mandibular fragments from the Djetis beds of Java. Man (J. Roy. Anthropol. Inst.), 5:2, 228–236, 2 figs., 3 tables.
1971A   Femoral anatomy of Australopithecus africanus and robustus. Amer. J. Phys. Anthropol., 35:2, 286 (abs.).

LOVEJOY, C. O., BURNSTEIN, A. H. and HEIPLE, K. G.
1972A   Primate phylogeny and immunological distance. Science (AAAS), 176:4036, 803–805, 1 fig., 1 table.

LOVEJOY, C. O. and HEIPLE, K. G.
   1970A   A reconstruction of the femur of *Australopithecus africanus*. Amer. J. Phys. Anthropol., 32:1, 33–40, 5 figs.
   1972A   Proximal femoral anatomy of *Australopithecus*. Nature, 235:5334, 175–176, 2 figs.

LOVEJOY, C. OWEN   See also: Heiple, K. G. and Lovejoy, C. O., 1971A.

LOVERING, J. F. and McELROY, C. T.
   1969A   The Geology of New South Wales. The Sydney Basin. Triassic System. Wianamatta Group. Geol. Soc. Austral., J., 16:1, 417–423, 1 fig., 1 table.

LOWTHER, GORDON R.   See: Schaller, G. B. and Lowther, G. R., 1969A.

LOZAN, M. N.
   1969A   [Principal Moldavian localities of upper Pleistocene and Holocene small mammals remains and their faunas.] Akad. Nauk Moldav. SSR, Izv., Ser. Biol. Khim. Nauk, 1969:1, 29–35, 6 tables (Russian).

LOZAN, M. N. and MEZHZHERIN, V. A.
   1969A   [The finding of fossil arctic shrew *Sorex arcticus* Kerr, 1792 (Insectivora, Mammalia) in late Pleistocene deposits of Moldavia.] Akad. Nauk Moldav. SSR, Izv., Ser. Biol. Khim. Nauk, 1969:1, 36–38, 1 fig., 2 tables (Russian).

LOZOVSKIĬ, V. R.
   1967A   Triasovye otlozheniiá tsentral'noĭ chasti Moskovskoĭ sineklizy. [Triassic deposits of the central part of Moscow syneclise.] Mosk. Obshchest. Ispyt. Prir., Biull., Otd. Geol., 42:6, 139–140 (Russian).

LOZOVSKIĬ, V. R. and ROZANOV, V. I.
   1969A   Stratigrafiiá triasovykh otlozheniĭ severnoĭ chasti moskovskoĭ sineklisy. [Stratigraphy of Triassic deposits in the northern part of Moscow syneclise.] Izv. Vyssh. Uchebn. Zaved., Geol. i Razv., 12:10, 15–22, 3 figs. (Russian).

LOZOVSKIĬ, V. R.   See also: Gorbatkina, T. E., Lozovskiĭ, V. R. and Strok, N. I., 1971A; Ochev, V. G., Lozovskiĭ, V. R. and Dubeĭkovskiĭ, S. G., 1972A; Vavilov, M. N. and Lozovskiĭ, V. R., 1970A.

LÜ, CHENG-RUEY
   1967A   China: 1964–1965. Asian Perspectives, 10, 59–65.

LUCAS, A. T.   See: Council for British Archaeology and Lucas, A. T. (eds.), 1964A.

LUCAS, KENNETH   See: Firby, J. and Lucas, K., 1970A.

LUKIN, EFIM IUDOVICH (= LOOKIN, E. I.)
   1968A   Nekotorye obshchie voprosy postroeniiá sistemy zhivotnogo mira. [Some general problems in establishing a system of animal kingdom.] In: Problemy evoliutsii, 1, 71–81 (Russian; English summary).

LUMLEY, HENRY DE (= LUMLEY-WOODYEAR, H. DE)
   1967B   Les fouilles de Terra Amata à Nice. Monaco, Mus. Anthropol. Préhist., Bull., 13, 29–51, 11 figs. (French).
   1969A   Étude de l'outillage Moustérien de la grotte de Carigüela. (Piñar-Grenade). L'Anthropologie, 73:3–4, 165–206, 19 figs., tables (French).
   1969B*   Une cabane acheuléenne dans la grotte du Lazaret (Nice). Soc. Préhist. Fr., Mém., 7, 237 pp., 150 figs., 11 tables (French).
         Rev.: Bánesz in Archeol. Roz., 22:2, 225–226; Collins in Antiquity, 44:173, 78–79; Grigor'ev in Vop. Antropol., 36, 173–175 (Russian).; Naber and Heller in Quartär, 21, 151–156.
   1969C   Les coprolithes de la cabane acheuléenne du Lazaret. I. – Étude morphologique. In: Lumley, H. de (ed.), 1969B, 121–122, 1 fig. (French).
   1969D   Le Paléolithique inférieur et moyen du Midi méditerranéen dans son cadre géologique. Tome I: Ligurie-Provence. Gallia Préhist., 5e suppl., 463 pp., 353 figs., tables (French).
         Rev.: Praslov in Sov. Arkheol., 1971:4, 280–282 (Russian); Richmond in Quaternary Res., 2:2, 257–258.
   1969E   A Paleolithic camp at Nice. Sci. Amer., 220:5, 42–50, illustr.
   1970A   Une cabane de chasseurs acheuléens vieille de 130,000 ans dans une grotte de Nice. Sci. Progrès Découverte, 3419, 119–131, 13 figs. (French).

LUMLEY, H. DE, GAGNIÈRES, S. and FOURNIER, A.
  1969A   Le paysage et le climat à la fin du Riss III sur le littoral niçois. Écologie des faunes et des flores.
           In: Lumley, H. de (ed.), 1969B, 129–133, 1 fig., 7 pls., 1 table (French).

LUMLEY, H. DE and LUMLEY, MARIE-ANTOINETTE DE
  1971A   Découverte de restes humains anténéandertaliens datés du début du Riss à la Caune de l'Arago
           (Tautavel, Pyrénées-Orientales). Acad. Sci., C.R., Sér. D, 272:13, 1739–1742, 2 figs., 1 pl.,
           1 table (French).

LUMLEY, MARIE-ANTOINETTE DE
  1970A   Le pariétal humain anténéandertalien de Cova Negra (Jativa, Espagne). Acad. Sci., C.R., Sér. D,
           270:1, 39–41, 1 pl. (French).

LUMLEY, M.-A. DE and PIVETEAU, JEAN
  1969A   Les restes humains de la grotte du Lazaret (Nice, Alpes-Maritimes). In: Lumley, H. de (ed.), 1969B,
           223–232, 5 figs. (French).

LUMLEY, MARIE-ANTOINETTE DE   See also: Lumley, H. de and Lumley, M.-A. de, 1971A.

LUND, RICHARD
  1970A   A new technique for chemical preparation of fossils. J. Paleontol., 44:3, 578.
  1970B   Fossil fishes from southwestern Pennsylvania. Part I: Fishes from the Duquesne limestones
           (Conemaugh, Pennsylvanian). Carnegie Mus., Ann., 41:8, 231–261, 17 figs.
  1972A   Elasmobranchiamorphs from the Bear Gulch limestones. Soc. Vert. Paleontol., Ann. Meeting, 32nd,
           1972, Abstr. (abs.).

LUNDBERG, JOHN G. and CASE, GERARD R.
  1970A   A new catfish from the Eocene Green River formation, Wyoming. J. Paleontol., 44:3, 451–457,
           2 figs., 2 pls., 2 tables.

LUNDBERG, JOHN G.   See also: Cavender, T. M., Lundberg, J. G. and Wilson, R. L., 1970A; Smith, G. R. and
           Lundberg, J. G., 1972A.

LUNDELIUS, ERNEST L., JR.
  1958A   Fossil bones in Longhorn Cavern. Speleo Digest, 1958, 2–110 (reprinted from Texas Caver, 3:1, 18).
  1969A   The age structure of a Tanupolama sample from South Texas and its ecological significance. Geol.
           Soc. Amer. Abstr., 121, 402–403 (abs.).
  1972A   A late Pleistocene mammalian fauna from Val Verde County, Texas. Soc. Vert. Paleontol., Ann.
           Meeting, 32nd, 1972, Abstr. (abs.).

LUNDELIUS, ERNEST L. and STEVENS, MARGARET S.
  1970A   Equus francisci Hay, a small stilt-legged horse, middle Pleistocene of Texas. J. Paleontol., 44:1, 148–
           153, 3 figs., 1 table.
           Rev.: Thenius in Zentralbl. Geol. Paläontol., Teil 2, 1970:5, 441.

LUNDELIUS, ERNEST L., JR.   See also: Turnbull, W. D. and Lundelius, E. L., Jr., 1970A.

LUNDIN, ROBERT F.   See: Lindsay, E. H. and Lundin, R. F., 1972A.

LUNGU, ALEKSANDR NIKOLAEVICH
  1964A   Predvaritel'nye soobshcheniia o raskopkakh zakhoroneniia sredne sarmatskikh mlekopitaiushchikh v
           raione s. Kalfa. [Preliminary report on excavation of middle Sarmatian mammals burial in the
           area of Kalfa village.] Nauch. Konf. Molod. Uch. Moldavii, 3-rd., Kishinev, Tr., Biol. Sel'sko-
           Khoz. Nauki, 2, 202–203 (Russian).
  1966A   [On middle Sarmatian Hipparion fauna of Moldavia.] Akad. Nauk Moldav. SSR, Izv., Ser. Biol. Khim.
           Nauk, 1966:10, 20–25 (Russian).
  1966B   [Comparison of middle Sarmatian hipparion faunas of Moldavia with hipparion faunas of western and
           eastern Europe.] Akad. Nauk Moldav. SSR, Izv., Ser. Biol. Khim Nauk., 1966:10, 26–31
           (Russian).
  1972A   K istorii roda Lagomeryx. [On the history of the genus Lagomeryx.] In: Pozvonochnye neogena i
           pleistotsena Moldavii, 24–36 (Russian).

LUNGU, A. N.   See also: David, A. I. and Lungu, A. N., 1972A; Kurochkin, E. N. and Lungu, A. N., 1970A,
           1970B.

LUNIN, B. V.
    1969A   K 70-letiŭ Mikhaila Evgen'evicha Massona. [Mikhail Evgen'evich Masson 70th anniversary.] Sov.
            Arkheol., 1969:2, 126—129, portr. (Russian).

LWOFF, STÉPHANE
    1968A   À propos de la plaquette de Laugerie-Basse, baptisée par l'abbé Landesque "la femme au renne". Soc.
            Préhist. Fr., Bull., C.R., 65:1, 18—19 (French).

LYARSKAYA, L. (= LĪARSKAĬA, L. A.)
    1972A   A classification of Devonian vertebrate localities of Latvia. Eesti NSV Tead. Akad., Toimet., Keem.
            Geol., 21:3, 259—268, 4 figs., 1 table (Esthonian and Russian summaries).

LYARSKAYA, L. and MARK-KURIK, E.
    1972A   Eine neue Fundstelle oberdevonischer Fische im Baltikum. Neues Jahrb. Geol. Paläontol., Monatsh.,
            1972:7, 407—414, 3 figs. (German; English summary).

LYCHEV, GENNADIĬ FEDOROVICH (= LYTSCHEV, G. F.)
    1970A   Novyĭ vid bobra iz oligotsena Severnogo Priaral'ia. [A new species of beaver from the Oligocene of
            northern Aral region.] Paleontol. Zh., 1970:2, 84—89, 1 fig., 1 table (Russian).

LYCHEV, GENNADIĬ FEDOROVICH and AUBEKEROVA, PIRUZA ABLAEVNA
    1971A   Iskopaemye bobry Kazakhstana. [Fossil beavers of Kazakhstan.] Akad. Nauk Kaz. SSR, Inst. Zool.,
            Mater. Fauny i Flory, 5, 12—33, 10 figs., 3 tables (Russian).

LYCHEV, G. F.   See also: Aubekerov, B. Zh., Aubekerova, P. A., Biriŭkov, M. D., Lychev, G. F. and
                Savinov, P. F., 1970A; Bazhanov, V. S., Biriŭkov, M. D., Vetrov, F. E., Kozhamkulova, B. S.,
                Lychev, G. F., Musakulova, L. T. and Savinov, P. F., 1971A.

LYELL, CHARLES
    1972A   Post-Pliocene period: bones of man and extinct Mammalia in Belgian caves. Post-Pliocene period:
            fossil human skulls of the Neanderthal and Engis caves. In: McCown, T. D. and Kennedy,
            K. A. R. (eds.), 1972A, 107—122, 2 figs. (reprinted from Lyell, 1863).

LYNCH, JOHN D.
    1971A   Evolutionary relationships, osteology, and zoogeography of leptodactyloid frogs. Kans., Univ., Mus.
            Natur. Hist., Misc. Publ., 53, 238 pp., 131 figs., 6 tables.

LYNCH, THOMAS F. and KENNEDY, KENNETH A. R.
    1970A   Early human cultural and skeletal remains from Guitarrero Cave, northern Peru. Science (AAAS),
            169:3952, 1307—1309, 3 figs.

LYON, JOHN
    1970A   The search for fossil man: Cinq personnages à la recherche du temps perdu. Isis, 61, 68—84.

MA, CHENG-RUEY
    1969A*   Far East. COWA, Surv. Bibliogr., Area 17, 4, 1—49.

McALESTER, A. LEE
    1968A   Rev.: Anon. in Calif., Div. Mines Geol., Miner. Inform. Serv., 23:5, 95.
    1970A   Animal extinctions, oxygen consumption, and athmospheric history. J. Paleontol., 44:3, 405—409,
            2 figs.

McALLISTER, D. E. and HARINGTON, C. R.
    1969A   Pleistocene grayling, Thymallus, from Yukon, Canada. Can. J. Earth Sci., 6:5, 1185—1190, 2 pls.,
            1 map, 1 table.

MACAROVICI, NECULAI
    1967A   Kritischer Überblick über Hipparion im Neogen von Rumänien. Österreich. Akad. Wiss., Math.-
            Naturwiss. Kl., Abt. I, Sitz.-Ber., 176, 81—90, 3 pls. (German).
            Rev.: Semaka in Zentralbl. Geol. Paläontol., Teil 2, 1969:1, 53—54.
    1972A   L'évolution de la faune des mammifères fossiles du Pliocène et du Pléistocène de la Roumanie. Int.
            Geol. Congr., 24th, Canada, Proc., Sec. 7, 563—568 (French).

1972B   Evoluția vieții în timpul paleozoicului. [Evolution of life in Paleozoic time.] Natura, Ser. Biol., 24:4, 11—27, 5 figs. (Rumanian).

1972C   Sur la faune "villafranchienne" de la Roumanie. Jassy, Univ. Cuza, An. Științ., Sec. 2, b. Geol., 18, 93—106 (French; Rumanian summary).

MACAROVICI, N. and JEANRENAUD, P.
1968A   On the stratigraphic position of the Meotian level. Int. Geol. Congr., 23rd, Czech., Rep., Abstr., Sec. 10, 280—281.

MACAROVICI, N. and JURCSÁK, T.
1968A   [On a Hipparion from the Pliocene of Derșida (Sălaj).] Jassy, Univ. Cuza, An. Științ., Sec. 2 (Științ. Nat.), b. Geol.-Geog., 14, 101—104, 5 figs. (Rumanian; French summary).

MACAROVICI, N. and PAGHIDA, N.
1966A   [Flora and fauna of upper Sarmatian from the hill Paun-Jassy.] Bucharest, Univ., An., Ser. Științ. Natur., Geol.-Geogr., 15:1, 67—81, 5 pls., 1 table (Rumanian; Russian and French summaries).

MACAROVICI, N. and SEMAKA, A.
1969A   Sur les espèces de chevaux fossiles du Quaternaire de la Roumanie. Folia Quaternaria, 34, 18 pp., 4 pls. (French; Polish and Russian summaries).
     Rev.: Semaka in Zentralbl. Geol. Paläontol., Teil 2, 1970:6, 521; Thenius in Zentralbl. Geol. Paläontol., Teil 2, 1971:1, 73.

MACAROVICI, N. and ZAHARIA, NECULAI
1968A   Nouvelles données sur quelques cétacés du Sarmatien inférieur du Nord de la Moldavie. Bucharest, Muz. Nat. Ist. Natur. "Grigore Antipa", Trav., 8, 587—590, 4 pls. (French; Rumanian summary).
1968B   Asupra unor mamifere fosile din Sarmațianul podișului Moldovenesc. [On some fossil mammals from the Sarmatian of the Moldavian Plateau.] Soc. Științ. Geol. R.S.R., Bul., 10, 217—227, 7 figs. (Rumanian; French and English summaries).

McBEATH, VIRGINIA   See: Molnar, S. and McBeath, V., 1968A.

McBROOM, PATRICIA
1971A   The scarred species. In: Holmes, L. D. (ed.), 1971A, 101—105 (reprinted from Science News, Nov. 23, 1968).

MacBURNEY, C. B. M.
1967B   Rev.: Mori in Quaternaria, 13, 427—428; Schwidetzky in Homo, 19:1, 56; Taute in Quartär, 21, 156—159.
1968A   Pleistocene and early post-Pleistocene archaeology of Libya. In: Geology and archaeology of Northern Cyrenaica, Libya (Petrol. Explor. Soc. Libya, 10th Ann. Field Conf.), 13—21, 8 figs.
1968B   The cave of Ali Tappeh and the epi-Palaeolithic in N.E. Iran. Prehist. Soc., Proc., 34:12, 385—413, illustr.

McCAIN, PEGGY
1971A   Who is Smilodon? S. Calif. Paleontol. Soc., Bull., 3:12, 1.

McCLUNG, ROBERT M.
1969A   Lost wild America. The story of our extinct and vanishing wildlife. Illustrated by Bob Hines. New York: William Morrow and Co., 240 pp., illustr.

McCOWN, THEODORE DONEY and KEITH, ARTHUR
1972A   The relationship of the fossil people of Mount Carmel to prehistoric and modern types. In: McCown, T. D. and Kennedy, K. A. R. (eds.), 1972A, 328—336 (reprinted from Stone Age of Mount Carmel, 1939).

McCOWN, THEODORE DONEY and KENNEDY, KENNETH A. R.
1972A*   Climbing man's family tree: a collection of major writings on human phylogeny, 1699 to 1971. Englewood Cliffs, New Jersey: Prentice-Hall, x + 485 pp., illustr.

McCOY, C. J.   See: Preston, R. E. and McCoy, C. J., 1971A.

McCRADY, ALLEN D.
1958A   Progress report from New Paris. Speleo Digest, 1958, 2—68 — 2—72, 2 figs. (reprinted from Netherworld News, 6:5, 106).
1959A   Prospecting limestone areas for Pleistocene vertebrate fossils. Speleo Digest, 1959, 2—121 — 2—129 (reprinted from Netherworld News, 7:8, 154—161).

McCRADY, A. D.   See also: Guilday, J. E., Hamilton, H. W. and McCrady, A. D., 1969A, 1971A.

MacCURDY, GEORGE GRANT
  1965A   Human origins. 2 vols. New York: Johnson Reprint Corp., v. 1, 478 pp., 254 figs.; v. 2, 532 pp.,
              410 figs. (reprint of MacCurdy, 1924).
              Rev.: Anon. in Arch. Suiss. Anthropol. Gén., 32, 155; J. M. in Anthropos, 62:3/4, 617.

McDERMOTT, JOHN FRANCIS
  1948A   Dr. Koch's wonderful fossils. Mo. Hist. Soc. Bull., 4, 233–256.

MacDONALD, GEORGE F.
  1968A   Rev.: Tuck in Amer. Antiquity, 36:2, 224.

MacDONALD, J.   See: Gaherty, G., Kettel, D., MacDonald, J., Niemann, L., Von Graeve, B. and Arima, E., 1969A.

MACDONALD, JAMES REID
  1968B   The dinosaurs are becoming extinct! Los Angeles Cty. Mus., Quart., 6:3, 19–20, 2 figs.
  1968C   People for planets. Los Angeles Cty. Mus., Quart., 7:1, 26–29, 1 pl.
  1969A   The quest for the fourteen toed horse. Los Angeles Cty. Mus., Quart., 7:3, 2 and 39, 1 fig.
  1969B   The dinosaurs are becoming extinct! S. Calif. Paleontol. Soc., Bull., 1:10, 1–3 (reprinted from
              Los Angeles Co. Mus. Natur. Hist. Quart., 6:3, 1968).
  1970A   Review of the Miocene Wounded Knee faunas of southwestern South Dakota. Los Angeles Cty. Mus.
              Natur. Hist. Sci., Bull., 8, 82 pp., 32 figs., 53 tables, 2 maps.

MACDONALD, J. R. and HARKSEN, J. C.
  1968A   Rosebud formation in South Dakota. S. Dak. Geol. Surv., Rep., 97, 13 pp., 5 figs., 2 tables.

MACDONALD, J. R. and SIBLEY, GRETCHEN
  1969A   Paleopathological ponderings or how to tell a sick saber-tooth. Los Angeles Cty. Mus., Quart., 8:2,
              26–30, 5 figs.

MACDONALD, J. R.   See also: Harksen, J. C. and Macdonald, J. R., 1967A, 1969A, 1969B.

MACDONALD, R.   See: Brock, P. W. G. and Macdonald, R., 1969A; Walker, A., Brock, P. W. G., and
              Macdonald, R., 1969A.

McDOWALL, R. M.
  1969A   Extinction and endemism in New Zealand land birds. Tuatara, 17:1, 1–12, 1 fig., 3 tables.

McDOWELL, S. B.
  1972A   The evolution of the tongue of snakes, and its bearing on snake origins. In: Dobzhansky, Th.,
              Hecht, M. K. and Steere, W. C. (eds.), 1972B, 191–273, 24 figs.

McELROY, C. T., et al.
  1969A   The geology of New South Wales. The Sydney Basin. Triassic System. Narrabeen group. Geol. Soc.
              Austral., J., 16:1, 388–407, 4 figs., 8 tables.

McELROY, C. T.   See also: Lovering, J. F. and McElroy, C. T., 1969A.

McGINNES, HELEN   See: Guilday, J. E. and McGinnes, H., 1972A.

McGOWAN, C.
  1972A   The distinction between latipinnate and longipinnate ichthyosaurs. Toronto, Roy. Ont. Mus., Life Sci.
              Occas. Pap., 20, 1–8, 4 figs., 1 table.
  1972B   Evolutionary trends in longipinnate ichthyosaurs with particular reference to the skull and fore fin.
              Toronto, Roy. Ont. Mus., Life Sci., Contrib., 83, 38 pp., 20 figs., 1 table.

McGOWEN, TOM
  1972A   Album of dinosaurs. Illustrated by Rod Ruth. New York and San Francisco: Rand McNally and Co.,
              60 pp., illustr.

McGOWRAN, BRIAN and MOORE, ALAN C.
  1971A   A reptilian tooth and upper Cretaceous microfossils from the lower Quarry at Needs Camp, South
              Africa. Geol. Soc. S. Afr., Trans, 74:2, 103–105, 1 pl.

McGREGOR, D. C.   See: Carroll, R. L., Belt, E. S., Dineley, D. L., Baird, D. and McGregor, D. C., 1972A, 1972B.

McGREW, PAUL O.
1971A   *Mesohippus* from the Vieja group of Texas. Pearce-Sellards Ser., Texas Mem. Mus., 18, 6—11, 2 figs., 2 tables.
         Rev.: Thenius in Zentralbl. Geol. Paläontol., Teil 2, 1971:6, 519.
1971B   Early and middle Eocene faunas of the Green River basin. Wyo., Univ., Contrib. Geol., 10:1, 65—68, 12 figs.
1971C   The Tertiary history of Wyoming. Wyo. Geol. Assoc. Guidebk., Ann. Field Confer., 23rd, 1971, 29—33, 6 figs.

McGREW, PAUL O. and SULLIVAN, RAYMOND
1970A   The stratigraphy and paleontology of Bridger A. Wyo., Univ., Contrib. Geol., 9:2, 66—85, 16 figs.

MACINTOSH, N. W. G.
1968A   The recovery and treatment of bone. In: Mulvaney, D. J. (ed.), 1968A, 175—191, 3 pls.
1969A   The Talgai cranium: the value of archives. Austral. Natur. Hist., 16:6, 189—195, 3 figs.
1970A   The Green Gully remains. Victoria, Nat. Mus., Mem., 30, 93—100.

MacINTYRE, GILES T.
1965A   The Miacidae (Mammalia: Carnivora). Part I: the systematics of *Ictidopappus* and *Protictis*. Diss. Abstr., 26:6, 3545 (abs.).
1972A   The trisulcate petrosal pattern of mammals. In: Dobzhansky, Th., Hecht, M. K. and Steere, W. C. (eds.), 1972B, 275—303, 8 figs., 1 table.

McKEE, EDWIN D. and ANDERSON, CHARLES A.
1971A   Age and chemistry of Tertiary volcanic rocks in north-central Arizona and relation of the rocks to the Colorado plateaus. Geol. Soc. Amer., Bull., 82:10, 2767—2782, 7 figs., 3 tables.

McKEE, EDWIN D. and BREED, WILLIAM J.
1969A   The Toroweap formation and Kaibab limestone. In: Summers, W. K. and Kottlowski, F. E. (eds.), 1969A, 12—26, 4 figs., 2 tables.

McKEE, EDWIN D. and GUTSCHICK, R. C.
1969A   History of the Redwall limestone of northern Arizona. Geol. Soc. Amer., Mem., 114, 726 pp., illustr.
1969B   Miscellaneous fossil groups: Algae and Stromatolites, Holothurians, Trilobites, Ostracodes, and Fish. In: McKee, E. D. and Gutschick, R. C., 1969A, 545—552, 2 figs.

McKELVEY, B. C., WEBB, P. N., GORTON, M. P. and KOHN, B. P.
1970A   Stratigraphy of the Beacon supergroup between the Olympus and Boomerang ranges, Victoria Land, Antarctica. Nature, 227:5263, 1126—1128, 1 fig., 1 table.

McKENNA, MALCOLM C.
1968B   Preliminary announcement of Arikareean mammals from high-level Tertiary sediments, Bighorn Mountains. Colorado, Univ. Mus., Field Confer. Guidebk., 38—49, 6 figs.
1969A   The origin and early differentiation of therian mammals. N.Y. Acad. Sci., Ann., 167:1, 217—240, 4 figs., 1 table.
1969B   Margaret C. Cook, 1899—1968. Soc. Vert. Paleontol., News Bull., 85, 59.
1971A   Fossil mammals and the Eocene demise of the De Geer north Atlantic dispersal route. Geol. Soc. Amer., Abstr., 3:7, 644 (abs.).
1971B   Condylarthra, Dermoptera, Dinocerata, Docodonta, Embrithopoda, Insectivora, Macroscelidea, Multituberculata, Pantodonta, Pantotheria, Primates, Symmetrodonta, Triconodonta. McGraw-Hill Encycl. Sci. Technol., illustr.
1972A   Vertebrate paleontology of the Togwotee Pass area, northwestern Wyoming. Field Conf. Tert. Bios., s. and w. Wyo., Guidebk., 80—101, 1 map.
1972B   The American Museum of Natural History. Soc. Vert. Paleontol., News Bull., 96, 12—14.
1972C   Eocene final separation of the Eurasian and Greenland-North American landmasses. Int. Geol. Congr., 24th, Canada, Proc., Sec. 7, 275—281.
1972D   Significance of an Arikareean mammalian assemblage from northwestern Wyoming. Soc. Vert. Paleontol., Ann. Meeting, 32nd, 1972, Abstr. (abs.).
1972E   Possible biological consequences of plate tectonics. BioScience, 22:9, 519—525, 5 figs.
1972F   Was Europe connected directly to North America prior to the middle Eocene? In: Dobzhansky, T., Hecht, M. K. and Steere, W. C. (eds.), 1972B, 179—188, 1 fig.

McKENNA, M. C. and LOVE, J. D.
1970A   Local stratigraphic and tectonic significance of *Leptoceratops*, a Cretaceous dinosaur in the Pinyon conglomerate, northwestern Wyoming. U.S. Geol. Surv., Prof. Paper, 700—D, D55—D61, 2 figs.
1972A   High-level strata containing early Miocene mammals on the Bighorn Mountains, Wyoming. Amer. Mus. Nov., 2490, 31 pp., 18 figs., 1 table.

McKENNA, M. C., MELLETT, J. S. and SZALAY, F. S.
1971A   Relationships of the Cretaceous mammal *Deltatheridium*. J. Paleontol., 45:3, 441–442.

McKENNA, M. C., RUSSELL, D. E. and SAVAGE, D. E.
1969A   *Protomomys* Teilhard de Chardin, 1927 (Mammalia): proposed suppression under the plenary powers.
             Bull. Zool. Nomencl., 25:4–5, 165.

McKENNA, MALCOLM C.   See also: Szalay, F. S. and McKenna, M. C., 1971A.

McKENZIE, DAN   See: Jardine, N. and McKenzie, D., 1972A.

McKERN, SHARON S. and McKERN, THOMAS W.
1970A   Tracking fossil man. An adventure in evolution. New York and London: Praeger Publishers, xiv +
             174 pp., frontispiece, 9 figs., 34 pls.

McKERN, SHARON   See also: McKern, T. W. and McKern, S., 1969A.

McKERN, THOMAS W. and McKERN, SHARON S.
1969A   Human origins, an introduction to physical anthropology. Englewood Cliffs, New Jersey: Prentice-
             Hall, xi + 204 pp., illustr.
             Rev.: Holloway in Amer. J. Phys. Anthropol., 34:2, 308–309; Johnston in Human Biol., 42:1, 147.

McKERN, THOMAS W.   See also: McKern, S. S. and McKern, T. W., 1970A; Rosen, S. I. and McKern,
                        T. W., 1971A.

McKINNEY, H. LEWIS
1972A   Wallace and natural selection. New Haven: Yale University Press.
             Rev.: Smith in New Sci., 56:815, 112.

MacLEAN, C. J.   See: Sofaer, J. A., Bailit, H. L. and MacLean, C. J., 1971A.

MacLEAN, WILLIAM P.
1970A   The braincase of *Labidosaurikos* (a Permian captorhinomorph reptile). J. Paleontol., 44:3, 458–463,
             10 figs.

McMILLAN, R. BRUCE
1972A   Pleistocene springs in Missouri. Explorer (Cleveland Mus. Natur. Hist.), 14:3, 22–24, 8 figs.

McMULLEN, TERRANCE L. and ZAKRZEWSKI, RICHARD J.
1972A   A new late Pleistocene fauna from northeastern New Mexico. N. Mex. Geol. Soc., Guidebk., Field
             Conf., 134–136, 1 fig.

McNEIL, PEARL L.
1969A   Legal safeguards for preserving the past. Tex. Archeol. Soc., Bull., 40, 267–280.

MacNEISH, RICHARD S.
1966A   Ancient Mesoamerican civilization. In: Graham, J. A. (ed.), 1966A, 39–45, 8 figs.
1971A   Early man in the Andes. Sci. Amer., 224:4, 36–46, 5 figs., 4 pls., 2 maps.
             Rev.: Anon. in Interamer., 18:6, 4.

MacNEISH, R. S., BYERS, D. S., *et al.*
1967A   The prehistory of the Tehuacan Valley. Vol. I. Environment and subsistence. In: Byers, D. S. (ed.),
             vol. 1, 1967B, viii + 331 pp.

McNULTY, C. L., JR.
1972A   A contribution to the question of the oral dentition of ganopristid sawfishes. Soc. Vert. Paleontol.,
             Ann. Meeting, 32nd, 1972, Abstr. (abs.).

McNULTY, C. L., JR. and KIENZLEN, GERALDINE
1970A   An enchodontid mandible from the Eagle Ford shale (Turonian), Dallas County, Texas. Tex. J. Sci.,
             21:4, 447–453, 3 figs.

McNULTY, C. L., JR. and SLAUGHTER, BOB H.
1969A   A vertebrate local fauna from the uppermost Woodbine formation (Cenomanian) of Tarrant County,
             Texas. Geol. Soc. Amer., Abstr., 121, 404–405 (abs.).
1970A   A request for opinions on a neotype for *Ptychotrygon triangularis* (Reuss). J. Paleontol., 44:1, 166.

MACUMBER, P. G.   See: Thorne, A. G. and Macumber, P. G., 1972A.

McWILLIAMS, B.
1967A   Fossil vertebrates of the Cromer forest bed in Norwich Castle Museum. Norwich: City of Norwich
           Museums Publ., 31 pp., 68 figs., 1 map.
1970A   Mammals of the Crag and Forest bed. Soc. Belge Géol. Paléontol. Hydrol., Bull., 79:2, 167—174.
           Rev.: Thenius in Zentralbl. Geol. Paläontol., Teil 2, 1971:6, 513.

MADARIAGA DE LA CAMPA, BENITO
1963A   Análisis paleontológico de la fauna terrestre y marina de la Cueva de la Chora. Exc. Arqueol. Españ.,
           26, 53—74, 1 fig., 4 pls. (Spanish).

MADARIAGA DE LA CAMPA, B.   See also: González Echegaray, J., García Guinea, M. A., Begines, A.,
           Madariaga de la Campa, B. and Leroi-Gourhan, Arl., 1966A.

MADDEN, CARY T.
1972A   Miocene mammals, stratigraphy and environment of Muruarot Hill, Kenya. PaleoBios, 14, 12 pp.,
           1 fig., 3 tables.

MADERSON, PAUL F. A.
1972A   When? Why? and How? : some speculations on the evolution of the vertebrate integument. Amer.
           Zool., 12:1, 159—171, 7 figs., 1 table.
1972B   On how an archosaurian scale might have given rise to an avian feather. Amer. Natur., 106:949, 424—
           428, 1 fig.

MADEYSKA-NIKLEWSKA, TERESA
1969A   Górnoplejstoceńskie osady jaskiń Wyżyny Krakowskiej. [Upper Pleistocene deposits in caves of the
           Cracow upland.] Soc. Géol. Pologne, Ann., 19, 341—392, 8 pls. (Polish; English summary).

MADSEN, J. H.
1964A   A general discussion of the Cleveland Lloyd quarry and the University of Utah cooperative dinosaur
           project. Translated by Ikuwo Obata. Natur. Sci. and Mus., 31:9—10, 133—139, cover plate
           (Japanese).

MAGALDI, D.   See: Borzatti von Löwenstern, E. and Magaldi, D., 1967A.

MAGLIO, VINCENT J.
1969A   A shovel-tusked gomphothere from the Miocene of Kenya. Breviora, 310, 10 pp., 2 figs., 1 table.
1969B   The status of the east African elephant "Archidiskodon exoptatus" Dietrich 1942. Breviora, 336,
           25 pp., 1 fig., 6 pls.
1970A   Early Elephantidae of Africa and a tentative correlation of African Plio-Pleistocene deposits. Nature,
           225:5230, 328—332, 2 figs., 1 table.
1970B   Four new species of Elephantidae from the Plio-Pleistocene of northwestern Kenya. Breviora, 341,
           43 pp., 4 figs., 7 pls., 4 tables.
1971A   Vertebrate fauna from the Kubi Algi, Koobi Fora and Ileret areas, east Rudolf, Kenya. Nature, 231:
           5300, 248—249, 1 table.
1971B   The nomenclature of intermediate forms: an opinion. Syst. Zool., 20:3, 370—373.
1972A   Vertebrate faunas and chronology of hominid-bearing sediments east of Lake Rudolf, Kenya. Nature,
           239:5372, 379—385, 4 figs., 4 tables.
1972B   Evolution of mastication in the Elephantidae. Evolution, 26:4, 638—658, 8 figs.

MAGLIO, VINCENT J. and HENDEY, Q. B.
1970A   New evidence relating to the supposed stegolophodont ancestry of the Elephantidae. S. Afr.
           Archaeol. Bull., 25, 85—87, 2 pls., 1 table.

MAGLIO, VINCENT J.   See also: Cooke, H. B. S. and Maglio, V. J., 1972A; Coryndon, S. C., Gentry, A. W.,
           Harris, J. M., Hooijer, D. A., Maglio, V. J. and Howell, F. C., 1972A.

MAHÉ, JOEL
1968A   Conséquence biologique tirée de l'orientation vestibulaire du crâne de Palaeopropithecus. Mus. Nat.
           Hist. Natur., Paris, Bull., 40:3, 634—639, 2 figs. (French).

MAHER, WILLIAM J.
1966A   Muskox bone of possible Wisconsin age from Banks Island, Northwest Territories. Arctic, 21, 260—
           266, 1 fig. (French and Russian summaries).

MAIER, WOLFGANG
1970A   Neue Ergebnisse der Systematik und der Stammesgeschichte der Cercopithecoidea. Z. Säugetierkunde,
         35:4, 193–214, 10 figs., 2 tables (German; English summary).
1970B   New fossil Cercopithecoidea from the lower Pleistocene cave deposits of the Makapansgat limeworks,
         South Africa. Palaeontol. Afr., 13, 69–107, 20 figs., 5 tables (German summary).
1971A   Two new skulls of *Parapapio antiquus* from Taung and a suggested phylogenetic arrangement of the
         genus *Parapapio*. S. Afr. Mus., Ann., 59:1, 1–16, 4 figs., 1 pl., 3 tables.
1972A   The first complete skull of *Simopithecus darti* from Makapansgat, South Africa, and its systematic
         position. J. Human Evol., 1:4, 395–405, 3 pls., 2 tables.

MAIS, KARL   See: Ehrenberg, K. and Mais, K., 1968A, 1970A, 1970B.

MAISURADZE, LAMARA SEMENOVNA   See: Gabelaia, Ts. D., Ramishvili, I. Sh. and Maisuradze, L. S., 1970A.

MAJZNER, Z.   See: Březinová, D., Losos, L. and Majzner, Z., 1968A.

MAKARENKO, G. F.
1971A   O sopostovlenii razrezov nizhnego karbona zapada Sibirskoi platformy. [Correlation of the lower
         Carboniferous sequences of the western part of the Siberian platform.] Mosk. Univ., Vestn.,
         Ser. Geol., 26:1, 88–93, 2 figs., 1 table (Russian).

MAKAROVA, INTERNA SERGEEVNA   See: Lipatova, V. V., Lopato, A. Iu., Makarova, I. S., Ochev, V. G.,
         Podgornyi, Iu. I., Starozhilova, N. N., Saidakovskii, L. Ia. and Shishkin, M. A., 1972A.

MALARODA, R.
1965A   Giorgio Dal Piaz paleontologo (1872–1962). Soc. Paleontol. Ital., Boll., 4:1, 3–8, portr. (Italian).

MALATESTA, ALBERTO
1970A   *Cynotherium sardous* Studiati, an extinct canid from the Pleistocene of Sardinia. Ist. Ital. Paleontol.
         Umana, n.s., 1, 1–72, 10 pls.
         Rev.: Thenius in Zentralbl. Geol. Paläontol., Teil 2, 1971:4, 338–339.

MALATESTA, ALBERTO and SURIANO, FRANCESCA
1971A   Avifauna pleistocenica di Alghero (Sardegna). Italy, Serv. Geol., Boll., 91 (1970), 149–158, 2 figs.,
         2 tables (Italian; English and German summaries).

MALDONADO-KOERDELL, MANUEL
1966A   Appendix on stratigraphy. In: Graham, J. A. (ed.), 1966A, 29–30, 1 fig.

MALEC, FRANZ and STORCH, G.
1970A   Zur Kenntniss der jungpleistozänen Wühlmaus *Pitymys melitensis* (Mammalia, Rodentia).
         Z. Säugetierkunde, 35:2, 75–80, 3 figs., 3 tables (German; English summary).

MALEC, FRANZ   See also: Bahlo, E. and Malec, F., 1969A, 1971A.

MALECHA, ADOLF   See: Šantrůček, P., Buzek, Č., Kopecký, L., Malecha, A. and Václ, J., 1968A.

MALEEV, EVGENII ALEKSANDROVICH
1968A   K sistematike karnozavrov. [On the systematics of carnosaurs.] In: Verkhnepaleozoiskie i mezozoiskie
         zemnovodnye i presmykaiushchiesia SSSR, 92–96 (Russian).

MALEEVA, A. G.
1970A   K probleme stanovleniia biogeotsenozov sovremennykh landshaftnykh zon Zapadnoi Sibiri. [On the
         problem of formation of modern landscape zone biogeocenoses in west Siberia.] Ekologiia,
         1970:1, 96–97 (Russian).

MALEEVA, A. G. and VOROB'EVA, T. D.
1970A   Predvaritel'noe soobshchenie o pozdnepleistotsenovoi stepnoi pestrushke (*Lagurus lagurus* Pall.) iz
         sostava "smeshannoi" fauny iuga Tiumenskoi oblasti. [Preliminary report on the late
         Pleistocene steppe lemming (*Lagurus lagurus* Pall.) from the "mixed" fauna of the southern
         Tiumen' Province.] Ural. Univ., Uch. Zap., 108, 35–42, 3 figs., 2 tables (Russian).

MALEEVA, A. G.   See also: Chernykh, I. I. and Maleeva, A. G., 1971A.

MALEGA, A. M.
1972A   Eotsenovoe mestonakhozhdenie ostatkov mlekopitaiushchikh Kyzylnura (Chatkal'skii khrebet).
         [Eocene locality of mammalian remains Kyzylnura (Chatkal Ridge).] Uzbek. Geol. Zh., 1972:3,
         66–67, 2 figs. (Russian).

MALEZ, MIRKO
1956A   Geološka i paleontološka istraživanja u pećini Veternici. [Geologische und paläontologische
           Forschungen in der Höhle Veternica.] Acta Geol., Zagreb, 1, 83—88, 1 fig., 4 pls.
           (Serbocroatian; German summary).
1956B   Novija istraživanja pećina u N. R. Hrvatskoj. [Explorations récentes des cavernes en Croatie.] Acta
           Geol., Zagreb, 1, 179—201, 3 figs., 6 pls. (Serbocroatian; French summary).
1960E   Etruskisches Nashorn — Dicerorhinus etruscus (Falconer) — aus altpleistozänen Brekzien der Halbinsel
           Marjan bei Split (Dalmatien). Anthropos, Brno, 1960 Suppl., 115—125, 2 pls., 3 tables
           (German; Russian summary).
1965L   Paleontološka istraživanja kvartara u 1963. godini. [Quaternary paleontological research in the year
           1963.] Jugoslav. Akad. Znanosti i Umjetnosti, Ljetopis, 70, 363—374, 8 pls. (Serbocroatian).
1966B   Paleontološka i speleološka istraživanja u 1964 godini. [Paleontological and speleological research in
           1964.] Jugoslav. Akad. Znanosti i Umjetnosti, Ljetopis, 71, 267—284, 4 pls. (Serbocroatian).
           Rev.: M. M. in Akad. savet FNRJ, Bull. Sci., Sec. A, 13:1—2, 26.
1967A   Paleolitska nalazišta Hrvatske. [Paleolithic sites in Croatia.] Arheol. Vestn., 18, 255—284, 6 pls.,
           1 map, 1 table (Croatian; German summary).
1967B   Gornjopleistocenska fauna Crvene stijene-Prethodno saopćenje. [Die Oberpleistozänfauna aus der
           Crvena stijena-Vorläufige Mitteilung.] Sarajevo, Zemaljski Muz., Glasnik, Arheol. (1966/1967),
           21—22, 67—80, 6 pls., 1 table (Serbocroatian; German summary).
           Rev.: Z. M. in Akad. savet FNRJ, Bull. Sci., Sec. A, 1968:9—10, 330.
1967C   Donjopleistocenska fauna koštane brece kod sela Dubci u Dalmaciji. [Early Pleistocene fauna from
           bone breccia near Dubci village in Dalmatia.] Jugoslav. Akad. Znanosti i Umjetnosti, Rad, 345,
           55—100, 7 figs., 1 pl., 2 tables (Serbocroatian; German summary).
           Rev.: M. M. in Akad. savet FNRJ, Bull. Sci., Sec. A, 13:1—2, 26.
1967D   Kvartarološka i speleološka istraživanja u 1965 godini. [Quaternary and speleological research in the
           year 1965.] Jugoslav. Akad. Znanosti i Umjetnosti, Ljetopis, 72, 405—417, 8 pls.
           (Serbocroatian).
1968B   Die altpleistozänische Vertebratenfauna in dem Gebiete des Dinarischen Karstes. Akad. savet FNRJ,
           Bull. Sci., Sec. A, 1968:5—6, 151—152, 1 fig. (German).
1968C   Ostaci zviždare u gornjem pleistocenu Jugoslavije. Pfeifhasenreste aus dem oberen Pleistozän in
           Jugoslawien. [Pika remains from upper Pleistocene of Yugoslavia.] Geol. Vjesnik, 21, 147—
           156, 4 figs. (Serbocroatian and German).
           Rev.: Kochansky-Devidé in Zentralbl. Geol. Paläontol., Teil 2, 1969:3, 298; M. M. in Bull. Sci.,
           Zagreb, Sec. A, 14:7—8, 258
1969A   Paleontološka i paleolitska istraživanja u 1966. godini. [Paleontological and Paleolithic research in
           the year 1966.] Jugoslav. Akad. Znanosti i Umjetnosti, Ljetopis, 73, 377—384, 8 pls.
           (Serbocroatian).
1969B   Diffusione del genere Ochotona nel Pleistocene superiore dell'Europa sud-orientale. Verona, Mus.
           Civ. Stor. Natur., Mem., Fuori Ser., 3, 67—74, 2 figs. (Italian; German summary).
1970A   Die Ergebnisse der Revision der pleistozänen Fauna aus Krapina. Krapina, 45—56, 1 table
           (Serbocroatian; German and English summaries).
           Rev.: Kochansky-Devidé in Zentralbl. Geol. Paläontol., Teil 2, 1971:5, 362.
1972A   Ostaci fosilnog čovjeka iz gornjeg pleistocena Šandalje kod Pule (Istra). [Remains of upper Pleistocene
           man from Šandalja near Pula in Istria (Croatia).] Palaeontol. Jugoslav., 12, 39 pp., 9 figs.,
           8 pls., 6 tables (Serbocroatian; English summary).

MALEZ, M. and PEPEONIK, Z.
1969A   Entdeckung des ganzen skelettes eines fossilen Leoparden in der Vjetrenica-Höhle auf dem Popovo
           Polje (Herzegowina). Akad. savet FNRJ, Bull. Sci., Sec. A, 14:5—6, 144—145, 3 figs. (German).

MALEZ, M. and VOGEL, J. C.
1970A   Die Ergebnisse der Radiocarbonanalysen der quartären Schichten der Velika Pećina in Nordwest-
           Kroatien. Akad. savet FNRJ, Bull. Sci., Sec. A, 15:11—12, 390—391, 1 fig. (German).

MALEZ, MIRKO   See also: Soklić, I. and Malez, M., 1969A.

MALINAS, Y.
1970A   La cavité pelvienne d'Australopithecus prometheus (Dart). Essai de paléo-obstétrique. Acad. Soc.
           Lorraines Sci., Bull., 9:1, 253—269, 15 figs. (French).

MALINOVSKIĬ, VIĀCHESLAV ĪUR'EVICH
1967A   Kaĭnozoĭ tsentral'noĭ chasti Kazakhskogo shchita. [Cenozoic of the central part of Kazakh shield.]
           In: Materialy po geologii Tsentral'nogo Kazakhstana, 7, 179—349, 24 figs., 4 tables (Russian).

MALINOWSKI, TADEUSZ
1970A*   Central Europe: part I. COWA Surv. Bibliogr., Area 5, 4, 22 pp.

MALLO VIESCA, MANUEL and PEREZ PEREZ, MANUEL
1969A   Primeras notas al estudio de la cueva "El Ramu" y su comunicación con "La Lloseta". Zephyrus,
           19–20, 7–25, 2 figs., 4 pls. (Spanish).

MALLO VIESCA, MANUEL   See also: Jordá Cerdá, F., Mallo, M. and Perez, M., 1970A.

MALPIERI, L.   See: Biddittu, I., Cassoli, P. and Malpieri, L., 1967A.

MALUQUER DE MOTES, J.   See: Pericot, L. and Maluquer de Motes, J., 1969A.

MALVESIN-FABRE, GEORGES
1955C   La datation relative par le microdosage du fluor dans les ossements fossiles. Les Eyzies, 5, 53–56
           (French).

MALZ, HEINZ
1970A   Zur Deutung permischer Ur-Amphibien. Natur Mus., 100:10, 430–434, 2 figs. (German).
           Rev.: Westphal in Zentralbl. Geol. Paläontol., Teil 2, 1971:1, 53.
1971A   Ein fossiler "Wildwechsel" im Wiehengebirge. Natur Mus., 101:10, 431–436, 2 figs. (German).

MALZAHN, ERICH
1972A   Zur Kenntnis des Kopfskeletts von Janassa bituminosa (Schloth.) aus dem hessischen Kupferschiefer.
           Geol. Jahrb., 90, 431–440, 2 pls. (German; English, French and Russian summaries).

MALZAHN, ERICH   See also: Bendix-Almgreen, S. E. and Malzahn, E., 1969A.

MAMAK, ALEXANDER
1970A   More speculations on the reduction of the canines. E. Anthropol., 23:1, 1–9.

MAMEDOV, M. A.   See: Akhundov, M. A. and Mamedov, M. A., 1968A.

MAMEDOV, TOFIK AKHMED OGLY
1971A   O razvitii paleontologo-stratigraficheskikh issledovaniǐ v Azerbaǐdzhane. [On the development of
           paleontological-stratigraphic research in Azerbaidzhan.] Baku, Azerbaǐdzh. Inst. Nefti Khimii,
           Uch. Zap., 9:4, 23–31 (Russian).

MANDELBAUM, D. G., LASKER, G. W. and ALBERT, E. M.
1963B*   Resources for the teaching of anthropology. Amer. Anthropol. Ass., Mem., 95, 316 pp.
           Rev.: Spaulding in Amer. Anthropol., 69, 746–747.

MANGUS, MARLYN   See: Schaeffer, B. and Mangus, M., 1970A.

MANIA, DIETRICH   See: Feustel, R., et al., 1971B.

MANLEY, GEOFFREY A.
1972A   A review of some current concepts of the functional evolution of the ear in terrestrial vertebrates.
           Evolution, 26:4, 608–621, 6 figs.

MANN, ALAN
1968A   The growth and development of Australopithecus and its cultural implications. Amer. Anthropol.
           Ass., Bull., 1:3, 88 (abs.).
1970A   "Telanthropus" and the single species hypothesis: a further comment. Amer. Anthropol., 72:3,
           607–609, 1 fig., 1 table.
1971A   Homo erectus. In: Dolhinow, P. and Sarich, V. M. (eds.), 1971, 166–177, 2 figs.

MANVILLE, RICHARD H. and WILSON, JERALD J.
1970A   Fossil walrus from Virginia waters. J. Mammal., 51:4, 810–811.

MANZIǏ, S. F. (= MANZYǏ, S. F.)
1968A   The peculiar features of evolution of thoracic limbs of primates and of human arm in the light of
           comparative anatomical data. Int. Congr. Anthropol. Ethnol. Sci., 7th, Moscow, 1964, Proc.,
           3, 523–529.

MARCHAL, ANATOLE F.
1965B   L'énigme des dinosauriens foudroyés. Rev. Gén. Belge, 5, 99–103 (French).

MARCHANT, S.
1972A   Evolution of the genus Chrysococcyx. Ibis, 114:2, 219–233, 3 figs.

MARCOZZI, V.
1966A   Relazione su un viaggio nelle regioni degli Australopitecidi. Osservazioni sui più recenti rinvenimenti.
         Riv. Antropol., 53, 125 (Italian).

MARCUS, LESLIE F.
1969A   Measurement of selection using distance statistics in the prehistoric orang-utan *Pongo pygmaeus
         palaeosumatrensis*. Evolution, 23:2, 301–307, 1 fig., 3 tables.

MARCUS, L. F.   See also: Ho, T. Y., Marcus, L. F. and Berger, R., 1969A.

MAREK, KURT W.   See: Ceram, C. W.

MARGALEF, RAMÓN
1962A   Adaptación, ecología y evolución: nuevas formas de plantear antiguos problemas. Discussions. Soc.
         Españ. Hist. Natur., Bol., Secc. Biol., 60, 231–246 (Spanish).

MARIN, ION   See: Grigorescu, D. and Marin, I., 1971A.

MARINOS, GEORGES P.
1970A   Professeur Maxime C. Mitzopoulos (1897–1968). Ann. Géol. Pays Hellén., 19 (1968), portr.

MARISOVA, I. V.
1968A   Pleĭstotsenovaĭa ornitofauna Podolii. [Pleistocene ornithofauna of Podolia.] Ornitologiĭa, 9, 316–322,
         1 fig., 1 table (Russian).

MARISOVA, I. V. and TATARINOV, K. A.
1962A   Pleĭstotsenovye ptitsy Krivchanskoĭ peshchery. [Pleistocene birds of Kryvche Cave.] Nauk. zap.
         Kremenets'k. Derzh. Pedag. Inst., 7, 63–75 (Ukrainian).
1965A   Iskopaemaĭa avifauna zapadnykh oblasteĭ Ukrainy i tempy mikroevoliutsii nekotorykh ptits. [Fossil
         avifauna of the western regions of Ukraine and rates of micro-evolution of some birds.]
         In: Novosti ornitologii. Materialy chetvertoĭ vsesoiuznoĭ ornitologicheskoĭ konferentsii, Alma-
         Ata, 1965, 232–233 (Russian).

MARISOVA, I. V.   See also: Tatarinov, K. A. and Marisova, I. V., 1962A, 1971A.

MARK-KURIK, EL'GA ĬULIUSOVNA (= MARK, E.)
1969A   Distribution of vertebrates in the Silurian of Estonia. Lethaia, 2:2, 145–152, 3 figs.
1971A   Obituary. Dmitri Obruchev 1900–1970. Soc. Vert. Paleontol., News Bull., 92, 64–65, portr.

MARK-KURIK, ELGA I. and NOPPEL, TIIU
1970A   Additional notes on the distribution of vertebrates in the Silurian of Estonia. Eesti NSV Tead. Akad.,
         Toimet., Keem. Geol., 19:2, 171–173, 1 table.

MARK-KURIK, EL'GA ĬULIUSOVNA   See also: Lyarskaya, L. and Mark-Kurik, E., 1972A.

MARK-KURIK, M.
1962A   [Certain adaptation phenomena in the psammosteids.] Geol. Markmed, 1, 30–34 (Esthonian).

MARKEVICH, V. I.   See: Grigor'eva, G. B., Markevich, V. I., Popova, T. A. and Chernysh, E. K., 1969A.

MARKMAN, HARVEY C.
1952A   Fossil mammals. Denver Mus. Natur. Hist., Mus. Pictorial, 4, 1–62, illustr.

MARKOTIĆ, VLADIMIR
1963A*   European Russia. COWA, Surv. Bibliogr., Area 8, 2, 1–12.
1966A*   European Russia. COWA, Surv. Bibliogr., Area 8, 3, 1–18.
1970A*   European Russia. COWA, Surv. Bibliogr., Area 8, 4, 19 pp.

MARKOV, C. C.   See: Markov, K. K.

MARKOV, K. K. (= MARKOV, C. C.)
1968A   L'Eurasie septentrionale pendant la période de refroidissement Pléistocène. L'Anthropologie, 72,
         97–106, 1 fig., 1 table (French).
1969A   Pervye desiat' knig "Biulletenia Frantsuzskoĭ assotsiatsii po izucheniiu chetvertichnogo perioda - AFEQ.
         [The first ten volumes of the "Bulletin de l'Association Française pour l'étude du Quaternaire -
         AFEQ".] Akad. Nauk SSSR, Kom. Izuch. Chetvertich. Perioda, Biull., 36, 154–159 (Russian).

MARKOV, K. K., VELICHKO, A. A., LAZUKOV, G. I. and NIKOLAEV, V. A.
    1968A   Pleĭstoĭsen. [Pleistocene.] Moscow: "Vysshaĭa Shkola" Press, 304 pp., 120 figs., 31 tables (Russian). Rev.: Sokoloff in Int. Geol. Rev., 11:7, 837.

MARKOVIĆ-MARJANOVIĆ, JELENA
    1970A   Data concerning the stratigraphy and the fauna of the lower and middle Pleistocene of Yugoslavia. Palaeogeogr., Palaeoclimatol., Palaeoecol., 8:2–3, 153–163, 3 figs.
    1972A   Dannye o stratigrafii i faune nizhnego i srednego pleĭstoĭsena Iugoslavii. [Data on the stratigraphy and fauna of the lower and middle Pleistocene of Yugoslavia.] In: Geologiĭa i fauna nizhnego i srednego pleĭstoĭsena Evropy, 153–161 (Russian).

MARSAC, MARTHE
    1970A   La châtellenie et les seigneurs de Montcuq. Soc. Hist. Archéol. Périgord, Bull., 97:1, 52–68 (French).

MARSH, OTHNIEL C.
    1879J   Additional characters of the Sauropoda. Amer. J. Sci., 117, 181–182.
    1972A   Fossil hunting on the plains of Kansas. Edited by George W. Bishop, Jr. Amer. West, 9:6, 34–41, illustr.

MARSHACK, ALEXANDER
    1969A   Polesini. A reexamination of the engraved upper Paleolithic mobilary materials of Italy by a new methodology. Riv. Sci. Preist., 24:2, 219–281, 41 figs. (Italian and French summaries).
    1970A   The baton of Montgaudier. Natur. Hist., 79:3, 56–63, 11 figs.
    1972A   The roots of civilization: the cognitive beginnings of man's first art, symbol and notation. New York: McGraw-Hill Book Co., 413 pp., 225 figs.
            Rev.: Lettvin in Natur. Hist., 81:7, 86–90; Morrison in Sci. Amer., 227:1, 117–118.

MARSHALL, LARRY G.
    1972A   Evolution of the peramelid tarsus. Roy. Soc. Victoria, Proc., 85:1, 51–60, 6 figs.

MARSTON, ALVAN T.
    1971A   Preliminary note on a new fossil human skull from Swanscombe, Kent. In: Leakey, L. S. B., Prost, J. and Prost, S. (eds.), 1971A, 253–256, 3 figs. (reprinted from Nature, August 1936).

MARTÍ JUSMET, F.
    1970A   Un nuevo arcantropino en Europa: el hombre de Vértesszöllös. Speleon, 17, 91–94 (Spanish; French summary).

MARTIN, J.   See: Jaeger, J.-J. and Martin, J., 1971A.

MARTIN, LARRY D.
    1969A   A vertebrate assemblage from the early Permian of Nebraska. Nebr. Acad. Sci., Proc., 79, 26–27 (abs.).
    1970A   Two microtine phylogenetic lineages. Nebr. Acad. Sci., Proc., 80, 35 (abs.).
    1971A   An early Pleistocene eagle from Nebraska. Condor, 73:2, 248–250, 1 fig.
    1971B   Paleozoic tetrapods from Nebraska. Nebr. Acad. Sci., Proc., 81, 49–50.
    1972A   The microtine rodents of the Mullen assemblage from the Pleistocene of north central Nebraska. Nebr. Univ. State Mus., Bull., 9:5, 173–182, 3 figs., 1 table.

MARTIN, LARRY D. and SCHULTZ, C. B.
    1971A   Stratigraphic position and paleoecology of the Angus local fauna. Geol. Soc. Amer., Abstr., 3:4, 270–271 (abs.).

MARTIN, LARRY D. and TATE, JAMES, JR.
    1970A   A new turkey from the Pliocene of Nebraska. Wilson Bull., 82, 214–218, 1 fig., 1 table.

MARTIN, LARRY D.   See also: Rasmussen, D. L., Martin, L. D., Chorn, J. D. and Slimmer, D. F., 1971A; Schultz, C. B. and Martin, L. D., 1970A, 1970B; Schultz, C. B., Schultz, M. R. and Martin, L. D., 1970A; Schultz, C. B., Tanner, L. G. and Martin, L. D., 1969A, 1972A; Tanner, L. G. and Martin, L. D., 1972A; Tate, J., Jr. and Martin, L. D., 1968A, 1969A.

MARTIN, P. G.
    1970A   The Darwin Rise hypothesis of the biogeographical dispersal of marsupials. Nature, 225:5228, 197–198, 1 fig.

MARTIN, P. G.   See also: Hayman, D. L., Kirsch, J. A. W., Martin, P. G. and Waller, P. F., 1971A.

MARTIN, PAUL S.
    1970A   Pleistocene niches for alien animals. BioScience, 20:4, 218—221, 2 figs., 2 tables.

MARTIN, P. S. and WRIGHT, H. E.
    1967A*   Rev.: Hlady in Manitoba Archaeol. News., 7:3, 23—24; Judson in Amer. Sci., 56:3, 330A—331A;
                Sadek-Kooros in Amer. Antiquity, 35:4, 502—503.

MARTIN, ROBERT
    1968A   Révision des mammifères fossiles du gisement quaternaire de Villereversure (Ain). Étude des
                carnivores, des cervidés et des équidés. Lyons, Fac. Sci., Lab. Géol., Doc., 27, 153 pp., 41 figs.,
                36 tables (French; English summary).
    1970A   Un nouveau gisement à *Hipparion* dans le Miocène supérieur rhodanien près de Valence (Drôme).
                Acad. Sci., C.R., Sér. D, 270:26, 3202—3203 (French).
    1971A   Les affinités de *Nyctereutes megamastoides* (Pomel) canidé du gisement Villafranchien de Saint-Vallier
                (Drôme, France). Palaeovertebrata (Montpellier), 4:2, 39—58, 8 figs. (French; German and
                English summaries).
                Rev.: Thenius in Zentralbl. Geol. Paläontol., Teil 2, 1971:2—3, 196—197.

MARTIN, ROBERT A.
    1968C   Further study of the Friesenhahn Cave *Peromyscus*. Southwest. Natur., 13:3, 253—266, 7 figs.,
                3 tables.
                Rev.: RLB in Caves Karst, 11:4, 32.
    1969A   Taxonomy of the giant Pleistocene beaver *Castoroides* from Florida. J. Paleontol., 43:4, 1033—1041,
                7 figs.
    1970A   Line and grade in the extinct *medius* species group of *Sigmodon*. Science (AAAS), 167:3924, 1504—
                1506, 3 figs.
    1970B   Fossil mammals of the Coleman II A local fauna, Sumter County, Florida. Diss. Abstr., 31:3, 1433B
                (abs.).
    1972A   Synopsis of late Pliocene and Pleistocene bats of North America and the Antilles. Amer. Midland
                Natur., 87:2, 326—335.

MARTIN, ROBERT D.   See: Charles-Dominique, P. and Martin, R. D., 1970A.

MARTIN, Y.   See: Graindor, M. and Martin, Y., 1971A.

MARTINELLI COCO, TEA
    1965A   Giuseppe Isetti [1922—1965]. Bull. Paletnol. Ital., n.s. 16, 74, 288—289 (Italian).

MARTINEZ, C.   See: Hoffstetter, R., Martinez, C., Mattauer, M. and Tomasi, P., 1971A; Hoffstetter, R.,
                Martinez, C., Muñoz-Reyes, J. and Tomasi, P., 1971A; Hoffstetter, R., Martinez, C. and
                Tomasi, P., 1972A.

MARTINEZ R., CARLOS and LIDICKER, WILLIAM Z., JR.
    1971A   Description of a new genus and species of fossil rodent from Australia. J. Mammal., 52:4, 775—781,
                4 figs., 1 table.

MARTINI, ERLEND
    1968A   Fisch-Otolithen aus Geschieben in Norddeutschland. Sammelgr. Geschiebek., Mitt., 2, 63—70, 1 fig.,
                2 pls. (German).
                Rev.: Weiler in Zentralbl. Geol. Paläontol., Teil 2, 1969:3, 286.

MARTINSON, GERBERT GENRIKHOVICH
    1969A   Biostratigrafiíà i fauna melovykh kontinental'nykh otlozheniĭ Tadzhikskoĭ depressii, Kyzylkumov i
                Pritashkentskikh Chuleĭ. [Biostratigraphy and fauna of continental Cretaceous deposits of
                Tadzhik basin, Kyzylkumy and Tashkent region Chuli.] In: Kontinental'nye obrazovaniíà
                vostochnykh raĭonov Sredneĭ Azii i Kazakhstana. (Litologiíà i biostratigrafiíà), 18—51, 1 fig.,
                1 chart, 5 pls. (Russian).
    1971A   Rol' nekotorykh biogeograficheskikh oblasteĭ v evolíùtsionnom proĭsesse kontinental'noĭ fauny.
                [Role of some biogeographic areas in the evolutionary process of continental fauna.] In:
                Tezisy dokladov XVII sessii Vsesoíùznogo paleontologicheskogo obshchestva, 25—29, íànv.
                1971g, 58—59 (Russian).

MARTINSON, G. G., SOCHAVA, A. V. and BARSBOLD, R.
    1969A   O stratigraficheskom raschlenenii verkhnemelovykh otlozheniĭ Mongolii. [On stratigraphic sub-
                division of upper Cretaceous sediments of Mongolia.] Akad. Nauk SSSR, Dokl., 189:5,
                1081—1084, 2 tables (Russian).

1970A   Stratigraphy of the upper Cretaceous of Mongolia. Akad. Nauk SSSR, Dokl., Earth Sci. Sec., 189,
            107–109, 2 tables. (Translated from Russian: Akad. Nauk SSSR, Dokl., 1969, 189:5, 1081–
            1084.)

MARTINSON, G. G., SOCHAVA, A. V. and KOLESNIKOV, CH. M.
1971A   Iskopaemye iaitsa dinozavrov iz pustyni Gobi. [Fossil dinosaur eggs from the Gobi Desert.] Akad.
            Nauk SSSR, Vestn., 1971:7, 95–98, 2 figs. (Russian).

MARTINSON, G. G.   See also: Verzilin, N. N., Martinson, G. G. and Khozatskii, L. I., 1970A, 1971A.

MARTYN, J. E.   See: Leakey, M., Tobias, P. V., Martyn, J. E. and Leakey, R. E. F., 1969A.

MARTYNOV, E. G.
1969A   K stratigrafii pleistotsenovykh otlozhenii srednego techeniia r. Al'my v Krymu. [On the stratigraphy
            of Pleistocene deposits of the middle course of Alma R. in Crimea.] Mosk. Obshchest. Ispyt.
            Prir., Biull., Otd. Geol., 44:5, 64–71, 4 figs., 1 table (Russian).

MARTYNOV, V. A.
1967A   Chetvertichnaia sistema. Iuzhnaia chast' Zapadno-Sibirskoi nizmennosti. [Quaternary system.
            Southern part of west-Siberian lowlands.] Geologiia SSSR, 14, Western Siberia (southern part),
            391–399 (Russian).
1968A   Pozdneneogenovye (ranneantropogenovye?) otlozheniia iuga Zapadnoi Sibiri. [Late Neogene (early
            Anthropogene?) deposits of the south of western Siberia.] In: Neogenovye i chetvertichnye
            otlozheniia Zapadnoi Sibiri, 5–14 (Russian).

MARTYNOV, V. A. and NIKITIN, V. P.
1968A   K stratigrafii neogenovykh otlozhenii iuzhnoi chasti Zapadno-Sibirskoi nizmennosti. [On stratigraphy
            of the Neogene sediments of the southern part of west Siberian lowland.] Geol. Geofiz.,
            1968:12, 3–15, 3 figs. (Russian).

MARTYNOVA, MARIIA IAKOVLEVNA   See: Bliakhova, S. M. and Martynova, M. Ia., 1971A.

MARYAŃSKA, TERESA
1970A   Remains of armoured dinosaurs from the uppermost Cretaceous in Nemegt Basin, Gobi Desert.
            In: Kielan-Jaworowska, Z. (ed.), 1970B, 23–32, 4 pls., 3 tables.
            Rev.: Chrulew in Zentralbl. Geol. Paläontol., Teil 2, 1972:3, 165–166.
1971A   New data on the skull of Pinacosaurus grangeri (Ankylosauria). In: Kielan-Jaworowska, Z. (ed.),
            1971B, 45–56, 1 fig., 2 pls.
            Rev.: Chrulew in Zentralbl. Geol. Paläontol., Teil 2, 1972:3, 166.

MÂRZA, IOAN
1971A   Prezența unor resturi de Mammuthus primigenius Blumb. în depositele cuaternare de la Moldova Nouă
            (Jud. Caraş-Severin). [Presence of some remains of Mammuthus primigenius Blumb. in the
            Quaternary deposits of Moldova Nouă (Jud. Caraş-Severin).] Cluj, Univ., Stud., Ser. Geol.-
            Mineral., 16:1, 29–32, 4 figs. (Rumanian; Russian and English summaries).

MARZKE, MARY WALPOLE
1971A   Origin of the human hand. Amer. J. Phys. Anthropol., 34:1, 61–84, 3 figs., 3 tables.

MASALI, MELCHIORRE
1967A   Notizie ed informazioni su presunti resti fossili umani delle grotte dei Balzi Rossi appartenenti alle
            collezioni del Museo di Antropologia di Torino. Riv. Antropol., 54, 175–186, 4 figs., 1 table
            (Italian; English summary).

MASALI, MELCHIORRE   See also: Fedele, F., Chiarelli, B. and Masali, M., 1966A.

MASCHER, JAN W.
1970A   Skedemosse – ett forntida fågelträsk på Öland. Vår Fågelvärld, 29:1, 1–5, 2 figs. (Swedish; English
            summary).
            Abs.: L.d.K.L. in Auk, 88:1, 222.

MASCLE, G.   See: Bianchini, G. and Mascle, G., 1971A.

MASSEY, WILLIAM C.
1966A   Archaeology and ethnohistory of Lower California. Handbk. Mid. Amer. Ind., 4, 38–58, 12 figs.

MASSOL, E.
1969A   Étude de quelques traces de petits tétrapodes dans les terrains triasiques de la région de Lodève. Soc.
         Hort. Hist. Natur. Hérault, Ann., 109:2, 109–114, 2 pls. (French).

MASUDA, KOICHIRO   See: Hatai, K., Hayasaka, S. and Masuda, K., 1963A; Hatai, K. and Masuda, K., 1966A.

MATEESCO, C. N.   See: Protopopesco-Pake, Em., Mateesco, C. N. and Grossu, Al. V., 1969A.

MATHIEU, G.
1970A   Observations stratigraphiques, sédimentologiques et structurales sur le Bassin houiller de Ronchamp -
         St.-Germain - Lomont. Poitiers, Univ., Inst. Géol. Anthropol. Préhist., Trav., 9 (1968), 186–
         213, 10 figs. (French).

MATHUR, D. P.   See: Verma, K. K. and Mathur, D. P., 1968A.

MATHUR, L. P.   See: Sahni, M. R. and Mathur, L. P., 1964A.

MATIUKHIN, A. E.
1972A   Arkhantrop ili Homo sapiens? [Archanthrope or Homo sapiens?] Priroda, 1972:5, 111 (Russian).
1972B   O sviazi avstralopitekovykh s drevneishimi kamennymi orudiiami. [On the connection between
         australopithecines and the oldest stone tools.] Vop. Antropol., 41, 60–71 (Russian).

MATIUSHIN, G. N.
1971A   Mikhail Mikhailovich Gerasimov [1907–1970]. Sov. Arkheol., 1971:2, 312–315, portr. (Russian).

MATSKHONASHVILI, K. G.   See: Adamiia, Sh. A., Dzotsenidze, N. M., Matskhonashvili, K. G. and Meladze,
         G. K., 1965A; Vekua, A. K. and Matskhonashvili, K. G., 1970A.

MATSUDA, GENJI   See: Goodman, M., Barnabas, J., Matsuda, G. and Moore, G. W., 1971A.

MATSUI, V. M. and MOS'KINA, OL'GA DMITRIEVNA
1968A   Biostratigraficheskoe raschlenenie antropogenovykh otlozhenii Zapadnogo Altaia. [Biostratigraphic
         subdivision of Anthropogene deposits of western Altai.] In: Problemy izucheniia
         chetvertichnogo perioda. Tezisy, 84–85 (Russian).

MATSUMOTO, HIKOSHICHIRO
1963B   [On the age of the bed with fossil remains and of the over and underlying beds of Hanaidzumi.]
         Nat. Sci. Mus., Tokyo, Bull., 6, 167–171 (Japanese; English summary).

MATSUMOTO, HIKOSHICHIRO and MORI, HAJIME
1968A   Spätpliozäne (oder frühpleistozäne) Faunen in Japan. Deut. Ges. Geol. Wiss., Ber., Reihe A, Geol.
         Paläontol., 13:3, 345–350, 1 fig., 4 pls. (German).
1971A   Das letzte Interglazial in Japan. Deut. Ges. Geol. Wiss., Ber., Reihe A, Geol. Paläontol., 16:2, 133–
         142, 1 fig., 10 pls. (German).

MATSUMOTO, MAYME
1971A*   Bibliography of vertebrate paleontology and related subjects. 1969–1970. Soc. Vert. Paleontol.,
         Bibliogr., 25, 121 pp.

MATSUMOTO, M. and NICHOLS, R.
1970A*   Bibliography of vertebrate paleontology and related subjects. 1968–1969. Soc. Vert. Paleontol.,
         Bibliogr., 24, 46 pp.

MATSUMOTO, M.   See also: Bacskai, J., Bartlett, S., Brajnikov, B., Munthe, K., Nichols, R. and Matsumoto, M.
         (eds.), 1972A.

MATTAUER, M.   See: Hoffstetter, R., Martinez, C., Mattauer, M. and Tomasi, P., 1971A.

MATTHES, HORST WERNER
1967D   Neue Wirbeltiere und Pflanzen aus dem Eozän des Geiseltales. Deut. Ges. Geol. Wiss., Ber. Reihe A,
         Geol. Paläontol., 12:6, 651–657 (German).
1967E   Eine neue Creodontier-Art aus der eozänen Geiseltalfauna. Deut. Ges. Geol. Wiss., Ber. Reihe A,
         Geol. Paläontol., 12:6, 659–665, 2 pls., 1 table (German).
1969A   Richard Hagen 1894–1966. Hall. Jahrb. Mitteldeut. Erdgesch., 9, 161–162, portr. (German).
1970A   Zur Paläogeographie und Stammesgeschichte der eozänen Wirbeltiere des Geiseltales. Hercynia, 7:1–3,
         199–249, 45 figs. (German).

1972A   *Propalaeotherium hassiacum* Haupt 1925 (Equidae) aus dem Mitteleozän des Geiseltales. Hall. Jahrb.
         Mitteldeut. Erdgesch., 11, 37–40, 2 pls., 2 tables (German).

MATTHEWS, JOHN V., JR.   See: Guthrie, R. D. and Matthews, J. V., Jr., 1971A.

MATTHEWS, WILLIAM H., III
    1968A   Wonders of fossils. New York: Dodd Publishing Co., 64 pp., illustr. (juvenile).
             Rev.: Neill in Audubon Mag., 70:3, 104.
    1968B   The story of the earth. New York: Harvey House, illustr. (juvenile).

MATTHEY, R.   See: Chaline, J. and Matthey, R., 1971A.

MATTIEVICH, E. and DANON, J.
    1971A   Use of Mössbauer spectroscopy in the study of fossils. Centro Brasil. Pesquis. Fís., Notas Fís., 17:5,
             237–246, illustr.

MATVEENKO, S. A.
    1969A   A. L. Andrzheevskiĭ - zoolog evoliutsionist pervoĭ poloviny XIX stoletiia. [A. L. Andrzhejowski -
             a zoologist-evolutionist of the first half of the 19th century.] Akad. Nauk Ukr. SSR, Inst.
             Zool., Vestn. Zool., 1969:1, 89–92, portr. (Russian).
    1971A   Rol' P. N. Veniukova v razvitii otechestvennoĭ paleontologii. [The role of P. N. Veniukov in the
             development of the native paleontology.] Akad. Nauk Ukr. SSR, Inst. Zool., Vestn. Zool.,
             1971:5, 86–89, portr. (Russian).

MATVEEV, BORIS STEPANOVICH (= MATVEJEV, B. S.)
    1963B   K 50-letiiu "Etiudov po teorii evoliutsii" A. N. Severtsova. [To the 50th anniversary of the "Essays
             on the theory of evolution" by A. N. Severtsov.] Zool. Zh., 42:8, 1129–1134 (Russian;
             English summary).
    1966A   Znachenie teoreticheskogo naslediia A. N. Severtsova v sovremennoĭ biologii. [Importance of the
             heritage of A. N. Severtsov for the modern biology.] Zool. Zh., 45:9, 1283–1295, 4 figs.
             (Russian; English summary).
    1968B   Proiskhozhdenie i puti evoliutsii pozvonochnykh zhivotnykh po sovremennym dannym. [Origin and
             ways of evolution of vertebrate animals accoring to recent data.] In: Problemy evoliutsii,
             1, 82–97, 2 figs. (Russian; English summary).
    1969A   O zadachakh evoliutsionnoĭ morfologii. [On the problems of evolutionary morphology.] Akad. Nauk
             Ukr. SSR, Inst. Zool., Vestn. Zool., 1969:4, 3–10 (Russian; English summary).
    1970A   Biologicheskiĭ progress i individual'noe razvitie. [Biological progress and ontogenesis.] Zool. Zh.,
             49:4, 505–516 (Russian; English summary).
    1970B   O proiskhozhdenii konodontov po dannym evoliutsionnoĭ morfologii. [The origin of conodonts as
             shown by evolutionary morphology data.] Vop. Ikhtiol., 10:60, 3–14, 10 figs. (Russian).

MATVEEVA, OL'GA VLADIMIROVNA   See: Arkhipov, S. A. and Matveeva, O. V., 1964A.

MAUBEUGE, PIERRE L.
    1968A   Quelques précisions sur le "monstre" des carrières d'Haudainville (Meuse). (Crocodilien aff.
             Machimosaurus). Acad. Soc. Lorraines Sci., Bull., 7:3, 203–209, 1 fig. (French).

MAUBEUGE, PIERRE L.   See also: Gaudant, J. and Maubeuge, P., 1971A.

MAURIN, V.   See: Flugel, H. and Maurin, V., 1959A.

MAVLIANOV, G. A., KAMBARIDDINOV, R. K. and MIRZABAEV, KH.
    1968A   [More precise age of loess rocks in Tadzhik basin with discovery of a fossil bone of horse.] Uzbek.
             Geol. Zh., 1968:5, 48–50, 1 fig., 1 table (Russian; Uzbek summary).

MAWBY, JOHN E.
    1968D   Pliocene vertebrates and stratigraphy in Stewert and Ione valleys, Nevada. Diss. Abstr., 29:4, 1406B
             (abs.).
    1969A   Pleistocene vertebrates from the Chiwondo beds of northern Malawi, central Africa. Geol. Soc.
             Amer., Abstr., Part 3, 41 (abs.).
    1970A   Fossil vertebrates from northern Malawi: preliminary report. Quaternaria, 13, 319–323, 1 fig.

MAWBY, JOHN E. and FIRBY, JEAN B.
    1970A   Pleistocene vertebrates from California aqueduct excavations, Merced County. S. Calif. Paleontol.
             Soc., Bull., 2:6, 5 (reprinted from S. Calif. Acad. Sci., 1970 Meetings, Abstr.).

MAXFIELD, JERRY L.   See: Zakrzewski, R. J. and Maxfield, J. L., 1971A.

MAXIMILIAN, C.
1972A   Evoluţia umană: probleme. [Human evolution: problems.] Natura, Ser. Biol., 24:4, 28—35
           (Rumanian).

MAY, JULIAN
1967A   They lived in the ice age. Illustrations by Jean Zallinger. New York: Holiday House, 38 pp., illustr.
           (juvenile).
1968A   The first men. Illustrated by Lorence F. Bjorklund. New York: Holiday House, 38 pp., illustr.
           (juvenile).
1968B   Horses - how they came to be. New York: Holiday House, unpaged, illustr. (juvenile).
           Rev.: Neill in Audubon Mag., 70:3, 104.

MAYER, GASTON
1967A   Muschelkalkaufschlüsse im südlichen Kraichgau. VIII. Bruchsal. Aufschluss, 18:12, 332—344,
           8 figs. (German).
1971A   Beiträge zur Geschichte der Badischen Landessammlungen für Naturkunde in Karlsruhe. II. Aus der
           Frühzeit der pleistozänen Fossilfundstelle Mauer bei Heidelberg. Naturk. Forsch.
           Südwestdeutschland, Beitr., 30:1, 77—83 (German).
1971B   Beiträge zur Geschichte der Badischen Landessammlungen für Naturkunde in Karlsruhe. III. Der
           Schädel des *Dicerorhinus mercki (kirchbergensis)* (Jäger) var. *brachycephalus* Schroeder von
           Daxlanden und seine Geschichte. Naturk. Forsch. Südwestdeutschland, Beitr., 30:2, 157—163
           (German).

MAYO, NÉSTOR A.
1969A   Nueva especie de Megalonychidae y descripción de los depósitos cuaternarios de la cueva del Vaho,
           Boca de Jaruco, La Habana. Univ. La Habana, Fac. Cienc., Mem., Ser. Cienc. Biol., 3, 1—58,
           14 figs., 2 maps, 6 tables (Spanish; English summary).

MAYR, ERNST
1963B   Rev.: Dunn in Isis, 55:2, 225—227.
1965G   Races in animal evolution. UNESCO (Int. Soc. Sci. J.), 17:1, 121—122.
1967B   Rev.: Haltenorth in Säugetierkundl. Mitt., 18, 289; Herre in Z. Tierzücht. Züchtungsbiol., 85:4, 404;
           Spindler in Anthropol. Ges., Mitt., 98, 96.
1968B   Museum of comparative zoology, report of the director, 1966—1967. Harvard Univ., Mus. Comp.
           Zool., Ann. Rep., 1966—1967, 1—57, illustr.
1969A   The biological meaning of species. Linn. Soc., Biol. J., 1:3, 311—320.
1969B   Introduction: The role of systematics in biology. In: Sibley, Ch. G. (ed.), 1969A, 4—15.
1969C   Grundgedanken der Evolutionsbiologie. Naturwiss., 56:8, 392—397 (German).
1969D   Principles of systematic zoology. New York, London, Sydney: McGraw-Hill Book Company, xi +
           428 pp., illustr.
           Rev.: Ashlock in Amer. Sci., 57:3, 260A—261A; Gill in Auk, 88:1, 190—192; Richards in Science
           (AAAS), 167:3924, 1477—1478.
1969E   Museum of comparative zoology, report of the director, 1967—1968. Harvard Univ., Mus. Comp.
           Zool., Ann. Rep., 1967—1968, 1—66, illustr.
1970A   Biologicheskoe znachenie vida. [The biological meaning of species.] Priroda, 1970:5, 48—54, portr.
           (Russian).
1970B   Museum of comparative zoology, report of the director, 1968—1969. Harvard Univ., Mus. Comp. Zool.,
           Ann. Rep., 1968—1969, 1—70, illustr.
1970C   Populations, species, and evolution. An abridgement of animal species and evolution. Cambridge,
           Mass.: Belknap Press of Harvard Univ. Press, 471 pp., illustr.
           Rev.: Anon. in Biologist, 53, 163; Kurth in Naturwiss. Rundsch., 24:1, 41; Schöneich in Biol.
           Zentralbl., 91:2, 263—264.
1970D   L'evoluzione delle specie animali. Translated by S. and A. Serafini. Torino: G. Einaudi, 2 vols.,
           xxxiii + 865 pp., 65 figs. (Italian).
           Rev.: Tortonese in Natura, 62:1, 136—138.
1972A   Continental drift and the history of the Australian bird fauna. Emu, 72:1, 26—28.
1972B   Lamarck revisited. J. Hist. Biol., 5:1, 55—94.
1972C   The taxonomic evaluation of fossil hominids. In: McCown, T. D. and Kennedy, K. A. R. (eds.),
           1972A, 372—386 (reprinted from Classification and Human Evolution, 1963).

MAYR, ERNST and CAMPBELL, BERNARD
1971A   Was Virchow right about neanderthal? Nature, 229:5282, 253—254.

MAYR, FRANZ X.
1964A   Die naturwissenschaftlichen Sammlungen der Philosophisch-theologischen Hochschule Eichstätt.
           400 Jahre Collegium Willibaldinum Eichstätt, Festschrift, 302—334 (German).

MAZAK, VRATISLAV
    1970A   On a supposed prehistoric representation of the Pleistocene scimitar cat, *Homotherium* Fabrini, 1890 (Mammalia; Machairodontidae). Z. Säugetierkunde, 35:6, 359–362, 4 figs. (German summary).

MAZONOWICZ, DOUGLAS
    1970A   Copying the world's oldest masters. Pac. Discovery, 23:3, 1–10, illustr.

MCHEDLIDZE, GURAM ANDREEVICH
    1966A   Ob ekogeneze kitoobraznykh. [On the ecogenesis of Cetacea.] Akad. Nauk Gruz. SSR, Inst. Paleobiol., Nauchn. Sess., 12, 41–42 (Russian and Georgian).
    1967B   K voprosu o progresse v filogeneze kitoobraznykh. [The problem of progress in the phylogenesis of cetaceans.] Akad. Nauk Gruz. SSR, Inst. Paleobiol., Obshch. Vop. Evoliūts. Paleobiol., 3, 92–99 (Russian; Georgian and English summaries).
    1968A   Elementy rekapituliāt̄sii v razvitii kitoobraznykh. [Elements of recapitulation in the development of cetaceans.] Akad. Nauk Gruz. SSR, Inst. Paleobiol., Nauchn. Sess., 14, 9–10 (Russian).
    1970A   Ob ekogeneze kitoobraznykh. [On the ecogenesis of cetaceans.] Akad. Nauk Gruz. SSR, Inst. Paleobiol., Obshch. Vop. Evoliūts. Paleobiol., 5, 69–76 (Russian; Georgian and English summaries).
    1970B   Nekotorye obshchie cherty istorii kitoobraznykh. Chast' I. [Some features of the historical development of the Cetacea. Part I.] Tbilisi: Akad. Nauk Gruz. SSR, Inst. Paleobiol., "Met̄sniereba" Press, 112 pp., 23 figs., 6 pls. (Russian; English summary).
    Rev.: Rothausen in Zentralbl. Geol. Paläontol., Teil 2, 1971:1, 65.

MEDVEDEV, V. V.   See: Bersenev, I. I., Ustinovskiĭ, Iu. B., Bur'ianova, I. Z., Nevolina, S. I. and Medvedev, V. V., 1969A.

MEDVEDEVA, IRINA M.
    1961A   K voprosu o proiskhozhdenii khoan amfibiĭ. [On the origin of choanae in amphibians.] Akad. Nauk SSSR, Dokl., 137:2, 468–471, 2 figs. (Russian).
    1965A   O lokalizat̄sii materiala v oboniatel'noĭ plakode khvostatykh amfibiĭ. [On localization of material in the olfactory placode of caudate amphibians.] Akad. Nauk SSSR, Dokl., 162:3, 709–712, 1 fig., 1 table (Russian).

MEESTER, J. and MEYER, I. J.
    1972A   Fossil *Suncus* (Mammalia: Soricidae) from southern Africa. Transvaal Mus., Ann., 27:14, 269–277, 4 tables.

MEGGERS, BETTY JANE
    1966A   Ecuador. London: Thames and Hudson, Ancient Peoples and Places, 49, 220 pp., 118 figs., 3 tables, 5 maps.
    Rev.: Adams in Amer. Anthropol., 69, 533–534; Collier in Amer. Antiquity, 33, 269–271.
    1972A   Prehistoric America. Chicago: Aldine Atherton, illustr.

MEHRINGER, P. J., JR., KING, J. E. and LINDSAY, E. H.
    1970A   A record of Wisconsin-age vegetation and fauna from the Ozarks of western Missouri. In: Dort, W., Jr and Jones, J. K., Jr. (eds.), 1970A, 173–183, 7 figs., 1 table.

MEHROTRA, DEEPAK KUMAR   See: Sahni, A., Mehrotra, D. K. and Jauhari, A. K., 1971A.

MEIBURG, P. and SIEGFRIED, P.
    1970A   Katalog der Typen und Belegstücke zur Paläozoologie im Geologisch-Paläontologischen Institut der Westfälischen Wilhelms-Universität Münster. Teil II: Vertebrata. Münstersche Forsch. Geol. Paläontol., 15, 84 pp., 3 figs. (German).
    Rev.: Häntzschel in Zentralbl. Geol. Paläontol., Teil 2, 1970:6, 449.

MEIN, PIERRE
    1969A   Le gisement lutétien de Lissieu dans le Mont d'Or Lyonnais. Colloque sur l'Éocène, Paris, mai 1968, Vol. III. Fr., Bur. Rech. Géol. Minières, Mém., 69, 399–401 (French).
    1969B   Réponse au problème posé par M. Freudenthal et Fahlbusch au sujet de *Cricetodon minus* Lartet, 1851 (Mammalia). Bull. Zool. Nomencl., 26:3–4, 122 (French).
    1970A   Les sciuroptères (Mammalia, Rodentia) néogènes d'Europe Occidentale. Géobios, 3:3, 7–77, 85 figs. (French; English summary).
    1971A   Jean Viret 1894–1970. Soc. Vert. Paleontol., News Bull., 91, 60, portr.

MEIN, P. and FREUDENTHAL, M.
1971A   Une nouvelle classification des Cricetidae (Mammalia, Rodentia) du Tertiaire de l'Europe. Scripta
         Geol., 2, 37 pp., 1 fig., 2 pls. (French; German and English summaries).
1971B   Les Cricetidae (Mammalia, Rodentia) du Néogène moyen de Vieux-Collonges. Partie 1: Le genre
         Cricetodon Lartet, 1851. Scripta Geol., 5, 38 pp., 13 figs., 6 pls., 1 table (French; German
         and English summaries).

MEIN, P. and MICHAUX, JACQUES
1970A   Un nouveau stade dans l'évolution des rongeurs pliocènes de l'Europe sud-occidentale. Acad. Sci.,
         C.R., Sér. D, 270:23, 2780–2783, 2 pls., 1 table (French).

MEIN, P., TRUC, G. and BALLÉSIO, R.
1972A   Âge des formations de la Côtière de Dombes à la lumière d'éléments paléontologiques nouveaux. Acad.
         Sci., C.R., Sér. D, 274:14, 2016–2018 (French).

MEIN, P., TRUC, G. and DEMARCQ, G.
1971A   Micromammifères et gastéropodes continentaux des biozones de Paulhiac et de la Romieu dans le
         Miocène de la Bastidonne et de Mirabeau (Vaucluse, Sud-Est de la France). Acad. Sci., C.R.,
         Sér. D, 273:5, 566–568 (French).

MEIN, PIERRE   See also: Bruijn, H. de, Dawson, M. R. and Mein, P., 1970A; Guérin, C. and Mein, P., 1971A;
                    Guérin, C., Mein, P., Philippe, M. and Truc, G., 1972A; Guérin, C., Mein, P. and Truc, G.,
                    1970A; Hugueney, M. and Mein, P., 1968A; Telles Antunes, M. and Mein, P., 1971A.

MEISE, WILHELM
1960A   Über Verbreitung, Verbreitungsgeschichte und Evolution afrikanischer Vögel. Int. Ornith. Congr.,
         12th, Proc., 499–506 (German).

MELADZE, GURAM KARLOVICH
1966A   K ekogenezu gipparionovoĭ fauny. [On the ecogenesis of Hipparion fauna.] Akad. Nauk Gruz. SSR,
         Inst. Paleobiol., Nauchn. Sess., 12, 42–44 (Russian and Georgian).
1967B   O print͡sipakh datirovki i stratigraficheskoĭ parallelizat͡sii kontinental'nykh otlozheniĭ po iskopaemym
         ostatkam pozvonochnykh (na primere Hipparion). [On the principles of dating and stratigraphic
         correlation of continental deposits by fossil remains of vertebrates (example of Hipparion).]
         Akad. Nauk Gruz. SSR, Inst. Paleobiol., Nauchn. Sess., 17–18 (Russian).
1970A   O nekotorykh osobennost͡siakh ekogeneza gipparionovoĭ fauny. [On some special features in the
         ecogenesis of the Hipparion fauna.] Akad. Nauk Gruz. SSR, Inst. Paleobiol., Obshch. Vop.,
         Evoli͡ut͡s. Paleobiol., 5, 77–84 (Russian; Georgian and English summaries).

MELADZE, G. K.   See also: Adamii͡a, Sh. A., Dzot͡senidze, N. M., Mat͡skhonashvili, K. G. and Meladze, G. K., 1965A.

MELÉNDEZ, BERMUDO
1962A   Los "eslabones" de las series evolutivas. Discussions. Soc. Españ. Hist. Natur., Bol., Secc. Biol., 60,
         151–166, 11 figs. (Spanish).

MELÉNDEZ, B.   See also: Crusafont, M., Meléndez, B. and Aguirre, E., 1966A.

MELENTIS, JOHANN K.
1963A   Studien über fossile Vertebraten Griechenlands. 3. Die Osteologie der pleistozänen Proboscidier des
         Beckens von Megalopolis im Peloponnes (Griechenland). Ann. Géol. Pays Hellén., 14, 1–107,
         16 figs., 12 pls., 26 tables (German).
1966F   Die pleistozänen Cerviden des Beckens von Megalopolis im Peloponnes (Griechenland). Ann. Géol.
         Pays Hellén., 16, 1–92, 9 figs., 12 pls., 19 tables (Greek and German).
1966G   Studien über fossile Vertebraten Griechenlands. 4. Die pleistozänen Nashörner des Beckens von
         Megalopolis in Peloponnes (Griechenland). Ann. Géol. Pays Hellén., 16, 363–402, 5 figs.,
         5 pls., 7 tables (German).
1966H   Studien über fossile Vertebraten Griechenlands. 6. Sus scrofa L. aus dem Jungpleistozän des
         Beckens von Megalopolis im Peloponnes (Griechenland). Ann. Géol. Pays Hellén., 16, 436–445,
         2 pls., 2 tables (German).
1966I   Studien über fossile Vertebraten Griechenlands. 7. Die Boviden des Jungpleistozäns des Beckens von
         Megalopolis im Peloponnes (Griechenland). Ann. Géol. Pays Hellén., 16, 446–472, 6 figs.,
         3 pls., 8 tables (German).
1966J   Studien über fossile Vertebraten Griechenlands. 8. Über Equus abeli aus dem Mittelpleistozän des
         Beckens von Megalopolis im Peloponnes (Griechenland). Ann. Géol. Pays Hellén., 17, 158–168,
         2 figs., 2 pls., 2 tables (German; Greek summary).

1966K   Studien über fossile Vertebraten Griechenlands. 10. *Clemmys caspica* aus dem Pleistozän des Beckens von Megalopolis im Peloponnes (Griechenland). Ann. Géol. Pays Hellén., 17, 169–181, 8 figs., 1 table (German).

1966L   Studien über fossile Vertebraten Griechenlands. 12. Neue Schädel- und Unterkieferfunde von *Pliohyrax graecus* aus dem Pont von Pikermi (Attika) und Halmyropotamos (Euboea). Ann. Géol. Pays Hellén., 17, 182–210, 10 figs., 7 pls., 4 tables (German; Italian and Greek summaries).

1966M   Studien über fossile Vertebraten Griechenlands. 13. *Archidiskodon meridionalis proarchaicus* n. ssp., die geologisch ältesten Elephantenreste aus Griechenland. Ann. Géol. Pays Hellén., 17, 211–220, 2 figs., 1 pl., 1 table (German; Italian and Greek summaries).

1966N   Studien über fossile Vertebraten Griechenlands. 14. Der erste Nachweis von *Brachyodus onoideus* (Mammalia, Anthracotheriidae) aus Griechenland und die Datierung der Fundschichten. Ann. Géol. Pays Hellén., 17, 221–235, 5 figs., 2 pls., 2 tables (German; Italian and Greek summaries).

1966O   Studien über fossile Vertebraten Griechenlands. 15. Fossile "Gehirne" aus dem Pont von Pikermi. Ann. Géol. Pays Hellén., 17, 236–246, 4 figs., 1 pl., 1 table (German; Greek summary).

1966P   Studien über fossile Vertebraten Griechenlands. 16. Die pleistozäne Säugetierfauna des Beckens von Haliakmon (Griechenland). Ann. Géol. Pays Hellén., 17, 247–266, 6 figs., 2 pls., 7 tables (German; Italian and Greek summaries).

1966Q   Studien über fossile Vertebraten Griechenlands. 18. *Stenofiber jaegeri* aus Ligniten von Serrae und die Datierung der Fundschichten. Ann. Géol. Pays Hellén., 17, 289–297, 1 fig., 1 pl., 1 table (German; Greek summary).

1967C   Studien über fossile Vertebraten Griechenlands. 20. *Orthogonoceros verticornis* aus dem Altpleistozän des Beckens von Haliakmon (Griechenland). Ann. Géol. Pays Hellén., 18, 447–455, 2 figs., 2 pls., 2 tables (German; Greek summary).

1967D   Studien über fossile Vertebraten Griechenlands. 21. Über *Coelodus münsteri* Ag. (Pisces) aus dem Cenoman von Griechenland. Ann. Géol. Pays Hellén., 18, 456–462, 1 fig., 1 pl., 1 table (German; Greek summary).
        Rev.: Thenius in Zentralbl. Geol. Paläontol., Teil 2, 1970:3/4, 246.

1967E   *Steneofiber jaegeri* aus Ligniten von Serrae und die Datierung der Fundschichten. Akad. Athenon, Prakt., 41, 40–50, 1 fig., 1 pl., 1 table (German; Greek summary).

1967F   Die Pikermifauna von Halmyropotamos (S. Euböa/Griechenland). Akad. Athenon, Prakt., 41, 261–266 (Greek; German summary).

1969A   Zur Morphologie und systematischen Stellung von *Pliocervus pentelici* (Gaudry) aus dem Pont von Attika. Akad. Athenon, Praktika, 43, 5–16, 1 fig., 5 pls., 1 table (German).

1970A   Die Pikermifauna von Halmyropotamos (Euböa, Griechenland). I Teil: Odontologie und Kraniologie. Ann. Géol. Pays Hellén., 19 (1968), 283–411, 28 figs., 23 pls., 26 tables (German; Greek and English summaries).

MELENTIS, J. K. and SCHNEIDER, HORST
1966A   Studien über fossile Vertebraten Griechenlands. 17. Eine neue Pikermifauna in der Nähe der Ortschaft Alifaka in Thessalien (Griechenland). Ann. Géol. Pays Hellén., 17, 267–288, 4 figs., 4 pls., 4 tables (German).

MELENTIS, J. K. and TOBIEN, HEINZ
1970A   Paläontologische Ausgrabungen auf der Insel Chios. (Eine Vorläufige Mitteilung). Ann. Géol. Pays Hellén., 19 (1968), 647–651, 1 map (German; Greek summary).

MELLARS, P. A.
1969A   The chronology of Mousterian industries in the Périgord region of south-west France. Prehist. Soc., Proc., 35:6, 134–171, 4 figs.

MELLETT, JAMES S.
1967A   Fossil mammals from the Oligocene Hsanda Gol formation, Mongolia. Part I: Insectivora, Rodentia and Deltatheridia with notes on the paleobiology of *Cricetops dormitor*. Diss. Abstr., 27:8, 2747B (abs.).

1969A   Carnassial rotation in a fossil carnivore. Amer. Midland Natur., 82, 287–289, 2 figs.

1969B   A skull of *Hemipsalodon* (Mammalia, Deltatheridia) from the Clarno formation of Oregon. Amer. Mus. Nov., no. 2387, 1–19, 12 figs., 3 tables.

MELLETT, JAMES S. and SZALAY, F. S.
1968A   *Kennatherium shirensis* (Mammalia, Palaeoryctoidea), a new didymoconid from the Eocene of Asia. Amer. Mus. Nov., 2342, 1–7, 4 figs.

MELLETT, JAMES S.   See also: McKenna, M. C., Mellett, J. S. and Szalay, F. S., 1971A.

MEL'NIKOV, O. A. and SHUSTOV, L. N.
1969A   O novoĭ nakhodke ostatkov kosteĭ drevnikh krupnykh pozvonochnykh na Sakhaline. [On a new finding of bone remains of ancient large vertebrates in Sakhalin.] Akad. Nauk SSSR, Sibirsk. Otd., Sakhalinsk. Kompleks. Nauch.-Issled. Inst., Trudy, 21, 41–43, 3 figs. (Russian).

MELTON, WILLIAM G., JR.
    1969A   A new Pennsylvanian fish fauna from central Montana. Geol. Soc. Amer., Abstr., Part 3, 41 (abs.).
    1969B   A new dorypterid fish from central Montana. Northwest Sci., 43:4, 196—205, 8 figs., 2 pls.
    1971A   The Bear Gulch fauna from central Montana. N. Amer. Paleontol. Conv., 1969, Proc., Part I. 1202—
             1207, 2 figs.

MELVILLE, R. V.
    1971A   *Protomomys* Teilhard de Chardin, 1927 (Mammalia): suppressed under the plenary powers. Bull.
             Zool. Nomen., 27:5—6, 227—228.

MÉNDEZ, B.   See: Comas, J., Castillo, H. de and Méndez, B., 1971A.

MENDREZ, CHRISTIANE HÉLÈNE
    1972A   Premières ébauches d'un palais secondaire chez les reptiles mammaliens. Acad. Sci., C.R., Sér. D,
             274:22, 260—261, 1 fig. (French).
    1972B   Les paléontologistes et la dérive des continents. La Recherche, 3:23, 476—477, 2 figs. (French).
    1972C   On the skull *Regisaurus jacobi*, a new genus and species of Bauriamorpha Watson and Romer 1956
             (= Scaloposauria Boonstra 1953), from the *Lystrosaurus*-zone of South Africa. In: Joysey,
             K. A. and Kemp, T. S. (eds.), 1972A, 191—212, 12 figs., 3 pls., 1 table.
    1972D   Revision du genre *Protocynodon* Broom 1949 et discussion de sa position taxonomique. Palaeontol.
             Afr., 14, 19—50, 6 figs. (French; English and German summaries).
    1972E   On *Cyrbasiodon boycei*, Broom 1931 (Cynodontia Procynosuchidae), from South Africa. Palaeontol.
             Afr., 14, 51—69, 12 figs., 1 pl.

MENESINI, E.
    1968A   Cirripedi, echinidi, elasmobranchi e pesci (s.s.) del Pliocene di Punta Ristola (Capo di Leuca - Puglia).
             Soc. Toscana Sci. Natur., Atti, Mem., Ser. A, 75:2, 579—596, 3 pls. (Italian; French summary).
    1969A   Ittiodontoliti miocenici di terra d'Otranto. Palaeontogr. Ital., 65, 1—61, 6 figs., 7 pls. (Italian;
             English summary).

MENESINI, E. and TAVANI, G.
    1968A   Resti di *Scaldicetus* (Cetacea) nel Miocene della Puglia. Soc. Paleontol. Ital., Boll., 7:2, 87—93, 1 fig.,
             4 pls. (Italian; English summary(.
             Rev.: Albanesi in Riv. Ital. Paleontol. Stratigr., 75:4, 883.

MENGEL, ROBERT M.
    1970A   The North American central plains as an isolating agent in bird speciation. In: Dort, W., Jr. and
             Jones, J. K., Jr. (eds.), 1970A, 279—340, 17 figs., 4 tables.

MENGHIN, OSWALD
    1968A   Vergessene Nachrichten über paläolithische Funde in Südosteuropa. Quartär, 19, 347—351 (German).

MENNER, VLADIMIR VLADIMIROVICH
    1968B   Rang, ob"em, podrazdelenia i nizhniaia granitsa antropogena (kvartera). [Rank, volume, subdivisions
             and lower boundary of the Anthropogene (Quaternary).] In: Granitsa tretichnogo i
             chetvertichnogo periodov, 5—8 (Russian; English summary).

MENNER, V. V., KRYLOVA, A. K., KOLODEZNIKOV, K. E. and FRADKIN, G. S.
    1970A   O korreliatsii srednedevonskikh otlozhenii Sibirskoi platformy. [On correlation of middle-Devonian
             deposits of the Siberian platform.] Akad. Nauk SSSR, Dokl., 193:6, 1360—1363, 1 fig.
             (Russian).

MENNER, V. V., NIKIFOROVA, K. V., PEVZNER, M. A., ALEKSEEV, M. N., GLADENKOV, IU. B., GURARII,
    G. Z. and TRUBIKHIN, V. M.
    1972A   Paleomagnetizm v detal'noi stratigrafii verkhnego kainozoia. [Paleomagnetism in the detailed
             stratigraphy of the upper Cenozoic.] Akad. Nauk SSSR, Izv., Ser. Geol., 1972:6, 3—17,
             9 figs. (Russian).

MENNER, V. V.   See also: Glushnitskii, O. T. and Menner, V. V., 1970A.

MENNESSIER, G.   See: Ginsburg, L. and Mennessier, G., 1970A; Ginsburg, L., Mennessier, G. and
                  Russell, D., 1967A.

MEN'SHIKOV, SLAVII FEOKTISTOVICH
    1971A   Vozrast otlozhenii drevnei doliny r. Aiaguz. [Age of the deposits of the ancient valley of Aiaguz R.]
             In: Materialy po geologii i poleznym iskopaemym iuzhnogo Kazakhstana, 4(29), 165—166
             (Russian).

MENU, HENRI and SIGÉ, BERNARD
　　1971A　　Nyctalodontie et myotodontie, importants caractères de grades évolutifs chez les chiroptères
　　　　　　　entomophages. Acad. Sci., C.R., Sér. D, 272:13, 1735–1738, 1 pl. (French).

MÉON-VILAIN, H.　　See: Combémorel, R., Guérin, C. and Méon-Vilain, H., 1970A; Guérin, C., Ballésio, R. and
　　　　　　　Méon-Vilain, H., 1969A.

MERCADAL, BENITO
　　1967A　　Nuevos yacimientos con Myotragus en Menorca y su cronología. Soc. Hist. Natur. Baleares, Bol., 13,
　　　　　　　63–70, 2 pls. (Spanish).

MERKLIN, ROMAN L'VOVICH
　　1966A*　　Stratigrafiía. Paleontologiía. [Stratigraphy. Paleontology.] Itogi Nauki, Seriía Geologiía, 10, 123 pp.,
　　　　　　　illustr. (Russian).

MÉROC, LOUIS
　　1967A　　Circonscription de Midi-Pyrénées. Gallia Préhist., 10:2, 389–411, 27 figs. (French).
　　1969A　　Informations archéologiques. Circonscription de Midi-Pyrénées. Gallia Préhist., 12:2, 485–503, 28 figs.
　　　　　　　(French).

MERRILEES, DUNCAN
　　1967C　　Cranial and mandibular characters of modern mainland wombats (Marsupialia, Vombatidae) from a
　　　　　　　paleontological viewpoint, and their bearing on the fossils called Phascolomys parvus by Owen
　　　　　　　(1872). S. Austral. Mus., Rec., 15:3, 399–418, 5 figs., 2 tables.
　　1969A　　A newly discovered bone-bearing deposit in Labyrinth Cave, near Augusta, Western Australia.
　　　　　　　W. Austral. Natur., 11:4, 86–87.
　　1970A　　Two new fossil finds representing the large extinct diprotodontid marsupial. W. Austral. Natur., 11:5,
　　　　　　　111–113, 1 fig.
　　1971A　　Resemblances between the extinct "cave goat" (Eutheria, Bovidae) of the Balearic Islands and
　　　　　　　phalangeroid marsupials. Helictite, 9:3, 51–60, 2 figs.

MESZOELY, CHARLES A. M.
　　1970A　　North American fossil anguid lizards. Harvard Univ., Mus. Comp. Zool., Bull., 139:2, 87–150, 17 figs.,
　　　　　　　2 pls., 6 tables.

MESZOELY, C. A. M.　　See also: Estes, R., Berberian, P. and Meszoely, C. A. M., 1969A.

METEL'TSEVA, ELIZAVETA PETROVNA　　See: Garutt, V. E., Metel'tseva, E. P. and Tikhomirov, B. A., 1970A.

METREWELI, C.　　See: Brothwell, D. R., Molleson, T. and Metreweli, C., 1968A.

MEULENKAMP, J. E.　　See: Bruijn, H. de and Meulenkamp, J. E., 1972A.

MEUNIER, FRANÇOIS　　See: Castanet, J., Gasc, J.-P., Meunier, F. and Ricqlès, A. de, 1970A.

MEURISSE, M., MICHAUX, J. and SIGÉ, B.
　　1969A　　Un remplissage karstique à micromammifères du Miocène inférieur à la Serre de Vergès, près St-Arnac
　　　　　　　(Pyrénées-Orientales). Soc. Géol. Fr., C.R., 1969:5, 166–168 (French).

MEYER, I. J.　　See: Meester, J. and Meyer, I. J., 1972A.

MEYER, KARL OTTO
　　1970A　　Dokumentation in naturwissenschaftlichen Museen. Natur Mus., 100:5, 224–228 (German).

MEZHZHERIN, V. A.
　　1969A　　Ob otnositel'nykh tempakh evoliútsii mlekopitaíushchikh v pleístotsene i prichinakh vymraniía krupnykh
　　　　　　　form. [On the relative rate of evolution of mammals during Pleistocene and on causes of extinc-
　　　　　　　tion of large forms.] In: Materialy po chetvertichnomu periodu Ukrainy, 144–154 (Russian;
　　　　　　　English summary).

MEZHZHERIN, V. A.　　See also: Lozan, M. N. and Mezhzherin, V. A., 1969A.

MEZZALIRA, SÉRGIO　　See: Paulo Couto, C. de and Mezzalira, S., 1971A.

MIALL, ANDREW D.
　　1970A　　A new lower Devonian rock unit in the Canadian Arctic islands: discussion. Can. J. Earth Sci., 7:3,
　　　　　　　1027–1029, 1 fig.

MIALL, A. D.　　See also: Broad, D. S., Dineley, D. L. and Miall, A. D., 1968A.

MICHAEL, HENRY N. and RALPH, ELISABETH K.
1971A*   Dating techniques for the archaeologist. Cambridge, Mass.: M.I.T. Press, xii + 228 pp., illustr.
          Rev.: Barker in Nature, 238:5363, 259–260; Morrison in Sci. Amer., 227:3, 198–204; Taylor
          in Science (AAAS), 177:4047, 419.

MICHAUX, JACQUES
1969A   Les gisements de vertébrés de la région montpelliéraine. 3. Gisements pliocènes. Fr., Bur. Rech.
         Géol. Minières, Bull. (Sér. 2), Sec. 1, 1969:1, 31–37, 3 tables (French; English summary).
         Rev.: Thenius in Zentralbl. Geol. Paläontol., Teil 2, 1971:6, 513–514.
1969B   Muridae (Rodentia) du Pliocène supérieur d'Espagne et du Midi de la France. Palaeovertebrata
         (Montpellier), 3:1, 25 pp., 1 fig., 2 pls., 7 tables (French; German and English summaries).
1970A   Les rongeurs (Arvicolidés, Muridés, et Gliridés) de la localité Arondelli à Villafranca d'Asti (Italie).
         Palaeontogr. Ital., 66, 67–80, 24 figs., 6 tables (French; English and Italian summaries).
1971A   Évolution et signification des peuplements de Muridés (Rodentia) en Europe sud-occidentale au Néogène
         supérieur. Acad. Sci., C.R., Sér. D, 273:3, 314–317, 2 figs. (French).
1971B   Arvicolinae (Rodentia) du Pliocène terminal et du Quaternaire ancien de France et d'Espagne.
         Palaeovertebrata (Montpellier), 4:5, 137–214, 26 figs., 11 tables (French; German and English
         summaries).

MICHAUX, JACQUES   See also: Barrière, J., Cappetta, H. and Michaux, J., 1970A; Barrière, J. and Michaux, J.,
         1970A; Berzi, A., et al., 1970A; Chaline, J. and Michaux, J., 1969A, 1969B; Crusafont Pairó, M.,
         Aguirre, E. de, and Michaux, J., 1969A; Leinders, J. and Michaux, J., 1969A; Mein, P. and
         Michaux, J., 1970A; Meurisse, M., Michaux, J. and Sigé, B., 1969A.

MICHEL, J. P. and CARITE, D.
1971A   Industrie paléolithique dans les alluvions quaternaires de la Seine, en aval de Paris (Flins). Cah. Géol.,
         87, 1149–1156, 5 figs. (French).

MICHELET, F.   See: Dubecq, X. J., Michelet, F. and Verger-Pratoucy, J., 1966A.

MICHENER, CHARLES D.
1970A   Diverse approaches to systematics. In: Dobzhansky, Th., Hecht, M. K. and Steere, W. C. (eds.),
         1970A, 1–38, 8 figs., 1 table.

MIDDLETON, J.   See: Halstead, L. B. and Middleton, J., 1972A.

MIELKE, JAMES H.   See: Armelagos, G. J., Mielke, J. H. and Winter, J., 1971A.

MIHĂILĂ, NICOLAE
1969A   Romanianul, termen stratigrafic final al Neogenului şi stratigrafia sa din sectorul Rîmnicu Vîlcea-
         Vîlsăneşti. [Romanian, the terminal stratigraphic term of the Neogene and its stratigraphy in
         the Rîmnicu Vîlcea-Vîlsanesti area.] Rom., Inst. Geol., Dări, 54:3(1967), 163–172, 1 fig.
         (Rumanian; French and English summaries).
1971A   Stratigrafia depozitelor pliocene şi cuaternare dintre valea Oltului şi valea Vîlsanului (sectorul Rîmnicu
         Vîlcea-Curtea de Argeş-Vîlsăneşti). [Stratigraphy of Pliocene and Quaternary deposits between
         the Oltul and Vîlsanul valleys (Rîmnicu Vîlcea-Curtea de Argeş-Vîlsăneşti District).] Rom., Inst.
         Geol., Stud. Teh. Econ., ser. J, 7, 145 pp., 11 figs., 27 pls., 4 maps, 16 tables (Rumanian;
         French and English summaries).

MIHĂILĂ, NICOLAE   See also: Ghenea, C., Bandrabur, T. and Mihăilă, N., 1967A.

MIKHEEV, A. V.
1967A   Nekotorye voprosy proiskhozhdeniia pereletov ptiĉ Palearktiki. [Some problems of the origin of
         Palearctic birds migrations.] Pribalt. Ornitol. Konf., 5th, Tartu, 1963, Tr., 17–24 (Russian).

MIKLASHEVSKAĬA, N. N.
1970A   K godovshchine so dnia smerti Georgiia Franĉevicha Debeĉsa. [Georgiĭ Franĉevich Debeĉs death
         anniversary.] Vop. Antropol., 35, 178 (Russian).

MIKULINA, T. M.   See: Shanĉer, E. V. and Mikulina, T. M., 1967A.

MILES, ROGER S.
1968A   Jaw articulation and suspension in Acanthodes and their significance. Nobel Symp., 4th, Stockholm,
         1967, Proc., 1968, 109–127, 4 figs.
1969A   Features of placoderm diversification and the evolution of the arthrodire feeding mechanism. Roy.
         Soc. Edinburgh, Trans., 68:6, 123–170, 14 figs.
1970A   Remarks on the vertebral column and caudal fin of acanthodian fishes. Lethaia, 3:4, 343–362, 8 figs.
1971A   Paleozoic fish. McGraw-Hill Yearbook Sci. Tech., 1971, 312–314, 2 figs.
1971B   The Holonematidae (Placoderm fishes), a review based on new specimens of Holonema from the upper
         Devonian of Western Australia. Roy. Soc. London, Phil. Trans., Ser. B, 263:849, 101–234,
         126 figs., 1 table.

MILLER, A. H.
    1962A   Rev.: D.L.S. in Emu, 63, 174–175.

MILLER, GEORGE J.
    1969A   Man and *Smilodon*: a preliminary report on their possible coexistence at Rancho La Brea.
                Los Angeles Cty. Mus., Contrib. Sci., 163, 8 pp., 4 figs.
                Rev.: Thenius in Zentralbl. Geol. Paläontol., Teil 2, 1970:3/4, 241.
    1969B   A new hypothesis to explain the method of food ingestion used by *Smilodon californicus* Bovard.
                Tebiwa, 12:1, 9–19, 4 pls., 4 tables.
    1969C   A study of cuts, grooves, and other marks on recent and fossil bone. I. Animal tooth marks.
                Tebiwa, 12:1, 20–26, 5 pls.
    1970A   The Rancho La Brea project: 1969–70. Los Angeles Cty. Mus., Quart., 9:1, 26–30, illustr.
    1971A   Science and education at the tar pits. Part one. Ward's Bull., 11:79, 1, 4, and 6, 3 photos.
    1972A   Science and education at the tar pits. Part two. Ward's Bull., 11:80, 1 and 4, 3 photos.

MILLER, GERRIT SMITH
    1972A   Conflicting views on the problem of man's ancestry. In: McCown, T. D. and Kennedy, K. A. R. (eds.),
                1972A, 218–228 (reprinted from Amer. J. Phys. Anthropol., 3:2, 213–223, 243–245).

MILLER, HALSEY W.
    1972A   The fossil origins of man. Champaign, Ill.: Stipes Publishing Co., 187 pp., 77 figs.
    1972B   The taxonomy of the Pteranodon species from Kansas. Kansas Acad. Sci. Trans.,74:1 (1971), 1–19,
                7 plates.
    1972C   A skull of *Pteranodon (Longicepia) longiceps* Marsh associated with wing and body bones. Kansas
                Acad. Sci. Trans., 74:1 (1971), 20–33, 4 plates, 2 tables.

MILLER, JOHN A.
    1972A   Dating Pliocene and Pleistocene strata using the potassium-argon and argon-40/argon-39 methods.
                In: Bishop, W. W. and Miller, J. A. (eds.), 1972A, 63–76, 4 figs.

MILLER, J. A.   See also: Bishop, W. W. and Miller, J. A. (eds.), 1972A; Bishop, W. W., Miller, J. A. and
                Fitch, F. J., 1969A; Fitch, F. J. and Miller, J. A., 1970A; Van Couvering, J. A. and Miller,
                J. A., 1969A, 1971A.

MILLER, LOYE HOLMES
    1970A   The interpretive naturalist. Interviews. With an introduction by Raymond B. Cowles. Berkeley:
                University of California, Bancroft Library. Mimeograph, 61 pp., illustr.
    1972A   Journal of first trip of University of California to John Day beds of eastern Oregon. Edited by
                J. Arnold Shotwell. Oreg., Univ., Mus. Natur. Hist., Bull., 19, 21 pp., 7 figs., 1 map.

MILLER, ROBERT C.
    1972A   Dinosaur quest. Pac. Discovery, 25:5, 1–2, 1 fig.

MILLER, R. R.   See: Cavender, T. M. and Miller, R. R., 1972A.

MILLER, T. H.   See: Floyd, D. N., Miller, T. H. and Berry, W. B. N., 1958A.

MILLER, WADE E.
    1971A   Pleistocene vertebrates of the Los Angeles Basin and vicinity (exclusive of Rancho La Brea).
                Los Angeles Cty. Mus. Natur. Hist. Sci., Bull., 10, 124 pp., frontispiece, 155 figs., 20 tables.
                Rev.: Thenius in Zentralbl. Geol. Paläontol., Teil 2, 1971:5, 413.
    1972A   A Pleistocene mammal fauna from Salt Lake City, Utah. Soc. Vert. Paleontol., Ann. Meeting, 32nd,
                1972, Abstr. (abs.).

MILLER, WADE E. and DOWNS, THEODORE
    1971A   A middle Pliocene fauna from Hungry Valley, southern California. Geol. Soc. Amer., Abstr., 3:2,
                160–161 (abs.).

MILLOTTE, J.-P.
    1969A   Informations archéologiques. Circonscription de Franche-Comté. Gallia Préhist., 12:2, 465–484,
                34 figs. (French).

MILLS, JAMES R. E.
    1970A   The dentition of *Morganucodon*. Linn. Soc., Biol. J., 2:4, 318 (abs.).

1971A   The dentition of *Morganucodon*. Linn. Soc., Zool. J., 50:suppl. 1, 29–63, 5 figs., 5 pls., 1 table. Rev.: Krebs in Zentralbl. Geol. Paläontol., Teil 2, 1972:3, 168–169.

MILLS, JAMES R. E.   See also: Clemens, W. A. and Mills, J. R. E., 1971A.

MILLS, RICHARD S.
1972A   Mice, men and mastodons. Explorer (Cleveland Mus. Natur. Hist.), 14:2, 9–12, 5 figs.

MILLS, RICHARD S. and GUILDAY, JOHN E.
1972A   First record of *Cervalces scotti* Ledekker from the Pleistocene of Ohio. Amer. Midland Natur., 88:1, 255.

MILLS, VERNON
1970A   Prehistoric animals. Illustrated by Vernon Mills, Frances Vargo, Andrew Farmer and Janet Smith. London: Purnel, 91 pp., illustr.

MILOŠEVIČ, VELIMIR M.
1967A   O nalasku fosilnih jaja u miocenskim sedimentima okoline Blaca u Toplici. [Fossil eggs from Miocene sediments near Blaca in Toplice basin.] Belgrad, Prirodn. Muz., Glas., Ser. A, 22, 17–42, 5 figs., 8 pls., 1 table (Serbocroatian; Russian summary).

MILTHERS, KELD
1959A   Beskrivelse til geologisk kort over Danmark. Kortbladene Fåborg, Svendborg og Gulstav. Dan. Geol. Unders., Raekke 1, 214, 1–112, illustr. (Danish; English summary).

MILTHERS, V.
1940A   Geologisk kort over Danmark. Kortbladet Vissenbjaerg. Dan. Geol. Unders., Raekke 1, 19, 143 pp., 31 figs., 2 maps (Danish; French summary).

MINATO, M., OHMORI, M., MIZUNO, T. and OBATA, I.
1968A*   Atlas of Japanese fossils. Tokyo: Tsukiji Shokan Pub. Co., vi + 256 pp., illustr. Rev.: Anon. in Natur. Sci. and Mus., 36:7–8, 194.

MINCH, J. A., SCHULTE, K. C. and HOFMAN, G.
1970A   A middle Miocene age for the Rosarito beach formation in northwestern Baja California, Mexico. Geol. Soc. Amer., Bull., 81:10, 3149–3154, 2 figs., 1 table.

MINIKH, M. G. (= MINICH, M. G.)
1969A   Znachenie ostatkov dvoiakodyshashchikh ryb (Dipnoi) dlia stratigrafii triasovykh otlozheniĭ vostoka Evropeĭskoĭ chasti SSSR. [Significance of lungfishes (Dipnoi) remains for the stratigraphy of Triassic deposits of the eastern European part of USSR.] In: Voprosy geologii Iuzhnogo Urala i Povolzh'ia, 6:1, 137–145 (Russian).

MINIKH, M. G.   See also: Rykov, S. P. and Minikh, M. G., 1969A, 1970A.

MINKOFF, ELI C.
1972A   A fossil baboon from Angola, with a note on *Australopithecus*. J. Paleontol., 46:6, 836–844, 3 figs., 3 tables.

MIROSCHEDJI, ALEXANDRE DE   See: Lapparent, A. F. de, Curnelle, R., Defaut, B., Miroschedji, A. de and Pallard, B., 1969A.

MIRZABAEV, KH.   See: Mavlianov, G. A., Kambariddinov, R. K. and Mirzabaev, Kh., 1968A.

MISHINA, ALLA VASIL'EVNA   See: Kudriavtsev, G. A., Agentov, V. B., Gatinskiĭ, Iu. G. and Mishina, A. V., 1969A.

MISHRA, V. P.   See: Sahni, A. and Mishra, V. P., 1972A.

MISRA, UMA SHANKER
1968A   Vertebrate fossils from Basoli Tahsil, District Kathua (Jammu and Kashmir). Indian Sci. Congr., Proc., 55, 238.
1971A   *Trilophodon kamalii* sp. nov. from the Siwalik beds of Dera-Gopipur, Tehsil, District Kangra, Himachal Pradesh. Indian Sci. Congr., Proc., 58, 315.

MISRA, VIRENDRA NATH
1967A   Pre- and proto-history of the Berach basin, south Rajasthan. Poona: Deccan College Postgraduate and Research Institute, xix + 216 pp., 67 figs., 10 pls., 42 tables. Rev.: Fairservis in Amer. Anthropol., 70, 1231.

MISZKIEWICZ, BRUNON   See: Bielicki, T. and Miszkiewicz, B., 1968A.

MITCHELL, EDWARD
1966B   Rev.: Rothausen in Zentralbl. Geol. Paläontol., Teil 2, 1971:1, 65–66.

MITCHELL, STEVEN W.
1971A   A new occurrence of the Devonian arthrodire *Holonema*. Ohio J. Sci., 71:2, 120–124, 1 fig.

MITTRE, VISHNU   See: Randhawa, M. S., Singh, J., Dey, A. K. and Mittre, V., 1969A.

MITZOPOULOS, MAXIMOS K.
1966A   *Zygolophodon borsoni* und *Anancus (Bunolophodon) arvernensis* aus dem Oberpliozän von Griechenland.
        Akad. Athenon, Prakt., 40, 376–386, 3 pls., 1 table (German; Greek summary).
1967B   Über das Vorkommen von *Archidiskodon meridionalis archaicus* im Becken von Ptolemais (Griechisch-
        Mazedonien). Ann. Géol. Pays Hellén., 18, 463–470, 1 fig., 2 pls. (German; Greek summary).

MIZUNO, T.   See: Minato, M., Ohmori, M., Mizuno, T. and Obata, I., 1968A.

MŁYNARSKI, MARIAN
1968A   Die plio-pleistozänen Schildkröten Mitteleuropas. Deut. Ges. Geol. Wiss., Ber., Reihe A, Geol.
        Paläontol., 13:3, 351–356, 2 figs. (German).
1968B   Notes on tortoises (Testudinidae) from the Tertiary of Mongolia. Palaeontol. Polonica, 19, 85–97,
        8 figs., 2 pls.
1969A   Fossile Schildkröten. Wittenberg: Ziemsen Press, "Neue Brehm-Bücherei", 396, 128 pp., 73 figs.,
        8 pls. (German).
        Rev.: Klemmer in Natur Mus., 100:10, 475–476; Wermuth in Salamandra, 6:1/2, 67–68; Westphal in
        Zentralbl. Geol. Paläontol., Teil 2, 1969:4, 328–329; Zapfe in Geol. Ges. Wien, Mitt., 61, 211;
        Zimmermann in Hercynia, 6:2, 211–212.
1972A   *Zangerlia testudinimorpha* n. gen., n. sp., a primitive land tortoise from the upper Cretaceous of
        Mongolia. In: Kielan-Jaworowska, Z. (ed.), 1972B, 85–92, 2 figs., 1 pl.

MŁYNARSKI, MARIAN and NARMANDACH, PAGAM
1972A   New turtle remains from the upper Cretaceous of the Gobi Desert, Mongolia. In: Kielan-Jaworowska,
        Z. (ed.), 1972B, 95–101, 4 figs.

MŁYNARSKI, MARIAN   See also: Borsuk-Białynicka, M. and Młynarski, M., 1968A; Khosatzky, L. I. and
        Młynarski, M., 1971A; Vergnaud-Grazzini, C. and Młynarski, M., 1969A.

MOCHANOV, IU. A.
1969A   Novaia verkhnepaleoliticheskaia kul'tura Severovostochnoi Azii. [A new upper Paleolithic culture of
        northeastern Asia.] In: Rybakov, B. A. (ed.), 1969A, 214–215 (Russian).
1969B   Mnogosloinaia stoianka Bel'kachi I i periodizatsiia kamennogo veka Iakutii. [Multilayered site
        Belkachi I and the periodization of the Stone Age of Iakutia.] Moscow: 206 pp., 49 pls.
        (Russian).
        Rev.: kv in Archeol. Roz., 22:3, 365.
1969C   Diuktaiskaia verkhnepaleoliticheskaia kul'tura i nekotorye aspekty ee genezisa. [Diuktai upper
        Paleolithic culture and some aspects of its genesis.] Sov. Arkheol., 1969:4, 235–239, 4 figs.
        (Russian).
1969D   Drevneishie etapy zaseleniia Severo-Vostochnoi Azii i Aliaski. (K voprosu o pervonachal'nykh
        migratsiiakh cheloveka v Ameriku. [Oldest stages of population of northeastern Asia and
        Alaska. (The problem of the primitive migrations of man to America).] Sov. Etnogr., 1969:1,
        79–86 (Russian; English summary).
1970A   Drevneishie etapy kamennogo veka Severo-Vostochnoi Azii. [The oldest stages of the Stone Age in
        northeastern Asia.] Geogr. Obshchest. SSSR, Vost.-Sibirsk. Otd., Izv., 67, 60–64 (Russian).
1972A   Novye dannye o beringomorskom puti zaseleniia Ameriki. (Stoianka Maiorych-pervyi verkhne-
        paleoliticheskii pamiatnik v doline Kolymy). [New data on the peopling of America across the
        Behring Sea. (Maiorych, the first upper Paleolithic site in the Kolyma valley).] Sov. Etnogr.,
        1972:2, 98–101, 2 figs. (Russian).

MOCHANOV, IU. A.   See also: Vereshchagin, N. K. and Mochanov, Iu. A., 1972A.

MODELL, WALTER
1969A   Horns and antlers. Sci. Amer., 220:4, 114–122, illustr.

MOHAPATRA, G. C.
1966A   Preliminary report of the exploration and excavation of Stone Age sites in eastern Punjab. Deccan
Coll. Res. Inst., Bull., 25, 221–237, 4 figs., 4 pls.

MOHEN, JEAN-PIERRE
1969A   Un bâton perforé et gravé de la Madeleine (Dordogne) au Musée de l'Armée à Paris. Soc. Hist. Archéol.
Périgord, Bull., 96:1, 70–74, 2 figs. (French).

MØHL, ULRIK
1972A   Contribution to the knowledge of late-glacial finds of giant deer, Megaloceros giganteus (Blumenbach)
in Denmark. Lutra, 14:1–3, 23–24, 1 pl.

MOHR, ERNA
1969A   Die Apfelschimmel von Pech-Merle. Z. Säugetierkunde, 34:5, 316–318, 4 figs. (German).

MOKROUSOV, V. P. and SADOVSKIĬ, N. D.
1964A   Chetvertichnai͡a sistema. [Quaternary system.] Geologii͡a SSSR, 31, Kamchatka, Kuril'skie and
Komandorskie Islands, 220–234, 3 figs., 1 table (Russian).

MOLI͡AVKO, GRIGORIĬ IVANOVICH
1958A   Neogenovye otlozhenii͡a Prichernomorskoĭ vpadiny. [Neogene deposits of the Black Sea region
depression.] Geologii͡a SSSR, 5, Ukrainian SSR, Moldavian SSR, 712–729, 3 figs., 1 table
(Russian).
1958B   Neogenovye otlozhenii͡a Ukrainskogo kristallicheskogo massiva. [Neogene deposits of the Ukrainian
crystalline massif.] Geologii͡a SSSR, 5, Ukrainian SSR, Moldavian SSR, 755–761 (Russian).

MOLINA, E., PÉREZ-GONZÁLEZ, A. and AGUIRRE, E.
1972A   Observaciones geológicas en el Campo de Calatrava. Estud. Geol. (Inst. Invest. Geol. "Lucas Mallada"),
28:1, 3–11, 8 figs., 1 map (Spanish; English summary).

MOLLENHAUER, D.   See: Peters, D. S., Mollenhauer, D. and Gutmann, W. F., 1971A.

MOLLESON, THEYA I., OAKLEY, K. P. and VOGEL, J. C.
1972A   The antiquity of the human footprints of Tana della Basura. J. Human Evol., 1:5, 467–471, 1 table.

MOLLESON, THEYA I.   See also: Brothwell, D. R., Molleson, T. and Metreweli, C., 1968A; Day, M. H. and
Molleson, T., 1971A; Oakley, K. P., Campbell, B. G. and Molleson, T. I. (eds.), 1971A.

MOLNAR, STEPHEN and McBEATH, VIRGINIA
1968A   Some facial-dental correlations and possible selective forces involved in canine development. Amer. J.
Phys. Anthropol., 29, 127 (abs.).

MONCHARMONT ZEI, MARIA
1970A   L'ittiofauna degli scisti lignitici di Tremembé e di Taubaté (Stato di San Paolo - Brasile). Accad. Sci.
Fis. Mat., Naples, Rendic., 37, 70–87, 9 figs., 14 pls. (Italian; French and English summaries).
Rev.: Albanesi in Riv. Ital. Paleontol. Stratigr., 76:4, 626.

MONES, ALVARO
1967A   Notas paleontológicas uruguayas. I. Trigodon Amegh., 1882 (Toxodonta, Notungulata) en la fauna
pliocena superior de las barrancas de San Gregorio, dpto. de San José, Uruguay. Mus. Hist.
Natur. Montevideo, Com. Zool., 9, 117, 1–4 (Spanish).
1970A   Notas paleontológicas uruguayas, II. Un nuevo Pseudoplohophorus Castell., 1926 (Hoplophorinae,
Edentata) de la R. O. del Uruguay Pseudoplohophorus francisi n. sp. Mus. Hist. Natur.
Montevideo, Com. Paleontol., 1:1, 1 pl., 2 tables (Spanish).

MONES, ALVARO   See also: Olazarri, J., Mones, A., Ximénez, A. and Philippi, M. E., 1970A.

MONGEREAU, N.   See: David, L., Evin, J., Guérin, C., Mongereau, N. and Walter, B., 1972A.

MONJUVENT, G.
1968A   Les formations pliocènes et quaternaires des environs de Villefranche-sur-Saône (Rhône). Rev. Géog.
Phys. Géol. Dyn., 10, 255–275, 10 figs. (French; English summary).

MONOD, THEODORE
1966A   The late Tertiary and Pleistocene in the Sahara. In: Howell, F. C. and Bourliere, F. (eds.), 1966A,
117–229, 14 figs., 3 tables.

MONTAGNA, WILLIAM   See: Harrison, R. J. and Montagna, W., 1969A; Noback, C. R. and Montagna, W.
          (eds.), 1970A.

MONTAGU, ASHLEY
     1964D   The science of man-an illustrated introduction to anthropology. New York: Odyssey Press Inc.,
          158 pp., illustr.
          Rev.: Hunt in Amer. J. Phys. Anthropol., 24, 129–130.
     1965A   Rev.: Kurth in Homo, 19:1, 44.
     1969A   Predators, tools, implements and weapons: a comment. Amer. Anthropol., 71, 312–313.
     1969B   Man: his first two million years. New York and London: Columbia University Press, vi + 262 pp.,
          67 illustr., 6 tables.
          Rev.: Schwidetzky in Homo, 21:3, 189; Wolpoff in Amer. J. Phys. Anthropol., 33:2, 273–274.

MONTENAT, CHRISTIAN
     1970A   Empreintes de pas de Reptiles dans le Trias moyen du plateau du Daüs près d'Aubenas (Ardèche).
          Bull. Sci. Bourgogne, 25, 369–389, 4 pls. (French).

MONTENAT, CHRISTIAN and CRUSAFONT PAIRÓ, M.
     1970A   Découverte de mammifères dans le Néogène et le Pléistocène du Levant espagnol (Provinces d'Alicante
          et de Murcia). Acad. Sci., C.R., Sér. D, 270:20, 2434–2437 (French).

MONTENAT, CHRISTIAN   See also: Dollé, P., Lapparent, A. F. de and Montenat, Ch., 1970A; Ginsburg, L.,
          Lapierre, F. and Montenat, C., 1967A; Janvier, P. and Montenat, C., 1970A.

MONTENAT, G.
     1968A   Contribution à l'étude des formations tertiaires continentales des Baronnies. Fr., Bur. Rech. Géol.
          Minières, Bull. (Sér. 2), Sec. 1, 1968:2, 1–18, 5 figs. (French).

MONTFORD, H. M.
     1970A   The terrestrial environment during upper Cretaceous and Tertiary times. Geol. Ass. (London), Proc.,
          81, 181–204, 2 figs.

MOODY, J. W. T.
     1971A   The reading of the Darwin and Wallace papers: an historical "non-event". Soc. Bibliogr. Natur.
          Hist., J., 5:6, 474–476.

MOODY, P. A.
     1970A   Introduction to evolution. Third edition. New York: Harper and Row, 527 pp., illustr.
          Rev.: Anon. in The Biologist, 53:1, 45.

MOODY, R. T. J. and WALKER, C. A.
     1970A   A new trionychid turtle from the British lower Eocene. Palaeontology, 13:3, 503–510, 5 figs., 1 pl.

MOODY-STUART, M.   See: Friend, P. F., Heintz, N. and Moody-Stuart, M., 1966A.

MOOK, CHARLES CRAIG
     1961A   Notes on the skull characters of Allognathosuchus polyodon. Amer. Mus. Nov., 2072, 1–5, 2 pls.

MOORE, ALAN C.   See: McGowran, B. and Moore, A. C., 1971A.

MOORE, G. WILLIAM   See: Goodman, M., Barnabas, J., Matsuda, G. and Moore, G. W., 1971A.

MOORE, JOHN G.   See: Fry, G. F. and Moore, J. G., 1969A.

MOORE, J. N. and SLUSHER, H. S.
     1970A*   Biology: a search for order in complexity. Grand Rapids, Mich.: Zondervan Publ. House, 458 pp.,
          illustr.
          Rev.: Milne, L. and Milne, M. in BioScience, 21:9, 445.

MOORE, RAYMOND C., et al.
     1968A   Developments, trends, and outlooks in paleontology. J. Paleontol., 42:6, 1327–1377, 3 figs.

MOORE, RUTH
     1970A   The search for mankind's ancestors. In: Young, L. B. (ed.), 1970A, 184–224, 14 figs. (reprinted
          from Moore, Ruth and the Editors of Life, 1962, "Evolution").
     1971A   The record in the rocks. Photography by R. Ratcliffe. Audubon Mag., 73:1, 13–29, 13 photos.

MOORE, WILLIAM
1972A   The big ugly tree-eater. San Francisco Chron., March 13, 1972, 6, 2 figs.

MOOREHEAD, ALAN
1969A   Darwin and the Beagle. New York: Harper and Row, 280 pp., frontispiece, illustr.
           Rev.: Carson in Natur. Hist., 79:1, 110—111, 1 fig.; Lindroth in Lychnos, 1971, 481—482 (Swedish);
                 Matthews in New Sci., 45:689, 367; Tooze in Nature, 224:5222, 973—974, 2 figs; Zirkle in
                 Isis, 61, 284—285.
1969B   Darwin and the Beagle. Paperback edition. London: Penguin Books, 280 pp., frontispiece, illustr.

MOORHEAD, PAUL S. and KAPLAN, MARTIN M.
1967A*   Mathematical challenges to the neo-darwinian interpretation of evolution. Wistar Inst. Symp. Monogr.
           5, 140 pp., illustr.
           Rev.: Hanelt in Biol. Zentralbl., 88:1, 120.

MOOSER, O.
1968A   Fossil Equidae from the middle Pliocene of the central plateau of Mexico. Southwest. Natur., 13:1,
           1—12, 13 figs., 3 tables.
1972A   A new species of Pleistocene fossil tortoise, genus Gopherus, from Aguascalientes, Mexico. Southwest.
           Natur., 17:1, 61—65, 4 figs., 1 table.

MORBECK, MARY E.
1972A   A re-examination of the forelimb of the Miocene Hominoidea. Diss. Abstr., 32:12, 6798B (abs.).

MOREAU, R. E.
1963A   Vicissitudes of the African biomes in the late Pleistocene. J. Zool., 141:2, 395—421, 4 maps.

MOREIRA, LUIZ EURICO
1971A   Os gliptodontes do Nordeste do Brasil. Acad. Brasil. Ciênc., An., 43 Suppl., 529—552, 18 figs.,
           4 tables (Portuguese; English summary).

MOREIRA, LUIZ EURICO and GOMES DE MELO, SHEILA MARIS
1971A   Mamíferos fósseis em Goiás e Distrito Federal. Acad. Brasil. Ciênc., An., 43 Suppl., 553—555, 2 figs.
           (Portuguese).

MORET, LÉON
1953A   Rev.: Hacquaert in Natuurwet. Tijdschr., 35:1—2, 61—62.
1958A   Rev.: Maréchal in Natuurwet. Tijdschr., 41:4, 136.

MORGAN, ELAINE
1972A   The descent of woman. New York:' Stein and Day, 258 pp.
           Rev.: Anon. in Interamer., 19:3, 8; Simms in New Sci., 56:815, 112—113; Stuttaford in San Francisco
                 Chron., "This world", June 4, 38.

MORI, HAJIME   See: Matsumoto, H. and Mori, H., 1968A, 1971A.

MORIN, PHILIPPE
1965A   Bibliographie analytique des sciences de la terre. Maroc et régions limitrophes (depuis le début des
           recherches géologiques à 1964). 2 vols. Morocco, Serv. Géol., Notes Mém., 182, 1 vol.,
           824 pp., 2 vol., 900 pp. (French).
           Rev.: Souville in L'Anthropologie, 72, 133—135.

MORLAN, RICHARD E.   See: Chard, C. S. and Morlan, R. E., 1970A.

MÖRNER, NILS-AEL
1970A   Comparison between late Weichselian and late Wisconsin ice marginal changes. Eiszeitalter Gegenwart,
           21, 173—176, 1 fig., 1 table (German summary).

MOROZOV, G. V.
1971A   K voprosu ob ispol'zovanii termolíuministsentsii karbonatov dlía geokhronologii. [On the problem of
           application of thermoluminescence of carbonates for geochronology.] In: Khronologiía
           lednikovogo veka. Materialy k simpoziumu, Leningrad, mart 1972g., 118—124 (Russian).

MOROZOV, V. A. and SOLEV'EV, V. K.
1967A   Chetvertichnaía (antropogenovaía) sistema. [Quaternary (Anthropogene) system.] Geologiía SSSR, 11,
           Povolzh'e and Prikam'e, 624—672, 9 figs. (Russian).

MOROZOV, V. A.   See also: Moskvitin, A. I. and Morozov, V. A., 1967A.

MORRES, NORA K.
1967A   Anthropology and geology. Santa Barbara Mus. Natur. Hist., Ann. Rep., 1967, 15–16.
1968A   Anthropology and geology. Santa Barbara Mus. Natur. Hist., Ann. Rep., 1968, 16.

MORRIS, DESMOND
1968A   Der nackte Affe. Translated from the English by Fritz Bolle. München-Zürich: Droemersche Verlag.,
               391 pp. (German).
               Rev.: Eibl-Eibesfeldt in Homo, 19:2, 120; Grebenščikov in Biol. Zentralbl., 87:5, 673–674;
               Haltenorth in Säugetierkundl. Mitt., 17:2, 195–196; Preuschoft in Anthropol. Anz., 31:3,
               218–219.

MORRIS, DONALD H.
1970A   On deflecting wrinkles and the Dryopithecus pattern in human mandibular molars. Amer. J. Phys.
               Anthropol., 32:1, 97–104, 7 figs.

MORRIS, RAMONA and MORRIS, DESMOND
1966A   Rev.: Napier in New Sci., 30:497, 545–546.

MORRIS, WILLIAM J.
1968B   A new early Tertiary perissodactyl, Hyracotherium seekinsi, from Baja California. Los Angeles Cty.
               Mus., Contrib. Sci., 151, 11 pp., 5 figs. (Spanish summary).
               Rev.: Thenius in Zentralbl. Geol. Paläontol., Teil 2, 1970:3/4, 246–247.
1969A   Late Cretaceous dinosaurs from Baja California. Geol. Soc. Amer., Abstr., 121, 209 (abs.).
1970A   Hadrosaurian dinosaur bills — morphology and function. Los Angeles Cty. Mus., Contrib. Sci., 193,
               1–14, 5 figs.
1970B   A new lineage of hollow crested dinosaur. S. Calif. Paleontol. Soc., Bull., 2:6, 5 (reprinted from
               S. Calif. Acad. Sci., 1970 Meetings, Abstr.).
1971A   Mesozoic and Tertiary vertebrates in Baja California. Nat. Geogr. Soc., Res.Reps., 1965, 195–198.
1972A   A giant hadrosaurian dinosaur from Baja California. J. Paleontol., 46:5, 777–779, 1 fig., 1 table.

MORRISON, LORRIN L.
1971A   Dr. Charles L. Camp receives the Wagner memorial award. J. West, 10:1, 203.

MORRISON, ROGER B. and WRIGHT, HERBERT E., JR.
1968A*   Means of correlation of Quaternary successions. Int. Ass. Quaternary Res., 7th Congr. (1965), Proc.,
               8, xi + 631 pp., illustr.

MOSKALENKO, TAMARA ALEKSANDROVNA
1968A   Llandoveriĭskie ostatki Agnatha v Sibiri. [Llandoverian remains of Agnatha in Siberia.] In: Ocherki
               po filogenii i sistematike iskopaemykh ryb i bezchelĭustnykh, 29–32, 2 figs. (Russian).

MOS'KINA, OL'GA DMITRIEVNA   See: Matsuĭ, V. M. and Mos'kina, O. D., 1968A.

MOSKVITIN, ALEKSANDR IVANOVICH
1970A   Stratigrafiĭa pleĭstotsena Tsentral'noĭ i Zapadnoĭ Evropy. [Pleistocene stratigraphy of central and
               western Europe.] Akad. Nauk SSSR, Geol. Inst., Tr., 193, 287 pp., 69 figs., 26 tables (Russian;
               German summary).

MOSKVITIN, A. I. and MOROZOV, V. A.
1967A   Neogenovaĭa sistema. [Neogene system.] Geologiĭa SSSR, 11, Povolzh'e and Prikam'e, 603–624,
               3 figs. (Russian).

MOSNA, S.   See: Anfossi, G. and Mosna, S., 1969A, 1969B, 1971A.

MOSS, JOHN LAWRENCE
1971A   The morphology and phylogenetic relationships of the lower Permian tetrapod Tseajaia campi Vaughn.
               Diss. Abstr., 32:2, 1106B (abs.).
1972A   The morphology and phylogenetic relationships of the lower Permian tetrapod Tseajaia campi Vaughn
               (Amphibia: Seymouriamorpha). Calif., Univ., Publ. Geol. Sci., 98, 72 pp., 18 figs., 7 pls.

MOSS, MELVIN L.
1969A   Evolution of mammalian dental enamel. Amer. Mus. Nov., no. 2360, 1–39, 29 figs.

MOSTECKÝ, VLASTIMIL
    1969A   Jungpleistozäne Säugetiere aus der "Chlupáč-Höhle" auf dem Hügel "Kobyla" bei Koněprusy
        (Böhmischer Karst). Prague, Sborn. Národního Muz. Praze, Rada B, 25:1, 55 pp., 6 figs.,
        1 pl., 7 tables (German).
        Rev.: Thenius in Zentralbl. Geol. Paläontol., Teil 2, 1971:1, 63—64.

MOSTLER, HELFRIED   See: Fuchs, G. and Mostler, H., 1969A.

MOSTNY, GRETE
    1968A   Association of human industries with Pleistocene fauna in central Chile. Current Anthropol., 9:2—3,
        214—215.

MOTTL, MARIA
    1960B   Gedanken über Probleme der jungpleistozänen Warmzeiten im Ostalpengebiet. Anthropos, Brno, 1960
        Suppl., 127—136, 1 table (German; Russian summary).
    1968A   Zusammenfassendes zur Datierung urgeschichtlicher Rastplätze SO-Österreichs. Quartär, 19, 199—217
        (German).
    1969A   Bedeutende Proboscidier-Neufunde aus dem Altpliozän (Pannonien) Südost-Österreichs. Österreich.
        Akad. Wiss., Denk., 115, 50 pp., 22 pls., 9 tables (German).
    1969B   Die Säugetierfunde von St. Oswald b. Gratwein, W von Graz in der Steiermark. Festband des
        Landesmuseums Joanneum (German).
    1970A   Die jungtertiären Säugetierfaunen der Steiermark, Südost-Österreichs. Graz, Joanneum, Mus. Berg.
        Geol. Techn., Mitt., 31, 92 pp., 3 figs., 7 pls. (German).

MOTUZKO, A. N.
    1970A   Nizhnepleĭstoĭsenovaĭa fauna mlekopitaĭushchikh iz razreza u s. Skorodum Omskoĭ oblasti. [Lower
        Pleistocene mammalian fauna from the section near Skorodum village, Omsk province.] Mosk.
        Univ., Vestn., Ser. Geog., 1970:4, 87—89, 2 tables (Russian; English summary).
    1970B   Paleontologicheskaĭa kharakteristika "diagonal'nykh" peskov v razreze u s. Urtam. [Paleontological
        characterization of "diagonal" sands near the village of Urtam.] Mosk. Univ., Vestn., Ser.
        Geog., 1970:3, 106—108, 2 figs. (Russian; English summary).

MOTUZKO, A. N., SUDAKOVA, N. G. and KHOREV, V. S.
    1969A   O vozraste suglinkov Aldanskikh terras. [On the age of loams of Aldan terraces.] In: Noveĭshaĭa
        tektonika, noveĭshie otlozheniĭa i chelovek, 1, 62—67, 1 fig., 1 table (Russian).

MOTUZKO, A. N.   See also: Agadzhanĭan, A. K., Dobredeev, O. P., Kursalova, V. I. and Motuzko, A. N.,
        1972A; Agadzhanĭan, A. K. and Motuzko, A. N., 1971A, 1972A.

MOUNT, JACK D.
    1969A   Late Pliocene vertebrates from the Newport Bay area, Orange County, California. S. Calif. Paleontol.
        Soc., Bull., 1:2, 2—3.
    1970A   A record of the extinct horse Pliohippus from the marine Pliocene of Los Angeles, California.
        S. Calif. Paleontol. Soc., Bull., 2:1, 1—3, 1 fig.

MOUSSA, MOUNIR T.
    1968A   Rev.: Häntzschel in Zentralbl. Geol. Paläontol., Teil 2, 1970:1, 10—11.

MOVIUS, HALLAM L., JR.
    1955C   Une fouille préliminaire à l'Abri Pataud, Les Eyzies (Dordogne). Les Eyzies, 5, 33—40, 2 figs. (French).
    1969A   The Châtelperronian in French archaeology: the evidence of Arcy-sur-Cure. Antiquity, 43:170, 111—
        123, 8 figs.

MOVSHOVICH, E. V.
    1970A   Triasovaĭa sistema. [Triassic system.] Geologiĭa SSSR, 46, Rostov, Volgograd, Astrakhan' Provinces
        and Kalmyk ASSR, 228—255, 3 figs., 3 tables (Russian).

MOY-THOMAS, J. A.
    1971A   Palaeozoic fishes. Second edition, extensively revised by R. S. Miles. London: Chapman and Hall
        Ltd., xi + 259 pp., illustr.
        Rev.: Andrews in Nature, 238:5360, 172; Anon. in S. Afr. J. Sci., 68:3, 87; Haas in Isr. J. Zool.,
        21:1, 53; Heintz in Nor. Geol. Tidsskr., 52:2, 212; Herre in Z. Zool. Syst. Evolut.-Forsch.,
        9:4, 320; Jonet in Soc. Belge Géol. Paléontol. Hydrol., Bull., 79:3—4, 275—277; Nelson in
        Copeia, 1972:1, 195; Romer in Palaeogeogr. Palaeoclimatol. Palaeoecol., 11:3, 214—215;
        Thomson in Science, 175:4026, 1102.

MOYES, JEAN
    1966A   Les faluns néogènes du Bordelais.   Bordeaux, Univ., Inst. Géol. Bassin Aquitaine, Bull., 1, 85–113,
                   11 figs. (French).

MROCZKOWSKI, MACIEJ
    1969A   Kilka słów o wystawie dynosaurów i polskich badaniach zoologicznych w Mongolskiej Republice
                   Ludowej.   [Some remarks on the exhibition of dinosaurs and the Polish zoological exploration
                   in the Mongolian People's Republic.] Przegl. Zool., 13:2, 262–267, 8 figs. (Polish).

MÜHLMANN, W.
    1968A   Geschichte der Anthropologie.   Second edition.   Frankfurt: Athenäum Verlag, 328 pp. (German).
                   Rev.:   Vallois in L'Anthropologie, 73:3–4, 297–298.

MUKHA, B. B.
    1970A   O novoĭ nakhodke skeleta Turicius turicensis Schinz.   [On a new find of Turicius turicensis Schinz
                   skeleton.] Paleontol. Sb., 7:1, 68–70 (Russian; English summary).

MÜLLER, ARNO HERMANN
    1968A   Rev.:   Boné in Rev. Quest. Sci., 30, 148–149.
    1970A   Über Dollopterus volitans (Osteichthyes, Chondrostei), ein Flugfisch aus dem germanischen Oberen
                   Muschelkalk sowie einige Bemerkungen zur Biostratinomie und zur Konkretionsbildung.
                   Freiberger Forschungsh., Reihe C, 256, 37–45, 9 figs. (German; Russian and English summaries).
    1970B   Lehrbuch der Paläozoologie.   Band III, Teil 3 Mammalia.   Jena: Gustav Fischer, xv + 855 pp., 820
                   figs. (German).
                   Rev.:   Boné in Rev. Quest. Sci., 32:3, 437; Haltenorth in Säugetierkundl. Mitt., 18, 391; Hölder in
                   Biol. Zentralbl., 90:4, 534; Niethammer in Bonner Zool. Beitr., 23:1, 75; Romer in Quart. Rev.
                   Biol., 46:1, 70; Sestini in Riv. Ital. Paleontol. Stratigr., 76:2, 340; Storch in Natur Mus., 100:
                   10, 545–546; Thenius in Geol. Ges. Wien, Mitt., 62, 213–214; Thenius in Zentralbl. Geol.
                   Paläontol., Teil 2, 1970:6, 446–448.
    1970C   Neue Tetrapoden-Fährten aus dem terrestrischen Zechstein.   Akad. Wiss. Berlin, Monatsbr., 12:2–3,
                   197–207, 2 figs., 2 pls., 1 table (German).
    1970D   Ein neuer Colobodus - Fund (Actinopterygii, Chondrostei) aus dem Oberen Muschelkalk des
                   Germanischen Triasbeckens.   Akad. Wiss. Berlin, Monatsber., 12:6–7, 511–520 (German).

MÜLLER, DIETER   See: Bolten, R. and Müller, D., 1969A; Gall, H. and Müller, D., 1970A.

MÜLLER, E. M., SCHRÖDER, E. and SCHMIDT, W.
    1960A   Zur Gliederung und Altersstellung des linkrheinischen Buntsandsteins.   Die stratigraphische Bedeutung
                   des Mechernicher Labyrinthodonten.   Hess. Landesamt Bodenforsch., Notizbl., 88, 246–265,
                   3 figs. (German).

MÜLLER, FABIOLA
    1968A   Zur Phylogenese des sekundären Kiefergelenks.   Rev. Suisse Zool., 75:2, 373–414, 7 figs., 9 pls.,
                   5 tables (German; French and English summaries).
    1968B   Methodische Gesichtspunkte zum Studium der Evolution der Säuger-Ontogenesetypen.   Rev. Suisse
                   Zool., 75:3, 630–643, 4 figs., 2 tables (German; French and English summaries).
    1969A   Zur Phylogenese des sekundären Kiefergelenks: Zeugniswert diarthognather Fossilien im Lichte neuer
                   ontogenetischer Befunde.   Rev. Suisse Zool., 76:3, 710–715, 2 figs., 1 table (German; French
                   and English summaries).

MÜLLER, H.
    1960A   Über Fossilfunde im Lias-Epsilon der Mistelgauer Ziegeleigrube.   Naturwiss. Ges. Bayreuth, Ber., 10
                   (1958/60), 91–114, 19 figs. (German).

MÜLLER, KLAUS and LANGER, W.
    1970A   Georg August Goldfuss.   1782–1848.   Math. Naturwiss., 1970, 163–167, 1 pl. (German).
                   Rev.:   Häntzschel in Zentralbl. Geol. Paläontol., Teil 2, 1971:2–3, 98.

MÜLLER-BECK, HANSJÜRGEN
    1967B   Lothar F. Zotz (1899–1967).   Bayer. Vorges., 32:1–2, 230–231 (German).
    1967C   Der Ort des Homo heidelbergensis in der Hominiden-Stratigraphie.   Fundamenta, Reihe B, 2, 313–320,
                   1 table (German).
    1969A   Die Stratigraphie des süddeutschen Jungpleistozäns.   Jahresschrift. Mitteldeutsch. Vorgesch., 53, 83–
                   102, 3 tables (German).

MÜLLER-KARPE, HERMANN
1966A   Rev.: Grigor'ev in Sov. Arkheol., 1972:1, 275—277 (Russian); Hančar in Anthropol. Ges., Mitt., 99, 221—223; Riek in Fundber. Schwaben, 19, 398—399; Rust in Z. Ethnol., 93:1—2, 283—284.

MULVANEY, DEREK JOHN
1968A*   Australian archaeology. A guide to field techniques. Canberra: Australian Institute of Aboriginal Studies, iii + 268 pp., illustr., tables.
           Rev.: Gould in Amer. Anthropol., 71, 565—566; McBryde in Man (J. Roy. Anthropol. Inst.), 4:1, 143—144.
1969A   The prehistory of Australia. London: Thames and Hudson, Ancient Peoples and Places, 65, 276 pp., 108 figs., 11 maps.
           Rev.: Clark in Antiquity, 43:172, 327—329.
1970A   The Green Gully burial. An introduction. Victoria, Nat. Mus., Mem., 30, 1—2.
1970B   Green Gully revisited: the later excavations. Victoria, Nat. Mus., Mem., 30, 59—77, 7 figs., pls. 3—6.
1972A   Prehistoric man in Australia. Nature, 240:5375, 9—10.

MULVANEY, D. J. and GOLSON, J.
1971A*   Aboriginal man and environment in Australia. Canberra: Australian National University Press, xxi + 389 pp., 31 pls.
           Rev.: Shawcross in Antiquity, 46:182, 163—164.

MULVEY, MINA WHITE
1969A   Digging up Adam: the story of L.S.B. Leakey. New York: David McKay and Co., 216 pp., 23 photos.
           Rev.: Anon. in Archeology, 24:1, 95—96.

MUNDLOS, RUDOLF
1967A   Solnhofen, Geschichte und Geschichten um das Steinbrecherdorf im Altmühltal. Aufschluss, 18:10, 275—283, 7 figs. (German).

MUNGAI, J. M.   See: Leakey, R. E. F., Mungai, J. M. and Walker, A. C., 1971A, 1972A.

MUÑOZ-REYES, J.   See: Hoffstetter, R., Martinez, C., Muñoz-Reyes, J. and Tomasi, P., 1971A.

MUNTHE, JENS, JR.
1971A   The earliest geomyine rodents: Dikkomys and Horatiomys. Geol. Soc. Amer., Abstr., 3:2, 169 (abs.).

MUNTHE, KATHLEEN   See: Bacskai, J., Bartlett, S., Brajnikov, B., Munthe, K., Nichols, R. and Matsumoto, M. (eds.), 1972A.

MURAKHOVSKAÏA, E. I.   See: Buvalkin, A. K., Zhaïmin, M. I., Murakhovskaïa, E. I., Orlovskaïa, E. R. and Sakulina, G. V., 1971A.

MURALIDHARA, VATSALA
1969B   The last supper. Frontiers, 34:2, 16—17, 1 fig.

MURATA, MASABUMI
1971A   [Notosaur from Utatsu region, Japan.] Chigaku Kenkyū, 22:11—12, 396—409 (Japanese).

MURATOV, V. M.   See: Vekilova, E. A., Muratov, V. M. and Fridenberg, E. O., 1969A.

MURCHISON, DUNCAN and WESTOLL, T. STANLEY
1968A*   Coal and coal-bearing strata. Edinburgh and London: Oliver & Boyd, 418 pp., 113 figs., 41 pls., 25 tables.

MURPHY, JAMES L.
1971A   Eryopsid remains from the Conemaugh group, Braxton County, West Virginia. Southeast. Geol., 13:4, 265—273, 2 pls.
1971B   A Physonemus spine from the lower Mercer limestone (Pennsylvanian) of Portage County, Ohio. Ohio J. Sci., 71:4, 240—242, 1 fig.

MURPHY, JOHN A.
1966A   Department of geology. Denver Mus. Natur. Hist., Ann. Rep., 1965, 13—14.
1967A   Department of geology. Denver Mus. Natur. Hist., Ann. Rep., 1966, 16—19, illustr.

MURRAY, BERTRAM G., JR.
1970A   A redescription of two Pliocene cormorants. Condor, 72:3, 293—298, 7 tables.

MURRAY, KEITH F.   See: Brame, A. H., Jr. and Murray, K. F., 1968A.

MUSAKULOVA, LÍAĬLÍA TALIPOVNA
1966A   Iskopaemye tragulidy na territorii Kazakhstana. [Fossil tragulids on the territory of Kazakhstan.] In: II Vsesoïuznoe soveshchanie po paleontologii mlekopitaïushchikh kaïnozoïa (Russian).
1971A   Mestonakhozhdeniïa iskopaemykh tragulid v Kazakhstane. [Localities of fossil tragulids in Kazakhstan.] Akad. Nauk Kaz. SSR, Inst. Zool., Mater. Fauny i Flory, 5, 52–56, 1 fig. (Russian).

MUSAKULOVA, L. T.   See also: Bazhanov, V. S., Birïukov, M. D., Vetrov, F. E., Kozhamkulova, B. S., Lychev, G. F., Musakulova, L. T. and Savinov, P. F., 1971A; Duïsebaev, Zh. D. and Musakulova, L. T., 1968A.

MUSGRAVE, JONATHAN H.
1971A   How dextrous was Neanderthal man? Nature, 233:5321, 538–541, 6 figs.

MUSIL, RUDOLF
1960C*   Mammalia pleistocaenica I. Anthropos, Brno, 1960 Suppl., 147 pp., illustr.
1960D   Československtí pracovníci v pleistocenní osteologii. [Czechoslovakian researchers in the field of Pleistocene osteology.] Anthropos, Brno, 1960 Suppl., 15–41 (Czechoslovakian, Russian and German).
1966C   Stránská skála près de Brno (Moravie). In: Filip, J. (ed.), 1966B, 28–29 (French).
1968B   Stránská skála: its meaning for Pleistocene studies. With comment. Current Anthropol., 9:5, II, 534–539, 4 figs., 3 tables.
1969A   Das Pleistozän von Süssenborn. Die Equiden-Reste aus dem Pleistozän von Süssenborn bei Weimar. Paläontol. Abh., Abt. A, 3:3–4, 617–666, 15 figs., 9 pls., 34 tables. II Internat. Paläont. Kolloquium 1966 in Weimar (German; Russian and English summaries).
    Rev.: Thenius in Zentralbl. Geol. Paläontol., Teil 2, 1970:3/4, 242.
1969B   Fauna pozvonochnykh verkhnego pleïstoïsena na territorii Ch. SSR. [Vertebrate fauna of upper Pleistocene on the territory of Czech. SSR.] In: Less-Periglïaïsial-Paleolit na territorii Sredneï i Vostochnoï Evropy. (VIII Kongress INKVA, Parizh, 1969), 179–182 (Russian).
1969C   Die Pferde der Pekárna-Höhle. Ein Beitrag zur Problematik der Evolution von Equiden. Z. Tierzücht. Züchtungsbiol., 86:2, 147–193, 2 figs., 5 tables (German).
    Rev.: Thenius in Zentralbl. Geol. Paläontol., Teil 2, 1970:5, 441–442.
1969D   Eine Karstspalte mit mittelpleistozänen Funden im Kalksteinbruch Žernavá. Brünn, Moravske Mus., Časopis, 54, 85–96, 4 figs., 2 pls. (German; Czechoslovakian summary).
1970A   Josef Augusta †. [1903–1968]. Quartär, 21, 107–118, portr.
1972A*   Stránská Skála I. 1910–1945. Anthropos, Brno, 20 (Czechoslovakian).

MUSIL, RUDOLF and VALOCH, KAREL
1966A   La grotte "Pod Hradem" dans le Karst Morave. In: Filip, J. (ed.), 1966B, 28 (French).

MUSIL, RUDOLF   See also: Feustel, R., et al., 1971A, 1971B; Valoch, K., Pelíšek, J., Musil, R., Kovanda, J. and Opravil, E., 1969A.

MUSKHELISHVILI, T. A.
1970A   Vozmozhnye puti proniknoveniïa presmykaïushchikhsïa na territoriïu Gruzii i nekotorye kharakternye osobennosti ikh rasprostraneniïa. [Possible dispersal routes of reptiles and some peculiarities of their spread in the territory of Georgia.] Akad. Nauk Gruz. SSR, Soobshch., 58:1, 209–212 (Russian; Georgian and English summaries).

MUSSETT, FRANCES
1967A   The phylogeny of the mammalian jaw joint. Mammal. Soc. Brit. Isles, Bull., 27, 2–3.

MUZIS, A. I.
1968A   Srednechetvertichnyĭ ozernyĭ vodoem Charskoĭ vpadiny (Olekmo-Vitimskaïa gornaïa strana). [Middle Quaternary lacustrine basin of Chara depression. (Olekma-Vitim mountains).] In: Mezozoĭskie i kaĭnozoĭskie ozera Sibiri, 125–138, 6 figs. (Russian).

MYERS, DIXIE P.
1970A   Oil, old bones, and irony. Los Angeles Cty. Mus., Quart., 8:4, 28–31, 5 figs.

MYERS, GEORGE S.
1969A   The endemic fish fauna of Lake Lanao, and the evolution of higher taxonomic categories. In: Ehrlich, P. R., et al. (eds.), 1969A, 247–261.

MYNAREK, H.
1967A   Der Mensch, das Sinnziel der Weltentwicklung. München-Paderborn-Wien: F. Schoning Verlag, xxxi + 499 pp. (German).
    Rev.: Spindler in Anthropol. Anz., 31:3, 212—213.

NAGASAWA, JOJI
1968A   On the *Parastegodon* obtained from Kanagawa prefecture and a part of fossil elephant. Tokyo Gakugei Univ., Bull., Ser. 4, no. 2, 19, 186—195, 4 pls., 2 tables.
1971A   A fossil California sea lion from the Shizu shell bed, Chiba prefecture in Japan. Tokyo, Gakugei Univ., Bull., Ser. 4, 23:4, 146—153, 4 pls.

NAIRN, A. E. M.
1965A*   Rev.: Dimbleby in London Univ., Inst. Archaeol., Bull., 6, 131—132.

NAKASEKO, K.   See: Ikebe, N., Chiji, M. and Nakaseko, K., 1969A.

NALIVKIN, DMITRIĬ VASIL'EVICH
1963B   Devonskaia sistema. [Devonian system.] Geologiia SSSR, 2, Arkhangel'sk and Vologda Provinces, and Komi ASSR, 255—345, 15 figs., 2 tables (Russian).

NALIVKIN, V. D., LARIONOVA, E. N. and SHERSHNEV, K. S.
1969A   Permskaia sistema. [Permian system.] Geologiia SSSR, 12:1, Perm, Sverdlovsk, Cheliabinsk, and Kurgan Provinces, 326—358, 5 figs. (Russian).

NAPIER, JOHN R.
1965A   The evolution of the human hand. Roy. Inst. Gt. Brit., Proc., 40:6, 544—557, 5 pls.
1967A   Evolutionary aspects of primate locomotion. Amer. J. Phys. Anthropol., 27, 333—342, 4 figs.
1967B   The antiquity of human walking. Sci. Amer., 216:4, 56—66, illustr.
1970A   The roots of mankind. Washington, D.C.: Smithsonian Inst. Press, 240 pp., frontispiece, 30 figs., 20 pls., 13 tables.
    Rev.: Ashton in J. Anat., 110:1, 127—128; Bramblett in Human Biol., 43:3, 459—460; Campbell in New Sci., 53:786, 560.
1970B   Paleoecology and catarrhine evolution. In: Napier, J. R. and Napier, P. H. (eds.), 1970A, 53—95, 3 figs.
1971A   Five steps to man. In: Holmes, L. D. (ed.), 1971A, 106—112, 1 fig. (reprinted from Discovery, June, 1964).

NAPIER, J. R. and NAPIER, P. H.
1970A*   Old world monkeys. Evolution, systematics, and behavior. New York and London: Academic Press, xvi + 660 pp., illustr.
    Rev.: Buettner-Janusch in Amer. J. Phys. Anthropol., 37:2, 318; Dorst in Mammalia, 35:1, 171—172; Fooden in Quart. Rev. Biol., 46:4, 438—439; Haltenorth in Säugetierkundl. Mitt., 20:1—2, 183—184; Kirsch in Amer. Sci., 60:2, 259; Martin in Nature, 232:5313, 659.

NAPIER, J. R.   See also: Groves, C. P. and Napier, J. R., 1968A; Leakey, L. S. B., Tobias, P. V. and Napier, J. R., 1971A.

NAPIER, PRUE H.
1970A   Monkeys and apes. London: Hamlyn Publishing Co., 159 pp., illustr.

NAPIER, P. H.   See also: Napier, J. R. and Napier, P. H. (eds.), 1970A.

NAPTON, LEWIS K.   See: Heizer, R. F. and Napton, L. K., 1969A.

NARMANDACH, PAGAM   See: Młynarski, M. and Narmandach, P., 1972A.

NARR, KARL J.
1966B*   Rev.: Maringer in Anthropos, 65:5—6, 1021; Reitinger in Oberösterr. Musealver., Jahrb., 113:1, 287—288; Ridley in London Univ., Inst. Archeol., Bull., 7, 141; Sørensen in Asian Perspectives, 10, 174.

NASIMOVICH, A. A. (= NASIMOWITSCH, A. A.) and FORMOZOV, A. A.
1970A   Veniamin Iosifovich Tsalkin (1903—1970). Zool. Zh., 49:10, 1589—1591, portr. (Russian).

NASIMOVICH, A. A.   See also: Heptner, W. G. and Nasimovich, A. A., 1967A.

NASIMOWITSCH, A. A.   See: Nasimovich, A. A.

NASSICHUK, W. W.
    1971A   *Helicoprion* and *Physonemus*, Permian vertebrates from the Assistance formation, Canadian Arctic
          archipelago. Can., Geol. Surv., Bull., 192, 83–93, 1 map, 2 pls. (French summary).

NASSICHUK, W. W. and SPINOSA, CLAUDE
    1970A   *Helicoprion* sp., a Permian elasmobranch from Ellesmere Island, Canadian Arctic. J. Paleontol., 44:6,
          1130–1132, 1 fig.

NEBBIA, L.   See: Bucci, G., Nebbia, L., Sacchi Vialli, G., Savi, A. and Basso, G., 1969A.

NECRASOV, OLGA
    1962-63A   Date cu privire la mugurele dentar uman descoperit în stratul paleolitic superior din peştera "La Adam"
          (Dobrogea). [Data concerning the human rudimentary tooth found in the upper Paleolithic
          layer of "La Adam" Cave (Dobrogea).] Acad. Repub. Soc. Rom., Inst. Speol. "Emile Rakoviţă",
          Lucr., 1–2, 285–291, 1 fig. (Rumanian; Russian and French summaries).
    1968A   Originea şi evoluţia omului. [Origin and evolution of men.] Natura, Ser. Biol., 20:5, 3–12, 1 table
          (Rumanian).

NEGADAEV-NIKONOV, KONSTANTIN NIKOLAEVICH
    1969A   Chetvertichnaîâ sistema. [Quaternary system.] Geologiîâ SSSR, 45, Moldavian SSR, 196–223, 3 figs.
          (Russian).
    1970A   Mezhdunarodnyĭ kollokvium po faune i geologii nizhnego i srednego pleĭstoŤsena Evropy.
          [International colloquium on fauna and geology of lower and middle Pleistocene of Europe.]
          Akad. Nauk Moldav. SSR, Izv., Ser. Biol. Khim. Nauk, 1970:3, 86–87 (Russian).

NEGADAEV-NIKONOV, K. N. and BUKATCHUK, P. D.
    1969A   [Early Quaternary deposits of lower Dnestr region.] Akad. Nauk Moldav. SSR, Izv., Ser. Biol. Khim.
          Nauk, 1969:2, 3–17, 6 figs. (Russian).

NEGADAEV-NIKONOV, K. N., DAVID, A. I. and Khubka, A. N.
    1970A   Tiraspol'skiĭ opornyĭ razrez pleĭstoŤsena Evropy. [Tiraspol' key section of European Pleistocene.]
          Akad. Nauk Moldav. SSR, Izv., Ser. Biol. Khim. Nauk, 1970:2, 74–84, 4 figs., 1 table
          (Russian).

NEILL, WILFRED T.
    1971A   The last of the ruling reptiles. Alligators, crocodiles and their kin. New York, London: Columbia
          University Press, xvii + 486 pp., 162 figs.
          Rev.: Cott in Nature, 237:5356, 468; King in BioScience, 22:2, 119; Russell in J. Natur. Hist.,
          London, 6:2, 243–244.

NEĬSHTADT, M. I.
    1964A   Bibliografiîâ izdaniĭ, podgotovlennykh k VI kongressu INQUA. [Bibliography of publications prepared
          for the VI INQUA Congress.] In: Nauchnye itogi VI kongressa mezhdunarodnoĭ assofsiafsii po
          izucheniîû chetvertichnogo perioda (INQUA). (Varshava, 1961), 113–133 (Russian).

NEĬSHTADT, M. I.   See also: Vereĭskiĭ, N. G., Ivanova, I. K. and Neĭshtadt, M. I., 1964A.

NELSON, ELMER R.
    1968A   Do we understand museum air conditioning? Curator, 11:2, 127–136, 4 figs.

NELSON, GARETH J.
    1968A   Gill-arch structure in *Acanthodes*. Nobel Symp., 4th, Stockholm, 1967, Proc., 1968, 129–143, 6 figs.
    1969A   Gill arches and the phylogeny of fishes, with notes on the classification of vertebrates. Amer. Mus.
          Natur. Hist., Bull., 141:4, 475–552, 26 figs., 14 pls., 1 table.
          Rev.: McAllister in Quart. Rev. Biol., 45:2, 209–210.

1969B   The problem of historical biogeography. Syst. Zool., 18:2, 243–246, 5 figs.
1969C   Origin and diversification of teleostean fishes. N.Y. Acad. Sci., Ann., 167:1, 18–30, 3 figs.
1972A   Cephalic sensory canals, pitlines, and the classification of esocoid fishes, with notes on galaxiids and other teleosts. Amer. Mus. Nov., 2492, 49 pp., 23 figs., 2 tables.

NELSON, HARRY   See: Brace, C. L., Nelson, H. and Korn, N., 1971A.

NELSON, MICHAEL E.
1972A   Age and stratigraphic relations of the Fowkes formation, southwestern Wyoming. Field Conf. Tert. Bios., S. and W. Wyo., Guidebk., 51–62, 1 fig.

NELSON, ROBERT S. and SEMKEN, HOLMES A.
1969A   Paleoecological and stratigraphic significance of the muskrat in Pleistocene deposits. Geol. Soc. Amer., Abstr., Part 7, 159–160 (abs.).
1970A   Paleoecological and stratigraphic significance of the muskrat in Pleistocene deposits. Geol. Soc. Amer., Bull., 81:12, 3733–3738, 7 figs.

NEMESKÉRI, JÁNOS and DEZSÖ, GYULA
1969A*   Evolutionary trends in fossil and Recent hominids. Symposium held in Budapest, 10–12 October, 1967. Symp. Biol. Hungarica, 9, 140 pp.
     Rev.: Anon. in J. Anthropol. Soc. Nippon, 78:3, 245–246; Coon in Human Biol., 42:3, 522–523; F. E. in Man in India, 51:4, 414; H. V. V. in L'Anthropologie, 74:5–6, 409–410; Harding and Washburn in Quart. Rev. Biol., 45:2, 224; Leguebe in Soc. Roy. Belge Anthropol. Préhist., Bull., 80, 244–245; MacConaill in Man (J. Roy. Anthropol. Inst.), 4:4, 653; Vogel in Quartär, 20, 234–236; Vogel in Z. Morphol. Anthropol., 62:2, 232–233.

NEMESKÉRI, JÁNOS   See also: Acsádi, Gy. and Nemeskéri, J., 1970A.

NEMKOVA, VERONIKA KONSTANTINOVNA   See: Iakhimovich, V. L. and Nemkova, V. K., 1969A.

NEQUIN, J.
1969A   Progress report on the Inventaria Archaeologica Africana. S. Afr. Archaeol. Bull., 23, 30.

NESOV, L. A.   See: Verzilin, N. N., Khozatskiĭ, L. I., Vu Din' Li and Nesov, L. A., 1970A.

NESTURKH, M. F.
1964D   Problema pervonachal'noĭ prarodiny chelovechestva. [The problem of the original native land of mankind.] In: U istokov chelovechestva. (Osnovnye problemy antropogeneza), 7–32, 5 figs. (Russian).
1970A   Proiskhozhdenie cheloveka. [The origin of man.] Second edition, revised and completed. Ia. Ia. Roginskiĭ, ed. Moscow: "Nauka" Press (Russian).
     Rev.: Iakimov in Vop. Antropol., 38, 166–167 (Russian).
1972A   Otkrytie cherepa pitekantropa VIII. [Discovery of the Pithecanthropus VIII skull.] Vop. Antropol., 40, 192–195, 3 figs. (Russian).
1972B   [Discussion.] Vop. Antropol., 41, 163 (Russian).

NETTING, M. GRAHAM
1967B   Vertebrate fossils. Carnegie Mus., Ann. Rep., 70, 14–16.
1969A   Vertebrate fossils. Carnegie Mus., Ann. Rep., 72, 20–21.

NEÚSTUPNÝ, JIŘÍ
1969A   National Museum, Prague: new presentation of the exhibit on prehistory. Mus., UNESCO, 22:1, 10–19, 20 photos (French and English).

NEVESSKAÏA, LIDIĬA ALEKSANDROVNA
1966A   Problema vida v paleontologii v svete politipicheskoĭ kontseptsii. [Problem of species in paleontology in the light of polytypic concept.] Itogi Nauki, Ser. Geol., 10, Stratigr. Paleontol., 5–35, 5 figs. (Russian).

NEVO, EVIATAR
1968A   Pipid frogs from the early Cretaceous of Israel and pipid evolution. Mus. Comp. Zool., Bull., 136:8, 255–318, 18 figs., 11 pls., 10 tables.

NEVO, EVIATAR and ESTES, RICHARD
1969A   Ramonellus longispinus, an early Cretaceous salamander from Israel. Copeia, 1969:3, 540–547, 7 figs., 1 table.
     Rev.: Westphal in Zentralbl. Geol. Paläontol., Teil 2, 1970:6, 515.

NEVOLINA, SERAFIMA IVANOVNA   See: Bersenev, I. I., Ustinovskiĭ, Iu. B., Bur'iănova, I. Z., Nevolina, S. I.
and Medvedev, V. V., 1969A.

NEWCOMB, R. C. and REPENNING, C. A.
1970A   Occurrence of mammoth fossils in the Touchet beds, south-central Washington. Northwest Sci., 44:1,
16–18, 2 figs.

NEWELL, NORMAN D.
1971A   The nature of the fossil record. In: Leakey, L. S. B., Prost, J. and Prost, S. (eds.), 1971A, 77–105,
9 figs. (reprinted from an address at the Amer. Phil. Soc. An. Meeting, 1959).

NEWMAN, B. H.
1970A   Stance and gait in the flesh-eating dinosaur Tyrannosaurus. Linn. Soc., Biol. J., 2:2, 119–123, 2 figs.

NICHOLS, RACHEL H.   See: Bacskai, J., Bartlett, S., Brajnikov, B., Munthe, K., Nichols, R. and Matsumoto, M.
(eds.), 1972A; Camp, C. L., Nichols, R. H., Brajnikov, B., Fulton, E. and Bacskai, J. A. (eds.),
1972A; Matsumoto, M. and Nichols, R. (eds.), 1970A.

NICOLL, P. G.   See: Halstead, L. B. and Nicoll, P. G., 1971A.

NICOLUSSI, CARLA MUSI
1971A   Biometria di molari elefantini di varie specie conservati nell' Istituto Geologico Universitario di Padova.
Accad. Patavina Sci. Let. Arti, Cl. Sci. Mat. Natur., Atti Mem., 83:2, 203–223, 27 figs. (Italian).

NIEMANN, L.   See: Gaherty, G., Kettel, D., MacDonald, J., Niemann, L., Von Graeve, B. and Arima, E., 1969A.

NIKIFOROVA, KSENIIĀ VLADIMIROVNA (= NIKIFOROVA, X. V.)
1969A   Osnovnye problemy antropogena Severnoĭ Evrazii. [Basic problems of north Eurasian Anthropogene.]
In: Osnovnye problemy geologii antropogena Evrazii. K VIII kongressu INQUA, Parizh, 1969,
5–15 (Russian; English summary).
1970A   The volume and subdivision of Pliocene. G. Geol., 35:1, 171–180, 1 chart (Russian summary).
1971A*   Pleĭstotsen Tiraspoliā. [Pleistocene of Tiraspol'.] Kishinev: "Ştiinţa" Press, 187 pp., illustr. (Russian).

NIKIFOROVA, K. V., IVANOVA, I. K. and KONSTANTINOVA, N. A.
1969A   Tiraspol' kak stratotip pleĭstotsena Vostochnoĭ Evropy. [Tiraspol' as a stratotype for the Pleistocene
of eastern Europe.] In: Mezhdunarodnyĭ kollokvium po geologii i faune nizhnego i srednego
pleĭstotsena Evropy. Tezisy dokladov, 3–5 and 61–63 (Russian and English).
1970A   Tiraspol' as a type locality for the Pleistocene of eastern Europe. Palaeogeogr., Palaeoclimatol.,
Palaeoecol., 8:2–3, 175–185, 2 figs.
1971A   Tiraspol' kak opornyĭ razrez pleĭstotsena Evropy. [Tiraspol' as the key section of European
Pleistocene.] In: Pleĭstotsen Tiraspoliā, 8–25 (Russian).

NIKIFOROVA, K. V.   See also: Gromov, V. I., Krasnov, I. I., Nikiforova, K. V. and Shantser, E. V., 1969A;
Gromov, V. I. and Nikiforova, K. V., 1968A, 1968B, 1968C, 1969A; Gromov, V. I.,
Vangengeĭm, E. A., Grichuk, V. P., Ivanova, I. K. and Nikiforova, K. V. (eds.), 1968A;
Gromov, V. I., Vangengeĭm, E. A. and Nikiforova, K. V., 1965B; Menner, V. V., Nikiforova,
K. V., Pevzner, M. A., Alekseev, M. N., Gladenkov, Iu. B., Gurariĭ, G. Z. and Trubikhin, V. M.,
1972A.

NIKIFOROVA, XENIA V. (= NIKIFOROVA, K. V.)
1968A   Die Korrelation der unter- und mittelpleistozänen Ablagerungen im nördlichen Eurasien. Deut. Ges.
Geol. Wiss., Ber., Reihe A, Geol. Paläontol., 13:3, 367–374 (German).

NIKITENKO, M. F.
1970A   Evoliutsiiā i mozg. [Evolution and brain.] Minsk: "Nauka i tekhnika" Press, 342 pp., illustr. (Russian).
Rev.: Iablokov in Zool. Zh., 49:12, 1888–1890.

NIKITIN, E. A.   See: Kostenko, N. N., Nikitin, E. A. and Liādzhina, K. A., 1971A; Kostenko, N. N., Nikitin,
E. A. and Polumiskova, L. A., 1971A; Kostenko, N. N., Nikitin, E. A., Polumiskova, L. A. and
Fedorenko, O. A., 1971A; Kostenko, N. N., Nikitin, E. A. and Savinova, A. P., 1971A.

NIKITIN, VADIM PETROVICH   See: Martynov, V. A. and Nikitin, V. P., 1968A.

NIKLEWSKI, J.   See: Laskowska-Wysoczańska, W. and Niklewski, J., 1969A.

NIKOLAEV, V. A.
1964A   Eopleĭstoĭsen Zapadno-Sibirskoĭ nizmennosti. [Eopleistocene of the western Siberian lowlands.]
        Akad. Nauk SSSR, Sib. Otd., Inst. Geol. Geofiz., Tr., 44, 92—108 (Russian).
1969A   Stratigrafiia chetvertichnykh dosamarovskikh otlozheniĭ Zapadno-Sibirskoĭ nizmennosti. [Stratigraphy
        of Quaternary pre-Samarovo deposits of west Siberian lowlands.] In: Problemy chetvertichoĭ
        geologii Sibiri, 62—73, 3 figs. (Russian; English summary).

NIKOLAEV, V. A.   See also: Markov, K. K., Velichko, A. A., Lazukov, G. I. and Nikolaev, V. A., 1968A.

NIKOLOV, IV.
1969A   [The finding of *Mammuthus primigenius* near the station Cherepish.] Bŭlg. Akad. Nauk., Geol. Inst.,
        Izv., Ser. Paleontol., 18, 105—110, 2 pls. (Bulgarian; Russian and German summaries).
1971A   Novi predstaviteli na rod *Hipparion* v Bŭlgariia. [New representatives of the genus *Hipparion* in
        Bulgaria.] Bŭlg. Akad. Nauk., Geol. Inst., Izv., Ser. Paleontol., 20, 107—122, 3 pls. (Bulgarian,
        Russian and German).
1972A   Vŭrkhu stratigrafskoto nivo na *Metaschizotherium fraasi* Koenigswald. [On the stratigraphic level of
        Metaschizotherium fraasi Koenigswald.] Bŭlg. Akad. Nauk., Geol. Inst., Izv., Ser. Paleontol.,
        21, 129—132, 1 fig. (Bulgarian; Russian and German summaries).

NIKOLOV, IV. and VELICHKOV, V.
1969A   [On the presence of the genus *Paraentelodon* in the Tertiary basin of Razlog.] Bŭlg. Akad. Nauk.,
        Geol. Inst., Izv., Ser. Paleontol., 18, 111—115, 1 fig. (Bulgarian; Russian and German summaries).
        Rev.: Thenius in Zentralbl. Geol. Paläontol., Teil 2, 1971:1, 70—71.

NIKONOV, A. A.
1971A   Kladbishcha drevnikh zhivotnykh v Tadzhikistane. [Cemeteries of ancient animals in Tadzhikistan.]
        Priroda, 1971:3, 85—91, 5 figs., 1 chart, portr. (Russian).

NIKONOV, A. A., PEN'KOV, A. V., TROFIMOV, B. A., VANGENGEĬM, E. A., DMITRIEVA, E. A. and
SOTNIKOVA, M. V.
1971A   Novye dannye po geologii i faune mlekopitaiushchikh verkhnego pliotsena i nizhnego pleĭstotsena
        Iuzhnogo Tadzhikistana. [New data on the geology and mammalian fauna of the upper
        Pliocene and lower Pleistocene of the southern Tadzhikistan.] Mosk. Obshchest. Ispyt. Prir.,
        Biull., Otd. Geol., 46:6, 146—147 (Russian).

NOBACK, CHARLES R. and MONTAGNA, WILLIAM
1970A*   Advances in primatology, volume 1. The primate brain. New York: Appleton-Century-Crofts,
        v + 320 pp., illustr.

NOBIS, GÜNTER
1967A   Über pleistozäne Equiden Eurasiens und das Problem der Pferdedomestikation. Fundamenta, Reihe B,
        2, 281—289, 3 tables (German).
1970A   Equiden aus dem Löss von Kärlich (Neuwieder Becken). Mainzer Naturwiss. Arch., 9, 297—302, 2 figs.,
        2 tables (German).

NOLF, DIRK
1966A   Bijdrage tot de studie van de ichthyologische fauna uit midden Eozeen. Brugge: Mimeographed
        report (Flemish).
        Rev.: Weiler in Zentralbl. Geol. Paläontol., Teil 2, 1968:6, 649—650.
1967A   Nieuwe gegevens over de fossielen op de spuiterreinen te Zeebrugge: de Fauna en de geremanieerde
        elementen uit het Jong-Kwartair. Werkgroep. Tert. Kwart. Geol., Meded., 4, 67—72 (Flemish).
        Rev.: Weiler in Zentralbl. Geol. Paläontol., Teil 2, 1969:3, 286.
1969A   Over de visfauna uit de glauconietzandstenen van de formatie van Aalter, geremanieerd langs de
        belgische kust el te Cadzand. Biol. Jaarboek, 37, 262—265 (Flemish).
1970A   Sur la faune ichthyologique d'un falun dans l'argile des Flandres, près de Courtrai (Belgique). Soc.
        Belge Géol. Paléontol. Hydrol., Bull., 79:1, 11—23, 24 figs., 1 chart, 1 table (French).
        Rev.: Weiler in Zentralbl. Geol. Paläontol., Teil 2, 1971:5, 402.
1970B   De geremanieerde eocene visfauna in de basis van het Pleistoceen te Merelbeke. Natuurwet. Tijdschr.
        (1969), 51:3—8, 111—124, 1 pl. (Flemish; French summary).
        Rev.: Weiler in Zentralbl. Geol. Paläontol., Teil 2, 1971:5, 402—403.
1970C   Ichthyologische Fauna uit de Formatie Mont Panisel en de Hoorn (Belgisch Eoceen). Ghent, Rijksuniv.
        Fac. Wetensch., Verh., 1970, 1—122, 18 pls., 7 charts, 3 tables (Flemish; French summary).
        Rev.: Weiler in Zentralbl. Geol. Paläontol., Teil 2, 1971:5, 401—402.

NOLF, DIRK   See also: Stinton, F. C. and Nolf, D., 1969A.

NOLTE, H., WOLFRAM, H.-J. and WÖLLNER, H.
1969A   Das Pleistozän von Süssenborn. Überblick über die Forschungsgeschichte der Pleistozän-Fundstelle
          Süssenborn bei Weimar. Paläontol. Abh., Abt. A, 3:3–4, 373–383, 7 figs., 1 table. II Internat.
          Kolloquium 1966 in Weimar (German).

NOPPEL, TIIU   See: Mark-Kurik, E. and Noppel, T., 1970A.

NORBERG, ULLA MARIA
1970A   Functional osteology and myology of the wing of Plecotus auritus Linnaeus (Chiroptera). Ark. Zool.,
          22:5, 483–543, 43 figs., 3 tables.

NORDMANN, V.
1958A   Beskrivelse til Geologisk Kort over Danmark. Dan. Geol. Unders., Raekke 1, 22A, 125 pp., 37 figs.,
          2 pls., 2 maps (Danish; English summary).

NORRIS, KENNETH S.
1968A   The evolution of acoustic mechanisms in odontocete cetaceans. In: Drake, E. T. (ed.), 1968A, 297–
          324, 6 figs., 4 tables.

NORTH, F. J.
1956A   W. D. Conybeare, his geological contemporaries and Bristol associations. Bristol Natur. Soc., Proc.,
          29:2, 133–146.

NORTHROP, STUART A.
1961B   Mississippian and Pennsylvanian fossils of the Albuquerque country. N. Mex. Geol. Soc., Guidebk.,
          Field Conf. 12, 105–112, 1 fig., tables.
1962A   New Mexico's fossil record. N. Mex. Quart., 32, suppl., 75 pp., 2 figs.
1966A   University of New Mexico contributions in geology, 1898–1964. N. Mex., Univ., Publ. Geol., 7,
          152 pp., 4 pls.
1969A   History of the New Mexico Geological Society, 1947–1968. N. Mex. Geol. Soc., Spec. Publ., 2,
          78 pp.

NOUGIER, LOUIS-RENÉ
1965A   L'expressionisme dans l'art préhistorique: les mammouths de Rouffignac. Toulouse, Univ., Inst.
          d'Art Préhist., Trav., 7, 93–113, 16 pls. (French).
1969A   In memoriam Camille Arambourg 1885–1969. Préhist. Spéléol. Ariége., 24, 102–103 (French).
1969B   In memoriam F. Ed. Koby. 18..–1969. Préhist. Spéléol. Ariége., 24, 103–104 (French).
1969C   In memoriam Edmond Vignard. 18..–1969. Préhist. Spéléol. Ariége., 24, 104–105 (French).

NOUGIER, L.-R. and BARRIÈRE, C.
1965B   La grotte ornée des Fieux (Commune de Miers, Lot). Toulouse, Univ., Inst. d'Art Préhist., Trav., 7,
          115–134, 18 figs. (French).

NOUGIER, L.-R. and ROBERT, ROMAIN
1968A   Scène d'initiation de la Grotte de la Vache à Alliat (Ariège). Préhist. Spéléol. Ariége., 23, 13–98,
          illustr. (French).
1970A   Pendeloque "au cheval sautant" du Magdalénien final des Pyrénées (Grotte de la Vache, Ariège).
          Préhist. Spéléol. Ariége., 25, 17–28, 1 fig., 7 pls. (French).
1971A   Galets gravés du Magdalénien final des Pyrénées (Grotte de la Vache, Alliat, Ariège). Préhist. Spéléol.
          Ariége., 26, 11–75, 11 figs., 15 pls., 3 diagr., 7 maps, 2 tables (French).

NOUGIER, LOUIS-RENÉ   See also: Caralp, E., Nougier, L.-R. and Robert, R., 1970A; Gailli, R., Nougier, L.-R.
          and Robert, R., 1969A; Robert, R. and Nougier, L. R., 1968A.

NOVACEK, MICHAEL J.
1972A   Insectivora of the late Eocene, San Diego, California. Soc. Vert. Paleontol., Ann. Meeting, 32nd, 1972,
          Abstr. (abs.).

NOVIKOV, G. A.
1971A   Pamĭati Veniamina Iosifovicha Tsalkina. [1903–1970]. [In the memory of V. I. Zalkin.] Mosk.
          Obshchest. Ispyt. Prir., Bĭull., Otd. Biol., 76:1, 5–17, portr. (Russian).
1971B   Obzor sovremennogo sostoĭaniĭa teriologii. [A review of the present status of theriology.] Mosk.
          Obshchest. Ispyt. Prir., Bĭull., Otd. Biol., 76:1, 147–158, 5 tables (Russian).

NOVITSKAĬA, LARISA ILLARIONOVNA (= NOVITSKAYA, LARISSE)
1968A   Novye amfiaspidy (Heterostraci) iz nizhnego devona Sibiri i klassifikatsiĭa Amphiaspidiformes. [New
          amphiaspids (Heterostraci) from lower Devonian of Siberia and classification of Amphiaspidiforme
          In: Ocherki po filogenii i sistamatike.

formes.] In: Ocherki po filogenii i sistematike iskopaemykh ryb i bezcheliùstnykh, 43–62, 10 figs., 5 pls. (Russian).

1970A   Pozdnesiluriĭskiĭ *Archegonaspis* na ostrove Vaĭgach. [Late Silurian *Archegonaspis* on the island Vaĭgach.] Paleontol. Zh., 1970:3, 105–113, 4 figs., 1 pl., 1 table (Russian).

1970B   Pervai̇a nakhodka *Archegonaspis* (Heterostraci) v verkhem silure Vaĭgacha. [First find of *Archegonaspis* (Heterostraci) in the upper Silurian of Vaĭgach Is.] In: Stratigrafiiâ i fauna siluriĭskikh otlozheniĭ Vaĭgacha, 236–237 (Russian).

1971A   O diagnosticheskoĭ otsenke ornamenta bezcheliùstnykh i ryb. [Diagnostic evaluation of ornamentation in Agnatha and Pisces.] Paleontol. Zh., 1971:4, 82–96, 6 figs., 1 pl. (Russian).

1971B   Les Amphiaspidés (Heterostraci) du Dévonien de la Sibérie. Cah. Paléontol., 130 pp., 81 figs., 23 pls. (French).

           Rev.: Anon. in Soc. Géol. Fr., C.R., 1971:6, 332–333.

1971C   Diagnostic evaluation of the ornamentation of Agnatha and Pisces. Paleontol. J., 5:4, 494–506, 6 figs.

1972A   O filogeneticheskikh sviâziâkh poraspid (Heterostraci). [On phylogenetic relationships of poraspids (Heterostraci).] Paleontol. Zh., 1972:3, 112–120, 4 figs. (Russian).

NOVITSKAYA, LARISSE   See: Novitskaiâ, Larisa Illarionovna

NOWIŃSKI, ALEKSANDER
1971A   *Nemegtosaurus mongoliensis* n. gen., s. sp. (Sauropoda) from the uppermost Cretaceous of Mongolia. In: Kielan-Jaworowska, Z. (ed.), 1971B, 57–81, 9 figs., 7 pls., 2 tables.

NÚÑEZ, LAUTARO
1969A   Nuevas perspectivas de la arqueologia en Checoslovaquia. Univ. Chile, Bol., 91, 26–31, 5 figs. (Spanish).

NYBELIN, O.
1964A   Versuch einer taxonomischen Revision der jurassischen Fischgattung *Thrissops* Agassiz. Göteborg, K. Vetensk. Vitterh. Samh., Handl., Ser. B, 9:4, 3–44, 9 pls., 2 tables (German).

O., D.
1969A   Uri Aleksandrovich Orlov. (1893–1966). Geol. Soc. London, Proc., 1651, 229–231.

OAKESHOTT, GORDON B.
1970A   Geology of the California Coast Ranges. Calif., Div. Mines Geol., Miner. Inform. Serv., 23:1, 7–10, 8 figs., map.

OAKLEY, KENNETH PAGE
1965C   Introduction. In: Henschen, F., 1965A.
1966A   Rev.: Ranov in Vop. Antropol., 36, 176–178 (Russian).
1966B   Rev.: Knussmann in Homo, 19:3–4, 233; Narr in Anthropos, 62:5–6, 961–962.
1968A   The date of the 'Red Lady' of Paviland. Antiquity, 42:168, 306–307.
1968B   The Piltdown skull. New Sci., 40:619, 154.
1968C   Cronología del hombre fósil. Barcelona: Labor Ed., 317 pp., 82 figs. (Spanish).
           Rev.: Nolla in Ampurias, 31–32, 397–398.
1969A   Man the skilled tool-maker. Antiquity, 43:171, 222–223.
1969B   An appreciation of Dr. Robert Broom, F.R.S. S. Afr. Archaeol. Bull., 23, 35–36.
1971A   Radiocarbon dating of proto-Solutrean in Wales. Nature, 231:5298, 112.
1971B   Die Datierung menschlicher Fossilien. German translation by G. Heberer and Elly Schefter. Stuttgart: G. Fischer, xi + 278 pp., 83 figs., 2 maps (German).
           Rev.: Haltenorth in Säugetierkundl. Mitt., 20:1–2, 184; Preuschoft in Zentralbl. Geol. Paläontol., Teil 2, 1972:3, 181; Roth-Lutra in Anat. Anz., 131:1–2, 172–173; Thenius in Geol. Ges. Wien, Mitt., 63, 255–256.

OAKLEY, K. P. and CAMPBELL, BERNARD GRANT
1967A *   Rev.: Knussmann in Homo, 19:1, 49.

OAKLEY, K. P., CAMPBELL, B. G. and MOLLESON, T. I
1971A *   Catalogue of fossil hominids. Part 2: Europe. London: Trustees of the British Museum (Natural History), xii + 379 pp.

OAKLEY, KENNETH P.   See also: Clark, J. D., Brothwell, D. R., Powers, R. and Oakley, K. P., 1968A; Heintz, N. and Oakley, K. P., 1969A; Howell, F. C., Cole, G. H., Kleindienst, M. R., Szabo, B. J. and Oakley, K. P., 1972A; Molleson, T. I., Oakley, K. P. and Vogel, J. C., 1972A.

OBATA, IKUWO
1966A   [A review on the relative growth of study in paleontology.] Natur. Sci. and Mus., 33:5–6, 88–96 (Japanese).

OBATA, I., HASEGAWA, Y. and OTSUKA, H.
1972A   Preliminary report on the Cretaceous reptile fossils from Hokkaido. Nat. Sci. Mus., Tokyo, Mem., 5, 213–222, 1 fig., 1 pl. (Japanese; English summary).

OBATA, I., HASEGAWA, Y. and SUZUKI, T.
1970A   [Discovery of elasmosaur from the upper Cretaceous Futaba group.] Geol. Soc. Jap., J., 76:3, 161–164, 2 figs. (Japanese).

OBATA, IKUWO   See also: Hasegawa, Y. and Obata, I., 1972A; Hasegawa, Y., Obata, I., Honda, H. and Fujishima, Y., 1972A; Hayami, I. and Obata, I., 1966A, 1966B; Minato, M., Ohmori, M., Mizuno, T. and Obata, I., 1968A; Ozaki, H., Kato, A. and Obata, I., 1965A; Ozaki, H. and Obata, I., 1963A, 1963B.

OBER, L. D. and WEAVER, W. G.
1971A   Three new fossil sites in south Florida. Fla. Acad. Sci., Quart. J., 34:1, suppl., 4 (abs.).

OBER, L. D.   See also: Weaver, W. G. and Ober, L. D., 1971A.

OBERC, J.   See: Glazek, J., Oberc, J. and Sulimski, A., 1971A, 1972A.

OBMORYSHEV, K. M.
1961A   K voprosu o detal'noĭ stratigrafii verkhneduĭskoĭ svity Mgachinskogo kamennougol'nogo mestorozhdeniĭa na o. Sakhaline. [The problem of detail stratigraphy of the upper Due suite of Mgachi coal deposit on Sakhalin Island.] Vses. Neft. Nauch.-Issled. Geologorazved. Inst., Tr., 181, 88–94, 2 figs. (Russian).

OBRHELOVÁ, NADĚŽDA
1969A   Die Karpfenfische im tschechoslowakischen Süsswassertertiär. Čas. Mineral. Geol., 14:1, 39–52, 5 figs., 2 tables (German).
    Rev.: Weiler in Zentralbl. Geol. Paläontol., Teil 2, 1971:5, 403–404.
1970A   Fische aus den Süsswasserablagerungen des Villafranchium im Süden der ČSSR. Geologie, 19:5, 569–587, 7 figs., 3 pls. (German; Czech , English and Russian summaries).
    Rev.: Weiler in Zentralbl. Geol. Paläontol., Teil 2, 1971:5, 404; Weiler in Zentralbl. Geol. Paläontol., Teil 2, 1971:5, 405.
1970B   Die Osteologie der Tinca-Vorläufer aus dem tschechoslowakischen Süsswassertertiär. Dresden, Staatl. Mus. Mineral. Geol., Abhandl., 99–209, 46 figs., 12 pls., 5 tables (German).
    Rev.: Weiler in Zentralbl. Geol. Paläontol., Teil 2, 1971:5, 404–405.
1971A   Vergleichende Osteologie der Gattung Leuciscus (Pisces) aus tertiären Schichten der nördlichen und westlichen ČSSR. Paläontol. Abh., Abt. A, 4:3, 549–660, 80 figs., 10 pls., 7 tables (German; Russian and English summaries).
1971B   Über einen Serranid (Pisces) aus dem nordböhmischen Süsswassertertiär. Čas. Mineral. Geol., 16:4, 371–387, 9 figs., 6 pls. (German; Czech summary).

O'BRIEN, PATRICIA J.
1968A   A mastodon (?) tusk from Manhattan, Kansas. Kan. Acad. Sci., Trans., 71, 90–91, 1 fig.

OBRUCHEV, DMITRIĬ VLADIMIROVICH (= OBRUTCHEV, D. V.)
1968A*   Ocherki po filogenii i sistematike iskopaemykh ryb i bezchelĭustnykh. [Outlines on phylogeny and systematics of fossil fishes and Agnatha.] Moscow: "Nauka" Press, 211 pp., illustr. (Russian).
1968B   Sovetskaĭa paleoikhtiologiĭa. [Soviet paleoichthyology.] In: Ocherki po filogenii i sistematike iskopaemykh ryb i bezchelĭustnykh, 5–9 (Russian).
1968C   Ob evolĭutsii Heterostraci. [On the evolution of Heterostraci.] In: Ocherki po filogenii i sistematike iskopaemykh ryb i bezchelĭustnykh, 21–28, 4 figs. (Russian).
1971A   Sovremennye teorii evolĭutsii nizshikh pozvonochnykh. [Contemporary theories on the evolution of lower vertebrates.] Akad. Nauk SSSR, Paleontol. Inst., Tr., 130, 332–346, 18 figs. (Russian).
1971B   Ĭuriĭ Aleksandrovich Orlov (12.vi. 1893–2.x. 1966). Akad. Nauk SSSR, Paleontol. Inst., Tr., 130, 356–368, portr. (Russian).
1972A   Nekotorye kriterii filogeneticheskikh issledovaniĭ na primere nizshikh pozvonochnykh. [Some criteria of phylogenetic research on the example of lower vertebrates.] Paleontol. Zh., 1972:3, 56–71, 9 figs. (Russian).

OBRUCHEV, DMITRIĬ VLADIMIROVICH and KARATAJŪTE-TALIMAA, VALENTINA NIKOLAEVNA
    1967A   Vertebrate faunas and correlation of the Ludlovian-lower Devonian in eastern Europe. Linn. Soc.,
                Zool. J., 47:311, 5–14, 12 figs., 2 pls., 2 tables.
    1968A   Fauny pozvonochnykh i korreliatsiia ludlovskikh i nizhnedevonskikh otlozheniĭ Vostochoĭ Evropy.
                [Vertebrate faunas and the correlation of Ludlovian and lower Devonian deposits of eastern
                Europe.] In: Ocherki po filogenii i sistematike iskopaemykh ryb i bezcheliustnykh, 63–70,
                2 tables (Russian).

OBRUCHEV, DMITRIĬ VLADIMIROVICH and SHIMANSKIĬ, VIKTOR NIKOLAEVICH
    1971A*   Sovremennye problemy paleontologii. [Current problems of paleontology.] Orlov, Ĭu. A. Festschrift.
                Akad. Nauk SSSR, Paleontol. Inst., Tr., 130, 380 pp., portr., illustr. (Russian).

OBRUCHEVA, OL'GA PAVLOVNA (= OBRUTCHEVA, O.)
    1962C   Pantsirnye ryby devona SSSR (kokkosteidy i dinikhtiidy). [Armored fishes of the Devonian of the
                USSR (coccosteids and dinichthyids).] Moscow: Univ. Press, 189 pp., 42 figs., 14 pls. (Russian).

OBRUCHEVA, O. P.   See also: Drushits, V. V. and Obrucheva, O. P., 1971A.

OCHEV, VITALIĬ GEORGIEVICH (= OTSCHEV, V. G.)
    1968A   Znachenie analiza filogeneticheskikh otnosheniĭ kapitozavroidnykh labirintodontov dlia korreliatsii
                kontinental'nykh triasovykh otlozheniĭ udalennykh regionov. [Significance of analysis of
                phylogenetic relationships of capitosauroid labyrintodonts for correlation of continental
                Triassic deposits of distant regions.] In: Zakonomernosti razvitiia organicheskogo mira po
                dannym paleontologii, 115–125, 1 fig., 1 table (Russian).
    1969A   O nekotorykh voprosakh taksonomii i filogenii po povodu raboty S. Vellesa i D. Kosgriffa "Reviziia
                labirintodontov sem. Capitosauridae". [On some questions of taxonomy and phylogeny in
                connection with the work by S. Welles and D. Cosgriff "A revision of the labyrinthodont
                family Capitosauridae".] In: Voprosy geologii iuzhnogo Urala i Povolzh'ia, 5:1, 61–79
                (Russian).

OCHEV, V. G., LOZOVSKIĬ, V. R. and DUBEĬKOVSKIĬ, S. G.
    1972A   Nekotorye zamechaniia o rabotakh G. I. Bloma po triasovym otlozheniiam Russkoĭ platformy. [Some
                remarks concerning G. I. Blom's works on Triassic deposits of the Russian platform.] Sov. Geol.,
                15:6, 145–149 (Russian).

OCHEV, V. G., SHISHKIN, M. A., GARIAINOV, V. A. and TVERDOKHLEBOV, V. P.
    1964A   Novye dannye o stratigraficheskom raschlenenii triasa Orenburgskogo Priural'ia po pozvonochnym.
                [New data on stratigraphic subdivision of Triassic in Orenburg sub-Urals region based on
                vertebrates.] Akad. Nauk SSSR, Dokl., 158:2, 363–365 (Russian).
    1965A   New data on the stratigraphic subdivision of the Triassic of the Orenburg Urals region by means of
                vertebrates. Akad. Nauk SSSR, Dokl., Earth Sci. Sec., 158, 47–49. (Translated from Russian:
                Akad. Nauk SSSR, Dokl., 1964, 158:2, 363–365.)

OCHEV, V. G. and TVERDOKHLEBOVA, GALINA IVANOVNA
    1970A   Znachenie nazemnykh pozvonochnykh dlia stratigrafii kontinental'nykh permskikh i triasovykh
                otlozheniĭ Russkoĭ platformy i Priural'ia (metodicheskiĭ ocherk). [Significance of land
                vertebrates for the stratigraphy of continental Permian and Triassic deposits of the Russian
                platform and Cisuralia (methodical outlines).] In: Voprosy geologii iuzhnogo Urala i
                Povolzh'ia, 7:1, 52–64 (Russian).

OCHEV, V. G.   See also: Kalandadze, N. N., Ochev, V. G., Tatarinov, L. P., Chudinov, P. K. and Shishkin,
                M. A., 1968A; Lipatova, V. V., Lopato, A. Ĭu., Makarova, I. S., Ochev, V. G., Podgornyĭ, Ĭu. I.,
                Starozhilova, N. N., Saĭdakovskiĭ, L. Ĭa. and Shishkin, M. A., 1972A; Polubotko, I. V. and
                Ochev, V. G., 1972A.

OCHOTERENA F., H. and SILVA-BARCENAS, A.
    1970A   *Cuvieronius arellanoi* sp. n., mastodonte del Pleistoceno del Estado de Oaxaca. México, Univ. Nac.,
                Inst. Geol., Paleontol. Mex., 33, 22 pp., 1 fig., 3 pls. (Spanish).

OCTOBON, F. C. E.
    1965B   Le Musée de Menton (salle de Préhistoire). Congr. Préhist. France, 16e Sess., Monaco 1959, C.R.,
                150–154, 1 fig. (French).

OCTOBON, R.
    1970A   Le commandant François-Charles Octobon (1881–1969). Soc. Préhist. Fr., Bull., C.R., 67:4, 98–99
                (French).

ODINTSOV, IGOR' ALEKSANDROVICH (= ODINTZOV, I. A.)
    1969A   Vidovoĭ sostav pliotsenovoĭ fauny odesskikh karstovykh peshcher. [Specific composition of the
                    Pliocene fauna from the karst caves of Odessa.] In: Stratigrafiia neogena Moldavii i Iuga
                    Ukrainy, 113–117 (Russian).

OEHSER, PAUL H.
    1970A   The Smithsonian Institution. Washington, D.C.: Praeger Publ., 275 pp.
                    Rev.: Swazey in J. Hist. Biol., 4:2, 374; Yochelson in GeoTimes, 15:9, 40.

OESCH, RONALD D.
    1969A   Pleistocene vertebrates from Missouri with emphasis on the Crankshaft Pit fauna. Abstract from
                    Proceedings, August 1968. Nat. Spel. Soc., Bull., 31:2, 45.
    1969B   Fossil Felidae and Machairodontidae from two Missouri caves. J. Mammal., 50:2, 367–368.

OESCH, RONALD D.   See also: Parmalee, P. W., Oesch, R. D. and Guilday, J. E., 1969A.

OGANESIÂN, D. A.   See: Garkusha, M. P., Engoian, M. A., Oganesiân, D. A. and Sukiasiân, S. S., 1971A.

OGAWA, TEIZO and HOSOKAWA, HIROSHI
    1969A   Some observations on the endocranial cast of the Amud man. Int. Congr. Anthropol. Ethnol. Sci.,
                    8th, Tokyo, 1968, Proc., Vol. I. Anthropology, 278–279, 1 table.

OGAWA, T., KAMIYA, T., SAKAI, S. and HOSOKAWA, H.
    1970A   Some observations on the endocranial cast of the Amud man. In: Suzuki, H. and Takai, F. (eds.),
                    1970A, 407–420, 8 figs., 8 pls., 1 table.

OGBURN, CHARLTON, JR.
    1968A   The forging of our continent. Consultant, William G. Melson. New York: American Heritage
                    Publishing Co., 160 pp., illustr.
                    Rev.: Wolfe in Archaeology, 23:4, 346–347.

OHE, FUMIO
    1970A   [Catalogue of Japanese fossil fishes.] Chigaku Kenkyu, Geosci. Mag., 21:7–8, 195–206, 1 fig.
                    (Japanese).

OHMORI, M.   See: Minato, M., Ohmori, M., Mizuno, T. and Obata, I., 1968A.

OKADA, Y. K.
    1963A   [Evolutionary history of vertebrates.] Natur. Sci. and Mus., 30:7–8, 1–38, 56 figs. (Japanese).

OKLADNIKOV, ALEKSEĬ PAVLOVICH (=UKLADNIKOV, A. P.)
    1970A   Yakutia before its incorporation into the Russian state. Anthropol. North, 8, xlii + 500 pp., 84 figs.,
                    4 maps.

OKLADNIKOV, A. P. and LARICHEV, V. E.
    1971A   Pamiati M. M. Gerasimova. [In memoriam M. M. Gerasimov.] Akad. Nauk SSSR, Sib. Otd., Izv., Ser.
                    Obshch. Nauk, 1971:1:1, 146–147 (Russian).

OKLADNIKOV, A. P., VASIL'EVSKIĬ, R. S., LARICHEV, V. E., DEREVIÂNKO, A. P., GOGOLEV, Z. V. and
TOSHCHAKOVA, E. M.
    1969A   Georgiĭ Frantsevich Debets (1905–1969). Akad. Nauk SSSR, Sibirsk. Otd., Izv., Ser. Obshch. Nauk,
                    6:2, 160–161 (Russian).

OKLADNIKOV, A. P.   See also: Boriskovskiĭ, P. I. and Okladnikov, A. P., 1970A; Derevianko, A. P. and
                    Okladnikov, A. P., 1969A.

OLAFSON, SIGFUS
    1970A   Mammoth and mastodon remains in Orange County, New York. Chesopiean, 8:1, 9.

OLAZARRI, J., MONES, A., XIMÉNEZ, A. and PHILIPPI, M. E.
    1970A   Lista de los ejemplares-tipo depositados en el Museo Nacional de Historia Natural de Montevideo,
                    Uruguay. I. Chordata. Mus. Hist. Natur. Montevideo, Com. Zool., 10:131, 12 pp. (Spanish).

OLIVER, JAMES A.
    1969A   The centennial convocation of the American Museum of Natural History. Mus. News, 47:9, 28–30,
                    1 photo.

OLIVER, ROLAND A. and FAGE, J. D.
    1962A   A short history of Africa. New York: New York Univ. Press, 280 pp., 19 maps.

OLIVER, ROLAND A.   See also: Fage, J. D. and Oliver, R. A. (eds.), 1970A.

OLIVIER, GEORGES
    1967C   Les pommettes et l'aplatissement facial des hommes fossiles. (Summary). Discussion. Soc. Anthropol.
                Paris, Bull. Mém., Sér. 12, 1:4, 495 (French).
    1967D   Teilhard de Chardin y el transformismo. An. Antropol., Mexico, 4, 9–17, 1 fig. (Spanish).
    1968A   Les méthodes de recherche en anthropologie. L'Anthropologie, 72:3–4, 353–362 (French).
    1969A   Réflexions sur l'évolution des hominidés fossiles. Symp. Biol. Hungarica, 9, 33–37, 1 fig. (French).
    1969B   L'évolution séculaire des populations subfossiles et récentes. Symp. Biol. Hungarica, 9, 65–72 (French).
    1969C   Practical anthropology. Foreword by H. V. Vallois. Translated by M. A. MacConaill. Springfield,
                Ill.: Charles C. Thomas, xii + 330 pp., 103 figs.
                Rev.: Kerley in Plains Anthropol., 14:46, 322.
    1971A   Estimation de l'écart-type de la capacité crânienne des Hominidés. Acad. Sci., C.R., Sér. D, 273:21,
                1925–1928, 2 figs., 2 tables (French).
    1972A   Capacité crânienne, langage articulé et définition du genre *Homo*. Acad. Sci., C.R., Sér. D, 274:10,
                1469–1472, 2 figs. (French).

OLSEN, STANLEY J.
    1959F   Fossil mammals of Florida. (Corrected copy). Fla. Geol. Surv., Spec. Publ. 6, 75 pp., 13 figs., 14 pls.
    1964D   Mammal remains from archaeological sites. Part 1. Southeastern and southwestern United States.
                Harvard Univ., Peabody Mus. Archaeol. Pap., 56:1, 162 pp., numerous figs.
    1965A   Vertebrate fossil localities in Florida. Fla. Geol. Surv., Spec. Publ. 12, 28 pp., 11 figs.
    1968C   Miocene vertebrates and north Florida shorelines. Palaeogeogr., Palaeoclimatol., Palaeoecol., 5, 127–
                134, 2 figs.
    1968D   Fish, amphibian and reptile remains from archaeological sites. Part I. Southeastern and southwestern
                United States. Appendix: the osteology of the wild turkey. Harvard Univ., Peabody Mus.
                Archaeol. Ethnol., Pap., 56:2, 137 pp., 86 figs., 2 pls.
                Rev.: Wing in Amer. Anthropol., 71, 775–776.
    1971A   Zooarchaeology: animal bones in archaeology and their interpretation. Reading, Massachusetts:
                Addison-Wesley Publishing Co., an Addison-Wesley Module, 30 pp., 9 figs.

OLSEN, WILLIAM H.   See: Riddell, F. A. and Olsen, W. H., 1969A.

OLSON, EVERETT C.
    1968C   Early fossil reptiles. In: Moore, R. C., *et al.*, 1968A, 1374–1375, 1 fig.
    1970A   New and little known genera and species of vertebrates from the lower Permian of Oklahoma.
                Fieldiana: Geol., 18:3, 359–434, 13 figs., 7 pls., 7 tables.
    1970B   *Trematops stonei* sp. nov. (Temnospondyli: Amphibia) from the Washington formation, Dunkard
                group, Ohio. Kirtlandia, 8, 12 pp., 2 figs.
    1970C   Current and projected impacts of computers upon concepts and research in paleontology. N. Amer.
                Paleontol. Conv., Proc., Part B, 135–153.
    1971A   Vertebrate paleozoology. New York, London, Sydney, Toronto: Wiley-Interscience, xv + 839 pp.,
                illustr.
                Rev.: Anon. in Biologist, 54:2, 95; Anon. in Soc. Géol. Fr., C.R., 1971:6, 330; Bardack in Evolution,
                26:3, 487–488; Black in Syst. Zool., 21:3, 347; Fantini Sestini in Riv. Ital. Paleontol. Stratigr.,
                77:2, 297; Jollie in Amer. Sci., 60:4, 505; Kermack in Nature, 234:5324, 111; R.P. in Geol. J.,
                8:1, iii–iv; Szalay in Amer. J. Phys. Anthropol., 36:3, 449–450; Van Valen in Science, 175:
                4027, 1237.
    1971B   A skeleton of *Lysorophus tricarinatus* (Amphibia: Lepospondili) from the Hennessey formation
                (Permian) of Oklahoma. J. Paleontol., 45:3, 443–449, 3 figs., 1 table.
                Rev.: Westphal in Zentralbl. Geol. Paläontol., Teil 2, 1971:5, 409–410.
    1972A   *Fayella chickashaensis*, the Dissorophoidea and the Permian terrestrial radiations. J. Paleontol., 46:1,
                104–114, 4 figs., 1 pl., 2 tables.
    1972B   The habitat: climatic change and its influence on life and habitat. In: Fiennes, R. N. (ed.), 1972A,
                267–305, 4 figs., 2 tables.
    1972C   *Diplocaulus parvus* n. sp. (Amphibia: Nectrididea) from the Chickasha formation (Permian:
                Guadalupian) of Oklahoma. J. Paleontol., 46:5, 656–659, 3 figs., 1 table.
    1972D   Vertebrates from the Chickasha formation of Oklahoma. Soc. Vert. Paleontol., Ann. Meeting, 32nd,
                1972, Abstr. (abs.).

OLSON, EVERETT C. and DALY, ELEANOR
    1972A   Notes on *Gnathorhiza* (Osteichthyes, Dipnoi). J. Paleontol., 46:3, 371–376, 3 figs., 1 pl.

OLSON, EVERETT C. and VAUGHN, PETER PAUL
1970A   The changes of terrestrial vertebrates and climates during the Permian of North America. Forma et Functio, 3, 113—138, 2 figs., 3 tables (French and German summaries).

OLSON, EVERETT C.   See also: Hueber, F. M. and Olson, E. C., 1972A.

OLSON, STORRS L.
1972A   A whooping crane from the Pleistocene of north Florida. Condor, 74:3, 341.

OLSSON, INGRID U.
1970A*   Radiocarbon variations and absolute chronology. Proceedings of the 12th Nobel Symposium, Uppsala University, 1969. New York and London: Wiley Interscience. Stockholm: Almquist and Wiksell, 652 pp., illustr.
         Rev.: Barker in Nature, 231:5300, 270.

ONODERA, SHINGO
1970A   [Discovery of fossil deer from Iwanoshita, Higashiyama-chō, Higashiiwai-gun, Iwate-ken.] Geol. Soc. Jap., J., 76:1, 27—28, 3 figs., 3 tables (Japanese).
1970B   [On the lower jaw of Megaceros kinryuensis Matsumoto et Mori.] Geol. Soc. Jap., J., 76:5, 265—266, 2 figs. (Japanese).

ONODERA, S., OOTAKA, S., SATO, J., TAKAHASHI, T. and YAMADA, Y.
1967A   A find of Desmostylus from the "Green Tuff" formations in the southern part of Shizukuishi-machi, Iwate prefecture. Geol. Soc. Jap., J., 73:6, 309—311, 3 figs. (Japanese)

ONORATINI, G.   See: Catzigras, F., Guérin, C. and Onoratini, G., 1971A.

OOTAKA, S.   See: Onodera, S., Ootaka, S., Sato, J., Takahashi, T. and Yamada, Y., 1967A.

OPPENHEIMER, ARMAND M.
1967A   In re "Tooth size reduction: a hominid trend". Amer. Anthropol., 69, 514—515.
1968A   Behavioral novelty — an evolutionary force. Amer. Anthropol., 70, 562—563.

OPRAVIL, E.   See: Valoch, K., Pelíšek, J., Musil, R., Kovanda, J. and Opravil, E., 1969A.

ORGHIDAN, TRAIAN
1970A*   Livre du centenaire Emile G. Racovitza 1868—1968. Bucharest: Acad. Rep. Soc. Rom. Press, 699 pp. (French).
         Rev.: Cornelius in Stud. Speleol., 2:3—4, 158—159.

ORGHIDAN, TRAIAN and DUMITRESCU, MARGARETA
1962-63A Studiu monografic al complexului carstic din defileul Vîrghişului. [Monographic study of the carstic complex of the Vîrghiş gorge.] Acad. Repub. Soc. Rom., Inst. Speol. "Emil Racoviţă", Lucr., 1—2, 69—178, 60 figs. (Rumanian; Russian and French summaries).

ORIEL, STEVEN S. and TRACEY, JOSHUA I., JR.
1970A   Uppermost Cretaceous and Tertiary stratigraphy of Fossil Basin, southwestern Wyoming. U.S. Geol. Surv., Prof. Paper, 635, vi + 53 pp., frontispiece, 16 figs., 4 tables.

ORLOV, J. A.
1968B   Some data on Hipparion fauna of Siberia and Kazakhstan. J. Palaeontol. Soc. India, 5—9, 5—8.

ORLOVSKAĬA, ELEONORA RAĬMUNDOVNA and SAVINOV, PAVEL FEDOROVICH
1971A   Golotipy, khraniàshchiesià v paleobiologicheskoĭ kollekṫsii Instituta zoologii AN Kaz. SSR v Alma-Ate. [Holotypes conserved in the paleobiological collection of the Institute of Zoology AN Kaz. SSR in Alma-Ata.] Akad. Nauk Kaz. SSR, Inst. Zool., Mater. Fauny i Flory, 5, 181—185 (Russian).

ORLOVSKAĬA, E. R.   See also: Buvalkin, A. K., Zhaĭmin, M. I., Murakhovskaià, E. I., Orlovskaià, E. R. and Sakulina, G. V., 1971A; Kozhamkulova, B. S. and Orlovskaià, E. R., 1971A.

ORÓ ALTISENT, ASUNCIÓN
1969A   Bibliografía geológica española (1967). Acta Geol. Hisp., 4:6, 145—168 (Spanish)
1970A   Bibliografía geológica española (1968). Acta Geol. Hisp., 5:5, 26 pp. (Spanish).
1971A   Bibliografía geológica española (1969). Acta Geol. Hisp., 6:6, 153—176 (Spanish).

ORTIZ, EUGENIO
1962A   Integración genética, selección natural y evolución. Discussions. Soc. Españ. Hist. Natur., Bol., Secc.
             Biol., 60, 259—262 (Spanish).

ORTLAM, DIETER
1967A   Fossile Böden als Leithorizonte für die Gliederung des Höheren Buntsandsteins im nördlichen
             Schwarzwald und südlichen Odenwald. Geol. Jahrb., 84, 485—590, 28 figs., 5 pls., 4 tables
             (German; English and French summaries).
1968A   Neue Ergebnisse aus dem höheren Buntsandstein des nördlichen Schwarzwaldes und des Kraichgaues.
             Geol. Jahrb., 86, 693—750, 6 figs., 1 pl. (German; English and French summaries).
1970A   Eocyclotosaurus woschmidti n.g. n. sp. — ein neuer Capitosauride aus dem Oberen Buntsandstein des
             nördlichen Schwarzwaldes. Neues Jahrb. Geol. Paläontol., Monatsh., 1970:9, 568—580, 5 figs.,
             1 table (German).
             Rev.: Westphal in Zentralbl. Geol. Paläontol., Teil 2, 1971:1, 53—54.

ØRVIG, TOR
1968A   Tanden i kultur, fantasi och verklighet. Naturhist. Riksmus. Småskrifter, 3, 23 pp., illustr. (Swedish).
1968B   The dermal skeleton; general considerations. Nobel Symp., 4th, Stockholm, 1967, Proc., 1968,
             373—397, 5 figs.
1968C*   Current problems of lower vertebrate phylogeny. Proceedings of the fourth Nobel symposium,
             Stockholm, 1967. New York: Interscience (Wiley); Stockholm: Almquist & Wiksell, 540 pp.,
             illustr.
             Rev.: Bellairs in J. Anat., 105:1, 179—180; F. R. P. in Geol. Mag., 106:3, 301; Martinsson in Geol.
             Fören. Stockholm, Förh., 91:1, 130—131; Romer in Science (AAAS), 164:3887, 1510—1511;
             Starck in Z. Zool. Syst. Evolut.-Forsch., 8:3, 237—240; Wake in Quart. Rev. Biol., 45:1, 93—
             96; Westphal in Zentralbl. Geol. Paläontol., Teil 2, 1969:2, 206—207.
1969A   The vertebrate fauna of the primaeva beds of the Fraenkelryggen formation of Vestspitsbergen and its
             biostratigraphic significance. Lethaia, 2:3, 219—239, 3 figs.
1969B   Cosmine and cosmine growth. Lethaia, 2:3, 241—260, 4 figs.
1969C   A new brachythoracid arthrodire from the Devonian of Dickson Land, Vestspitsbergen. Lethaia, 2:3,
             261—271, 3 figs.
1969D   Vertebrates from the Wood Bay group and the position of the Emsian-Eifelian boundary in the
             Devonian of Vestspitsbergen. Lethaia, 2:4, 273—328, 11 figs.
1969E   Thelodont scales from the Grey Hoek formation of Andrée Land, Spitsbergen. Nor. Geol. Tidsskr.,
             49, 387—401, 3 figs.
1971A   Comments on the lateral line system of some brachythoracid and ptyctodontid arthrodires. Zool.
             Scripta, 1:1, 5—35, 8 figs. (Russian summary).
1972A   The latero-sensory component of the dermal skeleton in lower vertebrates and its phyletic significance.
             Zool. Scripta, 1:3—4, 139—155, 3 figs. (Russian summary).

OSBORN, HENRY FAIRFIELD
1972A   Recent discoveries relating to the origin and antiquity of man. In: McCown, T. D. and Kennedy,
             K. A. R. (eds.), 1972A, 285—301, 3 figs. (reprinted from Palaeobiologica, 1, 189—202).

OSBORNE, P. J. and SHOTTON, F. W.
1968A   The fauna of the channel deposit of early Saalian age at Brandon, Warwickshire. Roy. Soc. London,
             Phil. Trans., Ser. B, 254:796, 417—424, 6 figs.

OSBORNE, R. H.   See: Laughlin, W. S. and Osborne, R. H. (eds.), 1967A.

OSIPOVA, V. A.   See: Speranskiĭ, V. S., Artem'eva, V. I., Osipova, V. A. and Rodionova, V. A., 1971A.

OSMÓLSKA, HALSZKA
1972A   Preliminary note on a crocodilian from the upper Cretaceous of Mongolia. In: Kielan-Jaworowska, Z.
             (ed.), 1972B, 43—47, 1 fig., 2 pls., 1 table.

OSMÓLSKA, HALSZKA and RONIEWICZ, EWA
1970A   Deinocheiridae, a new family of theropod dinosaurs. In: Kielan-Jaworowska, Z. (ed.), 1970B, 5—19,
             4 figs., 5 pls., 2 tables.
             Rev.: Chrulew in Zentralbl. Geol. Paläontol., Teil 2, 1972:3, 166—167.

OSMÓLSKA, H., RONIEWICZ, E. and BARSBOLD, R.
1972A   A new dinosaur, Gallimimus bullatus n. gen., n. sp. (Ornithomimidae) from the upper Cretaceous of
             Mongolia. In: Kielan-Jaworowska, Z. (ed.), 1972B, 103—143, 18 figs., 25 pls., 7 tables.

OSOLE, FRANC
1964-65D   Paleolitik Slovenije. [The Paleolithic of Slovenia.] Arheol. Vestn., 15—16, 9—20, 1 map (Slovenian;
             German summary).

1967A   Zakajeni spodmol, jamska paleolitska postaja. [Zakajeni Spodmol, a Paleolithic cave site.] Arheol.
               Vestn., 18, 25–40, 5 figs., 2 pls. (Slovenian; German summary).

OSTROM, JOHN H.
1962C   On the constrictor dorsalis muscles of *Sphenodon*. Copeia, 1962:4, 732–735, 1 fig.
1965B   The duck-billed dinosaur puzzle. Natur. and Sci., 3:3, 10–13, illustr. (juvenile).
1966D   The age of reptiles. A guide to the Rudolph Zallinger mural in the Peabody Museum, Yale University.
               Yale Univ., Peabody Mus. Natur. Hist., Spec. Publ., 9, 37 pp., 53 figs., 1 pl.
1968A   The Rocky Hill dinosaurs. N. England Geol. Conf., 60th Ann. Meeting, Guidebk., 12 pp., 6 figs.
1969A   A new theropod dinosaur from the lower Cretaceous of Montana. Postilla, 128, 17 pp., 8 figs.
               Rev.: Chrulew in Zentralbl. Geol. Paläontol., Teil 2, 1970:1, 70.
1969B   Terrible claw. Discovery, 5:1, 1–9, 8 figs.
1969C   The supporting chain. Discovery, 5:1, 10–16, 9 figs.
1969D   The case of the missing specimen. Discovery, 5:1, 50–51, 2 figs.
1969E   Reptilia fossils. McGraw-Hill Yearbook Sci. Tech., 1969, 294–298, 6 figs.
1969F   Terrestrial vertebrates as indicators of Mesozoic climates. N. Amer. Paleontol. Conv., Proc., Part D,
               347–376, 10 figs.
1969G   Osteology of *Deinonychus antirrhopus*, an unusual theropod from the lower Cretaceous of Montana.
               Yale Univ., Peabody Mus. Natur. Hist., Bull., 30, 165 pp., 83 figs., 13 tables (German and
               Russian summaries).
               Rev.: Chrulew in Zentralbl. Geol. Paläontol., Teil 2, 1971:1, 55–56.
1970A   *Archaeopteryx*: notice of a "new" specimen. Science (AAAS), 170:3957, 537–538, 2 figs.
               Rev.: Anon. in La Recherche, 1:7, 667; Groiss in Geol. Bl. Nordost-Bayern, 21:1, 61.
1970B   [*Archaeopteryx lithographica.*] Discovery, 6:1, 44, 1 fig.
1970C   Stratigraphy and paleontology of the Cloverly formation (lower Cretaceous) of the Bighorn Basin area,
               Wyoming and Montana. Yale Univ., Peabody Mus. Natur. Hist., Bull., 35, 234 pp., 9 figs.,
               27 pls., 24 maps, 7 charts, 5 tables (German and Russian summaries).
               Rev.: Langston in J. Paleontol., 46:6, 928–929.
1971A   On the systematic position of *Macelognathus vagans*. Postilla, 153, 10 pp., 1 fig.
1972A   Were some dinosaurs gregarious? Palaeogeogr., Palaeoclimatol., Palaeoecol., 11:4, 287–301, 5 figs.,
               1 table.

OTSUKA, HIROYUKI
1969A   Pleistocene vertebrate fauna from the Kuchinotsu group of west Kyushu. P. III. Proboscidean fossils.
               P. IV. Reptilian fossils. P. V. Concluding remarks on the vertebrate fauna from the
               Kuchinotsu group. Kagoshima Univ., Fac. Sci., Rep., 2, 53–84, 6 figs., 5 pls., 2 tables.
1970A   Tertiary Chelonia from northwestern Kyushu. Kagoshima Univ., Fac. Sci., Rep., 3, 23–28, 2 figs., 1 pl.
1970B   A fossil deer from the late Pleistocene Oe formation, Kyushu. Kagoshima Univ., Fac. Sci., Rep., 3,
               29–33, 2 figs., 1 pl.
1971A   Note on the mode of occurrence of the Tsubami vertebrate fauna from the Pleistocene Kuchinotsu
               group with remarks on the associated plant remains. Kagoshima Univ., Fac. Sci., Rep., 4,
               31–41, 6 figs., 1 pl., 3 tables (Japanese; English summary).
1972A   *Elaphurus shikamai* Otsuka (Pleistocene cervid) from the Akashi formation of the Osaka group, Japan,
               with special reference to the genus *Elaphurus*. Nat. Sci. Mus., Tokyo, Bull., 15:1, 197–210,
               3 figs., 3 pls., 1 table.

OTSUKA, HIROYUKI   See also: Obata, I., Hasegawa, Y. and Otsuka, H., 1972A.

OUELLETTE, CECIL M.
1972A   Caves of the Grand Coulee. Pac. Discovery, 25:2, 28–32, illustr.

OUELLETTE, CECIL and OUELLETTE, ELAINE
1970A   The John Day fossil beds. Pac. Discovery, 23:6, 1–6, illustr.

OUELLETTE, ELAINE   See: Ouellette, C. and Ouellette, E., 1970A.

OVERHAGE, PAUL
1965A   Die Evolution des Lebendigen. II. Die Kausalität. (Questiones Disputatae 26/27). Freiburg: Herder,
               280 pp. (German).
               Rev.: Heberer in Anthropol. Anz., 31:4, 299–300.
1966A   "*Homo habilis*". Theol. Phil., 41:3, 321–353, 3 figs.
               Abs.: Anon. in Anthropos, 62:1–2, 242.
1969A   Menschenformen im Eiszeitalter. Umwelten-Gestalten-Entwicklungen. Frankfurt a. M.: J. Knecht Verl
               456 pp., 25 figs., 19 tables (German).
               Rev.: Guenther in Naturwiss. Ver. Schleswig-Holstein, Schr., 41, 104–105; Roth-Lutra in Anat. Anz.,
               131:1–2, 157–158.

OVODOV, N. D.
1970A   Ostatki burykh medvedeĭ (*Ursus arctos* L.) v peshcherakh Sibiri i Dal'nego Vostoka. [Remains of
             brown bear (*Ursus arctos* L.) in the caves of Siberia and Far East.] Mosk. Obshchest. Ispyt.
             Prir., Bi̇ull., Otd. Biol., 75:4, 116—126, 1 fig., 2 tables (Russian; English summary).

OXNARD, CHARLES E.
1968A   A note on the fragmentary Sterkfontein scapula. Amer. J. Phys. Anthropol., 28, 213—218.
1968B   Primate evolution — a method of investigation. Amer. J. Phys. Anthropol., 28, 289—302.
1968C   A note on the Olduvai clavicular fragment. Amer. J. Phys. Anthropol., 29, 429—431, 2 figs.
1968D   Evolution of the human shoulder. Amer. Anthropol. Ass., Bull., 1:3, 105 (abs.).
1969A   Evolution of the human shoulder: some possible pathways. Amer. J. Phys. Anthropol., 30, 319—331,
             3 figs., 5 tables.
1972A   Some African fossil foot bones: a note on the interpolation of fossils into a matrix of extant species.
             Amer. J. Phys. Anthropol., 37:1, 3—12, 7 figs.

OXNARD, CHARLES E. and TUTTLE, RUSSELL
1969A   An analysis of the mechanical efficiency of the digital ray in the chimpanzee in relation to knuckle-
             walking postures and movement. Amer. J. Phys. Anthropol., 31, 265 (abs.).

OXNARD, C. E.   See also: Tuttle, R. H. and Oxnard, C. E., 1969A.

OZAKI, HIROSHI
1970A   [My personal history related to museum activities; a memorandum of the opening of the exhibition of
             "evolution of life" at the National Science Museum.] Natur. Sci. and Mus., 37:11—12, 235—
             264, 20 figs. (Japanese).

OZAKI, H. and HASEGAWA, YOSHIKAZU
1969A   [Fossil elephant (*Paleoloxodon naumanni* Makiyaha) from off Shodo-shima, Seto Inland Sea.] Natur.
             Sci. and Mus., 36:7—8, 195—201, 2 figs. (Japanese).

OZAKI, H., KATO, A. and OBATA, I.
1965A   [Mineralogical note on petrified dinosaur bone.] Natur. Sci. and Mus., 32:5—6, 73—78, 1 fig.,
             3 tables (Japanese).

OZAKI, H. and OBATA, I.
1963A   [Note on *Allosaurus*.] Natur. Sci. and Mus., 30:9—10, 6—12, 4 figs., cover photograph (Japanese).
1963B   [Notes on *Oreopithecus*.] Natur. Sci. and Mus., 30:11—12, 1—9, 3 figs., cover photograph (Japanese).

OZAKI, HIROSHI   See also: Shimoda, N. and Ozaki, H., 1967A.

OZANNE, PAUL
1969A   Atmospheric radiocarbon. W. Afr. Archaeol. News., 11, 9—11.

OZANSOY, FIKRET
1966A   Türkiye senozoik çağlarinda fosil insan formu problemi ve biostratigrafik dayanaklari. Ankara, Üniv.,
             D.T.C. Fak., Yainl., 172, 104 pp., 17 figs., 3 maps, 5 tables (Turkish).
1969A   [Un nouveau *Palaeoamasia kansui*; biozone fossile mammifère de Boyabat (Sinop) et documents
             paléontologiques.] Türk. Tarih Kurumu, Bell., 33:132, 581—585 (Turkish).
1969B   Sur la longevité des faunes à *Hipparion* et les faunes de vertébrés fossiles dans la région de la Mer Egée
             Anatolienne. Maden Tetkik Arama Enst. (Miner. Res. Explor. Inst. Turk.), Bull. (Foreign Ed.),
             72, 130—134.
1969C   Pleistocene fossil human footprints in Turkey. Maden Tetkik Arama Enst. (Miner. Res. Explor. Inst.
             Turk.), Bull. (Foreign Ed.), 72, 146—150, 2 figs., 7 photos.
1970A   *Ankarapithecus meteai*, pongidé fossile aux traits humain du Pliocène de Turquie. Türk Tarih
             Kurumu, Bell., 34:133, 1—15, 6 figs. (French; Turkish summary).

ÖZETI, NECLÂ and WAKE, DAVID B.
1969A   The morphology and evolution of the tongue and associated structures in salamanders and newts (family
             Salamandridae). Copeia, 69:1, 91—123, 17 figs., 1 table.

OZHIGOVA, A. P.
1968A   Osobennosti mieloarkhitektoniki korkovogo kont̃sa zritel'nogo analizatora v evoliũt̃sionnom riàdu
             primatov. [Particularities in the mieloarchitectonics of the cortical extremity of the visual
             analyser in the evolutionary line of Primates.] Int. Congr. Anthropol. Ethnol. Sci., 7th, Moscow,
             1964, Proc., 3, 537—541, 3 tables (Russian).

P., M.
 1964A   La vie et l'oeuvre de l'abbé Breuil, en Périgord. Les Eyzies, 13, 24–33 (French).

PACKARD, EARL LEROY
 1949B   A fossil sea-lion from Cape Blanco, Oregon. Oreg. Acad. Sci., Proc., 1, 81.
 1951A   Occurrences of ground sloths in Oregon. Oreg. Acad. Sci., Proc., 2, 15.

PACKARD, E. L., ALLISON, I. S. and CRESSMAN, L. S.
 1951A   Fossil mammalian tracks in Lake County, Oregon. Oreg. Acad. Sci., Proc., 2, 14.

PAGE, JAMES K., JR.
 1965A   Measuring past ages. Natur. and Sci., 2 :11, 7, illustr. (juvenile).

PAGEAU, YVON
 1968A   Nouvelle faune ichthyologique du Dévonien moyen dans les grès de Gaspé (Québec). I. Géologie et
             écologie. Natur. Can., 95:6, 1459–1497, 8 figs., 2 pls., 2 tables (French; English summary).
 1969A   Nouvelle faune ichthyologique du Dévonien moyen dans les grès de Gaspé (Québec). II. Morphologie
             et systématique. Première section: A. - Euryptérides, B. - Ostracodermes, C. - Acanthodiens et
             Sélaciens. Natur. Can., 96:3, 399–478, 8 figs., 22 pls., 5 tables (French; English summary).
 1969B   Nouvelle faune ichthyologique du Dévonien moyen dans les grès de Gaspé (Québec). II. Morphologie
             et systématique. Deuxième section: Arthrodires: Dolichothoraci. Natur. Can., 96:5, 805–889,
             6 figs., 13 pls., 3 tables (French; English summary).

PAGHIDA, N.   See: Macarovici, N. and Paghida, N., 1966A.

PAINTER, FLOYD
 1969A   Latest news on early man. Chesopiean, 7:4–5, 90–93.

PALES, LÉON
 1968A   Statuaire préhistorique et anatomie. Soc. Anthropol. Paris, Bull. Mém., Sér. 12, 3:1, 63–76, 5 figs.
             (French).
 1969A   Les gravures de la Marche. I. - Félins et ours. Bordeaux, Univ., Inst. Préhist., Publ., Mém., 7, 136 pp.,
             34 figs., 61 pls. (French).
             Rev.: Cassano in Quaternaria, 11, 289–291; Delporte in Soc. Préhist. Fr., Bull., C.R., 263–265.
 1970A   Le "Coco des Roseaux" ou la fin d'une erreur. Soc. Préhist. Fr., Bull., C.R., 67:3, 85–88, 1 pl.
             (French).
 1970B   Petite histoire de la Barma Grande (paléolithique). Objets et Mondes, 10:3, 225–230, 4 figs. (French).
 1972A   Atlas ostéologique pour servir à l'identification des mammifères du Quaternaire. 1. Les membres.
             I. Carnivores, 3 ff., 48 pls. II. Herbivores, 3 ff., 84 pls. Paris: CNRS, "Bibliogr. France"
             Press, 161:14, 562 pp. (French).

PALES, LÉON and TASSIN DE SAINT PEREUSE, MARIE
 1967A   Ces dames de la Marche. Objets et Mondes, 7:4, 307–320, 13 figs. (French).

PÁLFALVY, ISTVÁN   See: Jámbor, A., Korpás, L., Kretzoi, M., Pálfalvy, I. and Rákosi, L., 1971A; Kretzoi, M.
             and Pálfalvy, I., 1969A.

PALLARD, BERNARD   See: Lapparent, A. F. de, Curnelle, R., Defaut, B., Miroschedji, A. de and
             Pallard, B., 1969A.

PALMA DI CESNOLA, ARTURO
 1965C   Marina di Camerota (Salerno). Riv. Sci. Preist., 20, 366 (Italian).
 1965D   Francesco Zorzi [1900–1964]. Bull. Paletnol. Ital., n.s. 16, 74, 289–291 (Italian).
 1966A   Il Paleolitico superiore arcaico (facies uluzziana) della Grotta del Cavallo, Lecce (continuazione). Riv.
             Sci. Preist., 21:1, 3–59, 17 figs. (Italian; French and English summaries).
 1966B   Gli scavi nella Grotta del Cavallo (Lecce) durante il 1966. Riv. Sci. Preist., 21:2, 289–302, 4 figs.,
             2 tables (Italian; French and English summaries).
 1966C   Marina di Camerota (prov. di Salerno). Riv. Sci. Preist., 21:2, 419–420 (Italian).
 1969A   Datazione dell' Uluzziano col metodo del C14. Riv. Sci. Preist., 24:2, 341–348, 2 figs. (Italian;
             French and English summaries).
 1969B   Il musteriano della Grotta del Poggio a marina di Camerota (Salerno). Verona, Mus. Civ. Stor. Natur.,
             Mem., Fuori Ser., 3, 95–135, 14 figs. (Italian; French summary).
 1970A   Grotta Paglicci (Rignano Garganico, Prov. di Foggia). Riv. Sci. Preist., 25:2, 404–405 (Italian).

PALMA DI CESNOLA, A. and VIGLIARDI, A.
 1967A   Marina di Camerota (Prov. di Salerno). Riv. Sci. Preist., 22:2, 435 (Italian).

PALMQUIST, JOHN C.   See: Ray, C. E., Wills, D. L. and Palmquist, J. C., 1968A.

PALOMBO, MARIA R.   See: Accordi, F. S. and Palombo, M. R., 1971A.

PAMPE, WILLIAM R.
    1969A   Late Devonian fish remains from central Colorado. J. Paleontol., $\underline{43}$:5, 1111—1113, 1 pl.

P'AN, KIANG
    1962A   Abs.: Sci. Abstr. China, Earth Sci., $\underline{1}$:1, 11—12.
    1962B   Abs.: Sci. Abstr. China, Earth Sci., $\underline{1}$:3, 4.
    1964A   Abs.: Sci. Abstr. China, Earth Sci., $\underline{3}$:1, 7—8.

PANARINA, G. N.
    1969A   Drevneĭshie freski v peshcherakh. [Ancient frescoes in caves.] Peshchery, $\underline{7}$(8), 120 (Russian).

PANCHEN, A. L.
    1970A   Batrachosauria. Anthracosauria. Handb. Paläoherp., Teil 5/A, 84 pp., 20 figs., 3 tables.
                Rev.: Carroll in J. Paleontol., $\underline{46}$:3, 463—464; Fantini Sestini in Riv. Ital. Paleontol. Stratigr., $\underline{77}$:1,
                135; Haltenorth in Säugetierkundl. Mitt., $\underline{20}$:1—2, 185; Krumbiegel in Deut. Ges. Geol. Wiss.,
                Ber., Reihe A, Geol. Paläontol., $\underline{16}$:6, 720—722; Mertens in Natur Mus., $\underline{101}$:8, 367—368;
                Scherf in Naturwiss. Rundsch., $\underline{24}$:11, 499; Thenius in Geol. Ges. Wien, Mitt., $\underline{63}$, 250; Westphal
                in Zentralbl. Geol. Paläontol., Teil 2, $\underline{1971}$:2—3, 179—180.
    1972A   The skull and skeleton of *Eogyrinus attheyi* Watson (Amphibia: Labyrinthodontia). Roy. Soc. London,
                Phil. Trans., Ser. B, $\underline{263}$:851, 279—326, 16 figs., 2 pls., 1 table.
                Rev.: Westphal in Zentralbl. Geol. Paläontol., Teil 2, $\underline{1972}$:3, 164.
    1972B   The interrelationships of the earliest tetrapods. In: Joysey, K. A. and Kemp, T. S. (eds.), $\underline{1972A}$,
                65—87, 8 figs.
    1972C   Carboniferous tetrapods. In: Hallam, A. (ed.), $\underline{1972C}$, illustr.

PANDEY, J. and SASTRI, V. V.
    1968A   On a new species of *Sivapithecus* from the Siwalik rocks of India. Geol. Soc. India, J., $\underline{9}$:2, 206—211,
                1 pl., 2 tables.

PANFILOV, DMITRIĬ VIKTOROVICH
    1968A   Periodichnost' filogeneza i veroiât̃nye prichiny etogo iâvleniiâ. [Periodicity in phylogenesis and the
                probable causes of this phenomenon.] In: Zakonomernosti razvitiiâ organicheskogo mira po
                dannym paleontologii, 132—136 (Russian).

PANIN, N.
    1964A   [Coexistence of foot imprints of vertebrates with mecanoglyphs in the Miocene molasse of eastern
                Carpathians.] Stud. Cercet. Geol., Geofiz., Geogr., Ser. Geol., $\underline{9}$:2, 341—363, 4 figs., 8 pls.
                (Rumanian).
    1965A   Coexistence de traces de pas de vertébrés et des mécanoglyphes dans la molasse miocène des Carpathes
                Orientales. Rev. Roum. Géol. Géophys. Géogr., Sér. Géol., $\underline{9}$:2, 141—163, 22 figs. (French).

PANOV, B. S.   See: Kobelev, M. V., Panov, B. S. and Permiâkov, V. V., 1971A.

PANYCHEV, V. A.   See: Zudin, A. N. and Panychev, V. A., 1968A.

PAPP, ADOLF
    1968A   Maximos K. Mitzopoulos. Geol. Ges. Wien, Mitt., $\underline{61}$, 184—185.

PAQUET, M.   See: Coppens, Y., Gouzes, R., Le Floch, R. and Paquet, M., s.d.

PAREA, G. C.
    1964A   Le presunte orme di tetrapode nell'alberese di Pontassieve in Provincia di Firenze. Soc. Paleontol.
                Ital., Boll., $\underline{3}$:1, 8—11, 3 pls. (Italian).

PARKER, LEE R.
    1970A   A titanothere from the Eocene Green River formation of Utah. Geol. Soc. Amer., Abstr., $\underline{2}$:6, 400
                (abs.).

PARKES, KENNETH C.   See: Farner, D. S., King, J. R. and Parkes, K. C. (eds.), 1971A.

PARKINGTON, JOHN
    1969A   Symbolism in Palaeolithic cave art. S. Afr. Archaeol. Bull., $\underline{24}$:93, 3—13, 3 tables.

PARMALEE, PAUL W.
    1968A   Cave and archaeological faunal deposits as indicators of post-Pleistocene animal populations and
                 distribution in Illinois. In: Bergstrom, R. E. (ed.), 1968A, 104—113.
                 Rev.: JFQ in Caves Karst, 11:4, 32.
    1971A   Fisher and porcupine remains from cave deposits in Missouri. Ill. Acad. Sci., Trans., 64:3, 225—229,
                 3 figs.

PARMALEE, P. W., OESCH, R. D. and GUILDAY, J. E.
    1969A   Pleistocene and Recent vertebrate faunas from Crankshaft Cave, Missouri. Ill. State Mus., Rep. Invest.,
                 14, iv + 37 pp., 15 figs., 5 tables.

PARMALEE, PAUL W.   See also: Guilday, J. E. and Parmalee, P. W., 1972A.

PARRINGTON, F. R.
    1971A   On the upper Triassic mammals. Roy. Soc. London, Phil. Trans., Ser. B, 261:838, 231—272, 15 figs.

PARRIS, DAVID C. and GREEN, MORTON
    1969A   *Dinohyus* (Mammalia: Entelodontidae) in the Sharps formation, South Dakota. J. Paleontol., 43:5,
                 1277—1279, 2 figs.
                 Rev.: Thenius in Zentralbl. Geol. Paläontol., Teil 2, 1971:1, 71.

PARSONS, K. C.
    1968A   Application of modern plastics to fossil casting techniques. Foreword by N.W.G. Macintosh. In:
                 Mulvaney, D. J. (ed.), 1968A, 193—209, 2 pls.

PARSONS, THOMAS S.
    1970A   The nose and Jacobson's organ. In: Gans, C. (ed.), 1970A, 99—191, 51 figs.

PASA, ANGELO
    1969A   Appunti sul quaternario. Verona, Mus. Civ. Stor. Natur., Mem., Fuori Ser., 3, 15—38 (Italian; English
                 summary).

PASA, A.   See also: Bartolomei, G. and Pasa, A., 1969A.

PASCAL, RENÉ
    1965A   Gisement du Vallonnet. Congr. Préhist. France, 16e Sess., Monaco 1959, C.R., 943—948, 3 figs.
                 (French).

PASCUAL, ROSENDO, *et al.*
    1966A   Vertebrata. In: Borrello, A. V. (ed.), 1966A, fasc. IV, 202 pp., 101 pls., 3 tables (Spanish).

PASCUAL, ROSENDO and DÍAZ DE GAMERO, MARÍA LOURDES
    1969A   Sobre la presencia del género *Eumegamys* (Rodentia, Caviomorpha) en la formación Urumaco del
                 Estado Falcon (Venezuela). Su significación cronológica. Asoc. Venez. Geol., Minería, Petról.,
                 Bol. Inform., 12:10, 369—387, 1 fig., 1 pl. (Spanish).

PASCUAL, ROSENDO   See also: Patterson, P. and Pascual, R., 1968A, 1968B.

PASINI, GIANCARLO
    1969A   Fauna a mammiferi del Pleistocene superiore in un Paleoinghiottitoio corscio presso Monte Croara
                 (Bologna). Rev. Ist. Ital. Speleol., 2 (4), 1—36 (Italian).
                 Rev.: Thenius in Zentralbl. Geol. Paläontol., Teil 2, 1971:1, 64.
    1970A   Contributo alla conoscenza del tardo Würmiano e del Postwürmiano nei dintorni di Bologna (Italia).
                 G. Geol., 36:2 (1968), 687—700, 2 pls. (Italian).

PASQUARÈ, GIORGIO
    1968A   Geology of the Cenozoic volcanic area of central Anatolia. Accad. Naz. Lincei, Atti, Ser. 8, Cl. Sci.
                 Fis., Mat. Natur., Mem., 9:3, 55—204, 27 figs., 16 pls., 2 maps.

PASQUIER, LYNE
    1972A   Étude d'une population de *Mimomys savini* Hinton, 1910 (Arvicolinae, Rodentia) provenant de
                 l'upper Freshwater bed (Quaternaire ancien d'Angleterre). Mammalia, 36:2, 214—225, 7 figs.,
                 2 tables (French; English summary).

PATRULIUS, DAN and IORDAN, MAGDALENA
    1969A   Notă asupra prezenţei unor peşti placodermi în Devonianul din platforma moesică. [Note on the
                 occurrence of placoderms in the Devonian of Moesian platform.] Rom., Inst. Geol., Dări
                 (1966—67), 54:2, 17—23, 4 figs., 1 pl. (Rumanian; French and English summaries).

1970A   O nouă contribuţie la inventarul placodermilor şi ostracodermilor (?) din Devonianul platformei
           Moesice. [A new contribution to the list of Devonian placoderms and ostracoderms (?) of the
           Moesian platform.] Rom., Inst. Geol., Dări, 55:3, 181–186, 1 pl. (Rumanian; French and
           English summaries).

PATTE, ETIENNE
1966B   L'oeuvre scientifique du Docteur Henri–Martin. Soc. Archéol. Hist. Charente, Mém., 1965, 79–89,
           2 figs., portr., bibliogr. (French).
1968B   Quelques asiniens pleistocènes de la Charente, de la Dordogne, de la Vienne et du Val d'Oise. Ass. Fr.
           Étud. Quat., Bull., 15, 111–124, 14 figs. (French).
1968C   Enfant magdalénien de Fontarnaud (Gironde). (Collection J. Ferrier). Soc. Anthropol. Paris, Bull.
           Mém., Sér. 12, 3:4, 289–294, 5 figs. (French).

PATTEN, D. W.
1966A   The Biblical flood and the ice epoch. Seattle: Pacific Meridian Publ. Co., 336 pp., 27 figs., 13 tables.
           Rev.: Manten in Earth-Sci. Rev., 3:4, A253–A256.

PATTERSON, B., BEHRENSMEYER, A. K. and SILL, W. D.
1970A   Geology and fauna of a new Pliocene locality in north-western Kenya. Nature, 226:5249, 918–921,
           3 figs.

PATTERSON, B. and PASCUAL, ROSENDO
1968A   Evolution of mammals on southern continents. V. The fossil mammal fauna of South America.
           Quart. Rev. Biol., 43:4, 409–451, 13 figs., 12 tables.
1968B   New echimyid rodents from the Oligocene of Patagonia, and a synopsis of the family. Breviora, 301,
           14 pp., 3 figs., 1 table.
1972A   The fossil mammal fauna of South America. In: Keast, A., Erk, F. C. and Glass, B. (eds.), 1972A,
           247–309, 13 figs., 12 tables.

PATTERSON, BRYAN   See also: Hecht, M. K., Schaeffer, B., Patterson, B., Frank, R. van and Wood, F. D.,
           1972A; Hooijer, D. A. and Patterson, B., 1972A.

PATTERSON, COLIN
1968B   The caudal skeleton in Mesozoic Acanthopterygian fishes. Brit. Mus. (Natur. Hist.), Bull., Geol., 17:2,
           49–102, 28 figs.
1968C   *Menaspis* and the bradyodonts. Nobel Symp., 4th, Stockholm, 1967, Proc., 1968, 171–205, 15 figs.
1969A   Chondrichthyes. McGraw-Hill Yearbook Sci. Tech., 1969, 125–127, 3 figs.
1970A   Two upper Cretaceous salmoniform fishes from Lebanon. Brit. Mus. (Natur. Hist.), Bull., Geol., 19:5,
           205–296, 48 figs., 5 pls., 3 tables.
1970B   A clupeomorph fish from the Gault (lower Cretaceous). Linn. Soc., Zool. J., 49:3, 161–182, 6 figs.,
           1 pl.

PATTERSON, C. and GREENWOOD, P. H.
1967A *   Rev.: Thomson in J. Natur. Hist., London, 3, 301–302.

PATTERSON, COLIN   See also: Rosen, D. E. and Patterson, C., 1969A.

PATTERSON, THOMAS C.   See: Lanning, E. P. and Patterson, T. C., 1967A.

PATTON, THOMAS H., JR.
1967C   Miocene and Pliocene artiodactyls, Texas Gulf coastal plain. Diss. Abstr., 27:8, 2749B (abs.).
1969A   An Oligocene land vertebrate fauna from Florida. J. Paleontol., 43:2, 543–546, 1 fig.
1969B   Miocene and Pliocene artiodactyls, Texas Gulf coastal plain. Fla. State Mus., Bull., Biol. Sci., 14:2,
           115–226, 34 figs., 27 tables.
           Rev.: Thenius in Zentralbl. Geol. Paläontol., Teil 2, 1971:1, 71.

PATTON, THOMAS H. and TAYLOR, BERYL E.
1971A   The Synthetoceratinae (Mammalia, Tylopoda, Protoceratidae). Amer. Mus. Natur. Hist., Bull., 145:2,
           119–218, 37 figs., 15 tables.
           Rev.: Thenius in Zentralbl. Geol. Paläontol., Teil 2, 1971:6, 522–523.

PATTON, THOMAS H. and WEBB, S. D.
1970A   Fossil vertebrate deposits in Florida. Plaster Jacket, no. 14, 18 pp., 6 figs.

PAULA COUTO, CARLOS DE
1964B   Marcos da idade dos mamíferos na América do Sul. Soc. Brasil. Geol., Bol., 13:1–2, 5–21
           (Portuguese; English summary).

1967B   Estudos paleontológicos na Amazônia. Atas Simp. Biota Amazônica, 1, 11—34 (Portuguese).
1967C   Contribuição à paleontología do Estado do Pará, um sirênio na formação Pirabas. Atas Simp. Biota
          Amazônica, 1, 345—357, 3 figs. (Portuguese; English summary).
1970A   News on the fossil marsupials from the Riochican of Brazil. Acad. Brasil. Ciênc., An., 42:1, 19—34,
          8 figs., 4 tables.
1971A   On two small Pleistocene ground-sloths. Acad. Brasil. Ciênc., An., 43 Suppl., 499—513, 6 figs., 7 tables.

PAULA COUTO, C. DE and MEZZALIRA, S.
1971A   Nova conceituação geocronológica de Tremembé, Estado de São Paulo, Brasil. Acad. Brasil. Ciênc.,
          An., 43 Suppl., 473—488, 11 figs. (Portuguese; English summary).

PAVIA, GIULIO
1970A   Resti di *Anancus arvernensis* e flora ad affinità Plioceniche nel Villafranchiano inferiore della cava
          arboschio. Soc. Geol. Ital., Mem., 9:2, 157—176, 14 figs., 5 pls. (Italian).
          Rev.: Albanesi in Riv. Ital. Paleontol. Stratigr., 76:3, 482.

PAVLOVIĆ, MILORAD B.
1967A   Značaj fosilnih sisara za stratigrafsko raščlanjavanje neogenih tvorevine Topličkog basena. [Significance
          of fossil mammals for stratigraphic subdivision of Neogene formations of the Toplica basin.]
          Ann. Géol. Pén. Balkan., 33, 127—138, 2 figs. (Serbian; German summary).
1969A   Miocenski sisari Topličke kotline — paleontološko-stratigrafska studija. [Miocene mammals of Toplička
          basin — paleontological-stratigraphic study.] Ann. Géol. Pén. Balkan., 34, 269—394, 21 figs.,
          26 pls., 9 tables (Serbian; German summary).

PAVONI, NAZARIO   See: Kopp, K.-O., Pavoni, N. and Schindler, C., 1969A.

PAYNE, SEBASTIAN
1968A   The origins of domestic sheep and goats: a reconsideration in the light of the fossil evidence. Prehist.
          Soc., Proc., 34:11, 368—384, 2 tables.

PAYNTER, CHUCK
1969A   Volcanoes and archaeology. Screenings, 18:1, 3.

PEI, WEN-CHUNG
1957K   Discovery of lower jaws of giant ape in Kwangsi, south China. Sci. Record, New Ser., 1:3, 49—52,
          1 fig., 1 pl.
1965D   Abs.: Sci. Abstr. China, Earth Sci., 3:3, 10.
1972A   Discovery of palaeolithic chert in artifacts in Kuan-Yin-Tung Cave in Chien-Hsi-Hsien of Kweichow
          province. Int. J. Speleol., 4:2, 217 (abs.).

PELIŠEK, J.   See: Valoch, K., Pelišek, J., Musil, R., Kovanda, J. and Opravil, E., 1969A.

PELS, S.
1969A   The Geology of New South Wales. The Murrey Basin. Geol. Soc. Austral., J., 16:1, 499—511, 2 figs.

PENICK, JAMES
1971A   Professor Cope vs. Professor Marsh. Amer. Heritage, 22:5, 4—13 and 91—95, illustr.

PEN'KOV, A. V.   See: Nikonov, A. A., Pen'kov, A. V., Trofimov, B. A., Vangengeïm, E. A., Dmitrieva, E. A.
          and Sotnikova, M. V., 1971A.

PEOPLES, JOE WEBB
1967A   Dinosaur State Park. Conn. Geol. Natur. Hist. Surv., Bull., 100, 3—13, cover photo, 4 pls.
1969A   Dinosaur State Park. Conn. Geol. Natur. Hist. Surv., Bull., 102, 3—10, 24, 5 pls.

PEPEONIK, Z.   See: Malez, M. and Pepeonik, Z., 1969A.

PÉREZ, MANUEL   See: Jordá Cerdá , F., Mallo, M. and Pérez, M., 1970A; Mallo Viesca, M. and Pérez Pérez, M.,
          1969A.

PÉREZ-GONZÁLEZ, A., FUENTES VIDARTE, C. and AGUIRRE, E.
1970A   Nuevos hallazgos de *Elephas antiquus* en la terraza media del Jarama. Estud. Geol. (Inst. Invest. Geol.
          "Lucas Mallada"), 26:3, 219—223, 4 figs., 5 tables (Spanish).

PÉREZ-GONZÁLEZ, A.   See also: Molina, E., Pérez-González, A. and Aguirre, E., 1972A.

PERICOT GARCÍA, LUIS (= PERICOT, L.)
    1964A   Sobre algunos problemas del arte rupestre del Levante español. In: Pericot García, L. and Ripoll Perelló, E. (eds.), 1964A, 151–158 (Spanish; English abstract).

PERICOT GARCÍA, L. and MALUQUER DE MOTES, J.
    1969A   La humanidad prehistórica. Madrid-Barcelona: Salvat Ed., 187 pp., illustr. (Spanish).
        Rev.: Balout in L'Anthropologie, 74:1–2, 99–100; Bosch-Gimpera in An. Antropol., Mexico, 8, 331.

PERICOT GARCÍA, L. and RIPOLL PERELLÓ, EDUARDO
    1964A*   Prehistoric art of the western Mediterranean and the Sahara. Chicago: Aldine Publishing Co. (Viking Fund Publications in Anthropol., No. 39), xiv + 262 pp., illustr.
        Rev.: Levine in Amer. Anthropol., 68:5, 1301–1302; Llongueras Campañá in Ampurias, 28, 280–289; Sauter in Arch. Suiss. Anthropol. Gen., 30, 95–96.

PÉRINET, GUY
    1969A   Étude cristallographique de la fossilisation des ossements du Lazaret. In: Lumley, H. de (ed.), 1969B, 141 (French).
    1969B   Étude cristallographique des ossement brûlés de la cabane acheuléenne du Lazaret. In: Lumley, H. de (ed.), 1969B, 143–144, 1 table (French).

PERKINS, DEXTER, JR.
    1968A   The Pleistocene fauna from the Yabroud rockshelters. Ann. Archéol. Arabes Syrienne, 18, 123–130, 2 pls., 3 tables.

PERKINS, PHILIP L.
    1970A   Equitability and trophic levels in an Eocene fish population. Lethaia, 3:3, 301–310, 2 figs., 1 table.
    1970B   Notogoneus osculus Cope, an Eocene fish from Wyoming (Gonorynchiformes, Gonorynchidae). Postilla, 147, 18 pp., 8 figs.
    1970C   Fossil Lake, Wyoming, and its magnificent inhabitants. Discovery, 6:1, 33–40, 6 figs.
    1971A   The dipnoan fish Dipterus from the middle Devonian (Givetian) of Alaska. J. Paleontol., 45:3, 554–555, 1 fig.

PERMIAKOV, VADIM VASIL'EVICH   See: Kobelev, M. V., Panov, B. S. and Permiakov, V. V., 1971A.

PERSHINA, ANTONIDA IVANOVNA and TSYGANKO, VLADIMIR STEPANOVICH
    1971A   Stratigrafiia i korreliatsiia verkhnesiluriĭskikh, nizhne- i srednedevonskikh otlozheniĭ severa Urala. [Stratigraphy and correlation of upper Silurian, lower and middle Devonian deposits of the northern Urals.] Akad. Nauk SSSR, Komi Fil., Inst. Geol., Tr., 14, 37–44, 1 table (Russian).

PESCATORE, T.   See: Lirer, L., Pescatore, T. and Scandone, P., 1966A.

PETER, WALTER G., III
    1970A   Fundamentalist scientists oppose Darwinian evolution. BioScience, 20:19, 1067–1069.

PETERS, D. S., MOLLENHAUER, D. and GUTMANN, W. F.
    1971A   Bau, Konstruktion und Funktion des Organismus. Natur Mus., 101:5, 208–218, 1 fig. (German).

PETERS, JAMES A.
    1971A   Biostatistical programs in BASIC language for time-shared computors: coordinated with the book "Quantitative zoology." Smithson. Contrib. Zool., 69, 46 pp.

PETERSEN, ROBERT M.
    1969A   Würm II climate at Niah cave. Sarawak Mus. J., 17, 67–79, 1 fig., 1 table.

PETIT-MAIRE, NICOLE (= HEINTZ, N.; PETIT-MAIRE HEINZ, N.)
    1972A   Evolution trends and comparative ontogenesis in primate cranium. J. Human Evol., 1:1, 17–22, 9 figs., 1 table.

PETIT-MAIRE, NICOLE and CHARON, MICHEL
    1972A   Tendances évolutives de la denture inférieure permanente des Hominidés du Quaternaire. Acad. Sci., C.R., Sér. D, 274:3, 365–368, 6 figs. (French).

PETIT-MAIRE HEINTZ, NICOLE (= HEINTZ, N.; PETIT-MAIRE, N.)
    1970A   Morphogenèse du crâne des primates. Acad. Sci., C.R., Sér. D, 271:16, 1384–1386, 3 figs. (French).

PETIT-MAIRE HEINTZ, N. and DRICOT, J.-M.
    1970A   Croissance relative des parties sus-et sous-iniaques de l'écaille occipitale chez les singes cynomorphes, les
               pongidés et les hominidés actuels et fossiles. Soc. Anthropol. Paris, Bull. Mém., 6:3, 295–306
               (French; English summary).

PETIT-MAIRE HEINTZ, N., DRICOT, J.-M. and D'ANS, C.
    1970A   Croissance comparative des parties sus- et sous-iniaques de l'occipital chez l'homme, les pongidés et les
               singes cynomorphes. Position des hominidés fossiles par rapport aux formes actuelles. Acad.
               Sci., C.R., Sér. D, 270:15, 1886–1889, 1 fig., 2 tables (French).

PETKEWICH, RICHARD M. and FIELDS, R. W.
    1971A   The Burnt Hills faunule: a third Late Eocene mammalian assemblage from southwestern Montana.
               Geol. Soc. Amer., Abstr., 3:2, 178 (abs.).

PETRI, W.
    1969A   Neandertaler am Eismeer. Naturwiss. Rundsch., 22:2, 86–87 (German).

PETRONIO, CARMELO
    1970A   Scheletri di mammiferi pleistocenici montati nel Museo Paleontologico dell' Universitá di Roma dal
               1960 al 1970. Geol. Rom., 9, 137–148, 12 figs. (Italian; English summary).
               Rev.: Albanesi in Riv. Ital. Paleontol. Stratigr., 77:2, 296.
    1970B   I roditori pleistocenici della grotta di Spinagallo (Siracusa). Geol. Rom., 9, 149–194, 28 figs., 6 pls.,
               7 tables (Italian; English summary).
               Rev.: Albanesi in Riv. Ital. Paleontol. Stratigr., 77:2, 295–296.

PETSCHE, JEROME E.
    1968A*   Bibliography of salvage archeology in the United States. Foreword by John O. Brew. Salvage Archeol.
               Smithson. Inst., Publ., no. 10, iv + 162 pp.

PETTER, FRANCIS
    1968A   Un muridé quaternaire nouveau d'Algérie, *Paraethomys filfilae.* Ses rapports avec les muridés actuels.
               Mammalia, 32:1, 54–59, 5 figs. (French; English summary).

PETTER, FRANCIS   See also: Crusafont Pairó, M. and Petter, F., 1964A.

PETTER, GERMAINE and HEINTZ, EMILE
    1969A   Mammifères quaternaires de la grotte de Geula (Nord d'Haïfa, État d'Israël). Mus. Nat. Hist. Natur.,
               Paris, Bull., 41:5, 1292–1298, 1 pl., 1 table (French).
               Rev.: Thenius in Zentralbl. Geol. Paläontol., Teil 2, 1971:2–3, 192–193.

PETTER, GERMAINE   See also: Crusafont Pairó, M. and Petter, G., 1969A.

PETTIPAS, LEO
    1966A   The Lake Agassiz field survey. Manitoba Archaeol. News., 3:2, 3–4.

PEVZNER, M. A.   See: Menner, V. V., Nikiforova, K. V., Pevzner, M. A., Alekseev, M. N., Gladenkov, Iu. B.,
               Gurarií, G. Z. and Trubikhin, V. M., 1972A.

PEYER, BERNHARD
    1968A   Rev.: Knussmann in Homo, 20:4, 254.

PFEIFFER, JOHN E.
    1969A   The emergence of man. New York and London: Harper & Row, xxiii + 477 pp., illustr.
               Rev.: Bennett in Amer. Anthropol., 72:6, 1560–1562; Collins in Antiquity, 45:176, 331–332;
               Johnston in Human Biol., 42:2, 347–348; Mathur in E. Anthropol., 24:3, 211–213.
    1971A   When *Homo erectus* tamed fire, he tamed himself. In: Holmes, L. D. (ed.), 1971A, 177–186
               (reprinted from New York Times Magazine, Dec. 11, 1966).

PFLIEGER, WILLIAM L.
    1971A   A distributional study of Missouri fishes. Kans., Univ., Mus. Natur. Hist., Publ., 20:3, 225–570, 15 figs.,
               193 maps.

PHILIPPE, MICHEL   See: Guérin, C., Mein, P., Philippe, M. and Truc, G., 1972A; Hugueney, M., Truc, G. and
               Philippe, M., 1971A.

PHILIPPI, M. E.   See: Olazarri, J., Mones, A., Ximénez, A. and Philippi, M. E., 1970A.

PHILLIPSON, D. W.
  1966A   The early and middle Stone Age. In: Fagan, B. M. (ed.), 1966A, 33–55, 7 figs.

PIANESE, SIMONA PIERA
  1968A   Rassegna storica delle ricerche sul Paleolitico in Sicilia. Quaternaria, 10, 213–250, 7 figs. (Italian;
                French and English summaries).

PIÁTAKOV, V. V.   See: Vangengeĭm, E. A., Piatakov, V. V. and Shevchenko, V. K., 1969A, 1969B.

PICCARRETA, G. and RICCHETTI, G.
  1970A   I depositi del bacino fluvio-lacustre della Fiumara di Venosa-Matinelle del Torrente Basentello. Soc.
                Geol. Ital., Mem., 9:1, 121–134, 2 pls. (Italian; English summary).

PICCOLI, G., LADDAGA FORMENTIN, O., WINKLER DEL PUP, G. and ZANFERRARI VISENTIN, M. E.
  1970A   Studi su resti di crani di Elephas mnaidriensis Adams del Pleistocene di Sicilia. Padua, Univ., Ist.
                Geol. Miner., Mem., 27, 33 pp., 19 figs., 3 pls., 4 tables (Italian; English, French and German
                summaries).
                Rev.: Albanesi in Riv. Ital. Paleontol. Stratigr., 76:3, 483–484.

PIDOPLICHKO, IVAN GRIGOR'EVICH
  1962A*   Vykopni fauny Ukrainy i sumizhnykh terytoriĭ. [Fossil faunas of Ukraine and adjacent territories.
                Vol. 1.] Kiev: Ukr. RSR Akad. Nauk Press, 171 pp., 65 figs., 4 pls., 45 tables (Ukrainian;
                Russian summaries).
  1969A   Osnovnye itogi issledovaniĭ zoologov Akademii Nauk Ukrainskoĭ SSR za 50 let ee sushchestvovaniĭa.
                [Principal results of the zoological investigations of the Ukrainian Academy of Sciences for
                50 years of its existence.] Akad. Nauk Ukr. SSR, Inst. Zool., Vestn. Zool., 1969:1, 3–15,
                1 fig., 2 maps (Russian).
  1969B   Pozdnepaleoliticheskie zhilishcha iz losteĭ mamonta na Ukraine. [Late Paleolithic dwellings of
                mammoth bones in Ukraine.] Kiev: "Naukova Dumka" Press, 164 pp., illustr. (Russian).
                Rev.: Gvozdover in Vop. Antropol., 38, 168–169 (Russian).
  1970A   Pamĭati Veniamina Iosifovicha Tsalkina (1903–1970). [In memoriam Veniamin Iosifovich Tsalkin
                (1903–1970).] Akad. Nauk Ukr. SSR, Inst. Zool., Vestn. Zool., 1970:4, 90–92, portr.
                (Russian).
  1970B   Raskopki berislavskoĭ pozdnesarmatskoĭ gipparionovoĭ fauny. [Excavations of Berislav late Sarmatian
                hipparion fauna.] Prirodn. Obstan. i Fauny Proshl., 5, 3–24, 14 figs. (Russian).
  1970C   Man's influence upon the development of fauna in the Pleistocene and Holocene. Int. Congr.
                Anthropol. Ethnol. Sci., 7th, Moscow, 1964, Proc., 5, 527–530.

PIDOPLICHKO, I. G. and GOLDIN, G. K.
  1964A   Naibolee severnaĭa nakhodka iskopaemoĭ skorlupy ĭaĭtsa strausa v Evropeĭskoĭ chasti SSSR. [The
                northernmost find of fossil ostrich egg shell in the European part of the USSR.] In: Problemy
                ornitologii. Trudy tret'eĭ vsesoĭuznoĭ ornitologicheskoĭ konferentsii. Sentĭabr' 1962, 190–191,
                1 table (Russian).

PIDOPLICHKO, I. G., KISTĬAKOVSKIĬ, A. B., KORNEEV, A. P. and VERESHCHAGIN, N. K.
  1969A   Psevdonauka pod vidom poiskov neandertaloidov. [Pseudo-science under the guise of a search for
                Neanderthaloids.] Akad. Nauk Ukr. SSR, Inst. Zool., Vestn. Zool., 1969:4, 69–80 (Russian).

PIÉRON, H.
  1967A   L'homme rien que l'homme. Paris: Presses Universitaires de France, 172 pp. (French).
                Rev.: Tétry in L'Ann. Biol., 7:11–12, 732–733.

PIERSON, PEARL and KENDALL, BRUCE D.
  1969A   Petrified mammal remains in southern Monterey County. S. Calif. Paleontol. Soc., Bull., 1:12, 5–6
                (reprinted from Dinny's Doin's, 4:10, 1969).

PIGGOTT, STUART
  1969A   Hairy Russian fossil. New Sci., 42:654, 655.

PILBEAM, DAVID R.
  1967A   Man's earliest ancestors. Sci. J., 3:2, 47–53, 2 figs., 2 pls.
                Rev.: Preuschoft in Zentralbl. Geol. Paläontol., Teil 2, 1969:1, 55–59.
  1968C   Tertiary Pongidae of East Africa: taxonomy and evolutionary relationships. Diss. Abstr., 29:4, 1247B
                (abs.).
  1969A   Tertiary Pongidae of East Africa: evolutionary relationships and taxonomy. Yale Univ., Peabody Mus.
                Natur. Hist., Bull., 31, 185 pp., 31 figs., 50 tables, 3 appends. (German and Russian summaries).
  1969B   Newly recognized mandible of Ramapithecus. Nature, 222:5198, 1093–1094, 1 fig.

1969C   Possible identity of Miocene tali from Kenya. Nature, 223:5206, 648.
1969D   Early Hominidae and cranial capacity. Nature, 224:5217, 386.
1970A   The evolution of man. London: Thames and Hudson, New York: Funk and Wagnallis, 216 pp.,
          illustr.
          Rev.: Bilsborough in Man (J. Roy. Anthropol. Inst.), 5:4, 706—707; Brace in J. Human Evol., 1:2,
                 233—235; Campbell in New Sci., 46:705, 544; Greenberg in Sci. J., 6:12, 80; Napier in Nature,
                 226:5252, 1270—1271; Van Valen in Amer. J. Phys. Anthropol., 37:1, 313—314.
1970B   Gigantopithecus and the origins of Hominidae. Nature, 225:5232, 516—519, 2 figs.
1970C   Early hominids and cranial capacity (continued). Nature, 227:5259, 747—748, 2 figs.
1972A   The ascent of man. An introduction to human evolution. New York: Macmillan, Macmillan Series
          in Physical Anthropology, x + 208 pp., illustr.
          Rev.: Oxnard in Science (AAAS), 176:4035, 657—659.
1972B   An idea we could live without — the naked ape. Discovery, 7:2, 63—70, illustr.
1972C   Evolutionary changes in the hominoid dentition through geological time. In: Bishop, W. W. and
          Miller, J. A. (eds.), 1972A, 369—380, 1 fig., 1 table.

PILBEAM, D. R. and SIMONS, E. L.
1971A   Humerus of Dryopithecus from Saint Gaudens, France. Nature, 229:5284, 406—407.
1972A   Some problems of hominid classification. In: McCown, T. D. and Kennedy, K. A. R. (eds.), 1972A,
          400—421, 3 figs. (reprinted from Amer. Sci., 53:2, 237—259).

PILBEAM, DAVID R.   See also: Simons, E. L. and Pilbeam, D., 1971A, 1972A; Simons, E. L., Pilbeam, D. and
          Ettel, P. C., 1969A; Simons, E. L., Pilbeam, D. and Boyer, S. J., 1971A; Uzzell, T. and
          Pilbeam, D., 1971A.

PILLARD, BRIGITTE   See: Jullien, R. and Pillard, B., 1969A, 1969B.

PINKHAM, CARLOS F. A.
1971A   Peromyscus and Ochrotomys from the Pleistocene of Reddick, Florida. J. Mammal., 52:1, 28—40,
          6 figs., 4 tables.

PINNA, GIOVANNI
1969A   Lo scheletro di Camptosaurus browni Gilmore, dinosauro giurassico, del Museo Civico di Storia
          Naturale di Milano. Natura, 60:1, 5—9, 2 figs. (Italian; English summary).
1970A   La ricostruzione di Triceràtopo (Triceratops prorsus Marsh), dinosauro cretacico, esposta al Museo Civico
          di Storia Naturale di Milano. Natura, 61:3—4, 289—296, 11 figs. (Italian).

PINTAUD, ROLAND C.
1961B   Fragment de maxillaire d'enfant présumé néanderthalien dans les déblais du Placard. Les Eyzies, 10,
          116—118, 2 figs. (French).
1964A   Pierre David. 1903—1963. Les Eyzies, 13, 18—23, portr., biog. (French).

PINTER, LAWRENCE JOHN
1969A   Mr. Orr retires. Mus. Talk, 44:3, 32—33, 1 fig.

PIRLOT, PAUL
1969A   Morphologie évolutive des Chordés. Montréal: University of Montréal Press, 1068 pp., 454 figs.
          (French).
          Rev.: Bellairs in J. Anat., 105:3, 587; Cox in Nature, 224:5216, 292—293; Eaton in Evolution, 23:4,
                 725; Kaestner in Biol. Zentralbl., 89:2, 258—259; Leroy in Soc. Zool. Fr., Bull., 94:4, 705.

PISTSOV, IU. P. (= PISZOV)
1968A   Verkhnemezozoĭskie ozernye basseĭny Tsentral'nogo i Vostochnogo Zabaĭkal'ia. [Upper Mesozoic lake
          basins of central and eastern Transbaikalia.] In: Mezozoĭskie i kaĭnozoĭskie ozera Sibiri, 22—38,
          3 maps (Russian).

PITRAT, C. W.   See: Budding, A. J., Pitrat, C. W. and Smith, C. T., 1960A.

PIVETEAU, JEAN
1952B*   Rev.: A. H. in Natuurwet. Tijdschr., 37:1—4, 87—89.
1955E*   Rev.: A. Hacquaert in Natuurwet. Tijdschr., 37:7—8, 233.
1958B*   Rev.: A. H. in Natuurwet. Tijdschr., 41:5, 155.
1961A*   Rev.: Hacquaert in Natuurwet. Tijdschr., 43:7—8, 170.
1964C*   Rev.: Redactie in Natuurwet. Tijdschr., 48:1, 34—35.
1964G   Psicología del hombre de Neandertal. Col-Pa (Madrid, Univ., Fac. Cienc.), 1, 3—6, 2 figs. (Spanish).
          Rev.: H.-P. in Soc. Españ. Hist. Natur., Bol., Sec. Geol., 62, 274.

1966B*   Rev.: Müller in Biol. Zentralbl., 86:4, 542–543; Redactie in Natuurwet. Tijdschr., 48:6–8, 237–238.
1967C   De los primeros vertebrados al hombre. Barcelona: Labor Ed., 166 pp., 59 figs. (Spanish).
         Rev.: Campillo Valero in Ampurias, 31–32, 398–399.
1969A*   Traité de paléontologie. Tome IV, vol. 2. L'origine des vertébrés, leur expansion dans les eaux douces
         et le milieu marin. Gnathostomes, acanthodiens, placodermes, élasmobranches. Paris: Masson,
         790 pp., 384 figs., 90 in color, 2 tables (French).
         Rev.: Corrivault in Natur. Can., 96:3, 482; Krans in Geol. Mijnbouw, 48:4, 422–423; Müller in Biol.
         Zentralbl., 89:1, 133; Nelson in Quart. Rev. Biol., 45:1, 64–65; Westphal in Zentralbl. Geol.
         Paläontol., Teil 2, 1969:4, 326–327.
1969B   Gnathostomes. Poissons. Généralités. Classification. In: Piveteau, J. (ed.), 1969A, Traité de Paléo.,
         T. IV, vol. 2, 1–20, 12 figs., 1 table (French).
1969C   Cuvier. Anatomiste et zoologiste. J. Zool., 159:3, 269–272 (French).
1969D   Quelques aspects de l'évolution des primates non-humains. Symp. Biol. Hungarica, 9, 11–21 (French).
1970A   Les grottes de la Chaise (Charente). Paléontologie humaine. 1. – L'homme de l'abri Suard. Ann.
         Paléontol., Vertébrés, 56:2, 175–225, 26 figs. (French).
1972A   Un pariétal humain de la grotte du Lazaret (Alpes-Maritimes). Int. J. Speleol., 4:2, 210 (French; abs.).
1972B   La Grotte de Regourdou (Dordogne): paléontologie humaine. Int. J. Speleol., 4:2, 210 (French; abs.).

PIVETEAU, JEAN   See also: David, P. and Piveteau, J., 1953A; Debénath, A. and Piveteau, J., 1969A;
         Lumley, M.-A. de and Piveteau, J., 1969A.

PLACE, ROBIN
1968A   Introduction to archaeology. London: Newnes, xii + 168 pp., 11 figs., 24 pls.
         Rev.: Johnston in J. West, 9:1, 145.

PLANE, MICHAEL
1965B   Protemnodonts from the Pliocene of New Guinea. Austral. Mammal Soc., Bull., 2:2, 39–40.
1971A   A New Guinea fossil macropodid (Marsupialia) from the marine Pliocene of Victoria, Australia.
         Victoria, Nat. Mus., Mem., 33, 33–36, 1 fig., 1 pl., 2 tables.

PLAZIAT, JEAN-CLAUDE
1972A   Précisions nouvelles sur la position stratigraphique et structurale des conglomérats à ciment rouge de
         Coll de Nargó (Prov. de Lérida, Espagne). Acad. Sci., C.R., Sér. D, 274:17, 2431–2434, 2 figs.
         (French).

PLAZIAT, JEAN-CLAUDE   See also: Dughi, R., Plaziat, J.-C. and Sirugue, F., 1969A.

PLÉNIER, ALETH
1971A   L'art de la grotte de Marsoulas. Inst. Art Préhist. Toulouse, Mém., 296 pp., 181 figs. and pls., 1 map
         (French).
         Rev.: M.C. in Préhist. Spéléol. Ariége., 26, 153–154.
1971B   L'art de la grotte de Marsoulas. Préhist. Spéléol. Ariége., 26, 83–91, 7 figs. (French).

PLISNIER-LADAME, F. and COUPATEZ, P.
1969A   Étude morphologique de l'anneau sclérotique de Mosasaurus hoffmanni Mantell, 1829. Soc. Belge
         Géol. Paléontol. Hydrol., Bull., 78:3–4, 253–265, 9 figs., 1 table (French).

PLISNIER-LADAME, F. and QUINET, G. E.
1969A   Balaena belgica Abel 1938, cétacé du Merxemien d'Anvers. Inst. Roy. Sci. Natur. Belg., Bull., 45:3,
         1–6, 1 fig., 2 pls. (French).

PLUSQUELLEC, Y.
1968A   Découverte d'un Cervus elaphus Linné dans le Trieux (Côtes-du-Nord). Penn ar Bed, 6, n° 54, 305–
         307 (French).

POCKLINGTON, R.
1970A   Man's first route to America. Science (AAAS), 167:3926, 1670.

PODGORNYĬ, ĨU. I.   See: Lipatova, V. V., Lopato, A. ĩu., Makarova, I. S., Ochev, V. G., Podgornyĭ, ĩu. I.,
         Starozhilova, N. N., Saĭdakovskiĭ, L. ĩa. and Shishkin, M. A., 1972A.

POHLE, HERMANN
1959A   Ein kapitaler Elch in - Berlin. Gandert-Festschrift, Berliner Beit. Vor- und Frühgesch., 2, 126–127,
         1 pl. (German).

POKATILOV, A. G.
1968A   Stratigraficheskoe znachenie i osnovnye etapy razvitiia fauny melkikh mlekopitaiushchikh Zapadnogo Zabaĭkal'ia i Pribaĭkal'ia v antropogene. [Stratigraphic significance and principal evolution stages of small mammals fauna in western Transbaĭkal and Baĭkal regions during Anthropogene.] In: Problemy izucheniia chetvertichnogo perioda. Tezisy, 123–125 (Russian).

POKORNÝ, VLADIMÍR
1968A   Za prof. RNDr. Josefem Augustou, Dr.Sc. [In memory of Professor Josef Augusta, Dr.Sc.] Czech., Ústřed. Ústav Geol., Věstn., 43, 229–230 (Czech.).
1969A   Numerická taxonomie a principy biologické klasifikace. [Numerical taxonomy and principles of biological classification.] Čas. Mineral. Geol., 14:1, 83–90 (Czech.).

POLACH, H. A. and GOLSON, J.
1968A   The collection and submission of radiocarbon samples. In: Mulvaney, D. J. (ed.), 1968A, 211–239.

POLACH, H. A.   See also: Bowler, J. M., Thorne, A. G. and Polach, H. A., 1972A.

POLEVOĬ, L. L.
1961A   Arkheologicheskie svedeniia o rastitel'nom pokrove i faune mlekopitaiushchikh Prut-Dnestrovskogo mezhdurech'ia. [Archeological data on vegetation and mammalian fauna of Prut-Dnestr interfluve.] Akad. Nauk Moldav. SSR, Okh. Prir. Moldav., 2, 99–104, 1 chart, 1 table (Russian).

POLLARD, JOHN E.
1968A   The gastric contents of an ichthyosaur from the lower Lias of Lyme Regis, Dorset. Palaeontology, 11:3, 376–388, 2 figs., 2 pls., 1 table.

POLUBOTKO, INGA VLADIMIROVNA and OCHEV, VITALIĬ GEORGIEVICH
1972A   Novye nakhodki ikhtiozavrov v triase Severo-Vostoka SSSR i nekotorye zamechaniia ob usloviiakh ikh zakhoroneniia. [New finds of ichthyosaurs in the Triassic of the northwestern USSR and some remarks on the conditions of their burial.] Vyssh. Ucheb. Zaved., Izv., Geol. Razved., 15:3, 36–42, 4 figs. (Russian).

POLUMISKOVA, L. A.   See: Kostenko, N. N., Nikitin, E. A. and Polumiskova, L. A., 1971A; Kostenko, N. N., Nikitin, E. A., Polumiskova, L. A. and Fedorenko, O. A., 1971A.

PONOMARENKO, ALEKSANDR GEORGIEVICH and RASNITSYN, ALEKSANDR PAVLOVICH
1971A   O feneticheskoĭ i filogeneticheskoĭ sistemakh. [On phenetic and phylogenetic systems.] Zool. Zh., 50:1, 5–14, 2 figs. (Russian; English summary).
1971B   Simpozium po filosofskim problemam evoliutsionnoĭ teorii. [Symposium on philosophical problems of evolutionary theory.] Paleontol. Zh., 1971:3, 130–131 (Russian).

PONS, JOSÉ MARÍA   See: Crusafont Pairó, M. and Pons, J. M., 1969A.

POOLE, D. F. G.
1971A   An introduction to the phylogeny of calcified tissues. In: Dahlberg, A. A. (ed.), 1971A, 65–79, 10 figs.

POOLE, D. F. G.   See also: Stewart, J. H., Poole, F. G. and Wilson, R. F., 1972A.

POPESCU, ALEXANDRINA
1972A   Controverse asupra originii şi evoluţiei vertebratelor. [Controversy over the origin and evolution of vertebrates.] Natura, Ser. Biol., 24:2, 9–20, 2 figs. (Rumanian).

POPESCU, ANASTASE
1964A   O nouă descoperire. [A new discovery.] Natura, Ser. Biol., 16:3, 96 (Rumanian).

POPESCU, ANTON   See: Stancu, J., Gheorghian, M. D. and Popescu, A., 1971A.

POPLIN, C. M. and RICQLÈS, A. J. DE
1970A   A technique of serial sectioning for the study of undecalcified fossils. Curator, 13:1, 7–20, 14 figs.

POPLIN, FRANÇOIS
1971A   La faune fossile du lac Rodolphe. La Recherche, 14, 683–684, 1 fig. (French).

POPOV, ANDRIAN VASIL'EVICH
1971A   O znachenii vnutrennikh protivorechiĭ v razvitii organizmov. [On the significance of intrinsic contradictions in the development of organisms.] Akad. Nauk Kirgiz. SSR, Izv., 1971:1, 28–36 (Russian).

POPOV, GEORGIĬ IVANOVICH
1970A   Chetvertichnaĭa sistema. [Quaternary system.] Geologiĭa SSSR, 46, Rostov, Volgograd, Astrakhan' Provinces and Kalmyk ASSR, 447–491, 5 figs., 1 table (Russian).

POPOVA, T. A.   See: Grigor'eva, G. B., Markevich, V. I., Popova, T. A. and Chernysh, E. K., 1969A.

PORADA, EDITH
1970A   Stephan de Borhegyi. [Died Sept. 26, 1969.] Archaeology, 23:1, 49.

PORCAR, J. B.
1964A   Impresiones sobre el arte rupestre existente en el Maestrazgo. In: Pericot García, L. and Ripoll Perelló, E. (eds.), 1964A, 159–166, 1 fig. (Spanish; English summary).

PORSHNEV, B. F.
1969A   Problema reliktovykh paleoantropov. [The problem of relict Paleoanthropians.] Sov. Etnogr., 1969:2, 115–130 (Russian).
1969B   Trogloditidy i gominidy v sistematike i evolĭutsii vysshikh primatov. [The trogloditides and the hominides in the taxonomy and evolution of higher primates.] Akad. Nauk SSSR, Dokl., 188:1, 238–241 (Russian).
1971A   Vtoraĭa signal'naĭa sistema kak diagnosticheskiĭ rubezh mezhdu trogloditidami i gominidami. [Second signal system as a diagnostic border-line between Trogloditidae and Hominidae.] Akad. Nauk SSSR, Dokl., 198:1, 228–231 (Russian).

PORTA, J. DE
1969A   Les vertébrés fossiles de Colombie et les problèmes posés par l'isolement du continent Sud-Américain. Palaeovertebrata, 2:2, 77–94, 2 figs. (French; German and English summaries).
Rev.: Thenius in Zentralbl. Geol. Paläontol., Teil 2, 1971:6, 514.

PORTENKO, L. A.
1970A   Beringiĭskie svĭazi mezhdu Evrazieĭ i Severnoĭ Amerikoĭ v predstavlenii zoogeografov. [Beringian connections between Eurasia and North America as viewed by the zoogeographers.] In: Severnyĭ Ledovityĭ Okean i ego poberezh'e v kaĭnozoe, 530–536 (Russian).

PORTMANN, ADOLF
1969A   Einführung in die vergleichende Morphologie der Wirbeltiere. 4. überarbeitete und ergänzte Auflage. Basel-Stuttgart: Schwabe & Co. Verlag, 344 pp., 271 figs. (German).
Rev.: Gutmann in Natur Mus., 100:8, 380–381; Kritscher in Anthropol. Ges., Mitt., 99, 248–249; Kruska in Z. Säugetierkunde, 36:3, 191; Piechocki in Biol. Zentralbl., 89:4, 534; Rietschel in Umsch. Wiss. Tech., 72:5, 153; Schwidetzky in Homo, 20:4, 253; Vogel in Z. Morphol. Anthropol., 62:2, 231.

POSPELOVA, G. A.   See: Zudin, A. N. and Pospelova, G. A., 1970A.

POTAPOV, R. L.
1965A   Osnovnye etapy formirovaniĭa avifauny Pamira. [Basic stages in the formation of avifauna of the Pamir.] In: Novosti ornitologii. Materialy chetvertoĭ vsesoĭuznoĭ ornitologicheskoĭ konferentsii, Alma-Ata, 1965, 303–305 (Russian).
1970A   Rol' Beringiĭskoĭ sushi v istorii semeĭstva teterevinykh Tetraonidae. [The role of Beringian land in the history of the family Tetraonidae.] In: Severnyĭ Ledovityĭ Okean i ego poberezh'e v kaĭnozoe, 537–541 (Russian).
1971A   Nekotorye momenty evolĭutsii i rasseleniĭa glukhareĭ (Tetrao urogallus) v antropogene. [Some moments of evolution and distribution of the capercaillie (Tetrao urogallus) in the Anthropogene.] Zool. Zh., 50:6, 875–885, 2 figs., 1 table (Russian; English summary).

POTTER, I. C.   See: Hardisty, M. W. and Potter, I. C. (eds.), 1971A; Hubbs, C. L. and Potter, I. C., 1971A.

POULIANOS, ARIS N.
1967A   The place of the Petralonian man among Palaeoanthropoi. Akten des Anthropologischen Kongresses, Brno, 1965. Anthropos, Brno, 19, 216–221, 3 figs., 1 table.
1971A   Petralona: a middle Pleistocene cave in Greece. Archeology, 24:1, 6–11, illustr.

POWELL, CHARLES L., II
1971A   Sharktooth Hill. Parts I and II. S. Calif. Paleontol. Soc., Bull., 3:7, 5–6, 2 figs., 3:8, 1–3, figs. 3–4.

POWELL, JON S.
1969A   Reptilian fossils and geology of uppermost Cretaceous deposits of the San Juan Basin, New Mexico. Geol. Soc. Amer., Abstr., 121, 546 (abs.).

POWELL, JON S.   See also: Elliot, D. H., Colbert, E. H., Breed, W. J., Jensen, J. A. and Powell, J. S., 1970A.

POWERS, ROGER   See: Chard, C. S. and Powers, R., 1968A.

POWERS, ROSEMARY   See: Clark, J. D., Brothwell, D. R., Powers, R. and Oakley, K. P., 1968A.

PRADEL, L.
1959G   La grotte magdalénienne de la Marche, commune de Lussac-les-Chateaux (Vienne). Soc. Préhist. Fr.,
        Mém. (1958), 5, 170–191, 13 figs. (French).
1965E   Les abris moustériens Rousseau et du Dr. Sabourin, commune d'Angles-sur-l'Anglin (Vienne). Congr.
        Préhist. France, 16ᵉ Sess., Monaco 1959, C.R., 971–998, 13 figs., 2 tables (French).

PRASAD, K. N.
1964C   Fossil vertebrates from Gujarat. Indian Minerals, 18:1, 92.
1967A   Fossil mammals from Cutch district, Gujarat, India. Geol. Mining Met. Soc. India, Quart. J., 39:3,
        187–192, 2 pls.
1968A   Some observations on the Cretaceous dinosaurs of India. Geol. Soc. India, Mem., 2, seminar volume,
        248–255, 2 tables.
1969A   Observations of mid-Tertiary hominoids Sivapithecus and Ramapithecus. Amer. J. Phys. Anthropol.,
        31, 11–15, 1 fig.
1969B   Notes on Ramapithecus and Sivapithecus from the Siwaliks of India. Ned. Akad. Wetensch., Proc.,
        Ser. B, 72:1, 1–3.
1969C   Critical observations on the fossil anthropoids from the Siwalik system of India. Folia Primatol.,
        10:4, 288–317, 1 fig., 5 tables, 1 pl.
1969D   Fossil anthropoids from the Siwalik system of India. Int. Congr. Primat., 2nd, Atlanta, Ga. 1968,
        Proc., vol. 2, 131–134.
1971A   Observations on the dryopithecines of India and Europe. Int. Congr. Primat., 3rd, Zurich, 1970, Proc.,
        1, 74–78.

PRASAD, K. N. and DANIEL, J. A.
1968A   On the occurrence of Hypselephas hysudricus in the Pleistocene deposits of Tirunelveli, Madras State.
        Current Sci., 37:18, 516–517, 2 figs.

PRASAD, K. N. and SATSANGI, P. P.
1962B   Note on a fossil hoof of a bovid from Haritalyangar, Himachal Pradesh. Geol. Surv. India, Rec., 94:2,
        317–318, 1 pl.
1967A   Fossil tragulid from the Nagri beds of Haritalyangar, Himachal Pradesh. Geol. Surv. India, Rec., 95:2,
        537–540.
1967B   On a new fossil chelonian from the Siwalik beds of Himachal Pradesh. Geol. Surv. India, Rec., 95:2,
        533–536, 1 pl., 1 table.

PRASLOV, N. D.
1970A   [Problems of ancient archeology on the international conference on "loess-periglacial-Paleolithic of
        central Europe".] Sov. Arkheol., 1970:1, 303–306, 1 fig. (Russian).

PRAT, FRANÇOIS
1968A   Observations sur quelques ossements découverts dans la basse terrasse de l'Oise à Moru, Commune de
        Rhuis, Oise. In: R. Vaufray Festschrift, 1968A, 337–348, 3 figs., 1 pl., 3 tables (French;
        English summary).
1969A   Le cheval de Solutré. Soc. Anthropol. Paris, Bull. Mém., Sér. 12, 4, 403–404 (French).

PRAT, F. and SONNEVILLE-BORDES, D. DE
1969A   Découvertes récentes de Paléolithique supérieur à la grotte de Font-de-Gaume (Dordogne).
        Quaternaria, 11, 115–132, 6 figs. (French; English and Italian summaries).

PRAT, F. and SUIRE, CÉCILE
1971A   Remarques sur les cerfs contemporains des deux premiers stades würmiens. Soc. Préhist. Fr., Bull.,
        68:3, 75–79 (French).

PRAT, FRANÇOIS   See also: Delpech, F., Lachastre, J., Prat, F. and Suire, C., 1970A.

PRAUSNITZ, M. W.
1969A   The sequence of early to middle Paleolithic flint industries along the Galilean littoral. Isr. Explor. J.,
        19:3, 129–136, 3 figs.

PREDTECHENSKIĬ, N. N.
1966A   Devonskaia sistema. [Devonian system.] Geologiia SSSR, 29, Tuvinskaia ASSR, 175—201, 6 figs.,
         1 table (Russian).

PRESTON, ROBERT E. and McCOY, C. J.
1971A   The status of Emys twentei Taylor (Reptilia: Testudinidae) based on new fossil records from Kansas
         and Oklahoma. J. Herpetol., 5:1—2, 23—30, 4 figs., 1 table.

PREUSCHOFT, H.
1971A   Body posture and mode of locomotion in early Pleistocene hominids. Folia Primatol., 14, 209—240,
         15 figs.

PREVOSTI PELEGRÍN, ANTONIO
1962A   Dinámica de las poblaciones y selección natural. Discussions. Soc. Españ. Hist. Natur., Bol., Secc.
         Biol., 60, 247—258 (Spanish).
1969A   La selección natural. Acad. Cienc. Art. Barcelona, Mem., 39:10, 341—443 (Spanish; English summary).

PRICE, JOHN T.
1971A   The origin and evolution of life. London: English Universities Press, "Bridge Series", viii + 120 pp.
         Rev.: Boné in Rev. Quest. Sci., 33:1, 138.

PRICE, LLEWELLYN IVOR
1971A   A presença de Pterosauria no Cretácio inferior da Chapada do Araripe, Brasil. Acad. Brasil. Ciênc.,
         An., 43 Suppl., 451—461, 3 figs. (Portuguese; English summary).

PRICE, W. ARMSTRONG
1958A   Sedimentology and Quaternary geomorphology of south Texas. Gulf Coast Ass. Geol. Soc., Trans.,
         8, 41—75, 22 figs., 4 pls., 4 tables.

PRINGLE, LAURENCE
1968A   Dinosaurs and their world. New York: Harcourt, Brace and World, 63 pp. (juvenile).
         Rev.: Neill in Audubon Mag., 70:3, 104.

PROKHODSKIĬ, S. I.
1963A   Kamyshevskaia fauna mlekopitaiushchikh v drevnikh alluvial'nykh otlozheniiakh. [Kamyshev mammal
         fauna in ancient alluvial deposits.] Geogr. Obshchest. SSSR, Khar'kov. Otd., Izv., 1963, 33—34
         (Russian).

PROKOPEC, M.   See: Fetter, V., Prokopec, M., Suchy, J. and Titlbachová, S., 1967A.

PROSHLIAKOV, B. K.   See: Bogacheva, M. I., Vasil'ev, Iu. M., Proshliakov, B. K., Charygin, M. M. and
         Shleifer, A. G., 1965A.

PROST, JACK H.
1971A   An historical overview. In: Leakey, L. S. B., Prost, J. and Prost, S. (eds.), 1971A, 127—131
         (reprinted from Prost, J. H., 1968).

PROST, JACK H.   See also: Leakey, L. S. B., Prost, J. and Prost, S. (eds.), 1971A.

PROST, STEPHANIE   See: Leakey, L. S. B., Prost, J. and Prost, S. (eds.), 1971A.

PROTOPOPESCO-PAKE, EM., MATEESCO, C. N. and GROSSU, AL. V.
1969A   Formation des couches de civilisation de la station de Vădastra en rapport avec le sol, la faune
         malacologique et le climat. Quartär, 20, 135—162, 8 figs., 3 tables (French).

PRUDHOMMEAU, GERMAINE
1961A   Étude d'une caverne ornée: Font-de-Gaume. Les Eyzies, 10, 216—231, 36 figs., 1 table, graphs (French).

PRUDHOMMEAU, M.
1964A   La Recherche Préhistorique. Orientation actuelle — vues d'avenir. Les Eyzies, 13, 98—112, 4 figs.
         (French).
1966A   Les grandes dates de la Préhistoire. Les Eyzies, 15, 92—104 (French).

PTUKHIAN, ANOP EREMOVICH   See: Akopian, G. M., Veguni, A. T. and Ptukhian, A. E., 1970A.

PUGH, WALLY
    1969A   Fossil fish of the Los Angeles Basin. S. Calif. Paleontol. Soc., Bull., 1:7, 1—4 (reprinted from Gems
                 and Minerals, June 1965).

PUISSÉGUR, JEAN-JACQUES   See: Chaline, J., Clair, A. and Puisségur, J.-J., 1970A; Clair, A. and
                 Puisségur, J.-J., 1969A.

PULINA, MARIAN
    1969A   Karst and caves in Poland. Nat. Speleol. Soc., Bull., 31:1, 1—17, 19 figs.

PUMINOV, ALEKSANDR PETROVICH
    1964A   Nekotorye voprosy paleogeografii Minusinskogo progiba v kaĭnozoe. [Some problems of
                 paleogeography of the Minusinsk depression during Cenozoic.] In: Vsesoĭuznoe Soveshchanie
                 po Izucheniĭu Chetvertichnogo perioda, Novosibirsk, 1964, Tezisy Dokladov, Sektsiĭa
                 Paleogeografii, 84—87 (Russian).

PUNNING, J.-M., LIIVA, A. and ILVES, E.
    1968A   Spisok radiouglerodnykh datirovok Instituta zoologii i botaniki Akademii nauk Estonskoĭ SSR.
                 Soobshchenie III. [List of radiocarbon datings from the Institute of Zoology and Botanics of
                 the Academy of Sciences of the Esthonian SSR. Communication III.] Toimetised Eesti NSV
                 Tead. Akad., Ser. Biol., 17:4, 426—433 (Russian; Esthonian and German summaries).

PUNNING, J.-M.   See also: Ilves, E., Punning, J.-M. and Liiva, A., 1968A, 1969A.

PURRETT, LOUISE
    1971A   Magnetic reversals and biological extinctions. Sci. News, 100:18, 300—301.

PYLES, GERALD
    1969A   Notes on fossil and relic hunting in Florida. Rocks Miner., 44:12, 838—839.

QUAINTANCE, CHARLES W.
    1969A   Mylodon, furthest north in Pacific northwest. Amer. Midland Natur., 81, 593—594.

QUAM, LOUIS O.
    1971A*   Research in the Antarctic. Washington, D.C.: American Association for the Advancement of Science,
                 xv + 768 pp., illustr.

QUERNER, HANS
    1968A   Stammesgeschichte des Menschen. Stuttgart-Berlin-Köln-Mainz: Kohlhammer, 160 pp., 10 figs.
                 (German).
                 Rev.: Helmuth in Z. Morphol. Anthropol., 61:1, 118—119; Hemmer in Homo, 20:1, 71; Henschen in
                 Naturwiss., 56:1, 46—47; Simon in Aufschluss, 19, 371; Vogel in Naturwiss. Rundsch., 22:8,
                 361—362.

QUINET, GUY ÉLIE
    1965C   Le massif maxillo-dentaire, caractère évolutif essentiel. I. — La morphologie dentaire. Groupement
                 Int. Recherch. Sci. Stomatol., Bull., 8:3/4, 361—373, 3 figs. (French; English and German
                 summaries).
    1966D   Origine de la molaire inférieure tribosphénique placentaire. Groupement Int. Recherch. Sci. Stomatol.,
                 Bull., 9:3, 315—328, 4 figs. (French; English and German summaries).
    1966E   Sur la formule dentaire de deux primates du Landénien continental belge. Inst. Roy. Sci. Natur. Belg.,
                 Bull., 42:38, 1—6, 1 pl. (French).
    1966F   Les mammifères du Landénien continental Belge. 2d Tome. Étude de la morphologie dentaire
                 comparée des "carnivores" de Dormaal. Inst. Roy. Sci. Natur. Belg., Mém., 158, 64 pp., 4 figs.,
                 7 pls., 3 tables (French).
    1967A   Origine de la molaire supérieure tribosphénique placentaire. Groupement Int. Recherch. Sci. Stomatol.,
                 Bull., 10, 227—241, 6 figs. (French; English and German summaries).
    1967B   Tribosphénie et phylogenèse chez les mammifères. Groupement Int. Recherch. Sci. Stomatol., Bull.,
                 10, 343—355, 2 pls. (French; English and German summaries).
    1968A   Le mécanisme de l'audition chez Plioplatecarpus Dollo, 1882? Inst. Roy. Sci. Natur. Belg., Bull.,
                 44:3, 9 pp., 2 pls. (French).
    1969A   Extensions et applications de la théorie synthétique de la molaire mammalienne (G. Vandebroek, 1960—
                 1961). Inst. Roy. Sci. Natur. Belg., Bull., 45:2, 21 pp., 1 fig., 3 pls. (French; Engliah and
                 German summaries).

1969B   Apport de l'étude de la faune mammalienne de Dormaal à la stratigraphie générale du Paléocène supérieur européen et à la théorie synthétique de la molaire mammalienne. Inst. Roy. Sci. Natur. Belg., Mém., 162, 188 pp., 7 figs., 7 pls., 7 tables (French).

1970A   Les mosasauriens de la Belgique. Natur. Belg., 51:6, 257–270 (French).

1970B   Les mosasauriens de Belgique. 2 ème partie. II. Particularités des mosasauriens belges. Natur. Belg., 51:7, 313–325 (French).

QUINET, G. E., COUPATEZ, P. and WOUTERS, G.

1970A   Note préliminaire sur la faune ichthyologique et les otolithes de l'Yprésien belge de Montroeul-au-Bois, en Hainaut, Belgique. Inst. Roy. Sci. Natur. Belg., Bull., 46:33, 6 pp., 2 pls., 1 table (French).

QUINET, G. E. and VERLINDEN, W.

1970A   Sur l'*Hyracotherium* d'Erquelinnes (Jeumont). Inst. Roy. Sci. Natur. Belg., Bull., 46:34, 10 pp., 3 pls. (French).

    Rev.: Thenius in Zentralbl. Geol. Paläontol., Teil 2, 1971:4, 346.

QUINET, G. E., VERLINDEN, W. and COUPATEZ, P.

1971A   Sur un Condylarthre ? originaire de Maret (Brabant, Belgique). Inst. Roy. Sci. Natur. Belg., Bull., 47:7, 6 pp., 2 pls. (French).

    Rev.: Thenius in Zentralbl. Geol. Paläontol., Teil 2, 1971:6, 523.

QUINET, G. E.   See also: Plisnier-Ladame, F. and Quinet, G. E., 1969A.

QUINN, JAMES H.

1970A   Occurrence of *Sus* in North America. Geol. Soc. Amer., Abstr., 2:4, 298 (abs.).

1972A   University of Arkansas, Department of Geology. Soc. Vert. Paleontol., News Bull., 94, 39.

1972B   Extinct mammals in Arkansas and related C-14 dates circa 3000 years ago. Int. Geol. Congr., 24th, Canada, Abstr., 376.

QUINTERO, INDALECIO   See: Crusafont Pairó, M. and Quintero, I., 1970A.

R., C.

1965A   In memoriam do Abade Henri Breuil. Lisbon, Univ., Fac. Letr., Publ., Ser. 3, 9–10, 2 vols.

    Rev.: Lhote in L'Anthropologie, 73:3–4, 266–269.

R., S. K.

1970A   Dr. M. S. Krishnan [1898–1970]. Geol. Mining Met. Soc. India, Quart. J., 42:4, 151–152, portr.

RAAB, M.

1967A   *Enchodus elegans* Dartevelle and Casier from the Senonian of Israel. Isr. J. Earth-Sci., 16:3, 174–179, 2 figs., 1 pl.

    Rev.: Weiler in Zentralbl. Geol. Paläontol., Teil 2, 1969:3, 286.

RAATH, M. A.

1969A   A new coelurosaurian dinosaur from the Forest sandstone of Rhodesia. Arnoldia, 4:28, 25 pp., 6 figs., 5 pls., 12 tables.

1972A   Fossil vertebrate studies in Rhodesia: a new dinosaur (Reptilia: Saurischia) from near the Trias-Jurassic boundary. Arnoldia, 5:30, 37 pp., 13 figs., 8 pls., 11 tables.

1972B   First record of dinosaur footprints from Rhodesia. Arnoldia, 5:27, 5 pp., 1 fig., 1 pl.

RAATH, M. A., SMITH, C. C. and BOND, G.

1970A   A new upper Karroo dinosaur fossil locality on the lower Angwa river, Sipolilo district, Rhodesia. Arnoldia, 4:35, 10 pp., 3 figs., 1 table.

    Rev.: Chrulew in Zentralbl. Geol. Paläontol., Teil 2, 1972:3, 167.

RAATH, M. A.   See also: Bond, G., Wilson, J. F. and Raath, M. A., 1970A.

RABEDER, GERNOT

1970A   Die Wirbeltierfauna aus dem Alt-Pliozän (O-Pannon) vom Eichkogel bei Mödling (NÖ). I. Allgemeines - II. Insectivora. Naturhist. Mus. Wien, Ann., 74, 589–595 (German).

1972A   Ein neuer Soricide (Insectivora) aus dem Alt-Pleistozän von Deutsch-Altenburg 2 (Niederösterreich). Neues Jahrb. Geol. Paläontol., Monatsh., 1972:10, 635–642, 1 fig., 1 table (German; English summary).

RABEDER, G.   See also: Daxner-Höck, G. and Rabeder, G., 1971A.

RABISCHONG, P.   See: Genet-Varcin, E. and Rabischong, P., 1965A.

RACE, GEORGE J.
1968A   Identification of iron pigment in ancient Nubian bone. In: Wendorf, F., 1968F, 995.

RACHITSKIĬ, V. I.
1969A   O stratigraficheskom polozhenii nekotorykh mestonakhozhdeniĭ iskopaemoĭ fauny nazemnykh
pozvonochnykh deĭnotsefalovogo kompleksa. [On the stratigraphic position of some type
localities of terrestrial vertebrates fossil fauna of the deinocephalian complex.] In: Geologiĭa,
geokhimiĭa i razrabotka neftĭanykh i gazovykh mestorozhdeniĭ, 64–68 (Russian).

RADINSKY, LEONARD B.
1967D   The oldest primate endocast. Amer. J. Phys. Anthropol., 27, 385–388, 2 figs.
1968A   Evolution of somatic sensory specialization in otter brains. J. Comp. Neurol., 134:4, 495–505, 6 figs.
Rev.: Thenius in Zentralbl. Geol. Paläontol., Teil 2, 1970:5, 435.
1969A   The early evolution of the Perissodactyla. Evolution, 23:2, 308–328, 11 figs.
Rev.: Thenius in Zentralbl. Geol. Paläontol., Teil 2, 1970:5, 442.
1969B   Outlines of canid and felid brain evolution. N.Y. Acad. Sci., Ann., 167:1, 277–288, 6 figs.
Rev.: Thenius in Zentralbl. Geol. Paläontol., Teil 2, 1971:4, 339.
1970A   The fossil evidence of prosimian brain evolution. In: Noback, C. R. and Montagna, W. (eds.), 1970A,
209–224, 8 figs.
1971A   An example of parallelism in carnivore brain evolution. Evolution, 25:3, 518–522, 4 figs.
1972A   Oldest pongid brain. Soc. Vert. Paleontol., Ann. Meeting, 32nd, 1972, Abstr. (abs.).
1972B   Endocasts and studies of primate brain evolution. In: Tuttle, R. (ed.), 1972A, 175–184, 3 figs.

RADMILLI, A. M.
1965B   Grotta di S. Leonardo (Carso Triestino). Riv. Sci. Preist., 20, 363–364 (Italian).
1965C   Abruzzo. Valle della Vibrata (prov. di Teramo). Riv. Sci. Preist., 20, 365 (Italian).
1967A   Parabita (Prov. di Lecce). Riv. Sci. Preist., 22:2, 436–437 (Italian).

RADMILLI, A. M.   See also: Fornaca-Rinaldi, G. and Radmilli, A. M., 1968A.

RADO, GERTRUDE
1965A   Otolite din depozitele tortoniene de la Coşteiul de Sus. [Otoliths from Tortonian deposits of
Coşteiul de Sus.] Bucharest, Univ., An., Ser. Ştiint. Natur., Geol.-Geogr., 14, 55–71, 3 figs.,
5 pls., 2 tables (Rumanian; Russian and French summaries).
Rev.: Weiler in Zentralbl. Geol. Paläontol., Teil 2, 1968:6, 651.
1968A   Étude des otolithes sarmatiens de Copăcel-Chijic (Bassin du Crişul Repede). Bucharest, Muz. Nat. Ist.
Natur. "Grigore Antipa", Trav., 8, 581–585, 1 fig., 5 pls., 1 table (French; Rumanian summary).
Rev.: Weiler in Zentralbl. Geol. Paläontol., Teil 2, 1970:3/4, 225.
1969A   Grupe noi de organisme in fauna tortoniană de la Buituri (Amfinure şi peşti). [New groups of
organisms in the Tortonian fauna of Buituri (Amphineura and fishes).] Stud. Cercet. Geol.,
Geofiz., Geogr., Ser. Geol., 14:1, 189–204, 2 pls. (Rumanian; Russian summary).
Rev.: Weiler in Zentralbl. Geol. Paläontol., Teil 2, 1970:3/4, 226.

RADULESCO, COSTIN   See: Rădulescu, Costin.

RĂDULESCU, COSTIN (= RADULESCO, COSTIN)
1969A   Contribuţii la cunoaşterea ibexului fosil din România. [Contribution to the knowledge of fossil
mountain goats from Rumania.] Acad. Repub. Soc. Rom., Inst. Speol. "Emil Rakoviţă",
Lucr., 8, 179–199, 9 figs., 4 tables (Rumanian; English summary).

RĂDULESCU, COSTIN and HERMANN, WILHELM
1969A   Asupra prezenţei elanului (Alces alces L.) în pleistocenul superior al Transilvaniei. [On the presence of
elk (Alces alces L.) in the upper Pleistocene of Transylvania.] Acad. Repub. Soc. Rom., Inst.
Speol. "Emil Rakoviţă", Lucr., 8, 225–231, 5 figs., 2 tables (Rumanian; French summary).

RĂDULESCU, COSTIN and KOVÁCS, ALEXANDRU
1968A   Noi contribuţii la cunoaşterea faunei de mamifere fosile din Bazinul Baraolt (Depresiunea Braşov).
[New contribution to the knowledge of the mammalian fauna from the Baraolt basin
(depression of Braşov).] Acad. Repub. Soc. Rom., Inst. Speol. "Emil Rakoviţă", Lucr., 7, 231–
253, 9 figs. (Rumanian; English summary).

RĂDULESCU, COSTIN and SAMSON, PETRE
1965B   Soergelia elisabethae Schaub dans le Pléistocène moyen de l'Olténie (Roumanie). Eclogae Geol. Helv.,
58:2, 1107–1110, 1 fig. (French).

1972A   Nouvelles données sur les Castoridés (Rodentia, Mamm.) du Villafranchien inférieur de la Dépression de
         Braşov (Roumanie). Neues Jahrb. Geol. Paläontol., Monatsh., 1972:2, 95—107, 3 figs. (French;
         German and English summaries).

RĂDULESCU, COSTIN   See also: Alimen, H., Rădulescu, C. and Samson, P., 1968B; Dumitrescu, M.,
         Samson, P., Terzea, E., Rădulescu, C. and Ghica, M., 1963A; Samson, P. and Rădulescu, C.,
         1968A, 1969A; Samson, P., Radulesco, C. and Kisgyörgy, Z., 1971A.

RADWAŃSKI, ANDRZEJ
1968A   Szczątki chimer z albu-cenomanu obrzeżenia gór Świętokrzyskich. [Remains of Chimaerae from the
         Albian-Cenomanian of Świętokrzyskich Mts.] Acta Palaeontol. Pol., 13:2, 315—324, 1 fig.,
         1 pl. (Polish; English and Russian summaries).
         Rev.: Weiler in Zentralbl. Geol. Paläontol., Teil 2, 1969:3, 287.

RADWANSKI, PIERRE A.
1969A   Étude paléo-anthropologique de l'Île de Pâques. Int. Congr. Anthropol. Ethnol. Sci., 8th, Tokyo,
         1968, Proc., Vol. I. Anthropology, 180—182 (French).

RAEMSCH, B. E.   See: Timlin, J. P. and Raemsch, B. E., 1971A.

RAGE, JEAN-CLAUDE
1969A   Les amphibiens et les reptiles découverts sur le sol de la cabane acheuléenne du Lazaret. In: Lumley,
         H. de (ed.), 1969B, 107—110, 2 figs. (French).

RAGE, J.-C.   See also: Hoffstetter, R. and Rage, J.-C., 1972A.

RAHMOUNI, O., ROUSSILLOT, C. and ARMANET, F.
1970A   Laboratoire de datage par la méthode du carbone 14 d'Alger. Libyca, 18, 9—22, 13 figs. (French).

RAI, H.   See: Dixit, P. C., Kachroo, R. K., Rai, H. and Sharma, N. L., 1971A.

RAĬKOV, B. E.
1968A   Karl Ernst von Baer, 1792—1876. Sein Leben und sein Werk. Translated from Russian by H. von
         Knorre. Leipzig: J. A. Barth, 516 pp., illustr. (German).
         Rev.: Hamburger in Quart. Rev. Biol., 45:2, 173—176.
1969A   Germanskie biologi-evolifisionisty do Darvina. Lorenŝ Oken. Karl Fridrikh Burdakh. Martin Genrikh
         Ratke. [German biologists-evolutionists before Darwin. Lorenz Oken. Karl Friedrich Burdach.
         Martin Heinrich Rathke.] Leningrad: "Nauka" Press, 232 pp., portrs. (Russian).
         Rev.: Gaĭsinovich in Priroda, 1971:1, 109—112 (Russian).

RAITT, R. J.
1970A   Loye Holmes Miller, 1874—1970. Condor, 72:3, 379.

RAJAGURU, S. N.
1969A   On the late Pleistocene of the Deccan, India. Quaternaria, 11, 241—253, 4 figs. (Italian and German
         summaries).

RÁKOSI, L.   See: Jámbor, A., Korpás, L., Kretzoi, M., Pálfalvy, I. and Rákosi, L., 1971A.

RAKOVEC, IVAN
1965C   Pleistocene mammalian fauna from Risovaca near Arandjelovac (Serbia). Slovenska Akad. Znan. Umetn.,
         Ljubljana, Raz., 8, 223—317, 7 pls., 31 tables.
1967A   Sesalska favna Slovenije v pleistocenski dobi. [The mammal fauna of Slovenia in the Pleistocene epoch.]
         Arheol. Vestn., 18, 291—299 (Slovenian; English summary).
1967B   The cave bear from the Mokrica cave in the Savinja alps (Slovenia, Jugoslavia). Slovenska Akad. Znan.
         Umetn., Ljubljana, Raz., 10, 123—203, 1 pl., 20 tables (Slovenian; English summary).
         Rev.: Ehrenberg in Zentralbl. Geol. Paläontol., Teil 2, 1969:3, 293—294; I. R. in Akad. savet FNRJ,
         Bull. Sci., Sec. A, 1968:7—8, 262.
1968A   Über das älteste Pleistozän Jugoslawiens. Österreich. Akad. Wiss., Math.-Natur. Kl., Anz., 105, 169—
         176 (German).
1968B   O mastodontih iz Šaleške doline. [The mastodons from the Šalek Valley. (Slovenia, Yugoslavia).]
         Slovenska Akad. Znan. Umetn., Ljubljana, Raz., 11, 299—350, 1 fig., 5 pls. (Slovenian; English
         summary).
1969A   Su nuovi resti di Panthera (Leo) spelaea (Goldf.) rinvenuti in Slovenia (Jugoslavia). Verona, Mus. Civ.
         Stor. Natur., Mem., Fuori Ser., 3, 53—65, 7 figs., 3 tables (Italian; English summary).
         Rev.: I. R. in Akad. Savet FNRJ, Bull. Sci., Sec. A, 16:7—8, 243; Thenius in Zentralbl. Geol.
         Paläontol., Teil 2, 1971:1, 64.

RALPH, ELIZABETH K.
1971A   Carbon–14 dating. In: Michael, H. N. and Ralph, E. K. (eds.), 1971A, 1–48, 7 figs., 5 tables.

RALPH, ELIZABETH K.   See also: Michael, H. N. and Ralph, E. K., 1971A.

RAMISHVILI, I. SH.   See: Gabelaiâ, T̂s. D., Ramishvili, I. Sh. and Maïsuradze, L. S., 1970A.

RANDHAWA, M. S., SINGH, J., DEY, A. K. and MITTRE, V.
1969A   Evolution of life. New Delhi: Council of Scientific and Industrial Research, xviii + 360 pp., 100 figs.,
                   99 pls.
                   Rev.: Chanda in Sci. Culture, 36:8, 459–460.

RANKAMA, K.
1967A*   Rev.: Judson in Amer. Sci., 56:3, 330A–331A.

RANOV, V. A.   See: Bader, O. N., Erdeli, I. and Ranov, V. A., 1969A.

RAO, A. RANGA
1971A   New mammals from Murree (Kalakot zone) of the Himalayan foothills near Kalakot, Jammu and
                   Kashmir state, India. Geol. Soc. India, J., 12:2, 125–134, 6 pls., 2 tables.
                   Rev.: Thenius in Zentralbl. Geol. Paläontol., Teil 2, 1971:6, 523.

RAPPORT, SAMUEL and WRIGHT, HELEN
1967A*   Anthropology. New York: New York Univ. Press, xix + 332 pp.
                   Rev.: Schwidetzky in Homo, 20:3, 198.

RASMUSSEN, DONALD L.
1971A   Microvertebrates from a fissure deposit in the "driftless area" of southwestern Wisconsin. Geol. Soc.
                   Amer., Abstr., 3:4, 275–276 (abs.).

RASMUSSEN, D. L., MARTIN, L. D., CHORN, J. D. and SLIMMER, D. F.
1971A   Vertebrate assemblages from channel sandstones in the Pennsylvanian-Permian megacyclothems of
                   Kansas and Nebraska. Geol. Soc. Amer., Abstr., 3:4, 276 (abs.).

RASNIT̂SYN, ALEKSANDR PAVLOVICH   See: Ponomarenko, A. G. and Rasnit̂syn, A. P., 1971A, 1971B.

RAST̂SVETAEV, L. M.   See: Birman, A. S. and Rast̂svetaev, L. M., 1967A, 1969A; Birman, A. S., et al., 1971A.

RAU, REINHOLD
1969A   Über den Flügel von Archaeopteryx. Natur Mus., 99:1, 1–8, 5 figs. (German).

RAUP, DAVID M.
1972A   Approaches to morphologic analysis. In: Schopf, T. J. M. (ed.), 1972A, 28–44, 3 figs., 1 table.

RAUP, DAVID M. and STANLEY, STEVEN M.
1971A   Principles of paleontology. San Francisco: W. H. Freeman and Co., x + 388 pp., illustr.
                   Rev.: Anon. in Geotimes, 16:3, 39; Chlupáč in Čas. Mineral. Geol., 16:4, 433–434 (Czek); Cutler
                   in Amer. Ass. Petrol. Geol., Bull., 55:10, 1900–1901; Daber in Deut. Ges. Geol. Wiss., Ber.,
                   Reihe A, Geol. Paläontol., 16:6, 719–720; Fischer in Science, 172:3987, 1019–1020; Hubbard
                   in Nature, 230:5292, 316; Johnson in J. Geol., 79:6, 750–751; Martinsson in Geol. Fören.
                   Stockholm, Förh., 94:1, 129–130; O.M.B.B. in Geol. Mag., 108:6, 553; Olson in Quart. Rev.
                   Biol., 46:3, 285–286; P.J.B. in Geol. J., 8:1, vii; Reyment in Geol. Fören. Stockholm, Förh.,
                   94:1, 130–131; Rhodes in Geotimes, 16:8, 35–36; Steininger in Geol. Ges. Wien, Mitt., 63,
                   258–259; T.L.B. in Calif. Geol., 24:7, 135; Ubaghs in Rev. Quest. Sci., 32:3, 440–441;
                   Voorthuysen in Geol. Mijnbouw, 50:4, 630.

RAVEN, PETER H.   See: Ehrlich, P. R., Holm, R. W. and Raven, P. H. (eds.), 1969A.

RAVOUX, GEORGES and BAZILE, F.
1967A   Le Paléolithique de la grotte de Pâques (Commune de Collias, Gard). Cah. Ligures Préhist. Archéol.,
                   16, 15–26, 3 figs. (French).

RAVOUX, GEORGES   See also: Hugues, C., Lorblanchet, M. and Ravoux, G., 1969A.

RAVSKIĬ, E. I.
1968A   North Asiatic analogues of the Villafranchian and the position of the Neogene-Anthropogene boundary.
                   Int. Geol. Congr., 23rd, Czech., Rep., Abstr., Sec. 10, 281–282 (abs.).

1968B   Severoaziatskie analogi villafranka i polozhenie granit͡sy neogena i antropogena (chetvertichnogo perioda). [North Asiatic analogues of the Villafranchian and the position of the Neogene-Anthropogene (Quaternary period) boundary.] In: Granit͡sa tretichnogo i chetvertichnogo periodov, 23–31 (Russian; English summary).

1969A   Osnovnye cherty klimatov Sibiri v antropogene. [Main climatic features of Siberia in Anthropogene.] In: Osnovnye problemy geologii antropogena Evrazii. K VIII kongressu INQUA, Parizh, 1969, 111–120, 2 figs. (Russian; English summary).

RAVSKIĬ, E. I. and GERBOVA, V. G.

1970A   O razvitii antropogenovykh vpadin Zapadnogo Zabaĭkal'i͡a. [On the development of Quaternary basins of western Transbaĭkalia.] Akad. Nauk SSSR, Izv., Ser. Geol., 1970:12, 66–73, 1 fig. (Russian).

RAY, CLAYTON E.

1971A   Polar bear and mammoth on the Pribilof Islands. Arctic, 24:1, 9–18, 1 fig., 1 table.

RAY, C. E., DENNY, C. S. and RUBIN, M.

1970A   A peccary, *Platygonus compressus* LeConte, from drift of Wisconsinan age in northern Pennsylvania. Amer. J. Sci., 268:1, 78–94, 2 pls., 5 tables, 1 map.

RAY, C. E. and LIPPS, LEWIS

1970A   Southerly distribution of porcupine in eastern United States during late Quaternary time. Georgia Acad. Sci., Bull., 28:2, 24.

RAY, C. E., WETMORE, A., DUNKLE, D. H. and DREZ, P.

1968A   Fossil vertebrates from the marine Pleistocene of southeastern Virginia. Smithson. Misc. Coll., 153:3, 1–25, 2 figs., 2 pls.
      Abs.: C.F.S. in Auk, 88:1, 223.

RAY, C. E., WILLS, D. L. and PALMQUIST, J. C.

1968A   Fossil musk oxen of Illinois. Ill. Acad. Sci., Trans., 61, 282–292, 5 figs.

RAY, W. W.   See: Schultz, C. B., Tanner, L. G., Whitmore, F. C. and Ray, W. W., 1969A.

READ, DWIGHT W. and LESTREL, PETER

1972A   Phyletic divergence dates of hominoid primates. Evolution, 26:4, 669–670.

REED, CHARLES A.

1969A   They never found the ark. Ecology, 50:2, 343–346.

1970A   Extinction of mammalian megafauna in the Old World late Quaternary. BioScience, 20:5, 284–288.

REGEL', E. D.

1968A   Razvitie osevogo khri͡ashchevogo cherepa i ego svi͡azeĭ s verkhnim otdelom cheli͡ustnoĭ dugi u *Ranodon sibiricus* (Hynobiidae, Amphibia). [The development of the cartilaginous neurocranium and its connection with the upper part of mandibular arch in Siberian salamander *Ranodon sibiricus* (Hynobiidae, Amphibia).] Akad. Nauk SSSR, Zool. Inst., Trudy, 46, 5–85, 48 figs., 2 tables (Russian).

1970A   Voskhodi͡ashchiĭ otrostok nëbno-kvadratnogo khri͡ashcha khvostatykh amfibiĭ. [Processus ascendens palatoquadrati of caudate amphibians.] Akad. Nauk SSSR, Dokl., 194:4, 981–984, 4 figs. (Russian).

REHNELT, KURT

1959A   Neue Reptilfährten – Funde aus der germanischen Trias. Dresden, Staatl. Mus. Mineral. Geol., Jahrb., 1959, 97–103, 3 figs., 3 pls. (German; English summary).

REICHLEN, PAULETTE and HEIZER, ROBERT F.

1966A   The Ophir skull from Virginia City, Nevada. Calif. Archaeol. Surv., Rep., no. 66, 85–99, 1 table, 2 pls.

REIF, WOLF-ERNST

1971A   Fossil Lagerstätten. Zur Genese des Muschelkalk-Keuper-Grenzbonebeds in Südwestdeutschland. [On the genesis of the bone bed at the Muschelkalk-Keuper-boundary "Grenzbonebed" in s.w. Germany.] Neues Jahrb. Geol. Paläontol., Abh., 139:3, 369–404, 14 figs., 3 tables (German; English summary).

REIG, OSVALDO A.

1969A   Community structure in the Triassic vertebrate faunas: an attempt in evolutionary paleoecology. (Abstract.) Symp. Gondwana Stratigr., 401–404 (English and Spanish).

1970A   The Proterosuchia and the early evolution of the archosaurs; an essay about the origin of a major taxon. Harvard Univ., Mus. Comp. Zool., Bull., 139:5, 229–292, 16 figs., 1 table (Spanish summary).

REIG, OSVALDO A. and LINARES, OMAR J.
1969A   The occurrence of *Akodon* in the upper Pliocene of Argentina. J. Mammal., 50:3, 643–647, 2 figs., 1 table.

REIG, OSVALDO A. and SIMPSON, G. G.
1972A   *Sparassocynus* (Marsupialia, Didelphidae), a peculiar mammal from the late Cenozoic of Argentina. J. Zool., 167:4, 511–539, 9 figs., 9 pls., 2 tables.

REIG, O. A.   See also: Charig, A. J. and Reig, O. A., 1970A.

REILLY, EDGAR M., JR.   See: Funk, R. E., Fisher, D. W. and Reilly, E. M., Jr., 1970A.

REINHART, ROY H.
1971A   Fossil Sirenia of Florida. Plaster Jacket, 15, 1–10, 5 figs.

REISCH, L.
1968A   Die Exkursion der Hugo Obermaier-Gesellschaft 1967 in die Tschechoslowakei. Quartär, 19, 391–397, 1 pl. (German).

REISZ, ROBERT
1972A   *Petrolacosaurus*, the earliest known diapsid. Soc. Vert. Paleontol., Ann. Meeting, 32nd, 1972, Abstr. (abs.).
1972B   Pelycosaurian reptiles from the middle Pennsylvanian of North America. Harvard Univ., Mus. Comp. Zool., Bull., 144:2, 27–61, 20 figs.

REITINGER, JOSEF
1968A   Rev.: Joachim in Bonner Jahrb., 169, 539.

REMANE, JÜRGEN
1970A   Zusammenfassung der bisherigen palökologischen Ergebnisse über das limnische Pliozän von Willershausen (Kr. Osterode/Harz). Naturhist. Ges. Hannover, Ber., Beih., 114, 49–59 (German).

REMINGTON, J. E.
1968A   New exhibits. Discovery, 3:2, 55, 1 fig.

REMMERT, HERMANN
1969A   Der Wasserhaushalt der Tiere im Spiegel ihrer ökologischen Geschichte. Naturwiss., 56:3, 120–124, 6 figs. (German).

REMY, HORST   See: Boecker, M., Lehmann, E. v. and Remy, H., 1972A.

REMY, JEAN-ALBERT
1972A   Étude du crâne de *Pachynolophus lavocati* n. sp. (Perissodactyla, Palaeotheriidae) des Phosphorites du Quercy. Palaeovertebrata (Montpellier), 5:2, 45–78, 14 figs., 5 pls., 3 tables (French; German and English summaries).
1972B   Évolution d'une structure histologique chez les Périssodactyles: développement de la dentine péricanaliculaire. Acad. Sci., C.R., Sér. D, 274:14, 2026–2029, 3 figs., 1 pl. (French).

REMY, J. A.   See also: Crusafont Pairó, M. and Remy, J. A., 1970A.

RENNIE, GEORGE S., III
1969A   Reproduction of a skeleton. Discovery, 5:1, 17–22, 15 figs.

RENSBERGER, JOHN M.
1969A   A new iniid cetacean from the Miocene of California. Calif., Univ., Publ. Geol. Sci., 82, 43 pp., 2 figs., 4 pls., 12 tables.
1971A   Entoptychine pocket gophers (Mammalia, Geomyoidea) of the early Miocene John Day formation, Oregon. Calif., Univ., Publ. Geol. Sci., 90, vi + 209 pp., 76 figs., 22 pls., 15 tables.
1972A   Relationships of *Haplomys*. Soc. Vert. Paleontol., Ann. Meeting, 32nd, 1972, Abstr. (abs.).

RENSCH, BERNARD
1965A   Rev.: Smith in New Sci., 56:819, 351.
1966A   Rev.: Heberer in Biol. Zentralbl., 86:2, 261.

1968A   Biophilosophie auf erkenntnistheoretischer Grundlage (Panpsychistischer Identismus). Stuttgart:
            Fischer Verlag, xii + 293 pp., 6 figs. (German).
            Rev.:   Rossi Ronchetti in Riv. Ital. Paleontol. Stratigr., 76:4, 626–627; Schindewolf in Zentralbl.
            Geol. Paläontol., Teil 2, 1969:2, 110–113; Struve in Natur Mus., 101:2, 89; Vogel in Z. Morphol.
            Anthropol., 60:3, 338–339.

1968B*   Handgebrauch und Verständigung bei Affen und Frühmenschen. Bern: Verlag Hans Huber, 173 pp.,
            illustr. (German).
            Rev.:   Ankel in Folia Primatol., 9:3–4, 315; Schwidetzky in Homo, 19:3–4, 238; Winter in Naturwiss.
            Rundsch., 22:9, 409.

1968C   Manipulierfähigkeit und Komplikation von Handlungsketten bei Menschenaffen. In: Rensch,
            Bernhard (ed.), 1968B, 103–130, 9 figs. (German).

1970A   Evolution of matter and consciousness and its relation to panpsychistic identism. In: Hecht, M. K.
            and Steere, W. C. (eds.), 1970A, 97–119.

1970B   Homo sapiens. Vom Tier zum Halbgott. Third edition. Göttingen: Vandenhoeck and Ruprecht,
            231 pp., 12 figs., 4 pls. (German).
            Rev.:   Vogel in Naturwiss. Rundsch., 24:10, 451.

1971A   Biophilosophy. Translated by C. A. M. Sym. New York and London: Columbia University Press,
            xi + 377 pp.
            Rev.:   Simpson in Amer. J. Phys. Anthropol., 37:2, 311.

REPENNING, CHARLES A.
1968A   Mandibular musculature and the origin of the subfamily Arvicolinae (Rodentia). Acta Zool. Crac.,
            13:3, 29–72, 10 figs. (Polish and Russian summaries).

REPENNING, C. A., COOLEY, M. E. and AKERS, J. P.
1969A   Stratigraphy of the Chinle and Moenkopi formations, Navajo and Hopi Indian reservations, Arizona,
            New Mexico, and Utah. U.S. Geol. Surv., Prof. Paper, 521–B, iii + 34 pp., 10 figs., 2 pls.,
            1 table.

REPENNING, CHARLES A.   See also: Hendey, Q. B. and Repenning, C. A., 1972A; Newcomb, R. C. and
            Repenning, C. A., 1970A.

REPÉRANT, JACQUES
1970A   Moulages endocraniens de Tylopodes fossiles. Ann. Paléontol., Vertébrés, 56:2, 111–145, 11 figs.
            (French; English summary).
            Rev.:   Thenius in Zentralbl. Geol. Paläontol., Teil 2, 1971:2–3, 200.

RESHETOV, ĨU. G.
1972A   Vystuplenie. [Discussion.] Vop. Antropol., 41, 155–157 (Russian).

RESHETOV, V. ĨU.
1969A   Nekotorye osobennosti postkranial'nogo skeleta bizonov v svíazi s istorieĭ roda Bison. [Some
            particularities of the postcranial skeleton of bisons in connection with the history of the genus
            Bison.] Mosk. Obshchest. Ispyt. Prir., Bĩull., Otd. Geol., 44:6, 147 (Russian).
1971A   O gigantskom nosoroge iz mestonakhozhdeniĩa Bolatam. [On the gigantic rhinoceros from the fossil
            locality Bolatam.] Mosk. Obshchest. Ispyt. Prir., Bĩull., Otd. Geol., 46:2, 151 (Russian).

RESHETOV, V. ĨU.   See also: Kalandadze, N. N. and Reshetov, V. ĨU., 1971A, 1971B; Kurochkin, E. N.,
            Kalandadze, N. N. and Reshetov, V. ĨU., 1970A.

REY, ROGER
1968A   Observations à la note de L. Ginsburg relative à la Limagne du Sud. Soc. Géol. Fr., C.R., 1968:1,
            23–24 (French).
1968B   Sur l'âge oligocène moyen des sables bleutés du Var. Discussion. Soc. Géol. Fr., C.R., 1968:2, 31–32
            (French).

REYMENT, R. A.
1970A*   Symposium on biometrical methods in paleontology. Uppsala Univ., Geol. Inst., Bull., 2, 6 + 89 pp.,
            illustr.
1971A   Introduction to quantitative paleoecology. New York: Elsevier Publishing Co., xiv + 226 pp., illustr.
            Rev.:   Craig in Nature, 233:5319, 431; Gould in Earth-Sci. Rev., 8:1, 75–76; Hughes in Science, 175:
            4026, 1101–1102.

REYNOLDS, ROBERT E. and JEFFERSON, GEORGE T.
1971A   Late Pleistocene vertebrates from Valley Wells, Mojave Desert, California. Geol. Soc. Amer., Abstr.,
            3:2, 183 (abs.).

1971B   Late Pleistocene vertebrates from Valley Wells, Mojave Desert, California. S. Calif. Paleontol. Soc., Bull., 3:10, 6 (reprinted from Geol. Soc. Amer., Abstr., 3:2, 1971).

REYNOLDS, VERNON
1967B   Rev.: Ankel in Homo, 20:3, 201.

RHODES, F. H. T. and BLOXAM, T. W.
1971A   Phosphatic organisms in the Paleozoic and their evolutionary significance. N. Amer. Paleontol. Conv., Proc., Part K, 1485–1513, 7 tables.

RIABCHIKOVA, E. D.
1970A   Novye dannye po raschleneniiu chetvertichnykh otlozheniĭ Novokuznetskogo opornogo razreza. [New data on the subdivision of Quaternary deposits of the Novokuznetsk key section.] Tomsk., Politekh. Inst., Izv., 185, 44–47 (Russian).

RIABUKHINA, SVETLANA GEORGIEVNA   See: Belousova, Z. D. and Riabukhina, S. G., 1971A.

RIAZA, FERNANDO
1967A   El hombre como fenómeno evolutivo según Teilhard de Chardin. Arbor, 67:257, 5–21 (Spanish).

RICCHETTI, G.   See: Piccarreta, G. and Ricchetti, G., 1970A.

RICE, DAVID G.
1969A   A potential early man locality in south-central Washington. Northwest. Sci., 43:4, 149–155, 2 figs.

RICH, PATRICIA VICKERS
1972A   A fossil avifauna from the upper Miocene Beglia formation of Tunisia. Tunisia, Serv. Géol., Notes, 35, 29–66, 9 figs., 8 tables (French summary).

RICH, PATRICIA V. and RICH, THOMAS
1972A   The Dromornithidae, a group of extinct, giant ground birds from the Cenozoic of Australia. Soc. Vert. Paleontol., Ann. Meeting, 32nd, 1972, Abstr. (abs.).

RICH, P. V.   See also: Cracraft, J. and Rich, P. V., 1972A; Feduccia, J. A. and Rich, P. V., 1972A; Rich, Th. H. V. and Rich, P. V., 1971A.

RICH, THOMAS H. V.
1971A   Deltatheridia, Carnivora, and Condylarthra (Mammalia) of the early Eocene, Paris Basin, France. Calif., Univ., Publ. Geol. Sci., 88, 72 pp., 18 figs., 32 tables.
             Rev.: Thenius in Zentralbl. Geol. Paläontol., Teil 2, 1971:6, 518–519; Van Valen in J. Paleontol., 46:6, 929.

RICH, THOMAS H. V. and RICH, PAT VICKERS
1971A   Brachyerix, a Miocene hedgehog from western North America, with a description of the tympanic regions of Paraechinus and Podogymnura. Amer. Mus. Nov., 2477, 58 pp., 22 figs., 4 tables.

RICH, THOMAS H. V.   See also: Rich, P. V. and Rich, T., 1972A.

RICHARDSON, B. J.   See: Air, G. M., Thompson, O. P., Richardson, B. J. and Sharman, G. B., 1971A.

RICHARDSON, EUGENE S., JR.
1969A   Paleontological Convention notes. Chicago, Field Mus. Natur. Hist., Bull., 40:10, 10–11, 7 figs.
1972A   The early history of the geology department. Chicago, Field Mus. Natur. Hist., Bull., 43:5, 6–8, illustr.

RICHARDSON, EUGENE S., JR. and JOHNSON, R. G.
1971A   The Mazon Creek faunas. N. Amer. Paleontol. Conv., Proc., Part I, 1222–1235, 3 figs., 2 tables.

RICHMOND, ROLLIN   See: Levene, H., Ehrman, L. and Richmond, R., 1970A.

RICQLÈS, ARMAND DE
1969A   Recherches paléohistologiques sur les os longs des tétrapodes. II. – Quelques observations sur la structure des os longs des thériodontes. Ann. Paléontol., Vertébrés, 55:1, 3–52, 6 figs., 8 pls. (French).
1969B   Un reptile fossile africain rapproche-t-il les continents? Atomes, 265, 318–319, 2 figs. (French).
1970A   Entre reptiles et mammifères. La Recherche, 1:2, 181, 2 figs. (French).

1970B   En Afrique coexistence de l'australopithèque et de l'homme. La Recherche, 1:3, 277 (French).
1970C   Fil d'Ariane des tétrapodes. La Recherche, 1:7, 686—687, 2 figs. (French).
1971A   L'origine des oiseaux. La Recherche, 10, 213—221, 9 figs. (French).
1971B   Les performances d'*Archaeopteryx*. La Recherche, 14, 684 (French).
1971C   Les virus agents de l'évolution? La Recherche, 2:16, 878—879, 1 fig. (French).
1971D   La paléontologie aux États-Unis. La Recherche, 2:18, 1076—1077, 2 figs. (French).
1972A   Nature et signification des "surfaces épiphysaires" chez les tétrapodes fossiles. Acad. Sci., C.R.,
          Sér. D, 274:26, 3527—3530, 1 pl. (French).
1972B   Recherches paléohistologiques sur les os longs des tétrapodes. III. — Titanosuchiens, Dinocéphales
          et Dicynodontes. Ann. Paléontol., Vertébrés, 58:1, 17—77, 15 figs., 8 pls. (French; English
          summary).
1972C   Vers une histoire de la physiologie thermique. Les données histologiques et leur interprétation
          fonctionnelle. Acad. Sci., C.R., Sér. D, 275:16, 1745—1748, 1 fig. (French).
1972D   Vers une histoire de la physiologie thermique. L'apparition de l'endothermie et le concept de
          reptile. Acad. Sci., C.R., Sér. D, 275:17, 1875—1878 (French).

RICQLÈS, ARMAND J. DE   See also: Bonis, L. de, Lebeau, M.-O. and Ricqlès, A. de, 1972A; Castanet, J.,
          Gasc, J.-P., Meunier, F. and Ricqlès, A. de, 1970A; Poplin, C. M. and Ricqlès, A. J. de, 1970A.

RIDDELL, FRANCIS A.
1969A   Pleistocene faunal remains associated with carbonaceous material. Amer. Antiquity, 34, 177—180,
          2 figs.

RIDDELL, FRANCIS A. and OLSEN, WILLIAM H.
1969A   An early man site in the San Joaquin Valley, California. Amer. Antiquity, 34, 121—130, 7 figs.,
          1 table.

RIDE, W. D. L.
1967A   On *Sceparnodon ramsayi* Owen, 1884: the selection of a lectotype, the clarification of its type
          locality, and on its identity with *Phascolonus gigas* (Owen, 1859). S. Austral. Mus., Rec., 15:3,
          419—425, 3 figs.
1968A   On the past, present and future of Australian mammals. Austral. J. Sci., 31:1, 1—11, 6 figs.
1971A   On the fossil evidence of the evolution of the Macropodidae. Austral. Zool., 16:1, 2 figs., 1 table.

RIEK, GUSTAV
1969A   Bärenunterkieferhälften als Waffen oder Werkzeuge der Paläolithiker. Jahresschrift Mitteldeutsch.
          Vorgesch., 53, 141—147, 1 pl. (German).

RIETH, ADOLF
1970A   Wie hat der Urmensch ausgesehen? Kosmos (Stuttgart), 66:3, 102—109, 7 figs. (German).

RIGHTMIRE, G. P.
1972A   Multivariate analysis of an early hominid metacarpal from Swartkrans. Science (AAAS), 176:4031,
          159—161, 1 fig., 1 table.

RINGEADE, MICHEL
1967A   De quelques niveaux continentaux oligo-miocènes d'Aquitaine. Intérêt des faunes de rongeurs
          recueillies. Soc. Linn. Bordeaux, Actes, Sér. B, 104:6, 1—3 (French).
1967B   Étude en Aquitaine de niveaux continentaux à la limite éocène-oligocène. Découverte de rongeurs
          Théridomorphes. Soc. Linn. Bordeaux, Actes, Sér. B, 104:7, 1—3 (French).
1967C   Nouvelles découvertes paléontologiques dans les faciès continentaux dits de "la molasse de l'Agenais".
          Soc. Linn. Bordeaux, Actes, Sér. B, 104:18, 3—7 (French).
1967D   Sur de nouveaux points fossilifères en rongeurs et charophytes dans les faciès continentaux dits du
          "calcaire de Castillon" et de la "molasse du Fronsadais". Soc. Linn. Bordeaux, Actes, Sér. B,
          104:20, 1—3 (French).

RIPOLL PERELLÓ, EDUARDO
1964B   Para una cronología relativa del arte levantino español. In: Pericot García, L. and Ripoll Perelló, E.
          (eds.), 1964A, 167—175 (Spanish; English summary).
1964C   Problemas cronológicos del arte paleolítico. In: Pericot García, L. and Ripoll Perelló, E. (eds.),
          1964A, 83—100, 7 figs. (Spanish; English summary).
1966A   Abate André Glory (1906—1966). Ampurias, 28, 308—309 (Spanish).
1966B   Prof. Miguel Fusté Ara (1919—1966). Ampurias, 28, 309—311, portr. (Spanish).
1967A   Dr. Giuseppe Isetti (1922—1965). Ampurias, 29, 327 (Spanish).
1967B   Prof. Raymond Vaufray (1890—1967). Ampurias, 29, 327—331 (Spanish).
1967C   Prof. Lothar F. Zotz (1899—1967). Ampurias, 29, 334—335 (Spanish).

1968A*   Simposio de arte rupestre. Barcelona 1966. Barcelona: Diputación Provincial de Barcelona, 310 pp.,
           illustr. (Spanish).
           Rev.: Jordá Cerdá in Zephyrus, 19—20, 204—208; kv in Archeol. Roz., 23:2, 237—238 (Czech).
1969-70A   Grabados paleolíticos en Balzi Rossi (Liguria). Ampurias, 31—32, 231—232, 1 fig. (Spanish).
1969-70B   Louis Méroc (1904—1970). Ampurias, 31—32, 372—373 (Spanish).

RIPOLL PERELLÓ, EDUARDO   See also: Pericot García, L. and Ripoll Perelló, E. (eds.), 1964A .

RIQUET, R.
1966A   Variations historiques de quelques diamètres crâniens. (Summary). Soc. Anthropol. Paris, Bull. Mém.,
           Sér. 11, 9:4, 485—486 (French).
1969A   La race de Cro-Magnon: abus de langage ou réalité objective?   Int. Congr. Anthropol. Ethnol. Sci.,
           8th, Tokyo, 1968, Proc., Vol. I. Anthropology, 106—110, 2 tables (French).

RITCHIE, ALEXANDER
1968B   Phlebolepis elegans Pander, an upper Silurian thelodont from Oesel, with remarks on the morphology
           of thelodonts. Nobel Symp., 4th, Stockholm, 1967, Proc., 1968, 81—88, 4 figs.
1969A   Ancient fish of Australia. Austral. Natur. Hist., 16:7, 218—223, 4 figs.
1971A   Fossil fish discoveries in Antarctica. Austral. Natur. Hist., 17:3, 65—71.

RITCHIE, WILLIAM A.
1969A   The archaeology of New York state. Revised edition. New York: Natural History Press, 343 pp.,
           illustr.
           Rev.: Lloyd in Geotimes, 14:6, 37.

RITZKOWSKI, SIEGFRIED
1965A   Der Schlierbacher Muschelkalk-Graben und sein Buntsandsteinrahmen am Ostrande des Kellerwalds
           (nördliches Hessen). Hess. Landesamt Bodenforsch., Notizbl., 93, 147—175, 4 figs., 1 table
           (German).
1969A   Stratigraphie der eozaen/oligozaenen Sedimente im nördlichen Hessen und ihre Parallelisierung zu
           anderen Tertiaergebieten. Colloque sur l'Éocène, Paris, mai 1968, Vol. III. Fr., Bur. Rech.
           Géol. Minières, Mém., 69, 255—258 (German; French summary).

RIVAS, OSCAR E. ODREMAN
1969A   Los Polymorphinae, un diferente tipo adaptativo de los Proterotheriidae (Mammalia, Litopterna).
           Ameghiniana, 6:1, 57—64, 1 pl. (Spanish; English summary).

RIVIÈRE, ALPHONSE ENNEMOND AUGUSTE
1837B   Note sur un énorme fossile trouvé dans la Louisiane. Paris: Impr. de Fain, in 8º, 8 pp. (French).

RIXON, A. E.
1968A   The development of the remains of a small Scelidosaurus from a Lias nodule. Mus. J., 67:4, 315—321,
           5 figs.

ROBBA, ELIO
1970A   Otoliti del Tortoniano-tipo (Piemonte). Riv. Ital. Paleontol. Stratigr., 76:1, 89—172, 1 fig., 9 pls.,
           2 tables (Italian; English summary).
           Rev.: Weiler in Zentralbl. Geol. Paläontol., Teil 2, 1971:5, 406.

ROBBINS, LAWRENCE H.
1972A   Archeology in the Turkana district, Kenya. Science (AAAS), 176:4033, 359—366, 6 figs.

ROBERT, ROMAIN and NOUGIER, L. R.
1968A   Corne d'appel du Magdalénien final des Pyrénées. Quartär, 19, 369—372, 1 pl. (French).

ROBERT, ROMAIN   See also: Beltran, A., Robert, R. and Gailli, R., 1967A; Caralp, E., Nougier, L.-R. and
           Robert, R., 1970A; Gailli, R., Nougier, L.-R. and Robert, R., 1969A; Nougier, L. R. and
           Robert, R., 1968A, 1970A, 1971A.

ROBERTS, MICHAEL FOSTER
1970A   Late glacial and postglacial environments in southeastern Wyoming. Palaeogeogr. Palaeoclimatol.
           Palaeoecol., 8, 5—17, 6 figs.

ROBERTS, MIRIAM
1970A   Bibliography of the geology and mineral resources of Oregon (fourth supplement), Jan. 1, 1956 —
           Dec. 31, 1960. Bull. Dept. Geol. Min. Indust. Oregon, 67, 1—88.

ROBERTSON, GEORGE M.
1970A   The oral region of ostracoderms and placoderms: possible phylogenetic significance. Amer. J. Sci.,
            269:1, 39–64.
1970B   The oral region of ostracoderms and placoderms: possible phylogenetic significance. Amer. J. Sci.,
            269:3, 320.

ROBERTSON, JESSE S.
1969A   Fossil *Bison* from Florida. Plaster Jacket, 12, 10 pp., 5 figs., 1 map, 1 table.
1971A   Blancan mammals from Haile XV A, Alachua County, Florida. Diss. Abstr., 32:4, 2310B (abs.).

ROBINEAU, D.   See: Lessertisseur, J. and Robineau, D., 1969A, 1970A.

ROBINSON, JOHN T.
1966B   Adaptive radiations in the australopithecines and the origin of man. In: Howell, F. C. and
            Bourliere, F. (eds.), 1966A, 385–416, 9 figs.
1968A   Adaptive radiation in the australopithecines and the origin of man. In: Cohen, Y. A. (ed.), 1968A,
            156–171 (reprinted from Robinson, 1963).
1969A   Dentition and adaptation in early hominids. Int. Congr. Anthropol. Ethnol. Sci., 8th, Tokyo, 1968,
            Proc., Vol. I. Anthropology, 302–305, 5 figs.
1970A   Dental evidence of ecological differences among early hominids. Amer. J. Phys. Anthropol., 33:1,
            142 (abs.).
1970B   Comments. Curr. Anthropol., 11:1, 33–34.
1971A   Variation and taxonomy of the early hominids. In: Dolhinow, P. and Sarich, V. M. (eds.), 1971A,
            123–155, 5 figs., 7 tables (reprinted from Dobzhansky, Hecht and Steere, eds., 1967,
            Evolutionary biology, vol. 1).
1972A   Reply to Professor Tobias. Nature, 239:5373, 469.
1972B   The bearing of East Rudolf fossils on early hominid systematics. Nature, 240:5378, 239–240.
1972C   The origin and adaptive radiation of the Australopithecines. In: McCown, T. D. and Kennedy,
            K. A. R. (eds.), 1972A, 421–450, 5 figs. (reprinted from Evolution and Hominisation, 1968).

ROBINSON, PAMELA LAMPLUGH
1967C   The Indian Gondwana formations – a review. Int. Union Geol. Sci., 1st. Symp. Gondwana Stratigr.,
            Rev., 1967, 201–268, 8 figs., 3 tables.
1971A   A problem of faunal replacement on Permo-Triassic continents. Palaeontology, 14:1, 131–153,
            4 figs., 2 maps, 3 tables.
1971B   Second symposium on Gondwana stratigraphy and paleontology, South Africa, 1970. Geol. Soc.
            London, J., 127:2, 189–191.

ROBINSON, PETER
1957C   Species of *Notharctus* from the middle Eocene of North America. N. Mex. Geol. Soc., Guidebk.,
            Field Conf. 8, 254 (abs.).
1968C   Nyctitheriidae (Mammalia, Insectivora) from the Bridger formation of Wyoming. Wyo., Univ., Contrib.
            Geol., 7:2, 129–138, 2 pls., 2 tables.
1968D   Smaller mammals of the Split Rock formation of central Wyoming. Colorado, Univ. Mus., Field
            Confer. Guidebk., 82–84.
1968E   Comments on the smaller mammals of Miocene age from Middle Park, Colorado. Colorado, Univ.
            Mus., Field Confer. Guidebk., 194–197.
1972A   Miocene stratigraphy of central Tunisia. Soc. Vert. Paleontol., Ann. Meeting, 32nd, 1972, Abstr. (abs.).

ROBINSON, PETER and BLACK, CRAIG C.
1969A   Note préliminaire sur les vertébrés fossiles du Vindobonien (formation Béglia), du Bled Douarah,
            gouvernorat de Gafsa, Tunisie. Tunisia, Serv. Géol., Notes, 31, 67–70 (French).

ROCHE, JEAN
1966A   Souvenir de l'Abbé Breuil. Lisbon, Univ., Fac. Letr., Rev., Sér. 3, 10, 287–302 (French).
1972A   Faunes du Pléistocène supérieur et final de l'Estremadura, Portugal. Ann. Paléontol., Vertébrés, 58:2,
            229–242, 1 fig. (French; English summary).

ROCHE, J. and VEIGA FERREIRA, O. DA
1970A   Stratigraphie et faunes des niveaux paléolithiques de la Grotte de Salemas (Ponte de Lousa). Port.,
            Serv. Geol., Comun., 54, 263–269, 2 figs. (French).

RODENDORF, BORIS BORISOVICH
1970A   Znachenie nasekomykh v istoricheskom razvitii nazemnykh pozvonochnykh. [Significance of insects
            in the evolution of land vertebrates.] Paleontol. Zh., 1970:1, 10–18, 4 figs. (Russian).

RODIONOVA, V. A.   See: Speranskiĭ, V. S., Artem'eva, V. I., Osipova, V. A. and Rodionova, V. A., 1971A.

RODRIGO GAINZA, L.   See: Russo, A. and Rodrigo Gainza, L., 1965A.

RODZIANKO, G. N.
    1970A   Neogenovaia sistema. [Neogene system.] Geologiiă SSSR, 46, Rostov, Volgograd, Astrakhan'
                Provinces and Kalmyk ASSR, 410–447, 4 figs., 1 table (Russian).

ROE, DEREK ARTHUR
    1970A   Prehistory: an introduction. Berkeley: University of California Press, 288 pp., 142 figs.
                Rev.: Fleming in Prehist. Soc., Proc., 37:1, 246–247; Marks in Amer. Anthropol., 73:6, 1395–1397.

ROECK, BERND
    1968A   Ehemalige Interessenten für Geologie in Augsburg und dortige Fundmöglichkeiten. Aufschluss, 19,
                145–148, 6 figs. (German).

ROGACHEV, A. N.
    1972A   P. P. Efimenko i voprosy sotsiologii pervobytnogo obshchestva (kratkiĭ istoriograficheskiĭ ocherk).
                [P. P. Efimenko and the problems of sociology of the primitive society (a short historiographic
                sketch).] Akad. Nauk SSSR, Inst. Arkheol., Krat. Soobshch., 131, 5–10 (Russian).

ROGER, J.
    1970A   La paléoécologie. Soc. Écol., Bull., 1:4, 233–238 (French).

ROGERS, MALCOLM JENNINGS
    1966A   Rev.: Lambert in El Palacio, 74:4, 39–40.

ROGINSKIĬ, IA. IA. (= ROGUINSKY, Y. Y.)
    1965A   Links between physical and cultural evolution. UNESCO (Int. Soc. Sci. J.), 17:1, 131–134.
    1969A   Proiskhozhdenie cheloveka i stratigrafiia pleistotsena. [The origin of man and the Pleistocene
                stratigraphy.] In: Noveĭshaia tektonika, noveĭshie otlozheniia i chelovek, 1, 211–222 (Russian).
    1969B   Nakhodka drevneĭshego cheloveka v Vengrii. [The finding of earliest man in Hungary.] Vop.
                Antropol., 31, 171–172 (Russian).
    1969C   Alesh Grdlichka i problema pervonachal'nogo zaseleniia Ameriki. [Aleš Hrdlička and the problem of
                ancient population of America.] Vop. Antropol., 33, 8–11 (Russian).
    1969D   Problemy antropogeneza. [Problems of anthropogenesis.] Moscow: "Vysshaia Shkola" Press, 259 pp.,
                illustr. (Russian).
                Rev.: Uryson in Vop. Antropol., 36, 171–173 (Russian).
    1970A   Chto my dumaem o proiskhozhdenii cheloveka. Argumenty v pol'zu monotsentrizma. [What do we
                think about the origin of man. Arguments in favor of monocentrism.] Priroda, 1970:10,
                34–37, 5 figs., portr. (Russian).
    1972A   O nereshennykh problemakh vozniknoveniia cheloveka sovremennogo tipa. [On the unsolved
                problems of the emergence of man of the modern type.] Vop. Antropol., 40, 5–14 (Russian).

ROGINSKIĬ, IA. IA. and IAKIMOV, V. P.
    1968A   Teoreticheskoe nasledie A.N. Severtsova i nekotorye problemy antropogeneza. [The theoretical
                heritage of A.N. Severtsov and some problems of anthropogenesis.] Zh. Obshch. Biol., 29:1,
                68–77 (Russian; English summary).

ROGINSKIĬ, IA. IA.   See also: Aĭzenberg, D. M. and Roginskiĭ, Ia. Ia., 1970A.

ROGUINSKY, Y. Y.   See: Roginskiĭ, Ia. Ia.

ROLINGSON, MARTHA ANN and SCHWARTZ, DOUGLAS W.
    1966B   Late Paleo-Indian and early Archaic manifestations in western Kentucky. Stud. Anthropol., 3, 168 pp.,
                illustr.
                Rev.: Faulkner in Tenn. Archaeol., 22, 43–44.

ROLLIN, FRANÇOIS
    1969A   L'évolution humaine. Inform. Sci., 24:1, 7–22 (French).

ROMANOV, V. V.
    1970A   O vozraste tak nazyvaemoĭ perekhodnoĭ pachki v basseĭne r. Salmysh (Orenburgskaia obl.). [On the
                age of the so-called transition beds in the Salmysh R. basin (Orenburg Prov.).] In: Voprosy
                geologii Iuzhnogo Urala i Povolzh'ia, 7:1, 34–41 (Russian).

ROMANOVA, E. N.   See: Sementsov, A. A., Romanova, E. N. and Dolukhanov, P. M., 1969A.

ROMANOVSKÝ, A.   See: Špinar, Z. V., Boubelík, M. and Romanovský, A., 1971A.

ROMER, ALFRED SHERWOOD
1966C   Rev.: Morrison in Sci. Amer., 220:6, 142; Müller in Biol. Zentralbl., 87:1, 130—131; Roth-Lutra in
             Anat. Anz., 123:4, 477—478.
1966D   Rev.: Bauer in Biol. Zentralbl., 87:2, 267; Herre in Z. Tierzücht. Züchtungsbiol., 84:1, 97; Reisinger
             in Z. Zool. Syst. Evolut.-Forsch., 10:2, 158—159.
1968A   Rev.: Bishop in New Sci., 41:641, 648; Campillo Valero in Ampurias, 31—32, 394—395; Chrulew in
             Zentralbl. Geol. Paläontol., Teil 2, 1970:1, 1—4; Morrison in Sci. Amer., 220:6, 142; Roth-Lutra
             in Anat. Anz., 127:1, 127—128.
1968C   The procession of life. Cleveland, Ohio: World Publishing Company; London: Weidenfeld and
             Nicolson, 323 pp., 58 figs., 30 pls.
             Rev.: Inqlis in J. Natur. Hist., London, 3, 302—303; Simons in Austral. J. Sci., 31:5, 201; Smith in
             Quart. Rev. Biol., 44:3, 305.
1968D   Summary of vertebrate paleontology. In: Moore, R. C., et al., 1968A, 1371—1373.
1968E   Fossils and Gondwanaland. Amer. Phil. Soc., Proc., 112:5, 335—343, 6 figs.
1969A   The Chañares (Argentina) Triassic reptile fauna. V. A new chiniquodontid cynodont, Probelesodon
             lewisi — cynodont ancestry. Breviora, 333, 24 pp., 7 figs.
1969B   The cranial anatomy of the Permian amphibian Pantylus. Breviora, 314, 37 pp., 16 figs.
             Rev.: Westphal in Zentralbl. Geol. Paläontol., Teil 2, 1970:5, 431.
1969C   The Brazilian Triassic cynodont reptiles Belesodon and Chiniquodon. Breviora, 332, 16 pp., 9 figs.
1969D   Vertebrate history with special reference to factors related to cerebellar evolution. In: Llinás, R.
             (ed.), 1969A, 1—18, 16 figs.
1969E   A temnospondylous labyrinthodont from the lower Carboniferous. Kirtlandia, 6, 20 pp., 7 figs.
             Rev.: Westphal in Zentralbl. Geol. Paläontol., Teil 2, 1970:5, 431.
1969F   The 1968 British symposium. Soc. Vert. Paleontol., News Bull., no. 85, 55—56.
1969G   Cynodont reptile with incipient mammalian jaw articulation. Science (AAAS), 166:3907, 881—882,
             1 fig.
1969H   The Triassic faunal succession and the Gondwanaland problem. Symp. Gondwana Stratigr., 375—400
             (Spanish summary).
1969I   Vertebrate paleontology and zoology. Biologist, 51:2, 49—53.
1969J   Topics in therapsid evolution and classification. Indian Geol. Ass., Bull., 2:1—2, 15—26, 2 tables.
1969K   Teaching vertebrate paleontology. N. Amer. Paleontol. Conv., Proc., Part A, 39—46.
1970A   The Chañares (Argentina) Triassic reptile fauna. VI. A chiniquodontid cynodont with an incipient
             squamosal-dentary jaw articulation. Breviora, no. 344, 18 pp., 9 figs.
1970B   A new anthracosaurian labyrinthodont, Proterogyrinus scheelei, from the lower Carboniferous.
             Kirtlandia, no. 10, 16 pp., 8 figs.
             Rev.: Westphal in Zentralbl. Geol. Paläontol., Teil 2, 1971:4, 334—335.
1970C   The vertebrate body. Fourth edition. Philadelphia, London and Toronto: W. B. Saunders Co.,
             viii + 601 pp., 415 figs.
             Rev.: Kinch in Ohio J. Sci., 71:2, 72.
1971A   Unorthodoxies in reptilian phylogeny. Evolution, 25:1, 103—112, 3 figs.
1971B   The Chañares (Argentina) Triassic reptile fauna. VIII. A fragmentary skull of a large thecodont,
             Luperosuchus fractus. Breviora, 373, 8 pp., 4 figs.
1971C   The Chañares (Argentina) Triassic reptile fauna. IX. The Chañares formation. Breviora, 377, 1—8,
             1 table.
1971D   The Chañares (Argentina) Triassic reptile fauna. X. Two new but incompletely known long-limbed
             pseudosuchians. Breviora, 378, 1—10, 3 figs.
1971E   The Chañares (Argentina) Triassic reptile fauna. XI. Two new long-snouted thecodonts,
             Chanaresuchus and Gualosuchus. Breviora, 379, 1—22, 7 figs.
1971F   Major steps in vertebrate evolution. In: Dolhinow, P. and Sarich, V. M. (eds.), 1971A, 37—58, 4 figs.
             (reprinted from Science, 158, 1629—1637).
1971G   Vergleichende Anatomie der Wirbeltiere. Translated from English by H. Frick. Third edition.
             Hamburg: Parey Press, 590 pp., 415 figs. (German).
             Rev.: Haltenorth in Säugetierkundl. Mitt., 20:1—2, 187; Mayet in Anat. Anz., 131:3—4, 347;
             Niethammer in Bonner Zool. Beitr., 23:1, 74; Westphal in Zentralbl. Geol. Paläontol., Teil 2,
             1971:6, 431—432.
1972A   The Chañares (Argentina) Triassic reptile fauna. XII. The postcranial skeleton of the thecodont
             Chanaresuchus. Breviora, 385, 21 pp., 2 figs., 1 pl.
1972B   The Chañares (Argentina) Triassic reptile fauna. XIII. An early ornithosuchid pseudosuchian,
             Gracilisuchus stipanicicorum gen. et sp. nov. Breviora, 389, 24 pp., 9 figs., 1 pl., 1 table.
1972C   The Chañares (Argentina) Triassic reptile fauna. XIV. Lewisuchus admixtus gen. et sp. nov., a
             further thecodont from the Chañares beds. Breviora, 390, 13 pp., 8 figs.
1972D   The Chañares (Argentina) Triassic reptile fauna. XV. Further remains of the thecodonts Lagerpeton
             and Lagosuchus. Breviora, 394, 7 pp., 6 figs.
1972E   South American fossil reptiles as evidence of Gondwanaland. Austral. Natur. Hist., 17:6, 206—212,
             5 figs.

1972F   The Chañares (Argentina) Triassic reptile fauna. XVI. Thecodont classification. Breviora, 395, 24 pp.
1972G   The Chañares (Argentina) Triassic reptile fauna. XVII. The Chañares gomphodonts. Breviora, 396,
            9 pp., 7 figs.
1972H   Permian reptiles. In: Hallam, A. (ed.), 1972C, illustr.
1972I   A carboniferous labyrinthodont amphibian with complete dermal armor. Kirtlandia, 16, 8 pp., 4 figs.
1972J   Tetrapod vertebrates and Gondwanaland. Gondwana Symp., 2nd, Proc., Pap., 111–124.
1972K   Skin breathing-primary or secondary? Resp. Physiol., 14, 183–192, 2 figs.
1972L   The vertebrate as a dual animal-somatic and visceral. In: Dobzhansky, Th., Hecht, M. K. and Steere,
            W. C. (eds.), 1972B, 121–156, 9 figs.

RÖMISCH-GERMANISCHES ZENTRALMUSEUM, MAINZ and BUTLER, JAY J.
    1964A *   COWA surveys and bibliographies, western Europe: part II. COWA Surv. and Bibliog., Area 3, no. 2,
               35 pp.

RÓNAI, A.
    1968A   The Quaternary of the Hungarian Basin. Guide to Excursion 41C, Hungary. Int. Geol. Congr., 23rd,
               Czech., Guidebk., 74 pp., 19 figs., map.

RONIEWICZ, EWA   See: Osmólska, H. and Roniewicz, E., 1970A; Osmólska, H., Roniewicz, E. and
                        Barsbold, R., 1972A.

ROPER, MARILYN KEYES
    1969A   A survey of the evidence for intrahuman killing in the Pleistocene. With comments and reply. Current
               Anthropol., 10:4, 427–459, 5 tables.

ROSE, BRIAN
    1966A   New vistas of the past. Sci. S. Afr., 3:8, 5–8, illustr.

ROSE, FRANCIS L.
    1969A   Systematics, fossil history, and evolution of the genus Chrysemys. Amer. Phil. Soc.,,Yearb., 1968,
               330–332.

ROSE, KENNETH D.
    1972A   A new tillodont from the Eocene upper Willwood formation of Wyoming. Postilla, 155, 13 pp.,
               3 figs., 2 tables.

ROSE, WILLIAM D.
    1971A   Bibliography and index of Oklahoma geology. 1970. Okla. Geol. Notes, 31, 23–37.

ROSEN, DENNIS
    1968A   The jilting of Athene. New Sci., 39:613, 497–500, illustr.

ROSEN, DONN ERIC and PATTERSON, COLIN
    1969A   The structure and relationships of the paracanthopterygian fishes. Amer. Mus. Natur. Hist., Bull.,
               141:3, 361–474, 74 figs., 27 pls., 8 tables.
               Rev.: McAllister in Copeia, 1970:2, 400–401; McAllister in Quart. Rev. Biol., 45:2, 209.

ROSEN, S. I. and McKERN, THOMAS W.
    1971A   Several cranial indices and their relevance to fossil man. Amer. J. Phys. Anthropol., 35:1, 69–74,
               1 fig., 1 table.

ROSENFELD, ANDRÉE   See: Ucko, P. J. and Rosenfeld, A., 1967B.

ROSENKRANTZ, ALFRED
    1970A   Marine upper Cretaceous and lowermost Tertiary deposits in west Greenland. Dan. Geol. Foren., Medd
               19, 406–453, 16 figs. (Danish summary).

ROSHKA, VLADIMIR KHARLAMPIEVICH
    1969A   Neogenovaia sistema. Miotsen. [Neogene system. Miocene.] Geologiia SSSR, 45, Moldavian SSR,
               137–171, 5 figs. (Russian).

ROSIŃSKI, F.
    1970A   Comments. Curr. Anthropol., 11:1, 34–35.

ROSKOSZ, TADEUSZ   See: Jakubowski, G., Krysiak, K. and Roskosz, T., 1968A.

ROSSET, J.
    1962A   Réflexions sur le gigantisme. Est-il la cause de l'extinction des espèces? Cah. Étud. Biol., 1962:8–9,
             143–150 (French).

ROSSMANN, DAVID L.
    1971A   A comparison of root length of the anterior dentition from a modern population and the Krapina
             Neanderthal remains. Amer. J. Phys. Anthropol., 35:2, 294 (abs.).

ROTAĬ, AVRAAM PROKHOROVICH
    1963A   Permskaĭa sistema. Pechorskiĭ uglenosnyĭ basseĭn, Ural i Paĭ-Khoĭ. Nizhniĭ otdel. [Permian system.
             Pechora coal basin, Urals and Paĭ-Khoĭ. Lower section.] Geologiĭa SSSR, 2, Arkhangel'sk and
             Vologda Provinces, and Komi ASSR, 558–593, 2 tables (Russian).

ROTH, EDWARD L.
    1972A   Late Pleistocene mammals from Klein Cave, Kerr County, Texas. Tex. J. Sci., 24:1, 75–84.

ROTH, EDWARD L.   See also: Dalquest, W. W. and Roth, E., 1970A; Dalquest, W. W., Roth, E. and
             Judd, F., 1969A.

ROTHAUSEN, KARLHEINZ
    1966A   Fossile Flamingos im Tertiär des Mainzer Beckens. Rhein. Naturforsch. Ges., Z., 4, 26–31, 4 figs.
             (German).
    1967A   Die Klimabindung der Squalodontoidea (Odontoceti, Mamm.) und anderer mariner Vertebrata. Cologne,
             Univ., Geol. Inst., Sonderveröff., 13, 157–166 (German; English summary).
    1969A   Zonierung und Konnexe einer Abfolge oberaquitaner Land-Ökosysteme. Hess. Landesamt Bodenforsch.,
             Notizbl., 97, 81–97, 1 fig., 1 table (German; English summary).
    1970A   Marine reptilia and mammalia and the problem of the Oligocene-Miocene boundary. G. Geol., 35:1,
             181–190, 1 fig.
    1970B   *Praemegaceros* Portis, 1920 (Cervidae, Mamm.) als wichtiger stratigraphischer Beleg im Quartär von
             Kärlich/Neuwieder Becken (Mittelrhein). Mainzer Naturwiss. Arch., 9, 303–317, 4 figs., 1 pl.
             (German; English summary).
             Rev.: Thenius in Zentralbl. Geol. Paläontol., Teil 2, 1971:6, 523–524.
    1971A   *Cetotheriopsis tobieni* n. sp., der erste paläogene Bartenwal (Cetotheriidae, Mysticeti, Mamm.) nördlich
             des Tethysraumes. Hess. Landesamt. Bodenforsch., Abh., 60, 131–148, 3 figs., 3 pls., 1 table
             (German).

ROUSE, IRVING
    1972A   Introduction to prehistory: a systematic approach. New York: McGraw-Hill, xvii + 301 pp., illustr.

ROUSE, IRVING   See also: Cruxent, J. M. and Rouse, I., 1969A.

ROUSSEAU, GEORGES
    1969A   Lamarck et Darwin. Mus. Nat. Hist. Natur., Paris, Bull., 41:5, 1029–1041 (French).

ROUSSEAU, MICHEL
    1967A   Les grands félins dans l'art de notre préhistoire. Paris: Picard Ed., 200 pp., 125 figs., 14 pls. (French).
             Rev.: Alimen in Soc. Préhist. Fr., Bull., C.R., 64:7, 197–199.
    1969A   La scène du Puits de Lascaux. Hypothèses nouvelles. Sci. Progrès La Nature, 3408, 128–130, 3 figs.
             (French).
    1969B   Chefs-d'oeuvre de l'art paléolithique au Musée de Saint-Germain. Sci. Progrès Découverte, 3414, 386–
             388, 7 figs. (French).

ROUSSILLOT, C.   See: Rahmouni, O., Roussillot, C. and Armanet, F., 1970A.

ROUSSOT, ALAIN
    1970A   La grotte du Bison, commune de Meyrals (Dordogne). Une nouvelle main peinte. Soc. Hist. Archéol.
             Périgord, Bull., 97:1, 46–51, 3 figs. (French).

ROUSSOT, A., ANDRIEUX, C. and CHAUFFRIASSE, A.
    1968A   La grotte Nancy, commune de Sireuil (Dordogne). Soc. Hist. Archéol. Périgord, Bull., 95:1, 21–50,
             19 figs. (French).

ROUSSOT, A. and FERRIER, JEAN
    1970A   Le roc de Marcamps (Gironde). Quelques nouvelles observations. Soc. Préhist. Fr., Bull., Étud. Trav.,
             67:1, 293–303, 7 figs., 1 table (French).
    1971A   La grotte de Fontarnaud commune de Lugasson (Gironde). Soc. Préhist. Fr., Bull., Étud. Trav., 68:2,
             505–520, 11 figs., 2 tables (French).

ROUSSOT, A. and ROUSSOT-LARROQUE, J.
1968A   Notes de préhistoire en Périgord. II. Soc. Hist. Archéol. Périgord, Bull., 95:2, 139—153, 5 figs.
                    (French).

ROUSSOT-LARROQUE, J.   See: Roussot, A. and Roussot-Larroque, J., 1968A.

ROUTHIER, PIERRE and WATERLOT, GÉRARD
1968A   Pierre Pruvost (1890—1967). Soc. Géol. Fr., Bull., 10:5, 519—534, 1 portr.

ROUVREAU, MICHEL
1969A   Le gisement paléolithique "du Lycée," à Pons (Charente-Maritime). Soc. Préhist. Fr., Bull., C.R., 66:2,
                    37 (French).

ROUVREAU, MICHEL   See also: Lassarade, L., Rouvreau, M. and Texier, A., 1969A.

ROVNER, IRWIN and AGOGINO, G. A.
1969A   Minnesota man: archaeology's fickle female. Anthropol. J. Can., 7:1, 2—12.

ROVNER, IRWIN   See also: Agogino, G. A. and Rovner, I., 1969A.

ROWLAND, ROBERT W.
1972A   Paleontology and paleoecology of the San Diego formation in northwestern Baja California. San Diego
                    Soc. Natur. Hist., Trans., 25—32, 2 figs., 2 tables.

ROY, B. C.
1966A   General report of the Geological Survey of India for the year 1962—63. Geol. Surv. India, Rec., 97:1,
                    441 pp.

ROZANOV, V. I.   See : Lozovskiĭ, V. R. and Rozanov, V. I., 1969A.

ROZHDESTVENSKIĬ, ANATOLIĬ KONSTANTINOVICH (= ROZHDESTVENSKY, A. K.)
1968C   Gadrozavry Kazakhstana. [Hadrosaurs of Kazakhstan.] In: Verkhnepaleozoĭskie i mezozoĭskie
                    zemnovodnye i presmykaĭushchiesia SSSR, 97—141, 15 figs., 2 tables (Russian).
1969A   Na poiski dinozavrov v Gobi. [In search of dinosaurs in the Gobi.] Third edition, revised and
                    completed. Moscow: "Nauka" Press, 293 pp., illustr. (Russian).
1970A   O gigantskikh kogtevykh falangakh zagadochnykh reptiliĭ mezozoia. [On the gigantic claws of some
                    enigmatic Mesozoic reptiles.] Paleontol. Zh., 1970:1, 131—141, 7 figs. (Russian).
1970B   Giant claws of enigmatic Mesozoic reptiles. Paleontol. J., 4:1, 117—125, 7 figs.
                    Rev.: Chrulew in Zentralbl. Geol. Paläontol., Teil 2, 1971:1, 56—57.
1970C   Kompleksy mezozoĭskikh i kaĭnozoĭskikh nazemnykh pozvonochnykh Sredneĭ Azii i prilezhashchikh
                    raĭonov Kazakhstana i ikh stratigraficheskoe polozhenie. [Mesozoic and Cenozoic terrestrial
                    vertebrate complexes of central Asia and adjoining regions of Kazakhstan and their stratigraphic
                    position.] In: Biostratigraficheskie i paleobiofatsial'nye issledovaniia i ikh prakticheskoe
                    znachenie, 50—58 (Russian).
1971A   Ian Martynovich Eglon (1888—1971). Paleontol. Zh., 1971:4, 148—150, portr. (Russian).
1971B   Izuchenie dinozavrov Mongolii i ikh rol' v raschlenenii kontinental'nogo mezozoia. [The study of
                    Mongolian dinosaurs and their role in the subdivision of continental Mesozoic.] Sovm. Sovet.-
                    Mongol. Nauch.-Issled. Geol. Eksped., Tr., 3, 21—32, 2 tables (Russian).
1971C   Istoriia dinozavrovykh faun v svete paleobiogeografii. [History of dinosaur faunas in the light of
                    paleobiogeography.] In: Tezisy dokladov XVII sessii Vsesoiuznogo paleontologicheskogo
                    obshchestva, 25—29 ianv. 1971g., 70—72 (Russian).
1971D   Yan Martynovich Eglon (1888—1971). Paleontol. J., 5:4, 556—557.

ROZHDESTVENSKIĬ, A. K.   See also: Dmitriev, G. A. and Rozhdestvenskiĭ, A. K., 1968A.

RUBAĬLOVA, N. G.
1972A   Mysli Charlza Darvina o proiskhozhdenii cheloveka v zapisnykh knizhkakh o transmutatsii vidov 1837—
                    1839. [Charles Darwin's thoughts on the origin of man in the notebooks on transmutation of
                    species 1837—1839.] Vop. Antropol., 40, 32—44 (Russian).

RUBEN, JOHN A.
1971A   A Pliocene colubrid snake (Reptilia: Colubridae) from west-central Nevada. PaleoBios, 13, 19 pp.,
                    6 figs., 2 tables.

RUBIN, MEYER   See: Ray, C. E., Denny, C. S. and Rubin, M., 1970A.

RUBINGER, MARCOS
    1967A   El enfoque interdisciplinario sobre el origen del hombre desarrollado por la antropología soviética. Univ. Chile, Bol., 74, 32—35 (Spanish).

RUBINSHTEĬN, M. M. and GABUNIĬA, L. K.
    1972A   Nekotorye voprosy geokhronologii kaĭnozoĭa. [Some problems in Cenozoic geochronology.] Akad. Nauk SSSR, Izv., Ser. Geol., 1972:3, 3—8, 2 figs. (Russian).

RUBINSHTEĬN, M. M.   See also: Gabuniĭa, L. K. and Rubinshteĭn, M. M., 1965A, 1967A, 1968A, 1968B, 1968C.

RUCKENSTEINER, E.   See: Ehrenberg, K., Ruckensteiner, E., Adam, H. and Friedl, H., 1969A.

RUDKEVICH, M. ĬA.
    1964A   Verkhniĭ eotsen-nizhniĭ oligotsen (neraschlenennye). [Upper Eocene — lower Oligocene (undivided).] Geologiĭa SSSR, 44:1, West Siberian Lowlands, 160—163 (Russian).

RUDNER, IONE
    1970A   On how to prepare a fossil — a guide for beginners. S. Afr. Mus. Ass., Bull., 9:11, 402—408 (Dutch summary).

RUDNER, IONE   See also: Rudner, J. and Rudner, I., 1969A.

RUDNER, JALMAR and RUDNER, IONE
    1969A   Rock art in the Thirstland areas. S. Afr. Archaeol. Bull., 23, 75—89, 1 map, 1 table.

RUFFO, S.   See: Leonardi, P. and Ruffo, S., 1969A.

RUHE, ROBERT V.
    1961A   Landscapes and soils in the southern New Mexico desert: Organ Peak and Las Cruces quadrangles and adjacent areas, Dona Ana County. N. Mex. Geol. Soc., Guidebk., Field Conf. 12, 194—195 (abs.).

RUNCORN, STANLEY K.
    1971A*   Earth sciences. (The Royal Institution Library of Science, being the Friday evening discourses in physical science held at the Royal Institution 1851—1937). London: Applied Science, 3 vols., 1540 pp.
            Rev.: Eyles in Nature, 238:5364, 417—418; Stubbs in New Sci., 52:776, 282.

RUPRECHT, ANDRZEJ L.
    1971A   Słon leśny (*Palaeoloxodon antiquus*) w połnocno-wschodniej Polsce. [A straight-tusked elephant (*Palaeoloxodon antiquus*) in north-eastern Poland.] Folia Quaternaria, 37, 19—21, 1 pl. (Polish; English and Russian summaries).

RUSANOV, BORIS SERGEEVICH
    1968B   Biostratigrafiĭa kaĭnozoĭskikh otlozheniĭ ĭuzhnoĭ Ĭakutii. [Biostratigraphy of Cenozoic deposits of southern Iakutia.] Moscow: "Nauka" Press, 459 pp., 195 figs., 2 charts, 80 tables (Russian).

RUSSELL, DALE A.
    1966A   The skull of American mosasaurs. Diss. Abstr., 26:12, 7261 (abs.).
    1969A   A new specimen of *Stenonychosaurus* from the Oldman formation (Cretaceous) of Alberta. Can. J. Earth Sci., 6:4, 595—612, 17 figs., 8 tables.
    1970A   A skeletal reconstruction of *Leptoceratops gracilis* from the upper Edmonton formation (Cretaceous) of Alberta. Can. J. Earth Sci., 7:1, 181—184, 1 fig.
            Rev.: Chrulew in Zentralbl. Geol. Paläontol., Teil 2, 1971:1, 57.
    1970B   The vertebrate fauna of the Selma formation of Alabama: the mosasaurs. Fieldiana: Geol. Mem., 3:7, 363—380, 10 figs.
            Rev.: Westphal in Zentralbl. Geol. Paläontol., Teil 2, 1971:1, 52.
    1970C   Tyrannosaurs from the late Cretaceous of western Canada. Can. Nat. Mus., Publ. Pal., 1, 34 pp., 9 figs., 4 pls., tables (French summary).
    1970D   The dinosaurs of central Asia. Can. Geogr. J., 81:6, 208—215.
    1971A   The disappearance of dinosaurs. Can. Geogr. J., 83:6, 204—215, illustr.
    1972A   Ostrich dinosaurs from the late Cretaceous of western Canada. Can. J. Earth Sci., 9:4, 375—402, 10 figs., 7 tables.
    1972B   A pterosaur from the Oldman formation (Cretaceous) of Alberta. Can. J. Earth Sci., 9:10, 1338—1340, 1 fig., 1 table (French summary).

RUSSELL, DALE and TUCKER, WALLACE
1971A   Supernovae and the extinction of the dinosaurs. Nature, 229:5286, 553–554.

RUSSELL, DALE A.   See also: Colbert, E. H. and Russell, D. A., 1969A.

RUSSELL, DONALD E.
1967B   Le Paléocène continental d'Amérique du Nord. Mus. Nat. Hist. Natur., Paris, Mém., Sér. C, 16:2, 37–99, 3 figs. (French).

RUSSELL, DONALD E. and SIGÉ, B.
1970A   Révision des chiroptères lutétiens de Messel (Hesse, Allemagne). Palaeovertebrata (Montpellier), 3:4, 83–182, 29 figs., 6 pls., 5 tables (French; German and English summaries).

RUSSELL, DONALD   See also: Ginsburg, L., Mennessier, G. and Russell, D., 1967A; McKenna, M. C., Russell, D. E. and Savage, D. E., 1969A.

RUSSELL, LORIS S.
1967A   Rev.: D. Russell in Can. Field-Natur., 83:2, 177–178.
1968B   A new cetacean from the Oligocene Sooke formation of Vancouver Island, British Columbia. Can. J. Earth Sci., 5:4, 929–933, 3 figs., 2 pls.
1970A   Bibliography. Palaeontology. Toronto, Royal Ontario Museum, 4 pp., mimeographed.
1971A   Those remarkable dinosaurs. Rotunda, 4:1, 4–17, illustr.
1972A   A Paleocene faunule from the Ravenscrag formation of southwestern Saskatchewan. Soc. Vert. Paleontol., Ann. Meeting, 32nd, 1972, Abstr. (abs.).
1972B   Tertiary mammals of Saskatchewan part II: the Oligocene fauna, non-ungulate orders. Toronto, Roy. Ont. Mus., Life Sci., Contrib., 84, 97 pp., 17 figs.

RUSSI, V.
1968A   Sannicandro Garganico (Prov. di Foggia). Riv. Sci. Preist., 23:2, 400 (Italian).
1968B   Apricena (Prov. di Foggia). Riv. Sci. Preist., 23:2, 400–401 (Italian).

RUSSO, A. and RODRIGO GAINZA, L.
1965A   Estratigrafía y paleogeografía del Grupo Puca en Bolivia. Inst. Boliviano Petról., Bol., 5:3, 5–51 (Spanish).

RUST, B. R.   See: Dineley, D. L. and Rust, B. R., 1968A.

RUTTE, ERWIN
1970A   Die Cromer-Wirbeltierfundstelle Würzburg-Schalksberg. Naturwiss. Ver. (Würzburg) (1967), 8, 1–26 (German).
         Rev.: Thenius in Zentralbl. Geol. Paläontol., Teil 2, 1971:2–3, 193.
1971A   Fossilführender Mittlerer Muschelkalk in Unterfranken. Hess. Landesamt Bodenforsch., Abh., 60, 149–153, 2 figs. (German).

RUTTEN, M. G.
1962A   The geological aspects of the origin of life on earth. Amsterdam and New York: Elsevier Publishing Co., 146 pp., 36 figs.

RYAN, B.
1965A   The evolution of man: some theological, philosophical and scientific considerations. Westminster, Maryland: Newman Press.

RYBAKOV, B. A.
1969A*   Arkheologicheskie otkrytiiā 1968 goda. [Archeological discoveries of 1968.] Moscow: "Nauka" Press, 463 pp., illustr. (Russian).
1970A*   Arkheologicheskie otkrytiiā 1969 goda. [Archeological discoveries of 1969.] Moscow: "Nauka" Press, 456 pp., illustr. (Russian).

RYDER, MICHAEL L.
1969A   Animal bones in archaeology. Book of notes and drawings for beginners. (Mammal Society handbooks) Oxford and Edinburgh: Blackwell (Sci.), xxiv + 65 pp.
         Rev.: Fagg in New Sci., 43:657, 92; Haltenorth in Säugetierkundl. Mitt., 17:2, 198; Higgs in Antiquity 43:171, 246; Higgs in Nature, 222:5196, 904–905; Macintosh in Austral. J. Sci., 32:3, 114.

RYKOV, S. P. and MINIKH, M. G.
  1969A   O novykh nakhodkakh dipnoĭ v razreze gory Bol'shoe Bogdo. [On recent finds of Dipnoi in the
              quarry of Mount Bogdo.] Akad. Nauk SSSR, Dokl., 188:2, 414–416, 2 figs. (Russian).
  1970A   New finds of Dipnoi in the section of the Bol'shoye Bogdo Mountain. Akad. Nauk SSSR, Dokl.,
              Earth Sci. Sec., 188, 55–56, 2 figs. (Translated from Russian: Akad. Nauk SSSR, Dokl., 1969,
              188:2, 414–416.)

RYZIEWICZ, ZBIGNIEW
  1964A   Pleistozäne Säugetiere als klimatische Indicatoren des Eiszeitalters. Int. Ass. Quaternary Res., 6th Congr.
              (1961), Rept., 2, 573–576 (German).
  1969A   Szczątki waleni mioceńskich z Pińczowa. [Miocene whale remains from Pińczów.] Przegl. Zool., 13:2,
              225–226, 1 fig. (Polish; English summary).
  1969B   Badania nad niedźwiedziami plioceńskimi. [Research on Pliocene bears.] Acta Palaeontol. Pol., 14:2,
              199–252, 13 figs., 6 pls., 24 tables (Polish; English and Russian summaries).
              Rev.: Thenius in Zentralbl. Geol. Paläontol., Teil 2, 1970:5, 435–436.

RZEBIK, BARBARA (= RZEBIK-KOWALSKA, B.)
  1968A   Crocidura Wagler and other Insectivora (Mammalia) from the Quaternary deposits of Tornewton Cave
              in England. Acta Zool. Crac., 13:10, 251–263, 6 figs., 4 tables (Polish and Russian summaries).
  1971A   The Pliocene and Pleistocene insectivores (Mammalia) of Poland. I. Erinaceidae and Desmaninae.
              Acta Zool. Cracov., 16:9, 435–461, 9 figs., 7 tables (Russian and Polish summaries).

RZHONSNITSKAIÂ, MARIIÂ ADOL'FOVNA (= RŽONSNICKAJA, M. A.)
  1970A   Korreliatsiiâ devonskikh otlozheniĭ Kuznetskogo basseĭna s glavneĭshimi razrezami devona Zapadnoĭ
              Evropy. [Correlation of Kuznetskogo basin Devonian deposits with the principal sections of west
              European Devonian.] In: Ocherki po geologii Kuznetskogo i Donetskogo basseĭnov, 238–254
              (Russian).

RZHONSNITSKAIÂ, M. A.   See also: Iavorskiĭ, V. I. and Rzhonsnitskaiâ, M. A., 1967A.

SNG
  1970A   Anthropologische Ausstellung. Natur Mus., 100:8, 380 (German).

SABAN, R.
  1967B   Réflexions anatomiques sur la plaquette de la "Femme au Renne". Soc. Préhist. Fr., Bull., Étud.
              Trav., 64:1, 131–142, 6 figs. (French).

SABLOFF, PAULA LYNNE WEINBERG
  1968A*   Northwest Africa. COWA, Surv. Bibliogr., Area 10, 4, 1–13.

SACCHI VIALLI, GIULIA
  1965A   Imagini di vita nei fossili. Pavia, Univ., Ist. Geol., Atti, 16, 72–80, 2 pls. (Italian).
  1967A   Contributo alla conoscenza paleoistologica di ossa fossili. Pavia, Univ., Ist. Geol., Atti, 18, 65–81,
              1 table, 1 pl. (Italian; French, English and German summaries).
              Rev.: Fantini Sestini in Riv. Ital. Paleontol. Stratigr., 74:4, 1321–1322.

SACCHI VIALLI, G.   See also: Bucci, G., Nebbia, L., Sacchi Vialli, G., Savi, A. and Basso, G., 1969A.

SADOV, I. A.
  1970A   O stroenii skorlupy iaĭts iskopaemykh reptiliĭ i ptits. [On the eggshell structure of fossil reptiles and
              birds.] Paleontol. Zh., 1970:4, 88–91, 1 table (Russian).

SADOVSKIĬ, N. D.   See: Mokrousov, V. P. and Sadovskiĭ, N. D., 1964A.

SAFONOW, W. G.   See: Djoshkin, W. W. and Safonow, W. G., 1972A.

SAFRONOV, F. G.
  1971A   O zaselenii Ameriki pervobytnym chelovekom. [America's settling by primitive man.] Vses. Geogr.
              Obshchest., Izv., 103:5, 433–436 (Russian).

SAFRONOV, I. N. and LEBEDEVA, NATAL'IÂ ALEKSEEVNA
  1968A   Chetvertichnye kontinental'nye otlozheniiâ. [Quaternary continental deposits.] Geologiiâ SSSR, 9,
              Northern Caucasus, 447–465, 3 tables (Russian).

SAHLY, ALI
1961A   La plus petite main préhistorique du domaine Franco-Hispanique. Considérations sur les empreintes de mains d'enfants à Gargas. Toulouse, Univ., Inst. d'Art Préhist., Trav., 4, 169–174, 3 figs. (French).
1970A   Le problème des mains mutilées dans l'art préhistorique. Discussion. Int. Congr. Anthropol. Ethnol. Sci., 7th, Moscow, 1964, Proc., 5, 350–355 (French).

SAHNI, ASHOK
1969A   A review of Cretaceous mammals. J. Palaeontol. Soc. India, 12, 21–24, 1 table.
1969B   Techniques in prospecting for terrestrial microvertebrates. J. Palaeontol. Soc. India, 13, 38–43, 1 fig., 1 table.
1969C   The vertebrate fauna of the Judith River formation, Montana. Diss. Abstr., 29:7, 2497B–2498B (abs.).
1972A   The vertebrate fauna of the Judith River formation. Amer. Mus. Natur. Hist., Bull., 147:6, 323–412, 16 figs., 5 tables.

SAHNI, A., MEHROTRA, D. K. and JAUHARI, A. K.
1971A   Micro-fish fauna of the Baripada beds, Mayurbhanj district. Indian Sci. Congr., Proc., 58, 317.

SAHNI, A. and MISHRA, V. P.
1972A   A new species of Protocetus (Cetacea) from the middle Eocene of Kutch, western India. Palaeontology, 15:3, 490–495, 1 fig., 1 pl.

SAHNI, ASHOK   See also: Kapoor, H. M. and Sahni, A., 1971A.

SAHNI, M. R. and KHAN, E.
1968A   Boundary between the Tatrots and Pinjaurs. J. Palaeontol. Soc. India, 5–9, 29–30.
1968B   Probison dehmi n. g. n. sp. a recent find of an upper Sivalik bovid. Bayer. Staatssamml. Paläontol. Hist. Geol., Mitt., 8, 247–251, 1 pl., 1 table (German summary).

SAHNI, M. R. and MATHUR, L. P.
1964A   Stratigraphy of the Siwalik group. Int. Geol. Congr., 22nd, India, 1964, 24 pp., 2 maps, 3 charts.

SAIADIAN, IU. V.
1969A   Shirakskiĭ opornyĭ razrez chetvertichnykh kontinental'nykh otlozheniĭ v Zakavkaz'e. [Shiraki key section of continental Quaternary deposits in Transcaucasia.] Akad. Nauk Arm. SSR, Izv., Nauki Zemle, 22:3, 15–25, 1 fig., 1 table (Russian; Armenian summary).
1970A   O stratigraficheskom polozhenii i paleogeograficheskom znachenii fauny mlekopitaĭushchikh leninakanskogo faunisticheskogo kompleksa (Armeniĭa). [On the stratigraphic position and paleogeographic significance of the mammalian fauna of Leninakan faunal complex (Armenia).] Akad. Nauk SSSR, Kom. Izuch. Chetvertich. Perioda, Biull., 37, 63–67, 1 table (Russian).

SAID, R.   See: Wendorf, F., Schild, R. and Said, R., 1970A.

SAIDAKOVSKIĬ, L. IA.   See: Lipatova, V. V., Lopato, A. Iu., Makarova, I. S., Ochev, V. G., Podgornyĭ, Iu. I., Starozhilova, N. N., Saĭdakovskiĭ, L. Ia. and Shishkin, M. A., 1972A.

SAINT-BLANQUAT, HENRI DE
1969A   L'âge de l'homme moderne. Sci. Avenir, 270, 665–669, 684 (French).

SAINT-PÉRIER, RAYMONDE-SUZANNE DE
1962E   Hommage à M. le Chanoine Jean Bouyssonie. Les Eyzies, 11, 18–20, portr. (French).
1962F   Le Professeur Pittard. [1867–1962]. Les Eyzies, 11, 29, portr. (French).
1963A   Le Professeur Pittard. [1867–1962]. Les Eyzies, 12, 13–16, portr. (French).

SAINT-SEINE, P. DE and DEVILLERS, CH.
1969A   Holocéphales et Élasmobranches. Généralités. In: Piveteau, J. (ed.), 1969A, Traité de Paléo., T. IV, vol. 2, 693–701, 6 figs. (French).

SAJNER, JOSEF
1966A   Neue Forschungen über Gregor Mendel. Ver. Verbreitung Naturwiss. Kenntnisse Wien, Schrift 106, 163–182 (German).

SAKAI, SHIZU   See: Ogawa, T., Kamiya, T., Sakai, S. and Hosokawa, H., 1970A.

SAKANOUE, MASANOBU and YOSHIOKA, MITSUO
1970A   Radiochemical studies on fossil bones from the Amud Cave. In: Suzuki, H. and Takai, F. (eds.), 1970A, 425–427.

SAKHAROV, V. A.
1971A   Paleogenovaiā sistema. Nizhniĭ-sredniĭ oligotŝen. [Paleogene system. Lower-middle Oligocene.]
             Geologiiā SSSR, 34:1, Turgaĭ trough, 353–375, 3 figs., 3 tables (Russian).

SAKS, VLADIMIR NIKOLAEVICH
1969A   Znachenie trudov V. I. Gromova v razvitii chetvertichnoĭ geologii Sibiri. [Significance of V. I.
             Gromov's works for the development of Quaternary geology of Siberia.] In: Chetvertichnaiā
             geologiiā i geomorfologiiā Sibiri, Part 1, 3–10 (Russian).

SAKULINA, GALINA VLADIMIROVNA   See: Buvalkin, A. K., Zhaĭmin, M. I., Murakhovskaiā, E. I.,
             Orlovskaiā, E. R. and Sakulina, G. V., 1971A; Galiŝkiĭ, V. V., Gekker, R. F., Kostenko, N. N.
             and Sakulina, G. V., 1968A.

SAKURA, HAJIME
1969A   Dentition of the Amud man from the Amud Cave, Israel. Int. Congr. Anthropol. Ethnol. Sci., 8th,
             Tokyo, 1968, Proc., Vol. I. Anthropology, 300–301, 1 table.
1970A   State of the skeletons of the Amud man in situ. In: Suzuki, H. and Takai, F. (eds.), 1970A, 117–
             122, 3 figs., 1 table.
1970B   Dentition of the Amud man. In: Suzuki, H. and Takai, F. (eds.), 1970A, 207–229, 7 figs., 9 tables.

SALAMUNI, RIAD   See: Bigarella, J. J. and Salamuni, R., 1967A.

SALI, S. A.   See: Joshi, R. V. and Sali, S. A., 1971A.

SALIS, KATHARINA VON
1967A   Geologische und sedimentologische Untersuchungen in Molasse und Quartär südöstlich Wolhusen
             (Entlebuch, Kt. Luzern). Naturforsch. Ges. Luzern, Mitt., 21, 1–107, 27 figs., 1 map, 6 tables
             (German).
             Rev.: Weiler in Zentralbl. Geol. Paläontol., Teil 2, 1968:6, 651–652.

SALLER, KARL
1957-66A   Lehrbuch der Anthropologie. Third edition, 4 vols. Stuttgart: G. Fischer, 3000 pp., 1253 figs.
             Rev.: Koenigswald in Natur Mus., 99:9, 432–433.
1968A*   Rassengeschichte der Menschheit. Munich: Oldenbourg Verlag, 221 pp.
             Rev.: Schwidetzky in Homo, 20:1, 79; Vallois in L'Anthropologie, 74:1–2, 112–114.

SALOMONI, E.   See: Ambrosetti, P. and Salomoni, E., 1966A.

SALOV, I. N.
1963A   Nakhodka cherepa ovtŝebyka v Talashkinskom peschano-graviĭnom kar'ere (Smolenskiĭ raĭon). [Finding
             of musk ox skull in Talashkinskiĭ sand and gravel quarry (Smolensk district).] Smolensk. Gos.
             Pedag. Inst., Uch. Zap., 12, 54–57, 1 fig. (Russian).

SALZMANN, ZDENEK
1969A   Anthropology. New York: Harcourt, Brace & World, Inc., xi + 308 pp., illustr.

SAMAMA, J. C.   See: Demathieu, G. and Samama, J. C., 1970A.

SAMMET, E. ĬU.
1971A   Devonskaiā sistema. [Devonian system.] Geologiiā SSSR, 1, Leningrad, Novgorod, and Pskov
             Provinces, 173–245, 8 figs., 3 tables (Russian).

SAMSON, P. and HERMANN, WILHELM
1968A   Contribuţii la cunoaşterea perisodactilelor fosile din terasa inferioară a Tîrnavei Mari de la Brateiu.
             [A contribution to the knowledge of fossil Perissodactyla from the lower terrace of Tirnava
             Mare in Brateiu.] Acad. Repub. Soc. Rom., Inst. Speol. "Emil Racoviţă", Lucr., 7, 255–269,
             6 figs. (Rumanian; French summary).

SAMSON, P. and RĂDULESCU, COSTIN
1968A   Das mittlere Pleistozän in Rumänien. Deut. Ges. Geol. Wiss., Ber., Reihe A, Geol. Paläontol., 13:3,
             375–379, 1 table (German).
1969A   Faunele de mamifere cuaternare din bazienele Ciuc şi Borsec (jud. Harghita). [Quaternary mammalian
             faunas from Ciuc and Borsec basins (Harghita district).] Acad. Repub. Soc. Rom., Inst. Speol.
             "Emil Rakoviţă", Lucr., 8, 215–223, 1 table (Rumanian; English summary).

SAMSON, P., RADULESCO, C. and KISGYÖRGY, Z.
1971A   Nouvelles données sur la faune de mammifères du Villafranchien inférieur de Căpeni-Virghiş (Dépression de Braşov, Roumanie). Eiszeitalter Gegenwart, 22, 64--88, 5 figs., 1 pl., 2 tables (French; German and English summaries).

SAMSON, PETRE   See also: Alimen, H., Rădulescu, C. and Samson, P., 1968B; Dumitrescu, M., Samson, P., Terzea, E., Rădulescu, C. and Ghica, M., 1963A; Rădulescu, C. and Samson, P., 1965B, 1972A.

SANCHEZ, T. M.   See: Benedetto, J. L. and Sanchez, T. M., 1971A.

SANDARS, N. K.
1968A   Prehistoric art in Europe. Middlesex, Baltimore and Australia: The Penguin History of Art, Penguin Books Ltd., xxxix + 350 pp., 104 figs., 304 pls., 3 tables, 3 maps.
         Rev.: jf in Archeol. Roz., 21:4, 566–567 (Czech).

SANDERSON, J. L.   See: Foldvary, G. Z. and Sanderson, J. L., 1972A.

SANDISON, A. T.
1968A   Pathological changes in the skeletons of earlier populations due to acquired disease, and difficulties in their interpretation. In: Brothwell, D. R. (ed.), 1968A, 205–243, 3 figs.

SANDISON, A. T.   See also: Brothwell, D. R., Sandison, A. T. and Gray, P. H. K., 1969A.

SANGER, D.   See: MacDonald, G. F. and Sanger, D., 1968A.

SANTAFÉ LLOPIS, JOSÉ-VICENTE   See: Casanovas Cladellas, M. L. and Santafé Llopis, J.-V., 1971A.

ŠANTRŮČEK, P., BŮZEK, Č., KOPECKÝ, L., MALECHA, A. and VÁCL, J.
1968A   Tertiary basins and young volcanics of the Bohemian massif. Guide to excursion 13AC, Czechoslovakia. Int. Geol. Congr., 23rd, Czech., Guidebk., 13, 53 pp., 7 figs.

SARDENBERG SALGADO, MARISE   See: Silva Santos, R. da and Sardenberg Salgado, M., 1969A, 1970A, 1971A.

SARGENT, S. and SHOTWELL, J. ARNOLD
1951A   Preliminary report of a new Miocene vertebrate locality near Pendleton. Oreg. Acad. Sci., Proc., 2, 76.

SARICH, VINCENT M.
1970A   Primate systematics with special reference to old world monkeys. A protein perspective. In: Napier, J. R. and Napier, P. H. (eds.), 1970A, 175–226, 4 figs., 11 tables.
1971A   Human variation in an evolutionary perspective. In: Dolhinow, P. and Sarich, V. M. (eds.), 1971A, 182–191.
1971B   A molecular approach to the question of human origins. In: Dolhinow, P. and Sarich, V. M. (eds.), 1971A, 60–81, 4 figs., 3 tables.
1972A   Hominid origins revisited: 1971. In: McCown, T. D. and Kennedy, K. A. R. (eds.), 1972A, 450–460, 1 fig., 2 tables.

SARICH, V. M. and WILSON, A. C.
1967A   Rates of albumin evolution in primates. Nat. Acad. Sci., Proc., 58:1, 142–148, 2 figs., 5 tables.

SARICH, VINCENT M.   See also: Dolhinow,P. and Sarich, V. M., 1971A, 1971B; Wilson, A. C. and Sarich, V. M., 1969A.

SARJEANT, WILLIAM A. S.
1966A   A restudy of some fossil footprints from the Permian of Mansfield (Notts.). Mercian Geol., 1:4, 367– 373, 1 fig., 1 pl.
1967A   Fossil footprints from the middle Triassic of Nottinghamshire and Derbyshire. Mercian Geol., 2:3, 327–341, 4 figs., 4 pls.
1970A   Fossil footprints from the middle Triassic of Nottinghamshire and the middle Jurassic of Yorkshire. Mercian Geol., 3:3, 269–282, 5 figs., 2 pls.
         Rev.: Chrulew in Zentralbl. Geol. Paläontol., Teil 2, 1971:1, 57.
1971A   Vertebrate tracks from the Permian of Castle Peak, Texas. Texas J. Sci., 22:4, 343–366, 6 figs., 6 pls.

SARJEANT, WILLIAM A. S.   See also: Wills, L. J. and Sarjeant, W. A. S., 1970A.

SARKAR, R. M.
1970A   Fundamentals of physical anthropology. Second edition. Calcutta: Century Publishers, xx + 476 pp., 63 figs.
         Rev.: Bose in Man in India, 51:1, 79–80.

SARKAR, S. S.
1964B On the evolution of *Giraffa*. Indian Sci. Congr., 51, 192—193.
1971A On the growth in vertebrates. Indian Sci. Congr., Proc., 58, 319.

SARSONNEUR, C. and LAPPARENT, F. DE
1966A Un dinosaurien carnivore, *Halticosaurus*, dans le Rhétien d'Airel (Manche). Soc. Linn. Normandie, Bull. 10(7), 108—117, 5 figs., 2 pls. (French).
       Rev.: Huene in Zentralbl. Geol. Paläontol., Teil 2, 1968:6, 656.

SARTONO, S.
1968A Early man in Java: *Pithecanthropus* skull VII, a male specimen of *Pithecanthropus erectus* (I), and (II). Ned. Akad. Wetensch., Proc., Ser. B, 71:5, Part I: 396—407, 4 figs., 4 pls., 6 tables; Part II: 408—422, drawings and craniograms only, figs. 5—19.
1969A *Stegodon timorensis*. A pygmy species from Timor (Indonesia). Ned. Akad. Wetensch., Proc., Ser. B, 72:3, 192—202, 6 figs., 1 pl., 4 tables.
1970A On the stratigraphic position of pithecanthropus mandible — C. Bandung, Inst. Teknol., Proc., 4:4, 91—102, 6 figs. (Indonesian summary).
1971A Observations on a new skull of *Pithecanthropus erectus (Pithecanthropus VIII)* from Sangiran, central Java. Ned. Akad. Wetensch., Proc., Ser. B, 74:2, 183—194, 3 figs., 2 pls., 2 tables.
1971B [The Java man: a short note. Translated into Japanese by I. Fujiyama.] Natur. Sci. and Mus., 38: 9—10, 217—230, 7 figs., 6 tables (Japanese).

SASTRI, V. V. See: Pandey, J. and Sastri, V. V., 1968A.

SASTRY, M. V. A.
1966A Pleistocene vertebrates from Susunia, Bankura district, west Bengal. Indian Minerals, 20:3, 195—197.
1969A Mesozoic and Tertiary sequences in India. U.N., Econ. Comm. Asia Far East, Miner. Resour. Develop. Ser., 30, 107—111, 2 charts, 2 tables.

SASTRY, M. V. A. See also: Gosh, P. K. and Sastry, M. V. A., 1967A.

SASVARI, LOUIS
1968A Phylogénie et microévolution comme facteurs biologiques du développement évolutif des êtres vivants. Soc. Hist. Natur. Toulouse, Bull. 104:1—2, 252—259, 1 fig. (French).

SATŌ, JIRŌ
1962A Miocene fishes from the western area of Shizukuishi basin, Iwate prefecture, northeastern Japan. Earth Sci. (Chikyū Kagaku), 59, 1—29, 32 figs., 6 pls., 14 tables (Japanese summary).
1968A Miocene boney fish fossils from the western area of Shizukuishi town, Iwate pref. In: Minato, M. *et al.* (eds.), 1968A, 14, 5 figs. (Japanese).

SATŌ, J. See also: Onodera, S., Ootaka, S., Satō, J., Takahashi, T. and Yamada, Y., 1967A.

SATŌ, TOSHIHIKO
1969A Collogen fibrils in the teeth of fossil Proboscidea. Geol. Soc. Jap., J., 75:10, 549—552, 5 pls., 1 table (Japanese, English summary).

SATSANGI, P. P.
1964B A preliminary note on the Siwalik vertebrates of Jammu, Udhampur and Ramnagar areas of J. & K. state. Indian Minerals, 18:1, 91—92.

SATSANGI, P. P. See also: Prasad, K. N. and Satsangi, P. P., 1962B, 1967A, 1967B.

SATTONNET, R. See: David, E., Frachon, J.-C. and Sattonnet, R., 1968A.

SAUBADE, A. M. See: Chavanon, S. and Saubade, A. M., 1970A.

SAUER, E. G. FRANZ
1968A Calculations of struthious egg sizes from measurements of shell fragments and their correlation with phylogenetic aspects. Cimbebasia, Ser. A, 1:2, 27—55, 9 figs. (German summary).
       Abs.: R.W.S. in Auk, 88:2, 476.
1969A Taxonomic evidence and evolutionary interpretation of *Psammornis*. Bonner Zool. Beitr., 20:1—3, 290—310, 10 figs. (German summary).
1972A Ratite eggshells and phylogenetic questions. Bonner Zool. Beitr., 23:1, 3—48, 24 figs. (German summary).

SAUNDERS, JEFFREY JOHN
   1972A   Population dynamics of *Mammut* from Boney Spring, Missouri. Soc. Vert. Paleontol., Ann. Meeting, 32nd, 1972, Abstr. (abs.).

SAURIN, E.
   1966A   Le Paléolithique du Cambodge oriental. Asian Perspectives 9, 96–110, 4 figs., 7 pls. (French).
   1968A   La géologie du Quaternaire et les industries préhistoriques en Indochine. Asian Pac. Archaeol. Ser., 2, 63–84, 5 figs. (French).

SAUVAGE, JACQUELINE   See: Guernet, C. and Sauvage, J., 1971A.

SAVAGE, DONALD E.
   1971A   The University of California Museum of Paleontology, activities and accomplishments 1921–1971. Berkeley: University of California Museum of Paleontology, 51 pp., illustr.
   1971B   The Sparnacian-Wasatchian mammalian fauna, early Eocene, of Europe and North America. Hess. Landesamt Bodenforsch., Abh., 60, 154–158.

SAVAGE, D. E. and BARNES, LAWRENCE G.
   1972A   Miocene vertebrate geochronology of the west coast of North America. AAPG-SEPM Symp., 124–145, 4 figs., 1 map.

SAVAGE, D. E. and CURTIS, GARNISS H.
   1970A   The Villafranchian stage-age and its radiometric dating. Geol. Soc. Amer., Spec. Pap., 124, 207–231, 3 figs., 7 tables.

SAVAGE, D. E., WATERS, B. T. and HUTCHISON, J. H.
   1972A   Northwestern border of the Washakie Basin, Wyoming. Field Conf. Tert. Bios., S. and W. Wyo., Guidebk., 32–39, 3 tables, 1 map.
   1972B   Early Eocene fossiliferous strata, northwest Washakie Basin, Sweetwater County, Wyoming. Soc. Vert. Paleontol., Ann. Meeting, 32nd, 1972, Abstr. (abs.).

SAVAGE, D. E., WHISTLER, D. and HUTCHISON, H.
   1969A   Notes from members. West coast. Northern California. University of California, Berkeley. [Camp Bibliography of Fossil Vertebrates.] Soc. Vert. Paleontol., News Bull., no. 85, 39–40, 1 photo.

SAVAGE, DONALD E.   See also: Chappell, W. M., Durham, J. W. and Savage, D. E., 1970A; McKenna, M. C., Russell, D. E. and Savage, D. E., 1969A; Waters, B. T., Hutchison, J. H. and Savage, D. E., 1972A; Waters, B. T. and Savage, D. E., 1969A.

SAVAGE, JAY M.
   1969A   Evolution. Second edition. New York, Chicago, etc.: Holt, Rinehart and Winston, ix + 152 pp., illustr.

SAVAGE, ROBERT JOSEPH GAY
   1969A   Early Tertiary mammal locality in southern Libya. Geol. Soc. London, Proc., 1657, 167–171, 2 tables.

SAVAGE, R. J. G. and TCHERNOV, E.
   1968A   Miocene mammals of Israel. Geol. Soc. London, Proc., 1648, 98–101, 1 fig.

SAVAGE, R. J. G.   See also: Coryndon, S. C. and Savage, R. J. G., 1972A; Leakey, L. S. B. and Savage, R. J. G. (eds.), 1970A; Waldman, M. and Savage, R. J. G., 1972A.

SAVI, A.   See: Bucci, G., Nebbia, L., Sacchi Vialli, G., Savi, A. and Basso, G., 1969A.

SAVICH, V. P.
   1969A   Kostïanye izdeliïa stoïanki Lipa VI. [Bone artifacts of the locality Lipa VI.] Akad. Nauk SSSR, Kom. Izuch. Chetvertich. Perioda, Bïull., 36, 136–141, 1 fig. (Russian).
   1969B   Issledovanie pozdnepaleoliticheskoĭ stoïanki Kalychivka. [Research on late Paleolithic site Kulychivka.] In: Rybakov, B. A. (ed.), 1969A, 262–263 (Russian).

SAVINOV, PAVEL FEDOROVICH
   1970A   Tushkanchikovye (Dipodidae, Rodentia) neogena Kazakhstana. [Jerboas (Dipodidae, Rodentia) from the Neogene of Kazakhstan.] In: Materialy po evoliutsii nazemnykh pozvonochnykh, 91–134, 10 figs., 10 tables (Russian).

SAVINOV, PAVEL FEDOROVICH   See also: Aubekerov, B. Zh., Aubekerova, P. A., Birĭukov, M. D., Lychev,
G. F. and Savinov, P. F., 1970A; Bazhanov, V. S., Birĭukov, M. D., Vetrov, F. E., Kozhamkulova,
B. S., Lychev, G. F., Musakulova, L. T. and Savinov, P. F., 1971A; Eroshkin, A. F. and Savinov,
P. F., 1971A; Orlovskaĭa, E. R. and Savinov, P. F., 1971A.

SAVINOVA, ANNA POTAPOVNA   See: Kostenko, N. N., Nikitin, E. A. and Savinova, A. P., 1971A; Kostenko,
N. N. and Savinova, A. P., 1971A.

SAXENA, M. N.
     1968A   A note on the validity of the upper Siwalik vertebrate fossils for stratigraphic correlation. E. Anthropol.,
21:3, 319—321.

SAXON, J.
     1967A   Fossil fishes of Caithness and Orkney. Caithness Notebook, 6, 3/6, 3—30, illustr.
            Rev.: Stubbs in New Sci., 38:596, 306; Weiler in Zentralbl. Geol. Paläontol., Teil 2, 1968:6, 652.

SCANDONE, P.   See: Lirer, L., Pescatore, T. and Scandone, P., 1966A.

SCARLETT, R. J.
     1969A   On the alleged Queensland moa, *Dinornis queenslandiae* De Vis. Queensl. Mus., Mem., 15:3, 207—212,
1 pl.
     1970A   The genus *Capellirallus.* Notornis, 17:1, 68—74, 2 pls.
     1972A   Bone of a presumed odontopterygian bird from the Miocene of New Zealand. N.S. J. Geol. Geophys.,
15:2, 269—274, 2 figs.

SCARTASCINI, GUILLERMO
     1959A   El banco de calcáreo organógeno de Paraná. Mus. Argent. Cienc. Natur. "Bernardino Rivadavia", Comun.,
Geol., 1:16, 12 pp., 5 figs. (Spanish; English summary).

SCHAAFFHAUSEN, D.
     1971A   On the human skeleton from the Neander Valley. In: Leakey, L. S. B., Prost, J. and Prost, S. (eds.),
1971A, 159—164, 1 fig. (reprinted from Man's Place in Nature, 1858).

SCHAEFER, HANS
     1967A   Säugetierpaläontologie. Naturforsch. Ges. Basel, Verh., 78:1, 74—79 (German).
     1969A   Das Pleistozän von Süssenborn. Zwei Caniden-Reste (Carnivora, Mammalia) aus dem Altpleistozän von
Süssenborn bei Weimar. Paläontol. Abh., Abt. A, 3:3—4, 757—760, 2 figs. II Internat. Paläont.
Kolloquium 1966 in Weimar (German; Russian and English summaries).

SCHAEFER, HANS and ZAPFE, HELMUT
     1971A   *Chalicotherium grande* Blainv. und *Chalicotherium goldfussi* Kaup. Naturforsch. Ges. Basel, Verh., 81:2,
157—199, 31 figs. (German).
            Rev.: Thenius in Zentralbl. Geol. Paläontol., Teil 2, 1972:3, 178.

SCHAEFFER, BOBB
     1968B   A new actinopterygian fish from the Cretaceous of North America. Amer. Mus. Nov., 2344, 1—10,
5 figs.
     1968C   The origin and basic radiation of the Osteichthyes. Nobel Symp., 4th, Stockholm, 1967, Proc., 1968,
207—222, 4 figs.
     1968D   Fossil fishes. In: Moore, R. C., et al., 1968A, 1373—1374.
     1968E   Department of vertebrate paleontology. Amer. Mus. Natur. Hist., Ann. Rept., 99, 54—56, illustr.
     1969A   Adaptive radiation of the fishes and the fish-amphibian transition. N.Y. Acad. Sci., Ann., 167:1, 5—17,
7 figs., 1 table.
     1970A   Mesozoic fishes and climate. N. Amer. Paleontol. Conv., Proc., Part D, 376—388, 7 figs.
     1970B   Department of vertebrate paleontology. Amer. Mus. Natur. Hist., Ann. Rept., 101, 30.
     1971A   The braincase of the Holostean fish *Macrepistius*, with comments on neurocranial ossification in the
Actinopterygii. Amer. Mus. Nov., 2459, 34 pp., 11 figs., 1 table.
     1971B   Obituary. William King Gregory 1876—1970. Soc. Vert. Paleontol., News Bull., 92, 62—64, portr.
     1971C   Jurassic fishes from Antarctica. Antarctic J., 6:5, 190—191, 1 photo.
     1971D   Department of vertebrate paleontology. Amer. Mus. Natur. Hist., Ann. Rep., 102, 31—32.
     1972A   A Jurassic fish from Antarctica. Amer. Mus. Nov., 2495, 17 pp., 8 figs.

SCHAEFFER, B., HECHT, M. K. and ELDREDGE, N.
     1972A   Phylogeny and paleontology. In: Dobzhansky, Th., Hecht, M. K. and Steere, W. C. (eds.), 1972B,
31—46, 2 figs.

SCHAEFFER, B. and MANGUS, MARLYN
    1970A   *Synorichthys* sp. (Palaeonisciformes) and the Chinle-Dockum and Newark (Upper Triassic) fish faunas.
              J. Paleontol., 44:1, 17—22, 2 figs., 2 pls., 1 table.

SCHAEFFER, BOBB   See also: Hecht, M. K., Schaeffer, B., Patterson, B., Frank, R. van and Wood, F. D. 1972A.

SCHÄFER, W.
    1969A   Anthropologie im Rahmen der senckenbergischen Arbeitsgebiete. Natur Mus., 99:3, 127—130 (German).
    1969B   Prof. Dr. Robert Mertens 50 Jahre im Senckenberg. Natur Mus., 99:3, 134—135 (German).
    1969C   Aus dem Schaumuseum. Natur Mus., 99:6, 284—197, 6 figs. (German).
    1969D   Robert Mertens zum 75. Geburtstag. Natur Mus., 99:12, 584 (German).
    1970A   Erdgeschichte - Lebensgeschichte. Natur Mus., 100:3, 140—143 (German).
    1970B   Wirbeltier-Fossilien in ihrer schaumusealen Behandlung: Acht Leitsätze. Natur Mus., 100:4, 195—197
              (German).

SCHÄFER, W., *et al.*
    1970A   Jahresbericht zur Mitgliederversammlung der Senckenbergischen Naturforschenden Gesellschaft am 4.
              November 1970. Natur Mus., 100:11, 481—545, 27 figs., portrs. (German).

SCHAIRER, GERHARD   See: Janicke, V. and Schairer, G., 1970A.

SCHALLER, GEORGE B.
    1972A   Are you running with me, hominid? Natur. Hist., 81:3, 60—69, illustr.

SCHALLER, GEORGE B. and LOWTHER, GORDON R.
    1969A   The relevance of carnivore behavior to the study of early hominids. Southwest. J. Anthropol., 25:4,
              307—341, 2 figs., 2 tables.

SCHANFIELD, MELVIN and HARPENDING, HENRY
    1968A   A cluster analysis of the Neanderthals. Amer. J. Phys. Anthropol., 29, 125 (abs.).

SCHAUMBERG, G.
    1970A   Auf den Spuren der "Sintflut" im Richelsdorfer Gebirge. Aufschluss, 21:7—8, 259—265, 8 figs.
              (German).

SCHELLHORN, M.
    1969A   Probleme der Struktur, Organisation und Evolution biologischer Systeme. Jena: G. Fischer Verlag,
              134 pp. (German).
              Rev.: Bogsch in Földt, Közl., 100:4, 405 (Hungarian); Starostin in Zh. Obshch. Biol., 31:1, 123—126
              (Russian).

SCHILD, R.   See: Wendorf, F., Schild, R. and Said, R., 1970A.

SCHINDEWOLF, OTTO H.
    1968A   Homologie und Taxonomie. Acta Biotheoret., 18, 235—283, 14 figs. (German).
    1969A   Über den "Typus" in morphologischer und phylogenetischer Biologie. Akad. Wiss. Lit. Mainz, Mat.-
              Naturwiss. Kl., Abh., 1969:4, 59—131, 10 figs. (German).
              Rev.: Daber in Deut. Ges. Geol. Wiss., Ber., Reihe A, Geol. Paläontol., 16:1, 69—70; Kullmann in
              Zentralbl. Geol. Paläontol., Teil 2, 1970:5, 341—342; Ronchetti in Riv. Ital. Paleontol.
              Stratigr., 76:2, 340.

SCHINDLER, CONRAD   See: Kopp, K.-O., Pavoni, N. and Schindler, C., 1969A.

SCHLOMM, W.
    1970A   Versteinertes Drama im Weissjura von Solnhofen. Aufschluss, 21:5, 184, 1 fig. (German).

SCHMALHAUSEN, IVAN IVANOVICH
    1968A   Rev.: Wake in Copeia, 1971:4, 762—764.
    1968B   Faktory evolfufsii. Teorifa stabilizirufushchego otbora. [Factors of evolution. A theory of stabilizing
              selection.] Second edition, revised and completed. Moscow: "Nauka" Press, 451 pp., 41 figs.,
              10 tables (Russian).
    1969A   Problemy darvinizma. [Problems of darwinism. Second edition.] Leningrad: "Nauka" Press, 493 pp.,
              183 figs., 16 portrs. (Russian).
              Rev.: Smirnov in Priroda, 1970:6, 116—118.

SCHMID, ELISABETH
1972A   Atlas of animal bones. Amsterdam, London, New York: Elsevier Publishing Company, 159 pp.,
          27 figs., 8 tables, 37 pls. (English and German).
          Rev.: Anon. in Säugetierkundl. Mitt., 20:3, 263–264; Cornwall in Nature, 238:5365, 474; Dorst in
                 Mammalia, 36:2, 314; Herre in Z. Säugetierkunde, 37:4, 256; Olsen in Science, 178:4058, 297.

SCHMID, ELISABETH   See also: Feustel, R., et al., 1971A, 1971B.

SCHMIDT, B.   See: Hoffmann, W. and Schmidt, B., 1965A.

SCHMIDT, HERMANN
1969A   Stenopelix valdensis H. v. Meyer, der kleine Dinosaurier des norddeutschen Wealden. Paleontol. Z.,
          43:3/4, 194–198, 1 fig. (German; English summary).
          Rev.: Chrulew in Zentralbl. Geol. Paläontol., Teil 2, 1970:3/4, 230.

SCHMIDT, VIRGINIA
1969A   When giant lizards lived. Desert Mag., 32:4, 35–37, 3 figs.

SCHMIDT, WOLFGANG   See: Müller, E. M., Schröder, E. and Schmidt, W., 1960A.

SCHMIDT, ZOLTÁN
1969A   Nálezy mastodontných chobotnatcov na Slovensku. [Finds of mastodont proboscideans in Slovakia.]
          Svet Vedy, 16:4 (Czech).
1969B   Nálezy teplomilných foriem slonovitých chobotnatcov na Slovensku. [Finds of thermophilic forms of
          elephantine proboscideans in Slovakia.] Svet Vedy, 16:5 (Czech).

SCHMIDT, ZOLTÁN and HALOUZKA, RUDOLF
1970A   Nová fauna vertebrát villafranchienu zo Strekova na Hronskej pahorkatine (Podunajska nížina). [New
          vertebrate fauna of the Villafranchian from Strekov in the Hronská pahorkatina (Danube lowland).]
          Geol. Práce, Zpr., 51, 173–183, 2 figs., 6 pls., 2 tables (Czech; English summary).

SCHMIDT-KITTLER, NORBERT (= SCHMIDT, N.)
1969A   Eine alttertiäre Spaltenfüllung von Ehrenstein westlich Ulm. Bayer. Staatssamml. Paläontol. Hist.
          Geol., Mitt., 9, 201–208, 2 figs. (German; English summary).
1970A   Ein neuer Pseudosciuride von Ehrenstein westlich Ulm. Bayer. Staatssamml. Paläontol. Hist. Geol.,
          Mitt., 10, 433–440, 3 figs. (German; English summary).
1971A   Die obermiozäne Fossillagerstätte Sandelzhausen. 3. Suidae (Artiodactyla, Mammalia). Bayer.
          Staatssamml. Paläontol. Hist. Geol., Mitt., 11, 129–170, 23 figs., 2 pls. (German; English and
          French summaries).
1971B   Eine unteroligozäne Primatenfauna von Ehrenstein bei Ulm. Bayer. Staatssamml. Paläontol. Hist. Geol.,
          Mitt., 11, 171–204, 33 figs., 1 pl., 5 tables (German; English and French summaries).
1971C   Odontologische Untersuchungen an Pseudosciuriden (Rodentia, Mammalia) des Alttertiärs. Bayer.
          Akad. Wiss., Math.-Naturwiss. Kl., Abh., 150, 133 pp., 46 figs., 2 pls., 8 tables (German).
1972A   Odontologische Untersuchungen an Pseudosciuriden (Rodentia, Mammalia) des Alttertiärs. Bayer. Akad.
          Wiss., Math.-Naturwiss. Kl., Sitz.-Ber., 1971, 7*–10* (German; abs.).

SCHMIDT-KITTLER, NORBERT   See also: Bosma, A. and Schmidt-Kittler, N., 1972A; Fahlbusch, V., Gall, H.
          and Schmidt-Kittler, N., 1972A; Fahlbusch, V. and Schmidt, N., 1969A.

SCHMITZ-MOORMAN, N. and SCHMITZ-MOORMAN, K.
1971A*   Pierre Teilhard de Chardin: l'oeuvre scientifique. Pref. J. Piveteau. Olten and Freiburg i. Brisgau:
          10 vols. in - 8º, CXII + 4634 pp., 1 vol., 39 maps (French).
          Rev.: Anon. in Soc. Géol. Fr., C.R., 1971:6, 336.

SCHNEER, CECIL J.
1969A*   Toward a history of geology. Proceedings of the New Hampshire Inter-Disciplinary Conference on the
          History of Geology, September 7–12, 1967. Cambridge, Mass., and London, Engl.: The M.I.T.
          Press, 469 pp., illustr.
          Rev.: Faul in J. Geol., 79:4, 507–508.

SCHNEIDER, HORST E.
1968A   Zur quartärgeologischen Entwicklungsgeschichte Thessaliens (Griechenland). Beitr. Ur-u. Frühgesch.
          Archäol. Mittelmeer-Kulturr., 6, 127 pp., 65 pl., 1 map (German).
          Rev.: Pfannenstiel in Quartär, 19, 410–412.

SCHNEIDER, HORST E.   See also: Melentis, J. K. and Schneider, H., 1966A; Steiner, W. and
          Schneider, H. E., 1963B.

SCHOBINGER, JUAN
   1969A   Prehistoria de Suramérica. Barcelona: Editorial Labor, S.A., 296 pp., 79 figs. (Spanish).
            Rev.: Bosch-Gimpera in An. Antropol., Mexico, 7, 323–326.

SCHOPF, M.
   1969A   Einweihung des "Urmensch-Museum" in Steinheim/Murr, Württemberg. Anthropol. Anz., 31:3, 234–
            235, 1 fig. (German).
   1969B   Einweihung des "Urmensch-Museum" in Steinheim/Murr. Aufschluss, 20:3, 79–81, 5 figs. (German).

SCHOPF, THOMAS J. M.
   1972A*   Models in paleobiology. San Francisco: Freeman, Cooper and Co., 250 pp., illustr.

SCHOTT, LOTHAR
   1970A   Gab es eine "habiline" Hominisationsphase? Ethnogr.-Archäol. Z., 11:1, 39–50, 4 figs., 1 table
            (German).
   1970B   Lässt sich die Frage nach Haltung und Fortbewegungsart der Australopithecinen durch die Erörterung
            gliedermechanischer Zusammenhänge lösen? Ethnogr.-Archäol. Z., 11:2, 359–366, 2 figs.
            (German).

SCHRAM, FREDERICK R. and TURNBULL, WILLIAM D.
   1970A   Structural composition and dental variations in the murids of the Broom Cave fauna, late Pleistocene,
            Wombeyan Caves Area, N.S.W., Australia. Austral. Mus., Rec., 28:1, 24 pp., 5 figs., 3 pls.,
            4 tables.

SCHRIEFER, ALFONS
   1970A   Morphologische und topographische Korrelationen der allgemeinen Odontologie. Säugetierkundl. Mitt.,
            18:1, 62–67, 1 fig. (German; English summary).

SCHRÖDER, ECKART   See: Müller, E. M., Schröder, E. and Schmidt, W., 1960A.

SCHROEDER, DON
   1969A   Fossil department. Rocks Miner., 44:8, 607–608.
   1969B   Fossil department. Rocks Miner., 44:9–10, 686–687.
   1969C   Fossil department. Rocks Miner., 44:12, 828–829.
   1970A   Fossil department. Rocks Miner., 45:1, 14–15.
   1970B   Fossil department. Rocks Miner., 45:4, 254–255.
   1970C   Fossil department. Rocks Miner., 45:5, 326–327.
   1970D   Fossil department. Rocks Miner., 45:9, 541–543, 1 table.

SCHUBERTH, CHRISTOPHER J.
   1965A   Exploring for fossils. Natur. and Sci., 3:3, 6–7, illustr. (juvenile).

SCHULTE, KENNETH C.   See: Minch, J. A., Schulte, K. C. and Hofman, G., 1970A.

SCHULTZ, ADOLPH H.
   1966A   Der Mensch als Primat. Ver. Verbreitung Naturwiss. Kenntnisse Wien, Schrift. 106, 47–88, 15 figs.
            (German).
   1969A   The life of primates. New York: Universe Books, xi + 281 pp., 79 figs., 39 pls.
            Rev.: Bramblett in Human Biol., 42:4, 695–696.

SCHULTZ, C. BERTRAND
   1971A   1971 – the museum's centennial year. Nebr., Univ., State Mus., Univ. Nebr. News, Mus. Notes, 50:22,
            4 pp., illustr.
   1972A   100 years of museum growth. Nebr., Univ., State Mus., Univ. Nebr. News, Mus. Notes, 51:15, 4 pp.,
            8 figs.

SCHULTZ, C. B. and GUNDERSON, HARVEY L.
   1972A   The museum's centennial year. Nebr., Univ., State Mus., Univ. Nebr. News, Mus. Notes, 51:21, 4 pp.,
            4 figs.
   1972B   Henry Reider. Nebr. Univ., State Mus., Univ. Nebr. News, Mus. Notes, 51:21, p. 4.

SCHULTZ, C. B. and MARTIN, LARRY D.
   1970A   Machairodont cats from the early Pleistocene Broadwater and Lisco local faunas. Nebr. Univ. State
            Mus., Bull., 9:2, 33–38, 2 figs., frontispiece, 2 tables.
   1970B   Quaternary mammalian sequence in the central Great Plains. In: Dort, W., Jr. and Jones, J. K., Jr.
            (eds.), 1970A, 341–353, 3 figs., 1 table.
   1972A   Two lynx-like cats from the Pliocene and Pleistocene. Nebr. Univ. State Mus., Bull., 9:7, 197–203,
            3 figs., 2 tables, frontis.

SCHULTZ, C. B., SCHULTZ, M. R. and MARTIN, L. D.
1970A   A new tribe of saber-toothed cats (Barbourofelini) from the Pliocene of North America. Nebr. Univ. State Mus., Bull., 9:1, 31 pp., frontispiece, 13 figs., 2 tables.

SCHULTZ, C. B., TANNER, L. G. and MARTIN, L. D.
1969A   Evolutionary trends in certain phylogenetic lines of Quaternary mammals. Nebr. Acad. Sci., Proc., 79, 7 (abs.).
1972A   Phyletic trends in certain lineages of Quaternary mammals. Nebr. Univ. State Mus., Bull., 9:6, 183–195, frontispiece, 6 figs.

SCHULTZ, C. B., TANNER, L. G., WHITMORE, F. C. and RAY, W. W.
1969A   Geologic and faunal evidence of the Quaternary deposits at Big Bone Lick, Kentucky. Geol. Soc. Amer., Abstr., Part 2, 24–25 (abs.).

SCHULTZ, C. BERTRAND   See also: Martin, L. D. and Schultz, C. B., 1971A.

SCHULTZ, GERALD E.
1967B   The geology and paleontology of a late Pleistocene basin in southwest Kansas. Diss. Abstr., 27:7, 2417B–2418B (abs.).
1969A   Geology and paleontology of a late Pleistocene basin in southwest Kansas. Geol. Soc. Amer., Spec. Pap., no. 105, viii + 85 pp., 9 figs., 3 pls., 2 tables.
1972A   Vertebrate paleontology of the southern high plains. N. Mex. Geol. Soc., Guidebk., Field Conf., 23, 129–133, 1 fig., 1 table.
1972B   A skull of *Bison latifrons* from Lipscomb County, Texas. Tex. J. Sci., 23:3, 391–401, 2 figs., 1 table.

SCHULTZ, GERALD E. and CHEATUM, ELMER P.
1969A   *Bison occidentalis* and associated mollusks from the late Wisconsin of Randall County, Texas. Geol. Soc. Amer., Abstr., 121, 411 (abs.).
1970A   *Bison occidentalis* and associated invertebrates from the late Wisconsin of Randall County, Texas. J. Paleontol., 44:5, 836–850, 5 figs., 1 pl., 1 table.

SCHULTZ, MARIAN R.   See: Schultz, C. B., Schultz, M. R. and Martin, L. D., 1970A.

SCHULTZ, ORTWIN
1968A   Die Selachierfauna (Pisces, Elasmobranchii) aus den Phosphoritsanden (Unter-Miozän) von Plesching bei Linz, Oberösterreich. Naturkundl. Jahrb. Linz, 14, 61–102, 20 figs., 4 pls., 1 table (German; English summary).
           Rev.: Weiler in Zentralbl. Geol. Paläontol., Teil 2, 1969:6, 510–511.
1972A   Die Selachier-Fauna (Pisces, Elasmobranchii) des Wiener Beckens und seiner Randgebiete im Badenien (Miozän). Naturhist. Mus. Wien, Ann., 75, 311–341, 4 pls., 1 table (German; English summary).

SCHULTZ, ORTWIN   See also: Bachmayer, F., Kollmann, H. A., Schultz, O. and Summesberger, H., 1971A.

SCHULTZE, HANS-PETER
1969A   *Griphognathus* Gross, ein langschnauziger Dipnoer aus dem Oberdevon von Bergisch-Gladbach (Rheinisches Schiefergebirge) und von Lettland. Geol. Palaeontol., 3, 21–79, 43 figs., 9 pls., 1 table (German; English summary).
1969B   Die Faltenzähne der Rhipidistiiden Crossopterygier, der Tetrapoden und der Actinopterygier-Gattung *Lepisosteus*; nebst einer Beschreibung der Zahnstruktur von *Onychodus* (Struniiformer Crossopterygier). Palaeontogr. Ital., 65, 63–137, 26 figs., 28 pls. (German; Italian and English summaries).
1970A   Die Histologie der Wirbelkörper der Dipnoer. The histological structure of the centra of dipnoans. Neues Jahrb. Geol. Paläontol., Abh., 135:3, 311–336, 6 figs., 5 pls. (German; English summary).
1970B   *Indaginilepis rhombifera* n. gen. et n. sp., ein altertümlicher Palaeoniscoide (Pisces, Actinopterygii) aus dem Wealden von Norddeutschland. Palaeontol. Zeit., 44:1/2, 10–24, 3 figs., 1 pl. (German).
1970C   Über *Nothosaurus*. Neubeschreibung eines Schädels aus dem Keuper. Senckenbergiana Lethaea, 51: 2/3, 211–237, 15 figs., 2 pls., 1 table (German; English summary).
           Rev.: Anon. in Geol. Bl. Nordost-Bayern, 21:1, 64.
1970D   Folded teeth and the monophyletic origin of tetrapods. Amer. Mus. Nov., 2408, 1–10, 4 figs.
           Rev.: Westphal in Zentralbl. Geol. Paläontol., Teil 2, 1970:5, 431–432.
1972A   *Homalacanthus*, ein oberdevonischer Acanthodier mit Haifisch-ähnlichen Zähnen. Neues Jahrb. Geol. Paläontol., Monatsh., 1972:5, 315–320, 4 figs. (German; English summary).
1972B   New fossils from the lower upper Devonian of Miguasha. In: Carroll, R. L., *et al.*, 1972A, p. 94.

SCHULTZE, H.-P. and WILCZEWSKI, N.
1970A   Ein Nothosauride aus dem unteren Mittel-Keuper Unterfrankens. Göttinger Arb. Geol. Paläontol., 5,
          H. Martin-Festschrift, 101–112, 2 figs., 1 pl. (German; English summary).
          Rev.: Groiss in Geol. Bl. Nordost-Bayern, 21:1, 63.

SCHULZ, H.
1964A   On the zoomorphic representations. Summary. In: Pericot García, L. and Ripoll Perelló, E. (eds.),
          1964A, 253.

SCHUMACHER, GERT-HORST
1968A   In memoriam Richard N. Wegner. Anat. Anz., 123:5, 565–572, portr., bibliog.

SCHÜTRUMPH, R.   See: Gripp, K., Schütrumph, R. and Schwabedissen, H. (eds.), 1967A.

SCHÜTT, GERDA
1968A   Die cromerzeitlichen Bären aus der Einhornhöhle bei Scharzfeld. Hanover, Tech. Hochsch., Geol.
          Inst., Mitt., 1968:7, 1–121, 3 figs., 6 pls., 32 tables (German).
          Rev.: Ehrenberg in Zentralbl. Geol. Paläontol., Teil 2, 1968:6, 662–663.
1969A   Untersuchungen am Gebiss von Panthera leo fossilis (v. Reichenau 1906) und Panthera leo spelaea
          (Goldfuss 1810). Neues Jahrb. Geol. Paläontol., Abh., 134:2, 192–220, 2 figs., 2 pls., 5 tables
          (German; English summary).
          Rev.: Thenius in Zentralbl. Geol. Paläontol., Teil 2, 1970:5, 436.
1969B   Panthera pardus sickenbergi n. subsp. aus den Maurer Sanden. Neues Jahrb. Geol. Paläontol., Monatsh.,
          1969:5, 299–310, 12 figs., 3 tables (German; English summary).
          Rev.: Thenius in Zentralbl. Geol. Paläontol., Teil 2, 1970:3/4, 243.
1969C   Die jungpleistozäne Fauna der Höhlen bei Rübeland im Harz. Quartär, 20, 79–125, 3 pls. (German).
          Rev.: Thenius in Zentralbl. Geol. Paläontol., Teil 2, 1971:1, 64.
1970A   Nachweis der Säbelzahnkatze Homotherium in den altpleistozänen Mosbacher Sanden (Wiesbaden/Hessen).
          Neues Jahrb. Geol. Paläontol., Monatsh., 1970:3, 187–192, 1 fig., 1 table (German; English
          summary).
          Rev.: Thenius in Zentralbl. Geol. Paläontol., Teil 2, 1970:6, 519.
1970B   Ein Gepardenfund aus den Mosbacher Sanden (Altpleistozän, Wiesbaden). Mainzer Naturwiss. Arch.,
          9, 118–131, 3 figs., 2 tables (German; English summary).
          Rev.: Thenius in Zentralbl. Geol. Paläontol., Teil 2, 1971:5, 415.

SCHÜTT, GERDA   See also: Hemmer, H. and Schütt, G., 1969A, 1970A.

SCHÜZ, ERNST
1966A   175 Jahre Staatliches Museum für Naturkunde in Stuttgart. Ver. Vaterländ. Naturk. Württemberg,
          Jahresh., Suppl. to 122 (1967), 40 pp., 27 figs. (German).
1970A   125 Jahre Verein für vaterländische Naturkunde in Württemberg. Ges. Naturk. Württemberg, Jahresh.,
          125, 9–12 (German).
1970B   Alfred Brehm (der Tierleben-Brehm) und John W. v. Müller aus Kochersteinsfeld. Ges. Naturk.
          Württemberg, Jahresh., 125, 294–312, 2 portrs. (German).

SCHWABE, G. H.   See: Fittkau, E. J., Illies, J., Klinge, H., Schwabe, G. H. and Sioli, H. (eds.), 1969A.

SCHWABEDISSEN, H.   See: Gripp, K., Schütrumph, R. and Schwabedissen, H. (eds.), 1967A.

SCHWARTZ, DOUGLAS W.   See: Rolingson, M. A. and Schwartz, D. W., 1966B.

SCHWARZ, WALTER
1970A   Birgeria stensiöi Aldinger. In: Kuhn-Schnyder, E., and Peyer, B. †: Die Triasfauna der Tessiner
          Kalkalpen, XX. Schweiz. Paläontol. Abh. – Mém. Suisses Paléontol., 89, 93 pp., 75 figs., 2 pls.,
          6 tables (German; English, French and Italian summaries).

SCHWARZBACH, MARTIN
1950A   Rev.: Anon. in Natuurwet. Tijdschr., 32:5, 168.
1961A   Rev.: Hacquaert in Natuurwet. Tijdschr., 43:7–8, 168.

SCHWARZHANS, WERNER and WEILER, WILHELM
1971A   Ein ungewöhnlicher Fund von Otolithen "in situ" aus dem mitteloligozänen Meeressand des Mainzer
          Beckens. Senckenbergiana Lethaea, 52:5/6, 529–535, 5 figs. (German; English summary).

SCHWIDETZKY, ILSE
1959A   Das Menschenbild der Biologie. Stuttgart: Gustav Fischer Verlag, viii + 218 pp., 81 figs. (German).

1971A   Das Menschenbild der Biologie. Revised edition. Stuttgart: Gustav Fischer Verlag, 235 pp., 84 figs.
         (German).
         Rev.: Haltenorth in Säugetierkundl. Mitt., 20:1—2, 189; Jürgens in Naturwiss. Rundsch., 24:8, 365.
1972A   Moderne Trends in der prähistorischen Anthropologie. Umsch. Wiss. Tech., 72:17, 545—550, 6 figs.
         (German; English summary).

SCOTT, W. FRANK and CLEM, RICHARD
1967A   A mammoth from the Touchet beds near Walla Walla, Washington. Northwest Sci., 41:1, 60—61
         (abs.).

SEDDON, GEORGE
1969A   Conodont and fish remains from Gneudna formation, Carnarvon Basin, Western Australia. Roy. Soc.
         West. Austral., J., 52:1, 21—30, 1 fig., 2 pls., 3 tables.

SEELEY, H. G.
1967A   Rev.: Petzold in Biol. Zentralbl., 87:6, 814—815.

SEGALL, WALTER
1970A   Morphological parallelism of the bulla and auditory ossicles in some insectivores and marsupials.
         Fieldiana, Zool., 51:15, 169—205, 26 figs.

SEGRE, ALDO G.   See: Ascenzi, A. and Segre, Aldo G., 1971A, 1971B.

SEIFFERT, JÜRGEN
1969A   Urodelen-Atlas aus dem obersten Bajocien von SE - Aveyron (Südfrankreich). Palaeontol. Z., 43:1/2,
         32—36, 1 fig. (German; English and French summaries).
         Rev.: Westphal in Zentralbl. Geol. Paläontol., Teil 2, 1969:6, 511.
1969B   Sternalelement (Omosternum) eines mitteljurassischen Anuren von SE - Aveyron, Südfrankreich.
         Z. Zool. Syst. Evolut.-Forsch., 7:2, 145—153, 9 figs., 1 table (German; English and French
         summaries).
         Rev.: Westphal in Zentralbl. Geol. Paläontol., Teil 2, 1970:1, 68—69.
1972A   Ein Vorläufer der Froschfamilien Palaeobatrachidae und Ranidae im Grenzbereich Jura-Kreide. Neues
         Jahrb. Geol. Paläontol., Monatsh., 1972:2, 120—131, 2 figs., 2 pls. (German; English and
         French summaries).
         Rev.: Westphal in Zentralbl. Geol. Paläontol., Teil 2, 1972:3, 164.

SEILACHER, ADOLF
1967A   Fossil behavior. Sci. Amer., 217:2, 72—80, illustr.
1969A   Friedrich Freiherr von Huene, March 22, 1875—April 4, 1969. Soc. Vert. Paleontol., News Bull., 86,
         41, portr.
1970A   Arbeitskonzept zur Konstruktions-Morphologie. Lethaia, 3:4, 392—396, 1 fig. (German; English
         summary).
1970B   Begriff und Bedeutung der Fossil-Lagerstätten. Neues Jahrb. Geol. Paläontol., Monatsh., 1970:1,
         34—39 (German; English summary).
         Rev.: Häntzschel in Zentralbl. Geol. Paläontol., Teil 2, 1971:4, 251.
1972A   Otto H. Schindewolf (7. Juni 1896—10 Juni 1971). Neues Jahrb. Geol. Paläontol., Monatsh., 1972:2,
         69—71, portr. (German).

SEILACHER, A. and WESTPHAL, F.
1969A   Friedrich Freiherr von Huene. Ver. Vaterländ. Naturk. Württemberg, Jahresh., 124, 43—44, portr.
         (German).

SEILER, ROLF   See: Ehara, A. and Seiler, R., 1970A.

SELANDER, ROBERT K.
1969A   The ecological aspects of the systematics of animals. Discussions. In: Sibley, Ch. G. (ed.), 1969A,
         213—247, 5 figs.

SELIVERSTOV, ĪŪ. P.
1967A   Chetvertichnaĭa sistema. Zaĭsanskaĭa vpadina. [Quaternary. Zaĭsan basin.] Geologiĭa SSSR, 41:1,
         Eastern Kazakhstan, 213—219, 1 fig., 1 table (Russian).

SEMACA, A.   See: Macarovici, N. and Semaca, A., 1969A.

SEMENOV, G. I. and STOLIAROV, A. S.
    1970A   O korreliatsii razrezov raznofatsial'nykh otlozhenii oligotsena Mangyshlaka i Predkavkaz'ia. [On correlation of heterofacies deposits cross-sections of Mangyshlak and Precaucasus Oligocene.] Mosk. Obshchest. Ispyt. Prir., Biull., Otd. Geol., 45:1, 84–94, 2 figs. (Russian).

SEMENOV, IU. I.
    1971A   Ot kogo zhe proizoshel *Homo sapiens*? [From whom did *Homo sapiens* originate?] Priroda, 1971:11, 50–63, 11 figs. (Russian).

SEMENOV, S. A.
    1970A   Chto my dumaem o proiskhozhdenii cheloveka. Sotsial'naia rol' ognia. [What we think about the origin of man. Social role of fire.] Priroda, 1970:10, 40–43, 4 figs., portr. (Russian).

SEMENOV, S. A.   See also: Eritsian, B. G. and Semenov, S. A., 1971A.

SEMENTSOV, A. A., ROMANOVA, E. N. and DOLUKHANOV, P. M.
    1969A   Radiouglerodnye daty laboratorii LOIA. [Radiocarbon data from LOIA Laboratory.] Sov. Arkheol., 1969:1, 251–261 (Russian; French summary).

SEMKEN, HOLMES A., JR.
    1959B   Preliminary report on the Cave Without a Name fossil fauna. Speleo Digest, 1959, 2-131 – 2-132 (reprinted from Texas Caver, 4:3, 6).
    1969A   Paleoecological implications of micromammals from Peccary Cave, Newton County, Arkansas. Geol. Soc. Amer., Abstr., Part 2, 27 (abs.).
    1972A   Small mammals from Peccary Cave, northwestern Arkansas. Soc. Vert. Paleontol., Ann. Meeting, 32nd, 1972, Abstr. (abs.).
    1972B   Mammalian remains from Rattlesnake Cave, Kinney County, Texas (USA). Int. J. Speleol., 4:2, 213 (abs.).

SEMKEN, HOLMES A., JR.   See also: Nelson, R. S. and Semken, H. A., Jr., 1969A, 1970A; Straka, J. J., II and Semken, H. A., Jr., 1969A, 1969B.

SEN, D. and GHOSH, A. K.
    1966A*   Rev.: Fairservis in Asian Perspectives, 10, 176.

SENEŠ, JÁN   See: Cicha, I., Seneš, J. and Tejkal, J., *et al.*, 1967A.

SEREDA, T. T., ELLERN, S. S. and LIASHENKO, A. I.
    1967A   Devonskaia sistema. [Devonian system.] Geologiia SSSR, 11, Povolzh'e and Prikam'e, 130–226, 16 figs. (Russian).

SEREZHENKO, V. A.   See: Zhizhchenko, B. P., Serezhenko, V. A. and Churilova, E. V., 1968A.

SERGEANT, D. E.   See: Harington, C. R. and Sergeant, D. E., 1972A.

SERGI, SERGIO
    1959C   I tipi umani piu antichi. Preominidi e Ominidi fosili. In: Biasutti, R. (ed.), *et al.*, 1959A, vol. 1, 69–133, 41 figs., 1 pl., 1 table (Italian).
            Rev.: Comas in Cuad. Inst. Hist., Ser. Antropol. no. 6, 29–36.
    1966A   Gian Alberto Blanc (1879–1966). Riv. Antropol., 53, 129–135, portr. (Italian).
    1966B   Commemorazione di Alberto Carlo Blanc (1906–1960). Riv. Antropol., 53, 136–137 (Italian).
    1968A   La posizione dell'osso temporale nel cranio neandertaliano del Monte Circeo. Riv. Antropol., 55, 9–14, 3 figs. (Italian; English summary).
    1969A   Position of the temporal bone in the neandertalian skull of Mount Circeo. Accad. Naz. Lincei, Atti, Ser. 8, Cl. Sci. Fis., Mat. Natur., Rend., 46:4, 476–480, 2 figs. (Italian summary).
    1971A   The palaeanthropi in Italy: the fossil men of Saccopastore and Circeo. In: Leakey, L. S. B., Prost, J. and Prost, S. (eds.), 1971A, 229–237, 3 figs. (reprinted from Man, 48, 1948).

SERGIENKO, N. I.
    1971A   Iskopaemyi vid roda *Nerophis* (Teleostei). [A fossil species of the genus *Nerophis* (Teleostei).] Paleontol. Zh., 1971:4, 136–137, 1 fig. (Russian).
    1971B   A fossil species of *Nerophis* (Teleostei). Paleontol. J., 5:4, 544–545, 1 fig.

SERGIN, V. IA.
    1970A   Krupneishee otkrytie arkheologov. [A greatest discovery by archeologists.] Priroda, 1970:4, 116–117, 1 fig. (Russian).

SERONIE-VIVIEN, R.
1971A   Note préliminaire sur la faune des niveaux aziliens de la grotte de Pégourié (Caniac, Lot). Soc. Linn. Bordeaux, Bull., 1:2, 3–4, 1 fig. (French).

SERVANT, M., ERGENZINGER, P. and COPPENS, Y.
1969A   Datations absolues sur un delta lacustre quaternaire au Sud du Tibesti (Angamma). Soc. Géol. Fr., C.R., 1969:8, 313–314, 2 figs. (French).

SEVERTSOV, A. N.
1967A   Glavnye napravleniia evoliutsionnogo protsessa. [Main trends of the evolutionary process.] Moscow: Univ. Press, 139 pp. (Russian).

SEVERTSOV, A. S.
1969A   Proiskhozhdenie bazal'nykh elementov giobrankhial'nogo skeleta lichinok amfibii. [The origin of basal elements of the hyobranchial skeleton of amphibian larvae.] Akad. Nauk SSSR, Dokl., 187:3, 677–680, 4 figs. (Russian).
1971A   Mekhanizm zakhvatyvaniia pishchi khvostatymi amfibiiami. [Food-seizing mechanism of amphibians.] Akad. Nauk SSSR, Dokl., 197:3, 728–731, 2 figs. (Russian).

SEVRIUGIN, N. A.
1967A   Chetvertichnaia sistema. Zapadnaia Kalba (Charskaia i Zharminskaia zony). [Quaternary. West Kalba (Char and Zharmin zones).] Geologiia SSSR, 41:1, Eastern Kazakhstan, 227–231 (Russian).

SEVRIUGIN, N. A.   See also: Borisov, B. A. and Sevriugin, N. A., 1967A.

SHAKH, LIUBOV' NIKOLAEVNA
1968A   O novykh nakhodkakh predstavitelei roda Ptychodus iz melovykh otlozhenii Podolii. [On the new finds of the representatives of the genus Ptychodus from Cretaceous deposits of Podolia.] Paleontol. Sb., 5:1, 105–106, 1 pl. (Russian; English summary).

SHANTSER, EVGENII VIRGIL'EVICH
1964A   O rabote VI kongressa Mezhdunarodnoi assotsiatsii po izucheniiu chetvertichnogo perioda (INQUA) (Pol'sha, 1961g.). [On the work of the VI Congress of the International Association for Quaternary Research (INQUA) (Poland, 1961).] In: Nauchnye itogi VI kongressa mezhdunarodnoi assotsiatsii po izucheniiu chetvertichnogo perioda (INQUA). (Varshava, 1961), 5–71, 12 figs., 1 table (Russian).

SHANTSER, EVGENII VIRGIL'EVICH and MIKULINA, TAMARA MIKHAILOVNA
1967A   Geomorfologiia i antropogenovye otlozheniia severo-zapadnoi chasti Kazakhskogo shchita. [Geomorphology and Quaternary deposits of the northwestern part of Kazakh shield.] In: Materialy po geologii Tsentral'nogo Kazakhstana, 7, 7–176, 36 figs. (Russian).

SHANTSER, E. V.   See also: Gromov, V. I., Krasnov, I. I., Nikiforova, K. V. and Shantser, E. V., 1969A.

SHAPIRO, HARRY L.
1964A   From fins to fingers. Natur. and Sci., 2:7, 10–11, illustr. (juvenile).
1971A   The strange, unfinished saga of Peking man. Natur. Hist., 80:9, 8–10, 74–83, illustr.

SHARAKHMEDOV, SH. SH.   See: Kambariddinov, R. K., Kadyrov, M. Kh., Aripov, A. A. and Sharakhmedov, Sh. Sh., 1971A; Kambariddinov, R. K. and Sharakhmedov, Sh. Sh., 1971A.

SHARFMAN, V. S., TSETLIN, V. P. and SKRIPKO, K. A.
1965A   O santonskom iaruse na Orskom Urale. [On the Santonian stage in Orsk Urals.] In: Materialy po geologii i poleznym iskopaemym Iuzhnogo Urala, 4, 77–79 (Russian).

SHARKOV, A. A.   See: Dubrovo, I. A. and Sharkov, A. A., 1971A.

SHARMA, N. L.   See: Dixit, P. C., Kachroo, R. K., Rai, H. and Sharma, N. L., 1971A.

SHARMAN, G. B.   See: Air, G. M., Thompson, O. P., Richardson, B. J. and Sharman, G. B., 1971A.

SHAROV, ALEKSANDR GRIGOR'EVICH
1970A   Svoeobraznaia reptiliia iz nizhnego triasa Fergany. [A peculiar reptile from the lower Triassic of Fergana.] Paleontol. Zh., 1970:1, 127–130, 4 figs., 1 pl. (Russian).
1970B   An unusual reptile from the lower Triassic of Fergana. Paleontol. J., 4:1, 112–116, 4 figs., 1 pl.

1971A   Novye letaiushchie reptilii iz mezozoiă Kazakhstana i Kirgizii. [New flying reptiles from the
Mesozoic of Kazakhstan and Kirgizia.] Akad. Nauk SSSR, Paleontol. Inst., Tr., 130, 104–
113, 5 figs., 3 pls. (Russian).

SHARP, L.   See: Howell, F. C., Turnbull, C., Sharp, L., Clark, J. G. D. and DeVore, I., 1968A.

SHATSKIĬ, S. B.
1967A   Chetvertichnaiă sistema. Kolyvan'-Tomskaiă zona. [Quaternary system. Kolyvan'-Tomsk zone.]
Geologiiă SSSR, 14, Western Siberia (southern part), 406–409 (Russian).

SHATSKIĬ, S. B.   See also: Gurari, F. G., Zal'tsman, G., Teslenko, Yu. V. and Shatskiĭ, S. B., 1968A, 1968B.

SHAW, ALAN B.
1969A   Adam and Eve, paleontology, and the non-objective arts. J. Paleontol., 43:5, 1085–1098, 16 figs.
1971A   The butterfingered handmaiden. J. Paleontol., 45, 1–5, 3 tables.

SHAY, THOMAS C.
1971A   The Itasca bison kill site, an ecological analysis. St. Paul: Minnesota Historical Society, 133 pp.,
38 figs., 36 pls., 36 tables.
Rev.: Martin in Ecology, 52:6, 1137.

SHCHEGLOVA, VERA VASIL'EVNA
1964A   O vozmozhnosti bolee drobnogo raschleneniiă verkhnepleĭstotsenovykh otlozheniĭ po ostatkam
mamonta. [On the possibility of a more detailed subdivision of upper Pleistocene deposits by
mammoth remains.] In: Vsesoiŭznoe Soveshchanie po Izucheniiŭ Chetvertichnogo perioda,
Novosibirsk, 1964, Tezisy Dokladov, Sektsiiă Istorii Flory, Fauny i Drevnego Cheloveka, 11–12,
1 table (Russian).
1968A   Sushchestvovala li riss-wiŭrmskaiă "antikvusovaiă" fauna? [Did the Riss-Würm "antiquus" fauna
exist?] In: Voprosy geologii antropogena, 115–119 (Russian).

SHCHEGLOVA, V. V.   See also: Tsapenko, M. M. and Shcheglova, V. V., 1972A; Vozniăchuk, L. N.,
Shcheglova, V. V. and Kalechits, E. G., 1972A.

SHCHEPINSKIĬ, A. A.
1971A   Kogda obrazovalsiă iŭzhnyĭ bereg Kryma. [When the Crimea's southern coast came into existence.]
Priroda, 1971:12, 77–78, 2 figs. (Russian).

SHCHERBAKOVA, L. A.   See: Krasnenkov, R. V., Aleksandrova, L. P., Shcherbakova, L. A. and
Chepalyga, A. L., 1970A.

SHCHUKINA, E. N.
1967A   Chetvertichnaiă sistema. Biĭsko-Barnaul'skaiă vpadina. [Quaternary system. Biĭsk-Barnaul
depression.] Geologiiă SSSR, 14, Western Siberia (southern part), 399–406, 1 fig. (Russian).
1967B   Chetvertichnaiă sistema. Gornaiă Shoriiă i Kuznetskiĭ Alatau. [Quaternary system. Gornaiă Shoriiă
and Kuznetskiĭ Alatau.] Geologiiă SSSR, 14, Western Siberia (southern part), 413–414
(Russian).
1967C   Chetvertichnaiă sistema. Salair. [Quaternary system. Salair.] Geologiiă SSSR, 14, Western Siberia
(southern part), 415–417 (Russian).
1967D   Chetvertichnaiă sistema. Gornyĭ Altaĭ. [Quaternary system. Gornyĭ Altaĭ.] Geologiiă SSSR, 14,
Western Siberia (southern part), 417–425 (Russian).

SHELKOPLIĂS, V. N.
1971A   Datirovanie chetvertichnykh otlozheniĭ termoliuministsentnym metodom. [Dating Quaternary deposits
by the thermoluminescence method.] In: Khronologiiă lednikovogo veka. Materialy k
simposiumu, Leningrad, mart 1972g., 155–160 (Russian).

SHELTON, JOHN W.
1971A   Lungfish burrows in dolomite of the Wellington formation. Okla. Geol. Notes, 31, 50, cover photo.

SHEN-SJAO-CHZHOU
1963A   [Characteristics of the mammal fauna of Tibet and the history of its origin.] Acta Zool. Sinica, 15,
139–150, 1 map, 3 tables (Chinese; Russian summary).

SHER, ANDREĬ VLADIMIROVICH
1968B   Early Quaternary mammals of the northeastern USSR and the problem of the continental links
between Asia and America. Akad. Nauk SSSR, Dokl., Earth Sci. Sec., 177, 128–130.
(Translated from Russian: Akad. Nauk SSSR, Dokl., 1967, 177:6, 1430–1433.)

1968C   Fossil saiga in northeastern Siberia and Alaska. Int. Geol. Rev., 10:11, 1247—1260, 2 figs., 2 tables.

1969A   Paleogeografiiā i fauna mlekopitaiūshchikh nizov'ev Kolymy v kontse pleistotsena. [Paleogeography and mammalian fauna of the lower course of Kolyma at the end of Pleistocene.] In: Chetvertichnaiā geologiiā i geomorfologiiā Sibiri, Part 1, 173—188 (Russian).

1970A   Pleistotsenovaiā fauna mlekopitaiūshchikh ravninnykh poberezhiĭ Vostochno-Sibirskogo moriā i problema Beringiĭskoĭ sushi. [Pleistocene mammalian fauna of the coastal plains of the east-Siberian Sea and the problem of Beringian land.] In: Severnyĭ Ledovityĭ Okean i ego poberezh'e v kaĭnozoe, 516—524, 1 fig. (Russian).

1970B   Pleistotsenovye mlekopitaiūshchie Severnoĭ Ameriki i ikh stratigraficheskoe znachenie. [Pleistocene mammals of North America and their stratigraphic significance.] Itogi Nauki, Ser. Geol., 21 (1969), Obshch. Geol., Stratigr., Paleontol., 136—160, 1 fig., 2 tables (Russian).

1971A   Säugetierfunde und Pleistozänstratigraphie in der Kolyma-Niederung. Deut. Ges. Geol. Wiss., Ber., Reihe A, Geol. Paläontol., 16:2, 113—125, 1 fig. (German).

1971B   K voprosu o proiskhozhdenii subarkticheskoĭ fauny mlekopitaiūshchikh. [The problem of the origin of subarctic mammalian fauna.] Mosk. Obshchest. Ispyt. Prir., Biull., Otd. Geol., 46:2, 151—152 (Russian).

1971C   Mlekopitaiūshchie i stratigrafiiā pleistotsena kraĭnego Severo-Vostoka SSSR i Severnoĭ Ameriki. [Mammals and stratigraphy of the Pleistocene of the extreme northeast of USSR and North America.] Moscow: "Nauka" Press, 310 pp., 72 figs., 40 tables (Russian).

1972A   Zorgelia na Kolyme. [Soergelia on Kolyma.] Priroda, 1972:5, 109—110 (Russian).

SHER, A. V.   See also: Vangengeĭm, E. A. and Sher, A. V., 1969A, 1970A, 1972A.

SHERMAN, DIANE
    1964A   In search of the first man. Natur. and Sci., 2:7, 3—6, illustr. (juvenile).

SHERSHNEV, K. S.   See: Nalivkin, V. D., Larionova, E. N. and Shershnev, K. S., 1969A.

SHERSTIŪKOV, NIKOLAĬ MATVEEVICH
    1971A   Prokhorez i stratigraficheskoe rasprostranenie khobotnykh Severnogo Kavkaza i iūga SSSR. [Prochoresis and stratigraphic distribution of proboscideans of north Caucasus and the south of the USSR.] Grozny, USSR, Grozn. Neft. Nauch.-Issled. Inst., Tr., 33, 49—50 (Russian).

SHERWIN, L.
    1969A   Amphibian footprints in Hawkesbury sandstone. Quarry Mine and Pit, 1969, June, 6—8, 1 fig.

SHERWOOD, MORGAN B.
    1969A   Genesis, evolution, and geology in America before Darwin: the Dana-Lewis controversy, 1856—1857. In: Schneer, C. J. (ed.), 1969A, 305—316.

SHEVCHENKO, ANTONINA IVANOVNA
    1964A   Stratigraficheskoe znachenie melkikh mlekopitaiūshchikh (Rodentia). [Stratigraphic significance of small mammals (Rodentia).] In: Vsesoiūznoe Soveshchanie po Izucheniiū Chetvertichnogo perioda, Novosibirsk, 1964, Tezisy Dokladov, Sektsiiā Istorii Flory, Fauny i Drevnego Cheloveka, 13—15 (Russian).

    1968A   Pliotsenovye i drevnechetvertichnye kompleksy melkikh mlekopitaiūshchikh iūga SSSR. [Pliocene and early Quaternary small mammals complexes of the south of USSR.] In: Problemy izucheniiā chetvertichnogo perioda. Tezisy, 129 (Russian).

    1969A   O korreliātsii otlozheniĭ s tiraspol'skim faunisticheskim kompleksom i bakinskikh morskikh otlozheniĭ. [On the correlation of deposits with Tiraspol' faunistic complex and Bakinian marine deposits.] In: Mezhdunarodnyĭ kollokvium po geologii i faune nizhnego i srednego pleistotsena Evropy. Tezisy dokladov, 40—42 (Russian).

SHEVCHENKO, ANTONINA IVANOVNA and TROSHKINA, O. B.
    1967A   Ftorovyĭ metod opredeleniiā absoliūtnogo vozrasta kostnykh ostatkov mlekopitaiūshchikh iz kaĭnozoĭskikh otlozheniĭ. [Fluorine method of determining the absolute age of fossil bones of mammals in Cenozoic deposits.] Akad. Nauk. Gruz. SSR, Inst. Paleobiol., Nauchn. Sess., 13, 13—17 (Russian).

SHEVCHENKO, IŪ. G.
    1970A   Evoliūtsiiā kory mozga primatov i cheloveka. [Evolution of the cortex of primates and man.] Moscow: Univ. Press, 463 pp., illustr. (Russian). Rev.: Dzugaeva and Zvorykin in Vop. Antropol., 40, 196—198 (Russian).

SHEVCHENKO, V. K.   See: Vangengeĭm, E. A., Piātakov, V. V. and Shevchenko, V. K., 1969A, 1969B.

SHEVYREV, ALEKSANDR ALEKSANDROVICH
    1972A   Otto Heinrich Schindewolf (1896–1971). Paleontol. Zh., 1972:1, 156–157, portr. (Russian).

SHEVYREVA, NINA SEMENOVNA
    1969A   Melkie mlekopitaiushchie iz paleogena iuga Zaisanskoi kotloviny. [Small mammals from the Paleogene
                 of the southern part of Zaisan trough.] Mosk. Obshch. Ispyt. Prir., Biull., Otd. Geol., 44:6,
                 146 (Russian).
    1970A   K voprosu ob evoliutsii semeistva Zapodidae (Dipodoidea, Rodentia, Mammalia). [On the problem of
                 evolution of the family Zapodidae (Dipodoidea, Rodentia, Mammalia).] In: Materialy po
                 evoliutsii nazemnykh pozvonochnykh, 85–90, 1 fig. (Russian).
    1971A   Pervaia nakhodka eotsenovykh gryzunov v SSSR. [First find of Eocene rodents in USSR.] Akad.
                 Nauk Gruz. SSR, Soobshch., 61:3, 745–747, 1 fig. (Russian; Georgian and English summaries).
    1971B   Pervaia nakhodka v SSSR gryzunov semeistva Mylagaulidae. [The first find in USSR of rodents of
                 the family Mylagaulidae.] Akad. Nauk Gruz. SSR, Soobshch., 62:2, 481–484, 1 fig. (Russian;
                 Georgian and English summaries).
    1971C   Novye sredneoligotsenovye gryzuny Kazakhstana i Mongolii. [New middle Oligocene rodents from
                 Kazakhstan and Mongolia.] Akad. Nauk SSSR, Paleontol. Inst., Tr., 130, 70–86, 8 figs.
                 (Russian).
    1971D   K voprosu o sistematicheskom polozhenii "Tsaganomys altaicus" (Mammalia, Rodentia). [On the
                 question of the systematic position of "Tsaganomys altaicus" (Mammalia, Rodentia).] Mosk.
                 Obshchest. Ispyt. Prir., Biull., Otd. Geol., 46:6, 144 (Russian).
    1972A   Novye gryzuny iz paleogena Mongolii i Kazakhstana. [New rodents from the Paleogene of Mongolia
                 and Kazakhstan.] Paleontol. Zh., 1972:3, 134–145, 6 figs. (Russian).

SHEVYREVA, N. S.   See also: Birman, A. S., Zhegallo, V. I., Rastsvetaev, L. M., Khozatskii, L. I. and
                         Shevyreva, N. S., 1971A.

SHIKAMA, TOKIO
    1967A   A fossil Reptilia from the Tetori group. Natur. Sci. and Mus., 34:1–2, 13–16, 2 figs. (Japanese).
    1969A   On a Jurassic reptile from Miyama-cho, Fukui prefecture, Japan. Yokohama Nat. Univ., Sci. Repts.,
                 Sect. II, 15, 25–34, 3 figs., 1 pl.
    1970A   On some Mesosaurus skeletons kept in Japan. Yokohama Nat. Univ., Sci. Repts., Sect. II, 16, 29–49,
                 5 figs., 5 pls.
    1971A   Ushinawareta seibutsu. [Lost creature.] Shukan Asahi, 2720, 74–75, 1 photo (Japanese).
    1972A   Fossil Crocodilia from Tsochin, southwestern Taiwan. Yokohama Nat. Univ., Sci. Repts., Sect. II, 19,
                 125–132, 1 fig., 2 pls.

SHIKAMA, TOKIO and DOMNING, DARYL P.
    1970A   Pliocene Sirenia in Japan. Palaeontol. Soc. Jap., Trans. Proc., 80, 390–396, 4 figs., pl. 44 (Japanese
                 summary).

SHIKAMA, TOKIO and KANNO, SABURO
    1970A   On an elephant found at Ikebukuro station, Tokyo. Yokohama Nat. Univ., Sci. Repts., Sect. II, 16,
                 51–60, 4 figs., 2 pls.

SHIKAMA, TOKIO and TAKAYASU, YASUSUKE
    1971A   Fossil mammals from the Shibikawa formation, in Oga Peninsula, Akita prefecture. Yokohama Nat.
                 Univ., Sci. Repts., Sect. II, 18, 43–48, 1 pl.

SHIKAMA, TOKIO and YANAGISAWA, ICHIRO
    1971A   Fossil proboscidian tooth from Iwaki City, Hukushima prefecture. Yokohama Nat. Univ., Sci. Repts.,
                 Sect. II, 18, 37–42, 1 fig., 2 pls.

SHIMANSKII, VIKTOR NIKOLAEVICH   See: Obruchev, D. V. and Shimanskii, V. N. (eds.), 1971A.

SHIMODA, NOBUO and OZAKI, HIROSHI
    1967A   [Chemical research on lesser components in fossil bones. On the relationship between manganese
                 content and age of bones from Tsochen, Taiwan.] Nat. Sci. Mus., Tokyo, Bull., 10:3, 377–
                 381, 1 table (Japanese; English summary).

SHIREK, JUDITH   See: Washburn, S. L. and Shirek, J., 1967A.

SHISHKIN, MIKHAIL ALEKSANDROVICH
    1968B   On the cranial arterial system of the labyrinthodonts. Acta Zool. (Stockholm), 49:1–2, 1–22, 7 figs.
                 Rev.: Westphal in Zentralbl. Geol. Paläontol., Teil 2, 1970:1, 69.

1970A   Proiskhozhdenie Anura i teoriĭa "lissamfibiĭ". [Origin of Anura and the theory of "lissamphibia".]
         In: Materialy po evoliŭtsii nazemnykh pozvonochnykh, 30—44 (Russian).

SHISHKIN, M. A.   See also: Gekker, R. F., Shishkin, M. A. and Ĭakovlev, V. N., 1971A; Hecker, R. F.,
         Shishkin, M. A. and Yakovlev,V. N., 1971A; Kalandadze, N. N., Ochev, V. G., Tatarinov,
         L. P., Chudinov, P. K. and Shishkin, M. A., 1968A; Lipatova, V. V., et al., 1972A; Ochev,
         V. G., Shishkin, M. A., Garĭainov, V. A. and Tverdokhlebov, V. P., 1964A, 1965A.

SHKORBATOV, G. L.
1971A   Osnovnye cherty adaptatsii biologicheskikh sistem. [Principal features of adaptations of biological
         systems.] Zh. Obshch. Biol., 32:2, 131—142 (Russian; English summary).

SHLEĬFER, ANNA GEORGIEVNA   See: Bogacheva, M. I., Vasil'ev, Ĭu. M., Proshlĭakov, B. K., Charygin, M. M.
         and Shleĭfer, A. G., 1965A.

SHLEMON, ROY J.
1969A   Radiometric and faunal dating of Quaternary alluvium in the Sacramento area, California. Geol. Soc.
         Amer., Abstr., Part 3, 61 (abs.).

SHMIDT, E. A.
1963A   K istoricheskoĭ geografii Smolenskoĭ zemli. 1. O zaselenii Smolenskogo kraĭa v kamennom veke.
         [Contribution to the historical geography of the Smolensk land. 1. On the settlement of
         Smolensk territory in the Stone Age.] Smolensk. Gos. Pedag. Inst., Uch. Zap., 12, 303—317
         (Russian).

SHOR, ELIZABETH NOBLE
1971A   Fossils and flies. The life of a compleat scientist, Samuel Wendell Williston (1851—1918). Norman,
         Okla.: Univ. Oklahoma Press, xiv + 285 pp., illustr.
         Rev.: Fuller in Frontiers, 36:1, 30—31; Ostrom in Science, 174:4012, 937—938.

SHORT, LESTER L., JR.
1969A   A new genus and species of gooselike swan from the Pliocene of Nebraska. Amer. Mus. Nov.,
         no. 2369, 1—7, 1 fig.
1970A   Mid-Pleistocene birds from western Nebraska, including a new species of sheldgoose. Condor, 72:2,
         147—152, 2 figs.
1970B   A new anseriform genus and species from the Nebraska Pliocene. Auk, 87:3, 537—543, 2 figs.

SHOTTON, F. W.   See: Osborne, P. J. and Shotton, F. W., 1968A.

SHOTWELL, J. ARNOLD
1951A   A fossil sea-lion from Fossil Point, Oregon. Oreg. Acad. Sci., Proc., 2, 97 (abs.).
1954B   The McKay Reservoir local fauna, its age, and faunal relationships. Oreg. Acad. Sci., Proc., 3, 86.
1970A   Pliocene mammals of southeast Oregon and adjacent Idaho. Oreg., Univ., Mus. Natur. Hist., Bull., 17,
         103 pp., 43 figs., 26 tables.

SHOTWELL, J. ARNOLD   See also: Sargent, S. and Shotwell, J. A., 1951A.

SHOVKOPLIĂS, I. G.
1969A   Dobranichevskaĭa pozdnepaleoliticheskaĭa stoĭanka na Kievshchine. [Dobranichev late Paleolithic
         site in the Kiev region.] In: Materialy po chetvertichnomu periodu Ukrainy, 242—251
         (Russian; English summary).

SHTEGMAN, B. K.
1967A   Problema beringiĭskoĭ kontinental'noĭ svĭazi v ornitogeograficheskom osveshchenii. [The problem of
         Beringian continental connection in ornitho-geographical light.] Pribalt. Ornitol. Konf., 5th,
         Tartu, 1963, Tr., 25—36, 4 figs. (Russian).
1970A   Osobennosti morfologii kryla pingvinov. [Peculiarities of morphology of the wing in penguins.]
         Akad. Nauk SSSR, Zool. Inst., Trudy, 47, 236—248, 8 figs. (Russian).
1971A   Glubokiĭ sgibatel' pal'tsev v kryle ptits. [The deep digit flexor in the wings of birds.] Mosk.
         Obshchest. Ispyt. Prir., Biŭll., Otd. Biol., 76:1, 79—88, 5 figs. (Russian; English summary).

SHUL'GA, POLINA LUKINICHNA
1958A   Devonskie otlozheniĭa Volyno-Podol'skoĭ plity. [Devonian deposits of the Volyno-Podolian slab.]
         Geologiĭa SSSR, 5, Ukrainian SSR, Moldavian SSR, 460—466 (Russian).

SHUSHPANOV, K. I.   See: Khubka, A. N. and Shushpanov, K. I., 1971A; David, A. I. and
         Shushpanov, K. I., 1972A.

SHUSTOV, L. N.   See: Mel'nikov, O. A. and Shustov, L. N., 1969A.

SHUTLER, RICHARD, JR.
1967D   Radiocarbon dating and man in Southeast Asia, Australia, and the Pacific. In: Solheim, W. (ed.), 1967A, 79—87.

SHUVALOV, V. F.
1969A   O verkhneiurskikh krasnotsvetnykh kontinental'nykh otlozheniiakh Mongolii. [On the upper Jurassic continental red beds of Mongolia.] Akad. Nauk SSSR, Dokl., 189:5, 1088—1091 (Russian).
1970A   Continental red beds of the upper Jurassic of Mongolia. Akad. Nauk SSSR, Dokl., Earth Sci. Sec., 189, 112—114. (Translated from Russian: Akad. Nauk SSSR, 1969, 189:5, 1088—1091.)

SHVARTS, S. S.
1963A   Vnutrividovaia izmenchivost' mlekopitaiushchikh i metody ee izucheniia. [Intraspecific variability of mammals and methods of its study.] Zool. Zh., 42:3, 417—433, 4 figs. (Russian; English summary).
1965A   Uchenie o mikroevoliutsii i teoreticheskie voprosy sistematiki ptits. [The doctrine of micro-evolution and the theoretical problems of the systematics of birds.] In: Sovremenny problemy ornitologii. Chetvertaia vsesoiuznaia ornitologicheskaia konferentsiia, 65—86 (Russian).
1969A   Evoliutsionnaia ekologiia zhivotnykh. [Evolutionary ecology of animals.] Akad. Nauk SSSR, Ural. Fil., Inst. Ekol. Rast. Zhiv., Tr., 65, 198 pp., 9 figs., 13 tables (Russian).

SHVAZHAĬTE, R. A. (= ŠVAŽAITE, R. A.)
1968A   O zubak akul iz Esiàskoĭ svity nizhnego mela Shviàntoĭskogo basseĭna. [On shark teeth from Esiàskaia suite of lower Cretaceous of the Shviàntoĭia R. basin.] In: Materialy nauchnoĭ konferentsii molodykh uchenykh geologov Litvy, 18—19 (Russian).

SHVAZHAĬTE, R. A.   See also: Glikman, L. S. and Shvazhaĭte, R. A., 1971A.

SIBLEY, CHARLES G.
1969A*   Systematic biology. Proceedings of an international conference. Washington: National Academy of Sciences, Publication 1692, 632 pp., illustr.

SIBLEY, G.   See: Macdonald, J. R. and Sibley, G., 1969A.

ŠIBRAVA, V., FEJFAR, O., KOVANDA, J. and VALOCH, K.
1969A   Quaternary in Czechoslovakia. (History of investigations between 1919—1969). Prague: Academia, 149 pp., 24 pls.
          Rev.: Fridrich in Archeol. Roz., 22:4, 487.

SICARD, HARALD VON
1967A   Das Menschenbild der Altsteinzeit. Anthropos, 62:5/6, 940—943 (German).

SICARD, HENRI
1957A   L'Hominisation. Les Eyzies, 1957:1, 79—90 (French).
1961A   Les Néandertaliens. Les Eyzies, 10, 232—248, 1 fig. (French).
1961B   Teilhard de Chardin et l'Anthropogenèse. Les Eyzies, 10, 249—260 (French).
1963A   Les primates tertiaires et l'hominisation. Les Eyzies, 12, 89—101, 1 table (French).
1965A   L'hominisation et ses problèmes. Les Eyzies, 14, 172—181, 1 fig. (French).
1967A   Les origines de l'intelligence humaine. L'intelligence pratique. Les Eyzies, 16, 28—45 (French).

SICKENBERG, OTTO
1964B   Die Säugetierfauna der Höhle Petralona bei Thessaloniki. Athens. Inst. Geol. Ereun. Hypedaph., Geol. Geophys. Mel., 9:1, 5—16, 1 map (German and Greek).
1967A   Die unterpleistozäne Fauna von Wolaks (Griech.-Mazedonien). I. Eine neue Giraffe (Macedonitherium martini nov. gen. nov. spec.) aus dem unteren Pleistozän von Griechenland. Ann. Géol. Pays Hellén., 18, 314—330, 5 figs., 3 pls. (German).
1968B   Der Steppeniltis (Mustela [Putorius] eversmanni soergeli Éhik) in der Niederterrasse der Leine und seine klimageschichtliche Bedeutung. Eiszeitalter Gegenwart, 19, 147—163, 2 figs., 2 tables (German; English summary).
1969A   Die Säugetierfauna der Kalkmergel von Lehringen (Krs. Verden/Aller) im Rahmen der eemzeitlichen Faunen Nordwestdeutschlands. Geol. Jahrb., 87, 551—564, 2 figs., 2 tables (German; English and French summaries).
1970A   Die Unterpleistozäne Fauna von Wolaks (Griech.-Mazedonien). II. Die Carnivoren. Ann. Géol. Pays Hellén., 19, 621—645, 2 figs., 6 tables (German; French and English summaries).
          Rev.: Thenius in Zentralbl. Geol. Paläontol., Teil 2, 1969:6, 517—518.

SICKENBERG, OTTO and TOBIEN, HEINZ
1971A   New Neogene and lower Quaternary vertebrate faunas in Turkey. Newsl. Stratigr., 1:3, 51—61, 1 fig.,
         1 table (German summary).
         Rev.: Thenius in Zentralbl. Geol. Paläontol., Teil 2, 1971:6, 514—515.

SICKENBERG, OTTO   See also: Becker-Platen, J. D. and Sickenberg, O., 1968A.

SIEDLECKI, STANISLAW
1970A   A *Helicoprion* from the Permian of Spitzbergen. Nor. Polarinst., Årbok, 1968, 36—54, 4 figs., 2 pls.,
         1 table.

SIEGEL, BERNARD J.
1970A*   Biennial review of anthropology 1969. Stanford, Calif.: Stanford Univ. Press, vii + 404 pp.
         Rev.: Beidelman in Anthropos, 66:3—4, 584; Johnston in Human Biol., 43:1, 182; Schwidetzky in
         Homo, 21:2, 123; Spencer in Amer. Anthropol., 73:2, 306—308; Underwood in Amer. J. Phys.
         Anthropol., 36:2, 302—303.

SIEGEL, BERNHARD J. and BEALS, ALAN R.
1967A*   Rev.: Peter in Anthropol. Ges., Mitt., 98, 89—90; Schwidetzky in Homo, 19:3—4, 228.

SIEGFRIED, PAUL and GROSS, WALTER
1971A   Christian Heinrich Pander 1794—1865 und seine Bedeutung für die Paläontologie. Münstersche Forsch.
         Geol. Paläontol., 19, 101—183, 4 figs., 6 pls. (German).
         Rev.: Häntzschel in Zentralbl. Geol. Paläontol., Teil 2, 1971:4, 249—250.

SIEGFRIED, PAUL   See also: Meiburg, P. and Siegfried, P., 1970A.

SIEWING, ROLF
1969A   Lehrbuch der vergleichenden Entwicklungsgeschichte der Tiere. Hamburg-Berlin: Paul Parey, 531 pp.,
         196 figs. (German).
         Rev.: Bohlken in Z. Säugetierkunde, 36:1, 63; Gutmann in Natur Mus., 101:9, 410—411; Kritscher
         in Anthropol. Ges., Mitt., 99, 233; Reisinger in Z. Zool. Syst. Evolut.-Forsch., 7:3, 235—236;
         Vogel in Z. Morphol. Anthropol., 63:1, 135—136.
1971A*   Methoden der Phylogenie. Symposion vom 12. bis 13. Februar 1970 im I. Zoologischen Institut
         der Universität Erlangen-Nürnberg. Erlangen: Univ. Press, 88 pp., 12 figs. (German).
         Rev.: Roth-Lutra in Anat. Anz., 131:1—2, 175—176.

SIFTON, DAVID W.
1969A   The New York State Cultural Center. Museologist, no. 110, 14—16.

SIGÉ, BERNARD
1971A   Anatomie du membre antérieur chez un chiroptère molossidé (*Tadarida* sp.) du Stampien de Céreste
         (Alpes-de-Haute-Provence). Palaeovertebrata, 4:1, 38 pp., 9 figs., 1 pl., 2 tables (French;
         German and English summaries).
1971B   Les Didelphoidea de Laguna Umayo (formation Vilquechico, Crétacé supérieur, Pérou), et le
         peuplement marsupial d'Amérique du Sud. Acad. Sci., C.R., Sér. D, 273:25, 2479—2481,
         1 fig. (French).

SIGÉ, BERNARD   See also: Cappetta, H., Hartenberger, J. L., Sigé, B. and Sudre, J., 1968A; Cappetta, H. and
         Sigé, B., 1969A; Hartenberger, J. L., Sigé, B. and Sudre, J., 1969A; Hartenberger, J. L.,
         Sigé, B., Sudre, J. and Vianey-Liaud, M., 1970A, 1970B; Menu, H. and Sigé, B., 1971A;
         Meurisse, M., Michaux, J. and Sigé, B., 1969A; Russell, D. E. and Sigé, B., 1970A.

SIGMON, B. A.
1969A   Bipedal behavior as a selective force in the evolution of erect bipedalism in man. Amer. Anthropol.
         Ass., Bull., 2:3, 93—94 (abs.).

SIGOGNEAU, DENISE
1970A   Révision systématique des gorgonopsiens Sud-Africains. Cah. Paléontol., 416 pp., 243 figs., 93 pls.,
         6 tables (French).
1970B   Contribution à la connaissance des Ictidorhinidés (Gorgonopsia). Palaeontol. Afr., 13, 25—38, 7 figs.,
         3 pls. (French).

SIGOGNEAU, DENISE and TCHUDINOV, P. K.
1972A   Reflections on some Russian eotheriodonts (Reptilia, Synapsida, Therapsida). Palaeovertebrata
         (Montpellier), 5:3, 81—109, 30 figs., 1 table (French and German summaries).

SIGOV, A. P.
1969A   Melovaiā sistema. [Cretaceous system.] Geologiiā SSSR, 12:1, Perm, Sverdlovsk, Cheliābinsk, and
           Kurgan Provinces, 391—403, 1 fig., 1 table (Russian).
1969B   Paleogenovaiā sistema. [Paleogene system.] Geologiiā SSSR, 12:1, Perm, Sverdlovsk, Cheliābinsk,
           and Kurgan Provinces, 404—422, 1 fig., 7 tables (Russian).

SILL, WILLIAM D.
1969A   Congress of Latin American Zoologists. Soc. Vert. Paleontol., News Bull., no. 85, 56—57.
1969B   The tetrapod-bearing continental Triassic sediments of South America. Amer. J. Sci., 267:7, 805—
           821, 3 figs., 2 tables.
1971A   Implicaciones estratigráficas y ecológicas de los rincosaurios. Asoc. Geol. Argent., Rev., 26:2, 163—
           168, 2 figs., 1 pl. (Spanish; English summary).
1971B   Functional morphology of the rhynchosaur skull. Forma et Functio, 4:4, 308—318, 3 figs., 4 pls.
           (French and German summaries).

SILL, WILLIAM D.   See also: Patterson, B., Behrensmeyer, A. K. and Sill, W. D., 1970A.

SILVA-BARCENAS, ANGEL B.
1969A   Pleistocene vertebrate faunas of the Mexican Plateau. Geol. Soc. Amer., Abstr., 121, 279 (abs.).
1969B   Localidades de vertebrados fósiles en la República Mexicana. México, Univ. Nac., Inst. Geol.,
           Paleontol. Mex., 28, 34 pp., 1 map (Spanish).

SILVA-BARCENAS, A. B.   See also: Ochoterena, F. H. and Silva-Barcenas, A., 1970A.

SILVA SANTOS, RUBENS DA
1968A   A paleoictiofauna da formação Santana — Euselachii. Acad. Brasil. Ciênc. An., 40:4, 491—497, 3 pls.
           (Portuguese; English summary).
1969A   Sôbre um Lepidotes da formação Itaparica, Estado da Bahia. Rio de Janeiro, Univ. Fed., Inst.
           Geociênc., Bol., Geol., 4, 43—46, 1 fig., 1 pl. (Portuguese; English summary).
1970A   Nova evidência paleontológica da idade pleistocênica dos estratos da bacia do Paraíba. Eng.,
           Mineração, Met., 51:301, 10 (Portuguese).
1970B   A paleoitiofauna da formação Santana — Holostei: familia Girodontidae. Acad. Brasil. Ciênc. An.
           42:3, 445—452, 7 figs. (Portuguese; English summary).
1971A   Nouveau genre et espèce d'Elopidae du bassin sédimentaire de la Chapada do Araripe. Acad. Brasil.
           Ciênc., An., 43:2, 439—442, 6 figs. (French).

SILVA SANTOS, RUBENS DA and GOMES VALENCA, JOEL
1968A   A formação Santana e sua paleoictiofauna. Acad. Brasil. Ciênc. An., 40:3, 339—359, 6 figs., 2 pls.,
           3 tables (Portuguese; English summary).

SILVA SANTOS, RUBENS DA, and SARDENBERG SALGADO, MARISE
1969A   Enchodus longipectoralis (Shaeffer), um Teleostei do Cretáceo de Sergipe. Acad. Brasil. Ciênc. An.,
           41:3, 381—392, 5 figs., 1 table (Portuguese; English summary).
1970A   Um espinho de Xenacanthus do Carbonífero do Estado do Maranhão. Acad. Brasil. Ciênc. An.,
           42:2, 223—227, 2 figs. (Portuguese; English summary).
1971A   Contribuição à paleontologia do estado do Pará. Novos restos de peixes da formação Pirabas. Mus.
           Paraen. E. Goeldi, Bol., Geol., 16, 1—13, 1 table, 2 pls. (Portuguese; English summary).

SILVERBERG, ROBERT
1967A   The morning of mankind. Conn.: New York Graphical Society, 236 pp., 30 figs.
           Rev.: Burkitt in New Sci., 48:724, 192—194.
1970A   Mammoths, mastodons and man. New York and London: McGraw-Hill Book Co., 224 pp., illustr.

SIMAK, CLIFFORD D.
1971A   Prehistoric man. New York: St. Martin's Press, 192 pp., illustr.

SIMARD, SIMONE
1968A   Étude paléontologique et paléoclimatique de la microfaune du Régourdou (Montignac, Dordogne,
           France). Natur. Can., 95:6, 1435—1457 (French).

SIMKIN, G. N.
1969A   O proiskhozhdenii i evoliutsii morfo-biologicheskogo oblika pozvonochnykh. [On the origin and
           evolution of the morpho-biological aspect of vertebrates.] Nauchn. Dokl. Vyssh. Shkoly, Biol.
           Nauki, 1969:10, 128—144 (Russian).

SIMON, KLAUS H.
1971A   Wann und wo lebte der erste Mensch? Naturwiss. Rundsch., 24:10, 433–434 (German).

SIMON, WILHELM   See: Kräusel, W. and Simon, W., 1968A.

SIMONE, SUZANNE
1969A   Les formations de la mer du Mindel-Riss et les brèches à ossements rissiennes de la Grotte du Prince.
             Monaco, Mus. Anthropol. Préhist., Bull., 15, 5–90, 31 figs., 3 tables (French; English summary).

SIMONE, SUZANNE   See also: Barral, L. and Simone, S., 1968A, 1968B, 1968C, 1969A, 1970A.

SIMONNET, GEORGES and SIMONNET, ROBERT
1970A   Louis Méroc (1904–1970). Soc. Préhist. Fr., Bull., C.R., 67:9, 262–264, portr. (French).

SIMONS, ELWYN L.
1968C   Hunting the "dawn apes" of Africa. Discovery, 4:1, 19–32, 10 figs.
1969A   Late Miocene hominid from Fort Ternan, Kenya. Nature, 221:5179, 448–451, 1 fig.
1969B   Miocene monkey (Prohylobates) from northern Egypt. Nature, 223:5207, 687–689, 3 figs., 1 table.
1969C   The origin and radiation of the primates. N.Y. Acad. Sci., Ann., 167:1, 319–331, 8 figs.
1969D   Recent advances in paleoanthropology. Yearbk. Phys. Anthropol., 1967, 14–23, 1 fig.
1969E   In pursuit of man's pedigree.Yale Alumni Mag., Feb. 1969, 24–27, illustr.
1970A   The deployment and history of Old World monkeys (Cercopithecidae, Primates). In: Napier, J. R.
             and Napier, P. H. (eds.), 1970A, 97–137, 9 figs.
1971A   Relationships of Amphipithecus and Oligopithecus. Nature, 232:5311, 489–491, 3 figs.
1971B   Primates, fossil. McGraw-Hill Yearbook Sci. Tech., 1971, 347–348.
1971C   A current review on the interrelationships of Oligocene and Miocene Catarrhini. In: Dahlberg, A. A.
             (ed.), 1971A, 193–208, 8 figs.
1971D   The phyletic position of Ramapithecus. In: Leakey, L. S. B., Prost, J. and Prost, S. (eds.), 1971A,
             371–376, 2 figs. (reprinted from Postilla, Nov. 1961).
1971E   On the mandible of Ramapithecus. In: Leakey, L. S. B., Prost, J. and Prost, S. (eds.), 1971A, 385–
             395, 3 figs. (reprinted from Anthropology, 54, 1964).
1972A   Primate evolution. An introduction to man's place in nature. New York: Macmillan Co., xii +
             322 pp., 112 figs., 4 tables.
             Rev.: Tuttle in Science (AAAS), 177:4049, 601–602, cover photo.

SIMONS, E. L. and CHOPRA, S. R. K.
1969A   Gigantopithecus (Pongidae, Hominoidea) a new species from north India. Postilla, 138, 18 pp., 4 figs.,
             2 tables.
1969B   A preliminary announcement of a new Gigantopithecus species from India. Int. Congr. Primat., 2nd,
             Atlanta, Ga., Proc., 2, 135–142, 4 figs.

SIMONS, E. L. and ETTEL, PETER C.
1970A   Gigantopithecus. Sci. Amer., 222:1, 76–85, illustr.

SIMONS, E. L. and PILBEAM, DAVID R.
1971A   A gorilla-sized ape from the Miocene of India. Science (AAAS), 173:3991, 23–27, 3 figs.
1972A   Hominoid paleoprimatology. In: Tuttle, R. (ed.), 1972A, 36–62, 3 figs., 7 pls.

SIMONS, E. L., PILBEAM, D. R. and BOYER, S. J.
1971A   Appearance of Hipparion in the Tertiary of the Siwalik Hills of north India, Kashmir and West
             Pakistan. Nature, 229:5284, 408–409.

SIMONS, E. L., PILBEAM, D. R. and ETTEL, P. C.
1969A   Controversial taxonomy of fossil hominids. Science (AAAS), 166:3902, 258–259.

SIMONS, ELWYN L.   See also: Pilbeam, D. R. and Simons, E. L., 1971A, 1972A; Tattersall, I. M. and
             Simons, E. L., 1969A.

SIMONS, HOWARD
1965C   Third man at Olduvai. New Sci., 26:439, 158.
1967A   More fossilmanship. New Sci., 33:531, 207.

SIMONS, J. R.
1971A   Sharks, aeroplanes and evolution. Austral. Natur. Hist., 17:2, 59–64, 4 figs.

SIMPSON, D. D. A.   See: Coles, J. M. and Simpson, D. D. A. (eds.), 1968A.

SIMPSON, GEORGE GAYLORD
1950S	Lower Tertiary formations and vertebrate faunas of the San Juan Basin. N. Mex. Geol. Soc., Guidebk., Field Conf., 1, 85–89, 2 figs.
1961K	Rev.: A. E. in Vár Fágelvärld, 21:2, 149.
1968F	Fossil mammals. In: Moore, R. C., et al., 1968A, 1375–1377.
1969A	South American mammals. In: Fittkau, E. J., et al. (eds.), 1969A, vol. 2, 879–909, 3 figs., 7 tables (Spanish summary).
1969B	History of the fauna of Latin America. In: Ehrlich, P. R., et al. (eds.), 1969A, 333–361, 10 figs., 3 tables.
1969C	On the term brachydont. Syst. Zool., 18:4, 456–458.
	Rev.: Thenius in Zentralbl. Geol. Paläontol., Teil 2, 1971:1, 61.
1969D	The present status of the theory of evolution. Roy. Soc. Victoria, Proc., 82, 149–160.
1969E	La géographie de l'évolution. Paris: Masson et Cie, 204 pp., 45 figs. (French).
	Rev.: Gautier in Natuurwet. Tijdschr., 51:3–8, 224–225; Heberer in Biol. Zentralbl., 90:4, 539–540; Tétry in L'Ann. Biol., 9:11–12, 717–718.
1970A	Ages of fossil penguins in New Zealand. Science (AAAS), 168:3929, 361–362.
1970B	Drift theory: Antarctica and central Asia. Science (AAAS), 170:3959, 678.
1970C	Miocene penguins from Victoria, Australia, and Chubut, Argentina. Victoria, Nat. Mus., Mem., 31, 17–24.
1970D	Mammals from the early Cenozoic of Chubut, Argentina. Breviora, 360, 1–13, 5 figs., 3 tables.
	Rev.: Thenius in Zentralbl. Geol. Paläontol., Teil 2, 1971:2–3, 201.
1970E	The Argyrolagidae, extinct South American Marsupials. Mus. Comp. Zool., Bull., 139:1, 1–86.
1970F	Additions to knowledge of the Argyrolagidae (Mammalia, Marsupialia) from the late Cenozoic of Argentina. Breviora, 361, 1–9, 4 figs., 4 tables.
1970G	Addition to knowledge of Groeberia (Mammalia, Marsupialia) from the mid-Cenozoic of Argentina. Breviora, 362, 1–17, 7 figs., 1 table.
1970H	Obituary. A. T. Hopwood. Soc. Vert. Paleontol., News Bull., 90, 42.
1970I	Uniformitarianism. An inquiry into principle, theory, and method in geohistory and biohistory. In: Hecht, M. K. and Steere, W. C. (eds.), 1970A, 43–96.
1971A	Fossil penguin from the late Cenozoic of South Africa. Science, 171:3976, 1144–1145, 1 fig., 2 tables.
1971B	Recent literature on Mesozoic mammals. J. Paleontol., 45:5, 862–868.
1971C	A review of the pre-Pliocene penguins of New Zealand. Amer. Mus. Natur. Hist., Bull., 144:5, 319–378, 20 figs., 6 tables.
1971D	Forces of evolution and their integration. In: Dolhinow, P. and Sarich, V. M. (eds.), 1971A, 7–25 (reprinted from Simpson, 1967F, The meaning of evolution).
1971E	Concluding remarks: Mesozoic mammals revisited. Linn. Soc., Zool. J., 50:suppl. 1, 181–198.
	Rev.: Krebs in Zentralbl. Geol. Paläontol., Teil 2, 1972:3, 175–176.
1971F	The evolution of marsupials in South America. Acad. Brasil. Ciênc. An., 43 (suppl.), 103–118, 1 fig.
1971G	William King Gregory, 1876–1970. Amer. J. Phys. Anthropol., 35:2, 155–174, portr.
1972A	Didelphidae from the Chapadmalal formation in the Museo Municipal de Ciencias Naturales de Mar del Plata. Mar del Plata, Mus. Munic. Cienc. Natur., Publ., 2:1, 1–40, 4 figs., 10 tables (Spanish summary).
1972B	Conspectus of Patagonian fossil penguins. Amer. Mus. Nov., 2488, 37 pp., 1 fig., 3 tables.
1972C	William King Gregory (1876–1970). Amer. Phil. Soc. Yearb., 1971, 124–127, portr.
1972D	Leben der Vorzeit. Stuttgart: F. Enke Verlag, 197 pp., 47 figs. (German).
	Rev.: Laufeld in Geol. Fören. Stockholm, Förh., 94:3, 476; Warth in Kosmos, 68:9, 281.

SIMPSON, GEORGE G.   See also: Reig, O. A. and Simpson, G. G., 1972A.

SINEGUB, VALERIĬ VASIL'EVICH
1969A	Neogenovaĭa sistema. Pliotsen. [Neogene system. Pliocene.] Geologiĭa SSSR, 45, Moldavian SSR, 171–196, 4 figs. (Russian).

SINEL'NIKOVA, VALENTINA NIKOLAEVNA   See: Dubrovo, I. A. and Sinel'nikova, V. N., 1971A.

SINGER, RONALD
1971A	The Saldanha skull from Hopefield, South Africa. In: Leakey, L. S. B., Prost, J. and Prost, S. (eds.), 1971A, 315–326, 10 figs. (reprinted from Amer. J. Phys. Anthropol., 12, 1954).

SINGER, RONALD and WYMER, JOHN
1969A	Archaeological investigations at the Saldanha skull site in South Africa. S. Afr. Archaeol. Bull., 23:91, 63–74, 2 figs., 5 pls.

SINGH, GURCHARAN
1971A	Hypoprion horai, a shark tooth from lower Miocene beds of Baiwa-Dehdapur area, N.W. Kutch. Indian Sci. Congr., Proc., 58, 321.

SINGH, JAGJIT   See: Randhawa, M. S., Singh, J., Dey, A. K. and Mittre, V., 1969 A

SINGH, M. P.   See: Tewari, B. S., Chaturvedi, M. N. and Singh, M. P., 1968A.

SINITSA, SOF'IA MIKHAĬLOVNA
   1969A   Biostratigrafiia verkhnego mezozoia Vostochnogo Zabaĭkal'ia po ostrakodam. [Biostratigraphy of the upper Mesozoic of East Transbaikalia on ostracods.] Geogr. Obshchest. SSSR, Zabaĭkal. Fil., Izv., 5:4, 3—11, illustr. (Russian).

SIOLI, H.   See: Fittkau, E. J., Illies, J., Klinge, H., Schwabe, G. H. and Sioli, H. (eds.), 1969A.

SIRKS, M. J.
   1959A   Lamarck en Darwin, 1809—1859—1959. Natuurwet. Tijdschr., 41:2—3, 49—73, 13 figs. (Dutch; French abstract).

SIRUGUE, FRANÇOIS   See: Bessonnat, G., Dughi, R. and Sirugue, F., 1969A; Dughi, R., Plaziat, J.-C. and Sirugue, F., 1969A; Dughi, R. and Sirugue, F., 1968B.

SIRYK, I. M. and DUBROVO, I. A.
   1970A   Iskopaemyĭ zubatyĭ kit v miotsenovykh otlozheniiakh Iuzhnogo Sakhalina. [Fossil toothed whale in the Miocene deposits of southern Sakhalin.] Geol. Geofiz. (Akad. Nauk SSSR, Sib. Otd.), 1970:9, 123—129, 4 figs. (Russian).

SIRYK, I. M.   See also: Egorov, A. E., Zarubin, S. I. and Siryk, I. M., 1968A.

SITTLER, CLAUDE
   1969A   L'Éocène dans le fossé Rhénan. Colloque sur l'Éocène Paris, mai 1968, Vol. III. Fr., Bur. Rech. Géol. Minières, Mém., 69, 371—383, 1 table (French).

SKARYD, SUZANNE M.
   1971A   Trends in the evolution of the pongid dentition. Amer. J. Phys. Anthropol., 35:2, 223—240, 1 fig., 8 tables.
   1971B   Parallel trends in the evolution of pongid dentition. Amer. J. Phys. Anthropol., 35:2, 295 (abs.).

SKARYD, SUZANNE M.   See also: Wright, G. A. and Skaryd, S., 1972A.

SKINNER, MORRIS F.
   1968A   Rev.: Thenius in Zentralbl. Geol. Paläontol., Teil 2, 1970:6, 523—524.
   1972A   Early Pleistocene pre-glacial and glacial rocks and faunas of north-central Nebraska. Order Perissodactyla. Amer. Mus. Natur. Hist., Bull., 148:1, 117—125, 3 figs., 1 table.

SKINNER, MORRIS F. and HIBBARD, CLAUDE W., et al.
   1972A   Early Pleistocene pre-glacial and glacial rocks and faunas of north-central Nebraska. Amer. Mus. Natur. Hist., Bull., 148:1, 148 pp., illustr.

SKINNER, S. A.   See: Gumerman, G. J. and Skinner, S. A., 1968A.

SKOBLO, VADIMIR MAKSIMOVICH   See: Dmitriev, G. A. and Skoblo, V. M., 1966A.

SKORIK, A. F.
   1969A   Novoe mestonakhozhdenie ostatkov pozdnepliotsenovykh melkikh mlekopitaiushchikh v Nikolaevskoĭ oblasti USSR. [New locality with remains of Late Pliocene small mammals in Nikolaevsk province, Ukrainian SSR.] Akad. Nauk Ukr. SSR, Inst. Zool., Vestn. Zool., 1969:4, 83—85, 1 table (Russian).
   1972A   Kornezubye bestsementnye polevki roda Villanyia pozdnepliotsenovykh otlozheniĭ Iuga SSSR. [Teeth of the vole genus Villanyia from the upper Pliocene of southern USSR.] Prirodn. Obstan. i Fauny Proshl., 6, 35—51, 7 figs., 2 tables (Russian).

SKORIK, A. F.   See also: Topachevskyĭ, V. O. and Skoryk, O. F., 1971A.

SKORKOWSKI, EDWARD
   1967B   Czy tak zwane - "konie Przewalskiego" są rzeczywiście końmi? [Are really the so-called "Przewalski horses" - horses?] Przegl. Zool., 11:3, 345—348, 4 figs. (Polish; English summary).
   1969A   Koniowate Ameryki. [Equidae of America.] Przegl. Zool., 13:3, 266—270, 7 figs. (Polish; English summary).

SKRIPKO, K. A.   See: Sharfman, V. S., Tsetlin, V. P. and Skripko, K. A., 1965A.

SKVORTSOV, A. K.
> 1967A   Osnovnye etapy razvitiiā predstavleniĭ o vide. [The main stages in the development of the species concept.] Mosk. Obshchest. Ispyt. Prir., Biull., Otd. Biol., 72:5, 11–27 (Russian; English summary).

SKVORTSOVA, KSENIIĀ VASIL'EVNA
> 1972A   O zubakh akul v kalienosnykh otlozheniĭakh Predkarpat'iā. [On shark teeth in potassium deposits of Ciscarpathia.] Vses. Nauch.-Issled. Proektn. Inst. Gal., Tr., 56, 30–31 (Russian).

SKWARKO, S. K.
> 1969A   Bibliography of the Mesozoic paleontology of Australia and eastern New Guinea. Austral., Bur. Miner. Resour., Geol. Geophys., Bull., 108, 237–279.

SLAUGHTER, BOB H.
> 1964C   Cave with a past. Speleo Digest, 1964, 2-78–2-80 (reprinted from Texas Caver, 9:6, 89–92).
> 1968D   Holoclemensia instead of Clemensia Science, 162:3859, 1306.
> 1969A   Astroconodon, the Cretaceous triconodont. J. Mammal., 50:1, 102–107, 1 fig., 1 table.
> 1969B   Age of the second terrace of the upper Trinity river, Texas. Geol. Soc. Amer., Spec. Pap., 121, 412 (abs.).
> 1970A   Were the first Americans caucasoid? Texas. J. Sci., 21:4 483–486, 1 fig.
> 1970B   Evolutionary trends in chiropteran dentitions. In: Slaughter, B. H. and Walton, D. W. (eds.), 1970A, 51–83, 5 figs.
> 1970C   Middle Cretaceous marsupials and placentals from Texas. Linn. Soc., Biol. J., 2:4, 320 (abs.).
> 1971A   Mid-Cretaceous (Albian) therians of the Butler Farm local fauna. Linn. Soc., Zool. J., 50:suppl. 1, 131–143, 1 fig., 10 pls.
>   Rev.: Krebs in Zentralbl. Geol. Paläontol., Teil 2, 1972:3, 172–173.
> 1972A   Classification of skates and rays. Soc. Vert. Paleontol., Ann. Meeting, 32nd, 1972, Abstr. (abs.).

SLAUGHTER, BOB H. and WALTON, DAN W.
> 1970A*   About bats. A chiropteran biology symposium. Dallas: Southern Methodist Univ. Press, vii + 339 pp., illustr.

SLAUGHTER, BOB H.   See also: McNulty, C. L. and Slaughter, B. H., 1969A, 1970A.

SLIEPČEVIĆ, A.
> 1970A   Die bisherigen Resultate der Bestimmung des absoluten Alters der Fossilien aus Krapina mittels der Radiokohlenstoffmethode. Krapina, 141–146, 2 figs., 2 tables (Serbocroatian; English and German summaries).
>   Rev.: Kochansky-Devidé in Zentralbl. Geol. Paläontol., Teil 2, 1971:5, 419.

SLIMMER, D. F.   See: Rasmussen, D. L., Martin, L. D., Chorn, J. D. and Slimmer, D. F., 1971A.

SLIŠKOVIĆ, T.
> 1970A   Die stratigraphische Lage der Schichten mit Pachyophiidae aus Selište bei Bileća (Ostherzegowina). Akad. Savet. FNRJ., Bull. Sci., Sec. A, 15:11–12, 389–390 (German).

SLOAN, ROBERT E.
> 1970A   Cretaceous and Paleocene terrestrial communities of western North America. N. Amer. Paleontol. Conv., Proc., Part E, 427–453, 8 figs.

SLOAN, ROBERT E.   See also: Van Valen, L. and Sloan, R. E., 1972A, 1972B.

SLUSHER, H. S.   See: Moore, J. N. and Slusher, H. S., 1970A.

SMIRNOV, EVGENIĬ SERGEEVICH
> 1969A   Taksonomicheskiĭ analiz. [Taxonomic analysis.] Moscow: Moscow Univ. Press, 187 pp., illustr. (Russian).
>   Rev.: Shmidt in Zh. Obshch. Biol., 31:1, 121–123 (Russian).

SMIT, J.   See: Holst, H. K. H., Smit, J. and Veenstra, E., 1970A.

SMITH, A. GILBERT and HALLAM, A.
> 1970A   The fit of southern continents. Nature, 225:5228, 139–144, 2 figs., 2 tables.

SMITH, C. C.   See: Raath, M. A., Smith, C. C. and Bond, G., 1970A.

SMITH, C. LAVETT and BUERKLI, MARIA
    1969A   Should paratypes be included in lists of type specimens? Syst. Zool., 18:2, 247—250.

SMITH, C. T.   See: Budding, A. J., Pitrat, C. W. and Smith, C. T., 1960A.

SMITH, FRED H.
    1972A   Reconstruction of the D-skull from Krapina. Amer. J. Phys. Anthropol., 37:3, 450 (abs.).

SMITH, GERALD R.
    1972A   Fish diversity and extinction in the Glens Ferry formation (Pliocene) of Idaho. Soc. Vert. Paleontol.,
                Ann. Meeting, 32nd, 1972, Abstr., 15 (abs.).

SMITH, G. R. and LUNDBERG, J. G.
    1972A   The Sand Draw fish fauna. Amer. Mus. Natur. Hist., Bull., 148:1, 40—54, 12 figs.

SMITH, HOBART M.
    1970A   Nomina and taxa dubia. Syst. Zool., 19:1, 94.
    1972A   The palustral origin of mammals: a hypothesis. Colo.-Wyo. Acad. Sci., J., 7:2—3, 111—112.
    1972B   The palustral origin of mammals. Biologist, 54:2, 49—51.

SMITH, MEREDITH J.
    1971A   Small fossil vertebrates from Victoria Cave, Naracoorte, South Australia. I. Petoroinae (Macropodidae),
                Petauridae and Burramyidae (Marsupialia). Roy. Soc. S. Austral., Trans., 95:4, 185—198,
                11 figs., 9 tables.

SMITH, PHILIP E. L.
    1967A   New investigations in the late Pleistocene archaeology of the Kom Ombo plain (upper Egypt).
                Quaternaria, 9, 141—152, 1 map, 2 pls. (French and Spanish summaries).

SMITH, PHILIP E. L.   See also: Churcher, C. S. and Smith, P. E. L., 1972A.

SMOLLA, GÜNTER
    1967A   Epochen der menschlichen Frühzeit. München: K. Alber Verlag, 168 pp., 1 fig., 2 maps (German).
                Rev.: Schwidetzky in Homo, 19:3—4, 242.

SNYDER, DON O.
    1970A   Fossil evidence of Eocene age of Baca formation, New Mexico. N. Mex. Geol. Soc., Guidebk., Field
                Conf., 21, 65—67, 4 figs.

SOCHAVA, ANDREĬ V.
    1969A   Ĭaĭtsa dinozavrov iz verkhnego mela Gobi. [Dinosaur eggs from upper Cretaceous of the Gobi.]
                Paleontol. Zh., 1969:4, 76—88, 5 figs., 2 pls., 1 table (Russian).
    1969B   Dinosaur eggs from the upper Cretaceous of the Gobi Desert. Paleontol. J., 3:4, 517—527, 5 figs.,
                2 pls.
                Rev.: Chrulew in Zentralbl. Geol. Paläontol., Teil 2, 1971:1, 57—58.
    1970A   Mikrostruktura skorlupy ĭaĭts dinozavrov iz verkhnego mela Severnoĭ Gobi. [Microstructure of
                dinosaur egg shells from upper Cretaceous of northern Gobi.] Akad. Nauk SSSR, Dokl., 192:5,
                1137—1140, 3 figs. (Russian).
    1970B   Ĭaĭtsa dinozavrov v pustyne Gobi. [Dinosaur eggs in the Gobi Desert.] Priroda, 1970:10, 65—68,
                4 figs. (Russian).
    1970C   Microtexture of dinosaur eggshells from the upper Cretaceous of the northern Gobi. Akad. Nauk SSSR,
                Dokl., Earth Sci. Sec., 192, 203—205, 3 figs.
    1971A   Novoe o stroenii skorlupy ĭaĭts dinozavrov. [New data on the dinosaur egg shell structure.] Priroda,
                1971:8, 103—104, 2 figs. (Russian).
    1971B   Dva tipa skorlupy ĭaĭts senonskikh dinozavrov. [Two types of Senonian dinosaur egg shells.]
                Paleontol. Zh., 1971:3, 80—88, 2 pls. (Russian).
    1972A   Skelet embriona v ĭaĭtse dinozavra. [Skeleton of an embryo in a dinosaur egg.] Paleontol. Zh., 1972:4,
                88—92, 2 figs., 1 pl. (Russian).

SOCHAVA, ANDREĬ V.   See also: Kielan-Jaworowska, Z. and Sochava, A. V., 1969A; Kolesnikov, Ch. M. and
                Sochava, A. V., 1972A; Martinson, G. G., Sochava, A. V. and Barsbold, R., 1969A, 1970A;
                Martinson, G. G., Sochava, A. V. and Kolesnikov, Ch. M., 1971A.

SOERGEL, ELSBETH
    1966B   Die Teufels- oder Fuchsenlucken bei Eggenburg (NÖ.). 8. Die Vogelreste. Österreich. Akad. Wiss.
                Denk., 112, 93—107, 1 table (German).

SOFAER, J. A., BAILIT, H. L. and MacLEAN, C. J.
    1971A   A developmental basis for differential tooth reduction during hominid evolution. Evolution, 25:3,
               509–517, 1 fig., 7 tables.

SOKAL, ROBERT R.
    1967A   Sovremennye predstavleniĭa o teorii sistematiki. [Recent ideas on the theory of systematics.] Zh.
               Obshch. Biol., 28:6, 658–674, 2 figs. (Russian; English summary).
    1968A   Numericheskaĭa taksonomiĭa: metody i sovremennoe razvitie. [Numerical taxonomy: methodology
               and recent development.] Zh. Obshch. Biol., 29:3, 297–315, 8 figs. (Russian; English summary).

SOKHIN, V. K.   See: Bersenev, I. I. and Sokhin, V. K., 1969A.

SOKLIĆ, I. and MALEZ, M.
    1969A   Ein Fund der Art *Mastodon angustidens* in der bunten Folge bei Tuzla (Mittleres Miozän). Akad.
               savet. FNRJ., Bull. Sci., Sec. A, 14:11–12, 380–381, 2 figs. (German).

SOKOLOV, BORIS SERGEEVICH
    1968A*   Stratigrafiĭa nizhnego paleozoĭa Ṫsentral'noĭ Evropy. [Stratigraphy of lower Paleozoic of central
               Europe.] Int. Geol. Congr., 23rd, Czech., Rep. Sov. Geol., 154 pp. (Russian; English summaries).
    1972A   Akademik A. A. Borisĭak i razvitie sovetskoĭ paleontologii. [Academician A. A. Borisiak and the
               development of Soviet paleontology.] Paleontol. Zh., 1972:3, 3–20, portr. (Russian).

SOKOLOV, I. I.
    1968A   Proiskhozhdenie, polozhenie v sisteme i osnovnye napravleniĭa evoliŭtsii v semeĭstve kun'ikh,
               Mustelidae. [Origin, systematic position and major evolutionary trends of the Mustelidae
               family.] Mosk. Obshchest. Ispyt. Prir., Bĭull., Otd. Biol., 73:6, 5–16, 2 figs., 1 table (Russian;
               English summary).

SOKOLOV, MIKHAIL IVANOVICH
    1957A   Melovaĭa sistema. Nizov'ĭa Amu-Dar'i. [Cretaceous system. Lower Amu-Dar'ĭa region.] Geologiĭa
               SSSR, 22, Turkmenian SSR, 192–194, 1 fig. (Russian).

SOKOLOVSKAĬA, VALENTINA TIKHONOVNA   See: Sukachev, V. N. and Sokolovskaĭa, V. T., 1965A, 1966A.

SOLAGES, BRUNO DE
    1967A   Teilhard de Chardin. Témoignage et étude sur le développement de sa pensée. Paris-Toulouse: Privat,
               397 pp. (French).
               Rev.: Castelló in Arbor, 275, 100–101.

SOLECKI, RALPH S.
    1968A   Cave archaeology in the Zagros Mountains. Acta Archaeol. Carpathica, 10:1–2, 246–259, 10 figs.,
               2 maps (Polish summary).
    1968B   The Shemsi industry, a Tayacian-related industry at Yabroud, Syria. Preliminary report. In:
               R. Vaufray Festschrift, 1968A, 401–410, 8 figs. (French summary).
    1971A   Shanidar. The first flower people. New York: Alfred A. Knopf, xv + 290 pp., 8 figs., 34 pls.,
               3 maps.
               Rev.: Brace in Natur. Hist., 80:7, 82–86; Morrison in Sci. Amer., 225:3, 234, 237–238.
    1971B   Prehistory in Shanidar Valley, northern Iraq. In: Leakey, L. S. B., Prost, J. and Prost, S. (eds.),
               1971A, 397–424, 17 figs. (reprinted from Science, 1963).

SOLHEIM, WILHELM G., II
    1964B*   COWA surveys and bibliographies. Indonesia. COWA Surv. and Bibliog., Area 20, no. 3, 10 pp.
    1967A*   Archaeology at the Eleventh Pacific Science Congress. Asian Pac. Archaeol. Ser., 1, 132 pp., 7 figs.,
               18 pls., table, 3 maps.
               Rev.: Starr in Amer. Anthropol., 71, 154–155.
    1968A*   Anthropology at the Eighth Pacific Science Congress. Asian Pac. Archaeol. Ser., 2, 1968, ix + 285 pp.,
               illustr.
               Rev.: Scott in Amer. Anthropol., 71, 1226–1227.
    1969A   New directions in Southeast Asian prehistory. Anthropologica, 11:1, 31–44, 1 map (French summary)
    1969B*   Indonesia. COWA, Surv. Bibliogr., Area 20, 4, 1–10.

SOLLE, GERHARD
    1970A   Die Hünsruck-Insel im oberen Unterdevon. Hess. Landesamt Bodenforsch., Notizbl., 98, 50–80,
               1 fig., 1 pl. (German).

SOLOV'EV, VĬACHESLAV KAPITONOVICH   See: Morozov, V. A. and Solov'ev, V. K., 1967A.

SOMOV, V. D.
    1969A   Gekhinskaĭa svita oligoĭsena Chernykh gor i nekotorye osobennosti ee nakopleniĭa. [Oligocene Gekhinskaĭa suite of Chernye Mts. and some features of its deposition.] Sev.-Kavkaz. Neft. Nauch.-Issled. Inst., Tr., 4, 177—183 (Russian).
    1970A   Roshnenskiĭ gorizont i ego stratigraficheskoe znachenie. [Roshnenskiĭ horizon and its stratigraphic significance.] Sev.-Kavkaz. Neft. Nauch.-Issled. Inst., Tr., 7, 117—124 (Russian).

SONDAAR, P. Y.
    1968B   Rev.: Shotwell in Palaeogeogr. Palaeoclimatol. Palaeoecol., 6, 246.
    1969A   Some remarks on horse evolution and classification. Z. Säugetierkunde, 34:5, 307—311, 1 fig.
                Rev.: Thenius in Zentralbl. Geol. Paläontol., Teil 2, 1970:5, 443.
    1971A   The Samos *Hipparion.* Ned. Akad. Wetensch., Proc., Ser. B, 74:4, 417—441, 5 figs., 6 pls., 5 tables.

SONDAAR, P. Y.   See also: Bruijn, H. de, Sondaar, P. Y. and Zachariasse, W. J., 1971A; Crusafont Pairó, M. and Sondaar, P. Y., 1971A.

SONNEVILLE-BORDES, DENISE DE
    1967A   La préhistorie moderne. Périgueux: Pierre Fanlac, illustr. (French).
                Rev.: Bonavia in Curr. Anthropol., 10:2—3, 232.
    1970A   À propos du Colloque sur l'origine de l'homme moderne (Paris, UNESCO, 2—5 septembre 1969). Soc. Préhist. Fr., Bull., C.R., 67:1, 5—6 (French).

SONNEVILLE-BORDES, D. DE   See also: Bordes, F. and Sonneville-Bordes, D. de, 1967B; Prat, F. and Sonneville-Bordes, D. de, 1969A.

SOPER, TONY   See: Sparks, J. and Soper, T., 1970A.

SORBINI, LORENZO
    1970A   Un nuovo genere fossile nell'ittiofauna di M. Bolca: *Eolates* nov. gen. Verona, Mus. Civ. Stor. Natur., Mem., 18, 11—29 (Italian; English summary).

SORIANO, M.
    1970A   The fluoric origin of the bone lesion in the *Pithecanthropus erectus* femur. Amer. J. Phys. Anthropol., 32:1, 49—57, 10 figs.

SORRICK, MUIR
    1970A   The history of Orinda, gateway to Contra Costa County. With a prologue by Charles L. Camp. Orinda, Calif.: Orinda Library Board, x + 204 pp., illustr.

SORSKAĬA, L. S.   See: Utekhin, D. N. and Sorskaĭa, L. S., 1971A.

SOS BAYNAT, VICENTE
    1969A   Sobre un fragmento de húmero de elefante encontrado en Ciudad Rodrigo (Salamanca). Zephyrus, 19—20, 186—192, 5 figs., 1 pl. (Spanish).

SOTNIKOVA, M. V.   See: Nikonov, A. A., Pen'kov, A. V., Trofimov, B. A., Vangengeĭm, E. A., Dmitrieva, E. A. and Sotnikova, M. V., 1971A; Vangengeĭm, E. A., Erbaeva, M. N., Zhegallo, V. I. and Sotnikova, M. V., 1968A.

SOUCY, CLAUDE
    1967A   Pensée logique et pensée politique chez Teilhard de Chardin. Paris: P.U.F., 230 pp. (French).
                Rev.: Castelló in Arbor, 275, 98—100.

SOUSTELLE, JACQUES
    1967A   Mexico. Translated by James Hogarth. Archaeologia Mundi Series, Nagel Publishers, Geneva. Cleveland and New York: World Publishing Co., 284 pp., 184 illustr., 1 table, 3 maps.
                Rev.: Bernal in Amer. Anthropol., 70, 820—821.

SOUTHERN, H. N.   See: Berry, R. J. and Southern, H. N., 1970A.

SOUZA CUNHA, FAUSTO LUIZ DE
    1971A   Sôbre os holótipos de *Equus (Amerhippus) neogaeus* Lund, 1840 e *Equus (Amerhippus) curvidens* Owen, 1844. Acad. Brasil. Ciênc., An., 43 Suppl., 619—627, 4 figs. (Portuguese; English summary).

SOUZA CUNHA, FAUSTO LUIZ DE and JAIN, SOHAN LALL
  1968A   An inexpensive technique for drawing paleontological and biological specimens. Curator, 11:2, 123–
              126, 3 figs.

ŞOVA, C.   See: Cosmovici, N. L., Şova, C. and Tărăbuţă, C., 1964A.

SPAETH, W. v.   See: Behrens, M., Frank, H., Höllein, K., Spaeth, W. v. and Wurster, P., 1970A.

SPARKS, JOHN and SOPER, TONY
  1970A   Owls: their natural and unnatural history. New York: Newton Abbot, 206 pp., illustr.
              Rev.: Bezzel in J. Ornithol., 112:1, 104–105; R.P.P.-J. in Ibis, 113:3, 383; Schonewald in Pac.
              Discovery, 24:5, 30–31; Southern in New Sci., 49:744, 698–700.

SPERANSKIĬ, V. S., ARTEM'EVA, V. I., OSIPOVA, V. A. and RODIONOVA, V. A.
  1971A   Kraniometr dlia izucheniia cherepa v sisteme prostranstvennykh koordinat. [A craniometer for three-
              dimensioned study of the skull.] Vop. Antropol., 38, 161–164, 2 figs. (Russian).

SPILLMANN, FRANZ
  1969A   Neue Rhinocerotiden aus den oligozänen Sanden des Linzer Beckens. [New Rhinocerotidae from the
              Oligocene sands of the Linz Basin.] Oberösterr. Musealver., Jahrb., 114:1, 201–254, 16 figs.,
              8 pls. (German).
  1970A   Über den Nachweis cerebraler Wundernetzsysteme bei einem fossilen Zahnwal. Neues Jahrb. Geol.
              Paläontol., Monatsh., 1970:2, 116–126, 5 figs. (German; English summary)

SPINAGE, C. A.
  1970A   Giraffid horns. Nature, 227:5259, 735–736.

ŠPINAR, ZDENĚK V.
  1967C   Nové poznatky o Bieberových druzích fosilních žab Palaeobatrachus laubei a Protopelobates gracilis.
              [New findings on V. Bieber's species Palaeobatrachus laubei and Protopelobates gracilis.]
              Prague, Národ. Muz. Čas., Odd. Přírod., 136:1, 33–35, 2 figs., 2 pls. (Czech; English summary).
  1970A   Předkové našich žab. [The ancestors of our frogs.] Prague, Národ. Muz., Čas., Odd. Přírod., 137:3–4,
              74–88, 5 figs., 8 pls. (Czech; English summary).
  1972A   Dvacet let paleontologických vyzkumů lokality Bechlejovice u Děčina. [Twenty years of paleonto-
              logical research at the Bechlejovice locality near Děčin.] Čas. Mineral. Geol., 17:1, 99–104,
              2 figs., 4 pls. (Czech).
  1972B   Tertiary frogs from central Europe. Prague: Academia, 286 pp., 96 figs., 184 pls., 15 tables.
              Rev.: Estes in Science (AAAS), 177:4049, 603–604; Westphal in Zentralbl. Geol. Paläontol., Teil 2,
              1972:3, 164–165.

ŠPINAR, Z. V., BOUBELÍK, M. and ROMANOVSKÝ, A.
  1971A   A contribution to the phylogeny of the family Pelobatidae (Anura). Acta Univ. Carol., Geol.,
              1971:3, 279–285, 1 fig. (Czech summary).

SPINNER, P. JULIUS
  1968A   El biodinamismo pleistocénico, una consecuencia de los repetidos cambios del clima mundial.
              Valparaiso, Mus. Hist. Natur., An., 1, 77–112 (Spanish).

SPINOSA, C.   See: Nassichuk, W. W. and Spinosa, C., 1970A.

SPIRKIN, A. I.
  1970A   O drevnikh ozerakh Darkhatskoĭ kotloviny (Zapadnoe Prikhubsugul'e). [On ancient lakes of Darkhat
              trough (western Khubsugul area).] Sovm. Sovet.-Mongol. Nauch.-Issled. Geol. Eksped., Tr., 2,
              143–150, 3 figs. (Russian).

SPOCZYNSKA, J. O. I.
  1971A   Fossils: a study in evolution. London: Frederick Muller Ltd., 208 pp., 52 figs., 15 pls.
              Rev.: D.J.G. in Geol. Mag., 109:2, 183–184; Vaughn in Evolution, 26:4, 677–678.

SPRINKLE, G.   See: Bardack, D. and Sprinkle, G., 1969A.

SPUHLER, J. N.
  1967A*   Genetic diversity and human behavior. Chicago: Aldine Publishing Co., x + 291 pp., illustr.
              Rev.: Williams in Amer. Anthropol., 71, 165–167.

SQUIRES, DONALD F.
  1966A   Data processing and museum collections: a problem for the present. Curator, 9:3, 216–227, 7 figs.

SQUIRRELL, H. C.   See: Hall, I. H. S. and Squirrell, H. C., 1972A.

STAESCHE, KARL
    1969A   Übersicht über die Fauna des deutschen Rotliegenden (Unteres Perm). Stuttgarter Beitr. Naturk., 198,
                10 pp. (German).

STAFLEU, FRANS A.
    1969A   A historical review of systematic biology. In: Sibley, Ch. G. (ed.), 1969A, 16—44.

STAHL, GÜNTHER
    1971A   Zur Sedimentologie des tieferen Sandsteinkeupers in Nordbayern. Erlanger Geol. Abhandl., 84, 32 pp.,
                18 figs., 5 pls., 4 tables (German).

STALKER, A. MAC S.
    1969A   Geology and age of the early man site at Taber, Alberta. Amer. Antiquity, 34, 425—428, 1 table.

STALKER, A. MAC S. and CHURCHER, C. S.
    1972A   Glacial stratigraphy of the southwestern Canadian prairies; the Laurentian record. Int. Geol. Congr.,
                24th, Canada, Proc., Sec. 12, 110—119, 1 fig., 3 tables.

STALKER, A. MAC S.   See also: Churcher, C. S. and Stalker, A. Mac S., 1970A.

ŠTAMBERG, STANISLAV
    1970A   Reptilkoprolithen aus tertiären Diatomeenerden von Bechlejovice in Böhmen. Čas. Mineral. Geol.,
                15:3, 217—225, 4 pls., 1 table (German; Czech summary).

STANCU, JOSEFINA
    1970A   Otolitele sarmațiene de la Soceni (Banat-România). [Sarmatian otoliths of Soceni (Banat-Romania)].
                Rom., Inst. Geol., Dări, 56:3 (1968—1969), 5—24, 4 figs., 11 pls., 2 tables (Rumanian; French
                and English summaries).

STANCU, J., GHEORGHIAN, M. D. and POPESCU, A.
    1971A   Studii stratigrafice asupra Miocenului din versantul nordic al Dunării, între Dubova şi Pojejena
                (Carpaţii Meridionali). [Stratigraphic studies on the Miocene from the northern slope of the
                Danube between Dubova and Pojejena (south Carpathians).] Rom., Inst. Geol., Dări, 57:4,
                119—133, 8 pls., 1 map (Rumanian; French and English summaries).

STANDARD, J. C.
    1969A   The geology of New South Wales. The Sydney Basin. Triassic System. Hawkesbury sandstone.
                Geol. Soc. Austral., J., 16:1, 407—417, 3 figs., 2 tables.

STANLEY, STEVEN M.   See: Raup, D. M. and Stanley, S. M., 1971A.

STARCK, D., SCHNEIDER, R. and KUHN, H. J.
    1967A*   Rev.: Heberer in Biol. Zentralbl., 87:3, 384; Kaltenbach in Anthropol. Ges., Mitt., 98, 87;
                Knussmann in Homo, 20:3, 201.

STAROZHILOVA, NATAL'IĀ NIKOLAEVNA   See: Lipatova, V. V., Lopato, A. Iu., Makarova, I. S., Ochev,
                V. G., Podgornyĭ, Iu. I., Starozhilova, N. N., Saĭdakovskiĭ, L. Iã. and Shishkin, M. A., 1972A.

STEARNS, CHARLES E.
    1967A   Pleistocene geology of Cape Ashakar and vicinity. In: Howe, B., 1967A, 6—35, 14 figs., 1 table.

STEBBINS, G. LEDYARD
    1968B   Evolutionsprozesse. Stuttgart: Gustav Fischer Verlag, 196 pp., 75 figs. (German).
                Rev.: Czarnetzki in Anthropos, 65:1—2; Kaltenbach in Anthropol. Ges., Mitt., 99, 235; Vogel in
                Naturwiss. Rundsch., 22:12, 548.
    1971A   Processes of organic evolution. Second edition. New Jersey: Prentice-Hall, Inc., xiii + 193 pp.,
                illustr.

STEEGE, LOU
    1969A   Prehistoric man in the high plains and Wyoming. Wyo. Archaeol., 12:1, 16—26, 2 figs.

STEELE, NANCY
    1972A   The pigmy hippos of Cyprus. Frontiers, 36:3, 14—15, illustr.

STEEL, RODNEY
    1969A   Ornithischia. Handb. Paläoherp., Teil 15, 84 pp., 24 figs.
                 Rev.: Chrulew in Zentralbl. Geol. Paläontol., Teil 2, 1970:3/4, 230–232; Colbert in Copeia, 1970:1,
                       203–204; Fantini Sestini in Riv. Ital. Paleontol. Stratigr., 75:3, 685–686; Haltenorth in
                       Säugetierkundl. Mitt., 18:1, 93; Mertens in Natur Mus., 100:7, 341; Swinton in J. Paleontol.,
                       46:2, 321; Thenius in Geol. Ges. Wien, Mitt., 62, 211.
    1970A   Saurischia. Handb. Paläoherp., Teil 14, 87 pp., 23 figs.
                 Rev.: Chrulew in Zentralbl. Geol. Paläontol., Teil 2, 1971:1, 59–60; Haltenorth in Säugetierkundl.
                       Mitt., 18, 292; Krumbiegel in Deut. Ges. Geol. Wiss., Ber., Reihe A, Geol. Paläontol., 16:2,
                       157–158; Mertens in Natur Mus., 100:10, 475; Sestini in Riv. Ital. Paleontol. Stratigr., 72:2,
                       342; Thenius in Geol. Ges. Wien, Mitt., 62, 212.
    1970B   Die Dinosaurier. Wittenberg Lutherstadt: A. Ziemsen Verlag, "Die neue Brehm-Bücherei", 95 pp.,
                 70 figs. (German).
                 Rev.: Chrulew in Zentralbl. Geol. Paläontol., Teil 2, 1971:1, 58–59; Kleinschmidt in Kosmos, 68:1,
                       22; Zapfe in Geol. Ges. Wien, Mitt., 63, 263.

STEERE, WILLIAM C.   See: Dobzhansky, Th., Hecht, M. K. and Steere, W. C. (eds.), 1968A, 1969A, 1970A,
                         1972A, 1972B; Hecht, M. K. and Steere, W. C. (eds.), 1970A.

STEFANOVSKIĬ, V. V.
    1970A   Paleogeografiia vostochnogo sklona iuzhnogo Urala i Zaural'ia v Chetvertichnyi period. [Paleogeography
                 of the eastern slope of south Urals and Transuralia in the Quaternary.] Akad. Nauk SSSR, Kom.
                 Izuch. Chetvertich. Perioda, Biull., 37, 55–62, 1 fig. (Russian).

STEIDTMANN, JAMES R.   See: Dorr, J. A., Jr. and Steidtmann, J. R., 1970A.

STEINER, UTE and STEINER, WALTER
    1969A   Ergebnisse der Grabungen 1962 in den quartären Sedimenten und Bemerkungen zur Genese der
                 Rübeländer Höhlen/Harz. Jahresschrift Mitteldeutsch. Vorgesch., 103–140, 10 figs., 4 pls.,
                 3 tables (German).

STEINER, WALTER and SCHNEIDER, H. E.
    1963B   Zwei Fährtenplatten aus dem Rotliegenden von Tambach in der Sammlung des Instituts für Geologie
                 und technische Gesteinskunde Weimar. Weimar. Hochsch. Architekt. Bauw., Wiss. Z., 10, 71–
                 87, 12 figs. (German).

STEINER, WALTER   See also: Steiner, U. and Steiner, W., 1969A.

STEINERT, H.
    1972A   Saurierskelette in Antarktika. Frankfruter Allgemeine Zeitung, March 8, 1972, 33 (German).

STEININGER, FRIEDRICH
    1966A   Über eine Fossiliensammlung aus dem Stadtbereich von Linz. Naturkundl. Jahrb. Linz, 12, 7–10,
                 4 pls. (German).
    1969A   Das Tertiär des Linzer Raumes. Kat. Geol. Paläontol. Linz, 36–52, 14 pls., 1 table (German).
    1970A   Othmar Kühn. Geol. Ges. Wien, Mitt., 62, 175–184, portr. (German).

STEKELIS, M.
    1966A   Archaeological excavations at 'Ubeidiya, 1960–1963. Isr. Acad. Sci. Hum., Publ., 1966, 32 pp.,
                 42 pls.
                 Rev.: Czarnetzki in Anthropol. Anz., 30, 312–313.
    1966B   Un lissoir en os du Pléistocène moyen de la vallée du Jourdain. Lisbon, Univ., Fac. Letr., Rev.,
                 Sér. 3, 339–343, 1 fig. (French).

STEKLOV, A. A.   See: Timofeev, E. M., Steklov, A. A. and Alekseeva, L. I., 1970A.

STEL, J. H.
    1970A   Dinosaurier-eieren het uitsterven van de dinosauriers. Natuur Tech., 38:8, 324–334 (Dutch).

STENHOUSE, N. S.   See: Freedman, L. and Stenhouse, N. S., 1972A.

STENSIÖ, ERIK
    1968A   The cyclostomes with special reference to the diphyletic origin of the Petromyzontida and
                 Myxinoidea. Nobel Symp., 4th, Stockholm, 1967, Proc., 1968, 13–71, 22 figs.
    1969A   Anatomie des Arthrodires dans leur cadre systématique. Ann. Paléontol., Vertébrés, 55:2, 151–192
                 (French).

1969B   Elasmobranchiomorphi. Placodermata. Arthrodires. In: Piveteau, J. (ed.), 1969A, Traité de Paléo.,
             T. IV, vol. 2, 71–692, 275 figs. (French).
1971A   Anatomie des Arthrodires dans leur cadre systématique (suite). Ann. Paléontol., Vertébrés, 57:1,
             45–83 (French).
1971B   Anatomie des Arthrodires dans leur cadre systématique (suite et fin). Ann. Paléontol., Vertébrés,
             57:2, 158–186 (French).

STEPHAN, B.   See: Fischer, K. and Stephan, B., 1971A, B.

STERN, JACK T., JR.
1970A   The meaning of "adaptation" and its relation to the phenomenon of natural selection. In:
             Dobzhansky, Th., Hecht, M. K. and Steere, W. C. (eds.), 1970A, 39–66.

STERN, PHILLIP VAN DOREN
1969A   Prehistoric Europe. From Stone Age man to the early Greeks. New York: W. W. Norton and Co.,
             Inc., 383 pp., illustr.
             Rev.: Bhattacharya in E. Anthropol., 24:1, 101–104; MacConaill in Man (J. Roy. Anthropol. Inst.),
             5:3, 527; Pfeiffer in Natur. Hist., 78:8, 83–84; Walker in New Sci., 47:713, 305–306.

STERNBERG, CHARLES M.
1970A   Comments on dinosaurian preservation in the Cretaceous of Alberta and Wyoming. Can., Nat. Mus.,
             Publ. Pal., 4, vi + 9 pp., 6 pls.

STĘŚLICKA–MYDLARSKA, WANDA (= STĘŚLICKA, W.)
1968A   Linia genealogiczna Homo erectus (Pithecanthropus) – Ngandong – wspólcześni Australijezycy.
             [Genealogical line Homo erectus (Pithecanthropus) – Ngandong man – living Australian
             aborigines.] Mater. Prace Antropol., 76, 143–156, 2 figs., 8 tables (Polish; English summary).
1971A   Odlewy wnętrz czaszkowych kopalnych i współczesnych Hominidae. [The endocranial casts of fossil
             and living Hominidae.] Przegl. Antropol., 37:1, 107–116, 2 figs., 1 table (Polish; French and
             English summaries).

STEVE, MARIE-JOSEPH   See: Alimen, M.-H. and Steve, M.-J. (eds.), 1966A.

STEVENS, JAMES B.   See: Stevens, M. S., Stevens, J. B. and Dawson, M. R., 1969A.

STEVENS, MARGARET SKEELS
1970A   Merychyus verrucomalus, a new species of oreodont (Mammalia, Artiodactyla) from the middle
             Miocene Runningwater formation. Amer. Mus. Nov., no. 2425, 11 pp., 5 figs., 1 table.

STEVENS, M. S., STEVENS, J. B. and DAWSON, M. R.
1969A   New early Miocene formation and vertebrate local fauna, Big Bend National Park, Brewster County,
             Texas. Pearce-Sellards Ser., Texas Mem. Mus., 15, 52 pp., 15 figs., 9 tables.

STEVENS, MARGARET S.   See also: Lundelius, E. L. and Stevens, M. S., 1970A.

STEWART, ALEXANDER D.   See: Halstead, L. B. and Stewart, A. D., 1970A.

STEWART, JOHN H.
1969A   Major upper Triassic lithogenetic sequences in Colorado Plateau region. Amer. Ass. Petrol. Geol.,
             Bull., 53:9, 1866–1879, 5 figs.

STEWART, J. H., POOLE, F. G. and WILSON, R. F.
1972A   Stratigraphy and origin of the Triassic Moenkopi formation and related strata in the Colorado Plateau
             region. U.S. Geol. Surv., Prof. Paper, 691, v + 195 pp., 11 figs., 5 pls., 8 tables.

STEWART, T. D.
1969A   Laguna Beach man re-examined in the light of direct C-14 dating. Amer. J. Phys. Anthropol., 31,
             255–256 (abs.).
1969B   The evolution of man in Asia as seen in the lower jaw. Int. Congr. Anthropol. Ethnol. Sci., 8th,
             Tokyo, 1968, Proc., Vol. I. Anthropology, 263–266, 8 figs.

STEYSKAL, GEORGE C.
1970A   The language of zoological names. Syst. Zool., 19:1, 94–97.

STIEBER, JÓZSEF
1969A   A hazai későglaciális vegetációtörténet anthrakotómiai vizsgálatok alapján. [Anthracotomical
             determination of the Late Glacial vegetation of Hungary.] Földt. Közl., 99:2, 188–193, 7 figs.,
             1 table (Hungarian and Italian).

STINSON, MELVIN C.
    1964A   A trip to... a vertebrate fossil locality. Calif., Div. Mines Geol., Miner. Inform. Serv., 17:9, 160–163,
             4 figs., 1 map.
    1971A   A trip to a vertebrate fossil locality. S. Calif. Paleontol. Soc., Bull., 3:1, 1–4, map.

STINTON, FREDERIC CHARLES and KISSLING, DANIEL
    1968A   Quelques otolithes de téléostéens de la Molasse oligocène de Suisse occidentale. Soc. Phys. Hist.
             Natur. Genève., C.R., 3:3, 140–154, 4 figs., 1 pl. (geology in French; paleontology in English).
             Rev.: Weiler in Zentralbl. Geol. Paläontol., Teil 2, 1970:3/4, 226.

STINTON, FREDERIC CHARLES and NOLF, DIRK
    1969A   A teleost otolith fauna from the sands of Lede, Belgium. Soc. Belge Géol. Paléontol. Hydrol., Bull.,
             78:3–4, 219–234, 24 figs., 1 table.
             Rev.: Weiler in Zentralbl. Geol. Paläontol., Teil 2, 1971:5, 406–407.

STINTON, F. C.   See also: Edwards, N. and Stinton, F. C., 1971A.

STIRTON, RUBEN A.
    1965C   A classification of the Marsupialia. Austral. Mammal Soc., Bull., 2:2, 37.

STIRTON, R. A., TEDFORD, R. H. and MILLER, A. H.
    1961A   Rev.: D.L.S. in Emu, 63, 174.

STIRTON, R. A., TEDFORD, R. H. and WOODBURNE, M. O.
    1968A   Rev.: Anon. in Austral. Mammal Soc., Bull., 2:6, 179.

STOCK, A. DEAN and STOKES, WILLIAM LEE
    1969A   A re-evaluation of Pleistocene bighorn sheep from the Great Basin and their relationship to living
             members of the genus Ovis. J. Mammal., 50:4, 805–807.

STÖCKLIN, J.   See: Lapparent, A. F. de and Stöcklin, J., 1971A.

STÖHR, MICHAEL
    1968A   Fundmöglichkeiten in einer Ziegeleitongrube in Berg bei Donauwörth am Riesrand. Aufschluss, 19,
             148–149, 1 fig. (German).

STOKES, EVELYN
    1968A   The six days and the Deluge: some ideas on earth history in the Royal Society of London 1660–1775.
             Earth Sci. J. (Waikato Geol. Soc.), 3:1, 13–39.

STOKES, WILLIAM LEE   See: Stock, A. D. and Stokes, W. L., 1969A.

STOLIAROV, A. S.   See: Semenov, G. I. and Stoliarov, A. S., 1970A.

STONE, WILLIAM J.   See: Stout, T. M. and Stone, W. J., 1971A.

STONEHOUSE, B.
    1969A   Environmental temperatures of Tertiary penguins. Science, 163:3868, 673–675, 2 figs.

STORCH, GERHARD
    1969A   Über Kleinsäuger der Tundra und Steppe in jungeiszeitlichen Eulengewöllen aus dem nordhessischen
             Löss. Natur Mus., 99:12, 541–551, 4 figs. (German).

STORCH, GERHARD   See also: Malec, F. and Storch, G., 1970A.

STORER, JOHN E.
    1969A   An upper Pliocene neohipparion from the Flaxville gravels, northern Montana. Can. J. Earth Sci.,
             6:4, 791–794, 1 fig.
    1970A   New rodents and lagomorphs from the upper Miocene Wood Mountain formation of southern
             Saskatchewan. Can. J. Earth Sci., 7:4, 1125–1129, 22 figs.
    1972A   The Wood Mountain fauna: an upper Miocene mammalian assemblage from southern Saskatchewan.
             Diss. Abstr., 32:12, 7204B (abs.).
    1972B   Ischyrhiza (Chondrichthyes: Batoidea) from the Cretaceous of Alberta. Soc. Vert. Paleontol., Ann.
             Meeting, 32nd, 1972, Abstr. (abs.).

STOUT, THOMSON M. and STONE, WILLIAM J.
   1971A   Fossil beavers in Tertiary caprocks in North Dakota and Montana. Geol. Soc. Amer., Abstr., 3:4, 281—282 (abs.).

STRAHLER, ARTHUR NEWELL
   1971A   The earth sciences. Second edition. New York: Harper and Row, vii + 824 pp., illustr.
              Rev.: Craig in J. Geol., 80:3, 370—371; Mickelson in Ohio J. Sci., 72:1, 60—61.

STRAKA, JOSEPH J., II and SEMKEN, HOLMES A., JR.
   1969A   A dinichthyid in middle Devonian of Iowa. J. Paleontol., 43:6, 1423—1428, 3 figs., 1 pl., 2 tables.
   1969B   *Dunkleosteus* in the middle Devonian of Iowa. Geol. Soc. Amer., Spec. Pap., 121, 670.

STRAUCH, F.   See: Gliese, J. and Strauch, F., 1969A.

STRAUS, WILLIAM L., JR.
   1967A   The great Piltdown hoax. In: Rapport, S. and Wright, H. (eds.), 1967, 45—55, 1 table (reprinted from Science, 119, 265—269).
   1968A   Time and stratigraphy in the evolution of man: nature of the problem and the evidence. In: Genovés, T., *et al.* eds.), 1968A, 42—59, 11 figs. (reprinted from Publ. Nation. Acad. Sci., 1965).

STRELKOV, S. A.
   1970A   K istorii peremeshcheniia beregovoĭ linii Arkticheskogo basseĭna v kaĭnozoe. [On the history of shifting of the shore line of the Arctic basin during the Cenozoic.] In: Severnyĭ Ledovityĭ Okean i ego poberezh'e v kaĭnozoe, 222—227 (Russian).

STRELKOV, S. A.   See also: Deviatkin, E. V. and Strelkov, S. A., 1968A.

STRELKOVSKIĬ, VASILIĬ IL'ICH
   1966B   Nekotorye soobrazheniia ob usloviiakh ekogeneticheskogo protsessa. [Some considerations on the conditions of ecogenetic process.] Akad. Nauk Gruz. SSR, Inst. Paleobiol., Nauchn. Sess., 12, 25—26 (Russian and Georgian).
   1968A   O sovremennom sostoianii biogeneticheskogo zakona. [The present state of the biogenetic law.] Akad. Nauk Gruz. SSR, Inst. Paleobiol., Nauchn. Sess., 14, 4—7 (Russian).
   1970A   K voprosu o faktorakh i usloviiakh ekogeneza. [On factors and conditions of ecogenesis.] Akad. Nauk Gruz. SSR, Inst. Paleobiol., Obshchie Vop. Evoliuts. Paleobiol., 5, 5—25 (Russian; Georgian and English summaries).

STROK, N. I.   See: Gorbatkina, T. E., Lozovskiĭ, V. R. and Strok, N. I., 1971A.

STRONG, EMORY
   1968A   The Scottsbluff projectile point. Screenings, 17:9, 2, 1 fig.
   1969A   Stone age in the Great Basin. Portland, Ore.: Binfords and Mort, ix + 274 pp., 143 figs., 6 charts.

STRUVE, W.
   1970A   Zum 70. Geburtstag von Herta Schmidt. Natur Mus., 100:6, 282—286 (German).
   1970B   In memoriam Franz Michels. Natur Mus., 100:6, 290—292, portr. (German).

STUART, A. J.   See: Barnes, B., Edwards, B. J. N., Hallam, J. S. and Stuart, A. J., 1971A.

STUART, GENE S.   See: Stuart, G. E. and Stuart, G. S., 1969A.

STUART, GEORGE E. and STUART, GENE S.
   1969A   Discovering man's past in the Americas. Washington, D.C.: National Geographic Society Special Publication, 211 pp., illustr.

STUBBLEFIELD, C. J.
   1970A   Drashaw N. Wadia. Roy. Soc. London, Biogr. Mem., 16, 543—562, portr.

STUBBS, PETER and WICK, GERALD
   1969A   Human ancestors four million years old. New Sci., 44:669, 9.
   1969B   Did sub-standard eggs destroy the dinosaurs? New Sci., 44:673, 223.
   1969C   Drifting Antarctica yields spectacular fossil bed. New Sci., 44:679, 542.

STUBBS, PETER   See also: Chedd, G. and Stubbs, P., 1969A; Chedd, G., Stubbs, P. and Wick, G., 1970A.

STUMP, THOMAS E.   See: Kern, J. P., Stump, T. E. and Dowlen, R. J., 1971A.

STÜRMER, WILHELM
1970A   Versteinerungen mit Röntgen-Augen gesehen. Die Röntgenaufnahme als Hilfsmittel der Paläontologie.
             Neue Erlangen, 22, 1640–1647 (German).
1971A   Moderne physikalische Hilfsmittel der Paläontologie. (Demonstriert am Beispiel einer ? Urodele in
             einem bulgarischen Ölschiefer). Hess. Landesamt Bodenforsch., Abh., 60, 175–177, 3 pls.,
             1 table (German).

SU, TE-TSAO
1963A   Abs.: Sci. Abstr. China, Earth Sci., 2:1, 5.

SUCHY, J.   See: Fetter, V., Prokopec, M., Suchy, J. and Titlbachová, S., 1967A.

SUDAKOVA, N. G.   See: Motuzko, A. N., Sudakova, N. G. and Khorev, V. S., 1969A.

SUDILOVSKAĨA, A. M.
1964A   K istorii ornitologicheskogo sobraniĩa Zoologicheskogo Muzeĩa Moskovskogo Universiteta. [On the
             history of the ornithological collection of the Zoological Museum of Moscow University.]
             In: Problemy ornitologii. Trudy tret'eĩ vsesoiũznoĩ ornitologicheskoĩ konferentsii. Sentĩabr'
             1962, 207–213 (Russian).

SUDRE, JEAN
1969A   Acquisitions récentes pour la faune des Mammifères de Robiac (Eocène supérieur). Soc. Géol. Fr.,
             C.R., 1969:4, 125–127, 1 fig. (French).
             Rev.: Thenius in Zentralbl. Geol. Paläontol., Teil 2, 1971:6, 516.
1969B   Les gisements de Robiac (Eocène supérieur) et leurs faunes de mammifères. Palaeovertebrata
             (Montpellier), 2:3, 96–156, 21 figs., 6 tables (French; German and English summaries).
             Rev.: Thenius in Zentralbl. Geol. Paläontol., Teil 2, 1971:6, 515–516.
1971A   Étude de la variabilité chez Lophiodon lautricense Noulet. Palaeovertebrata (Montpellier), 4:3, 67–
             95, 11 figs., 4 pls., 5 tables (French; English and German summaries).
             Rev.: Thenius in Zentralbl. Geol. Paläontol., Teil 2, 1971:4, 346–347.
1972A   Révision des artiodactyles de l'Éocène moyen de Lissieu (Rhône). Palaeovertebrata (Montpellier),
             5:4, 111–156, 17 figs., 7 tables (French; German and English summaries).

SUDRE, JEAN   See also: Cappetta, H., Hartenberger, J. L., Sigé, B. and Sudre, J., 1968A; Hartenberger, J. L.,
             Sigé, B. and Sudre, J., 1969A; Hartenberger, J. L., Sigé, B., Sudre, J. and Vianey-Liaud, M.,
             1970A, 1970B.

SUGA, SHŌICHI   See: Kobayashi, I. and Suga, S., 1971A.

SUGIE, T., et al.
1967A   Special issue in commemoration of the 90th anniversary of the National Science Museum. Natur. Sci.
             and Mus., 34:11–12, 201–370, 26 figs., 16 pls., 2 plans, 57 tables (Japanese).

SUIRE, CÉCILE
1968A   À propos d'une canine inférieure de félin, Felis cf. pardus L., découverte à La Chaise (Charente). Soc.
             Linn. Bordeaux, Actes, Sér. B, 105:5, 7 pp., 4 figs., 3 tables (French).
1970A   Contribution à l'étude des dents de "Felis spelæa" Goldf. Ass. Fr. Étud. Quat., Bull., 7:25, 243–252
             (French; English summary).

SUIRE, C.   See also: Delpech, F., Lachastre, J., Prat, F. and Suire, C., 1970A; Prat, F. and Suire, C., 1971A.

SUKACHEV, V. N., GROMOV, V. I. and BADER, O. N.
1966A   Rev.: Karlov in Akad. Nauk SSSR, Kom. Izuch. Chetvertich. Perioda, Biull., 37, 145–148 (Russian).

SUKACHEV, V. N. and SOKOLOVSKAĨA, V. T.
1965A   O likhvinskoĩ mezhlednikovoĩ flore pod Moskvoĩ. [The Likhvin interglacial flora in the environs of
             Moscow.] Akad. Nauk SSSR, Dokl., 165:1, 194–197 (Russian).
1966A   Likhvin interglacial flora near Moscow. Akad. Nauk SSSR, Dokl., Earth Sci. Sec., 165, 200–202.
             (Translated from Russian: Akad. Nauk SSSR, Dokl., 1965, 165:1, 194–197.)

SUKHANOV, VLADIMIR BORISOVICH
1968A   Obshchaĩa sistema simmetrichnoĩ lokomotsii nazemnykh pozvonochnykh i osobennosti peredvizheniĩa
             nizshikh tetrapod. [General system of symmetric locomotion in terrestrial vertebrates and
             peculiarities of locomotion in lower tetrapods.] Moscow: "Nauka" Press, 227 pp., 109 figs.,
             36 photos (Russian).
             Rev.: Gambariãn in Zool. Zh., 48:9, 1428–1429 (Russian).

SUKHORUKOV, A. M.
  1964A   Osnovnye cherty razvitiia gidroseti i akkumuliatsii alluviia v antropogene na vostochnom sklone
             Srednego Urala i v Zaural'e. [Main traits of drainage system development and alluvium
             accumulation in Anthropogene on the eastern slopes of middle Urals and in Transuralia.]
             In: Vsesoiuznoe Soveshchanie po Izucheniiu Chetvertichnogo perioda, Novosibirsk, 1964,
             Tezisy Dokladov, Sektsiia Paleogeografii, 73–76 (Russian).

SUKHOV, VLADIMIR PAVLOVICH (= SUCHOV, V. P.)
  1967B   Melkie mlekopitaiushchie srednego akchagyla i nizhnego apsherona Bashkirskogo Predural'ia (po
             stratotipicheskomu razrezu Akkulaevo). [Small mammals of middle Akchagylian and lower
             Apsheronian of Bashkirian Predural'e (stratotypic cross-section Akkulaevo).] In: Materialy
             Iubileinoi Nauchnoi Sessii po voprosam geologii Iuzhnogo Urala i Russkoi platformy. Tezisy
             dokladov, 56–57 (Russian).
  1968A   Discovery of the remains of molar-toothed zokors of the genus *Prosiphneus* (Rodentia, Mammalia)
             in the Bashkirian part of the Cisural region and some aspects of the taxonomy of the family
             Myospalacidae. Akad. Nauk SSSR, Dokl., Earth Sci. Sec., 177, 256–258, 1 fig. (Translated
             from Russian: Akad. Nauk SSSR, Dokl., 1967, 177:3, 695–698.)
  1970A   Pozdnepliotsenovye melkie mlekopitaiushchie Akkulaevskogo mestonakhozhdeniia v Bashkirii. [Late
             Pliocene small mammals from Akkulaevo faunal locality in Bashkiria.] Moscow: "Nauka"
             Press, 94 pp., 264 figs., 5 tables (Russian).

SUKIASIAN, S. S.   See: Garkusha, M. P., Engoian, M. A., Oganesian, D. A. and Sukiasian, S. S., 1971A.

SULIMIRSKI, TADEUSZ
  1970A   Prehistoric Russia: an outline. London: John Baker Publishers Ltd., xxiii + 449 pp., 91 figs., 50 pls.,
             23 tables, 32 maps.
             Rev.: Klein in Amer. Anthropol., 73:6, 1423–1424; Pittioni in Archaeol. Austriaca, 48, 33–34;
             Pleslová in Archeol. Roz., 22:5, 625; Thompson in Antiquaries J., 51:1, 106–108.

SULIMSKI, ANDRZEJ
  1968B   Paleocene genus *Pseudictops* Matthew, Granger & Simpson 1929 (Mammalia) and its revision.
             Palaeontol. Pol., 19, 101–129, 4 figs., 5 pls., 2 tables.
  1970A   On some Oligocene insectivore remains from Mongolia. In: Kielan-Jaworowska, Z. (ed.), 1970B,
             53–70, 2 figs., 2 pls., 6 tables.
  1972A   *Adamisaurus magnidentatus* n. gen., n. sp. (Sauria) from the upper Cretaceous of Mongolia. In:
             Kielan-Jaworowska, Z. (ed.), 1972B, 33–40, 2 figs., 1 pl., 1 table.

SULIMSKI, A.   See also: Glazek, J., Oberc, J. and Sulimski, A., 1971A, 1972A.

SULLIVAN, BRIAN
  1972A   Animal bones hold clues to the study of ancient man. Screenings, 21:1, 1.

SULLIVAN, RAYMOND   See: McGrew, P. O. and Sullivan, R., 1970A.

SULLIVAN, WALTER
  1968A   Neanderthal man liked flowers. Chesopiean, 6:6, 162–164.
  1971A   A pre-Neanderthal skull found in Pyrenees cave. Chattanooga Times, Oct. 14, 1971, 27.

SULTANOV, KADYR MAMEDOVICH and DZHAFAROVA, ZHANNET DZHAMIL'KYZY
  1967A   Nekotorye dannye o biogeokhimicheskoi izuchennosti kostei iskopaemykh organizmov. [Some data on
             biogeochemistry of bones of fossil organisms.] Baku, Azerbaidzh. Univ., Uch. Zap., Ser. Geol.-
             Geogr., 1967:1, 3–7 (Russian).

SUMMERS, W. K. and KOTTLOWSKI, F. E.
  1969A*   The San Andres limestone, a reservoir for oil and water in New Mexico. Symposium. N. Mex. Geol.
             Soc., Spec. Publ., 3, 51 pp., figs., 12 pls.

SUMMESBERGER, HERBERT   See: Bachmayer, F., Kollman, H. A., Schultz, O. and Summesberger, H., 1971A.

SUN, AI-LIN
  1961A   Abs.: Sci. Abstr. China, Earth Sci., 1:2, 9.
  1964A   Abs.: Sci. Abstr. China, Earth Sci., 2:3, 9–10.

SURIANO, F.   See: Malatesta, A. and Suriano, F., 1971A.

SUTCLIFFE, ANTHONY J.
 1969A   Adaptations of spotted hyaenas to living in the British Isles. Mammal Soc. Brit. Isles, Bull., 31,
           10–14, 2 figs.
           Rev.: Thenius in Zentralbl. Geol. Paläontol., Teil 2, 1971:2–3, 197.

SUTTON, JOHN F.
 1972A   A multituberculate from the Oligocene of Jackson Hole, Wyoming. Soc. Vert. Paleontol., Ann.
           Meeting, 32nd, 1972, Abstr. (abs.).
 1972B   Additional rodent material from the Split Rock local fauna, Miocene of Wyoming. Tex. Tech. Univ.,
           Mus., Occas. Pap., 4, 8 pp., 1 fig., 1 table.

SUTTON, JOHN F. and BLACK, CRAIG C.
 1972A   Oligocene and Miocene deposits of Jackson Hole, Wyoming. Field Conf. Tert. Bios., S. and W. Wyo.,
           Guidebk., 73–79.

SUZUKI, HISASHI
 1969A   The Amud man and the Shanidar man. Int. Congr. Anthropol. Ethnol. Sci., 8th, Tokyo, 1968, Proc.,
           Vol. I. Anthropology, 273–278, 9 figs., 1 table.
 1970A   Introduction. In: Suzuki, H. and Takai, F. (eds.), 1970A, 3–6.
 1970B   The skull of the Amud man. In: Suzuki, H. and Takai, F. (eds.), 1970A, 123–206, 28 figs., 16 pls.,
           28 tables.
 1970C   General conclusions. In: Suzuki, H. and Takai, F. (eds.), 1970A, 421–422.

SUZUKI, HISASHI, et al.
 1966A   Hamakita man and the site of Nekata limestone quarry at Hamakita. Jour. Anthropol. Soc. Nippon,
           74:750–751, 101–176, 29 figs., 9 pls., 15 tables (Japanese; English summaries).
           Rev.: Hemmer in Homo, 18:4, 271.

SUZUKI, HISASHI and TAKAI, FUYUJI
 1970A*   The Amud man and his cave site. Tokyo: University of Tokyo, frontispiece, xvi + 439 pp., 138 figs.,
           64 pls.
           Rev.: Anon. in J. Anthropol. Soc. Nippon, 79:3, 287–289; Comas in An. Antropol., Mexico, 9,
           292–295; Stewart in Amer. J. Phys. Anthropol., 37:2, 413–415.

SUZUKI, MASAO
 1970A   Preliminary report on fission track date of animal bone from the Amud Cave. In: Suzuki, H. and
           Takai, F. (eds.), 1970A, 428.

SUZUKI, T.   See: Obata, I., Hasegawa, Y. and Suzuki, T., 1970A.

SVICHENSKAIA, ALEKSANDRA ANDREEVNA (= SWITCHENSKA, A. A.)
 1968A   Novyĭ rod semeĭstva Sphyraenidae iz miotsena Zakavkaz'ia. [New genus of the family Sphyraenidae
           from middle Miocene of Transcaucasia.] In: Ocherki po filogenii i sistematike iskopaemykh
           ryb i bezcheliustnykh, 157–161, 2 figs., 1 pl. (Russian).
           Rev.: Weiler in Zentralbl. Geol. Paläontol., Teil 2, 1970:5, 428–429.

SVISTUN, VLADIMIR IL'ICH
 1971A   Novye nakhodki ostatkov verbliudov (Tylopoda, Camelidae) v otlozheniiakh ponta iuga Evropeĭskoĭ
           chasti SSSR. [New finds of camel remains (Tylopoda, Camelidae) in Pontian deposits of the
           south of the European part of the USSR.] Akad. Nauk Ukr. SSR, Inst. Zool., Vestn. Zool.,
           1971:1, 64–68, 4 figs., 2 tables (Russian; English summary).

SVISTUN, V. I.   See also: Danilova, E. I. and Svistun, V. I., 1969A.

SWIFT, CAMM and ELLWOOD, BROOKS
 1972A   Hypsocephalus atlanticus, a new genus and species of lutjanid fish from marine Eocene limestones of
           northern Florida. Los Angeles Cty. Mus., Contrib. Sci., 230, 29 pp., 7 figs.

SWINDLER, D. R.
 1968A   The maxillary incisors and evolution of Old World monkeys. In: Chiarelli, B. (ed.), 1968C, 57–67,
           2 figs.

SWINTON, W. E.
 1960F   Archaeopteryx. Brit. Ornithol. Club, Bull., 80:9, 153–154.
 1970A   The dinosaurs. London: Allen and Unwin, 331 pp., 65 figs., 8 pls., 7 maps.
           Rev.: Anon. in Biologist, 53:1, 46; Chrulew in Zentralbl. Geol. Paläontol., Teil 2, 1970:5, 432–434;
           Cox in Nature, 227:5265, 1375; Eaton in J. Paleontol., 45:4, 740–741; Fantini Sestini in Riv.
           Ital. Paleontol. Stratigr., 76:4, 628, Kermack in Sci. Progress, 59:235, 444–445.

SYCH, LUCJAN
   1971A   Mixodontia, a new order of mammals from the Paleocene of Mongolia. In: Kielan-Jaworowska, Z.
            (ed.), 1971B, 147–158, 4 pls., 1 table.

SYCHEVSKAÎA, E. K. (= SYTCHEVSKAYA, E. K.)
   1968A   Iskopaemye Umbridae iz oligoťsena Zapadnoĭ Sibiri. [Fossil Umbridae from the Oligocene of
            western Siberia.] In: Ocherki po filogenii i sistematike iskopaemykh ryb i bezcheliustnykh,
            162–166, 1 pl.(Russian).
            Rev.: Weiler in Zentralbl. Geol. Paläontol., Teil 2, 1970:5, 429–430.

SYCHEVSKAÎA, E. K. and LEBEDEV, V. D.
   1971A   Presnovodnaîa neogenovaîa ikhtiofauna Kotloviny Bol'shikh Ozer. [Freshwater Neogene
            ichthyofauna of the Bol'shie Ozera basin.] Sovm. Sovet.-Mongol. Nauch.-Issled. Geol. Eksped.,
            Tr., 3, 49–57, 2 pls. (Russian).

SYDOW, W.
   1969A   The discovery of a Boskop skull at Otjiseva near Windhoek, S.W.A. S. Afr. J. Sci., 65, 77–81, 1 fig.

SYKES, E.
   1969A   Elephants in Central America. New World Antiq., 16:1–2, 8–9.

SYKES, J. H.
   1971A   A new dalatiid fish from the Rhaetic bone bed at Barnstone, Nottinghamshire. Mercian Geol., 4:1,
            13–22.

SZABO, BARNEY J.
   1971A   A comment concerning the applicability of the "open system" model to dating of fossil bones from
            San Joaquin soil, California. Earth Planet. Sci. Lett., 10, 252, 1 table.

SZABO, B. J.   See also: Gard, L. M. and Szabo, B. J., 1971A; Howell, F. C., Cole, G. H., Kleindienst, M. R.,
            Szabo, B. J. and Oakley, K. P., 1972A.

SZALAY, FREDERICK S.
   1967B   Mixodectids, microsyopids and the insectivore-primate transition. Diss. Abstr., 28:3, 1289B–1290B
            (abs.).
   1968B   The Picrodontidae, a family of early primates. Amer. Mus. Nov., 2329, 1–55, 34 figs., 3 tables.
   1968C   Origins of the Apatemyidae (Mammalia, Insectivora). Amer. Mus. Nov., 2352, 1–11, 4 figs., 1 table.
   1969A   The Hapalodectinae and a phylogeny of the Mesonychidae (Mammalia, Condylarthra). Amer. Mus.
            Nov., no. 2361, 1–26, 19 figs.
            Rev.: Thenius in Zentralbl. Geol. Paläontol., Teil 2, 1971:1, 73.
   1969B   Uintasoricinae, a new subfamily of early Tertiary mammals (? Primates). Amer. Mus. Nov., no. 2363,
            1–36, 25 figs., 3 tables.
   1969C   Mixodectidae, Microsyopidae, and the insectivore-primate transition. Amer. Mus. Natur. Hist., Bull.,
            140:4, 197–330, 28 figs., 41 pls., 21 tables.
   1969D   Origin and evolution of function of the mesonychid condylarth feeding mechanism. Evolution, 23:4,
            703–720, 7 figs.
   1970A   Late Eocene *Amphipithecus* and the origins of catarrhine primates. Nature, 227:5256, 355–357, 1 fig.
   1971A   Cranium of the late Palaeocene primate *Plesiadapis tricuspidens*. Nature, 230:5292, 324–325, 2 figs.
   1971B   The European adapid primates *Agerina* and *Pronycticebus*. Amer. Mus. Nov., 2466, 19 pp., 13 figs.,
            1 table.
   1971C   Relationships of the alleged primate *Gesneropithex peyeri* Hürzeler, 1946. J. Mammal., 52:4, 824–
            826, 1 fig.
   1971D   Biological level of organization of the Chesowanja robust australopithecine. Nature, 234:5326,
            229–230, 2 figs.
   1971E   Significance of the basicranium of early Tertiary primates for the phylogeny of the order. Amer. J.
            Phys. Anthropol., 35:2, 297 (abs.).
   1972A   *Amphipithecus* revisited. Nature, 236:5343, 179–180.
   1972B   Cranial morphology of the early Tertiary *Phenacolemur* and its bearing on primate phylogeny.
            Amer. J. Phys. Anthropol., 36:1, 59–76, 16 figs.
   1972C   Paleobiology of the earliest primates. In: Tuttle, R. (ed.), 1972A, 3–35, 9 figs., 9 pls., 1 table.

SZALAY, F. S. and McKENNA, M. C.
   1971A   Beginning of the age of mammals in Asia: the late Paleocene Gashato fauna, Mongolia. Amer. Mus.
            Natur. Hist., Bull., 144:4, 269–318, 35 figs., 3 tables.

SZALAY, FREDERICK S.   See also: McKenna, M. C., Mellett, J. S. and Szalay, F. S., 1971A; Mellett, J. S. and
          Szalay, F. S., 1968A; Wilson, R. W. and Szalay, F. S., 1972A.

SZARSKI, HENRYK
     1969A   Z badań ewolucji ryb spodoustych (Elasmobranchii). [On some studies of the evolution of
          Elasmobranchs.] Przegl. Zool., 13:2, 148–151 (Polish; English summary).

T., L.
     1971A   Des australopithèques et des hommes. Sci. Progrès Découverte, 3437, 23–24 (French).

TABRUM, ALAN R.
     1970A   Comments on new tyrannosaurid material from Montana. S. Calif. Paleontol. Soc., Bull., 2:6, 6
          (reprinted from S. Calif. Acad. Sci., 1970 Meetings, Abstr.).

TACOMA, J.   See: Erdbrink, D. P. and Tacoma, J., 1967A, 1968A; Erdbrink, D. P., Tacoma, J. and
          Visser, H., 1966A.

TAÏEB, MAURICE
     1971A   Aperçus sur les formations quaternaires et la néotectonique de la basse vallée de l'Aouache (Afar
          méridional, Éthiopie). Soc. Géol. Fr., C.R., 1971:2, 63–65, 2 figs. (French).

TAÏEB, M., COPPENS, Y., JOHANSON, D. C. and KALB, J.
     1972A   Dépôts sédimentaires et faunes du Plio-pléistocène de la basse vallée de l'Awash (Afar central,
          Éthiopie). Acad. Sci., C.R., Sér. D, 275:7, 819–822, 1 map (French).

TAÏEB, MAURICE   See also: Bonnefille, R., Chavaillon, N. and Taïeb, M., 1970A.

TAKAHASHI, T.   See: Onodera, S., Ootaka, S., Sato, J., Takahashi, T. and Yamada, Y., 1967A.

TAKAI, FUYUJI
     1970A   Fossil mammals from the Amud Cave. In: Suzuki, H. and Takai, F. (eds.), 1970A, 53–76, 1 fig.,
          6 pls., 1 table.

TAKAI, FUYUJI   See also: Suzuki, H. and Takai, F., 1970A.

TAKAMIYA, HIROE
     1967A   Archaeological work in the Ryukyu Islands, 1961-1965. In: Solheim, W. (ed.), 1967A, 11–18, 1 pl.

TAKAYASU, Y.   See: Shikama, T. and Takayasu, Y., 1971A.

TAKŠIĆ, A.
     1968A   Die Vertebratenfauna aus dem Goručičatal bei Sinj. Akad. savet FNRJ, Bull. Sci., Sec. A, 1968:3–4,
          74–75, 1 fig. (German).

TALENT, J. A., DUNCAN, P. M. and HANDBY, P. L.
     1966A   Early Cretaceous feathers from Victoria. Emu, 66:2, 81–86, 1 fig., 2 pls.

TALIPOV, M. A.
     1968A   Nekotorye voprosy biostratigrafii chetvertichnykh otlozheniĭ na primere opornogo razreza Kirgizskogo
          Tiàn'-Shanià. [Some biostratigraphic problems of Quaternary deposits on the example of the
          key section of Kirgizian Tian-Shan.] In: Problemy izucheniià chetvertichnogo perioda, Tezisy,
          126–127 (Russian).

TALIPOV, M. A. and KOROLEV, V. G.
     1970A   Dzhergalanskiĭ razrez kak stratotip chetvertichnykh otlozheniĭ Severnogo Tiàn'-Shanià. [Dzhergalan
          section as the stratotype of Quaternary deposits of northern Tian-Shan.] In: Materialy po
          geologii kaĭnozoià i noveĭsheĭ tektonike Tiàn'-Shanià, 72–88 (Russian).

TALIPOV, M. A.   See also: Kambariddinova, T. K. and Talipov, M. A., 1969A.

TAMERS, MURRY
     1969A   Datage non destructif des os fossiles. Acad. Sci., C.R., Sér. D, 268:3, 489–492, 1 fig., 1 table
          (French).

TANABE, GIICHI
    1970A   Fluorine content of the skeleton of the Amud man. In: Suzuki, H. and Takai, F. (eds.), 1970A, 429.

TANNER, LLOYD G.
    1969A   A new rhinoceros from the Nebraska Miocene. Nebr. Univ. State Mus., Bull., 8:6, 395—412, 10 figs., 2 tables.
    1970A   Notes on the genera *Aphelops* and *Peraceras* with a suggested tribal classification. Nebr. Acad. Sci., Proc., 80, 38 (abs.).
    1972A   A new species of *Menoceras* from the Marsland formation of Nebraska. Nebr. Univ. State Mus., Bull., 9:8, 205—213, frontispiece, 4 figs., 3 tables.

TANNER, LLOYD G. and MARTIN, LARRY D.
    1972A   Notes on the deciduous and permanent dentition of hyracodonts. Nebr. Acad. Sci., Trans., 1, 12 pp., 6 pls.

TANNER, LLOYD G.   See also: Schultz, C. B., Tanner, L. G. and Martin, L. D., 1969A, 1972A; Schultz, C. B., Tanner, L. G., Whitmore, F. C. and Ray, W. W., 1969A.

TAPALOV, E. D.
    1971A   Novye dannye po stratigrafii neogenovykh otlozheniĭ Mugodzhar i ikh periferii. [New data on the stratigraphy of Neogene deposits of the Mugodzhary and of their periphery.] Akad. Nauk Kaz. SSR, Vestn., 1971:6, 16—22 (Russian).

TAPPEN, NEIL C.
    1969A   The relationship of weathering cracks to split-line orientation in bone. Amer. J. Phys. Anthropol., 31, 191—198, 4 figs., 2 pls.
    1970A   On Hemmer's new view of human evolution. Curr. Anthropol., 11:1, 79.
    1972A   Structure of bone in Neanderthal fossils. Amer. J. Phys. Anthropol., 37:3, 453 (abs.).

TAQUET, PHILIPPE
    1969A   Première découverte en Afrique d'un reptile Captorhinomorphe (Cotylosaurien). Acad. Sci., C.R., Sér. D, 268:5, 779—781, 1 fig. (French).
    1970A   Sur le gisement de dinosauriens et de crocodiliens de Gadoufaoua (République du Niger). Acad. Sci., C.R., Sér. D, 271:1, 38—40 (French).
    1972A   Un crâne de *Ctenochasma* (Pterodactyloidea) du Portlandien inférieur de la Haute-Marne, dans les collections du Musée de Saint-Dizier. Acad. Sci., C.R., Sér. D, 274:3, 362—364, 1 pl. (French).

TAQUET, PHILIPPE   See also: Ginsburg, L., Hilly, J. and Taquet, P., 1968A.

TARABUKIN, B. A.
    1968B   Novyĭ vid gippariona iz s. Chimishliia MSSR. [New species of *Hipparion* from Chimishliia village MSSR.] Akad. Nauk Moldav. SSR, Okh. Prir. Moldav., 5, 70—78, 3 figs., 2 tables (Russian; English summary).

TĂRĂBUŢĂ, C.   See: Cosmovici, N. L., Şova, C. and Tărăbuţă, C., 1964A.

TARASHCHUK, VLADIMIR IVANOVICH
    1971A   Cherepakhi neogenovykh i antropogenovykh otlozheniĭ Ukrainy. Soobshchenie I. Semeĭstvo bol'shegolovykh cherepakh (Platysternidae). [Turtles of Neogene and Anthropogene deposits of Ukraine. Communication I. Family of large-headed turtles (Platysternidae).] Akad. Nauk Ukr. SSR, Inst. Zool., Vestn. Zool., 1971:2, 56—62, 1 fig. (Russian; English summary).
    1971B   Vykopni cherepakhy rodyny Emydidae z neogenovykh ta antropogenovykh vidkladiv Ukraïny. [Fossil turtles of the family Emydidae from Neogene and Quaternary deposits of Ukraine.] Akad. Nauk Ukr. RSR, Zool. Muz., Zb. Prats', 34, 100—112, 5 figs. (Ukrainian; Russian and English summaries).

TARASOV, L. M.
    1969A   Issledovanie gagarinskogo poseleniia. [Investigation of Gagarino dwelling.] In: Rybakov, B. A. (ed.), 1969A, 39—41 (Russian).
    1971A   Statuetka iz Gagarino. [Statuette from Gagarino.] Akad. Nauk SSSR, Inst. Arkheol., Krat. Soobshch., 126, 63—67, 1 fig. (Russian).
    1972A   Dvoĭnaia skul'ptura cheloveka iz Gagarino. [A double sculpture of man from Gagarino.] Akad. Nauk SSSR, Inst. Arkheol., Krat. Soobshch., 131, 14—19, 3 figs. (Russian).

TARASOV, SERGEĬ ALEKSEEVICH
   1970A   K voprosu o stratigrafii paleogen-neogenovykh otlozheniĭ Kochkorskoĭ vpadiny. [On the problem of
                the stratigraphy of Paleogene-Neogene deposits of Kochkorka depression.] In: Materialy po
                geologii kaĭnozoiă i noveĭsheĭ tektonike Tiăn'-Shaniă, 52–68 (Russian).

TARDON, K. K.
   1971A   On the discovery of mammalian and reptilian remains from the middle Eocene rocks of S.W. Kutch,
                India. Curr. Sci., 40:16, 436–437.

TARLING, DON H. and TARLING, MAUREEN P.
   1971A   Continental drift: a study of the earth's moving surface. New York: Doubleday and Co., 112 pp.,
                illustr.
        Rev.:   Anon. in Sci. on the March, 52:1, 14; Meyerhoff in Geotimes, 17:4, 34–36; Morrison in Sci.
                Amer., 225:6, 111–112; Osmaston in New Sci., 50:1, 47.

TARLING, MAUREEN P.   See: Tarling, D. H. and Tarling, M. P., 1971A.

TARLO, L. B. HALSTEAD (= HALSTEAD, L. B.)
   1967E   Age of the first mammal. New Sci., 34:550, 730–731.
   1968A   An outline classification of the squamates. Brit. J. Herpetol., 4:2, 32–35.

TASCH, PAUL
   1970A   Paleolimnology of some Antarctic nonmarine deposits. Antarctic J., 5:4, 85–86.

TASNÁDI-KUBACSKA, ANDRÁS
   1968A*   Bevor der Mensch kam. (Eine Entwicklungsgeschichte des Lebens). Leipzig, Jena, Berlin: Urania
                Verlag (German).
   1968B   Leben und Tod in der Vorzeit. In: Tasnádi-Kubacska, A. (ed.), 1968A, 446–509 (German).
   1969A   Dr. Vértes László emlékezete. (1914–1968). Földt. Közl., 99:4, 305–307, portr. (Hungarian).

TASNÁDI-KUBACSKA, ANDRÁS and CSERGEZÁN, P.
   1968A   Az élet fejlödése képekben. [The evolution of life in pictures.] Budapest: Gondolat Kiadó, 160 pp.
                (Hungarian).

TASNÁDI-KUBACSKA, ANDRÁS   See also: Fülöp, J. and Tasnádi-Kubacska, A., 1969A.

TASSIN DE SAINT PEREUSE, MARIE   See: Pales, L. and Tassin de Saint Pereuse, M., 1967A.

TATARINOV, KONSTANTIN ADRIANOVICH
   1962A   Pleĭstotsenovi i golotsenovi ssavtsi Kremenets'kikh gir. [Pleistocene and Holocene mammals of
                Kremenets mountains. (Preliminary report).] Nauk. zap. Kremenets'k. Derzh. Pedag. Inst.,
                7, 45–62 (Ukrainian).
   1969A   Cheliŭst' peshchernogo l'va iz rusla reki Vishni. [A jaw of cave lion from the bed of Vishniă river.]
                Akad. Nauk Ukr. SSR, Inst. Zool., Vestn. Zool., 1969:2, 48–53, 2 figs., 2 tables (Russian;
                English summary).
   1971A   Pleĭstotsen-golotsenovye ptitsy i mlekopitaiŭshchie rechnogo alliŭviiă Volynskogo Poles'iă.
                [Pleistocene-Holocene birds and mammals from the river alluvium of Volynskoe Poles'e.]
                Geogr. Obshchest. Ukr. SSR, L'vov. Otd., Dokl. Soobshch., 1971, 46–50 (Russian).

TATARINOV, K. A. and BACHINSKIĬ, G. A.
   1968A   Peshchernye zakhoroneniiă pliotsenovykh i antropogenovykh pozvonochnykh v zapadnykh oblastiăkh
                Ukrainy. [Cave burials of Pliocene and Anthropogene vertebrates in the western regions of the
                Ukraine.] Mosk. Obshchest. Ispyt. Prir., Biŭll., Otd. Biol., 73:5, 114–122, 5 tables (Russian;
                English summary).

TATARINOV, K. A. and MARISOVA, I. V.
   1962A   Zemnovodni z antropogenovikh vidkladiv okolits' Krementsiă. [Amphibia from Quaternary deposits
                near Krementsă.] Nauk. zap. Kremenets'k. Derzh. Pedag. Inst., 7, 77–78 (Ukrainian).
   1971A   Iskopaemye antropogenovye ptitsy zapadnykh oblasteĭ Ukrainy. [Fossil Pleistocene birds of western
                Ukraine.] Akad. Nauk Ukr. SSR, Inst. Zool., Vestn. Zool., 1971:6, 67–75, 2 figs., 1 table
                (Russian; English summary).

TATARINOV, K. A.   See also: Marisova, I. V. and Tatarinov, K. A., 1962A, 1965A.

TATARINOV, LEONID PETROVICH
1968B   Nakhodka primitivnogo khvostatogo zemnovodnogo v verkhneĭ permi Povolzh'ia. [The finding of a
            primitive tailed amphibian in the upper Permian of Povolzh'e.] In: Verkhnepaleozoĭskie i
            mezozoĭskie zemnovodnye i presmykaĭushchiesia SSSR, 7–10, 1 fig. (Russian).
1968C   Novye teriodonty iz verkhneĭ permi SSSR. [New theriodonts from upper Permian of USSR.] In:
            Verkhnepaleozoĭskie i mezozoĭskie zemnovodnye i presmykaĭushchiesia SSSR, 32–46, 7 figs.,
            1 pl. (Russian).
1968D   Stroenie mozgovoĭ korobki dvinii i nekotorye problemy evoliutsii endokraniia mlekopitaĭushchikh.
            [Structure of the brain case of Dvinia and some problems of evolution of the endocranium of
            mammals.] In: Verkhnepaleozoĭskie i mezozoĭskie zemnovodnye i presmykaĭushchiesia SSSR,
            47–64, 6 figs. (Russian).
1970A   Nekotorye problemy filogeneticheskikh issledovaniĭ po nizshim tetrapodam. [Some problems of
            phylogenetic research on lower tetrapods.] In: Materialy po evoliutsii nazemnykh pozvonochnykh,
            8–29 (Russian).
1971A   K morfologii i sistematike severodvinskikh tsinodontov. [On the morphology and taxonomy of north
            Dvina cynodonts.] Akad. Nauk SSSR, Paleontol. Inst., Tr., 130, 114–141, 6 figs. (Russian).
1972A   Paleontologiia i zakonomernosti filogeneza nizshikh nazemnykh pozvonochnykh. [Paleontology and
            the regularities of the phylogenesis of lower land vertebrates.] Paleontol. Zh., 1972:3, 121–133,
            1 fig. (Russian).
1972B   Seymouriamorphen aus der Fauna der USSR. Handb. Paläoherp., 5B, 70–80, 3 figs. (German).

TATARINOV, L. P.   See also: Kalandadze, N. N., Ochev, V. G., Tatarinov, L. P., Chudinov, P. K. and
                        Shishkin, M. A., 1968A.

TATE, JAMES, JR. and MARTIN, LARRY D.
1968A   Horned lark and black-billed magpie from the Pleistocene of Nebraska. Condor, 70:2, 183.
1969A   A Canada goose from the middle Pleistocene of Nebraska. Condor, 71:1, 81.

TATE, JAMES, JR.   See also: Martin, L. D. and Tate, J., Jr., 1970A.

TATE, ROBERT B.
1969A   The Anceney local mammal fauna. Geol. Soc. Amer., Spec. Pap., 121, 641.

TATIEVA, K. G.
1960A   O prisutstvii oligotsena v Mardachaĭskoĭ sinklinali i v razreze reki Abastumnis-Gele. [On the presence
            of Oligocene in Mardachaĭ syncline and in the Abastumnis-Gele river section.] Akad. Nauk Gruz.
            SSR, Soobshch., 25:6, 699–703 (Russian).

TATTERSALL, IAN M.
1969A   Ecology of north Indian Ramapithecus. Nature, 221:5192, 451–452.
1969B   More on the ecology of north Indian Ramapithecus. Nature, 224:5221, 821–822.
1969C   Evolution of early man. McGraw-Hill Yearbook Sci. Tech., 1969, 27–35, 13 figs.
1970A   Man's ancestors. An introduction to primate and human evolution. London: John Murray, 64 pp.,
            frontispiece, illustr.
            Rev.: Brace in Amer. Anthropol., 1431–1432; Wolpoff in Amer. J. Phys. Anthropol., 37:3, 420–421.
1972A   Crania and dentitions of Archaeolemurinae (Lemuroidea, Primates). Diss. Abstr., 33:1, 350B–351B
            (abs.).

TATTERSALL, I. M. and SIMONS, E. L.
1969A   Notes on some little-known primate fossils from India. Folia Primatol., 10:1–2, 146–153, 3 figs.

TATTERSALL, IAN M.   See also: Howell, F. C. and Tattersall, I. M., 1971A.

TAUTE-WIRSING, MARIE-LUISE
1969A   Robert Wetzel (1898–1962). In: Wetzel, R. and Bosinski, G., 1969A, 11–12, portr.

TAVANI, G.   See: Menesini, E. and Tavani, G., 1968A.

TAVERNE, LOUIS
1969A   Sur un squelette caudal d'ostéoglossomorphe (Brychaetus?) dans le Paléocène (Montien) de Landana
            (Enclave de Cabinda). Établissement d'une nouvelle espèce pour les restes de Brychaetus de
            Landana: Brychaetus caheni sp. nov. Rev. Zool. Bot. Afr., 79:1–2, 125–131 (French).
1969B   Sur la présence d'un Aspidorhynchidae (Pisces Holostéens, ordre des Aspidorhynchiformes) dans les
            terrains éocrétaciques de la Guinée Équatoriale. Rev. Zool. Bot. Afr., 79:3–4, 261–264, 1 fig.
            (French).

1969C   Sur une nouvelle espèce de Clupavidae (Pisces, Leptolepiformes) dans le Crétacé supérieur de Vonso
           (Bas-Congo): *Clupavus casieri* sp. nov. Rev. Zool. Bot. Afr., 80:3—4, 352—358, 2 figs.
           (French).
1969D   Sur des dents de séladens du Tertiaire de Bogenfels (Afrique du Sud). Quelques considérations sur
           l'âge du gisement. Rev. Zool. Bot. Afr., 80:3—4, 377—384 (French).
1970A   Les poissons fossiles et quelques dents de reptiles récoltés par C. R. Hoffmann dans le Crétacé
           supérieur de Vonso (Bas-Congo). Mus. Roy. Afr. Cent., Ann., Sér. in-8°, Sci. Géol., 70,
           44 pp., 6 figs., 8 pls., 2 tables (French).

TAVERNE, LOUIS   See also: Casier, E. and Taverne, L., 1971A.

TAYLOR, BERYL E.   See: Frick, C. and Taylor, B. E., 1971A; Patton, T. H. and Taylor, B. E., 1971A.

TAYLOR, EDWARD HARRISON
1968A   The caecilians of the world. A taxonomic review. Lawrence: Univ. Kansas Press, VIII + 848 pp.,
           illustr.
           Rev.: Bellairs in Endeavors, 28:104, 103; Gorham in Can. Field-Natur., 84:1, 70—71.

TAYLOR, FRANK
1968A   California Mitchell Caverns. Desert Mag., 31:11, 8—9, 3 figs.

TAYLOR, JAMES V.
1970A   Implication of the tibia for the classification of southwest Asian neanderthals. Amer. J. Phys.
           Anthropol., 33:1, 144 (abs.).

TAYLOR, K.
1972A   New fossiliferous localities in the upper Old Red Sandstone of the Ystradfellte-Cwm Taff district of
           Breconshire. Gt. Brit., Geol. Surv., Bull., 38, 11—14, 1 fig.

TAYLOR, R. E., BERGER, R. and DIMSDALE, B.
1968A   Electronic data processing for radiocarbon dates. Amer. Antiquity, 33, 180—184, 2 figs., 1 table.

TCHERNOV, EITAN
1968B   Succession of rodent faunas during the later Quaternary of Israel. Mammal. Depicta, 1968, 7—152,
           130 figs., 40 tables.
           Rev.: Fahlbusch in Zentralbl. Geol. Paläontol., Teil 2, 1968:6, 665—667; Sickenberg in Eiszeitalter
           Gegenwart, 20, 268—269.
1968C   A Pleistocene faunule from a karst fissure filling near Jerusalem, Israel. Naturforsch. Ges. Basel,
           Verh., 79:2, 161—185, 50 figs., 11 tables.

TCHERNOV, EITAN   See also: Savage, R. J. G. and Tchernov, E., 1968A.

TCHOUMAKOV, I. S. (= CHUMAKOV, I. S.) and ALEXEEVA, L. I.
1971A   Un nouveaux gisement de mammifères villafranchiens en Tunisie. Lyons, Fac. Sci., Lab. Géol., Doc.,
           45, 149—151 (French).

TEDFORD, RICHARD H.
1961B   Tertiary land mammals from Australia. Austral. Mammal Soc., Bull., 1:4, 14—18.
1967C   Ruben Arthur Stirton, 1901—1966. Austral. Mammal Soc., Bull., 2:4, 92—93.
1970A   Principles and practices of mammalian geochronology in North America. N. Amer. Paleontol. Conv.,
           Proc., Part F, 666—703, 7 figs.
1971A   Marsupials and global tectonics. Geol. Soc. Amer., Abstr., 3:7, 730—731 (abs.).

TEICHERT, CURT
1965A   Devonian rocks and paleogeography of central Arizona. U.S. Geol. Surv., Prof. Paper, 464,
           v + 181 pp., 40 figs., 32 pls., 8 tables.

TEICHERT, CURT   See also: Kummel, B. and Teichert, C., 1970A, 1970B.

TEICHERT, MANFRED
1971A   Die Knochenreste aus der Wildpferdjägerstation Bad Frankenhausen. Alt-Thüring., Mus. Ur-
           Frühgesch., Jahresschr., 11, 227—234, 5 tables (German).

TEILHARD DE CHARDIN, P.
1964C   Auswahl aus dem Werk. Freiburg i. Br.: Walter Press, Das moderne Sachbuch, 25, 307 pp. (German).
1969A   Comment je crois. Paris: Ed. du Seuil, 294 pp., 5 figs., 1 portr. (French).

TEJKAL, JIŘÍ
1970A   K šedesátinám doc. dr. Vladimíra Kalabise. [Sixty years of Dr. Vladimír Kalabis.] Czech., Ústřed.
         Ústav Geol., Vestn., 45, 243—246 (Czech).

TEJKAL, JIŘÍ   See also: Cicha, I., Seneš, J. and Tejkal, J., et al., 1967A.

TEKKAYA, İBRAHIM
1969A   Preliminary report on the Bovidae fauna from Kayadibi, Kenya. Maden Tetkik Arama Enst. (Miner.
         Res. Explor. Inst. Turk.), Bull. (Foreign Ed.) 73, 140—144, 5 pls.
1970A   A horn-core of Gazella deperdita Gervais (n. var.) from middle Sinap. Maden Tetkik Arama Enst.
         (Miner. Res. Explor. Inst. Turk.), Bull. (Foreign Ed.), 74, 59—60, 1 pl.

TELEPNEVA, V. P.
1964A   Novye dannye o pliotsenovykh cherepakhakh Moldavii i Ukrainy. [New data on Pliocene turtles of
         Moldavia and Ukraine.] In: Voprosy gerpetologii (Russian).

TELLES ANTUNES, MIGUEL
1960C   Notes sur la géologie et la paléontologie du Miocène de Lisbonne. II. Carnassiers fissipèdes. Soc.
         Geol. Port., Bol., 13, 269—292, 7 figs., 5 pls., 7 tables (French; English summary).
1961F   Notes sur la géologie et la paléontologie du Miocène de Lisbonne. III. Cainotherium. Soc. Geol.
         Port., Bol., 14, 73—82, 1 pl., 2 tables (French; English summary).
1966E   Notes sur la géologie et la paléontologie du Miocène de Lisbonne. V. Un schizotheriiné du genre
         Phyllotillon (Chalicotherioidea, Perissodactyla) dans l'Helvétien V-b de Charneca do Lumiar.
         Remarques écologiques sur la faune de mammifères. Soc. Geol. Port., Bol., 16:1—2, 159—178,
         2 figs., 2 pls., 2 tables (French).
1970A   Sur Lamna cattica ssp. totuserrata. Un cas de distribution antiéquatoriale. Lisbon, Univ., Fac. Ciênc.,
         Rev., Sér. 2, C (Ciênc. Natur.), 16:1, 37—62, 7 figs., 6 pls. (French; English summary).
1970B   Mamíferos não marinhos do Miocénico de Lisboa: ecología e estratigrafía. (Nota preliminar). Soc.
         Geol. Port., Bol. (1969—1970), 17:1, 75—85 (Portuguese).

TELLES ANTUNES, M. and JONET, S.
1970A   Requins de l'Helvétien supérieur et du Tortonien de Lisbonne. Lisbon, Univ., Fac. Ciênc., Rev.,
         Sér. 2, C (Ciênc. Natur.), 16:1, 119—280, 14 figs., 1 table, 20 pls. (French).
         Rev.: Weiler in Zentralbl. Geol. Paläontol., Teil 2, 1971:5, 395—397.

TELLES ANTUNES, M. and MEIN, PIERRE
1971A   Notes sur la géologie et la paléontologie du Miocène de Lisbonne. IX. Rongeurs et insectivores
         (Burdigalien inférieur et Helvétien inférieur). Lisbon, Univ., Fac. Ciênc., Rev., Sér. 2, C
         (Ciênc. Natur.), 16:2, 327—349, 1 fig., 4 pls., 1 table (French; English summary).

TELLES ANTUNES, M. and TORQUATO, JOAQUIM RAÚL
1970A   Notes sur la géologie et la paléontologie du Miocène de Lisbonne. VI. La coupe de Quinta da
         Silvéria (Helvétien V-b et V-c): stratigraphie et évolution morphologique. Soc. Geol. Port.,
         Bol. (1969—1970), 17:1, 1—30 (French).

TEMPLADO, JOAQUÍN
1968A   Los primeros esquemas filogenéticos del reino animal. Soc. Espñ. Hist. Natur., Bol., Secc. Biol.,
         66:3—4, 177—182, 2 figs. (Spanish).
1969A   Las ideas evolucionistas de Lamarck. Arbor, 73:283—284, 41—53 (Spanish).
1971A   El curso de la evolución. Arbor, 78:301, 7—16 (Spanish).

TEMPLE, PAUL H.
1969A   Some biological implications of a revised geological history for Lake Victoria. Linn. Soc., Biol. J.,
         1:4, 363—371.

TERZEA, ELENA
1968A   Observații asupra speciilor de Lagurus descoperite în pleistocenul României. [Remarks on the species
         of Lagurus discovered in Rumanian Pleistocene.] Acad. Repub. Soc. Rom. Inst. Speol. "Emil
         Racoviță", Lucr., 7, 271—290, 6 figs., 3 tables (Rumanian; French summary).
1972A   Sur la présence du genre Lemmus (Rodentia, Mammalia) dans le Pléistocène de la Roumanie. Folia
         Quaternaria, 40, 57—65, 3 figs., 1 table (French; Polish and Russian summaries).

TERZEA, ELENA and JURCSÁK, TIBERIU
1967A   Asupra unui nou punct fosilifer descoperit la Betfia. [On a new fossiliferous site discovered at
         Betfia.] Acad. Repub. Soc. Rom., Inst. Speol. "Emil Rakoviță", Lucr., 6, 193—209, 6 figs.
         (Rumanian; French summary).

1968A   Bermerkungen über die mittelpleistozänen Faunen von Betfia. Deut. Ges. Geol. Wiss., Ber., Reihe A, 13:3, 381–390, 1 table (German).

1969A   Contribuţii la cunoaşterea faunelor pleistocene medii de la Betfia (România). [Contribution to the knowledge of Middle Pleistocene faunas of Betfia (Rumania).] Acad. Repub. Soc. Rom., Inst. Speol. "Emil Rakoviţă", Lucr., 8, 201–214, 3 pls., 2 tables (Rumanian; French summary).
           Rev.: Thenius in Zentralbl. Geol. Paläontol., Teil 2, 1970:6, 517.

TERZEA, ELENA   See also: Dumitrescu, M., Samson, P., Terzea, E., Rădulescu, C. and Ghica, M., 1963A.

TESLENKO, IÛRIĬ VLADIMIROVICH   See: Gurari, F. G., Zal'tsman, G., Teslenko, Iu. V. and Shatskiĭ, S. B., 1968A, 1968B.

TESSIER, F., HEBRARD, L. and LAPPARTIENT, J.-R.
1971A   Découverte de fragments d'oeufs de *Psammornis* et de *Struthio* dans le Quaternaire de la presqu'île du Cap Blanc (République Islamique de Mauritanie). Acad. Sci., C.R., Sér. D, 273:25, 2418–2421 (French).

TESSMAN, NORM
1969A   Fossil land carnivores of Florida. Plaster Jacket, 11, 14 pp., 9 figs.

TESSMAN, NORM   See also: Webb, S. D. and Tessman, N., 1968A.

TETIÛKHIN, G. F.   See: Islamov, A. I. and Tetiûkhin, G. F., 1969A.

TEWARI, B. S. and BADAM, G. L.
1969A   A new species of fossil turtle from the upper Siwaliks of Pinjore, India. Palaeontology, 12:4, 555–558, 2 figs., 1 table.

TEWARI, B. S., CHATURVEDI, M. N. and SINGH, M. P.
1968A   Two new species of shark teeth from Gaj beds of Matanumarh, Kutch. J. Palaeontol. Soc. India, 5–9, 74–76, 1 pl., 1 table.

TEXIER, ALAIN   See: Lassarade, L., Rouvreau, M. and Texier, A., 1969A.

TEZUKA, HIDEO and ISHIBASHI, ICHIRO
1971A   An exhibition of the evolution of life at the National Science Museum. Natur. Sci. and Mus., 38:1–2, 46–61, 13 figs. (Japanese).

THALER, LOUIS
1965A   Rev.: Adrover in Teruel, 35, 167.
1969A   Rongeurs nouveaux de l'Oligocène moyen d'Espagne. Palaeovertebrata (Montpellier), 2:5, 191–207, 9 figs. (French; English and German summaries).
1971A   Les dinosaures: au sec! Sci. Progrès Découverte, 3431, 30 (French).
1971B   Les hommes de l'Omo. Sci. Progrès Découverte, 3433, 32–33, 2 figs. (French).
1972A   Les rongeurs (Rodentia et Lagomorpha) du Monte Pellegrino et la question des anciens isthmes de la Sicile. Acad. Sci., C.R., Sér. D, 274:2, 188–190, 2 pls. (French).

THALER, LOUIS   See also: Crusafont, M., Golpe, J.-M., Gibert, J. and Thaler, L., 1971A.

THENIUS, ERICH
1959B   Rev.: Hacquaert in Natuurwet. Tijdschr., 41:5, 153.
1960C   *Equus (Asinus) hydruntinus* Reg. aus dem Jungpleistozän von Brünn (Brno, ČSSR). Anthropos, Brno, 1960 Suppl., 137–142, 3 figs., 3 tables (German; Russian summary).
1966G   Die Teufels- oder Fuchsenlucken bei Eggenburg (NÖ.). 5. Die Cervidae und Perissodactyla (Equidae, Rhinocerotidae). Österreich. Akad. Wiss., Denk., 112, 61–82, 5 pls., 4 tables (German).
1968A   Zur systematischen Stellung von *Kyzylkakhippus* (Perissodactyla, Mamm.) aus dem Oligozän von Kasachstan. Österreich. Akad. Wiss., Math.-Natur. Kl., Anz., 105, 347–354, 2 figs. (German).
           Rev.: Thenius in Zentralbl. Geol. Paläontol., Teil 2, 1970:3/4, 246.
1968B   Emil Weinfurter. Geol. Ges. Wien, Mitt., 61, 188–191 (German).
1969A   Othmar Kühn 5.11.1892–26.3.1969. Palaeontol. Z., 43:3/4, 113–114 (German).
1969B   Über das Vorkommen fossiler Schneeleoparden (Subgenus *Uncia*, Carnivora, Mammalia). Säugetierkundl. Mitt., 17:3, 234–242, 2 figs., 1 table (German; English summary).
           Rev.: Thenius in Zentralbl. Geol. Paläontol., Teil 2, 1970:5, 437.
1969C   Über einige Probleme der Stammesgeschichte der Säugetiere. Z. Zool. Syst. Evolut.-Forsch., 7:3, 157–179, 9 figs. (German; English summary).
           Rev.: Thenius in Zentralbl. Geol. Paläontol., Teil 2, 1970:5, 437–438.

1969D   Stammesgeschichte der Säugetiere (einschliesslich der Hominiden). Handb. Zool., Bd. 8, Teil 2(1), nos. 47—48, 722 pp., 715 figs. (German).

    Rev.: Claude in Naturforsch. Ges. Zürich, Vierteljahrsschr., 115:4, 488—489; Fantini Sestini in Riv. Ital. Paleontol. Stratigr., 76:4, 628—629; Halle in Gegenbaurs Morph. Jahrb., 116:1, 144—145; Heinemann in Umsch. Wiss. Tech., 72:3, 103; Kahmann in Säugetierkundl. Mitt., 20:1—2, 190; Kruska in Z. Säugetierkunde, 36:5, 318—319; Kühnelt in Zool.-Bot. Ges. Wien, Verh., 110/111, 188—189; Storch in Natur Mus., 101:3, 138; Zapfe in Geol. Ges. Wien, Mitt., 62, 220—221.

1970A   Paläontologie. Stuttgart: Franckh'sche Verlags., 143 pp., 49 figs.

    Rev.: Sittig in Aufschluss, 21:12, 385—386; Thomas in Naturforsch. Ges. Zürich, Vierteljahrsschr., 115:4, 488; Westphal in Naturwiss. Rundsch., 23, 440; Zapfe in Geol. Ges. Wien, Mitt., 62, 220.

1970B   Ergebnisse der Bearbeitung von *Microstonyx antiquus* (Suidae, Mammalia) aus dem Alt-Pliozän von Niederösterreich. Österreich. Akad. Wiss., Math.-Naturwiss. Kl., Anz., 107:3, 65—68 (German).

    Rev.: Thenius in Zentralbl. Geol. Paläontol., Teil 2, 1971:1, 72.

1970C   Einige jungpleistozäne Säugetiere *(Platygonus, Arctodus* und *Canis dirus)* aus dem Valsequillo, Mexico. Quartär, 21, 57—66, 4 figs. (German).

    Rev.: Thenius in Zentralbl. Geol. Paläontol., Teil 2, 1971:5, 413.

1970D   Zur Evolution und Verbreitungsgeschichte der Suidae (Artiodactyla, Mammalia). Z. Säugetierkunde, 35:6, 321—342, 5 figs., 1 table (German; English summary).

    Rev.: Thenius in Zentralbl. Geol. Paläontol., Teil 2, 1971:2—3, 201.

1971A   Sozialverhalten vorzeitlicher Schweine. Umschau, 71:7, 248, 2 figs. (German).

1971B   Zum gegenwärtigen Verbreitungsbild der Säugetiere und seiner Deutung in erdgeschichtlicher Sicht. Natur Mus., 101:5, 185—196, 5 figs. (German; English summary).

    Rev.: Thenius in Zentralbl. Geol. Paläontol., Teil 2, 1971:6, 506—507.

1972A   Säugetierausbreitung in der Vorzeit. Umsch. Wiss. Tech., 72:5, 148—153, 4 figs., 1 chart (German; English summary).

1972B   Versteinerte Urkunden. Second edition. Verständ. Wiss., 81, xii + 211 pp., 89 figs. (German).

    Rev.: Laufeld in Geol. Fören. Stockholm, Förh., 94:3, 475—476.

1972C   Grundzüge der Verbreitungsgeschichte der Säugetiere. Jena: Gustav Fischer Verlag, 345 pp., 115 figs., 6 tables (German).

    Rev.: Dorst in Mammalia, 36:1, 169—170; Haltenorth in Säugetierkundl. Mitt., 20:1—2, 190; Reinig in Kosmos, 68:6, 195.

THÉOBALD, NICOLAS

1969A   La vie et l'oeuvre de Georges Cuvier. [The life and work of Georges Cuvier.] Besançon, Univ., Ann. Sci., Sér. 3, 6, 3—8 (French).

1970A   Chronologie des dépôts quaternaires à l'est de Rosheim et de Bischoffsheim (B.-R.). Ass. Fr. Étude Quat., Bull., 7:22, 35—39, 1 pl. (French).

THÉOBALD, N., BLANC, M. and DAVID, E.

s.d.   Découverte d'ossements de dynosaures *Plateosaurus* cf. *polignensis* (Pidancet et Chopard) dans les marnes irisées supérieures des environs de Salins (Jura). Soc. Hist. Natur. Doubs, s.d., 21—25, 2 figs. (French).

THÉOBALD, N. and GAMA, A.

1969A   Paléontologie. Éléments de paléobiologie. Paris: Éditions Doin, 584 pp., 299 figs., 40 pls. (French).

THOMA, ANDOR

1969A   Le caractère aromorphotique de l'évolution humaine à la lumière des nouveaux fossiles. Symp. Biol. Hungarica, 9, 39—46 (French).

1969B   Biometrische Studie über das Occipitale von Vértesszöllös. Z. Morphol. Anthropol., 60:3, 229—241, 3 figs., 4 tables (German; English summary).

    Rev.: Vallois in L'Anthropologie, 74:3—4, 285—286.

1972A   On Vértesszöllös man. Nature, 236:5348, 264—265.

1972B   Cranial capacity, taxonomical and phylogenetical status of Vértesszöllös man. J. Human Evol., 1:5, 511—512.

THOMAS, DAVID H.

1969A   Great Basin hunting patterns: a quantitative method for treating faunal remains. Amer. Antiquity, 34, 392—401, 1 fig., 2 tables.

THOMAS, HOMER L.   See: Laet, S. J. de and Thomas, H. L. (eds.), 1969A.

THOMEL, GÉRARD   See: Bidar, A., Demay, L. and Thomel, G., 1972A, 1972B.

THOMPSON, O. P.   See: Air, G. M., Thompson, O. P., Richardson, B. J. and Sharman, G. B., 1971A.

THOMSON, KEITH STEWART
 1968C   A critical review of the diphyletic theory of rhipidistian-amphibian relationships. Discussion:
            H. Szarski. Nobel Symp., 4th, Stockholm, 1967, Proc., 1968, 285—306, 11 figs.
            Rev.: Westphal in Zentralbl. Geol. Paläontol., Teil 2, 1969:2, 209.
 1968D   Experiments on lungfish respiration. Discovery, 4:1, 13—18, 3 figs.
 1969A   The environment and distribution of Paleozoic sarcopterygian fishes. Amer. J. Sci., 267:4, 457—464,
            1 fig., 1 table.
 1969B   The biology of the lobe-finned fishes. Biol. Rev., 44:1, 91—154, 11 figs., 3 tables.
 1971A   The adaptation and evolution of early fishes. Quart. Rev. Biol., 46:2, 139—166, 13 figs.
 1972A   Identification of the sensory components in cosmine. Soc. Vert. Paleontol., Ann. Meeting, 32nd,
            1972, Abstr. (abs.).

THOMSON, K. S. and BOSSY, K. H.
 1970A   Adaptive trends and relationships in early Amphibia. Forma et Functio, 3, 7—31, 8 figs. (French
            and German summaries).

THOMSON, K. S. and CAMPBELL, K. S. W.
 1971A   The structure and relationships of the primitive Devonian lungfish - Dipnorhinchus süssmilchi
            (Etheridge). Yale Univ., Peabody Mus. Natur. Hist., Bull., 38, 109 pp., 95 figs. (German and
            Russian summaries).

THOMSON, K. S. and VAUGHN, P. P.
 1968A   Vertebral structure in Rhipidistia (Osteichthyes, Crossopterygii) with description of a new Permian
            genus. Postilla, 127, 1—19, 10 figs.

THORNE, A. G.
 1972A   Recent discoveries of fossil man in Australia. Austral. Natur. Hist., 17:6, 191—195, 5 figs.

THORNE, A. G. and MACUMBER, P. G.
 1972A   Discoveries of late Pleistocene man at Kow Swamp, Australia. Nature, 238:5363, 316—319, 4 figs.,
            4 tables.

THORNE, A. G.   See also: Bowler, J. M., Jones, R., Allen, H. and Thorne, A. G., 1970A; Bowler, J. M.,
            Thorne, A. G. and Polach, H. A., 1972A.

THORNLEY, A. L.
 1970A   Epidermal remnants of Proterosuchus vanhoepeni. Palaeontol. Afr., 13, 57—60, 6 figs.

THUILLIER, PIERRE
 1972A   L'évolutionnisme entre le mythe et la science. La Recherche, 3:26, 787—790, 4 figs. (French).

THULBORN, RICHARD A.
 1970A   The skull of Fabrosaurus australis, a Triassic ornithischian dinosaur. Palaeontology, 13:3, 414—432,
            9 figs.
 1970B   The systematic position of the Triassic ornithischian dinosaur Lycorhinus angustidens. Linn. Soc.,
            Zool. J., 49, 235—245, 5 figs.
 1971A   Origins and evolution of ornithischian dinosaurs. Nature, 234:5324, 75—78, 4 figs.
 1971B   Tooth wear and jaw action in the Triassic ornithischian dinosaur Fabrosaurus. J. Zool., 164:2, 165—
            179, 9 figs.
 1972A   The post-cranial skeleton of the Triassic ornithischian dinosaur Fabrosaurus australis. Palaeontology,
            15:1, 29—60, 14 figs.

THURBER, D. L.   See: Butzer, K. W., Brown, F. H. and Thurber, D. L., 1969A; Butzer, K. W. and Thurber,
            D. L., 1969A.

THURMOND, JOHN T.
 1969A   New name for the mosasaur Compressidens Dollo, 1924. J. Paleontol., 43:5, 1298.
 1969B   Notes on mosasaurs from Texas. Tex. J. Sci., 21:1, 69—80, 2 figs., 1 table.
 1970A   Lower vertebrates and paleoecology of the Trinity group (lower Cretaceous) in north central Texas.
            Diss. Abstr., 31:4, 2156B (abs.).
 1971A   Stratigraphic significance of lower vertebrate faunas from the Trinity group (lower Cretaceous), north
            central Texas. Geol. Soc. Amer., Abstr., 3:5, 352—353 (abs.).
 1971B   Cartilagenous fishes of the Trinity group and related rocks (lower Cretaceous) of north central Texas.
            Southeast. Geol., 13:4, 207—227, 14 figs.
 1972A   Ciudad Real fauna, late Pleistocene, from the Guatemalan highlands. Soc. Vert. Paleontol., Ann.
            Meeting, 32nd, 1972, Abstr. (abs.).

TIEGHEM, ABBÉ G.
1969A   La préhistoire du Nord et du Pas-de-Calais: aperçu d'ensemble. Soc. Géol. Nord, Ann., 89:1, 127–
         129 (French; English summary).

TIGER, LIONEL and FOX, ROBIN
1971A   The imperial animal. New York: Holt, Rinehart and Winston, xii + 308 pp.
         Rev.: Barnard in Nature, 235:2333, 114–115; Eisenberg in Science, 175:4019, 289; Shapiro in
         Natur. Hist., 80:8, 90–98.

TIKHIĬ, VSEVOLOD NIKOLAEVICH
1972A   Chto zhe prinadlezhit eĭfel'skomu ĭarusu na Russkoĭ platforme? [What does finally belong to the
         Eifelian stage on the Russian platform?] Sov. Geol., 15:6, 33–44, 1 fig. (Russian).

TIKHOMIROV, B. A.   See: Garutt, V. E., Metel'tseva, E. P. and Tikhomirov, B. A., 1970A.

TIKHVINSKAĬA, E. I.
1967A   Permskaĭa sistema. Kazanskiĭ ĭarus. [Permian system. Kazanian stage.] Geologiĭa SSSR, 11,
         Povolzh'e and Prikam'e, 369–395, 4 figs. (Russian).

TIMASHEV, I. E.
1972A   O stratigrafii pleĭstotsena zapadnoĭ okrainy Ĭano-Indigirskoĭ nizmennosti. [On Pleistocene stratigraphy
         of the western border of Ĭana-Indigirka lowlands.] Vyssh. Ucheb. Zaved., Izv., Geol. Razved.,
         1972:10, 21–25 (Russian).

TIMLIN, JOSEPH P. and RAEMSCH, B. E.
1971A   Pleistocene tools from the northeast of North America. The Timlin site. Yager Mus., Publ. Anthropol.,
         Bull., 3, 21 pp., 39 figs., 1 table.

TIMOFEEV, E. M., STEKLOV, A. A. and ALEKSEEVA, L. I.
1970A   O prisutstvii pliotsenovykh otlozheniĭ na mezhdurech'e Pechory i Vychegdy. [On the presence of
         Pliocene deposits on the interfluve Pechora and Vychegda.] Prirodn. Obstan. i Fauny Proshl.,
         5, 160–165 (Russian).

TIMOFEEV-RESOVSKIĬ, N. V., VORONTSOV, N. N. and ĬABLOKOV, A. V.
1969A   Kratkiĭ ocherk teorii evoliutsii. [An outline of evolutionary concepts.] Moscow: "Nauka" Press,
         407 pp., 129 figs., 10 tables (Russian).
         Rev.: Bruckmoser in Naturwiss., 58:7, 375–376; Dobzhansky in Quart. Rev. Biol., 45:2, 189;
         Grebenščikov in Biol. Zentralbl., 89:1, 132–133; Polĭanskiĭ in Zh. Obshch. Biol., 31:3, 365–
         367 (Russian); Starobogatov in Zool. Zh., 49:5, 803–804; Zenkevich in Priroda, 1970:10,
         114–115.

TIMUSH, A. V.
1965A   K stratigrafii paleogena i neogena tsentral'noĭ chasti Iliĭskoĭ vpadiny. [On the stratigraphy of
         Paleogene and Neogene in the central part of Ili depression.] In: Materialy po geologii i
         poleznym iskopaemym Ĭuzhnogo Kazakhstana, 3, 51–61 (Russian).

TINÈ, S.
1968A   Balzi Rossi (Grimaldi). Riv. Sci. Preist., 23:2, 394–395 (Italian).

TING, MENG-LIN, et al.
1965A   Abs.: Sci. Abstr. China, Earth Sci., 3:2, 4.

TINTANT, HENRI
1969A   L'espèce et le temps. Point de vue du paléontologiste. Soc. Zool. Fr., Bull., 94:4, 559–576, 1 pl.
         (French).

TITAEVA, N. A.
1970A   Nekotorye dannye po opredeleniĭu vozrasta chetvertichnykh otlozheniĭ ionievym metodom (po kostnym
         ostatkam). [Some data on age determination of Quaternary deposits by the Ionium method
         (on bone remains).] Mosk. Univ., Vestn., Ser. Geol., 1970:4, 65–69, 3 tables (Russian).

TITKOV, A. S.   See: Baranova, Ĭu. P., Biske, S. F., Goncharov, V. F., Kulkova, I. A. and Titkov, A. S., 1968A.

TITLBACHOVÁ, S.   See: Fetter, V., Prokopec, M., Suchy, J. and Titlbachová, S., 1967A.

TIWARI, KRISHNA KANT
 1969A   A new fossil percoid fish from the lower Tertiary Fuller's earth deposits of Kapurdi, Barmer district,
         Rajasthan. Zool. Soc. India, J. (1968), 20:1–2, 95–103, 2 figs., 1 pl.

TLEGENOV, T. T. and TROFIMOV, V. I.
 1970A   O drevnem areale bol'shoĭ peschanki *(Rhombomys opimus)* v Prikaspiĭskoĭ nizmennosti. [Ancient range
         of the great gerbil *(Rhombomys opimus)* in the Caspian lowlands.] Zool. Zh., 49:7, 1101–1104,
         2 figs., 2 tables (Russian; English summary).

TOBIAS, PHILLIP V.
 1967A   Rev.: Fagan in Archaeology, 21:4, 310–314; Heberer in Homo, 19:1, 49; Howell in Amer. Anthropol.,
         70, 1028–1030; Steegmann in Asian Perspectives, 10, 181–182.
 1968D   The taxonomy and phylogeny of the Australopithecines. In: Chiarelli, B. (ed.), 1968C, 277–315,
         9 figs.
 1968E   The pattern of venous sinus grooves in the robust australopithecines and other fossil and modern
         hominoids. In: K. Saller Festschrift, 1968, 1–10, 7 figs., 1 table.
 1969A   Bigeneric nomina: A proposal for modification of the rules of nomenclature. Amer. J. Phys.
         Anthropol., 31, 103–105.
 1969B   Early man in East Africa. In: Ehrlich, P. R., *et al.* (eds.), 1969A, 496–522, 12 figs., 4 tables.
 1971A   The brain in hominid evolution. New York: Columbia University Press, xviii + 170 pp., 36 figs.,
         17 tables.
         Rev.: Pilbeam in Science, 175:4026, 1101.
 1971B   The Olduvai Bed I hominine with special reference to its cranial capacity. In: Leakey, L. S. B.,
         Prost, J. and Prost, S. (eds.), 1971A, 439–442, 2 figs., 1 table (reprinted from Nature, April
         1964).
 1972A   "Dished faces", brain size and early hominids. Nature, 239:5373, 468–469.
 1972B   Progress and problems in the study of early man in sub-Saharan Africa. In: Tuttle, R. (ed.), 1972A,
         63–93, 4 figs., 9 tables.

TOBIAS, P. V. and HUGHES, A. R.
 1969A   The new Witwatersrand University excavation at Sterkfontein. S. Afr. Archaeol. Bull., 24:95–96,
         158–169, 2 figs., 5 pls.

TOBIAS, P. V.   See also: Leakey, L. S. B., Tobias, P. V. and Napier, J. R., 1971A; Leakey, M., Tobias, P. V.,
         Martyn, J. E. and Leakey, R. E. F., 1969A.

TOBIEN, HEINZ
 1968G   Typen und Genese tertiärer Säugerlagerstätten. Eclogae Geol. Helv., 61:2, 549–575, 2 figs. (German;
         French and English summaries).
 1968H   Paläontologische Ausgrabungen nach jungtertiären Wirbeltieren auf der Insel Chios (Griechenland) und
         bei Maragheh (NW-Iran) Ver. Freunde Univ. Mainz, Jahrb., 17, 51–58, 7 figs. (German).
 1968I   *Anancus arvernensis* (Croizet et Jobert) und *Mammut borsoni* (Hays) (Proboscidea, Mamm.) aus den
         pleistozänen Mosbacher Sanden bei Wiesbaden (Hessen). Mainzer Naturwiss. Arch., 7, 35–54,
         7 figs., 4 tables (German; English and French summaries).
 1969A   *Kopidodon* (Condylarthra, Mammalia) aus dem Mitteleozän (Lutetium) von Messel bei Darmstadt
         (Hessen). Hess. Landesamt. Bodenforsch., Notizbl., 97, 7–37, 7 figs., 3 pls., 9 tables (German;
         English and French summaries).
 1969B   Wirbeltiergrabungen im Miozän der Insel Chios (Ägäis), 2. vorläufige Mitteilung. Akad. Athenon,
         Praktika, 43, 151–157, 1 pl., 1 map (German; English, French and Greek summaries).
 1969C   Die alttertiäre (mitteleozäne) Fossilfundstätte Messel bei Darmstadt (Hessen). Mainzer Naturwiss. Arch.,
         8, 149–180, 11 figs., 1 table (German; English and French summaries).
 1970A   Biostratigraphy of the mammalian faunas at the Pliocene-Pleistocene boundary in middle and western
         Europe. Palaeogeogr., Palaeoclimatol., Palaeoecol., 8:2–3, 77–93, 2 tables.
 1970B   Subdivision of Pontian mammalian faunas. G. Geol., 35:1, 191–195, 2 figs. (Italian summary).
 1970C   Lagomorpha (Mammalia) im Unter-Miozän des Mainzer Beckens und die Altersstellung der
         Fundschichten. Hess. Landesamt Bodenforsch., Abh., 56:14–36, 5 figs., 2 tables (German;
         French, English summaries).
 1970D   Die mitteleozäne Fossilfundstätte Grube Messel. Chronik der Grube Messel, 1970, 33–42, 8 figs.,
         1 table (German).
 1971A   Mikromammalier aus dem Melanienton von Nordhessen. Teil 1: Marsupialia, Insectivora, Primates.
         Hess. Landesamt Bodenforsch., Notizbl., 99, 9–29, 1 fig., 3 pls., 2 tables (German; English and
         French summaries).
 1971B   Ein umgelagerter oligozäner Anthracotheriden-Rest (Mammalia) aus den pleistozänen Mosbacher Sanden
         bei Wiesbaden (Hessen). Mainz. Naturwiss. Arch., 10, 203–211, 2 figs., 1 table (German; English
         and French summaries).

1971C   *Moeritherium, Palaeomastodon, Phiomia* aus dem Paläogen Nordafrikas und die Abstammung der
         Mastodonten (Proboscidea, Mammalia). Hanover, Tech. Hochsch., Geol. Inst., Mitt., 10, 141–
         163, 10 figs., 1 table (German; English and French summaries).
1972A   K biostratigrafii Srednei i Zapadnoi Evropy na granitse pliotsena i pleistotsena (po faune
         mlekopitaiushchikh). [On the biostratigraphy of central and western Europe at the limit of
         Pliocene and Pleistocene (according to mammalian fauna).] In: Geologiia i fauna nizhnego i
         srednego pleistotsena Evropy, 45–71 (Russian).

TOBIEN, HEINZ   See also: Melentis, J. K. and Tobien, H., 1970A; Sickenberg, O. and Tobien, H., 1971A.

TODD, ELIZABETH J.   See: Greenwood, P. H. and Todd, E. J., 1970A.

TOEPFER, VOLKER
1954B   Stand und Aufgaben der urgeschichtlichen Erforschung der Harzhöhlen bei Rübeland. Jahresschrift
         Mitteldeutsch. Vorgesch., 38, 1–33, 7 figs., 4 pls. (German).
1968B   Löss – Periglazial – Paläolithikum im Desna-Tal. Bericht über eine Exkursionstagung, 1967. Ethnogr.-
         Archäol. Z., 9:2, 185–189 (German).
1970A   Die Alt- und Mittelsteinzeit im Magdeburger Raum. Jahresschrift Mitteldeutsch. Vorgesch., 54, 57–82,
         10 figs., 3 pls. (German).
1971A   Säugetierfaunen paläolithischer Fundplätze im Gebiet der Deutschen Demokratischen Republik.
         Ausgrabung. u. Funde, 16:1, 7–12 (German).

TOFAN, V. E.   See: Khozatskii, L. I. and Tofan, V. E., 1970A.

TOLOCHKO, V. V. and AUBEKEROVA, PIRUZA ABLAEVNA
1971A   Eotsen-Pliotsenovye otlozheniia srednei chasti basseina r. Aiaguz. [Eocene-Pliocene deposits of the
         central part of the Aiaguz R. basin.] In: Materialy po geologii i poleznym iskopaemym
         iuzhnogo Kazakhstana, 4(29), 154–160 (Russian).

TOMASI, P.   See: Hoffstetter, R., Martinez, C., Muñoz-Reyes, J. and Tomasi, P., 1971A; Hoffstetter, R., Martinez,
         C., Mattauer, M. and Tomasi, P., 1971A; Hoffstetter, R., Martinez, C. and Tomasi, P., 1972A.

TOMIĆ-KAROVIĆ, KRUNA
1969A   Lovac kamennog doba i njegova spiljska umjetnost. [The hunter of the Stone Age and his pictorial
         art.] Priroda (Zagreb), 56:10, 306–312, 9 figs. (Serbocroatian).
1970A   Einige Eigentümlichkeiten und pathologische Veränderungen an den Überresten des Neandertalers von
         Krapina. Krapina, 177–181, 4 figs. (Serbocroatian; German summary).
         Rev.: Kochansky-Devidé in Zentralbl. Geol. Paläontol., Teil 2, 1971:5, 419.
1970B   Neandertaler von Krapina und Kannibalismus. Krapina, 183–187, 3 figs. (Serbocroatian; German
         summary).
         Rev.: Kochansky-Devidé in Zentralbl. Geol. Paläontol., Teil 2, 1971:5, 419.

TOMODA, YOSHIO
1969A   [Origin and evolution of fish. Part I.] Natur. Sci. and Mus., 36:9–10, 219–229, 5 figs. (Japanese).
1970A   [Origin and evolution of fish. Part II.] Natur. Sci. and Mus., 37:3–4, 71–91, 16 figs. (Japanese).

TONNI, EDUARDO P.
1969A   La presencia de *Anas leucophrys* (Aves, Anseriformes) en sedimentos de edad Ensenadense (Pleistoceno
         medio) de la Provincia de Buenos Aires. Ameghiniana, 6:4, 309–313, 1 fig. (Spanish; English
         summary).
1970A   *Foetopterus ambiguus* Moreno et Mercerat, 1891 (Aves, Falconiformes): su assignación a *Chloephaga
         picta* (Aves, Anseriformes). Ameghiniana, 7:3, 279–280, 1 fig. (Spanish).
         Rev.: Kuhn in Zentralbl. Geol. Paläontol., Teil 2, 1972:3, 167.

TOOTS, H.   See: Voorhies, M. R. and Toots, H., 1970A.

TOPACHEVSKII, VADIM ALEKSANDROVICH (= TOPACHEVS'KYI, V. O.)
1971A   Ostatki kitaiskogo belkoobraznogo burunduka (Rodentia, Sciuridae) iz verkhnemiotsenovykh otlozhenii
         Prichernomor'ia Ukrainy. [Remains of chinese striped squirrel (Rodentia, Sciuridae) from the
         upper Miocene deposits of the Ukrainian Black Sea area.] Akad. Nauk Ukr. SSR, Inst. Zool.,
         Vestn. Zool., 1971:4, 46–50, 1 fig. (Russian; English summary).

TOPACHEVS'KYI, V. O. (= TOPACHEVSKII, V. A. = TOPATSHEVSKY)
1962A   Vykopni vykhukholi rodu *Desmana* z neogenovykh ta antropogenovykh vidkladiv Evropeis'koi
         chastyny SRSR. [Fossil desmans of the genus *Desmana* from Neogene and Anthropogene
         deposits of the European part of the USSR.] In: Vykopni fauny Ukrainy i sumizhnykh
         terytorii, 1, 5–90, 16 figs., 25 tables (Ukrainian; Russian summary).

1971B   Davni polivkovi (Rodentia, Microtidae) z pizn'ogo miotsenu Skhidnoĭ Evropy. [Ancient voles
             (Rodentia, Microtidae) from the late Miocene of eastern Europe.] Akad. Nauk Ukr. RSR, Dopo
             Ser. B, 1971:1, 81–83, 1 fig. (Ukrainian; English and Russian summaries).
1971C   *Pseudoalactaga minuta* gen. et sp. nov. - svoeridnyĭ p'iatipalyĭ tushkanchik (Rodentia, Dipodidae) z
             pizn'ogo pliotsenu pivdniă Ukrainy. [*Pseudoalactaga minuta* gen. et sp. nov. - a peculiar five
             toed jerboa (Rodentia, Dipodidae) from late Pliocene of southern Ukraine.] Akad. Nauk Ukr.
             RSR, Dopov., Ser. B, 1971:2, 175–177, 1 fig. (Ukrainian; English and Russian summaries).

TOPACHEVS'KYĬ, V. O. and SKORYK, O. F.
1971A   Novyĭ rid p'iatypalogo tushkanchyka z verkhn'opliotsenovykh vidkladiv pivdniă Ukrainy. [A new genu
             of pentadactyl jerboa from the upper Pliocene deposits of southern Ukraine.] Akad. Nauk Ukr.
             RSR, Zool. Muz., Zb. Praĉs', 34, 112–120, 12 figs., 1 table (Ukrainian; Russian and English
             summaries).

TOPINARD, PAUL
1972A   The origin of man. In: McCown, T. D. and Kennedy, K. A. R. (eds.), 1972A, 166–181 (reprinted
             from Topinard, 1876).

TOPORKOV, V. ÎA.   See: Glazyrina, N. S. and Toporkov, V. Îa., 1971A.

TORQUATO, JOAQUIM RAÚL   See: Telles Antunes, M. and Torquato, J. R., 1970A.

TORRE, D.
1967B   Analisi di alcune differenze nell'apparato masticatorio dei leoni e delle pantere. Soc. Toscana Sci.
             Natur., Atti, Mem., Ser. B, 74, 59–67, 6 figs., 3 pls., 2 tables (Italian; English summary).
             Rev.: Albanesi in Riv. Ital. Paleontol. Stratigr., 74:4, 1321.

TORRE, D.   See also: De Giuli, C., Ficcarelli, G. and Torre, D., 1970A; Ficcarelli, G. and Torre, D., 1967B,
             1968A, 1970A.

TORRES PEREZHIDALGO, T. J. DE (= TORRES, T. DE)
1969A   Un hiénido de las cavernas de Pedraza de la Sierra (Segovia). Spain, Inst. Geol. Mineró, Bol. Geol.
             Minero, 80:3, 29–32, 9 figs. (Spanish; French summary).
1971A   Fauna fósil de la "Cueva de los Muñecos", Abenojar (Ciudad Real). Bol. Geol. Min., España, 82:1,
             37–46, 19 figs. (Spanish; French and English summaries).

TORRES PEREZHIDALGO, T. J. DE   See also: Espejo, J. A. and Torres, T. de, 1969A.

TORREY, THEODORE W.
1971A   Morphogenesis of the vertebrates. Third edition. New York: Wiley and Co., 529 pp., illustr.
             Rev.: Griffith in J. Natur. Hist., London, 6:1, 119–120.

TOSHCHAKOVA, E. M.   See: Okladnikov, A. P., Vasil'evskiĭ, R. S., Larichev, V. E., Dereviănko, A. P.,
             Gogolev, Z. V. and Toshchakova, E. M., 1969A.

TOTTEN, DAVID K., JR.
1969A   A middle Miocene shark of the genus *Isurus* from the Topanga formation, Griffith Park, Los Angeles,
             California. S. Calif. Paleontol. Soc., Bull., 1:3, 3–4, 1 fig.

TOURAINE, FERNAND
1968A   Sul l'âge oligocène des sables bleutés du Var. Soc. Géol. Fr., C.R., 1968:2, 29–31, 1 fig. (French).
1970A   Sur une contestation de l'âge oligocène des couches terminales du Cengle (Bouches-du-Rhône). Soc.
             Géol. Fr., C.R., 1970:4, 113–114 (French).
1971A   Présence d'un poisson Cyprinidés, *Barbus rudeli* Piton 1936, dans les calcaires "à Bithynies" du Var.
             Soc. Géol. Fr., C.R., 1971:6, 329 (French).
1972A   Présence d'un poisson Cyprinidé, *Barbus rudeli* Piton 1936, dans les calcaires "à Bithynies" du Var.
             Besançon, Univ., Ann. Sci., Sér. 3, 16(1971), 97–99, 1 pl. (French).

TOWERS, BERNARD   See: Lewis, J. and Towers, B., 1969A.

TOZZI, CARLO
1965B   La Grotta del Colombo a Toirano. Riv. Studi Liguri, 31:1–2, 5–43, 22 figs. (Italian).
1969A   Segnalazione di una grotta con fauna fossile a Borgio (Savona). Soc. Toscana Sci. Natur., Atti, Mem.,
             Ser. A, 76, 195–208, 3 figs. (Italian; English summary).
1970A   La grotta di S. Agostino (Gaeta). Riv. Sci. Preist., 25:1, 3–87, 13 figs., 7 tables (Italian; French and
             English summaries).

TRACEY, JOSHUA I., JR.   See: Oriel, Steven S. and Tracey, Joshua I., Jr., 1970A.

TREISTMAN, JUDITH M.
1972A   The prehistory of China. Garden City, New York: Doubleday and Co., Inc., 156 pp., 22 figs.

TRET'IAKOV, P. N.
1970A   Petr Petrovich Efimenko. 1884—1969. Sov. Arkheol., 1970:1, 310—312, portr. (Russian).

TRETTIN, H. P.
1969A   Pre-Mississippian geology of northern Axel Heiberg and northwestern Ellesmere islands, Arctic
         archipelago. Can., Geol. Surv., Bull., 171, 82 pp., 11 figs., 4 pls., 3 maps, 13 tables (French
         summary).

TRIAT, J.-M., TRUC, G. and HUGUENEY, M.
1971A   Lithostratigraphie des couches d'âge oligocène inférieur et moyen constituant le toit du gypse dans la
         carrière de Malemort (Vaucluse): données sédimentologiques et paléontologiques. Provence,
         Univ., Ann., Sci., 46, 235—246, 1 chart (French; English summary).

TRIMMEL, HUBERT
1968A   Höhlenkunde. Braunschweig: Friedr. Vieweg & Sohn, 300 pp., 88 figs. (German).
         Rev.: Salzer in Geol. Ges. Wien, Mitt., 62, 223—224.

TRIPATHI, C.
1967A   The Pleistocene alluvial deposits around Nevasa Ahmadnagar district, Maharashtra. Geol. Surv. India,
         Rec., 95:2, 355—366, 6 pls., 1 table.

TRISCHLER, J. and WINKLER, H.
1968A   Eine neue unteroligozäne Spaltenfüllung. Bayer. Staatssamml. Paläontol. Hist. Geol., Mitt., 8, 323—
         326, 1 fig., 1 table (German).

TROFIMOV, BORIS ALEKSANDROVICH
1969A   Pamiati Zhorzha Kiuv'e. (K 200-letiiu so dnia rozhdeniia. [In memoriam to Georges Cuvier
         (commemoration of 200th birth anniversary).] Paleontol. Zh., 1969:4, 114—117 (Russian).
1971A*   Fauna mezozoia i kainozoia Zapadnoi Mongolii. [Mesozoic and Cenozoic fauna of western Mongolia.]
         Sovm. Sovet.-Mongol. Nauch.-Issled. Geol. Eksped., Tr., 3, 136 pp., illustr.

TROFIMOV, BORIS ALEKSANDROVICH and CHUDINOV, PETR KONSTANTINOVICH
1970A   Novye dannye o mestonakhozhdeniiakh pozvonochnykh Mongolii. [New data on Mongolian vertebrate
         localities.] In: Materialy po evoliutsii nazemnykh pozvonochnykh, 152—160 (Russian).

TROFIMOV, B. A.   See also: Nikonov, A. A., Pen'kov, A. V., Trofimov, B. A., Vangengeim, E. A., Dmitrieva,
         E. A. and Sotnikova, M. V., 1971A.

TROFIMOV, D. M.   See: Gatinskii, Iu. G., Gerus, E. A., Klochko, V. P. and Trofimov, D. M., 1967A.

TROFIMOV, V. I.   See: Tlegenov, T. T. and Trofimov, V. I., 1970A.

TRÖGER, KARL-ARMIN
1969A   Zur Paläontologie, Biostratigraphie und faziellen Ausbildung der unteren Oberkreide (Cenoman bis
         Turon). Teil II. Stratigraphie und fazielle Ausbildung des Cenomans und Turons in Sachsen,
         dem nördlichen Harzvorland (subherzyne Kreide) und dem Ohm-Gebirge. Dresden, Staatl. Mus.
         Mineral. Geol. Abh., 13, 1—70, 7 figs., 18 maps and charts, 15 tables (German).

TROPIN, N. N.
1971A   Proshloe rasprostranenie bol'shoi peschanki (Rhombomys opimus) v Volgo-Ural'skom mezhdurech'e i
         ee veroiatnoe epizootologicheskoe znachenie. [Past distribution of the great gerbil (Rhombomys
         opimus) in the region between Volga and Ural rivers and its probable epizootical significance.]
         Zool. Zh., 50:1, 110—116, 1 fig., 1 table (Russian; English summary).

TROSHKINA, O. B.   See: Shevchenko, A. I. and Troshkina, O. B., 1967A.

TRUBIKHIN, V. M.   See: Menner, V. V., Nikiforova, K. V., Pevzner, M. A., Alekseev, M. N., Gladenkov, Iu. B.,
         Gurarii, G. Z. and Trubikhin, V. M., 1972A.

TRUC, GEORGES
1969A   L'Éocène près de Malaucène et dans la région de Mormoiron-Bédoin. Colloque sur l'Éocène, Paris,
         mai 1968, Vol. III. Fr., Bur. Rech. Géol. Minières, Mém., 69, 405—406 (French).

TRUC, GEORGES   See also: Demarcq, G. and Truc, G., 1969A; Guérin, C., Mein, P., Philippe, M. and Truc, G., 1972A; Guérin, C., Mein, P. and Truc, G., 1970A; Hugueney, M., Truc, G. and Philippe, M., 1971A; Mein, P., Truc, G. and Ballésio, R., 1972A; Mein, P., Truc, G. and Demarcq, G., 1971A; Triat, J.-M., Truc, G. and Hugueney, M., 1971A.

TRUDZIK, ZBIGNIEW
   1969A   O właściwe ujęcie procesu antropogenezy. [On the right approach to the process of anthropogenesis.] Archeol. Polski, 14:2, 433–444 (Polish).

TRUMLER, EBERHARD
   1969A   Morphologische und taxonomische Studien am Schädel und Gehirn rezenter und fossiler Einhufer. Vorläufige Mitteilung. Säugetierkundl. Mitt., 17:2, 173–180, 3 figs. (German; English summary).

TRUMP, DAVID   See: Bray, W. and Trump, D., 1970A.

TRUSWELL, J. F.
   1967A   A critical review of stratigraphic terminology as applied in South Africa. Geol. Soc. S. Afr., Trans., 70, 81–116, 2 figs., 11 tables.

TSAGARELI, ARCHIL LUKICH
   1964A   Chetvertichnaia sistema. [Quaternary system.] Geologiia SSSR, 10, Georgian SSR, 332–352, 2 figs., 2 tables (Russian).

TSALKIN, V. I. (= ZALKIN, V. I.)
   1968A   K shestidesiatiletiiu Nikolaia Kuz'micha Vereshchagina. [On the 60th birthday of Nikolai Kuz'mich Vereshchagin.] Mosk. Obshchest. Ispyt. Prir., Biull., Otd. Biol., 73:5, 149–155 (Russian).

TSAPENKO, MARGARITA MSTISLAVOVNA and SHCHEGLOVA, VERA VASIL'EVNA
   1972A   Ob ostatkakh antropogenovykh mlekopitaiushchikh u Smorgoni. [On the remains of Quaternary mammals near Smorgon'.] In: Voprosy geologii antropogena, 2, 25–28 (Russian).

TSEGEL'NIUK, P. D.
   1969A   Stratigrafiia i vozrast siluriiskikh i nizhnedevonskikh otlozhenii Pridnestrov'ia. [Stratigraphy and age of Silurian and Devonian sediments of Dnestr region.] Geol. Zh., 29:4, 61–68, 1 chart (Russian).

TSEĬTLIN, S. M. (= ZEITLIN, S. M.)
   1968A   Skhemy geologicheskoi periodizatsii paleolita razlichnykh raionov Sibiri i ikh korreliatsiia. [Schemes of geological periodization of the Paleolithic from different regions of Siberia and their correlation.] In: Problemy izucheniia chetvertichnogo perioda. Tezisy, 128 (Russian).
   1968B   Voprosy korreliatsii kontinental'nykh verkhnepleistotsenovykh otlozhenii Severnoi Evrazii i geologicheskaia periodizatsiia paleolita. [Correlation problems of upper Pleistocene continental deposits of northern Eurasia and a geological periodization of the Paleolithic.] In: Granitsa tretichnogo i chetvertichnogo periodov, 113–114 (Russian; English summary).
   1969A   Novaia verkhnepaleoliticheskaia stoianka na Enise Buzunovo II. [New upper Paleolithic site on Enisei R. Buzunovo II.] Akad. Nauk SSSR, Kom. Izuch. Chetvertich. Perioda, Biull., 36, 141–143, 1 fig. (Russian).
   1972A   Resul'taty obsuzhdeniia knigi B. S. Rusanova "Biostratigrafiia kainozoiskikh otlozhenii iuzhnoi Iakutii", M., "Nauka", 1968. [Results of the discussion of B. S. Rusanov's book "Biostratigraphy of Cenozoic deposits of Southern Iakutia", M., "Nauka", 1968.] Akad. Nauk SSSR, Kom. Izuch. Chetvertich. Perioda, Biull., 38, 172–185 (Russian).

TSEĬTLIN, S. M.   See also: Ravskii, E. I. and Tseitlin, S. M., 1968A.

TSETLIN, V. P.   See: Sharfman, V. S., Tsetlin, V. P. and Skripko, K. A., 1965A.

TSYGANKO, VLADIMIR STEPANOVICH   See: Pershina, A. I. and Tsyganko, V. S., 1971A.

TSZIA, L.-P., GAI, P. and LI, Y.-S.
   1964A   [New findings from the Paleolithic site Shuidungou.] Vert. Palasiatica, 8:1, 75–86, 8 figs., 3 pls. (Chinese; Russian summary).

TUCKER, W.   See: Russell, D. and Tucker, W., 1971A.

TUFTY, BARBARA
   1967B   Peking man refound. Sci. News, 92:25, 592–593, 3 figs.

1971A   Dr. Louis S. B. Leakey, the man and his discoveries. In: Holmes, L. D. (ed.), 1971A, 96–105
                (reprinted from Science News, Feb. 25, 1967).

TUREKIAN, KARL K.
1971A*   The late Cenozoic glacial ages. New Haven and London: Yale University Press, xii + 606 pp., illustr.
                Rev.: Cooke in Amer. Sci., 60:6, 784–785; Dionne in Natur. Can., 99:3, 249–250; Goldthwait in
                Science, 174:4013, 1016; Nairn in Earth-Sci. Rev., 8:1, 76; Robin in New Sci., 52:773, 121.

TUREKIAN, KARL K. and BADA, JEFFREY L.
1972A   The dating of fossil bones. In: Bishop, W. W. and Miller, J. A. (eds.), 1972A, 171–185, 4 figs.,
                2 tables.

TURNBULL, COLIN   See: Howell, F. C., Turnbull, C., Sharp, L., Clark, J. G. D. and DeVore, I., 1968A.

TURNBULL, WILLIAM D.
1969A   Pliocene mammals from western Victoria, Australia. Amer. Phil. Soc., Yearb., 1968, 341–343.
1970A   Mammalian masticatory apparatus. Fieldiana: Geol., 18:2, 149–356, 48 figs., 13 tables, appendix.
                Rev.: Haltenorth in Säugetierkundl. Mitt., 18, 394; Kittel in Gegenbaurs Morph. Jahrb., 116:2, 280;
                Landry in J. Mammal., 52:2, 482–484.
1971A   The Trinity therians: their bearing on evolution in marsupials and other therians. In: Dahlberg,
                Albert A. (ed.), 1971A, 151–179, 6 figs., 4 tables.
1972A   The Washakie formation of Bridgerian-Uintan ages, and its related faunas. Field Conf. Tert. Bios.,
                S. and W. Wyo., Guidebk., 20–31, 2 figs.
1972B   The Allen titanothere quarry. Soc. Vert. Paleontol., Ann. Meeting, 32nd, 1972, Abstr. (abs.).

TURNBULL, W. D. and LUNDELIUS, E. L., JR.
1970A   The Hamilton fauna. A late Pliocene mammalian fauna from the Grange Burn, Victoria, Australia.
                Fieldiana: Geol., 19, 163 pp., 2 figs., 31 pls., 10 graphs, 8 tables.
                Rev.: Woodburne in J. Paleontol., 46:6, 930.

TURNBULL, WILLIAM D.   See also: Schram, F. R. and Turnbull, W. D., 1970A.

TURNER, B. R.
1972A   Revision of the stratigraphic position of cynodonts from the upper part of the Karroo (Gondwana)
                system in Lesotho. Geol. Mag., 109:4, 349–360, 3 figs.

TURNER, DONALD L.
1969A   K-Ar dating of Tertiary foraminiferal stages and their correlation with North American mammalian ages.
                Geol. Soc. Amer., Abstr., 121, 300 (abs.).

TURNER, SUSAN
1970A   Timing of the Appalachian/Caledonian orogen contraction. Nature, 227:5253, 90.

TURNER, SUSAN and DIXON, JAMES
1971A   Lower Silurian thelodonts from Prince of Wales Island, Northwest Territories. Lethaia, 4:4, 385–392,
                7 figs.

TURNER, SUSAN   See also: Halstead, L. B. and Turner, S., 1970A.

TUTTLE, RUSSELL H.
1969A   The way apes walk. Sci. J., London, 5A:5, 66–72, 5 figs.
1969B   Knuckle-walking and the problem of human origins. Science (AAAS), 166:3908, 953–961, 8 figs.
1972A*   The functional and evolutionary biology of primates. Chicago: Aldine-Atherton, xii + 488 pp.,
                15 pls.
                Rev.: Day in Science (AAAS), 177:4045, 252.

TUTTLE, RUSSELL H. and OXNARD, C. E.
1969A   Knuckle-walking and possible evolutionary pathways of the great apes and man. Amer. J. Phys.
                Anthropol., 31, 265 (abs.).

TUTTLE, RUSSELL H.   See also: Oxnard, C. and Tuttle, R. H., 1969A.

TVERDOKHLEBOV, V. P.
1970A   O podrazdelenii vetluzhskoĭ serii (indskogo ĭarusa) v predelakh Iùzhnogo Priural'ià i Obshchego Syrta.
                [On the subdivision of the Vetlugian series (Indian stage) within the southern Cisuralian and
                Obshchiĭ Syrt territories.] Akad. Nauk SSSR, Izv., Ser. Geol., 1970:12, 101–105 (Russian).

1970B   Baskunchakskie otlozheniia levoberezh'ia basseĭna r. Samary i Obshchego Syrta (Orenburgskoe i Bashkirskoe Priural'e). [Baskunchak deposits of the left bank of Samara R. basin and Obshchiĭ Syrt.] In: Voprosy geologii Iuzhnogo Urala i Povolzh'ia, 7:1, 96—101 (Russian).

TVERDOKHLEBOV, V. P.   See also: Ochev, V. G., Shishkin, M. A., Garyainov, V. A. and Tverdokhlebov, V. P., 1964A, 1965A.

TVERDOKHLEBOVA, GALINA IVANOVNA (= TVERDOCHLEBOVA, G. I.)
1968A   O rodakh *Chroniosuchus* i *Jugosuchus* iz verkhnetatarskikh otlozheniĭ SSSR. [On the genera *Chroniosuchus* and *Jugosuchus* from upper Tatarian deposits of USSR.] In: Verkhnepaleozoĭskie i mezozoĭskie zemnovodnye i presmykaiushchiesia SSSR, 11—15, 1 fig., 1 pl. (Russian).
1969A   Ob usloviiakh zakhoroneniia batrakhozavrov v mestonakhozhdenii Donguz VI. [On the conditions of burial of batrachosaurs in the fossil locality Donguz VI.] In: Voprosy geologii Iuzhnogo Urala i Povolzh'ia, 6:1, 70—76 (Russian).
1972A   Novyĭ rod batrakhozavrov iz verkhneĭ permi Iuzhnogo Priural'ia. [New genus of bathrachosaurians from upper Permian of the southern Cisuralia.] Paleontol. Zh., 1972:1, 95—103, 3 figs. (Russian).
1972B   A new batrachosauran genus from the upper Permian of southern Cisuralia. Paleontol. J., 6:1, 84—90, 3 figs.

TVERDOKHLEBOVA, GALINA IVANOVNA   See also: Ochev, V. G. and Tverdokhlebova, G. I., 1970A.

TWEEDIE, MICHAEL
1970A   Fossil elephants. Animals, 12:10, 436—438, illustr.
1970B   Exciting fossil discovery. Animals, 12:11, 494—495, illustr.
1971A   Giant reptiles of the sea. Animals, 13:11, 508—511.

TYLER, JAMES C.
1968A   A monograph on plectognath fishes of the superfamily Triacanthoidea. Phila., Acad. Natur. Sci., Monogr., 16, 364 pp., 209 figs., 35 tables.
    Rev.: Myers in Copeia, 1970:1, 204—205.

UCKO, PETER J. and ROSENFELD, ANDRÉE
1967B   Arte paleolítico. Madrid: Ed. Guadarrama, 254 pp., 106 illustr. (Spanish).
    Rev.: Ripoll Perelló in Ampurias, 29, 348—352; Schaafsma in El Palacio, 74:4, 38—39.

UDALOV, N. F.
1969A   O nakhodke iskopaemykh ostatkov bizona v chetvertichnykh otlozheniiakh Kokmaĭnokskoĭ vpadiny (Severnyĭ Tĭan'-Shan'). [On the finding of fossil remains of bison in the Quaternary deposits of Kokmaĭnok depression (northern Tian-Shan).] Akad. Nauk Kirgiz. SSR, Izv., 1969:5, 11—12, 1 fig. (Russian).

UDRIS, K. P.
1971A   Paleogenovaia sistema. Morskie otlozheniia paleogena. [Paleogene system. Marine deposits of the Paleogene.] Geologiia SSSR, 34:1, Turgaĭ trough, 299—341, 4 figs., 1 table (Russian).
1971B   Neogenovaia sistema. Miotsen. [Neogene system. Miocene.] Geologiia SSSR, 34:1, Turgaĭ trough, 412—425, 2 figs. (Russian).

UDVARDY, MIKLOS D. F.
1969A   Dynamic zoogeography with special reference to land animals. New York, Toronto, London and Melbourne: van Nostrand Reinhold, xviii + 446 pp., 174 figs., 4 pls., 14 tables.
    Rev.: Bennett in Geogr. Rev., 61:1, 155—157; Howden in Ecology, 52:1, 191; J.M.W. in Ostrich, 41:4, 272; Jaczewski in Przegl. Zool., 16:1, 86; K.H.V. in Ardea, 60:1—2, 134—135; Kühnelt in Zool.-Bot. Ges. Wien, Verh., 110/111, 169—170; Shtegman in Zool. Zh., 49:12, 1887—1888 (Russian).

UENO, TERUYA
1970A   [On middle Tertiary bony fishes of Tsushima Islands, Japan.] Nat. Sci. Mus., Tokyo, Mem., 3, 33—34 (Japanese; English summary).

UENO, TERUYA   See also: Hasegawa, Y. and Ueno, T., 1967A.

UKLADNIKOW, A. P. (= OKLADNIKOV, A. P.)
1968C   Nuevos descubrimientos de remotos testimonios artísticos de la humanidad en el Asia. Univ. Chile, Bol., 82, 51—56 (Spanish).

ULLRICH, HERBERT
1967A   Plastische Gesichtsrekonstruktionen urgeschichtlicher Menschen nach der Methode von Gerasimov. Neue Museumskunde 10, 456—475, illustr. (German).

ULLRICH, WOLFGANG
1970A   Ernährung und Verhaltensweisen des Nahrungserwerbes der Prähominiden und frühen Euhominiden. Ethnogr.-Archäol. Z., 11:1, 55—59 (German).

ULRIX-CLOSSET, MARGUERITE
1968A   Le site préhistorique de Montaigle (Province de Namur) et l'industrie Moustérienne du Trou du Sureau. Soc. Roy. Belge Anthropol. Préhist., Bull., 79, 67—90, 25 figs. (French).

ÜNALAN, GÜNER   See: Guillemot, J. and Ünalan, G.

UNDERWOOD, GARTH
1970A   The eye. In: Gans, C. (ed.), 1970A, 1—97, 29 figs., 3 tables.

URYSON, M. I.
1964C   Nachal'nye etapy stanovleniĩa cheloveka (drevneĩshie i drevnie lĩudi). [Initial stages in the making of man (the most ancient and ancient men).] In: U istokov chelovechestva. (Osnovnye problemy antropogeneza), 83—151, 20 figs. (Russian).
1966D   Sovremennaĩa nauka o proiskhozhdenii cheloveka. [Contemporaneous science on the origin of man.] Moscow: "Znanie" Press (Russian).
1968A   Interrelations of the principal morphological peculiarities of man's skull in the process of anthropogenesis. Int. Congr. Anthropol. Ethnol. Sci., 7th, Moscow, 1964, Proc., 3, 542—546.
1969A   Nekotorye problemy proiskhozhdeniĩa cheloveka v svete novykh dannykh. [Some problems of the origin of man in the light of new data.] Nauchn. Dokl. Vyssh. Shkoly, Biol. Nauki, 1969:6, 150—160 (Russian).
1969B   Pamĩati Georgiĩa Franĩsevicha Debeĩsa (1905—1969). [In memoriam Georgiĩ Franĩsevich Debeĩs (1905—1969).] Vop. Antropol., 32, 195—197, portr. (Russian).
1969C   Rabota A. Grdlichki "Neandertal'skaĩa faza cheloveka" i ee znachenie dlĩa sovremennoĩ nauki. ["The Neanderthal phase of man" by A. Hrdlička and its significance for modern science.] Vop. Antropol., 33, 12—15 (Russian).
1970A   Sootnositel'naĩa izmenchivost' komponentov sagittal'nogo svoda cherepa u sovremennogo i iskopaemogo cheloveka. [Correlative variability of components of the sagittal cranial vault in modern and fossil man.] Vop. Antropol., 34, 31—39, 4 tables (Russian).
1970B   Nekotorye problemy antropogeneza v svete novykh paleoantropologicheskikh otkrytiĩ. [Some problems of anthropogenesis in the light of new paleoanthropological discoveries.] Itogi Nauki, Ser. Biol., 1969 (Russian).
1972A   Pamĩati Sergeĩa Ivanovicha Uspenskogo [1913—1971]. [In memoriam Sergeĩ Ivanovich Uspenskiĩ [1913—1971].] Vop. Antropol., 40, 189—191, portr. (Russian).
1972B   Vystuplenie. [Discussion.] Vop. Antropol., 41, 153—155 (Russian).

USPENSKIĬ, S. I.
1964A   O nekotorykh biologicheskikh predposylkakh ochelovecheniĩa obez'ĩan. [On some biological preconditions for humanization of monkeys.] In: U istokov chelovechestva. (Osnovnye problemy antropogeneza), 33—51, 4 figs. (Russian).
1969A   Polozhenie iskopaemykh deteĩ iz peshcher Starosel'e i Teshik-Tash v evolĩutsionnoĩ sisteme gominid po dannym stereomorfologii neĩrokranov. [The position of fossil children from Starosel'e and Teshik-Tash caves in the evolutionary system of hominids according to the data of neurocranial stereomorphology.] Vop. Antropol., 31, 113—124, 5 tables (Russian).

USTINOVSKIĬ, IU. B.   See: Bersenev, I. I., Ustinovskiĩ, Iu. B., Bur'ĩanova, I. Z., Nevolina, S. I. and Medvedev, V. V., 1969A.

UTEKHIN, DONAT NIKOLAEVICH
1971A   Devonskaĩa sistema. Sredniĩ otdel. [Devonian system. Middle section.] Geologiĩa SSSR, 4, Center of the European part of the USSR, 127—154, 9 figs. (Russian).

UTEKHIN, D. N. and SORSKAĨA, L. S.
1971A   Devonskaĩa sistema. Verkhniĩ otdel. [Devonian system. Upper section.] Geologiĩa SSSR, 4, Center of the European part of the USSR, 154—188, 6 figs. (Russian).

UZZELL, THOMAS and PILBEAM, DAVID
1971A   Phyletic divergence dates of hominoid primates: a comparison of fossil and molecular data. Evolution, 25:4, 615—635, 3 figs., 5 tables.

VÁCL, JAROSLAV   See: Šantrůček, P., Bůzek, Č., Kopecký, L., Malecha, A. and Václ, J., 1968A.

VAHL, JOHANNA
    1971A   Applicability of combined biocrystallographical and ultrastructural research methods in paleontology.
        N. Amer. Paleontol. Conv., 1969, Proc., Part K, 1535–1562, 20 figs.

VAĬNSHTEĬN, B. A.
    1968A   O chislovoĭ taksonomii. [On numerical taxonomy.] Zh. Obshch. Biol., 29:2, 153–167, 4 figs.,
        5 tables (Russian; English summary).
    1970A   O printsipakh postroeniĭa estestvennoĭ sistemy. [On the principles of constructing a natural system.]
        Zool. Zh., 49:12, 1749–1757 (Russian; English summary).

VALDEMAR, A. E.
    1970A   A new assessment of the occupation of the Cefn Cave in relation to the Bont Newydd Cave and the
        river Elwy. Cave Res. Group Gt. Brit., Trans., 12:2, 109–112, 2 maps, 1 pl.
    1970B   A preliminary report on the archaeological and palaeontological caves and rock shelters of Wales.
        Cave Res. Group Gt. Brit., Trans., 12:2, 113–126, 8 maps.

VALDEMAR, A. E. and JONES, R. D.
    1970A   An initial report on the archaeological and palaeontological caves and rock shelters in north Wales.
        Cave Res. Group Gt. Brit., Trans., 12:2, 99–107, 1 map.

VALENTINE, JAMES W.
    1971A   Resource supply and species diversity patterns. Lethaia, 4:1, 51–61, 1 fig.
    1972A   Conceptual models in ecosystem evolution. In: Schopf, T. J. M. (ed.), 1972A, 192–215, 3 figs.

VALLOIS, HENRI VICTOR
    1968A   Jack C. Trevor. [July 15, 1907–July 16, 1967]. L'Anthropologie, 72, 184–185 (French).
    1968B   Le centenaire de la découverte des hommes de Cro-Magnon. L'Anthropologie, 72:1–2, 198–199
        (French).
    1968C   Nouvelles précisions sur le sixième crâne du Pithécanthrope. L'Anthropologie, 72:3–4, 409–410
        (French).
    1968D   Un homme de Néanderthal en Turquie? L'Anthropologie, 72:3–4, 410–411 (French).
    1968E   Réflexions sur la soi-disant ancienneté de la posture bipède chez l'homme. In: K. Saller
        Festschrift, 1968, 18–27 (French).
    1969A   Un nouvel homme fossile au Japon. L'Anthropologie, 73:1–2, 138–140 (French).
    1969B   Recherche anthropologique en Australie. L'Anthropologie, 73:1–2, 140–142 (French).
    1969C   Symposium international canarien à l'occasion du centenaire de la découverte de l'homme de Cro-
        Magnon. L'Anthropologie, 73:3–4, 314–317 (French).
    1969D   Le temporal néandertalien H 27 de La Quina. Étude anthropologique. L'Anthropologie, 73:5–6,
        365–400, 11 figs., 1 pl., 8 tables (French).
    1969E   La fin d'un mythe: les soi-disant hommes fossiles de Denise. L'Anthropologie, 73:5–6, 444–445
        (French).
    1969F   Un Pithécanthrope au Maroc. L'Anthropologie, 73:5–6, 445–446 (French).
    1969G   Nouveaux restes d'Australopithèques en Éthiopie. L'Anthropologie, 73:5–6, 456–457 (French).
    1969H   Récents documents sur l'homme fossile de Rhodésie. L'Anthropologie, 73:5–6, 457–459 (French).
    1969I   La morphologie du temporal des Néandertaliens. Summary and discussion. Soc. Anthropol. Paris,
        Bull. Mém., Sér. 12, 4, 375–376 (French).
    1969J   L'os temporal des néandertaliens. Ass. Anat., C.R., 144, 1710–1716 (French).
    1971A   Le squelette paléolithique de Saint-Germain-la-Rivière et les Cro-Magnoïdes magdaléniens. Acad. Sci.,
        C.R., Sér. D, 272:21, 2677–2680, 2 figs. (French).
    1971B   Le crâne trépané magdalénien de Rochereil. Soc. Préhist. Fr., Bull., Étud. Trav., 68:2, 485–495,
        8 figs. (French).

VALOCH, KAREL
    1965B   Rev.: Kozłowski in Archeol. Polski, 15:1, 265–268 (Polish).
    1969A   Über einige Entwicklungsfragen des Mitteleuropäischen Jungpaläolithikums. Archeol. Roz., 21:3,
        342–354 (German).
    1969B   Nachalo verkhnego paleolita v Srednei Evrope. [Beginning of the upper Paleolithic in central
        Europe.] Akad. Nauk SSSR, Kom. Izuch. Chetvertich. Perioda, Biúll., 36, 63–74, 4 figs.,
        1 table (Russian).
    1970A   Early middle Pleistocene (stratum 14) in the Kůlna Cave near Sloup in the Moravian karst
        (Czechoslovakia). World Archaeol., 2:1, 28–38, 4 figs., 4 pls.
    1970B   Oeuvres d'art et objets en os du Magdalénien de Moravie (Tchécoslovaquie). Préhist. Spéléol.
        Ariége., 25, 79–93, 9 figs. (French).

VALOCH, K., PELÍŠEK, J., MUSIL, R., KOVANDA, J. and OPRAVIL, E.
1969A   Die Erforschung der Külna-Höhle bei Sloup im Mährischen Karst (Tschechoslowakei). Quartär, 20, 1—45, 9 figs., 2 pls., 3 tables (German).

VALOCH, KAREL   See also: Musil, R. and Valoch, K., 1966A; Šibrava, V., Fejfar, O., Kovanda, J. and Valoch, K., 1969A.

VAN ASCH, TH. W. J.   See: Erdbrink, D. P. and Van Asch, Th. W. J., 1972A.

VAN BEMMEL, A. C. U.
1971A   On reconstructions of the giant deer, *Megaloceros giganteus* (Blumenbach). Lutra, 12:3, 73—78, 1 fig. (Dutch summary).

VAN BERGIJK, W. A.
1966A   Evolution of the sense of hearing in vertebrates. Amer. Zool., 6:3, 371—377, 4 figs.

VAN COUVERING, JOHN A.
1972A   Radiometric calibration of the European Neogene. In: Bishop, W. W. and Miller, J. A. (eds.), 1972A, 247—271, 2 figs., 2 tables.
1972B   K-Ar calibration of Miocene history in the Mediterranean region. Soc. Vert. Paleontol., Ann. Meeting, 32nd, 1972, Abstr. (abs.).

VAN COUVERING, J. A. and MILLER, J. A.
1969A   Miocene stratigraphy and age determinations, Rusinga Island, Kenya. Nature, 221:5181, 628—632, 2 figs., 1 table.
1971A   Late Miocene marine and non-marine time scale in Europe. Nature, 230:5296, 559—563, 2 figs., 1 table.

VAN COUVERING, JUDITH
1972A   Faunal associations in the Miocene of Rusinga Island, Kenya. Soc. Vert. Paleontol., Ann. Meeting, 32nd, 1972, Abstr. (abs.).

VANDEBOSCH, ARTHUR
1952A   Les raclettes ou pièces à retouches abruptes. Les Eyzies, 2, 31—34 (French).
1955A   Les hommes fossiles de la grotte Schmerling à Engis. Les Eyzies, 5, 66—72, 2 figs. (French).
1957A   À propos des origines de l'homme. Chercheurs Wallonie, Bull.,16, 20—29 (French).
1957B   Note relative au premier ossement fossile d'un siluroide trouvé en Belgique. Chercheurs Wallonie, Bull., 16, 339—342 (French).

VANDEBROEK, GEORGES
1966B   Caractères morphologiques évolutifs des post-canines temporaires humaines. (Summary of report at the 2nd reunion of the G.I.R.S., Toulouse, 1966). Groupement Int. Recherch. Sci. Stomatol., Bull., 9:3, 345 (French).
1967A   Origin of the cusps and crests of the tribosphenic molar. Jour. Dental Res., 46:5, 796—804, 7 figs.
1969A   Évolution des vertébrés. De leur origine à l'homme. Paris: Masson et Cie., xx + 583 pp., 390 figs. (French).
           Rev.: Anon. in La Recherche, 1:5, 491—492; Cox in Nature, 226:5246, 676—677; Crochet in Rev. Quest. Sci., 31, 337—338; Fantini Sestini in Riv. Ital. Paleontol. Stratigr., 75:4, 889; Gautier in Natuurwet. Tijdschr., 51:3—8, 224; Kaestner in Biol. Zentralbl., 90:3, 404—405; Kuhn-Schnyder in Naturwiss., 57:11, 553; Leroy in Soc. Zool. Fr., Bull., 95:4, 870—871; Montalenti in Scientia, 106:11—12, 1120; Romer in Quart. Rev. Biol., 45:2, 190—191; Tétry in L'Ann. Biol., 10:3—4, 233—234.
1969B   Evolutionary characters of the human dentition. (Abstract). Int. Congr. Anthropol. Ethnol. Sci., 8th, Tokyo, 1968, Proc., Vol. I. Anthropology, 302.

VAN DE FLIERT, J. R.
1970A   Fundamentalism and the fundamentals of geology. Faith and Thought, 98:1, 11—42.

VANDEL, ALBERT
1968A   La genèse du vivant. Paris: Masson et Cie., Collection "Les grands problèmes de la biologie", P.-P. Grassé (ed.), Monogr. 6, 279 pp., 39 figs., pls. (French).
           Rev.: Brien in L'Ann. Biol., 8:5—6, 375—376; Hertwig in Biol. Zentralbl., 88:6, 814—815; Oppenheimer in Quart. Rev. Biol., 44:3, 295.

VAN DER FEEN, P. J.
1968A   A fossil skull fragment of a walrus from the mouth of the river Scheldt (Netherlands). Bijdr. Dierkunde, 38, 23—30, 1 fig., 1 pl., 1 table.

VANDERMEERSCH, BERNARD
1969A Un nouvel Australopithèque découvert en Éthiopie. Atomes, no. 261, 52–53, 2 figs. (French).
1969B Les grottes de Grimaldi aident à mieux comprendre le Quaternaire méditerranéen. Atomes, 264, 261–262, 2 figs. (French).
1969C Les nouveaux squelettes moustériens découverts à Qafzeh (Israël) et leur signification. Acad. Sci., C.R., Sér. D, 268:21, 2562–2565, 1 pl. (French).
1969D L'origine de l'*Homo sapiens*. [The origin of *Homo sapiens*.] Rev. Quest. Sci., 30, 333–339 (French).
1970A Les origines de l'homme moderne. Atomes, 272, 5–12, 10 figs. (French).
1970B Une sépulture moustérienne avec offrandes découverte dans la grotte de Qafzeh. Acad. Sci., C.R., Sér. D, 270:2, 298–301, 1 fig., 1 pl. (French).
1970C Éthiopie: le plus vieil outil du monde. Atomes, 25:274, 209–210, 1 fig. (French).
1971A Une mâchoire de 200,000 ans dans les Pyrénées. La Recherche, 1:8, 79, 1 fig. (French).
1971B L'australopithèque: ancêtre ou cousin? La Recherche, 2:15, 778–779, 2 figs. (French).
1972A Les australopithèques du lac Rodolphe. La Recherche, 3:26, 785–786, 2 figs. (French).

VANDERMEERSCH, B.   See also: Duport, L. and Vandermeersch, B., 1972A.

VANGENGEĬM, ELEONORA ALEKSEEVNA
1963A Fauna chetvertichnykh mlekopitaiŭshchikh o. Bol'shogo Liakhovskogo. [The fauna of Quaternary mammals from Bol'shoĭ Liakhovskiĭ Island.] Arkt. i Antarkt. Nauchn.-Issl. Inst., Trudy, 224, 73–87, 6 figs., 8 tables (Russian).
1968A Stratigraficheskoe znachenie fauny mlekopitaiŭshchikh v sviazi s problemoĭ gomotaksisa. [Stratigraphi significance of mammalian fauna in connection with the problem of homotaxis.] In: Problemy izucheniia chetvertichnogo perioda. Tezisy, 102–103 (Russian).
1968B Faunisticheskie kompleksy mlekopitaiŭshchikh antropogena Vostochnoĭ Sibiri i Zabaĭkal'ia i printsipy korreliatsii raznoprovintsial'nykh faun. [Mammalian faunistic complexes of Anthropogene of eastern Siberia and Transbaĭkalia and the principles of correlation of faunas of different provinces.] In: Problemy izucheniia chetvertichnogo perioda. Tezisy, 103–104 (Russian).

VANGENGEĬM, E. A., ERBAEVA, M. A., ZHEGALLO, V. I. and SOTNIKOVA, M. V.
1968A Novye dannye o geologii i faune pozdnepliotsenovogo mestonakhozhdeniia u fermy Beregovoĭ. [New data on geology and fauna of the late Pliocene key locality near Beregovaia farm.] In: Voprosy geologii Pribaĭkal'ia i Zabaĭkal'ia, 3:5, 251–252 (Russian).

VANGENGEĬM, E. A., PIATAKOV, V. V. and SHEVCHENKO, V. K.
1969A Novye nakhodki ostatkov mlekopitaiŭshchikh v Zabaĭkal'e. [New finds of mammal remains in Transbaĭkalia.] In: Voprosy geologii Pribaĭkal'ia i Zabaĭkal'ia, 6:4, 87–92 (Russian).
1969B Novye nakhodki ostatkov mlekopitaiŭshchikh v Zabaĭkal'e. [New finds of mammalian remains in Transbaĭkalia.] Geogr. Obshch. SSSR, Zabaĭkal'. Filial, Zap., 38, 87–92 (Russian).

VANGENGEĬM, E. A. and SHER, ANDREĬ VLADIMIROVICH
1969A Analogi tiraspol'skogo faunisticheskogo kompleksa v Sibiri. [Siberian equivalents of the Tiraspolian faunal complex.] In: Mezhdunarodnyĭ kollokvium po geologii i faune nizhnego i srednego pleĭstotsena Evropy. Tezisy dokladov, 35–38 and 72–74 (Russian and English).
1970A Siberian equivalents of the Tiraspol faunal complex. Palaeogeogr., Palaeoclimatol., Palaeoecol., 8:2–3, 197–207, 1 fig., 1 table.
1972A Analogi tiraspol'skogo faunisticheskogo kompleksa v Sibiri. [Analogues of Tiraspol' faunal complex in Siberia.] In: Geologiia i fauna nizhnego i srednego pleĭstotsena Evropy, 245–255 (Russian)

VANGENGEĬM, E. A. and ZAZHIGIN, VLADIMIR SEMENOVICH
1969A Fauny mlekopitaiŭshchikh eopleĭstotsena Sibiri i ikh sopostavlenie s vostochno-evropeĭskimi. [Mammal faunas of Siberian Eopleistocene and their correlation with east European.] In: Osnovnye problemy geologii antropogena Evrazii. K VIII kongressu INQUA, Parizh, 1969, 47–59, 2 tables (Russian; English summary).

VANGENGEĬM, E. A., ZHEGALLO, V. I. and ZAZHIGIN, V. S.
1972A Etapy razvitiia fauny mlekopitaiŭshchikh pozdnego neogena i nachala antropogena v Severnoĭ Azii. [Stages of the development of mammalian fauna of the late Neogene and beginning Anthropogene in north Asia.] Geol. Geofiz. (Akad. Nauk SSSR, Sib. Otd.), 1972:6, 58–65, 1 table (Russian).

VANGENGEĬM, E. A.   See also: Gromov, V. I., Vangengeĭm, E. A., Grichuk, V. P., Ivanova, I. K. and Nikiforova, K. V. (eds.), 1968A; Gromov, V. I., Vangengeĭm, E. A. and Nikiforova, K. V., 1965B; Nikonov, A. A., Pen'kov, A. V., Trofimov, B. A., Vangengeĭm, E. A., Dmitrieva, E. A. and Sotnikova, M. V., 1971A.

VANGEROW, E.-F.
 1970A   Zur Entwicklung der Landtiere. Kosmos (Stuttgart), 1970:6, 194 (German).

VANOSSI, M.   See: Fierro, G. and Vanossi, M., 1965A.

VAN VALEN, LEIGH
 1962A   A study of fluctuating asymmetry. Evolution, 16:2, 125—142, 1 fig., 7 tables.
 1963D   On evolutionary theories. Brit. J. Phil. Sci., 14:54, 146—152.
 1968A   Rev.: Rothausen in Zentralbl. Geol. Paläontol., Teil 2, 1971:1, 66.
 1968B   On the origin of races. Current Anthropol., 9:1, 65.
 1969A   A classification of the primates. Amer. J. Phys. Anthropol., 30, 295—296.
 1969B   Variation genetics of extinct animals. Amer. Natur., 103, 193—224.
 1969C   Evolution of dental growth and adaptation in mammalian carnivores. Evolution, 23:1, 96—117,
                     13 figs., 1 table.
 1969D   The multiple origins of the placental carnivores. Evolution, 23:1, 118—130, 11 figs.
                     Rev.: Thenius in Zentralbl. Geol. Paläontol., Teil 2, 1970:3/4, 243.
 1969E   Climate and evolutionary rate. Science (AAAS), 166:3913, 1656—1658, 2 figs.
 1970A   Late Pleistocene extinctions. N. Amer. Paleontol. Conv., Proc., Part E, 469—485, 1 table.
 1971A   Scientific bibliography 1958—1971. Mimeograph, 10 pp.
 1971B   Adaptive zones and the orders of mammals. Evolution, 25:2, 420—428, 1 fig.
 1971C   Toward the origin of artiodactyls. Evolution, 25:3, 523—529.

VAN VALEN, LEIGH and SLOAN, ROBERT E.
 1972A   Ecology and the extinction of the dinosaurs. Int. Geol. Congr., 24th, Canada, Abstr., 247 (abs.).
 1972B   Ecology and the extinction of the dinosaurs. Int. Geol. Congr., 24th, Canada, Proc., Sec. 7, 214.

VAN ZINDEREN BAKKER, EDWARD MEINE
 1966-67A*   Palaeoecology of Africa. Vols. 1—3. Cape Town-Amsterdam: A. A. Balkema, 3 vols., 600 pp.,
                     38 figs., 8 pls., 11 tables, 4 maps.
                     Rev.: Biberson in L'Anthropologie, 72:3—4, 349—351.

VAN ZYLL DE JONG, C. G.   See: Jong, C. G. van Zyll de

VARAGNAC, ANDRÉ
 1960A*   Rev.: Wiedemer in Schweiz. Ges. Urgesch., Jahrb., 52, 119—120.

VARDI, SHMUEL
 1972A   Dinosaur footprints in the Judean hills. Rocks Miner., 47:1, 16—17, 1 fig.

VARIŪKHINA, LILIĪA MIKHAĬLOVNA   See: Chalyshev, V. I. and Variŭkhina, L. M., 1966A, 1968A.

VARLAMOV, I. P.
 1959A   Nekotorye dannye o vykhodakh neogenovykh (kinel'skikh?) obrazovaniĭ i proiavlenii noveĭsheĭ
                     tektoniki v doline r. Zilima. [Some data on outcrops of Neogene (Kinelian?) formations and
                     newest tectonics manifestations in the Zilim river valley.] In: Voprosy geologii vostochnoĭ
                     okrainy Russkoĭ Platformy i Ĭuzhnogo Urala, 4, 123—127 (Russian).

VARNAVSKIKH, B. E.   See: Gus'kova, A. I., Duĭsebaev, Zh. D., Zhylkibaev, K. Zh. and Varnavskikh, B. E., 1971A.

VARONA, LUIS S.
 1966A   Notas sobre los crocodílidos de Cuba y descripción de una nueva especie del pleistoceno. Poeyana,
                     Ser. A, 16, 1—34, 11 figs., 6 tables (Spanish).

VARSANOF'EVA, V. A.
 1963A   Ordovikskaia i siluriĭskaia sistemy Urala, Paĭ-Khoia i Timana. [Ordovician and Silurian systems of
                     Urals, Paĭ-Khoĭ and Timan.] Geologiia SSSR, 2, Arkhangel'sk and Vologda Provinces, and
                     Komi ASSR, 169—255, 11 figs., 2 tables (Russian).

VASIL'EV, ĪU. M.
 1969A   Formirovanie antropogenovykh otlozheniĭ lednikovoĭ i vnelednikovoĭ zon. [Formation of
                     Anthropogene deposits of the glacial and extra-glacial zones.] [For the VIII INQUA Congress.
                     Paris, 1969.] Moscow: "Nauka" Press, 184 pp., 63 figs., 5 tables (Russian; French summary).

VASIL'EV, ĪU. M.   See also: Bogacheva, M. I., Vasil'ev, Ĭu. M., Proshliàkov, B. K., Charygin, M. M. and
                     Shleĭfer, A. G., 1965A.

VASIL'EV, V. A.
1965A   Kaĭnozoĭskie kontinental'nye otlozheniiã Pamira. [Cenozoic continental deposits of the Pamirs.]
            Akad. Nauk SSSR, Dokl., 161:4, 899–902, 1 table (Russian).

VASIL'EV, V. I.   See: Danilevich, A. M. and Vasil'ev, V. I., 1966A.

VASIL'EVSKIĬ, R. S.   See: Okladnikov, A. P., Vasil'evskiĭ, R. S., Larichev, V. E., Derevĭanko, A. P., Gogolev,
            Z. V. and Toshchakova, E. M., 1969A.

VAS'KOVSKIĬ, ALEKSEĬ PETROVICH
1963A   O nekotorykh ranneantropogenovykh tolshchakh Severo-Vostoka SSSR. [On some early Quaternary
            rocks of the northeast of USSR.] Kolyma, 1963:2, 29–32 (Russian).
1966B   Srednechetvertichnyĭ los' na Kamchatke. [Middle Quaternary elk in Kamchatka.] Kolyma, 1, 37
            (Russian).

VAUGHN, PETER PAUL
1969A   Further evidence of close relationship of the trematopsid and dissorophid labyrinthodont amphibians
            with a description of a new genus and new species. S. Calif. Acad. Sci., Bull., 68:3, 121–130,
            1 fig.
1969B   Upper Pennsylvanian vertebrates from the Sangre de Cristo formation of central Colorado. Los
            Angeles Cty. Mus., Contrib. Sci., 164, 28 pp., 5 figs.
1969C   Early Permian vertebrates from southern New Mexico and their paleozoogeographic significance.
            Los Angeles Cty. Mus., Contrib. Sci., 166, 21 pp., 2 figs.
1970A   Alternation of neural spine height in certain early Permian tetrapods. S. Calif. Acad. Sci., Bull.,
            60:2, 80–86, 1 fig.
1970B   Lower Permian vertebrates of the Four Corners and the midcontinent as indices of climatic differences.
            N. Amer. Paleontol. Conv., Proc., Part D, 388–408, 3 figs.
1971A   A Platyhystrix-like amphibian with fused vertebrae, from the upper Pennsylvanian of Ohio.
            J. Paleontol., 45:3, 464–469, 1 fig.
            Rev.: Westphal in Zentralbl. Geol. Paläontol., Teil 2, 1971:5, 410.
1972A   More vertebrates, including a new microsaur, from the upper Pennsylvanian of central Colorado.
            Los Angeles Cty. Mus., Contrib. Sci., 223, 30 pp., 6 figs.

VAUGHN, PETER PAUL   See also: Olson, E. C. and Vaughn, P. P., 1970A; Thomson, K. S. and Vaughn,
            P. P., 1968A.

VAVILOV, MIKHAIL NIKOLAEVICH and LOZOVSKIĬ, V. R.
1970A   K voprosu o ĭarusnom raschlenenii nizhnego triasa. [On the subdivision of lower Triassic into
            stages.] Akad. Nauk SSSR, Izv., Ser. Geol., 1970:9, 93–99, 2 tables (Russian).

VEENSTRA, E.   See: Holst, H. K. H., Smit, J. and Veenstra, E., 1970A.

VEGUNI, A. T.   See: Akopĭan, G. M., Veguni, A. T. and Ptukhĭan, A. E., 1970A; Arzumanian, S. K., Veguni,
            A. T. and Davtĭan, A. R., 1970A.

VEIGA FERREIRA, O. DA   See: Roche, J. and Veiga Ferreira, O. da, 1970A.

VEKILOVA, E. A., MURATOV, V. M. and FRIDENBERG, E. O.
1969A   Novoe v issledovanii krymskogo paleolita. [New in Crimean Paleolithic research.] In: Rybakov,
            B. A. (ed.), 1969A, 258–259 (Russian).

VEKILOVA, E. A. and ZUBOV, A. A.
1972A   Antropologicheskie ostatki iz must'erskikh sloev Akhshtyrskoĭ peshchery. [Anthropological remains
            from Mousterian strata of Akhshtyrskaiã Cave.] Akad. Nauk SSSR, Inst. Arkheol., Krat.
            Soobshch., 131, 61–64, 1 fig. (Russian).

VEKUA, A. K.
1967A   O prisutstvii Hipparion crusafonti Villalta v pozdnem pliotŝene Kvabebi (Vostochnaiã Gruziiã). [On
            the presence of Hipparion crusafonti Villalta in the late Pliocene of Kvabebi (eastern Georgia).]
            Akad. Nauk Gruz. SSR, Soobshch., 48:3, 689–692, 2 figs. (Russian; Georgian summary).
1967B   Novyĭ predstavitel' Lagomyidae iz paleolita Gruzii. [New representative of Lagomyidae from
            Paleolithic of Georgia.] Akad. Nauk Gruz. SSR, Soobshch., 45:1, 139–143, 2 figs. (Russian;
            Georgian summary).
1970A   Novyĭ predstavitel' tragelafin iz pliotsena Gruzii. [A new representative of Tragelaphini from the
            Pliocene of Georgia.] In: Fauna mezozoiã i kaĭnozoiã Gruzii i ee geoistoricheskoe znachenie,
            120–137, 1 fig., 4 tables (Russian; Georgian summary).

1972A   Kvabebskaia fauna akchagyl'skikh pozvonochnykh. [Kvabebi fauna of Akchagylian vertebrates.] Moscow: "Nauka" Press, 392 pp., illustr. (Russian).

VEKUA, A. K. and KHUKHIA, N. V.
1972A   O geologicheskom vozraste kostenosnykh peskov Kvemo-Kedi (Vostochnaia Gruziia). [On the geological age of the bone-bearing sands of Kvemo-Kedi (eastern Georgia).] Akad. Nauk Gruz. SSR, Soobshch., 65:1, 241–243, 1 fig. (Georgian; Russian and English summaries).

VEKUA, A. K. and MATSKHONASHVILI, K. G.
1970A   Pervaia nakhodka "diliuvial'nogo" byka v pleistotsene Gruzii. [First find of a "diluvial" ox in the Pleistocene of Georgia.] Akad. Nauk Gruz. SSR, Soobshch., 60:2, 501–504, 2 figs. (Russian; Georgian and English summaries).

VEKUA, A. K.   See also: Burchak-Abramovich, N. I. and Vekua, A. K., 1971A; Gabuniia, L. K. and Vekua, A. K., 1968A, 1968B, 1968C.

VELICHKO, ANDREI ALEKSEEVICH
1968A   Glavnyi klimaticheskii rubezh i etapy pleistotsena. [Main climatic boundary and stages of the Pleistocene.] Akad. Nauk SSSR, Izv., Ser. Geogr., 1968:3, 5–17, 5 figs. (Russian).
1971A   Sviaz' dinamiki prirodnykh izmenenii v pleistotsene s razvitiem pervobytnogo cheloveka. [Correlation of environmental change dynamics in Pleistocene with the development of ancient man.] Vop. Antropol., 37, 3–18, 3 figs. (Russian).

VELICHKO, A. A.   See also: Markov, K. K., Velichko, A. A., Lazukov, G. I. and Nikolaev, V. A., 1968A.

VELICHKOV, V.   See: Nikolov, Iv. and Velichkov, V., 1969A.

VENCL, SLAVOMIL
1966B   La station Paléolithique de Lubná près de Rakovník (Bohême). In: Filip, J. (ed.), 1966B, 25–26 (French).
1966C   La station Magdalénienne de Hostim près de Beroun (Bohême). In: Filip, J. (ed.), 1966B, 26–27 (French).

VENZO, S.   See: Grichuk, V. P., Hey, R. W. and Venzo, S., 1964A.

VEREISKII, N. G., IVANOVA, I. K. and NEISHTADT, M. I.
1964A   Nauchnye vystavki na VI kongresse INQUA. [Scientific exhibitions at the VI INQUA Congress.] In: Nauchnye itogi VI kongressa mezhdunarodnoi assotsiatsii po izucheniiu chetvertichnogo perioda (INQUA). (Varshava, 1961), 72–79, 2 figs. (Russian).

VERESHCHAGIN, NIKOLAI KUZ'MICH (= VEREŠČAGIN, N. K.)
1960C   Obez'iany i lednikovyi period Kavkaza. [Monkeys and the Ice Age in Caucasus.] Akad. Nauk Gruz. SSR, Soobshch., 25:3, 299–303, 3 figs. (Russian).
1963A   Osnovnye cherty formirovaniia teriofaun Golarktiki v antropogene. [Fundamental features of Holarctic theriofauna formation in Anthropogene.] Zool. Zh., 42:11, 1686–1698, 4 figs. (Russian; English summary).
1970A   Osvoenie zhivotnogo mira pervobytnym chelovekom na territorii SSSR. [The exploitation of animal world by primitive man on the territory of USSR.] Int. Congr. Anthropol. Ethnol. Sci., 7th, Moscow, 1964, Proc., 5, 531–536 (Russian).
1970B   The mammoth horizon. Animals, 12:10, 438–441.
1970C   Kartografirovanie v paleozoologii. [Mapping in paleozoology.] Vses. Geogr. Obshchest., Izv., 102:3, 264–270, 4 figs. (Russian).
1971A   A mammoth cemetery in Siberia. Illustr. London News, 258:6868, 26–27, illustr.
1971B   Peshchernyi lev i ego istoriia v Golarktike i v predelakh SSSR. [The cave lion and his history in Holarctic and within the USSR.] Akad. Nauk SSSR, Zool. Inst., Tr., 49, 123–199, 42 figs., 14 pls., 17 tables (Russian; English summary).
1971C   Okhoty pervobytnogo cheloveka i vymiranie pleistotsenovykh mlekopitaiushchikh v SSSR. [The hunting of the primitive man and the extinction of the Pleistocene mammals in the USSR.] Akad. Nauk SSSR, Zool. Inst., Tr., 49, 200–232, 20 tables (Russian; English summary).
1971D   Novye fakty o mamontakh. [New facts about mammoths.] In: Tezisy dokladov XVII sessii Vsesoiuznogo paleontologicheskogo obshchestva, 25–29 ianv. 1971g., 13 (Russian).
1972A   O proiskhozhdenii mamontovykh kladbishch. [On the origin of mammoth cemeteries.] Prirodn. Obstan. i Fauny Proshl., 6, 131–148, 8 figs. (Russian).

VERESHCHAGIN, N. K., ALEKSEEVA, L. I., DAVID, A. I. and BAĬGUSHEVA, V. S.
1969A   Iskopaemaîa vintorogaîa antilopa *Pontoceros ambiguus* gen. n. et sp. n. severnogo Prichernomor'îa.
          [Fossil screw-horned antelope *Pontoceros ambiguus* gen. nov. et sp. nov. from northern Black
          Sea region.] In: Mezhdunarodnyĭ kollokvium po geologii i faune nizhnego i srednego
          pleĭstofsena Evropy. Tezisy dokladov, 12–14 (Russian).

VERESHCHAGIN, N. K. and DAVID, A. I.
1968A   Die Säugetierfauna aus den frühanthropogenen Kiesen von Tiraspol. Deut. Ges. Geol. Wiss., Ber.,
          Reihe A, Geol. Paläontol., 13:3, 391–397, 1 table (German).
1971A   Mlekopitaîushchie epokhi otlozhenîi tiraspol'skogo graviîa. [Mammals of the age of deposition of
          Tiraspol' gravel.] Akad. Nauk SSSR, Zool. Inst., Tr., 49, 30–43, 4 figs., 3 pls., 2 tables
          (Russian; English summary).

VERESHCHAGIN, N. K. and MOCHANOV, ÎU. A.
1972A   Samye severnye v mire sledy verkhnego paleolita. [The world's northernmost traces of upper
          Paleolithic.] Sov. Arkheol., 1972:3, 332–336, 4 figs. (Russian).

VERESHCHAGIN, N. K.   See also: Alekseeva, E. V. and Vereshchagin, N. K., 1969A, 1970A; Pidoplichko, I. G.,
          Kistîakovskiĭ, A. B., Korneev, A. P. and Vereshchagin, N. K., 1969A.

VERGER-PRATOUCY, J.
1967A   La carie dentaire existait-elle chez l'homme du Plaéolithique. Soc. Préhist. Fr., Bull., C.R., 64:3,
          91–95 (French).

VERGER-PRATOUCY, J.   See also: Dubecq, X. J., Michelet, F. and Verger-Pratoucy, J., 1966A.

VERGNAUD-GRAZZINI, COLETTE
1968B   Amphibiens pléistocènes de Bolivie. Soc. Géol. Fr., Bull., 10:6, 688–695, 2 pls. (French).
          Rev.: Westphal in Zentralbl. Geol. Paläontol., Teil 2, 1970:3/4, 228.
1970A   Les Amphibiens fossiles du gisement d'Arondelli. Palaeontogr. Ital., 66, 47–65, 4 figs., 2 pls.
          (French).

VERGNAUD-GRAZZINI, C. and HOFFSTETTER, ROBERT
1972A   Présence de Palaeobatrachidae (Anura) dans des gisements tertiaires français. Caractérisation,
          distribution et affinités de la famille. Palaeovertebrata (Montpellier), 5:4, 157–177, 2 figs.,
          2 pls. (French; German and English summaries).

VERGNAUD-GRAZZINI, C. and MŁYNARSKI, MARIAN
1969A   Position systématique du genre *Pliobatrachus* Fejérvári 1917. Acad. Sci., C.R., Sér. D, 268:20, 2399–
          2402, 1 pl. (French).
          Rev.: Westphal in Zentralbl. Geol. Paläontol., Teil 2, 1970:1, 69.

VERLINDEN, W.   See: Quinet, G. E. and Verlinden, W., 1970A; Quinet, G. E., Verlinden, W. and
          Coupatez, P., 1971A.

VERMA, B. C.
1969A   *Procynocephalus pinjorii*, sp. nov. a new fossil primate from Pinjor beds (lower Pleistocene), east of
          Chandigarh. J. Palaeontol. Soc. India, 13, 53–57, 1 pl.

VERMA, K. K.
1968A   Bagh Beds - their fauna and affinities with south Indian Cretaceous formations. Geol. Soc. India,
          Mem., 2, seminar volume, 239–247, 4 figs.

VERMA, K. K. and MATHUR, D. P.
1968A   On the occurrence of a horncore of a bovid in the Rajahmundry sandstones of Pangadi. Current
          Sci., 37:16, 465–466, 2 figs.

VERNET, ROLAND   See: Broin, F. de, Grenot, C. and Vernet, R., 1971A.

VÉRTES, LÁSZLÓ
1964A*   Rev.: Müller-Beck in Schweiz. Ges. Urgesch., Jahrb., 52, 128.
1968A   Archäologische Forschungen im Jahre 1967. Urzeit. Vértesszöllös. Archaeol. Értesítö, 95:1, 129–130
          (German).
1969A   On the speed of evolution in Palaeolithic technology. Symp. Biol. Hungarica, 9, 47–50.
1969B   Kavics ösvény. A vértesszölösi elöember regénye. [Pebble trail. The story of the Vértesszölös
          hominid.] Budapest: Gondolat Publ., 237 pp., 46 figs., color pls., illustr. (Hungarian).

VERZILIN, N. N., KHOZAŤSKIĬ, L. I., VU DIN' LI and NESOV, L. A.
1970A   Novye paleontologicheskie dannye o granitše mezhdu nizhnim i verkhnim melom v Fergane. [New paleontological data on the limit between lower and upper Cretaceous in Fergana.] Leningrad, Univ., Vestn., 1970:18, 43—50, 1 fig. (Russian; English summary).

VERZILIN, N. N., MARTINSON, G. G. and KHOZAŤSKIĬ, L. I.
1970A   Novye dannye o paleontologicheskoĭ datirovke verkhneiūrskikh otlozheniĭ Ferganskoĭ vpadiny. [New data on paleontological dating of upper Jurassic deposits of Fergana trough.] Akad. Nauk SSSR, Dokl., 191:2, 407—409 (Russian).
1971A   New data on the paleontologic dating of the upper Jurassic of the Fergana depression. Akad. Nauk SSSR, Dokl., Earth Sci. Sec., 191, 48—49. (Translated from Russian: Akad. Nauk SSSR, Dokl., 1970, 191:2, 407—409.)

VETROV, FEDOR EGOROVICH   See: Bazhanov, V. S., Birĭukov, M. D., Vetrov, F. E., Kozhamkulova, B. S., Lychev, G. F., Musakulova, L. T. and Savinov, P. F., 1971A.

VEZIAN, JEAN   See: Vezian, J. and Vezian, J., 1966A, 1970A.

VEZIAN, JOSEPH and VEZIAN, JEAN
1966A   Les gisements de la grotte de Saint-Jean-de-Verges (Ariège). Gallia Préhist., 9:1, 93—130, 19 figs. (French).
1970A   Les gisements de la grotte de Saint-Jean-de-Verges (Ariège). Préhist. Spéléol. Ariége, 25, 29—77, 19 figs. (French).

VEZZANI, LIVIO
1967A   Osservazioni sul bacino lacustre del Fiume Mèrcure. Accad. Gioenia Sci. Natur. Catania, Atti, 18 suppl., 229—235, 1 map (Italian; English summary).

VIALLARD, PIERRE   See: Crouzel, F. and Viallard, P., 1968A.

VIÂLOV, OLEG STEPANOVICH
1968A   Materialy k klassifikatšii sledov i sledov zhiznedeĭatel'nosti organizmov. [Materials for classification of fossil traces and traces of life activity of organisms.] Paleontol. Sb., 5:1, 125—129, 5 tables (Russian; English summary).
    Rev.: Häntzschel in Zentralbl. Geol. Paläontol., Teil 2, 1970:1, 12—13.
1968B   Fossil traces of animals and their activity and their classification. Int. Paleontol. Union, Congress, Prague, 1968, Abstr., 55—56 (abs.).
    Rev.: Häntzschel in Zentralbl. Geol. Paläontol., Teil 2, 1970:1, 13.
1970A   Vykopni slidy patologichnykh iavishch— vnutrishni kameni. [Fossil traces of pathological phenomena — calculi.] Akad. Nauk Ukr. RSR, Dopov., Ser. B, 1970:4, 308—309 (Ukrainian; Russian and English summaries).
    Rev.: Häntzschel in Zentralbl. Geol. Paläontol., Teil 2, 1971:4, 266.
1972A   The classification of the fossil traces of life. Int. Geol. Congr., 24th, Canada, Abstr., 247—248 (abs.).
1972B   The classification of the fossil traces of life. Int. Geol. Congr., 24th, Canada, Proc., Sec. 7, 639—644, 2 figs.

VIANEY-LIAUD, MONIQUE
1969A   Rongeurs de l'Oligocène moyen provenant de nouvelles fouilles dans les Phosphorites du Quercy. Palaeovertebrata (Montpellier), 2:5, 209—239, 16 figs., 2 tables (French; German and English summaries).
1971A   Données nouvelles sur l'évolution des genres Eucricetodon et Pseudocricetodon à l'Oligocène en Europe Occidentale. Acad. Sci., C.R., Sér. D, 273:6, 619—622, 1 fig., 1 table (French).
1972A   Un cas de parallélisme intragénérique: l'évolution du genre Theridomys (Rodentia, Theridomyidae) à l'Oligocène moyen. Acad. Sci., C.R., Sér. D, 274:7, 1007—1010, 2 figs., 1 table (French).
1972B   Contribution à l'étude des Cricétidés oligocènes d'Europe Occidentale. Palaeovertebrata, 5:1, 46 pp., 12 figs., 5 pls., 8 tables (French; English and German summaries).

VIANEY-LIAUD, MONIQUE   See also: Hartenberger, J. L., Sigé, B., Sudre, J. and Vianey-Liaud, M., 1970A, 1970B; Helmer, D. and Vianey-Liaud, M., 1970A.

VICOVEANU, D.   See: Apostol, L. and Vicoveanu, D., 1970A.

VIDAL, PIERRE
1967B   Le problème de la conservation des grottes préhistoriques: l'exemple de Font-de-Gaume. Soc. Hist. Archéol. Périgord, Bull., 94:3, 154—165, 3 figs., 1 table (French).

VIDARTE, CAROLINA FUENTES (= FUENTES VIDARTE, CAROLINA)
  1966A   Estudio de dos cráneos de *Elephas meridionalis* Nesti, de la Vega de Granada. Soc. Españ. Hist.
           Natur., Bol., Secc. Biol., 64:3, 277—313, 16 figs., 5 tables (Spanish; English summary).

VIGLIARDI, ALDA
  1968A   L'industria litica della grotta di S. Teodoro, in provincia di Messina. (Scavi Graziosi-Maviglia). Riv.
           Sci. Preist., 23:1, 33—144, 27 figs., 4 tables (Italian; French and English summaries).
  1968B   Il Musteriano della Grotta Taddeo (Marina di Camerota, Salerno). Riv. Sci. Preist., 23:1, 245—259,
           4 figs. (Italian; French and English summaries).
  1968C   Prima campagna di scavi nel deposito paleolitico superiore di Grotta Calanca (Marina di Camerota,
           Salerno). Riv. Sci. Preist., 23:2, 271—314, 8 figs., 3 tables (Italian; French and English
           summaries).

VIGLIARDI, ALDA   See also: Palma di Cesnola, A. and Vigliardi, A., 1967A.

VILAR FIOL, R.
  1967A   La discriminación de las formaciones endonasales de los mamíferos y el etmoides. Col-Pa (Madrid,
           Univ., Fac. Cienc.), 1967:10, 3—5 (Spanish).

VILASECA, S.
  1969-70A   Dr. André Cheynier (1898—1968). Ampurias, 31—32, 363—365.

VILLEVEYGOUX, ABBÉ   See: Glory, Abbé André and Villeveygoux, Abbé, 1966A.

VILLIERS, ALAN
  1969A   In the wake of Darwin's Beagle. Illustrated by James L. Stanfield. Nat. Geogr. Mag., 136:4, 449—
           495, illustr.

VINOKUR, I. S.
  1969A   Dinoteriĭ na Podolii. [*Dinotherium* in Podolia.] Priroda, 1969:2, 104 (Russian).

VISSER, H.   See: Erdbrink, D. P., Tacoma, J. and Visser, H., 1966A.

VITA-FINZI, CLAUDIO
  1969A   Late Quaternary continental deposits of central and western Turkey. Man (J. Roy. Anthropol. Inst.),
           4:4, 605—619, 6 figs., 1 table.

V'IUSHKOV, B. P. (= VJUSHKOV, B. P.)
  1969A   Novye diĭsinodonty iz triasa ĭuzhnogo Priural'ia. [New dicynodonts from the Triassic of southern
           Cisuralia.] Paleontol. Zh., 1969:2, 99—106, 2 figs. (Russian).
  1969B   New dicynodonts from the Triassic of southern Cisuralia. Paleontol. J., 3:2, 237—242, 2 figs.

VJUSHKOV, B. P.   See: V'iushkov, B. P.

VLADIMIRSKAÍA, ELENA VLADIMIROVNA and BLAGONRAVOV, V. A.
  1966A   Siluriĭskaíâ sistema. [Silurian system.] Geologiíâ SSSR, 29, Tuvinskaíâ ASSR, 143—175, 2 figs.,
           1 table (Russian).

VLČEK, EMANUEL
  1967B   Der Jungpleistozäne Menschenfund aus Svitávka in Mähren. Akten des Anthropologischen Kongresses,
           Brno, 1965. Anthropos, Brno, 19, 262—270, 9 figs., 1 map (German).
  1968B   Nalez pozůstatků neandertálce v Šali na Slovensku. [The find of remains of the Neanderthal man at
           Sal'a in Slovakia.] Czech., Ústřed. Ústav Geol., Sborn. Geol. Věd, Rada A: Antropozoikum,
           5, 105—124, 6 figs., 8 pls., 2 tables (Czech; English and Russian summaries).
  1969A   Neandertaler der Tschechoslowakei. Prague: Academia, 276 pp., 144 figs., 57 pls., 54 tables, 4 maps
           (German).
           Rev.: Faulhaber in An. Antropol., Mexico, 8, 301—302; Ferembach in L'Anthropologie, 74:3—4,
           284—285; Guenther-Peters in Quartär, 20, 233; Íakimov in Vop. Antropol., 37, 164—165
           (Russian); Knussmann in Homo, 20:4, 255; ms in Archeol. Roz., 21:6, 834—835 (Czech);
           Maringer in Anthropos, 66:3—4, 596; Pittioni in Archaeol. Austriaca, 49, 64; Preuschoft in
           Zentralbl. Geol. Paläontol., Teil 2, 1970:3/4, 248—249; Roth-Lutra in Anat. Anz., 129:3,
           355—356; Žebera in Czech., Ústřed. Ústav. Geol., Věstn., 44:6, 378.
  1969B   Le métopisme au cours de l'évolution onto- et phylogénétique de l'espèce *Homo sapiens*. Int. Congr.
           Anthropol. Ethnol. Sci., 8th, Tokyo, 1968, Proc., Vol. I. Anthropology, 110—112, 2 figs.
           (French).

1970A Étude comparative onto-phylogénétique de l'enfant du Pech-de-l'Azé par rapport à d'autres enfants néandertaliens. Arch. Inst. Paléontol. Hum., Mém., 33, 149–180, 9 figs. (French).

VOGEL, CHRISTIAN
1968B The phylogenetical evaluation of some characters and some morphological trends in the evolution of the skull in Catarrhine primates. In: Chiarelli, B. (ed.), 1968C, 21–55, 17 figs., 4 tables.
1969A Funktionelle und phylogenetische Aspekte der Morphologie des Schädels höherer Primaten einschliesslich der Hominiden. Z. Morphol. Anthropol., 60:3, 242–262, 6 figs. (German; English summary).
1970A Gegenwärtige Probleme der Morphologie in der Stammesgeschichte von Primaten und Mensch. Z. Morphol. Anthropol., 62:2, 185–206, 4 figs. (German; English summary).

VOGEL, J. C. and BEAUMONT, P. B.
1972A Revised radiocarbon chronology for the Stone Age in South Africa. Nature, 237:5349, 50–51.

VOGEL, J. C. See also: Malez, M. and Vogel, J. C., 1970A; Molleson, T. I., Oakley, K. P. and Vogel, J. C., 1972A.

VOGELTANZ, RUDOLF
1968A Bericht über eine grosse Fossilgrabung im Salzburger Alpenvorland. Aufschluss, 19, 42–44, 3 figs. (German).
1969A Fischfunde aus der Salzburger Obertrias. Aufschluss, 20:4, 96–99, 4 figs. (German).
1970A Sedimentologie und Paläogeographie eines eozänen Sublitorals im Helvetikum von Salzburg (Österreich). Austr. Geol. Bundesanst., Verh., 1970:3, 373–451, 14 figs., 5 pls., 3 tables (German; English summary).

VOGT, HANS-HEINRICH
1970A Warum sind die Tiere einst aus dem Wasser gestiegen? Kosmos (Stuttgart), 66:3, 110–113, 1 fig. (German).
1970B Schlafen und Träumen. Kosmos (Stuttgart), 1970:11, 482–489, 7 figs. (German).
1971A Neuer Archaeopteryx-Fund. Naturwiss. Rundsch., 24:7, 312 (German).
1971B 25 Jahre Radiocarbondatierung. Kosmos (Stuttgart), 67:11, 478–483, 5 figs. (German).
1972A Wie gut flog der Urvogel? Kosmos, 68:7, 299–302, illustr. (German).

VOICHIN, IRINA
1966A Dinosaurul Mamenchisaurus hochuanensis. [Dinosaur Mamenchisaurus hochuanensis.] Natura, Ser. Biol., 18:3, 94, 3 figs. (Rumanian).

VOĬNO, M. S.
1972A Nekotorye problemy evolíutsii mozga i profsess gominizatsii. [Some problems of brain evolution and the hominization process.] Vop. Antropol., 41, 150–152 (Russian).

VOINSTVENSKIĬ, M. A.
1963A Iskopaemaia ornitofauna Kryma. [Fossil ornithofauna of Crimea.] Akad. Nauk Ukr. SSR, Kompl. Karst. Eksped., Tr., 1, 106–123 (Russian).
1965A Nekotorye cherty sovremennoĭ ornitofauny Kryma i ee istoriia na protiazhenii antropogena. [Some traits of the Modern ornithofauna of Crimea and its history during the Anthropogene.] In: Nazemni khrebetni Ukrainy, 51–63 (Russian).

VOLKHEIMER, WOLFGANG
1971A Aspectos paleoclimatológicos del Terciario Argentino. Mus. Argent. Cien. Natur. "Bernardino Rivadavia", Rev., Paleontol., 1:8, 243–262, 3 figs., 2 pls., 5 tables (Spanish; German summary).

VOLKOV, I. A. See: Alekseeva, E. V. and Volkov, I. A., 1969A.

VOLKOVA, V. S.
1970A Geologicheskoe stroenie pozdnepliotsenovykh i chetvertichnykh otlozhenii osnovnykh stratoraĭonov. [Geological structure of late Pliocene and Quaternary deposits of the principal strato-regions.] Akad. Nauk SSSR, Sib. Otd., Inst. Geol. Geofiz., Tr., 92, 20–47 (Russian).

VOLOSHIN, V. E. See: Bukatchuk, P. D., Burdenko, B. V. and Voloshin, V. E., 1968A, 1968B.

VÖLPEL, ALFRED
1966A Innere Gezetzmässigkeiten paläontologischer Entwicklungsabläufe. Naturwiss. Ver. Hamburg, Abh. Verh., 11, 79–100, 2 figs., 1 table (German).

VON GRAEVE, B.   See: Gaherty, G., Kettel, D., MacDonald, J., Niemann, L., Von Graeve, B. and Arima, E.,
                        1969A.

VONDERBANK, KLAUS
   1970A   Geologie und Fauna der Tertiären Ablagerungen Zentral-Spitsbergen. Nor. Polarinst. Skr., no. 153,
                  1–120, 31 figs., 21 pls. (German).

VONDRA, C. F., JOHNSON, G. D., BOWEN, B. E. and BEHRENSMEYER, A. K.
   1971A   Preliminary stratigraphical studies of the east Rudolf Basin, Kenya. Nature, 231:5300, 245–248,
                  3 figs., 1 table.

VOORHIES, MICHAEL R.
   1968B   Evidence of seasonal growth in Tertiary vertebrate fossils. Geol. Soc. Amer., Spec. Pap., 115, 230
                  (abs.).
   1969A   An Eocene sea cow tooth from Twiggs County, Georgia. Georgia Acad. Sci., Bull., 27:2, 92–94
                  (abs.).
   1969B   Taphonomy and population dynamics of an early Pliocene vertebrate fauna, Knox County, Nebraska.
                  Wyo., Univ., Contrib. Geol., Spec. Pap., 1, 69 pp., 29 figs., 13 pls., 12 tables.
   1970A   Paleontological evidence for Pliocene age of "high-level gravels", Taylor County, Georgia. Geol.
                  Soc. Amer., Abstr., 2:3, 246–247 (abs.).
   1970B   Sampling difficulties in reconstructing late Tertiary mammalian communities. N. Amer. Paleontol.
                  Conv., Proc., Part E, 454–468, 7 figs.
   1971A   Paleoclimatic significance of crocodilian remains from the Ogallala group (upper Tertiary) in north-
                  eastern Nebraska. J. Paleontol., 45:1, 119–121, 2 figs.
   1971B   The Watkins quarry: a new Late Pleistocene mammal locality in Glynn County, Georgia. Georgia
                  Acad. Sci., Bull., 29:2, 128.
   1971C   Study of a Pliocene fauna of Nebraska. Nat. Geogr. Soc., Res. Reps., 1965, 239–240.
   1972A   A family group (?) of megatheres from Georgia. Soc. Vert. Paleontol., Ann. Meeting, 32nd, 1972,
                  Abstr. (abs.).

VOORHIES, M. R. and TOOTS, H.
   1970A   An unusual burrow of a Tertiary vertebrate. Wyo., Univ., Contrib. Geol., 9:1, 7–8, 2 figs.

VOROB'EVA, EMILIĨA IVANOVNA (= VOROBYEVA, E. I.)
   1966A   O mono- ili polifileticheskom proiskhozhdenii tetrapod. [On mono- or polyphyletic origin of
                  tetrapods.] Zool. Zh., 45:9, 1355–1368, 7 figs. (Russian; English summary).
   1971A   K evoliŭtsii ripidistnykh kisteperykh ryb. [On the evolution of rhipidistian crossopterygian fishes.]
                  Paleontol. Zh., 1971:3, 3–16, 3 figs. (Russian).
   1971B   Etmoidnaĩa oblast Panderichthys i nekotorye problemy morfologii kisteperykh. [The ethmoid region
                  of Panderichthys and some problems of the cranial morphology of crossopterygians.] Akad.
                  Nauk SSSR, Paleontol. Inst., Tr., 130, 142–159, 8 figs., 2 pls. (Russian).
   1971C   Novyĩ vid osteolepid iz srednego devona Latvii. [A new osteolepid species from the middle Devonian
                  of Latvia.] Paleontol. Stratigr. Pribalt. Belorus., 3, 209–213, 2 figs. (Russian; English summary).
   1971D   Evolution of the Rhipidistia (Crossopterygii). Paleontol. J., 5:3, 283–293, 3 figs.
   1972A   Novyĩ rod dvoĩakodyshashchikh iz émĩaksinskoĩ svity Iakutii. [New Dipnoi genus from Emĩaksin
                  formation of Iakutia.] Paleontol. Zh., 1972:2, 94–100, 3 figs., 1 pl. (Russian).

VOROB'EVA, EMILIĨA IVANOVNA and LIARSKAĨA, LIŬBOV' ANATOL'EVNA
   1968A   Ostatki kisteperykh i dvoĩakodyshashchikh iz amatskikh sloev Latvii i ikh zakhoronenie. [Remains of
                  crossopterygians and dipnoans from Amata beds of Latvia and their burial.] In: Ocherki po
                  filogenii i sistematike iskopaemykh ryb i bezcheliustnykh, 71–86, 9 figs., 2 pls. (Russian).

VOROB'EVA, T. D.   See: Maleeva, A. G. and Vorob'eva, T. D., 1970A.

VOROBYEVA, E. I.   See: Vorob'eva, E. I.

VORONIN, IŬRIĨ IVANOVICH   See: Barsbold, R., Voronin, Iu. I. and Zhegallo, V. I., 1971A.

VORONTSOV, NIKOLAĨ NIKOLAEVICH (= VORONTZOW, N. N. = WORONZOW, N. N.)
   1963C   Neravnomernost' tempov preobrazovaniĩa organov i printsip kompensatsii funktsiĩ. [Irregularity of
                  tempo in organ transformation and the principle of the compensation of functions.] Zool. Zh.,
                  42:9, 1289–1305, 4 figs. (Russian; English summary).
   1967A   Evoliutsiĩa pishchevaritel'noĩ sistemy gryzunov (mysheobraznye). [Evolution of the alimentary system
                  in myomorph rodents.] Novosibirsk: "Nauka" Press, 235 pp., 148 figs., 14 tables (Russian).
                  Rev.: Polivanov in Quart. Rev. Biol., 43:3, 347–348; Zusman in Zool. Zh., 47:8, 1272–1274
                  (Russian).

1968A   Istoricheskaĭa zoogeografiĭa mysheobraznykh (Muroidea) gryzunov. [Historical zoogeography of the muroid rodents.] In: Problemy evoliŭtsii, 1, 116—141, 18 figs. (Russian; English summary).

VORONTSOV, N. N.   See also: Timofeev-Resovskiĭ, N. V., Vorontsov, N. N. and Iablokov, A. V., 1969A.

VOROSHILOVA, ANASTASIĬA GRIGOR'EVNA
1971A   K stratigrafii miotsenovykh otlozheniĭ Azerbaĭdzhana. [On the stratigraphy of Miocene deposits of Azerbaĭdzhan.] In: Stratigrafiĭa neogena Vostoka Evropeĭskoĭ chasti SSSR, 288—301 (Russian).

VORUZ, CATHERINE
1970A   Origine des dents bilophodontes des Cercopithecoidea. Mammalia, 34:2, 269—293, 16 figs., 2 pls. (French; English summary).

VORUZ, CATHERINE   See also: Blot, J. and Voruz, C., 1970A.

VORZIMMER, PETER J.
1971A   Darwin's "Lamarckism" and the "flat-fish controversy" (1863—1871). Lychnos, 1971, 121—170, 6 figs.
1970A   Charles Darwin: the years of controversy. Philadelphia: Temple Univ. Press, xix + 300 pp. Rev.: de Beer in New Sci., 54:794, 288—289.
1972A   Charles Darwin: the years of controversy. London: University of London, xix + 300 pp. Rev.: Barrington in Nature, 239:5370, 291.

VOSS-FOUCART, MARIE-FRANÇOISE
1971A   Est-il possible d'expliquer l'extinction des dinosaures à la fin du Crétacé. Natur. Belg., 52:2, 101—108 (French).

VOZNIACHUK, L. N., SHCHEGLOVA, V. V. and KALECHITS, E. G.
1972A   O pervoĭ nakhodke ostatkov severnogo olenia (Rangifer tarandus L.) v podmorennykh otlozheniĭakh Belorussii. [On the first find of remains of reindeer (Rangifer tarandus L.) in the submorainic deposits of Belorussia.] Akad. Navuk BSSR, Dokl., 16:1, 50—52, 1 fig., 1 table (Russian).

VRBA, E. S.
1971A   A new fossil alcelaphine (Artiodactyla: Bovidae) from Swartkrans. Transvaal Mus., Ann., 27:5, 59—82, 10 figs., 3 pls.
1972A   Statistical evaluation of the taxonomic status of a fossil member of the Bovidae (Mammalia: Artiodactyla). Transvaal Mus., Ann., 28:2, 17—26, 1 fig., 6 tables.

VU DIN' LI   See: Verzilin, N. N., Khozatskiĭ, L. I., Vu Din' Li and Nesov, L. A., 1970A..

VUILLEUMIER, B. S.
1971A   Pleistocene changes in the fauna and flora of South America. Science, 173:3999, 771—780, 4 figs., 3 tables.

W., F. S.
1966A   Professor L. S. Palmer. Geol. Ass. (London), Proc., 77, 167—168.

WAAGE, K. M.   See: Dunbar, C. O. and Waage, K. M., 1969A.

WADE, NICHOLAS
1972A   Creationists and evolutionists: confrontation in California. Science, 178:4062, 724—729.

WADE, ROBERT E., et al.
1969A   Museum model making. Los Angeles Cty. Mus., Quart., 7:2, 37—44, 11 illustr.

WADE, WILLIAM D.
1967A*   Miscellaneous papers in paleopathology: I. Mus. North Ariz., Tech. Ser., 7, v + 60, illustr. Rev.: Merbs in Amer. Anthropol., 71, 168—170; Turner in Amer. J. Phys. Anthropol., 32:1, 151.

WAGNER, CAROL DAILY
1969A   Paleontology at the University of California: the history of Bacon Hall. J. West, 8, 169—182, 2 pls.

WAGNER, FRANCES J. E.
1970A   Faunas of the Pleistocene Champlain Sea. Can., Geol. Surv., Bull., 181, 1–104, 2 figs., 7 pls., 2 table

WAGNER, G. A.   See: Faul, H. and Wagner, G. A., 1971A.

WAGNER, WARREN H.
1969A   The construction of a classification. Discussions. In: Sibley, Ch. G. (ed.), 1969A, 67–103, 7 figs.

WAGSTAFFE, REGINALD and FIDLER, J. HAVELOCK
1968A   Rev.: Stansfield in Mus. J., 69:1, 31–32.

WAHLERT, GERD VON
1968A   Latimeria und die Geschichte der Wirbeltiere. Eine evolutionsbiologische Untersuchung. Fortschr.
         Evolutionsforsch., 4, 133 pp., 63 figs. (German).
    Rev.: Fischer in Deut. Ges. Geol. Wiss., Ber., Reihe A, 14:6, 746–747; Gutmann in Natur Mus.,
         101:11, 477; Kähsbauer in Naturhist. Mus. Wien, Ann., 75, 670; Kaltenbach in Anthropol.
         Ges., Mitt., 99, 223; Kietz in Gegenbaurs Morph. Jahrb., 113:1, 159–160; Kuhn in Anthropos,
         63/64:5/6, 1002–1003; Kuhn in Säugetierkundl. Mitt., 17:3, 284; Marinelli in Zool.-Bot. Ges.
         Wien, Verh., 108/109, 181–182; Mergner in Naturwiss. Rundsch., 22:5, 276; Remmert in
         Naturwiss., 56:7, 384; Romer in Quart. Rev. Biol., 44:4, 416–417; Rossi Ronchetti in Riv.
         Ital. Paleontol. Stratigr., 75:3, 684; Roth-Lutra in Anat. Anz., 129:3, 340–341; Schindewolf
         in Zentralbl. Geol. Paläontol., Teil 2, 1969:2, 113–115; Thenius in Geol. Ges. Wien, Mitt.,
         61, 219; Wegelin in Biol. Zentralbl., 88:6, 816.

WAHLERT, GERD VON and WAHLERT, HEIDI VON
1967A   Bau und Funktion der paddelförmigen Unpaarflossen von Latimeria chalumnae J. L. B. Smith
         (Actinistia, Osteichthyes). Stuttgarter Beitr. z. Naturk., 172, 3 pp. (German).

WAHLERT, HEIDI VON   See: Wahlert, G. von and Wahlert, H. von, 1967A.

WAHLERT, JOHN H.
1968A   Variability of rodent incisor enamel as viewed in thin section, and the microstructure of the
         enamel in fossil and recent rodent groups. Breviora, 309, 18 pp., 3 figs., 4 tables.

WAKE, DAVID B.   See: Özeti, N. and Wake, D. B., 1969A.

WAKE, MARVALEE H.   See: Estes, R. and Wake, M. H., 1972A.

WAKEFIELD, JOHN
1972A   The halfway bird. Frontiers, 37:1, 24–27, illustr.

WAKEFIELD, NORMAN A.
1967A   Mammal bones in the Buchan district. Victorian Natur., 84, 211–214, 2 tables.
1967B   Preliminary report on McEachern's Cave, S.W. Victoria. Victorian Natur., 84, 363–383, 5 figs.,
         3 tables.
1972A   Palaeoecology of fossil mammal assemblages from some Australian caves. Roy. Soc. Victoria, Proc.,
         85:1, 1–26, 1 fig., 3 pls., 4 tables.

WAKEFIELD, NORMAN A.   See also: Warren, J. W. and Wakefield, N. A., 1972A.

WALDMAN, MICHAEL
1969A   On an immature specimen of Kritosaurus notabilis (Lambe) (Ornithischia: Hadrosauridae) from the
         upper Cretaceous of Alberta, Canada. Can. J. Earth Sci., 6:4, 569–576, 2 pls., 1 table.
1969B   Ichthyodectes and Holcolepis from the Cretaceous of Lac des Bois, Northwest Territories, Canada.
         Can. J. Earth Sci., 6:5, 1316–1319, 2 pls., 1 table.
1970A   A teiid lizard jaw from the Cretaceous of Alberta, Canada. Can. J. Earth Sci., 7:2, 542–547, 3 figs.
1970B   Comments on a Cretaceous coprolite from Alberta, Canada. Can. J. Earth Sci., 7:3, 1008–1012, 1 pl.
         Rev.: Häntzschel in Zentralbl. Geol. Paläontol., Teil 2, 1970:6, 472–473.
1970C   A third specimen of a lower Cretaceous feather from Victoria, Australia. Condor, 72, 377, 1 fig.
         Rev.: McK. in Emu, 71, 186.
1971A   Hexanchid and orthacodontid shark teeth from the lower Tertiary of Vancouver Island, British
         Columbia. Can. J. Earth Sci., 8:1, 166–170, 1 pl.
1971B   Fish from the freshwater lower Cretaceous of Victoria, Australia, with comments on the palaeo-
         environment. Spec. Pap. Palaeontol., 9, 124 pp., 37 figs., 18 pls., 6 tables.
1971C   A re-examination of Psilichthys selwyni Hall, from the lower Cretaceous of Victoria. Roy. Soc.
         Victoria, Proc., 84:2, 263–266, 3 pls.

WALDMAN, MICHAEL and HOPKINS, W. S., JR.
1970A   Coprolites from the upper Cretaceous of Alberta, Canada, with a description of their microflora. Can. J. Earth Sci., 7:5, 1295—1303, 59 figs.

WALDMAN, MICHAEL and SAVAGE, ROBERT JOSEPH GAY
1972A   The first Jurassic mammal from Scotland. Geol. Soc. London, J., 128:2, 119—125, 2 figs.

WALDREN, WILLIAM and KOPPER, JOHN S.
1968A   An extinct antelope and prehistoric man. Discovery, 3:2, 39—44, 6 figs.

WALDROP, JOHN
1969A   Fossil horses of Florida. Plaster Jacket, 9, 10 pp., 8 figs.

WALENGA, ARLINE J.   See: Garn, S. M., Lewis, A. B. and Walenga, A. J., 1969A.

WALKER, ALAN C.
1969A   True affinities of Propotto leakeyi Simpson 1967. Nature, 223:5206, 647—648, 1 fig., 1 table.
1970A   Post-cranial remains of the Miocene Lorisidae of East Africa. Amer. J. Phys. Anthropol., 33:2, 249—261, 8 figs., 4 tables.
1972A   Chesowanja australopithecine. Nature, 238:5359, 108—109, 2 figs.
1972B   The dissemination and segregation of early primates in relation to continental configuration. In: Bishop, W. W. and Miller, J. A. (eds.), 1972A, 195—218, 3 figs., 2 tables.

WALKER, A. C., BROCK, P. W. G. and MACDONALD, R.
1969A   Fossil mammal locality on Mount Elgon, eastern Uganda. Nature, 223:5206, 591—593, 2 tables.

WALKER, A. C.   See also: Day, M. H. and Walker, A. C., 1969A; Hill, A. and Walker, A., 1972A; Leakey, R. E. F., Mungai, J. M. and Walker, A. C., 1971A, 1972A.

WALKER, ALICK D.
1969A   The reptile fauna of the 'Lower Keuper' sandstone. Geol. Mag., 106:5, 470—476, 1 fig.
1970A   A revision of the Jurassic reptile Hallopus victor (Marsh), with remarks on the classification of crocodiles. Roy. Soc. London, Phil. Trans., Ser. B, 257:816, 323—372, 19 figs., 2 tables.
1972A   New light on the origin of birds and crocodiles. Nature, 237:5353, 257—263, 9 figs.

WALKER, C. A.   See: Harrison, C. J. O. and Walker, C. A., 1970A, 1971A, 1972A; Moody, R. T. J. and Walker, C. A., 1970A.

WALKER, MYRL V.
1970A   George Fryer Sternberg, August 26, 1883—October 23, 1969. Soc. Vert. Paleontol., News Bull., 88, 77.

WALLACE, ALFRED RUSSELL
1972A   Darwinism applied to man. In: McCown, T. D. and Kennedy, K. A. R. (eds.), 1972A, 181—187 (reprinted from Wallace, 1889).

WALLACE, CHARLOTTE
1969A   A study of evolution. Glasgow and London: Blackie, 149 pp., illustr.
         Rev.: George in Nature, 223:5204, 424.

WALLER, P. F.   See: Hayman, D. L., Kirsch, J. A. W., Martin, P. G. and Waller, P. F., 1971A.

WALTER, B.   See: David, L., Evin, J., Guérin, C., Mongereau, N. and Walter, B., 1972A.

WALTER, H.
1970A   Grundriss der Anthropologie. Munich and Vienna: BLV Verlagsgesellschaft, 234 pp., 117 figs., 35 pls. (German).
         Rev.: Haltenorth in Säugetierkundl. Mitt., 20:1—2, 191; May in Naturwiss. Rundsch., 24:12, 543—544; Schwidetzky in Homo, 21:4, 251.

WALTON, DAN W.
1969A   Evolution of the chiropteran scapula. Tex. J. Sci., 21:1, 85—90, 1 fig.

WALTON, DAN W.   See also: Slaughter, B. H. and Walton, D. W. (eds.), 1970A.

WANG, BAN-YUE
1965A   Abs.: Sci. Abstr. China, Earth Sci., 3:2, 5.

WANG, CUN-YI and ZHEN, SHOU-NAN
1963A   Abs.: Sci. Abstr. China, Earth Sci., 2:2, 7.

WANG, TZE-YI and HU, CHANG-KANG
1963A   Abs.: Sci. Abstr. China, Earth Sci., 2:2, 6—7.

WANG, Y.-Y., HSUEH, H.-H., HO, J.-C. and CHANG, K.-W.
1969A   Quaternary stratigraphy of northern Shansi and eastern Kansu loess district. Int. Geol. Rev., 11:7, 787—802, 9 figs., 1 table.

WARNICKA, JAMES M. and WILLIAMSON, T.
1968A   The Milnesand site — revisited. Amer. Antiquity, 33, 16—24, 5 figs., table.

WARNOCK, FRANK B.
1972A   The Pleistocene mammal fauna and associated artifacts of the San Pedro Springs, Pecos County, Texas. Diss. Abstr., 33:4, 1696B (abs.).

WARREN, ANNE
1972A   Queensland trace fossils pose a 230 million years old problem. Austral. Natur. Hist., 17:5, 160—162, 3 figs.

WARREN, JAMES W.
1969A   Chelid turtles from the mid-Tertiary of Tasmania. J. Paleontol., 43, 179—182, 2 figs.
1969B   A fossil chelonian of probable lower Cretaceous age from Victoria, Australia. Victoria, Nat. Mus., Mem., 29, 23—28, 2 figs., 1 pl.

WARREN, JAMES W. and WAKEFIELD, NORMAN A.
1972A   Trackways of tetrapod vertebrates from the upper Devonian of Victoria, Australia. Nature, 238:5365, 469—470, 3 figs.

WARRINGTON, GEOFFREY
1970A   The stratigraphy and palaeontology of the "Keuper" series of the central Midlands of England. (Discussions.). Geol. Soc. London, Quart. J., 126:1—2, 183—223, 8 figs., 7 pls., 1 table.

WARTER, STUART L.   See: Howard, H. and Warter, S. L., 1969A.

WASHBURN, SHERWOOD L.
1967B   The strategy of physical anthropology. In: Rapport, S. and Wright, H. (eds.), 1967A, 76—93, 1 table (reprinted from Kroeber, 1953, Anthropology today).
1968A   On Holloway's "Tools and teeth." Amer. Anthropol., 70, 97—101.
1968B   The study of human evolution. Condon Lectures, 48 pp., 25 figs.
1968C   One hundred years of biological anthropology. In: Brew, J. O. (ed.), 1968A, 97—115, 242—248.
1969A   The analysis of primate evolution with particular reference to the origin of man. In: Ehrlich, P. R., et al. (eds.), 1969A, 523—540, 1 fig.
1969B   Origin of man. Amer. Anthropol. Ass., Bull., 2:3, 109 (abs.).
1971A   The study of human evolution. In: Dolhinow, P. and Sarich, V. M. (eds.), 1971A, 82—117, 23 figs. (reprinted from Condon Lectures, 1968).
1972A   The new physical anthropology. In: Jennings, J. D. and Hoebel, E. A. (eds.), 1972A, 87—93, illustr. (reprinted from N.Y. Acad. Sci., Trans., 13:7, 298—304).
1972B   Human evolution. In: Dobzhansky, Th., Hecht, M. K. and Steere, W. C. (eds.), 1972B, 349—361, 1 table.

WASHBURN, S. L. and HARDING, R. S.
1972A   Evolution of primate behavior. In: Dolhinow, P. (ed.), 1972A, 338—351.

WASHBURN, S. L. and JAY, P. C.
1968A*   Perspectives on human evolution. I. New York: Holt, Rinehart & Winston, 287 pp., illustr.
               Rev.: Harlow in Amer. Anthropol., 71, 354—356; Hooijer in Genetica, 40:3, 434—435; Neville in Amer. J. Phys. Anthropol., 32:1, 162—163.

WASHBURN, S. L. and LANCASTER, C. S.
1968A   The evolution of hunting. In: Lee, R. B. and DeVore, I. (eds.), 1968A, 293—303.
1971A   The evolution of hunting. In: Dolhinow, P. and Sarich, V. M. (eds.), 1971A, 387—405 (reprinted from Lee and DeVore, eds., 1969, Man the hunter).

WASHBURN, S. L. and SHIREK, JUDITH
    1967A   Human evolution. In: Hirsch, J. (ed.), 1967A, 10—21.

WASHBURN, S. L.   See also: DeVore, I. and Washburn, S. L., 1972A.

WATANABE, HITOSHI
    1969A   Neanderthalers vs. *H. sapiens*. Behavorial adaptability to arctic winter. Int. Congr. Anthropol. Ethnol.
                  Sci., 8th, Tokyo, 1968, Proc., Vol. I. Anthropology, 280—283.
    1970B   A symposium on the origin of *Homo sapiens*. J. Anthropol. Soc. Nippon, 78:4, 339 (Japanese).

WATERLOT, GÉRARD
    1969A   Aperçu géologique de la région de Lille. Soc. Géol. Nord, Ann., 89:1, 67—77, 4 figs. (French;
                  English summary).

WATERLOT, GÉRARD   See also: Routhier, P. and Waterlot, G., 1968A.

WATERMAN, A. J., *et al.*
    1971A   Chordate structure and function. New York: Macmillan Co.; London: Collier-Macmillian Ltd.,
                  587 pp., illustr.
                  Rev.: Wood in BioScience, 21:11, 549.

WATERS, B. T., HUTCHISON, J. H. and SAVAGE, D. E.
    1972A   Early Eocene fossiliferous continental strata, northwest Washakie basin, Sweetwater County,
                  Wyoming. Geol. Soc. Amer., Abstr., 4:6, 420 (abs.).

WATERS, B. T. and SAVAGE, D. E.
    1969A   Skeletal specializations in the Diprotodontidae (Mammalia; Marsupialia). Geol. Soc. Amer., Abstr.,
                  Part 3, 72 (abs.).

WATERS, BARBARA T.   See also: Savage, D. E., Waters, B. T. and Hutchison, J. H., 1972A, 1972B.

WATSON, KAREN ANN
    1970A   Neanderthal and upper Palaeolithic burial patterns: a re-examination. Mankind, 7:4, 302—306,
                  4 tables.

WATSON, LYALL
    1971A   The omnivorous ape. New York : Coward, McCann and Geoghegan, Inc., 222 pp.

WATSON, WILLIAM
    1966A   Early civilization in China. New York: McGraw-Hill Book Co., 143 pp., 134 illustr.
                  Rev.: Chang in Amer. Anthropol., 69, 537.

WEAVER, W. G. and OBER, L. D.
    1971A   A preliminary analysis of a late Pleistocene vertebrate fauna from south Florida. Fla. Acad. Sci.,
                  Quart. J., 34:1 suppl., 14 (abs.).

WEAVER, W. G.   See also: Ober, L. D. and Weaver, W. G., 1971A.

WEBB, P. N.   See: McKelvey, B. C., Webb, P. N., Gorton, M. P. and Kohn, B. P., 1970A.

WEBB, S. DAVID
    1969A   The Pliocene Canidae of Florida. Fla. State Mus., Bull., Biol. Sci., 14:4, 273—308, 8 figs., 9 tables.
                  Rev.: Thenius in Zentralbl. Geol. Paläontol., Teil 2, 1970:6, 519—520.
    1969B   Extinction-origination equilibria in late Cenozoic land mammals of North America. Evolution, 23:4,
                  688—702, 4 figs., 3 tables.
    1969C   The Burge and Minnechaduza Clarendonian mammalian faunas of north-central Nebraska. Calif.,
                  Univ., Publ. Geol. Sci., 78, 191 pp., 46 figs., 52 tables.
                  Rev.: Romer in Palaeogeogr., Palaeoclimatol., Palaeoecol., 10, 77—78; Wetzig in Gegenbaurs Morph.
                  Jahrb., 114:3, 455.
    1970A   Reconnaissance of late Cenozoic vertebrate deposits in southern Honduras. Amer. Phil. Soc., Yearb.,
                  1969, 336.
    1970B   Fossil xenarthrans of Florida. Plaster Jacket, no. 13, 9 pp., 5 figs.
    1972A   Locomotor evolution in camels. Forma et Functio, 5:2, 99—112, 5 figs. (French and German summaries).
    1972B   Fossil peccaries of Florida. Plaster Jacket, 17, 10 pp., 4 figs.

WEBB, S. DAVID and TESSMAN, NORM
1968A   A Pliocene vertebrate fauna from low elevation in Manatee County, Florida. Amer. J. Sci., 266:9, 777–811, 5 figs., 4 tables.

WEBB, S. DAVID   See also: Patton, T. H. and Webb, S. D., 1970A.

WEBER, T. J.
1968A   Avoiding evolution: an appraisal of current hominid thinking. Wyo. Archaeol., 11:1, 10–15.

WEDDELL, G.
1972A   In memoriam. Wilfrid Edward Le Gros Clark. J. Anat., 111:1, 181–184, portr.

WEI, CHEN-YI
1964A   Abs.: Sci. Abstr. China, Earth Sci., 3:1, 4.

WEIDENREICH, FRANZ
1972A   Facts and speculations concerning the origin of Homo sapiens. In: McCown, T. D. and Kennedy, K. A. R. (eds.), 1972A, 336–353 (reprinted from Amer. Anthropol., 49:2).

WEIDMANN, MARC
1969A   Le mammouth de Praz-Rodet (Le Brassus, Vaud). Note préliminaire. Soc. Vaudoise Sci. Natur., Bull., 70:6, 229–239, 3 figs., 3 pls., 1 table (French).
1970A   Le mammouth de Praz-Rodet (Le Brassus, Vaud). Note préliminaire. Lausanne Univ., Lab. Géol., Bull., 179, 12 pp., 3 figs., 3 pls., 1 table (French).

WEIGEL, ROBERT D.
1962C   Fossil vertebrates of Vero, Florida. Fla. Geol. Surv., Spec. Publ. 10, 59 pp., 6 figs., 5 tables.

WEILER, WILHELM
1968A   Otolithi piscium. Fossilium Catalogus. I. Animalia, 117, 196 pp.
               Rev.: Martini in Zentralbl. Geol. Paläontol., Teil 2, 1971:2–3, 177–178; Weiler in Zentralbl. Geol. Paläontol., Teil 2, 1969:3, 288.
1969A   Fisch-Otolithen aus der Unter-Kreide der Umgebung von Hannover und aus dem Unter-Eozän von Fehmarn. Senckenbergiana Lethaea, 50:4, 357–366, 8 figs. (German; English summary).
               Rev.: Weiler in Zentralbl. Geol. Paläontol., Teil 2, 1970:5, 430.
1970A   Fischfunde aus dem Tertiär des Wadi Araba-Grabens in Jordanien. Geol. Jahrb., 89, 193–208, 3 pls. (German).
               Rev.: Weiler in Zentralbl. Geol. Paläontol., Teil 2, 1971:5, 407.
1971A   Palealbula ventralis n. sp. (Pisces, Clupeiformes) aus dem Neocom (Unter-Hauterive) von Engelbostel bei Hannover. Senckenbergiana Lethaea, 52:1, 1–3, 3 figs. (German; English summary).
               Rev.: Weiler in Zentralbl. Geol. Paläontol., Teil 2, 1971:5, 407–408.
1971B   Fish-Otolithen aus dem Jungtertiär Süd-Siziliens. Senckenbergiana Lethaea, 52:1, 5–37, 2 pls. (German; English summary).
               Rev.: Weiler in Zentralbl. Geol. Paläontol., Teil 2, 1971:5, 408–409.
1971C   Bemerkungen zum Skelettbau von Aeoliscus heinrichi (Heckel 1850). Hess. Landesamt Bodenforsch., Abh., 60, 187–194, 1 pl. (German).

WEILER, W.   See also: Schwarzhans, W. and Weiler, W., 1971A.

WEINER, J. S.
1971A   The natural history of man. New York: Universe Books, xii + 255 pp., 58 figs., 22 pls.
               Rev.: Harrison in Nature, 232:5311, 504; Sarma in Human Biol., 44:3, 589–599.
1971B   Excerpts from "The Piltdown forgery". In: Leakey, L. S. B., Prost, J. and Prost, S. (eds.), 1971A, 327–347, 3 figs. (reprinted from Weiner, J. S., 1955).

WEINFURTER, E.
1967B   Otolithen aus tiefen Gosauschichten Österreichs. Naturhist. Mus. Wien, Ann., 71, 353–361, 1 pl. (German).
               Rev.: Weiler in Zentralbl. Geol. Paläontol., Teil 2, 1968:6, 655.

WEISS, JOSEF
1963A   Die "Würzburger Lügensteine". Naturwiss. Ver. (Würzburg), 4, 107–136, 15 figs. (German).

WELBOURNE, ROBERT G.
1969A   Bibliography of Quaternary African palaeontology. Palaeontol. Afr., 12, 151–202.

WELC, ANDRZEJ   See: Kozłowski, J. K., Kubiak, H. and Welc, A., 1970A.

WELCH, DAN
1965A   Death trap of old Los Angeles. Natur. and Sci., 3:3, 2—3, illustr. (juvenile).

WELCOMME, J.-L.   See: Janvier, Ph. and Welcomme, J.-L., 1969A.

WELLER, J. MARVIN
1965C   Palaeontology, evolution and taxonomy. In: Jhingran, A. G., et al. (eds.), 1965A, 215—225.
1969A   The course of evolution. New York: McGraw-Hill, 696 pp., 507 figs., 46 tables.
            Rev.: Eldredge in Syst. Zool., 18:4, 446—447; Leigh in Amer. Sci., 58:2, 211; McKinney in J.
            Paleontol., 46:6, 931—932; Romer in Quart. Rev. Biol., 45, 382.

WELLES, SAMUEL P.
1969A   Collecting Triassic vertebrates in the plateau province. J. West, 8, 231—246.
1970A   Dilophosaurus (Reptilia: Saurischia), a new name for a dinosaur. J. Paleontol., 44:5, 989.
1970B   The longest neck in the ocean. Nebr., Univ., State Mus., Univ. Nebr. News, Mus. Notes, 50:9, 2 pp.,
            1 fig.
1971A   Dinosaur footprints from the Kayenta formation of northern Arizona. Plateau, 44:1, 27—38, 4 figs.,
            1 table.
1972A   Dinosaurs come to the Academy. Pac. Discovery, 25:5, 3—11, illustr.
1972B   Fossil-hunting for tetrapods in the Chinle formation: a brief pictorial history. Mus. North. Ariz.,
            Bull., 47, 13—18, 11 figs.

WELLES, S. P. and ESTES, RICHARD
1969A   Hadrokkosaurus bradyi from the upper Moenkopi formation of Arizona. With a review of the
            brachyopid labyrinthodonts. Calif., Univ., Publ. Geol. Sci., 84, 56 pp., 27 figs., 2 pls., 3 tables.
            Rev.: Westphal in Zentralbl. Geol. Paläontol., Teil 2, 1970:5, 432.

WELLES, S. P. and GREGG, D. R.
1971 A   Late Cretaceous marine reptiles of New Zealand. Canterbury Mus., Rec., 9:1, 1—111, frontispiece,
            58 figs.

WELLES, SAMUEL P.   See also: Fleming, C. A., Gregg, D. R. and Welles, S. P., 1971A.

WELLNHOFER, PETER
1967A   Ein Schildkrötenrest (Thalassemydidae) aus den Solnhofener Plattenkalken. Bayer. Staatssamml.
            Paläontol. Hist. Geol., Mitt., 7, 181—192, 2 figs., 1 pl. (German; English summary).
1969A   Ein neu aufgefundenes Mastodon-Skelett aus der Oberen Süsswassermolasse von Reisensburg bei
            Günzburg a.d. Donau. Bayer. Staatssamml. Paläontol. Hist. Geol., Mitt., 9, 215—220, 3 figs.
            (German).
1970A   Die Pterodactyloidea (Pterosauria) der Oberjura-Plattenkalke Süddeutschlands. Bayer. Akad. Wiss.,
            Math.-Naturwiss. Kl., Abh., 141, 133 pp., 28 figs., 14 pls., 1 table (German; English summary).
            Rev.: Groiss in Geol. Bl. Nordost-Bayern, 21:1, 62.
1970B   Plesiosaurier-Reste aus dem Opalinuston von Amberg (Oberpfalz). Bayer. Staatssamml. Paläontol.
            Hist. Geol., Mitt., 10, 261—270, 5 figs. (German; English summary).
            Rev.: Author's summary in Geol. Bl. Nordost-Bayern, 21:2/3, 153.
1971A   Die Atoposauridae (Crocodylia, Mesosuchia) der Oberjura-Plattenkalke Bayerns. [The Atoposauridae
            (Crocodylia, Mesosuchia) of the upper Jurassic Plattenkalke in Bavaria.] Palaeontographica,
            Abt. A, 138:5—6, 133—165, 16 figs., 6 pls., 1 table (German; English summary).
1971B   Ergänzende Bemerkungen zu Plesiosaurier-Resten aus Bayern. Bayer. Staatssamml. Paläontol. Hist.
            Geol., Mitt., 11, 123—124 (German).

WELLS, CALVIN
1964A   Rev.: Roth-Lutra in Anat. Anz., 122:2, 180; Wilkinson in Mich. Archaeol., 13:1, 31—32.
1967A   Ancient bones: their photography and what they reveal. Visual, 6:2, 24—29.

WELLS, G. P.   See: Wells, H. G., Huxley, J. S. and Wells, G. P., 1970A.

WELLS, H. G., HUXLEY, J. S. and WELLS, G. P.
1970A   The facts supporting evolution. In: Young, L. B. (ed.), 1970A, 31—57, 12 figs. (reprinted from
            Wells, H. G., Huxley, J. S. and Wells, G. P., 1929, "The science of life").

WELLS, L. H.
1969A   Faunal subdivision of the Quaternary in southern Africa. S. Afr. Archaeol. Bull., 24:95—96, 93—95.
1969B   Homo sapiens afer Linn.-content and earliest representatives. S. Afr. Archaeol. Bull., 24:95—96,
            172—173.

1970A   A late Pleistocene faunal assemblage from Driefontein, Cradock district, C.P. S. Afr. J. Sci., 66 59—61.
1970B   The fauna of the Aloes bone deposit: a preliminary note. S. Afr. Archaeol. Bull., 25:97, 22—23.
1971A   Africa and the ancestry of man. S. Afr. J. Sci., 67:4, 276—283.

WELTER, JACK
1972A   North-South fight on official state fossil. San Francisco Chron., June 20, 6.

WELTON, BRUCE J.
1972A   Fossil sharks in Oregon. Ore Bin, 34:10, 161—170, 2 figs., 1 pl.

WELZEL, ERHARD
1968A   Neue Fossilfunde im Sandsteinkeuper der Hassberge. Geol. Bl. Nordost-Bayern, 18, 251—253, 4 figs. (German).

WENDORF, FRED
1968A*   The prehistory of Nubia. Vol. 1. Fort Burgwin Res. Cent., Publ., no. 5, xi + 531 pp., illustr.
         Rev.: Adams in Antiquity, 44:174, 158—160; Evans in Man (J. Roy. Anthropol. Inst.), 4:1, 142— 143; Farrand in Science (AAAS), 164:3880, 702—705; Goedicke in Amer. J. Archaeol., 73:3, 380—381; ll in Archeol. Roz., 21:3, 413—414 (Czech).
1968B   Preface [to The prehistory of Nubia]. In: Wendorf, F. (ed.), 1968A, vii—x.
1968C   Introduction [to The prehistory of Nubia]. In: Wendorf, F. (ed.), 1968A, 3—18, 4 figs.
1968D*   The prehistory of Nubia. Vol. 2. Fort Burgwin Res. Cent., Publ., no. 5, 532—1084, illustr.
1968E   Late Paleolithic sites in Egyptian Nubia. In: Wendorf, F. (ed.), 1968D, 791—953, 97 figs., 28 tables.
1968F   Site 117: a Nubian final Paleolithic graveyard near Jebel Sahaba, Sudan. In: Wendorf, F. (ed.), 1968D, 954—995, 36 figs., 3 tables.
1968G   Summary of Nubian prehistory. In: Wendorf, F. (ed.), 1968D, 1041—1059, 8 figs.
1970A   The Lubbock subpluvial. In: Dort, W., Jr. and Jones, J. K., Jr. (eds.), 1970A, 23—35, 5 figs.

WENDORF, F., SCHILD, R. and SAID, R.
1970A   Problems of dating the late Paleolithic age in Egypt. Nobel Symp., 12th, Uppsala Univ., 1969, Proc., 57—79, 1 fig.

WENDT, HERBERT
1968A   Rev.: Bishop in New Sci., 40:628, 684—685.

WENZ, SYLVIE
1968C   Note préliminaire sur la faune ichthyologique du Jurassique supérieur de Montsech (Espagne). Soc. Géol. Fr., C.R., 1968:2, 59—60 (French).
         Rev.: H.-P. in Soc. Españ. Hist. Natur., Bol., Secc. Geol., 67:2, 220.
1969A   Note sur quelques poissons actinoptérygiens du Crétacé supérieur de Bolivie. Soc. Géol. Fr., Bull., 11:3, 434—438, 1 fig., 1 pl. (French).
1969B   Note sur quelques poissons Actinoptérygiens du Crétacé supérieur de Bolivie. Soc. Géol. Fr., C.R., 1969:3, 100 (French).
1970A   Sur un Metriorhynchus à museau court du Callovien des Vaches Noires (Calvados). Soc. Géol. Fr., C.R., 1970:3, 92 (French).
1971A   Anatomie et position systématique de Vidalamia, poisson holostéen du Jurassique supérieur du Montsech (Province de Lérida, Espagne). Ann. Paléontol., Vertébrés, 57:1, 43—67, 3 figs., 2 pls. (French; English summary).
1971B   Sur un Metriorhynchus à museau court du Callovien des Vaches Noires (Calvados). Soc. Géol. Fr., Bull. (1970), 12:2, 390—397, 3 figs., 1 pl. (French).

WERNERT, PAUL
1968A   Beutestücke der Höhlenhyänen in anatomischem Verband aus Achenheimer Lössen. Quartär, 19, 55—64, 2 pls. (German).

WERNERT, PAUL and WOLF, MARGUERITE
1970A   Un repaire d'hyènes quaternaires à Hermolsheim dans la vallée de la Bruche (Bas-Rhin). Congr. Nat. Soc. Savantes, 92e, Strasbourg-Colmar, 1967, C.R., 1967:2, 467—470 (French).

WERNERT, SUSAN
1969A   The dashing dinosaurs? Natur. and Sci., 6:16, 11—12, illustr. (juvenile).

WESCOTT, ROGER W.
1967B   Hominid uprightness and primate display. Amer. Anthropol., 69, 738.
1970A   Man without speech: speculations on hominid proto-culture. Anthropol. J. Can., 8:2, 27—32, 4 tables.

WEST, R. G.
1968A   Rev.: Shotton in New Sci., 39:610, 350—351.

WEST, ROBERT M.
1969A   *Paramys wyomingensis,* a small rodent from the middle Eocene of Wyoming. J. Paleontol., 43, 175—
             178, 2 figs., 1 table.
1969B   Biostratigraphy of fluvial sediments of the upper Wasatch formation in the northern Green River
             Basin, Wyoming. Wyo., Univ., Contrib. Geol., 8:2, 184—196, 4 figs., 1 table, map.
1969C   Temporal relations between tongues of the Wasatch formation, northern Green River Basin, Wyoming.
             Geol. Soc. Amer., Abstr., 121, 315 (abs.).
1970A   Distribution and correlative importance of the early Tertiary Phenacodontidae (Condylarthra:
             Mammalia). Geol. Soc. Amer., Abstr., 2:2, 157—158 (abs.).
1970B   Sequence of mammalian faunas of Eocene age in the northern Green River Basin, Wyoming.
             J. Paleontol., 44:1, 142—147, 2 figs., 1 table.
1970C   *Tetraclaenodon puercensis* (Mammalia: Phenacodontidae), Goler formation, Paleocene of California,
             and distribution of the genus. J. Paleontol., 44:5, 851—857, 1 fig., 1 pl., 1 table.
1971A   Late Eocene apatemyid insectivores—Utah and California west. Geol. Soc. Amer., Abstr., 3:2, 215
             (abs.).
1971B   Deciduous dentition of the early Tertiary Phenacodontidae (Condylarthra, Mammalia). Amer. Mus.
             Nov., 2461, 37 pp., 23 figs.
             Rev.: Thenius in Zentralbl. Geol. Paläontol., Teil 2, 1971:6, 524.
1972A   New late Paleocene apatemyid (Mammalia, Insectivora) from Bison Basin, central Wyoming.
             J. Paleontol., 46:5, 714—718, 2 figs., 1 table.
1972B   Minimammals and Bridger biostratigraphy. Field Conf. Tert. Bios., S. and W. Wyo., Guidebk., 40—50,
             3 figs.
1972C   The North American Eocene apatemyid insectivores. Amer. Phil. Soc., Yearb., 1971, 357—359.
1972D   Upper deciduous dentition of the Oligocene insectivore *Leptictis (= Ictops) acutidens.* Carnegie Mus.,
             Ann., 44:3, 25—32, 4 figs., 1 table.

WEST, ROBERT M. and ATKINS, EDWARD G.
1970A   Additional middle Eocene (Bridgerian) mammals from Tabernacle Butte, Sublette County, Wyoming.
             Amer. Mus. Nov., 2404, 26 pp., 9 figs., 3 tables.

WEST, ROBERT M. and BAIRD, DONALD
1970A   *Protogonia subquadrata* Cope, 1881 (Mammalia): proposed suppression of generic and specific names
             under the plenary powers. Z.N.(s.) 1890. Bull. Zool. Nomen., 26:5/6, 230—232.

WESTENHÖFER, M.
1953A   Le problème de la genèse de l'homme. Brussels: s. Frechkop, 52 pp., 12 figs. (French).
             Rev.: Redactie in Natuurwet. Tijdschr., 35:1—2, 63—64.

WESTOLL, T. STANLEY
1968A   Vertebrate faunas of coal-bearing strata. In: Murchison, D. and Westoll, T. S. (eds.), 1968A, 179—
             193, 4 figs.

WESTOLL, T. STANLEY   See also: Andrews, S. M. and Westoll, T. S., 1970A, 1970B; Murchison, D. and
             Westoll, T. S. (eds.), 1968A.

WESTPHAL, FRANK
1970A   Neue Riesensalamander-Funde (*Andrias,* Amphibia) aus der Oberen Süsswassermolasse von Wartenberg
             in Bayern. Bayer. Staatssamml. Paläontol. Hist. Geol., Mitt., 10, 253—260, 3 figs. (German;
             English summary).
             Rev.: Westphal in Zentralbl. Geol. Paläontol., Teil 2, 1971:2—3, 180.
1970B   Phytosaurier-Hautplatten aus der Trias von Madagaskar - ein Beitrag zur Gondwana-Paläogeographie.
             Neues Jahrb. Geol. Paläontol., Monatsh., 1970:10, 632—638, 1 fig. (German).

WESTPHAL, FRANK and WESTPHAL, ISOLDE
1967A   Die Pflasterzahnsaurier (Placodontia) der Germanischen Trias. Aufschluss, 18:9, 249—255, 6 figs.
             (German).
             Rev.: Huene in Zbl. Geol. Pal., Teil 2, 1968, 208.

WESTPHAL, FRANK   See also: Gregory, J. T. and Westphal, F., 1969A; Seilacher, A. and Westphal, F., 1969A.

WESTPHAL, ISOLDE   See: Westphal, F. and Westphal, I., 1967A.

WETMORE, ALEXANDER
1967B   Pleistocene Aves from Ladds, Georgia. Georgia Acad. Sci., Bull., 25:3, 151—153, 1 map.
             Abs.: C.F.S. in Auk, 88:1, 224.

1969A   Remington Kellogg. October 5, 1892—May 8, 1969. Soc. Vert. Paleontol., News Bull., 87, 48—49.

WETMORE, ALEXANDER   See also: Ray, C. E., Wetmore, A., Dunkle, D. H. and Drez, P., 1968A.

WETTSTEIN-WESTERSHEIMB, OTTO
          1966B   Die Teufels- oder Fuchsenlucken bei Eggenburg (NÖ.). 7. Kleinere Wirbeltiere. Österreich. Akad.
                    Wiss., Denk., 112, 89—92, 1 table (German).

WETZEL, R. and BOSINSKI, G.
          1969A   Die Bocksteinschmiede im Lonetal (Markung Rammingen, Kreis Ulm). Baden-Württemberg, Staatl.
                    Amt Denkmalpflege, Stuttgart. Veröff., Reihe A, 230 pp., 56 figs., 166 pls. (German; English
                    and French summaries).
                    Rev.: Heller in Quartär, 21, 159—161.

WHEAT, JOE BEN
          1967A   A Paleo-Indian bison kill. Sci. Amer., 216:1, 44—52, illustr.
          1970A   A Paleo-Indian bison kill. In: Fagan, B. M. (ed.), 1970A, 135—149, illustr. (reprinted from Scientific
                    American, Jan. 1967).
          1971A   Lifeways of early man in North America. Arctic Anthro., 8:2, 22—31.

WHISTLER, DAVID P.
          1969A   Later Tertiary lizards and snakes of the Mojave desert. Geol. Soc. Amer., Abstr., Part 3, 73 (abs.).

WHISTLER, DAVID P.   See also: Savage, D., Whistler, D. and Hutchison, H., 1969A.

WHITE, ERROL IVOR
          1955C   Notes on African Tertiary sharks. Gt. Brit., Inst. Geol. Sci., Overseas Geol. Miner. Resour., 5:3,
                    319—325, 2 pls.
          1968A   Devonian fishes of the Mawson-Mulock area, Victoria Land, Antarctica. Trans-Antarctic Exped.
                    1955—1958, Sci. Repts., 16, 26 pp., 16 figs., 3 pls.
          1969A   The deepest vertebrate fossil and other arctolepid fishes. Linn. Soc., Biol. J., 1:3, 293—310, 38 figs.,
                    2 pls.

WHITE, JOHN A.
          1969A   Late Cenozoic bats (subfamily Nyctophylinae) from the Anza-Borrego Desert of California. Kans.,
                    Univ., Mus. Natur. Hist., Misc. Publ., 51, 275—282, 8 figs., 2 tables.
          1970A   Late Cenozoic porcupines (Mammalia, Erethizontidae) of North America. Amer. Mus. Nov., 2421,
                    1—15, 4 figs., 2 tables.

WHITE, J. A.   See also: Downs, Th. and White, J. A., 1968B.

WHITE, TED
          1971A   Seal drys for bone preservation. Soc. Vert. Paleontol., News Bull., 92, 67.

WHITFIELD, GEORGE R. and BRAMWELL, CHERRIE
          1971A   Palaeoengineering: birth of a new science. New Sci., 52:775, 202—205, 9 figs.

WHITFIELD, G. R.   See also : Bramwell, C. D. and Whitfield, G. R., 1970A.

WHITING, H. P.
          1972A   Cranial anatomy of the ostracoderms in relation to the organization of larval lampreys. In: Joysey,
                    K. A. and Kemp, T. S. (eds.), 1972A, 1—20, 1 fig., 6 pls.

WHITING, JOHN W. M.   See: Deevey, E. and Whiting, J. W. M., 1968A.

WHITMORE, FRANK C., JR.
          1969A   Ecologic and stratigraphic implications of some Cenozoic vertebrates in the Atlantic coastal plain.
                    Geol. Soc. Amer., Abstr., 7, 236 (abs.).
          1971A   Calvert Cliffs project. Science, 173:3993, 192—193.
          1972A   Oligocene Cetacea from South Carolina. Soc. Vert. Paleontol., Ann. Meeting, 32nd, 1972, Abstr.
                    (abs.).

WHITMORE, F. C., JR.   See also: Gard, L. M., Lewis, G. E. and Whitmore, F. C., Jr., 1972A; Schultz, C. B.,
                    Tanner, L. G., Whitmore, F. C. and Ray, W. W., 1969A.

WICK, GERALD   See: Chedd, G., Stubbs, P. and Wick, G., 1970A; Stubbs, P. and Wick, G., 1969A, 1969B,
                    1969C.

WICKLER, W.
1970A   Stammesgeschichte und Ritualisierung. Munich: Piper, 284 pp. (German).
         Rev.: Jacobs in Naturwiss., 58:5, 276.

WIESNER, ERICH
1971A   Das Frankfurter Gebiet zur Unter-Miozän-Zeit. Natur Mus., 101:11, 445–457, 5 figs. (German).

WILCZEWSKI, N.   See: Schultze, H.-P. and Wilczewski, N., 1970A.

WILD, RUPERT
1968A   Ein Humerus-Rest eines Plesiosauriers aus dem Oberen Lias von Baden (Kt. Aargau). Eclogae Geol.
         Helv., 61:2, 581–591, 6 figs. (German; English summary).
1971A   Dorygnathus mistelgauensis n. sp., ein neuer Flugsaurier aus dem Lias Epsilon von Mistelgau
         (Fränkischer Jura). Geol. Bl. Nordost-Bayern, 21:4, 178–195, 1 fig., 2 pls., 4 tables (German;
         English summary).
1972A   Die Wirbeltierfaunen der fränkischen und südalpinen Mitteltrias (ein Vergleich). Deut. Geol. Ges., Z.,
         123, 229–234, 1 table (German).

WILDER, HARRIS HAWTHORNE
1972A   Summary: the phylogenetic tree of the primates; the pedigree of the human race. In: McCown, T. D.
         and Kennedy, K. A. R. (eds.), 1972A, 250–256, 3 figs. (reprinted from Wilder, 1926).

WILKINSON, H. E.
1969A   Description of an upper Miocene albatross from Beaumaris, Victoria, Australia, and a review of fossil
         Diomedeidae. Victoria, Nat. Mus., Mem., 29, 41–51, 2 pls., 2 tables.
         Rev.: Anon. in Emu, 70:1, 39–40; Kuhn in Zentralbl. Geol. Paläontol., Teil 2, 1970:5, 434.
1971A   The Duck Ponds fossil marsupial fauna, Hovell's Creek, Lara, Victoria, Australia. Victoria, Nat. Mus.,
         Mem., 33, 41–45, 1 pl.

WILL, HANS-JOACHIM
1969A   Untersuchungen zur Stratigraphie und Genese des Oberkeupers in Nordwestdeutschland. Geol. Jahrb.,
         Suppl. 54, 239 pp., 50 figs., 1 chart, 3 pls., 2 tables (German).

WILLEY, GORDON R.
1968A   One hundred years of American archaeology. In: Brew, J. O. (ed.), 1968A, 29–53, 227–237.

WILLEY, GORDON R.   See also: Ekholm, G. F. and Willey, G. R. (eds.), 1966A.

WILLIAMS, CLYDE THOMAS
1969A   Evolution of the Caninae and Borophaginae (Canidae). Geol. Soc. Amer., Abstr., Part 3, 74 (abs.).
1971A   The Mio-Pliocene event. Geol. Soc. Amer., Abstr., 3:2, 216–217 (abs.).

WILLIAMS, ERNEST E.   See: Estes, R., Frazzetta, T. H. and Williams, E. E., 1970A.

WILLIAMS, MICHAEL E.
1972A   The origin of "spiral coprolites". Kans., Univ., Paleontol. Contrib., Pap., 59, 19 pp., 10 figs., 8 pls.,
         1 table.

WILLIAMS, PATRICIA M.
1969A   Ptom-, Diken-, and Ariaspis? Chicago, Field Mus. Natur. Hist., Bull., 40:9, 6–8, 4 figs.
1970A   The unique gift of Charles R. Knight. Chicago, Field Mus. Natur. Hist., Bull., 41:6, 4–6, 3 figs.
1972A   Who's who in geology. Chicago, Field Mus. Natur. Hist., Bull., 43:5, 14–16, illustr.

WILLIAMS, TREVOR I.
1969A*   A biographical dictionary of scientists. London: A. & C. Black, xi + 592 pp.
         Rev.: Hall in Endevour, 28:105, 155.

WILLIAMSON, T.   See: Warnicka, J. M. and Williamson, T., 1968A.

WILLIMON, EDWARD L.
1972A   New local faunas and paleoecology (Pleistocene) of north central Texas. Tex. J. Sci., 23:4, 449–469,
         7 figs., 2 tables.

WILLMER, E. N.
1970A   Cytology and evolution. Second edition. New York and London: Academic Press, x + 649 pp.
         Rev.: Barrington in Nature, 228:5268, 294–295.

WILLS, DONALD L.   See: Ray, C. E., Wills, D. L. and Palmquist, J. C., 1968A.

WILLS, LEONARD J.
1970A   The Bunter formation at the Bellington pumping station of the East Worcestershire Waterworks
            Company. Mercian Geol., 3:4, 387—397.

WILLS, LEONARD J. and SARJEANT, WILLIAM A. S.
1970A   Fossil vertebrate and invertebrate tracks from boreholes through the Bunter series (Triassic) of
            Worcestershire. Mercian Geol., 3:4, 399—414, 3 pls.

WILSON, A. C. and SARICH, V. M.
1969A   A molecular time scale for human evolution. Nat. Acad. Sci., Proc., 63, 1088—1093.

WILSON, A. C.   See also: Sarich, V. M. and Wilson, A. C., 1967A.

WILSON, DOROTHY D.
1971A   "They came to hunt". Early man in the San Luis Valley. N. Mex. Geol. Soc., Guidebk., Field Conf.,
            22, 203—207.

WILSON, J. F.   See: Bond, G., Wilson, J. F. and Raath, M. A., 1970A.

WILSON, JERALD J.   See: Manville, R. H. and Wilson, J. J., 1970A.

WILSON, JOHN ANDREW
1969A   Additions to El Gramal local fauna, Nejapa, Oaxaca, Mexico. Geol. Soc. Amer., Spec. Pap., 121, 322.
1971A   Early Tertiary vertebrate faunas, Vieja group, Trans-Pecos, Texas: Agriochoeridae and Merycoidodontidae
            Tex. Mem. Mus., Bull., 18, 83 pp., 30 figs., 36 tables.
            Rev.: Thenius in Zentralbl. Geol. Paläontol., Teil 2, 1971:5, 416.
1971B   Early Tertiary vertebrate faunas, Vieja group, Trans-Pecos, Texas: Entelodontidae. Pearce-Sellards Ser.,
            Texas Mem. Mus., 17, 3—17, 6 figs., 2 tables.
1972A   Vertebrate biostratigraphy of Trans-Pecos, Texas and northern Mexico. Int. Geol. Congr., 24th, Canada,
            Abstr., 251 (abs.).

WILSON, LEONARD G.
1970A   Sir Charles Lyell's scientific journals on the species question. New Haven: Yale Univ. Press, lxii +
            572 pp., illustr.
            Rev.: Anon. in Tulane Stud. Geol. Paleontol., 8:4, 223—224; Ash in Amer. Sci., 59:1, 124; Gould in
            Science, 169:3946, 663—664.
1971A   Sir Charles Lyell and the species question. Amer. Sci., 59:1, 43—55, 1 fig.

WILSON, MICHAEL
1972A   Late Cretaceous hybodont sharks from Wyoming, Montana, and Alberta: stratigraphy and morphology.
            Geol. Soc. Amer., Abstr., 4:6, 422—423 (abs.).
1972B   Fossil Bison from the Casper site, Wyoming. Soc. Vert. Paleontol., Ann. Meeting, 32nd, 1972, Abstr.
            (abs.).

WILSON, R. F.   See: Stewart, J. H., Poole, F. G. and Wilson, R. F., 1972A.

WILSON, RICHARD L.
1968B   Systematics and faunal analysis of a lower Pliocene vertebrate assemblage from Trego County, Kansas.
            Diss. Abstr., 29:3, 1066B (abs.).

WILSON, RICHARD L.   See also: Cavender, T. M., Lundberg, J. G. and Wilson, R. L., 1970A.

WILSON, ROBERT W.
1953A   Fixing of geologic age and position within section. Bull. Zool. Nomencl., 8, 43—44.
1968A   Insectivores, rodents, and intercontinental correlation of the Miocene. Int. Geol. Congr., 23rd, Czech.,
            Rep., Abstr., sec. 10, 282 (abs.).
1968B   Insectivores, rodents and intercontinental correlation of the Miocene. Int. Geol. Congr., 23rd, Czech.,
            Rep., Proc., 10, 19—25, 1 table.
1971A   Recovery of small mammals from the Oligocene of South Dakota. Nat. Geogr. Soc. Res. Reps., 1965,
            279—287, 3 tables.
1972A   Evolution and extinction in early Tertiary rodents. Int. Geol. Congr., 24th, Canada, Abstr., 252 (abs.).
1972B   Thomas Emmett Reynolds. Soc. Vert. Paleontol., News Bull., 96, 45—46.
1972C   Evolution and extinction in early Tertiary rodents. Int. Geol. Congr., 24th, Canada, Proc., Sec. 7,
            217—224, 4 figs., 1 table.
1972D   Late Miocene and early Pliocene mammalian faunas of eastern Austria. Soc. Vert. Paleontol., Ann.
            Meeting, 32nd, 1972, Abstr. (abs.).

WILSON, R. W. and SZALAY, F. S.
1972A   New paromomyid primate from middle Paleocene beds, Kutz Canyon area, San Juan Basin,
         New Mexico. Amer. Mus. Nov., 2499, 18 pp., 13 figs., 1 table.

WILSON, R. W.   See also: Bachmayer, F. and Wilson, R. W., 1970A.

WIMSATT, WILLIAM A.
1970A*   Biology of bats. Volume 1. New York and London: Academic Press, xii + 406 pp., illustr.
         Rev.: Cockrum in Science, 173:3999, 806–807; Fenton in Can. Field-Natur., 86:2, 202; Haltenorth
         in Säugetierkundl. Mitt., 20:1–2, 192; Matthews in New Sci., 50:753, 536; Stebbings in
         J. Animal Ecol., 41:1, 254–255.

WINKLER, H.   See: Trischler, J. and Winkler, H., 1968A.

WINKLER DEL PUP, GIUSEPPINA   See: Piccoli, G., Ladaga Formentin, O., Winkler del Pup, G. and
         Zanferrari Visentin, M. E., 1970A.

WINTER, JOHN   See: Armelagos, G. J., Mielke, J. H. and Winter, J., 1971A.

WINTREBERT, P.
1962A   Le vivant créateur de son évolution. Paris: Masson et Cie., Ed., 416 pp. (French).

WIRTH, E.
1969A   Die Probleme des Eozäns im deutschen Anteil der Oberrheinebene und ihrer Randzonen. Colloque
         sur l'Éocène, Paris, mai 1968, Vol. III. Fr., Bur. Rech. Géol. Minières, Mém., 69, 287–306,
         1 map, 1 table (German; French summary).

WITT, W.   See: German, R., Filzer, P., Dehm, R., Freude, H., Jung, W. and Witt, W., 1968A.

WITWICKA, EMILIA
1970A   XVI Sesja Wszechzwiązkowego Towarzystwa Paleontologicznego. [XVI Session of the All-Union
         Paleontological Society.] Przegl. Geol., 1970:7, 351 (Polish).

WÓJCIK, MARIAN
1971A   Niedźwiedź jaskiniowy z plejstoceńskich osadów jaskini Nietoperzowej. [Cave bear from the
         Pleistocene deposits of Nietoperzowa cave.] Folia Quaternaria, 37, 1–17, 4 figs., 9 tables
         (Polish; English and Russian summaries).

WÓJCIK, ZBIGNIEW
1966A   Geneza i wiek klastycznych osadów jaskiń tatrzańskich. [On the origin and age of clastic deposits in
         the Tatra caves.] Warsaw, Muz. Ziemi, Pr., 9, 3–130, 52 figs., 19 pls., 35 tables (Polish and
         English).

WÓJCIK, ZBIGNIEW   See also: Gradziński, R. and Wójcik, Z., 1966A.

WOLBERG, DONALD L.
1970A   Late Pleistocene extinction: a note. Amer. Anthropol., 72:1, 106–107.
1970B   The hypothesized osteodontokeratic culture of the Australopithecinae: a look at the evidence and
         the opinions. Curr. Anthropol., 11:1, 23–30.
1970C   Reply. Curr. Anthropol., 11:1, 35–37.

WOLDSTEDT, PAUL
1969A   Quartär. In: Handb. Strat. Geol., 2, viii + 263 pp., 77 figs., 16 tables.
         Rev.: B. in Przegl. Geol., 1970:6, 307 (Polish); C.P.H. in Geol. Mag., 106:6, 618–619; Czabnetzki in
         Naturwiss. Rundsch., 23, 344–345; Guenther in Quartär, 20, 231–232; Klug in Naturwiss. Ver.
         Schleswig-Holstein, Schr., 40, 109–110; Königsson in Geol. Fören. Stockholm, Förh., 92:1,
         121–122; Müller in Kosmos (Stuttgart), 1970:4, 140–141; Ruske in Geologie (Berlin), 19:10,
         1213–1214; Schönhals in Eiszeitalter Gegenwart, 20, 274–275; Schwarzbach in Earth-Sci. Rev.,
         5:4, A200–A201; Struve in Natur Mus., 101:11, 474.

WOLF, M.   See: Wernert, P. and Wolf, M., 1970A.

WOLFF, RONALD G.   See: Arambourg, C. and Wolff, R. G., 1969A; Howell, F. C., Fichter, L. S. and
         Wolff, R., 1969A.

WOLFRAM, HANS-JOACHIM   See: Nolte, H., Wolfram, H.-J. and Wöllner, H., 1969A.

WOLLIN, JAY C.   See: Mac Fall, R. P. and Wollin, J. C., 1972A.

WÖLLNER, HEINTZ   See: Nolte, H., Wolfram, H.-J. and Wöllner, H., 1969A.

WOLPOFF, MILFORD H.
 1968A   *"Telanthropus"* and the single species hypothesis. Amer. Anthropol., 70, 477–493, 1 fig., 3 tables,
                    bibliography.
 1969A   Facts and theories in the taxonomy of *"Paranthropus"* and *"Australopithecus"* (*Homo*). Amer. J. Phy
                    Anthropol., 31, 256 (abs.).
 1969B   Cranial capacity and taxonomy of Olduvai hominid 7. Nature, 223:5202, 182–183.
 1969C   The taxonomy of Australopithecine variation. Amer. Anthropol. Ass., Bull., 2:3, 113 (abs.).
 1970A   Taxonomy and cranial capacity of Olduvai hominid 7 (continued). Nature, 227:5259, 747.
 1970B   The evidence for multiple hominid taxa at Swartkrans. Amer. Anthropol., 72:3, 576–607, 5 figs.,
                    6 tables.
 1971A   Is the new composite cranium from Swartkrans a small robust australopithecine? Nature, 230:5293,
                    398–401, 2 figs., 1 table.
 1971B   Is Vértesszöllös II an occipital of European *Homo erectus*? Nature, 232:5312, 567–568, 2 tables.
 1971C   Metric trends in hominid dental evolution. Case West. Reserve Univ., Stud. Anthropol., 2, xii + 244 p,
                    147 tables.
 1971D   A functional measure of tooth size. Southwest. J. Anthropol., 27:3, 279–286, 3 tables.
 1971E   Vértesszöllös and the presapiens theory. Amer. J. Phys. Anthropol., 35:2, 209–216, 3 tables.
 1972A   Allometry of the upper dentition. Amer. J. Phys. Anthropol., 37:3, 457 (abs.).

WOLPOFF, MILFORD H.   See also: Brose, D. S. and Wolpoff, M. H., 1971A.

WOO, JU-KANG
 1959F   Liukiang man - earliest representative of modern man in east Asia. Sci. Record, New Ser., 3:4, 165–
                    168, 1 pl., 1 table.
 1960D   New discoveries of palaeoanthropology in China. Sci. Record, New Ser., 4:2, 120–125, 1 pl., 1 table.
 1962D   Recent advances of palaeoanthropology in China. Sci. Abstr. China, Earth Sci., 1:3, 9–10.
 1963A   *Gigantopithecus* and the taxonomic system of Hominidae. Sci. Abstr. China, Earth Sci., 1:4, 8–9.
 1964G   Abs.: Sci. Abstr. China, Earth Sci., 2:2, 7–8.
 1966C   Abs.: Sci. Abstr. China, Earth Sci., 4:2, 7–8.

WOO, JU-KANG and BAI, HUI-YING
 1965A   Abs.: Sci. Abstr. China, Earth Sci., 3:3, 10.

WOOD, ALBERT E.
 1969A   Rodents and lagomorphs from the *"Chadronia* pocket," early Oligocene of Nebraska. Amer. Mus. Nov.
                    no. 2366, 1–18, 2 figs., 3 tables.
 1970A   The early Oligocene rodent *Ardynomys* (family Cylindrodontidae) from Mongolia and Montana. Amer.
                    Mus. Nov., 2418, 1–18, 4 figs., 1 table.
 1970B   The European Eocene paramyid rodent, *Plesiarctomys*. Naturforsch. Ges. Basel, Verh., 80:2, 237–278,
                    15 figs., 5 tables.
 1971A   Lagomorpha. McGraw-Hill Encycl. Sci. Technol., 7, 430, 2 figs.
 1971B   Rodentia. McGraw-Hill Encycl. Sci. Technol., 11, 662–664.
 1972A   An Eocene hystricognathous rodent from Texas: its significance in interpretations of continental drift.
                    Science, 175:4027, 1250–1251, 1 fig.
 1972B   Interrelations of humans, dogs and rodents. Science (AAAS), 176:4033, 437.

WOOD, ALBERT E.   See also: Ferrusquia-Villafranca, I. and Wood, A. E., 1969A; Harris, J. M. and Wood, A. E.,
                    1969A; Loring, S. H. and Wood, A. E., 1969A.

WOOD, B. A.   See: Day, M. H. and Wood, B. A., 1968A, 1969A.

WOOD, FLORENCE D.   See: Hecht, M. K., Schaeffer, B., Patterson, B., Frank, R. van and Wood, F. D., 1972A.

WOOD, ROGER CONANT
 1970A   A review of the fossil Pelomedusidae (Testudines, Pleurodira) of Asia. Breviora, 357, 1–24, 3 figs.,
                    4 pls., 1 table.
 1972A   A Pliocene vertebrate fauna from northern Venezuela. Soc. Vert. Paleontol., Ann. Meeting, 32nd,
                    1972, Abstr. (abs.).

WOOD, ROGER CONANT and DIAZ DE GAMERO, MARIA LOURDES
    1971A   *Podocnemis venezuelensis*, a new fossil pelomedusid (Testudines, Pleurodira) from the Pliocene of
                Venezuela and a review of the history of *Podocnemis* in South America. Breviora, 376, 1–23,
                3 figs., 5 pls.

WOODBURNE, MICHAEL O.
    1968A   Rev.: Thenius in Zentralbl. Geol. Paläontol., Teil 2, 1971:1, 72.
    1969A   Systematics, biogeography, and evolution of *Cynorca* and *Dyseohyus* (Tayassuidae). Amer. Mus. Natur.
                Hist., Bull., 141:2, 275–355, 14 figs., 11 pls., 17 tables.
                Rev.: Thenius in Zentralbl. Geol. Paläontol., Teil 2, 1971:1, 72–73; Webb in Quart. Rev. Biol., 45:1,
                62–63.
    1969B   A late Pleistocene occurrence of the collared peccary, *Dicotyles tajacu*, in Guatemala. J. Mammal.,
                50:1, 121–125, 2 figs.
                Rev.: Thenius in Zentralbl. Geol. Paläontol., Teil 2, 1971:1, 72.
    1969C   A lower mandible of *Zygomaturus gilli* from the Sandringham sands, Beaumaris, Victoria, Australia.
                Victoria, Nat. Mus., Mem., 29, 29–39, 2 figs., 1 table.
    1969D   The Alcoota fauna: an integrated geologic and paleontologic study. Diss. Abstr., 30:3, 1421B (abs.).

WOODBURNE, MICHAEL O. and GOLZ, DAVID J.
    1972A   Stratigraphy of the Punchbowl formation Cajon Valley, southern California. Calif., Univ., Publ. Geol.
                Sci., 92, 57 pp., 12 figs., 7 pls., 2 tables.

WOODBURNE, MICHAEL O.   See also: Jepsen, G. L. and Woodburne, M. O., 1969A.

WOODHOUSE, H. C.   See: Lee, D. N. and Woodhouse, H. C., 1970A.

WOODROW, DONALD L. and FLETCHER, FRANK W.
    1969A   Devonian dipnoan aestivation cylinders. Geol. Soc. Amer., Abstr., 121, 383–384 (abs.).

WOODWARD, ARTHUR SMITH   See: Dawson, C. and Woodward, A. S., 1971A, 1971B.

WORMINGTON, H. M.
    1967A   The Paleo-Indian. In: Gruber, J. W. (ed.), 1967A, 55–66.

WORSLEY, THOMAS R.
    1971A   Terminal Cretaceous events. Nature, 230:5292, 318–320, 2 figs.

WOUTERS, G.   See: Quinet, G. E., Coupatez, P. and Wouters, G., 1970A.

WRESCHNER, E.
    1967A   The Geula caves - Mount Carmel. Excavation, finds and summary. Quaternaria, 9, 69–89, 10 figs.,
                8 pls. (French and German summaries).

WRIGHT, D. J. M.
    1971A   Syphilis and Neanderthal man. Nature, 229:5284, 409.

WRIGHT, GARY A. and SKARYD, SUZANNE
    1972A   Do fossil elephants date the South African australopithecines? Nature, 237:5353, 291.

WRIGHT, H. E., JR. and FREY, D. G.
    1969A*   [The Quaternary of the United States. Russian translation.] Moscow: "Mir" Press, 2 vols., illustr.
                (Russian).

WRIGHT, H. E., JR.   See also: Morrison, R. B. and Wright, H. E., Jr. (eds.), 1968A.

WRIGHT, HELEN   See: Rapport, S. and Wright, H. (eds.), 1967A.

WU, KENT   See: Frost, H. M. and Wu, K., 1967A.

WU, XIN-ZHI, *et al.*
    1966A   Abs.: Sci. Abstr. China, Earth Sci., 4:2, 8.

WUNDERLICH, MANFRED D.
    1971A   Did early Wurm Neanderthal suffer from vitamin D deficiency? Nebr. Acad. Sci., Proc., 81, 9–10.

WURSTER, P.   See: Behrens, M., Frank, H., Höllein, K., Spaeth, W. v. and Wurster, P., 1970A.

WYCKOFF, RALPH W. G.
 1969A   Sur la composition de quelques protéines dinosauriennes. Acad. Sci., C.R., Sér. D, 269:16, 1489—
                1491, 1 table (French).
 1971A   Trace elements and organic constituents in fossil bones and teeth. N. Amer. Paleontol. Conv., Proc.,
                Part K, 1514—1524, 5 figs., 1 table.

WYMER, JOHN
 1968A   Lower Paleolithic archaeology in Britain as represented by the Thames Valley. London: John Baker,
                x + 429 pp., frontispiece, 110 figs., 36 pls.
                Rev.: Grigor'ev in Vop. Antropol., 37, 165—166 (Russian); Lacaille in Antiquaries J., 50:1, 110—111;
                Mellars in Prehist. Soc., Proc., 36, 385—386; Searle in Advan. Sci., 26:127, 54—56; Roe in
                Antiquity, 43:172, 326—327; Walker in New Sci., 44:663, 393.
 1971A   A further fragment of the Swanscombe skull. In: Leakey, L. S. B., Prost, J. and Prost, S. (eds.),
                1971A, 349—351 (reprinted from Nature, Sept. 1955).

WYMER, JOHN   See also: Singer, R. and Wymer, J., 1969A.

WYSOCZAŃSKI-MINKOWICZ, TADEUSZ
 1969A   Próba oznaczania wieku względnego kości kopalnych metodą fluoro-chloro-apatytową. [An attempt at
                relative age determination of fossil bones by fluorine-chlorine-apatite method.] Stud. Geol. Pol.,
                28, 9 figs., 4 charts, 10 tables (Polish; English summary).
 1969B   Application of fluorine-chlorine-apatite method for dating fossil bones. Geogr. Pol., 17, 93—96.

WYSOCZAŃSKI-MINKOWICZ, T.   See also: Borsuk-Białynicka, B. and Wysoczański-Minkowicz, T., 1969A.

XIMÉNEZ, A.   See: Olazarri, J., Mones, A., Ximénez, A. and Philippi, M. E., 1970A.

XU, YU-XUAN
 1965A   Abs.: Sci. Abstr. China, Earth Sci., 3:2, 7—8.

XU, YU-XUAN and CHIU, CHAN-SIANG
 1962A   Abs.: Sci. Abstr. China, Earth Sci., 1:2, 11.

YAKIMOV, V. P.   See: Iakimov, V. P.

YAKOVLEV, V. N.   See: Hecker, R. F., Shishkin, M. A. and Yakovlev, V. N., 1971A.

YALDEN, D. W.
 1971A   Flying ability of Archaeopteryx. Nature, 231:5298, 127.
 1971B   The flying ability of Archaeopteryx. Ibis, 113:3, 349—356, 4 figs., 2 tables.
 1971C   Archaeopteryx again. Nature, 234:5330, 478—479.

YAMADA, YATARO   See: Onodera, S., Ootaka, S., Sato, J., Takahashi, T. and Yamada, Y., 1967A.

YANAGISAWA, I.   See: Shikama, T. and Yanagisawa, I., 1971A.

YEH, HSIANG-K'UEI
 1963A   Abs.: Sci. Abstr. China, Earth Sci., 2:2, 4.
 1965A   Abs.: Sci. Abstr. China, Earth Sci., 3:2, 6—7.

YIN, T.-H., CHOW, M.-C. and HSU, J.
 1965A   Abs.: Sci. Abstr. China, Earth Sci., 3:1, 4.

YOCHELSON, ELLIS L.
 1969A   Fossils - the how and why of collecting and storing. In: Cohen, D. M. and Cressey, R. F. (eds.),
                1969A, Biol. Soc. Wash., Proc., 82, 585—601.
 1970-71A*   Proceedings of the North American Paleontological Convention. 2 vols., 12 parts. Lawrence, Kansas:
                Allen Press, 1674 pp.
                Rev.: McAlester in Amer. Sci., 60:4, 498—499.

1971A   Phylum and class nomenclature in systematics. Syst. Zool., 20, 245–249.

YOSHIOKA, MITSUO   See: Sakanoue, M. and Yoshioka, M., 1970A.

YOUNG, CHUNG-CHIEN
1957E   The significance of the lower Triassic reptilian fauna from Wuhsiang of Shansi. Sci. Record, New Ser., 1:4, 265–270, 1 fig., 2 tables.
1959J   Paleontologiĭa nizshikh chetveronogikh. [Paleontology of lower tetrapods.] Priroda, 1959:10, 69–73, 4 figs. (Russian).
1959K   On a new Lacertilia from Chingning, Chekiang, China. Sci. Record, New Ser., 3:10, 520–524, 1 fig., 1 pl.
1961B   Abs.: Sci. Abstr. China, Earth Sci., 1:2, 8.
1963A   Abs.: Sci. Abstr. China, Earth Sci., 1:4, 6.
1963B   Abs.: Sci. Abstr. China, Earth Sci., 2:1, 8–9.
1964C   Abs.: Sci. Abstr. China, Earth Sci., 2:4, 7–8.
1965A   Abs.: Sci. Abstr. China, Earth Sci., 3:4, 8.
1965B   Abs.: Sci. Abstr. China, Earth Sci., 3:3, 9.
1972A   [Mamenchisaurus from Ho Chuan.] Chinese Sci. Inst. Vert. Paleontol. Paleoanthropol., Monogr., Ser. A, 8, 30 pp., 12 figs., 15 pls., 10 tables (Chinese).

YOUNG, CHUNG-CHIEN and CHOW, MIN-CHEN
1962A   Abs.: Sci. Abstr. China, Earth Sci., 1:2, 9–10.

YOUNG, CHUNG-CHIEN and DONG, ZHI-MING
1972A   [On the aquatic reptiles of the Triassic in China.] Vert. Paleontol., Mem., 9, 34 pp., 7 figs., 8 pls., 4 tables (Chinese).

YOUNG, CHUNG-CHIEN and YEH, HSIANG-K'UEI
1963A   Abs.: Sci. Abstr. China, Earth Sci., 2:1, 8.

YOUNG, J. Z.
1971A   An introduction to the study of man. Oxford: Oxford University Press, xxv + 719 pp., illustr.
         Rev.: Dawson in Tuatara, 19:2, 103; Newth in New Sci., 52:773, 114–115; Weiner in Nature, 240: 5379, 282–283.

YOUNG, L. M.
1971A   A prehistoric find in Australia. Anthropol. J. Can., 9:4, 28.

YOUNG, LOUISE B.
1970A*   Evolution of man. New York: Oxford University Press, xiv + 648 pp., illustr.
         Rev.: Johnston in Human Biol., 43:1, 182–183; Maples in Amer. Anthropol., 73:6, 1426–1427.

ZACHARIASSE, W. J.   See: Bruijn, H. de, Sondaar, P. Y. and Zachariasse, W. J., 1971A.

ZAHARIA, NECULAI   See: Macarovici, N. and Zaharia, N., 1968A.

ZAÏONŤS, I. L.   See: Generalov, P. P., Kuzin, I. L., ZaïonŤs, I. L. and Krapivner, R. B., 1970A.

ZAKI, ANDRZEJ
1967A   Notatki archeologiczne z Andow. Cz. III. 5. Szczątki kostne człowieka paleolitycznego w Lauricocha. [Notes archéologiques des Andes. III. Ossements d'homme paléolithique de Lauricocha.] Acta Archaeol. Carpathica, 9:2, 131–138, 11 figs. (Polish; French summary).

ZAKRZEWSKI, RICHARD J.
1969A   The rodents from the Hagerman local fauna, upper Pliocene of Idaho. Mich., Univ., Mus. Paleontol., Contrib., 23:1, 1–36, 13 figs., 7 tables.
1969B   The rodents from the Hagerman local fauna, upper Pliocene of Idaho. Diss. Abstr., 30:1, 262B (abs.).
1970A   Notes on kangaroo rats from the Pliocene of southwestern Kansas, with the description of a new species. J. Paleontol., 44:3, 474–477, 1 fig., 2 tables.
1972A   Fossil microtines from late Cenozoic deposits in the Anza-Borrego Desert, California, with the description of a new subgenus of Synaptomys. Los Angeles Cty. Mus., Contrib. Sci., 221, 12 pp., 2 figs.

ZAKRZEWSKI, R. J. and MAXFIELD, J. L.
1971A   Occurrence of *Clethrionomys* in the late Pleistocene of Kansas. J. Mammal., 52:3, 620—621, 1 fig.

ZAKRZEWSKI, RICHARD J.   See also: Hibbard, C. W. and Zakrzewski, R. J., 1972A; McMullen, T. L. and
Zakrzewski, R. J., 1972A.

ZALKIND, N. G.
1970A   75 let so dnia rozhdeniia Ia. Ia. Roginskogo. [Ia. Ia. Roginskiĭ's 75-th anniversary.] Vop. Antropol.,
36, 168—169 (Russian).
1970B   K 75-letiiu M. F. Nesturkha. [M. F. Nesturkh's 75th anniversary.] Vop. Antropol., 36, 169 (Russian).

ZAL'TSMAN, I. G.
1964A   Nizhniĭ-sredniĭ oligotsen (neraschlenennye). [Lower-middle Oligocene (undivided).] Geologiia SSSR,
44:1, West Siberian Lowlands, 163—171 (Russian).
1967B   Neogenovaia sistema. Iuzhnaia chast' Zapadno-Sibirskoĭ nizmennosti. [Neogene system. Southern part
of west-Siberian lowlands.] Geologiia SSSR, 14, Western Siberia (southern part), 364—371
(Russian).
1968A   Sopostavlenie kontinental'nykh paleogenovykh i neogenovykh otlozheniĭ Zapadno-Sibirskoĭ
nizmennosti, Urala, Turgaĭskogo progiba i Severnogo Priaral'ia. [Correlation of continental
Paleogene and Neogene deposits of west-Siberian lowlands, Urals, Turgaĭ depression and
northern Aral region.] Sov. Geol., 1968:12, 26—34, 1 chart (Russian).

ZAL'TSMAN, I. G.   See also: Gurari, F. G., Zal'tsman, G., Teslenko, Iu. V. and Shatskiĭ, S. B., 1968A, 1968B.

ZAMORIĬ, P. K.
1958A   Chetvertichnye otlozheniia. [Quaternary deposits.] Geologiia SSSR, 5, Ukrainian SSR, Moldavian
SSR, 766—816, 15 figs., 3 tables (Russian).

ZANFERRARI VISENTIN, MARIA E.   See: Piccoli, G., Ladaga Formentin, O., Winkler del Pup, G. and
Zanferrari Visentin, M. E., 1970A.

ZANGERL, RAINER
1968A   A revision of the chelonian genus *Bothremys* (Pleurodira: Pelomedusidae). Fieldiana: Geol., 16:7,
193—239, 22 figs.
1968B   The morphology and the developmental history of the scales of the Paleozoic sharks *Holmesella* ? sp.
and *Orodus*. Nobel Symp., 4th, Stockholm, 1967, Proc., 1968, 399—412, 17 figs.
1969A   *Bandringa rayi*, a new ctenacanthoid shark from the Pennsylvanian Essex fauna of Illinois. Fieldiana:
Geol., 12:10, 157—169, 7 figs.
1969B   The turtle shell. In: Gans, C. (ed.), 1969A, 311—339, 15 figs., 2 tables.
1971A   Two toxochelyid sea turtles from the Landenian sands of Erquelinnes (Hainaut), of Belgium. Inst.
Roy. Sci. Natur. Belg., Mém., 169, 1—32, 18 figs., 9 pls.

ZANGERL, RAINER   See also: Bardack, D. and Zangerl, R., 1971A.

ZANINA, IRINA EVGEN'EVNA
1968A   Paleontologi Sovetskogo Soiuza. Spravochnik. [Paleontologists of the Sovet Union. Reference book.]
Leningrad: "Nauka" Press, 214 pp. (Russian).

ZAPFE, HELMUTH
1966D   Die Teufels- oder Fuchsenlucken bei Eggenburg (NÖ.). 2. Die Höhlenbärenreste. Österreich. Akad.
Wiss., Denk., 112, 15—22 (German).
1966E   Die Teufels- oder Fuchsenlucken bei Eggenburg (NÖ.). 3. Die übrigen Carnivoren (ausser Höhlenhyäne
und Höhlenbär). Österreich. Akad. Wiss., Denk., 112, 23—38, 2 figs., 7 tables (German).
1966F   Die Teufels- oder Fuchsenlucken bei Eggenburg (NÖ.). 9. Lebensspuren. Österreich. Akad. Wiss.,
Denk., 112, 109—122, 2 figs., 4 pls. (German).
1969A   Das Vorkommen fossiler Landwirbeltiere im Jungtertiär Österreichs und besonders des Wiener Beckens.
Österreich. Akad. Wiss., Math.-Naturwiss. Kl., Abt. I, Sitz.-Ber., 177, 65—87, 2 figs., 1 table
(German).

ZAPFE, H.   See also: Bachmayer, F. and Zapfe, H., 1969A, 1969B; Schaefer, H. and Zapfe, H., 1971A.

ZARKHIDZE, V. S.
1970A   Kaĭnozoĭskaia istoriia poberezh'ia evropeĭskogo severo-vostoka. [Cenozoic history of the coastal area
of the European north-east.] In: Severnyĭ Ledovityĭ Okean i ego poberezh'e v kaĭnozoe, 281—
286 (Russian).

ZARRINA, E. P.   See: Krasnov, I. I. and Zarrina, E. P., 1964A.

ZARUBIN, S. I.   See: Egorov, A. E., Zarubin, S. I. and Siryk, I. M., 1968A.

ZAVERNIAEV, F. M.
1970A   Novaia verkhnepaleoliticheskaia stoianka v raione g. Brianska. [New upper Paleolithic site in Briansk area.] In: Rybakov, B. A. (ed.), 1970A, 44—45 (Russian).

ZAZHIGIN, VLADIMIR SEMENOVICH
1969A   Znachenie pestrushek (Rodentia, Microtinae) dlia stratigrafii i korreliatsii otlozhenii eopleistotsena Vostochnoi Evropy i Zapadnoi Sibiri. [Significance of steppe lemmings Lagurini (Rodentia, Microtinae) for stratigraphy and correlation of Eopleistocene deposits of east Europe and west Siberia.] In: Mezhdunarodnyi kollokvium po geologii i faune nizhnego i srednego pleistotsena Evropy. Tezisy dokladov, 38—40, and 74—77 (Russian and English).
1969B   K istorii razvitiia pestrushek (Rodentia, Microtinae) v antropogene Evrazii. [A contribution to the history of the development of lemmings (Rodentia, Microtinae) in the Anthropogene of Eurasia.] Akad. Nauk SSSR, Dokl., 188:3, 722—725, 1 fig. (Russian).
1970A   Significance of lagurins (Rodentia, Microtinae, Lagurini) for the stratigraphy and correlation of Eopleistocene deposits of eastern Europe and western Siberia. Palaeogeogr., Palaeoclimatol., Palaeoecol., 8:2—3, 237—249, 7 figs.

ZAZHIGIN, V. S.   See also: Vangengeim, E. A. and Zazhigin, V. S., 1969A; Vangengeim, E. A., Zhegallo, V. I. and Zazhigin, V. S., 1972A.

ZÁZVORKA, VLASTISLAV
1965A   Čelist mosasaurida ze svrchní křídy Východních Čech. [A mosasaurid jaw from the upper Cretaceous of eastern Bohemia.] Prague, Národ. Muz., Čas. Odd. Přírod, 134:4, 217—219, 1 fig., 1 pl. (Czech; Esperanto summary).

ZBYSZEWSKI, GEORGES
1953A   Note sur l'apparition d'ossements de mammifères dans les argiles de Coja (Arganil). Soc. Geol. Port., Bol., 11, 59—64, 2 pls. (French).
1953B   Note sur une mandibule d'Isocetus trouvée à Mutela. Soc. Geol. Port., Bol., 11, 91—92, 1 pl. (French).
1966A   Adieu l'abbé Breuil! Lisbon, Univ., Fac. Letr., Rev., Sér. 3, 10, 361—372, portr. (French).

ZELIKMAN, A. L.
1968A   Ekologicheskie predposylki deistviia estestvennogo otbora. [Ecological premises of the effect of natural selection.] Zh. Obshch. Biol., 29:6, 658—669 (Russian; English summary).

ZEUNER, F. E.
1967A   Geschichte der Haustiere. München: Bayrischer Landwirtschaftsverlag GmbH, 448 pp. (German). Rev.: Kurth in Homo, 19:1, 57.

ZHAI, REN-JIE
1963A   Abs.: Sci. Abstr. China, Earth Sci., 1:2, 12.
1963B   Abs.: Sci. Abstr. China, Earth Sci., 2:1, 6—7.
1964A   Abs.: Sci. Abstr. China, Earth Sci., 2:2, 8.

ZHAIMIN, M. I.   See: Buvalkin, A. K., Zhaimin, M. I., Murakhovskaia, E. I., Orlovskaia, E. R. and Sakulina, G. V., 1971A.

ZHEGALLO, VLADIMIR IL'ICH (= JEGALLO, V. I.)
1971A   Gippariony iz neogenovykh otlozhenii Zapadnoi Mongolii i Tuvy. [Hipparions from the Neogene deposits of western Mongolia and Tuva.] Sovm. Sovet.-Mongol. Nauch.-Issled. Geol. Eksped., Tr., 3, 98—119 (Russian).

ZHEGALLO, VLADIMIR IL'ICH and BORISOV, B. A.
1968A   Paleontologicheskie issledovaniia v Zaisanskoi vpadine. [Paleontological research in Zaisan basin.] Authors' summary. Mosk. Obshchest. Ispyt. Prir., Biull., Otd. Geol., 43:1, 152 (Russian).

ZHEGALLO, VLADIMIR IL'ICH   See also: Barsbold, R., Voronin, Iu. I. and Zhegallo, V. I., 1971A; Birman, A. S., Zhegallo, V. I., Rastsvetaev, L. M., Khozatskii, L. I. and Shevyreva, N. S., 1971A; Vangengeim, E. A., Erbaeva, M. N., Zhegallo, V. I. and Sotnikova, M. V., 1968A; Vangengeim, E. A., Zhegallo, V. I. and Zazhigin, V. S., 1972A.

ZHEĬBA, STASIS IOZOVICH
1971A   Novye dannye po faune i stratigrafii narovskogo gorizonta ĩuzhnoĭ Pribaltiki. [New data on tĩ
           fauna and stratigraphy of the Narova horizon of southern Pribaltika.] Vyssh. Ucheb. Zav
           Lit. SSR, Nauch. Tr., Geogr. Geol., 8, 195–199 (Russian, Lithuanian and German summ

ZHELEZKO, V. I. and GLIKMAN, L. S.
1971A   O senomanskikh otlozheniĩakh Zapadnogo Kazakhstana i nekotorykh melovykh akulakh-sklerofa
           In: Problemy geologii Zapadnogo Kazakhstana, 179–188, 2 pls. (Russian).

ZHIZHCHENKO, B. P., SEREZHENKO, V. A. and CHURILOVA, E. V.
1968A   Neogenovaĩa sistema. [Neogene system.] Geologiĩa SSSR, 9, Northern Caucasus, 388–441, 11
           3 tables (Russian).

ZHUKOV, IŨ. V.
1970A   O nakhodke ostatkov mlekopitaĩushchikh v kokturpakskoĭ svite khrebta Kungeĭ Alatau. [On th
           find of mammalian remains in the Kokturpak suite of Kungeĭ Alatau Range.] In: Materi
           po geologii kaĩnozoĩa i noveĩsheĭ tektonike Tĩan'-Shanĩa, 69–71 (Russian).

ZHYLKIBAEV, KIĨANTAĬ ZH.
1969A   Slon Vĩusta iz Aktĩubinskoĭ oblasti. [Wüst's elephant from Aktĩubinsk province.] Akad. Nauk
           SSR, Izv., Ser. Biol., 1969:2, 42–50, 3 tables (Russian; Kazakh summary).

ZHYLKIBAEV, KIĨANTAĬ ZH.   See also: Gus'kova, A. I., Duĩsebaev, Zh. D., Zhylkibaev, K. Zh. and
           Varnavskikh, B. E., 1971A.

ZÍDEK, JIŘÍ
1965A   Poznámky k vertikálnímu rozpětí a bentosní adaptaci xenakantidŭ (Pisces). [Remarks on vertica
           distribution and benthic adaptation of xenacanthids (Pisces).] Prague, Národ. Muz., Čas. (
           Přírod., 134:2, 65–68, 1 fig. (Czech).
1967A   Revision of the systematic position of the species Hypospondylus bohemicus Jaekel, 1911 (Pisc
           Prague, Národ. Muz., Čas. Odd. Přírod., 136:2, 67–72, 4 figs., 1 pl. (Czech summary).
1967B   Janassa lacustris sp. n., a new bradyodont species (Pisces) from the lower Permian of Czechoslo
           Prague, Národ. Muz., Čas. Odd. Přírod., 136:4, 201–207, 2 figs., 1 pl. (Czech summary).
1969A   Upper Carboniferous hybodontoid remains and problematic ichthyodorulites of Bohemia, Part 1
           Hybodus vestitus. Prague, Národ. Muz., Čas. Odd. Přírod., 137:1–2, 70–76, 1 fig.
           (Czech summary).
1971A   Labidosaurikos meachami, a lower Permian reptile. Okla. Geol. Notes, 31:5, 90, cover picture.

ZIEGLER, ALAN C.
1969A   A theoretical determination of tooth succession in the therapsid Diademodon. J. Paleontol., 4ĩ
           771–778, 2 figs.
1971A   A theory of the evolution of therian dental formulas and replacement patterns. Quart. Rev. Bi
           46:3, 226–249, 4 figs.

ZIHLMAN, ADRIENNE L.
1971A   The question of locomotor differences in Australopithecus. Int. Congr. Primat., 3rd, Zurich, 19
           Proc., 1, 54–66, 3 tables.

ZIMINA, R. P. and GERASIMOV, I. P.
1971A   Perigliatsial'naĩa ekspansiĩa surkov (Marmota) v Sredneĭ Evrope v techenie verkhnego pleĩstoĩsena
           [Periglacial expansion of marmots (Marmota) in middle Europe during the upper Pleistoce
           Mosk. Obshchest. Ispyt. Prir., Biull., Otd. Biol., 76:1, 37–49, 2 figs. (Russian; English
           summary).

ZIMINA, VERA GRIGOR'EVNA
1969A   O vozraste pospelovskoĭ svity i vremeni poĩavleniĩa gondvanskikh elementov v permskoĭ flore
           ĩuzhnogo Primor'ĩa. [On the age of the Pospelov series and on the date of appearance o
           Gondwana elements in the Permian flora of the South Littoral.] Akad. Nauk SSSR, Dok
           189:5, 1073–1076, 1 fig. (Russian).
1970A   Age of the Pospelovskaya suite and time of appearance of Gondwana elements in the Permian f
           of the south Maritime region. Akad. Nauk SSSR, Dokl., Earth Sci. Sec., 189, 101–103,
           1 fig. (Translated from Russian: Akad. Nauk SSSR, Dokl., 1969, 189:5, 1073–1076.)

ZIMMERMANN, W.
1969A   Vererbung "erworbener Eigenschaften" und Auslese. Second edition. Stuttgart: Gustav Fische
           XII + 247 pp. (German).
           Rev.: Peters in Natur Mus., 101:11, 475; Thenius in Geol. Ges. Wien, Mitt., 61, 220.

ZINGESER, MAURICE R.
1969A   Cerecopithecoid canine tooth honing mechanisms. Amer. J. Phys. Anthropol., 31, 205–214, 3 figs., 1 table.

ZINSMEISTER, WILLIAM J.
1971A   A late Pliocene macrofossil fauna of Newport Beach, Orange County, California. S. Calif. Acad. Sci., Bull., 69:3–4, 120–125, 1 table.

ZORICHEVA, A. I.
1963A   Permskaiã sistema. Verkhniĭ otdel. Kazanskiĭ iãrus i tatarskiĭ iãrus. [Permian system. Upper section. Kazan' and Tatar stages. North of Russian platform.] Geologiiã SSSR, 2, Arkhangel'sk and Vologda Provinces, and Komi ASSR, 488–532, 4 figs. (Russian).
1963B   Triasovaiã sistema. Sever Russkoĭ platformy. [Triassic system. North of Russian platform.] Geologiiã SSSR, 2, Arkhangel'sk and Vologda Provinces, and Komi ASSR, 605–625, 4 figs. (Russian).

ZUBAKOV, V. A.
1966B   O kriteriiãkh stratigraficheskogo raschleneniiã i taksonomicheskom range chetvertichnogo etapa geologicheskoĭ istorii Zemli. [On the criteria of stratigraphic subdivision and on the taxonomic rank of the Quaternary stage of the geological history of the earth.] Vses. Paleontol. Obshchest., Tr., VIII sess., 190–199 (Russian).
1969A   La chronologie des variations climatiques au cours du Pléistocène en Sibérie Occidentale. Union Internationale pour l'Étude du Quaternaire, 8e Congrès, Paris, 1969. Rev. Géogr. Phys. Géol. Dyn., 11:3, 315–323, 2 figs., 2 tables (French).

ZUBOV, A. A.
1972A   Sistematicheskie kriterii roda Homo i ego evoliutsiiã. [Systematic criteria of the genus Homo and its evolution.] Vop. Antropol., 41, 148–150 (Russian).

ZUBOV, A. A.   See also: Vekilova, E. A. and Zubov, A. A., 1972A.

ZUDIN, A. N. and PANYCHEV, V. A.
1968A   Osobennosti razreza Priobskogo stepnogo plato u sela Kalistratikha. [Special features of the cross-section of Priobian steppe plateau at Kalistratikha village.] In: Neogenovye i chetvertichnye otlozheniiã Zapadnoĭ Sibiri, 29–33 (Russian).

ZUDIN, A. N. and POSPELOVA, G. A.
1970A   O vozrastnom polozhenii pliotsen-chetvertichnykh tolshch Priobskogo plato po paleomagnitnym dannym. [On the age of Pliocene-Quaternary strata of the Ob' plateau based on paleomagnetic data.] Akad. Nauk SSSR, Dokl., 195:6, 1402–1404, 1 chart (Russian).

ZUG, G. R.
1969A   Fossil chelonians, Chrysemys and Clemmys, from the upper Pliocene of Idaho. Great Basin Natur., 29:2, 82–87, 1 fig.

ZUIDEMA, HENRY P.
1970A   Fossil sea mammal. Sea Front., 16:1, 20–24, 5 figs.
1970B   Fossil sea mammal. S. Calif. Paleontol. Soc., Bull., 2:4, 2–4 (reprinted from Sea Frontiers, 16:1, 1970).

ZULLO, JANET LEWIS
1969A   Annie Montague Alexander: her work in paleontology. J. West, 8, 183–199.

ZULLO, VICTOR A.
1969A   Geology. Calif. Acad. Sci., Ann. Rep., 1968–1969, 18, 1 fig.

ZVORYKIN, V. P.
1968A   Modification morphologique de l'analyseur auditif liée à la réduction de la gamme des sons audibles chez les Primates. Int. Congr. Anthropol. Ethnol. Sci., 7th, Moscow, 1964, Proc., 3, 517–522, 4 tables (French).

ZWELL, MICHAEL
1972A   On the supposed "Kenyapithecus africanus" mandible. Nature, 240:5378, 236–239, 2 figs., 1 table.

SUBJECT INDEX

SUBJECT INDEX

This index has been revised in format and some changes made in the major subject headings used in previous volumes. Series of area terms, age terms, and class names have been added to the first-order headings. Each of the major topics is subdivided into second- and third-order subject headings to facilitate location of a particular item. The area terms include names of continents, countries, states or provinces, and general regions. Age terms are limited to geologic periods and eras. Class names used in this index are Amphibia, Aves, Mammalia, Pisces and Reptilia.

Many of the major subject headings (ABSOLUTE AGE, PALEOANTHROPOLOGY, PALEOCLIMATOLOGY, PALEOECOLOGY, VERTEBRATE FAUNAS) may also be found as second-order headings under area terms. CORRELATION and GEOCHRONOLOGY may appear as second-order headings under the age terms. Publications where appropriate, have been indexed both under a major subject heading or class name and under an age or area.

Papers dealing with a taxon from a particular place have been indexed both under an area term and under a class name. Under the area term the class, but not the particular taxon, is listed in the third-order heading. More detailed information is provided under the class name in the third-order heading.

Biogeography, Evolution, or age terms may also be used as second-order headings under a class name. Publications describing the anatomy of an organ system, functional anatomy, or functional adaptations of a taxon are grouped under the class name under the second-order term Anatomy.

Articles on the age of deposits containing vertebrate materials as determined by radiometric or other physical methods have been indexed under ABSOLUTE AGE, DATES, and grouped under the method used, with the area or locality in the third-order. Papers dealing with dating methods in general have been indexed under ABSOLUTE AGE, METHODS.

Publications discussing the correlation of one area with another on the basis of vertebrate fossils have been indexed both under CORRELATION and under age terms. Those discussing biostratigraphy have been indexed both under GEOCHRONOLOGY and under age terms. Papers dealing with the correlation or geochronology of a particular Tertiary Epoch are indexed under TERTIARY, with the name of the Epoch in the third-order heading.

Publications on the evolution of life and vertebrate evolution in general have been indexed under EVOLUTION. Under MUSEUMS have been placed papers on collections of vertebrate fossils, as well as annual reports of museums, reports on current activities, etc. Articles on field and laboratory techniques and general paleontological topics including textbooks have been indexed under PALEONTOLOGY.

Several subjects appear as second-order headings under VERTEBRATE. These include vertebrate anatomy in general, taphonomy, expeditions and field conferences. Publications on paleobiology of vertebrates have also been indexed under VERTEBRATE with names of particular taxa appearing in the third-order.

PALEOANTHROPOLOGY comprises a large section of the subject index and includes articles on physical anthropology, human evolution, and paleolithic art depicting vertebrates. Papers dealing with hominid remains are indexed in this section according to locality and culture or stage.

Papers dealing with continental drift as related to vertebrate evolution have been included under PALEO-GEOGRAPHY.

Publications on VERTEBRATE FAUNAS are listed under that topic, and grouped by age as the second-order heading. Tertiary faunal reports appear under the second-order term Tertiary, with the epoch or age listed in the third-order. Papers on Pleistocene cave faunas have been grouped under the second-order heading Quaternary Cave. Area, locality, and classes of vertebrates involved are listed in the third-order.

Subject Index Abbreviations

Amph.	Amphibia	n.	new
Calif.	California	n. gen.	new genus
Carb.	Carboniferous	n. sp.	new species
Cen.	Cenozoic	Ord.	Ordovician
Cret.	Cretaceous	Paleoz.	Paleozoic
Czech.	Czechoslovakia	Penn.	Pennsylvanian
Co.	County	Perm.	Permian
Dev.	Devonian	Pleist.	Pleistocene
Fm.	Formation	Prov.	Province
frag.	fragment	Quat.	Quaternary
Is.	Island	R.	River
Jur.	Jurassic	Rept.	Reptilia
Mam.	Mammalia	Sil.	Silurian
Mes.	Mesozoic	Tert.	Tertiary
Miss.	Mississippian	Tri.	Triassic
Mts.	Mountains	V.	Valley
		verts.	vertebrates

AMPHIBIA - cont.
Anura
Pliocene; Nebraska, Egelhoff Quarry; morphology
(Chantell, C. J.) 1971A
Tadpole nests
(Cameron, B., Estes, R.) 1971A
Tert.; Europe, central; systematics; phylogeny;
distribution; n. taxa
(Špinar, Z. V.) 1972B
Tert.; Italy, Arondelli; systematics; distribution
(Vergnaud-Grazzini, C.) 1970A
Batrachoseps
Evolution
(Brame, A. H., Murray, K. F.) 1968A
Benthosuchus
Triassic, lower; USSR, Tikhvino; skull; n. sp.
(Ivakhnenko, M. F.) 1972A
Biogeography
Carboniferous
(Panchen, A. L.) 1972C
Paleozoic; labyrinthodonts
(Brown, D. A.) 1968A
Triassic; labyrinthodonts
(Brown, D. A.) 1968A
Brachyopidae
Morphology; evolution; n. sp.
(Cosgriff, J. W.) 1969A
Branchiosauridae
Morphology, variation; sexual dimorphism; n. fam.
(Boy, J. A.) 1971A
Caeciliidae
Paleocene; Brazil, São José de Itaboraí;
vertebra; n. gen.
(Estes, R., Wake, M. H.) 1972A
Systematics
(Anon.) 1972AU
(Taylor, E. H.) 1968A
Capitosauridae
Systematics; phylogeny
(Ochev, V. G.) 1969A
Capitosauroidea
Phylogeny
(Ochev, V. G.) 1968B
Catalogs
Germany, Bavaria; taxonomic
(Kuhn, O.) 1967E
Taxonomic
(Kuhn, O.) 1968B,D
Urodela
(Brame, A. H.) 1967A
Caudata
Tert.; Italy, Arondelli; systematics; distribution
(Vergnaud-Grazzini, C.) 1970A
Chroniosuchidae
Perm., upper; USSR, Donguz R.; skull, skeleton;
n. taxa
(Tverdokhlebova, G. I.) 1972A
Cyclotosaurus mechernichensis
Nomenclature
(Müller, E. M., Schröder, E., Schmidt, W.) 1960A
Diplocaulus
Perm.; Oklahoma, Chickasha Fm.; skull,
skeleton; n. sp.
(Olson, E. C.) 1972C
Dissorophidae
Penn., upper; Ohio; vertebrae; n. gen.
(Vaughn, P. P.) 1971A

AMPHIBIA - cont.
Dissorophidae
Perm., upper; Oklahoma, Blaine Co.;
skull; systematics
(Olson, E. C.) 1972A
Eodiscoglossus
Jurassic, upper; Spain; morphology;
breeding habits
(Hecht, M. K.) 1970A
Eogyrinus
Carb.; England, Northumberland; shoulder
girdle; systematics
(Andrews, S. M.) 1972A
Carb.; England; skull, skeleton; systematics;
restoration
(Panchen, A. L.) 1972A
Eryopidae
Carb., upper; West Virginia, Braxton Co.;
skull, limbs
(Murphy, J. L.) 1971A
Perm., lower; Germany, Saar; skull
(Boy, J. A.) 1971B
General
Choanae, evolution
(Medvedeva, I. M.) 1961A, 1965A
Classification
(Kuhn, O.) 1972A
Evolution; systematics
(Kuhn, O.) 1970E
Palatoquadrate
(Regel', E. D.) 1970A
Respiration
(Romer, A. S.) 1972K
Systematics
(Kuhn, O.) 1970B
Greererpeton
Miss.; West Virginia, Greer; skull, skeleton
(Romer, A. S.) 1969E, 1972I
Labyrinthodontia
Triassic; Antarctica; jaw
(Anon.) 1968AK,BA
(Baranov, A. S.) 1969A
(Colbert, E. H.) 1969E
Leptodactylidae
Systematics; evolution
(Lynch, J. D.) 1971A
Lissamphibia
Pliocene; Siberia, Pavlodar; morphology
(Iskakova, K. I.) 1969A
Skull roof bones
(Lebedkina, N. S.) 1968A
Lysorophus
Permian; Oklahoma, Cleveland Co.; skeleton
(Olson, E. C.) 1971B
Lystrosaurus
Triassic; Antarctica
(Anon.) 1970AW,AY, 1972AE
(Jensen, J. A.) 1972A
Micromelerpeton
Skeleton; systematics
(Malz, H.) 1970A
Microsauria
Penn., upper; Colorado, Fremont Co.;
skeleton; systematics; n. taxa
(Vaughn, P. P.) 1972A
Ophiderpetontidae
Penn., upper; Colorado, central; n. gen.
(Vaughn, P. P.) 1969B

ANATOMY. See under class name, Vertebrate.

ANGOLA
  Paleontology
    Mam.; Pleist.; Leba
      (Minkoff, E. C.)   1972A
    Pisces; Miocene
      (Telles Antunes, M.)   1970A

ANTARCTICA
  Paleontology
    Amph.; Triassic
      (Colbert, E. H.)   1969E
    Amph.; Triassic; Coalsack Bluff
      (Jensen, J. A.)   1972A
    Pisces; Jurassic, lower; Queen Alexandra Range
      (Schaeffer, B.)   1971C, 1972A
  Vertebrate Faunas
    Dev.; Pisces
      (Ritchie, A.)   1969A
    Dev.; Victoria Land; Pisces
      (McKelvey, B. C., et al.)   1970A
      (White, E. I.)   1968A
    Jurassic; Pisces
      (Tasch, P.)   1970A
    Mesozoic
      (Colbert, E. H.)   1971C
    Mesozoic; Pisces
      (Ritchie, A.)   1971A
    Triassic
      (Anon.)   1970BD
      (Colbert, E. H.)   1970A,C, 1972A,B
      (Elliot, D. H., et al.)   1970A
      (Kitching, J. W., et al.)   1972A
      (Steinert, H.)   1972A
      (Stubbs, P., Wick, G.)   1969C
    Triassic; Coalsack Bluff
      (Colbert, E. H.)   1970B,E,G
    Triassic, lower; McGregor Glacier
      (Colbert, E. H.)   1971A
      (Kitching, J. W.)   1971A

ANTHROPOLOGY. See Paleoanthropology.

ANTILLES
  Paleontology
    Mam.; Pleist.
      (Martin, R. A.)   1972A
    Mam.; Pliocene
      (Martin, R. A.)   1972A
  Vertebrate Faunas
    Pleistocene
      (Hooijer, D. A.)   1972C

ARCTIC
  Paleogeography
    Cenozoic
      (Strelkov, S. A.)   1970A
  Vertebrate Faunas
    Dev.; Axel Heiberg Is.; Pisces
      (Trettin, H. P.)   1969A
    Dev.; Prince of Wales Is.; Pisces
      (Broad, D. S., Dineley, D. L.,
        Miall, A. D.)   1968A
    Pleist.; Mam.
      (Sher, A. V.)   1971B

ARGENTINA
  Paleoclimatology
    Tertiary
      (Volkheimer, W.)   1971A
  Paleontology
    Aves; Miocene; Chubut
      (Simpson, G. G.)   1970C

ARGENTINA - cont.
  Paleontology
    Aves; Miocene, lower; Patagonia Fm.
      (Simpson, G. G.)   1972B
    Aves; Pleist.; Buenos Aires
      (Holyoak, D. T.)   1971A
      (Tonni, E. P.)   1969A
    Mam.; Eocene; Chubut
      (Simpson, G. G.)   1970D
    Mam.; Eocene; Mendoza
      (Simpson, G. G.)   1970G
    Mam.; Oligocene; Patagonia
      (Patterson, B., Pascual, R.)   1968B
    Mam.; Pleist.
      (Simpson, G. G.)   1970F
    Mam.; Pleist., lower
      (Simpson, G. G.)   1972A
    Mam.; Pliocene; Chapadmalal
      (Reig, O. A., Linares, O. J.)   1969A
    Mam.; Plio-Pleistocene
      (Reig, O. A., Simpson, G. G.)   1972A
    Pisces; Cret.; Yacoraite Fm.
      (Leanza, A. F.)   1969A
    Rept.; Cret.
      (Gasparini, Z. B. de)   1972A
    Rept.; Cret.; Paso de Indios
      (Corro, G. del)   1966A
    Rept.; Eocene
      (Gasparini, Z. B. de)   1972A
    Rept.; Jur., upper; San Luis Prov.
      (Bonaparte, J. F.)   1969F
    Rept.; Mesozoic; Hualtarán
      (Bonaparte, J. F.)   1971C
    Rept.; Triassic
      (Bonaparte, J. F.)   1969B
    Rept.; Triassic; Chañares
      (Cox, C. B.)   1968A
      (Jenkins, F. A.)   1970B
      (Romer, A. S.)   1969A, 1970A,
                 1971B,D,E, 1972A,B,C,D,G
    Rept.; Triassic; Las Malvinas
      (Bonaparte, J. F.)   1969A
    Rept.; Tri., upper; La Rioja
      (Bonaparte, J. F.)   1971B
  Vertebrate Faunas
    Cenozoic; Buenos Aires Prov.
      (Pascual, R., et al.)   1966A
    Cenozoic, Cret.; Corrientes
      (Herbst, R.)   1971A
    Cret.; Salta Prov.
      (Benedetto, J. L., Sanchez, T. M.)   1971A
    Pleist.; Malacara; Mam.
      (Kraglievich, J. L.)   1959C
    Pliocene; Paraná; Pisces
      (Scartascini, G.)   1959A
    Tert., upper; northwestern; Mam.
      (Castellanos, A.)   1969A
    Triassic; Rept.
      (Bonaparte, J. F.)   1969C
    Triassic; San Juan-La Rioja
      (Bonaparte, J. F.)   1969E

ARIZONA
  Paleontology
    Amph.; Triassic; Moenkopi Fm.
      (Welles, S. P., Estes, R.)   1969A
    Mam.; Oligocene; central
      (Lindsay, E. H., Lundin, R. F.)   1972A

ARTIFACTS WITH FAUNAS - cont.

France

Paleolithic; Les Eyzies; reindeer fauna
(Movius, H. L.)   1955C
Paleolithic; Nice, Terra Amata; verts.
(Lumley, H.)   1969E
Paleolithic; Pas-de-Calais; verts.
(Bourdier, F.)   1969A
Paleolithic; Pons; verts.
(Lassarade, L., Rouvreau, M.,
Texier, A.)   1969A
Paleolithic, upper; Saint-Jean-de-Verge
Cave; verts.
(Vezian, J., Vezian, J.)   1966A, 1970A
Paleolithic; verts.
(Bouchud, J.)   1957A
Perigordian; Perigueux; verts.
(Celerier, G.)   1967A

General

Cave bear jaws
(Riek, G.)   1969A
Chelléen; verts.
(Denizot, G.)   1965A
Paleolithic; bird faunas
(Grimm, H.)   1970A, 1972A

Germany

Magdalénien; Feldkirchen-Gönnersdorf; verts.
(Bosinski, G.)   1968A, 1969A
Mousterian; Bocksteinschmiede; verts.
(Wetzel, R., Bosinski, G.)   1969A
Mousterian; Munzingen; verts.
(Guenther, E. W.)   1968A
Paleolithic; Lommersum; verts.
(Hahn, J.)   1970B
Paleolithic; Magdeburg; verts.
(Toepfer, V.)   1970A
Paleolithic; Rhineland; verts.
(Bosinski, G., Brunnacker, K.)   1969A
Paleolithic; verts.
(Hoffmann, W.)   1965A, 1966A, 1968A
(Hoffmann, W., Schmidt, B.)   1965A

Great Britain

Paleolithic, upper; Cefn Cave; verts.
(Valdemar, A. E.)   1970A

Hungary

Mousterian; Érd; verts.
(Gábori-Csánk, V.)   1967A, 1968A
(Gábori-Csánk, V., Kretzoi, M.)   1968A

Illinois

Paleo-Indian; verts.
(Griffin, J. B.)   1968A

India

Paleolithic, lower; Rajasthan; verts.
(Misra, V. N.)   1967A
Paleolithic; Nandur-Madhmeshwar; vert. f.
(Joshi, R. V., Sali, S. A.)   1971A
Paleolithic; Punjab; turtle
(Mohapatra, G. C.)   1966A

Israel

Acheulian; 'Evron; verts.
(Issar, A., Kafri, U.)   1969A
Paleolithic; Galilee; verts.
(Prausnitz, M. W.)   1969A

Italy

Acheulean; Prince Cave; verts.
(Barral, L., Simone, S.)   1969A

ARTIFACTS WITH FAUNAS - cont.

Italy

Aurignacian; Vibrata V.; verts.
(Radmilli, A. M.)   1965C
Mousterian; Grimaldi; verts.
(Barral, L., Simone, S.)   1968C
Mousterian; Grotta del Leone; verts.
(Leonardi, P., Allegranzi, A.)   1965A
Mousterian; Manie; verts.
(Anon.)   1969BM
Mousterian; Prazziche; verts.
(Borzatti von Löwenstern, E.)   1966A
Mousterian; St. Leonardo Cave; verts.
(Radmilli, A. M.)   1965B
Mousterian; Sannicandro Garganico;
verts.
(Russi, V.)   1968A
Mousterian; Santa Caterina; Mam.
(Borzatti von Löwenstern, E.)   1966B
Mousterian; Sora; verts.
(Biddittu, I., Cassoli, P.,
Malpieri, L.)   1967A
Mousterian; Taddeo Cave; verts.
(Vigliardi, A.)   1968A,B
Paleolithic; Alto Cave; verts.
(Borzatti von Löwenstern, E.,
Magaldi, D.)   1967A
Paleolithic; Azzurra Cave; verts.
(Cannarella, D., Cremonesi, G.)   1967A
Paleolithic; Balzi Rossi; verts.
(Tinè, S.)   1968A
Paleolithic; Borgosesia; verts.
(Fedele, F.)   1968A
Paleolithic, lower; Pontecorvo;
verts.
(Biddittu, I., Cassoli, P.)   1968A
Paleolithic, lower; Sicily; verts.
(Graziosi, P.)   1968A
Paleolithic; Sicily; Elephas
(Bianchini, G., Mascle, G.)   1971A
Paleolithic; Uluzzo Bay; verts.
(Borzatti von Löwenstern, E.)   1965C
Paleolithic, upper; Calauca Cave; verts.
(Vigliardi, A.)   1968C

Kentucky

Paleo-Indian; western; verts.
(Rolingson, M. A., Schwartz, D. W.)   1966B

Kenya

Paleolithic; Lake Rudolf; verts.
(Leakey, M. D.)   1970A

Louisiana

Paleo-Indian; Avery Island; verts.
(Anon.)   1971AG

Mauritania

Acheuléan; Adrar; verts.
(Biberson, P.)   1969B
Acheuléan; Zouérat; verts.
(Coppens, Y., Gouzes, R.,
Le Floch, R., Paquet, M.)   (s.d.)

Mexico

Paleo-Indian; Arroyo de Malpais;
horse kill
(Di Peso, C. C.)   1966A
Paleo-Indian; Lake Texcoco; mammoth
(Griffin, J. B.)   1966A
Paleo-Indian; Puebla; mastodon
(Paynter, C.)   1969A
(Sykes, E.)   1969A

ARTIFACTS WITH FAUNAS - cont.
USSR
Mousterian; Altaĭ, Ust'-Kanskaĭa Cave; verts.
(Anisîutkin, N. K., Astakhov, S. N.)   1970A
Mousterian; Armenia, Erevan; Mam.
(Eritsîân, B. G., Semenov, S. A.)   1971A
Mousterian; Crimea; verts.
(Shchepinskiĭ, A. A.)   1971A
Mousterian; northern; verts.
(Petri, W.)   1969A
Mousterian; Pechora; verts.
(Bader, O. N.)   1969B
Mousterian; Smolensk Prov.; mammal fauna
(Shmidt, E. A.)   1963A
Mousterian; southern; verts.
(Kleĭn, R. G.)   1967B
Mousterian; Volchiĭ Cave; mammoth fauna
(Bader, O. N.)   1969D
Mousterian; western; verts.
(Kleĭn, R. G.)   1969A,B
Paleolithic; Altaĭ; verts.
(Adamenko, O. M., Gaĭduk, I. M.)   1967A
Paleolithic; Chernoozer'e II; verts.
(Gening, V. F.)   1969A
Paleolithic; Desna V.; mammoth fauna
(Toepfer, V.)   1968B
Paleolithic; Îakutia; verts.
(Mochanov, Îu. A.)   1969B
Paleolithic; Kazakhstan; verts.
(Alpysbaev, Kh. A.)   1968A
Paleolithic; Kul'bulak; verts.
(Kasymov, M. R.)   1969A
Paleolithic; lower; verts.
(Adamenko, O. M.)   1970A
Paleolithic; Moldavia; verts.
(Ketraru, N. A.)   1965C
Paleolithic; Oselivka; mammoth fauna
(Chernysh, A. P.)   1971A
Paleolithic; Ukrainia; mammoth bone dwellings
(Kolinko, V.)   1971A
Paleolithic, upper; Brîansk; mammoth
(Zavernîaev, F. M.)   1970A
Paleolithic, upper; Kulychivka; verts.
(Savich, V. P.)   1969B
Paleolithic; verts.
(Vereshchagin, N. K.)   1970A
Paleolithic; western; fish remains
(Fedorov, V. V.)   1963A
Paleolithic; western; mammal faunas
(Bader, O. N.)   1971B
Paleolithic; Yakutia; mammoth
(Anon.)   1972AO
Venezuela
Paleo-Indian; Falcon; mastodon
(Anon.)   1969AS
Paleo-Indian; verts.
(Cruxent, J. M.)   1970A
Wyoming
Paleo-Indian; Casper; bison kill
(Anon.)   1971AI
Paleo-Indian; Rawlins; bison, mammoth
(Anon.)   1961DL
Paleo-Indian; Union Pacific; mammoth kill
(Irwin, H. T.)   1970A

ASIA
Paleoanthropology
Paleolithic art
(Panarina, G. N.)   1969A
Paleontology
Mam.; Eocene
(Mellett, J. S., Szalay, F. S.)   1968A
Mam.; Pleist.; eastern
(Ovodov, N. D.)   1970A
Mam.; Pliocene; Siwalik Hills
(Hussain, S. T.)   1971A,B
Pisces; Tertiary; southwestern
(Danil'chenko, V. P.)   1972A
Vertebrate Faunas
Cenozoic; Mam.
(Bazhanov, V. S., et al.)   1971A
(Vangengeĭm, E. A., Zhegallo, V. I.,
Zazhigin, V. S.)   1972A
Cenozoic, upper; Mam.
(Flerow, C. C.)   1971B
Oligocene; Mam.
(Flerov, K. K., Îanovskaîa, N. M.)   1971A
ASSOCIATIONS
All-Union Paleontological Society
16th session
(Witwicka, E.)   1970A
British Symposium of Vertebrate Paleontology
and Comparative Anatomy
Reading Univ., 1968
(Romer, A. S.)   1969F
Centennial Colloquium
Les Eyzies, 1968
(Boulinier, G.)   1968A, 1969A
(Vallois, H. V.)   1968B, 1969C
Colloquium of Pleistocene Geology and
Faunal Studies
URSR, 1969
(Biberson, P.)   1970B
Colloquium on the Paleolithic of Slovenia
Lubljana, 1965
(Broglio, A.)   1965B
Commemorative Meeting
Heidelberg man site, 1967
(Heberer, G.)   1968C
Eocene Colloquium
France, 1968
(Brabb, E. E.)   1969A
Darwin centenary
Report
(Anon.)   1971AR
Hugo-Obermaier Gesellschaft
Marbach am Neckar, 1968
(Geer, K.)   1969A
INQUA
Publications
(Markov, K. K.)   1969A
INQUA Congress
Paris, 1969; 8th
(Anon.)   1969BJ, 1970BA
(Bordes, F.)   1972A
(Davies, O.)   1970A
(Duphorn, K., et al.)   1969A
Warsaw, 1961; 6th
(Shanîser, E. V.)   1964A

AUSTRALIA - cont.
Paleontology
Mam.; Pleist., upper; Fromm's Landing
(Archer, M.)   1971A
Mam.; Pleist.; Wellington Caves
(Martinez R., C., Lidicker, W. Z.)   1971A
Mam.; Pleist.; western
(Merrilees, D.)   1970A
Mam.; Pliocene; Darling Downs
(Bartholomai, A.)   1971A
Mam.; Pliocene; Lake Tyers
(Plane, M.)   1971A
Mam.; Pliocene, upper; Dunolly
(Gill, E. D.)   1972A
Mam.; Tert.; Beaumaris
(Woodburne, M. O.)   1969C
Pisces; Cret.; Victoria
(Waldman, M.)   1971C
Pisces; Dev.
(Thomson, K. S., Campbell, K. S. W.)   1971A
Pisces; Dev.; Dare Plain
(Gilbert-Tomlinson, J.)   1968A
Pisces; Dev., middle; Carnarvon Basin
(Seddon, G.)   1969A
Pisces; Dev., upper; western
(Miles, R. S.)   1971B
Pisces; Dev.; Wilson Cliffs
(Gross, W.)   1971C
Rept.; Cret., lower; Carapook
(Warren, J. W.)   1969B
Vertebrate Faunas
Aves
(Mayr, E.)   1972A
Cenozoic; Mam.
(Ride, W. D. L.)   1968A
Cenozoic; Murray Basin; Pisces
(Pels, S.)   1969A
Cret., lower; Victoria; Pisces
(Waldman, M.)   1971B
Dev.; Gogo; Pisces
(Anon.)   1969BD
Dev.; New South Wales; Pisces
(Conolly, J. R., Hall, L. R., Rose, G.)   1969A
Dev.; Pisces
(Ritchie, A.)   1969A
Dev.; western; Pisces
(Miles, R. S.)   1971A
Jurassic; Great Artesian Basin; Pisces
(Hind, M. C., Helby, R. J.)   1969A
Jurassic; Talbragar; Pisces
(Dulhunty, J. A., Eadie, J.)   1969A
Miocene, upper; Alcoota
(Woodburne, M. O.)   1969D
Pleist.; Labyrinth Cave
(Merrilees, D.)   1969A
Pleist.; Lara; Mam.
(Wilkinson, H. E.)   1971A
Pleist.; Mabel, Pyramid Caves; Mam.
(Wakefield, N. A.)   1967A
Pleist.; McEachern's Cave; Mam.
(Wakefield, N. A.)   1967B
Pleist.; Mam.
(Calaby, J. H.)   1971A
(Mulvaney, D. J.)   1969A
Pleist.; Victoria Cave; Mam.
(Smith, M. J.)   1971A

AUSTRALIA - cont.
Vertebrate faunas
Pliocene; Grange Burn; Mam.
(Turnbull, W. D., Lundelius, E. L.)   1970A
Pliocene; Victoria; Mam.
(Turnbull, W. D.)   1969A
Tertiary; Mam.
(Tedford, R. H.)   1961B
Triassic, lower
(Bartholomai, A., Howie, A.)   1970A
Triassic; Sydney Basin
(Lovering, J. F., McElroy, C. T.)   1969A
(McElroy, C. T., et al.)   1969A
(Standard, J. C.)   1969A
Triassic; western
(Cosgriff, J. W.)   1967B
AUSTRIA
Paleontology
Mam.; Neogene; Vienna Basin
(Schaefer, H., Zapfe, H.)   1971A
Mam.; Oligocene; Reisetbauer quarry
(Spillmann, F.)   1969A
Mam.; Pleist.; Deutsch-Altenburg
(Rabeder, G.)   1972A
Mam.; Pleist.; Eggenburg
(Adam, K. D.)   1966D
(Thenius, E.)   1966G
Mam.; Pleist.; Hundsheim
(Daxner, G.)   1968A
Mam.; Pleist.; Teufels Cave
(Lehmann, U.)   1966B
Mam.; Pliocene, lower; Kohfidisch fissures
(Bachmayer, F., Wilson, R. W.)   1970A
Mam.; Pliocene, lower; Mödling
(Daxner-Höck, G.)   1970A
Mam.; Pliocene, lower; northern
(Thenius, E.)   1970B
Mam.; Pliocene; southeast
(Mottl, M.)   1969A
Mam.; Pliocene; Vienna Basin
(Daxner-Höck, G.)   1972A
Pisces; Cret., upper; East Alps
(Weinfurter, E.)   1967B
Vertebrate Faunas
Eocene; Salzburg; Pisces
(Vogeltanz, R.)   1968A, 1970A
Miocene; Eibiswald; Mam.
(Flugel, H., Maurin, V.)   1959A
Miocene, lower; Plesching; Pisces
(Schultz, O.)   1968A
Miocene; Vienna Basin; Pisces
(Schultz, O.)   1972A
Neogene; Mam.
(Kollmann, K.)   1964A
Oligo-Miocene; Plesching; Pisces
(Steininger, F.)   1966A
Pleist., lower; Eichkogels
(Daxner-Höck, G., Rabeder, G.)   1971A
Pleist.; Ruppersthal; Mam.
(Bachmayer, F., Kollmann, H. A.,
Schultz, O., Summesberger, H.)   1971A
Pleist.; Schlenkendurchgang's Cave
(Ehrenberg, K., Mais, K.)   1968A, 1970A,B
Pleist.; Teufels, Fuchsen Caves
(Ehrenberg, K.)   1966F
(Wettstein-Westersheimb, O.)   1966B
(Zapfe, H.)   1966D

AVES - cont.
Cimolopterygidae
Cret., upper; Wyoming; n. gen.
(Brodkorb, P.)   1969C
Conurus
Pleist.; Argentina, Buenos Aires; nomenclature
(Holyoak, D. T.)   1971A
Corvidae
Miocene, upper; Colorado, Logan Co.;
limb; n. gen.
(Brodkorb, P.)   1972A
Pliocene, upper; Kansas, Meade Co.; limb; n. sp.
(Brodkorb, P.)   1972A
Cretaceous
Australia, Koonwarra; feathers
(Talent, J. A., Duncan, P. M.,
Handby, P. L.)   1966A
Cuculidae
Pleist.; Cuba, Pio-Domingo; morphology
(Fischer, K., Stephan, B.)   1971B
Dendragapus
Variation
(Jehl, J. R.)   1969A
Dinornis
Nomenclature
(Scarlett, R. J.)   1969A
Diomedeidae
Miocene, upper; Australia, Beaumaris;
bill; n. sp.
(Wilkinson, H. E.)   1969A
Dromornithidae
Cenozoic; Australia; morphology
(Rich, P., Rich, T.)   1972A
Evolution
General
(Burchak-Abramovich, N. I.)   1967B
Phylogeny; morphology
(Walker, A. D.)   1972A
Radiation
(Brodkorb, P.)   1971B
Foetopterus
Nomenclature
(Tonni, E. P.)   1970A
Galliformes
Pleist.; USSR, Moldavia
(Gania, I. M.)   1969B
Gallirallus
Pleist., upper; New Zealand, Te Waka;
limbs, n. sp.
(Scarlett, R. J.)   1970B
Gallus
Pleist.; USSR, Georgia; domestication
(Burchak-Abramovich, N. I.,
Bendukidze, O. G.)   1971A
Gastroliths
Eocene; France; *Diatryma, Gastornis*
(Cailleux, A.)   1969A
Pleist.; Alaska
(Hoskin, C. M., Guthrie, R. D.,
Hoffman, B. L. P.)   1970A
General
Distribution
(Mikheev, A. V.)   1967A
Geochronology; environmental studies
(Burchak-Abramovich, N. I.)   1967C

AVES - cont.
General
Micro-evolution
(Shvarts, S. S.)   1965A
Origin
(Galton, P. M.)   1970B
Origin; phylogeny
(Ricqlès, A. de)   1971A
Origin; radiation
(Bock, W. J.)   1969C
Paleornithology
(Kurochkin, E. N.)   1971B
Systematics
(Dement'ev, G. P.)   1965A
(Iudin, K. A.)   1970A
Geranoididae
Eocene; USSR, Zaisan; limb; n. gen.
(Bendukidze, O. G.)   1971A
Systematics; evolution; n. taxa
(Cracraft, J.)   1969A
Grus
Pleist., lower; Cuba, Pio-Domingo;
skeleton; n. sp.
(Fischer, K., Stephan, B.)   1971A
Pleist., upper; Florida; Jefferson Co.
(Olson, S. L.)   1972A
Halcyornis
Eocene; England, Kent; systematics;
skull; n. taxa
(Harrison, C. J. O., Walker, C. A.)   1972A
Icteridae
Pleist.; Cuba, Pio-Domingo; morphology; n. sp.
(Fischer, K., Stephan, B.)   1971B
Macrorhamphus
Pliocene; Mongolia; morphology; n. sp.
(Kurochkin, E. N.)   1971A
Mancalla
Morphologic variation; n. sp.
(Howard, H.)   1970A
Musophagidae
Oligocene; Germany, Gaimersheim bei
Ingolstadt; humerus
(Ballman, P.)   1970A
Numenius
Endocranial casts
(Dechaseaux, C.)   1970B
Odontopterygia
Miocene; New Zealand, North Canterbury;
humerus
(Scarlett, R. J.)   1972A
Ornitholithus
Eocene; France; eggs
(Dughi, R., Plaziat, J.-C.,
Sirugue, F.)   1969A
Paleocene; France; eggs
(Dughi, R., Sirugue, F.)   1968B
Palaeophasianus
Systematics
(Cracraft, J.)   1968C
Paloelodus
Tert.; Germany, Mainz Basin; skull, skeleton
(Rothausen, K.)   1966A
Phalacrocorax
Pliocene; Idaho; skeleton
(Murray, B. G.)   1970A

AVES - cont.
Tutor
Nomenclature
(Kurochkin, E. N.) 　　　1969A,B
Zenaidura
Pliocene, upper; Kansas, Rexroad;
limb; n. sp.
(Brodkorb, P.) 　　　1968B
BELGIUM
Paleoanthropology
Schmerling Cave; fossil hominids
(Vandebosch, A.) 　　　1955A
Paleontology
Mam.; Eocene; Hainaut
(Quinet, G. E., Verlinden, W.) 　　　1970A
Mam.; Paleocene
(Quinet, G. E.) 　　　1966E,F
Mam.; Paleocene; Brabant
(Quinet, G. E., Verlinden, W.,
Coupatez, P.) 　　　1971A
Mam.; Plio-Pleistocene; Anvers
(Plisnier-Ladame, F., Quinet, G. E.) 　　　1969A
Pisces; Eocene
(Nolf, D.) 　　　1970C
Pisces; Eocene; Lede
(Stinton, F. C., Nolf, D.) 　　　1969A
Pisces; Miocene, middle; Antwerpen
(Gaemers, P. A. M.) 　　　1969A, 1971A
Pisces; Pleist.
(Casier, E.) 　　　1957C
Rept.
(Quinet, G. E.) 　　　1970B
Rept.; Cret.; Eben
(Plisnier-Ladame, F., Coupatez, P.) 　　　1969A
Rept.; Eocene
(Casier, E.) 　　　1968A
Rept.; Eocene, lower; Erquelinnes
(Zangerl, R.) 　　　1971A
Vertebrate Faunas
Eocene; Aalter; Pisces
(Nolf, D.) 　　　1969A
Eocene; Merelbeke; Pisces
(Casier, E., et al.) 　　　1966A
(Nolf, D.) 　　　1970B
Eocene; Montroeul-au-Bois; Pisces
(Quinet, G. E., Coupatez, P.,
Wouters, G.) 　　　1970A
Eocene; Pisces
(Nolf, D.) 　　　1966A
Paleocene; Dormaal; Pisces
(Casier, E.) 　　　1967B
Paleogene; Zeebrugge; Pisces
(Nolf, D.) 　　　1967A
Pleist.; Mam.
(McWilliams, B.) 　　　1970A
Pleist., upper; Le Trou Dubois Cave; Mam.
(Destexhe Jamotte, J.) 　　　1970A
Pleist., upper; Pisces
(Vandebosch, A.) 　　　1957B
Tert.; Pisces
(Nolf, D.) 　　　1970A
BIBLIOGRAPHY
Anthropology
Africa
(Gibson, G. D.) 　　　1969A

BIBLIOGRAPHY - cont.
Anthropology
Europe, central
(Malinowski, T.) 　　　1970A
European USSR
(Markotić, V.) 　　　1963A, 1970A
Far East
(Ma, C.-R.) 　　　1969A
Human evolution
(Beckham, R. S.) 　　　1963A
New World
(Franch, J. A.) 　　　1964A
North America
(Ballesteros-Gaibrois, M.,
Franch, J. A.) 　　　1964A, 1965A
Archaeology
Africa
(Nequin, J.) 　　　1969A
California
(Heizer, R. F., Elsasser, A. B.,
Clewlow, C. W.) 　　　1970A
Europe
(Römisch-Germanisches Zentralmuseum,
Mainz, Butler, J. J.) 　　　1964A
Great Britain
(Council for British Archaeology,
Lucas, A. T.) 　　　1964A
Manitoba
(Hlady, W. M.) 　　　1966B
West Africa
(Calvocoressi, D.) 　　　1969A
Coprolites
Vertebrate
(Häntzschel, W., El-Baz, F.,
Amstutz, G. C.) 　　　1968A
Earth Sciences
Hungary, 1968
(Kilényi, I.) 　　　1969A
Hungary, 1969
(Kilényi, I., Jantsky, Zs.) 　　　1970A
Evolutionary sciences
Book list
(Deason, H. J.) 　　　1970A
Fossil Birds
Hildegarde Howard
(Howard, H.) 　　　1969C
Fossil Mammals
General
(Anderson, S., et al.) 　　　1972A
Fossil Man
Old World, 1963–1968
(Fay, G. E.) 　　　1969A
Fossil Vertebrates
1964–1968
(Camp, C. L., et al.) 　　　1972A
1967–1968
(Clark, J. K.) 　　　1969A
1968–1969
(Matsumoto, M., Nichols, R.) 　　　1970A
1969–1970
(Matsumoto, M.) 　　　1971A
1970–1971
(Bacskai, J., et al.) 　　　1972A
Notice of publication
(Savage, D., Whistler, D.,
Hutchison, H.) 　　　1969A

BIOGRAPHY - cont.
Zdeněk Burian
  (Klíma, B.)   1970A
Charles L. Camp
  (Morrison, L. L.)   1971A
  Bibliography
    (Anon.)   1972AD
Czech paleontologists
  (Musil, R.)   1960D
W. D. Conybeare
  (North, F. J.)   1956A
Miguel Crusafont Pairó
  (Golpe Posse, J. M.)   1971B
Georges Cuvier
  (Anthony, J.)   1970A
  (Heller, F.)   1969A
  (Kuhn-Schnyder, E.)   1969A
  (Piveteau, J.)   1969C
  (Théobald, N.)   1969A
  (Trofimov, B. A.)   1969A
Giorgio Dal Piaz
  (Malaroda, R.)   1965A
Charles Darwin
  (Barry, D. G.)   1971A
  (Herbert, S.)   1971A
  (Moorehead, A.)   1969A,B
  (Villiers, A.)   1969A
  (Vorzimmer, P. J.)   1972A
Pierre David
  (Pintaud, R. C.)   1964A
Georgiĭ F. Debets
  (Miklashevskaĭa, N. N.)   1970A
Robert Denison
  (Williams, P. M.)   1969A
Theodosius Dobzhansky
  Bibliography
    (Levene, H., Ehrman, L.,
    Richmond, R.)   1970A
B. A. Dombrovskiĭ
  (Anon.)   1970AA
Tilly Edinger
  (Hofer, H.)   1969A
P. P. Efimenko
  (Editors)   1972A
  (Rogachev, A. N.)   1972A
Ian Martynovich Eglon
  (Rozhdestvenskiĭ, A. K.)   1971A
Loren Eiseley
  (Eiseley, L.)   1971A
Evolutionists
  Germany; pre-Darwin
    (Raĭkov, B. E.)   1969A
Géza Gyula Fejérváry
  (Boros, I., Dely, O. G.)   1968A
  (Dely, O. G.)   1968A
Ioanni Filip
  (Anon.)   1970AC
Mikhail M. Gerasimov
  (Anon.)   1968BK
André Glory
  (Bergounioux, F. M.)   1967A
  (Blanchard, V.)   1967A
Georg August Goldfuss
  (Langer, W.)   1970A, 1970B
  (Müller, K., Langer, W.)   1970A

BIOGRAPHY - cont.
Professor Gorjanović
  (Kochansky-Devidé, V.)   1970A
P. P. Grassé
  (Anon.)   1968BC
William King Gregory
  (Simpson, G. G.)   1972C
  Bibliography
    (Simpson, G. G.)   1971G
V. I. Gromov
  (Saks, V. N.)   1969A
Johann J. Haeckel
  Bibliography
    (Heberer, G.)   1968B
Richard Hagen
  (Matthes, H. W.)   1969A
Eugene Raymond Hall
  Bibliography
    (Durrant, S. D.)   1969A
T. S. Hall
  (Gill, E. D.)   1970A
Aleš Hrdlička
  (Anon.)   1969CI
  (Fetter, V.)   1969A
  (Roginskiĭ, Ia. Ia.)   1969C
  (Uryson, M. I.)   1969C
Julian Huxley
  (Huxley, J.)   1970A
Huxleys
  (Clark, R. W.)   1968A
Nikolaĭ Nikolaevich Iakovlev
  (Iavorskiĭ, V. I., et al.)   1970A
Werner Janensch
  (Jaeger, H.)   1971A
Hope Johnson
  (Bush, H.)   1969A
Vladimír Kalabis
  (Tejkal, J.)   1970A
Johann Jakob Kaup
  (Hefele, G.)   1959A
  (Heldmann, G.)   1955A
C. J. van der Klaauw
  (Boschma, H.)   1968A
  Bibliography
    (Anon.)   1968AJ
Charles R. Knight
  (Williams, P. M.)   1970A
Veronika I. Kochetkova
  Bibliography
    (Anon.)   1971CB
V. O. Kovalevskiĭ
  (Davitashvili, L. Sh.)   1968A
Alfred Kroeber
  (Kroeber, T.)   1970A
Othmar Kühn
  (Anon.)   1967BQ
  Bibliography
    (Steininger, F.)   1970A
L. S. B. Leakey
  (Mulvey, M. W.)   1969A
  (Tufty, B.)   1971A
Theodore Doney McCown
  Bibliography
    (Brooks, S.)   1970A

BIOGRAPHY - cont.
V. I. Zalkin
(Novikov, G. A.)   1971A
Lothar Zotz
(Freund, G., Guenther, E. W.)   1968A
BIOSTRATIGRAPHY. See under Geochronology.
BOLIVIA
Paleontology
Mam.; Oligocene; Salla-Luribay Basin
(Hoffstetter, R., Lavocat, R.)   1970A
Pisces; Cret., upper
(Wenz, S.)   1969A,B
Vertebrate Faunas
Neogene; Altiplano; Mam.
(Hoffstetter, R., Martinez, C.,
Tomasi, P.)   1972A
Oligocene; Lacayani; Mam.
(Hoffstetter, R., Martinez, C.,
Mattauer, M., Tomasi, P.)   1971A
Pleist.; Amph.
(Vergnaud-Grazzini, C.)   1968B
Pleist.; Ñuapua
(Hoffstetter, R.)   1968E
BRAZIL
Paleontology
Amph.; Paleocene;
Sao José de Itaborai
(Estes, R., Wake, M. H.)   1972A
Mam.; Miocene; Pará
(Paula Couto, C. de)   1967C
Mam.; Paleocene;
Sao José de Itaborai
(Paula Couto, C. de)   1970A
Mam.; Pleist.; Goiás
(Moreira, L. E., Gomes de Melo, S. M.) 1971A
Mam.; Pleist.; São Paulo
(Paula Couto, C. de)   1971A
Mam.; Pleist.; Tremembe
(Silva Santos, R. da)   1970A
Mam.; Pleist., upper; northeast
(Moreira, L. E.)   1971A
Pisces; Carb., lower; Maranhão
(Silva Santos, R. da; Sardenberg
Salgado, M.)   1970A
Pisces; Cret., lower; Araripe
(Silva Santos, R. da)   1970B, 1971A
Pisces; Cret., lower; Bahía
(Silva Santos, R. da)   1969A
Pisces; Cret., lower; Santana Fm.
(Silva Santos, R. da)   1968A
Pisces; Cret., upper; Ganhamaroba R.
(Silva Santos, R. da; Sardenberg
Salgado, M.)   1969A
Pisces; Miocene, lower; Pará
(Silva Santos, R., Sardenberg
Salgado, M.)   1971A
Rept.; Cret., lower; Araripe
(Price, L. I.)   1971A
Rept.; Permian; São Paulo
(Shikama, T.)   1970A
Rept.; Triassic
(Colbert, E. H.)   1970F
(Romer, A. S.)   1969C
Rept.; Triassic; Rio Grande do Sul
(Barberena, M. C.)   1971A

BRAZIL - cont.
Vertebrate Faunas
Cret.; Santana Fm.; Pisces
(Silva Santos, R. da,
Gomes Valenca, J.)   1968A
Neogene; Taubaté; Pisces
(Moncharmont Zei, M.)   1970A
Paleocene
(Estes, R.)   1972A
Permian; São Paulo; Rept.
(Amaral, S. E. de)   1971A
Pleist.; Santa Cruz do Capibaribe;
Mam.
(Lins Rolim, J.)   1971A
BRITISH COLUMBIA
Paleontology
Mam.; Oligocene; Vancouver Is.
(Russell, L. S.)   1968B
Mam.; Pleist.; Dease Lake
(Harington, C. R.)   1968A
Mam.; Pleist.; Quesnel Forks
(Harington, C. R.)   1971B
Pisces; Dev.; Wokkpash Creek
(Jessen, H.)   1968A
Pisces; Tert., lower; Vancouver Is.
(Waldman, M.)   1971A
BULGARIA
Paleoanthropology
Magourata Cave; Paleolithic art
(Anati, E.)   1969A
Paleontology
Mam.; Oligocene; Razlog
(Nikolov, Iv., Velichkov, V.)   1969A
Mam.; Pleist.; Cherepish
(Nikolov, Iv.)   1969A
Mam.; Pliocene; Kalimantsi
(Nikolov, Iv.)   1972A
Mam.; Tert.
(Nikolov, Iv.)   1971A
Pisces; Paleocene; Plevna region
(Dachev, D.)   1967A
Pisces; Paleogene
(Dachev, D. M.)   1971A
Vertebrate Faunas
Pleist.; Peshketo Cave; Mam.
(Dzhambazov, N.)   1970A
Pliocene; northeast; Mam.
(Khalvadzhiev, M.)   1969A
CALIFORNIA
Absolute Age
Laguna Beach; fossil hominid
(Stewart, T. D.)   1969A
Paleo-Indian bone collagen
(Berger, R., et al.)   1971A
Sacramento; Pleist. alluvium, verts.
(Shlemon, R. J.)   1969A
Sacramento; Riverbank Fm., verts.
(Hansen, R. O., Begg, E. L.)   1970A
Sacramento, San Joaquin soil, verts.
(Szabo, B. J.)   1971A
Paleoanthropology
Tranquillity; fossil hominids
(Angel, J. L.)   1966A

CANARY ISLANDS
 Paleoanthropology
  Guanche mummy
   (Brothwell, D. R., Sandison, A. T.,
    Gray, P. H. K.)   1969A
 Paleontology
  Mam.; Pleist.; Tenerife Is.
   (Crusafont Pairó, M., Petter, F.)   1964A
CARBON-14 DATING. See under Absolute Age, Dates
and Absolute Age, Methods.
CARBONIFEROUS
 Correlation
  Siberia; fishes
   (Makarenko, G. F.)   1971A
CATALOGS. See under class term, Vertebrate.
CAVE and ROCK PAINTINGS. See Paleolithic Art
under Paleoanthropology.
CAVE FAUNAS. See Quaternary Caves under age term.
CELEBES
 Paleontology
  Mam.; Pleist.
   (Hooijer, D. A.)   1969A
CENOZOIC
 Correlation
  Asia; mammals
   (Bazhanov, V. S., Kostenko, N. N.)   1964A
  Eurasia; mammals
   (Gabuniĩa, L. K., Rubinshteĭn, M. M.)
                    1965A, 1967A, 1968A,B,C
  Eurasia; vertebrates
   (Rubinshteĭn, M. M., Gabuniĩa, L. K.) 1972A
  Europe; rodents
   (Michaux, J.)   1970A
  India, Siwaliks; mammals
   (Saxena, M. N.)   1968A
  No. America; mammals
   (Gabuniĩa, L. K., Rubinshteĭn, M. M.)
                    1965A, 1967A, 1968A,B,C
  No. America; vertebrates
   (Rubinshteĭn, M. M., Gabuniĩa, L. K.) 1972A
  Turkey; mammals
   (Sickenberg, O., Tobien, H.)   1971A
 Geochronology
  Asia, northern; mammals
   (Vangengeĭm, E. A., Zhegallo, V. I.,
    Zazhigin, V. S.)   1972A
  Eurasia; mammals
   (Kowalski, K.)   1971B
   (Gabuniĩa, L. K., Rubinshteĭn, M. M.)
                    1965A, 1967A, 1968A,B,C
  Eurasia; vertebrates
   (Rubinshteĭn, M. M., Gabuniĩa, L. K.) 1972A
  Mammals
   (Evernden, J. F., Evernden, R. K. S.) 1970A
  No. America; mammals
   (Gabuniĩa, L. K., Rubinshteĭn, M. M.)
                    1965A, 1967A, 1968A,B,C
  No. America; vertebrates
   (Rubinshteĭn, M. M., Gabuniĩa, L. K.) 1972A
  So. America; mammals
   (Paula Couto, C. de)   1964B
  Texas, Trans Pecos; vertebrates
   (Wilson, J. A.)   1972A
  Turkey; mammals
   (Sickenberg, O., Tobien, H.)   1971A

CEYLON
 Vertebrate Faunas
  Cenozoic
   (Cooray, P. G.)   1967A
  General
   (Deraniyagala, P. E. P.)   1965D
  Miocene
   (Deraniyagala, P. E. P.)   1967B, 1969B
  Miocene; Arna Kallu
   (Deraniyagala, P. E. P.)   1969C
  Miocene; Malu member
   (Deraniyagala, P. E. P.)   1969D
  Tertiary
   (Deraniyagala, P. E. P.)   1969A
CHEMICAL COMPOSITION
 Amino Acids
  Fossil bone
   (Bucci, G., et al.)   1969A
  Hominid bone collagen
   (Corrain, C., Capitano, M.)   1969A
  Mammalian bone collagen
   (Ho, T.-Y.)   1967A
  Myoglobin; hemoglobin; kangaroo
   (Air, G. M., et al.)   1971A
 Biochemistry
  Fossil bones
   (Sultanov, K. M.,
    Dzhafarova, Zh. D.)   1967A
 Calcium Content
  Cyclic variations in fossil bone
   (Castanet, J., et al.)   1970A
 Collagen
  Vertebrate fossils
   (Grishchenko, M. N.)   1969A
   (Krueger, H. W.)   1965A
 Fluorine Content
  Fossil bone; Israel, Amud Cave
   (Tanabe, G.)   1970A
 Fossil Bone
  Weathering, split-line analysis
   (Tappen, N. C.)   1969A
 Magnesium Content
  Vertebrate fossils
   (Shimoda, N., Ozaki, H.)   1967A
 Manganese Content
  Neanderthal skeleton
   (Hamaguchi, H.)   1970A
 Paleoserology
  Nubia; fossil hominids
   (Race, G. J.)   1968A
 Proteins
  Dinosaur bone
   (Wyckoff, R. W. G.)   1969A
  Elephas tooth dentine
   (Hotta, S.)   1968A
  Fossil bones, teeth
   (Wyckoff, R. W. G.)   1971A
  Fossil hominid bone
   (Lengyel, I.)   1969A
 Steroid Hormones
  Hominid bones
   (Khrisanfova, E. N.)   1971A
 Substitution
  Salt deposits; USSR, Ukraine; Permian
   (Aleksandrov, I. M.)   1971A

CHEMICAL COMPOSITION - cont.
Uranium Content
Fossil bones
(Anon.) 1971BA
Fossil hominids; Israel, Amud Cave
(Sakanoue, M., Yoshioka, M.) 1970A
CHILE
Paleontology
Mam.; Pleist.; Lonquimay
(Casamiquela, R.) 1968A
Vertebrate Faunas
Cret., upper; Ovalle; Rept.
(Casamiquela, R. M., Corvalán, J., ·
Franquesa, F.) 1969A
Jurassic; Cerritos Bayos
(Biese, W.) 1961A
CHINA
Paleoanthropology
Chou K'ou Tien; fossil hominids
(Andersson, J. G.) 1967A
(Black, D.) 1971A,B
(Tufty, B.) 1967B
(Watson, W.) 1966A
Fossil hominids
(Aigner, J. S.) 1972A
(Chêng, T-k.) 1966A
(Lü, C.-R.) 1967A
(Treistman, J. M.) 1972A
(Woo, J-k.) 1960D, 1962D
Gongwangling; fossil hominids
(Chia, L-p.) 1965A
Lantian; fossil hominids
(Larichev, V. E.) 1970A
(Lisowski, F. P.) 1965A
Liukiang, Tung-tien-yen Cave; fossil hominids
(Woo, J-k.) 1959F
Shensi; fossil hominids
(Hoyanagi, M.) 1969A
Paleontology
Mam.; Eocene; Lushih
(Chow, M.) 1958G
Mam.; Miocene; Inner Mongolia
(Dubrovo, I. A.) 1970A
Mam.; Oligocene
(Chiu, C.-s.) 1965A
Mam.; Pleist.; Kwangsi
(Pei, W.-c.) 1957K
Mam.; Pleist.; Szechuan Prov.
(Deraniyagala, P. E. P.) 1965B
Mam.; Pliocene; Taiwan
(Chiu, H. T.) 1972A
Mam.; Plio-Pleistocene; Shansi
(Erdbrink, D.-P.) 1968A
Rept.
(Young, C-c.) 1959J
Rept.; Jurassic; Ho chuan
(Young, C-c.) 1972A
(Voichin, I.) 1966A
Rept.; Jurassic; upper; Chingning
(Young, C.-c.) 1959K
Rept.; Triassic
(Young, C.-c., Dong, Z.-m.) 1972A
Vertebrate Faunas
Pleist.; Chen-chia-ou; Mam.
(Chow, M.-c., Li, C.-k.) 1965B
Pleist.; Inner Mongolia
(Cultural Relics Working Party) 1963A

CHINA - cont.
Vertebrate Faunas
Pleist.; Kansu, Shansi; Mam.
(Wang, Y.-y., et al.) 1969A
Pleist.; Shuidungou; Mam.
(Tszia, L.-p., Gai, P., Li, Y.-s.) 1964A
Triassic, lower; Wuhsiang; Rept.
(Young, C-c.) 1957E
CIRCULATORY SYSTEM. See Anatomy under
class name.
CLASSIFICATION. See Systematics under Vertebrate.
CLIMATOLOGY. See Paleoclimatology.
COLLECTIONS. See under Museums.
COLOMBIA
Paleontology
Mam.; Eocene; Gualanday
(Hoffstetter, R.) 1970D
Rept.; Miocene, upper
(Auffenberg, W.) 1971A
Vertebrate Faunas
Cenozoic
(Porta, J. de) 1969A
Cretaceous
(Porta, J. de) 1969A
COLORADO
Absolute Age
Eastern; Paleo-Indian
(Breternitz, D. A.) 1969A
Paleontology
Amph.; Penn., upper; central
(Vaughn, P. P.) 1969B
Aves; Miocene, upper; Logan Co.
(Brodkorb, P.) 1972A
Mam.; Oligocene; northeastern
(Galbreath, E. C.) 1969A
Mam.; Pleist.
(Lewis, G. E.) 1970A
Mam.; Pliocene, upper; Logan Co.,
Ogallala Group
(Schultz, C. B., Martin, L. D.) 1972A
Rept.; Jurassic, upper; Garden Park
(Walker, A. D.) 1970A
Rept.; Penn., upper; central
(Vaughn, P. P.) 1969B
Vert.; Penn., upper; Fremont Co.
(Vaughn, P. P.) 1972A
Vertebrate Faunas
Dev.; central; Pisces
(Pampe, W. R.) 1969A
Miocene; Bighorn Mts.; Mam.
(McKenna, M. C.) 1968B
Miocene; Middle Park; Mam.
(Izett, G. A.) 1968A
Miocene; Troublesome Fm.; Mam.
(Lewis, G. E.) 1969A
Neogene; Dry Union Fm.
(Anon.) 1969CF
Neogene; Mam.
(Anon.) 1970BR
Perm.; Cutler Fm.
(Kirkland, P. L.) 1963A
Pleist.; Laramie Basin; Mam.
(Hager, M. W.) 1972A
Pleist.; southeast
(Hager, M. W.) 1972B
Triassic, upper; Colorado Plateau
(Stewart, J. H.) 1969A

COMPARATIVE ANATOMY.   See Anatomy under
class term, Vertebrate.
CONGO
    Paleontology
        Pisces; Cret., upper; Vonso
            (Taverne, L.)   1969C
    Vertebrate Faunas
        Cret.; Bokungu; Pisces
            (Casier, E.)   1969A
        Cret., upper; Vonso
            (Taverne, L.)   1970A
        Miocene; Mam.
            (Hooijer, D. A.)   1970B
        Pleist.; Lake Albert-Lake Edward Rift
            (Lepersonne, J.)   1970A
CONGRESSES, CONFERENCES, COLLOQUIA.
    See Associations.
CONNECTICUT
    Vertebrate Faunas
        Triassic; Pisces
            (McKenna, M. C.)   1972B
CONTINENTAL DRIFT.   See under Paleogeography.
COPROLITES.   See under class term, Vertebrate.
CORRELATION
    Africa
        Pleist.; mammals
            (Arambourg, C.)   1969A,B
        Pleist.; northern; vertebrates
            (Biberson, P.)   1969A
        Tertiary; elephants
            (Maglio, V. J.)   1970A
    Africa, South
        Pleist.; Australopithecines, elephants
            (Wright, G. A., Skaryd, S.)   1972A
        Triassic; Morganucodontidae
            (Attridge, J., Charig, A. J.)   1967B
    Argentina
        Cretaceous, upper; reptiles
            (Bonaparte, J. F., Bossi, G.)   1967A
    Asia
        Cenozoic; mammals
            (Bazhanov, V. S., Kostenko, N. N.) 1964A
        Pleistocene; eastern; mammals
            (Alekseev, M. N.)   1969A
    Canada
        Devonian; vertebrates
            (Miall, A. D.)   1970A
    Ethiopia
        Pleist.; Omo V.; vertebrates
            (Heinzelin de Braucourt, J. de) 1969A
    Europe
        Cenozoic; rodents
            (Michaux, J.)   1970A
        Devonian; fishes
            (Obruchev, D., Karatajute-Talimaa, V.) 1967A
        Miocene; mammals
            (Cicha, I., et al.)   1972A
        Pleist.; eastern; mammals
            (Vangengeĭm, E. A., Zazhigin, V. S.) 1969A
        Pleist.; eastern; microtines
            (Zazhigin, V. S.)   1969A
        Pleist.; mammals
            (Arambourg, C.)   1969A,B
            (Moskvitin, A. I.)   1970A
            (Nikiforova, K. V.)   1968A
            (Nikiforova, K. V., et al.)   1971A
            (Nikiforova, K. V., Ivanova, I. K.,
              Konstantinova, N. A.)   1969A, 1970A

CORRELATION - cont.
    Europe
        Pleist.; vertebrates
            (Biberson, P.)   1969A
        Plio-Pleistocene; mammals
            (Tobien, H.)   1970A
        Tertiary; mammals
            (Hooker, J. J.)   1972A
        Villafranchian; mammals
            (Azzaroli, A.)   1970A
    Eurasia
        Cenozoic; mammals
            (Gabuniĭa, L. K., Rubinshteĭn, M. M.)
                1965A, 1967A, 1968A,B,C
        Cenozoic; vertebrates
            (Rubinshteĭn, M. M.,
              Gabuniĭa, L. K.)   1972A
        Tertiary; sharks
            (Glikman, L. S.)   1965A
        Triassic; amphibians
            (Belousova, Z. D.,
              Rĭabukhina, S. G.)   1971A
    Germany
        Miocene; Lagomorpha
            (Tobien, H.)   1970C
        Triassic; phytosaurs
            (Gregory, J. T.)   1969B
    Greece
        Miocene; mammals
            (Van Couvering, J. A., Miller, J. A.) 1971A
    India
        Cenozoic; Siwaliks; mammals
            (Saxena, M. N.)   1968A
        Permian; vertebrates
            (Chakravarti, D. K.)   1968A
    Methods
        Land vertebrates
            (Ochev, V. G.,
              Tverdokhlebova, G. I.)   1970A
        Mammals
            (Kostenko, N. N.;
              Kozhamkulova, B. S.)   1964A
        Paleomagnetic correlation,
           biostratigraphic subdivisions
            (Menner, V. V., et al.)   1972A
        Pleistocene; East Africa
            (Bishop, W. W.)   1968A
        Triassic capitosauroids
            (Ochev, V. G.)   1968B
    Mongolia
        Mesozoic; dinosaurs
            (Rozhdestvenskiĭ, A. K.)   1971B
    North America
        Cenozoic; mammals
            (Gabuniĭa, L. K., Rubinshteĭn, M. M.)
                1965A, 1967A, 1968A,B,C
        Cenozoic; vertebrates
            (Rubinshteĭn, M. M.,
              Gabuniĭa, L. K.)   1972A
        Eocene; mammals
            (Savage, D. E.)   1971B
        Paleozoic; Appalachian-Caledonian
           orogeny; fishes
            (Turner, S.)   1970A
        Tertiary; mammal ages
            (Turner, D. L.)   1969A

CZECHOSLOVAKIA - cont.
Paleontology
 Mam.; Plio-Pleistocene; Slovakia
  (Hünermann, K. A.)   1971A
 Mam.; Slovakia
  (Schmidt, Z.)   1969A,B
 Pisces; Carb., upper; Kounov
  (Zídek, J.)   1969A
 Pisces; Miocene
  (Brzobohatý, R.)   1969A
 Pisces; Miocene; Carpathian Mts.
  (Brzobohatý, R.)   1967C
 Pisces; Miocene, lower; Bohemia, northern
  (Obrhelová, N.)   1971B
 Pisces; Oligocene; Pouzdřany
  (Brzobohatý, R.)   1966A
 Pisces; Perm., lower; Koštálov
  (Zídek, J.)   1967B
 Pisces; Pleist.
  (Obrhelová, N.)   1970A
 Pisces; Tertiary
  (Obrhelová, N.) 1969A, 1970B, 1971A
 Rept.; Cret., upper; Bohemia
  (Zázvorka, V.)   1965A
 Rept.; Miocene; Neudorf an der March
  (Estes, R.)   1969J
Vertebrate Faunas
 Cenozoic; Mam.
  (Fejfar, O.)   1966D, 1968A
 Miocene, lower; Bechlejovice
  (Špinar, Z. V.)   1972A
 Oligocene; Krumvíř; Pisces
  (Kalabis, V.)   1966A
 Pleist.; Bohemia; Mam.
  (Mostecký, V.)   1969A
 Pleist.; Chlum cave; Mam.
  (Beneš, J.)   1970A
 Pleist.; Kůlna Cave; Mam.
  (Valoch, K.)   1970A
  (Valoch, K., et al.)   1969A
 Pleist.; Mam.
  (Musil, R.)   1969B
 Pleist.; Pod Hradem Cave; Mam.
  (Musil, R., Valoch, K.) 1966A
 Pleist.; Stránská Skála
  (Musil, R.)   1966C, 1968B
 Pleist.; Strekov; Mam.
  (Schmidt, Z., Halouzka, R.) 1970A
 Pleist.; Žernavá; Mam.
  (Musil, R.)   1969D
 Tert.; Bohemia
  (Hurnik, S., Knobloch, E.) 1966A
DATING. See Absolute Age, Dates and
 Absolute Age, Methods.
DENMARK
Paleontology
 Mam.; Pleist.
  (Degerbøl, M., Fredskild, B.) 1970A
Vertebrate Faunas
 Pleist.; Mam.
  (Milthers, V.) 1940A, 1959A
 Tert.; Mam.
  (Nordmann, V.)   1958A

DENTITION. See appropriate taxon under class name.
DEVONIAN
Correlation
 Canada; vertebrates
  (Miall, A. D.)   1970A
 Europe; fishes
  (Obruchev, D.,
   Karatajute-Talimaa, V.) 1967A
 Siberia; fishes
  (Menner, V. V., et al.) 1970A
 USSR; fishes
  (Glushnitskiĭ, O. T., Menner, V. V.) 1970A
  (Rzhonsnitskaia, M. A.) 1970A
Geochronology
 Canada; vertebrates
  (Miall, A. D.)   1970A
 Spitsbergen; fishes
  (Ørvig, T.)   1969A
 USSR, Russian Platform; ichthyofauna
  (Tikhiĭ, V. N.)   1972A
DISEASE. See Paleopathology under Paleoanthropology,
 Vertebrate.
DISTRIBUTION. See appropriate taxon under class name.
EAST AFRICA
Absolute Age
 Miocene verts.
  (Bishop, W. W., Miller, J. A.,
   Fitch, F. J.)   1969A
Paleoanthropology
 Fossil hominids
  (Aguirre, E.)   1970A
  (Howell, F. C.)   1972A
  (Isaac, G. L.)   1969A
  (Leakey, L. S. B.) 1966D, 1971B
  (Tobias, P. V.)   1969B
Paleoclimatology
 Olduvai Gorge
  (Gautier, A.)   1964A
Paleontology
 Mam.; Cenozoic, upper
  (Bishop, W. W.)   1971A
 Mam.; Miocene
  (Churcher, C. S.)   1972A
  (Koenigswald, G. H. R. von) 1969A
 Mam.; Miocene, lower
  (Walker, A.)   1970A
 Mam.; Pleist.
  (Hooijer, D. A.)   1969B
Vertebrate Faunas
 Cenozoic; Mam.
  (Kingdon, J.)   1971A
EAST GERMANY
Paleoanthropology
 Paleolithic art
  (Feustel, R.)   1970A
Paleontology
 Mam.; Pleist.; Orlishausen
  (Kahlke, H.-D.)   1971A
 Mam.; Pleist.; Süssenborn
  (Fejfar, O.)   1969A
  (Flerov, K. K.)   1969B
  (Guenther, E. W.)   1969A
  (Hünermann, K. A.)   1969B
  (Kahlke, H.-D.) 1969B,C,D,E
  (Kretzoi, M.)   1969A

ETHIOPIA - cont.
  Paleoanthropology
    Omo V.; fossil hominids
      (Anfray, F.) 1968A
      (Butzer, K. W.) 1969A,B
      (Butzer, K. W., Brown, F. H.,
        Thurber, D. L.) 1969A
      (Coppens, Y.) 1970A, 1971C
      (Day, M. H.) 1969C
      (Howell, F. C.) 1969A,B,C
      (Leakey, R. E. F.) 1969B
      (Thaler, L.) 1971B
      (Vallois, H. V.) 1969G
  Paleontology
    Mam.; Pleist.; Omo V.
      (Arambourg, C., Chavaillon, J.,
        Coppens, Y.) 1969A
      (Howell, F. C., Fichter, L. S.,
        Wolff, R.) 1969A
    Vertebrate Faunas
      Cen.; Awash V.; Mam.
        (Taïeb, M., et al.) 1972A
      Pleist.; Gomboré; Mam.
        (Chavaillon, J., Chavaillon, N.) 1971A
      Pleist.; Hadar R.; Mam.
        (Taïeb, M.) 1971A
      Pleist.; Melka Kontouré; Mam.
        (Chavaillon, J., Chavaillon, N.) 1969A,B
      Pleist.; Omo V.
        (Heinzelin de Braucourt, J. de,
          Brown, F. H.) 1969A
        (Howell, F. C.) 1968A
        (Howell, F. C., Butzer, K. W.) 1968A
        (Howell, F. C., Fichter, L. S., Eck, G.) 1969A
      Pleist.; Omo V.; Mam.
        (Arambourg, C.) 1969C
        (Chavaillon, J.) 1970A
      Plio-Pleistocene; Omo V.
        (Butzer, K. W.) 1971A
EURASIA
  Paleoanthropology
    Northern; fossil hominids
      (Ivanova, I. K.) 1969C
  Paleontology
    Mam.; Pleist.
      (Nobis, G.) 1967A
      (Zazhigin, V. S.) 1969B, 1970A
EUROPE
  Paleoanthropology
    Central, eastern; fossil hominids
      (Bárta, J.) 1965E
    Encyclopedia
      (Filip, J.) 1969B
    Fossil hominids
      (Coles, J. M.) 1968A
      (Coles, J. M., Simpson, D. D. A.) 1968A
      (Ferembach, D.) 1963B
      (Laet, S. J. de) 1967A
    North-east; fossil hominids, migration
      (Bader, O. N.) 1968D
    Northern; fossil hominids, distribution
      (Bader, O. N.) 1971B
    Paleolithic art
      (Lhote, H.) 1966A
      (Pericot García, L., Ripoll Perelló, E.) 1964A
      (Rousseau, M.) 1967A

EUROPE - cont.
  Paleoanthropology
    Western; fossil hominids
      (Bailit, H. L.) 1966A
  Paleontology
    Amph.; Tert.; central
      (Špinar, Z. V.) 1972B
    Aves; Tert.; western
      (Cracraft, J., Rich, P. V.) 1972A
    Mam.; Eocene
      (Hartenberger, J.-L.) 1971A, 1972A
      (Wood, A. E.) 1970B
    Mam.; Eocene; central
      (Hartenberger, J.-L.) 1969A
    Mam.; Neogene
      (Mein, P.) 1970A
    Mam.; Neogene; southwest
      (Michaux, J.) 1971A
    Mam.; Oligocene; western
      (Bonis, L. de) 1970A
      (Vianey-Liaud, M.) 1972B
    Mam.; Pleist.
      (Beneš, J.) 1972A
      (Flerov, K. K.) 1969C
      (Friant, M.) 1970A
      (Hemmer, H.) 1971C
      (Koenigswald, G. H.) 1972A
    Mam.; Pleist.; central
      (Hemmer, H.) 1971A
    Mam.; Pleist., lower
      (Alekseeva, L. I.) 1970A
    Mam.; Pliocene; southwest
      (Mein, P., Michaux, J.) 1970A
    Mam.; Tert.
      (Fahlbusch, V.) 1970A
      (Friant, M.) 1971C
    Pisces; Dev.; Baltic Sea
      (Gross, W.) 1971A
    Rept.; Paleogene
      (Berg, D. E.) 1969A
    Rept.; Triassic
      (Gregory, J. T., Westphal, F.) 1969A
  Vertebrate Faunas
    Cenozoic; Mam.
      (Tobien, H.) 1972A
    Cenozoic, upper; Mam.
      (Flerow, C. C.) 1971B
    Dev., lower; eastern; Pisces
      (Obruchev, D.,
        Karatajute-Talimaa, V.) 1967A
    Eocene; Mam.
      (Hartenberger, J.-L.) 1972B
    Miocene; central, western; Mam.
      (Cicha, I., et al.) 1972A
    Pleist.; eastern; Mam.
      (Alekseeva, L. I.) 1969B
    Pleist.; Mam.
      (Bartolomei, G.) 1969C
      (Bonifay, M.-F.) 1969B
      (Jánossy, D.) 1969A,B
      (Negadaev-Nikonov, K. N.,
        David, A. I., Khubka, A. N.) 1970A
    Pleist., middle; Makarikha R.; Mam.
      (Zarkhidze, V. S.) 1970A
    Pleist.; western; Mam.
      (Bout, P.) 1968A
      (Koby, F.-E.) 1960B

EXTINCTION - cont.
  Causes
    Pleist. mammals
      (Mezhzherin, V. A.)   1969A
      (Reed, C. A.)   1969A, 1970A
      (Van Valen, L.)   1970A
      (Vereshchagin, N. K.)   1963A
      (Pidoplichko, I. G.)   1970C
    Radiation
      (Filipescu, M. G.)   1968A
    Reptiles, mammals
      (Gabuniã, L. K.)   1969A
  Dinosaurs
    Cretaceous, upper
      (Voss-Foucart, M.-F.)   1971A
    Cretaceous; Wyoming, Lance Fm.
      (Folinsbee, R. E., Baadsgaard, H.,
        Cumming, G. L.)   1970A
  Elephas primigenius
    Pleist.; USSR, Ukraine
      (Korniets', N. L.)   1962A
  Mammals
    Cenozoic, upper; North America
      (Webb, S. D.)   1969B
    Pleist.; USSR
      (Vereshchagin, N. K.)   1971C
  Mammoths
    General
      (Anon.)   1967BT
  Mammut
    Pleist.; North America, eastern
      (Dreimanis, A.)   1968A
  Megaselachus megalodon
    Neogene; Pacific and Indian Oceans
      (Belîaev, G. M., Glikman, L. S.)   1970A
FAUNAS. See Vertebrate Faunas.
FLORIDA
  Paleontology
    Aves; Pleist.; Reddick
      (Brewer, R.)   1968A
    Aves; Pleist., upper; Jefferson Co.
      (Olson, S. L.)   1972A
    Mam.; Cenozoic
      (Reinhart, R. H.)   1971A
      (Tessman, N.)   1969A
      (Waldrop, J.)   1969A
      (Webb, S. D.)   1972B
    Mam.; Pleist.
      (Robertson, J. S.)   1969A
      (Webb, S. D.)   1970B
    Mam.; Pleist.; Reddick
      (Pinkham, C. F. A.)   1971A
    Mam.; Pleist.; Sante Fe R.
      (Martin, R. A.)   1969A
    Mam.; Pliocene
      (Webb, S. D.)   1969A
    Pisces; Eocene; Milton's Cave
      (Swift, C., Ellwood, B.)   1972A
  Vertebrate Faunas
    Cenozoic
      (Olson, S. J.)   1965A
      (Patton, T. H., Webb, S. D.)   1970A
    Cenozoic; Mam.
      (Olson, S. J.)   1959F
    Cretaceous
      (Patton, T. H., Webb, S. D.)   1970A

FLORIDA - cont.
  Vertebrate Faunas
    Miocene
      (Olsen, S. J.)   1968C
    Oligocene; Gainesville
      (Patton, T. H.)   1969A
    Pleistocene
      (DuBar, J. R.)   1958B
    Pleist.; Alachua Co.
      (Dolan, E. M., Allen, G. T.)   1961A
    Pleist.; Arredondo; Aves
      (Frailey, C. D.)   1972A
    Pleist.; Coleman II A; Mam.
      (Martin, R. A.)   1970B
    Pleist.; Haile XV A; Mam.
      (Robertson, J. S.)   1971A
    Pleist.; southern
      (Ober, L. D., Weaver, W. G.)   1971A
    Pleist., upper; Dale Co.
      (Weaver, W. G., Ober, L. D.)   1971A
    Pleist.; Vero Beach
      (Weigel, R. D.)   1962C
    Pliocene; Aves
      (Brodkorb, P.)   1970C
    Pliocene; Manatee Co.
      (Webb, S. D.)   1970B
FOOTPRINTS. See Tracks and Traces.
FRANCE
  Absolute Age
    Auvergne, Velay; Pleist. verts.
      (Bout, P.)   1970A
    Central; Pleist. mammals
      (Bout, P.)   1972A
    Isère; Pleist. verts.
      (David, L., et al.)   1972A
  Paleoanthropology
    Abri Lartet; ritual; reindeer
      (Duport, L.)   1972A
      (Duport, L., Vandermeersch, B.)   1972A
    Abri Pataud; fossil hominids
      (Billy, G.)   1971A
    Alliat; Paleolithic art
      (Nougier, L.-R., Robert, R.)   1971A
    Arago Cave; fossil hominids
      (Lumley, H. de, Lumley, M.-A. de)   1971A
      (Vandermeersch, B.)   1971A
    Arcy-sur-Cure; fossil hominids
      (Movius, H. L.)   1969A
    Ardèche; Paleolithic art
      (Combier, J., Drouot, E.,
        Huchard, P.)   1959A
    Auvergne; fossil hominids
      (Delporte, H.)   1970A
    Barma Grande; fossil hominids
      (Pales, L.)   1970B
    Bergerac; fossil hominids
      (Marsac, M.)   1970A
    Bison Cave; Paleolithic art
      (Roussot, A.)   1970A
    Charente; fossil hominids
      (Guillien, Y.)   1970A
    Denise; fossil hominids
      (Vallois, H. V.)   1969E
    Dordogne; fossil hominids
      (Billy, G.)   1969A
      (Bouchud, J.)   1966G

FRANCE - cont.
Paleontology
Mam.; Eocene; Issel
  (Calas, G.)   1969A
Mam.; Eocene, middle; Lissieu
  (Sudre, J.)   1972A
Mam.; Miocene
  (Ginsburg, L.)   1968C, 1970B
Mam.; Miocene; l'Agenais
  (Baudelot, S., Bonis, L. de)   1968A
Mam.; Miocene; Anjou
  (Janvier, P.)   1969A
Mam.; Miocene; Artenay
  (Ginsburg, L., Heintz, E.)   1968A
Mam.; Miocene, lower; Bouches-du-Rhône
  (Catzigras, F., et al.)   1971A
Mam.; Miocene, middle; Vaucluse,
  Vaison-la-Romaine
  (Guérin, C., et al.)   1972A
Mam.; Miocene; Pontigné
  (Ginsburg, L.)   1969A
Mam.; Miocene; Pyrénées
  (Bergounioux, F. M., Crouzel, F.)   1970A
Mam.; Miocene; St. Gaudens
  (Pilbeam, D., Simons, E. L.)   1971A
Mam.; Miocene; Sansan
  (Baudelot, S.)   1968A, 1970A
Mam.; Neogene; Lyonnais
  (Hugueney, M., Mein, P.)   1969A
Mam.; Neogene, middle; Rhône,
  Vieux-Collonges
  (Mein, P., Freudenthal, M.)   1971B
Mam.; Oligocene; Céreste
  (Sigé, B.)   1971A
Mam.; Oligocene; Quercy
  (Bonis, L. de)   1971A
  (Eisenmann, V.)   1969A
  (Lange, B.)   1969A, 1970A
  (Vianey-Liaud, M.)   1969A
Mam.; Oligocene; Saint-Emilion
  (Chavanon, S., Saubade, A. M.)   1970A
Mam.; Oligocene; Saint-Martin-de-Castillon
  (Hugueney, M.)   1971A
Mam.; Oligocene; Saint-Paul-des-Landes
  (Bonis, L. de)   1969C
Mam.; Oligocene; Saint-Victor-la-Coste
  (Hugueney, M.)   1968A
Mam.; Oligocene; Saverdun
  (Bergounioux, F. M., Crouzel, F.)   1971A
Mam.; Oligocene; Villebramar
  (Brunet, M.)   1972A
Mam.; Paleogene; Quercy
  (Remy, J.-A.)   1972A
Mam.; Pleist.
  (Bergounioux, F. M., Crouzel, F.)   1964B
  (Bouchud, J.)   1957B
  (Chaline, J.)   1970B, 1972A
  (Coppens, Y.)   1965E
  (Heintz, E.)   1970A
  (Patte, E.)   1968B
Mam.; Pleist.; Ain, Villereversure
  (Guérin, C.)   1970A
Mam.; Pleist.; Bas-Rhin
  (Théobald, N.)   1970A
Mam.; Pleist.; Bernard Cave
  (Ficat, C.)   1963A

FRANCE - cont.
Paleontology
Mam.; Pleist.; Chilhac
  (Beden, M.)   1970B
Mam.; Pleist.; Clain V.
  (Beden, M.)   1970A
Mam.; Pleist.; Cornerives
  (David, E., Frachon, J.-C.,
  Sattonnet, R.)   1968A
Mam.; Pleist.; L'Escale and Lunel-Viel
  (Hemmer, H.)   1972A
Mam.; Pleist.; Isturitz Cave
  (Beaufort, F. de, Jullien, R.)   1968A
Mam.; Pleist.; La Chaise
  (Suire, C.)   1968A, 1970A
Mam.; Pleist.; Nice
  (Jullien, R., Pillard, B.)   1969A, ▮
Mam.; Pleist.; Palaminy
  (Méroc, L.)   1967A
Mam.; Pleist.; Pas-de-Calais
  (Bouchud, J.)   1964B
Mam.; Pleist.; Philippeville
  (Petter, F.)   1968A
Mam.; Pleist.; Praz-Rodet
  (Weidmann, M.)   1969A, 1970A
Mam.; Pleist.; Régourdou
  (Simard, S.)   1968A
Mam.; Pleist.; Saint-Vallier
  (Martin, R.)   1971A
Mam.; Pleist.; Senèze
  (Ballesio, R.)   1964A
Mam.; Pleist.; Solutré
  (Prat, F.)   1969A
Mam.; Pleist.; southeast
  (Bonifay, M.-F.)   1971A
Mam.; Pleist.; southwest
  (Bouchud, J.)   1966J
Mam.; Pleist.; Trieux
  (Plusquellec, Y.)   1968A
Mam.; Pleist., upper
  (Prat, F., Suire, C.)   1971A
Mam.; Pleist.; Vaulx-en-Velin
  (Jeannet, M.)   1971A
Mam.; Pliocene
  (Michaux, J.)   1969B
Mam.; Pliocene; Gard, St.-Laurent-des-
  Arbres
  (Guérin, C., et al.)   1969A
Mam.; Pliocene; Senèze
  (Cuscani Politi, P.)   1963D
Mam.; Pliocene; Vaucluse, Mont Lebéron
  (Heintz, E.)   1971B
Mam.; Pliocene; Vincent
  (David, E., Duplessis-
  Kergomard, D.)   1967A
Mam.; Plio-Pleistocene
  (Michaux, J.)   1971B
Mam.; Tert.; Allier
  (Hugueney, M.)   1972A
Pisces; Miocene, lower; Hérault,
  Lespignan
  (Cappetta, H.)   1972A
Pisces; Oligocene; Var
  (Touraine, F.)   1971A
Pisces; Perm., lower; Surmoulin
  (Heyler, D.)   1971A

FRANCE - cont.
Vertebrate Faunas
Paleozoic; Blanzy-Montceau; Pisces
   (Anon.)   1969AV
Permian
   (Heyler, D.)   1969A
Pleistocene
   (Bonifay, M. F.)   1969C
   (Bouchud, J.)   1957A
Pleist.; Achenheimer loess; Mam.
   (Wernert, P.)   1968A
Pleist.; Allier
   (Bouchud, J.)   1959B
Pleist.; Angles-sur-l'Anglin; Mam.
   (Pradel, L.)   1965E
Pleist.; Aquitaine; Mam.
   (Bordes, F.)   1970A
Pleist.; Arago Cave; Mam.
   (Chaline, J.)   1971A
Pleist.; Ariège, Mano Cave
   (Astre, G.)   1968B
Pleist.; Auvergne, Velay; Mam.
   (Bout, P.)   1967A
Pleist.; Balme-d'Épy; Mam.
   (Guèrin, C.)   1971A
Pleist.; Basses-Alpes, Puimoisson; Mam.
   (Dubar, M.)   1969A
Pleist.; Baume; Mam.
   (Bouchud, J.)   1966I, 1968D
Pleist.; Bédeilhac Cave
   (Beltrán, A., Robert, R., Gailli, R.) 1967A
Pleist.; Bernard Cave
   (Bertouille, H., Bertouille, M.,
   Bouchud, J.)   1968A
Pleist.; Blassac-La Girondie; Mam.
   (Beden, M., Guth, C.)   1970B
Pleist.; Calviac; Mam.
   (Champagne, F., Espitalié, R.)   1970A
Pleist.; Caniac; Mam.
   (Bensch, Cl.)   1971A
Pleist.; Carrière Caves; Mam.
   (Clot, A.)   1970A
Pleist.; Cessac
   (Delpech, F.)   1971A
Pleist.; Chagny; Mam.
   (Chaline, J., Clair, A., Puisségur, J.-J.) 1970A
Pleist.; Charente; Mam.
   (Guillien, Y.)   1970A
Pleist.; Châtillon-St.-Jean; Mam.
   (Bonnet, A.)   1970A
Pleist.; Chilhac; Mam.
   (Beden, M., Guth, C.)   1970A
Pleist.; Cornille
   (Bonifay, M.-F.)   1968B
Pleist.; Cubjac; Mam.
   (Delpech, F.)   1969A
Pleist.; Duruthy
   (Delpech, F.)   1968A
Pleist.; East Castaigne Cave; Mam.
   (Duport, L.)   1966A
Pleist.; Eure V.; Mam.
   (Dewolf, Y.)   1970A
Pleist.; Flageolet
   (Delpech, F.)   1970C
Pleist.; Font-de-Gaume; Mam.
   (Prat, F., Sonneville-Bordes, D. de) 1969A

FRANCE - cont.
Vertebrate Faunas
Pleist.; Fontalès
   (Bouchud, P., Bouchud, J.)   1957A
Pleist.; Fustié Cave; Mam.
   (Bertouille, H., Bouchud, J.)   1969A
Pleist.; Haute-Garonne, Tarté Cave; Mam.
   (Astre, G.)   1968A
Pleist.; Hermolsheim; Mam.
   (Wernert, P., Wolf, M.)   1970A
Pleist.; Jura; Mam.
   (Frachon, J. Cl.)   1965A
Pleist.; La Canéda; Mam.
   (Delpech, F.)   1970A
Pleist.; La Fage à Noailles
   (Couchard, J.)   1963A
Pleist.; Landes, Duruthy
   (Delpech, F.)   1970B
Pleist.; Landes; Mam.
   (Legigan, P.)   1970A
Pleist.; Languedoc-Roussillon; Mam.
   (Escalon de Fonton, M.)   1970A
Pleist.; Lascaux Cave; Mam.
   (Bouchud, J.)   1961C
   (Glory, A.)   1965B
Pleist.; Lille; Mam.
   (Waterlot, G.)   1969A
Pleist.; Liveyre Cave
   (Daniel, R.)   1969A
Pleist.; Lunel-Viel
   (Bonifay, E.)   1968A
Pleist.; Lussac-les-Châteaux
   (Pradel, L.)   1959G
Pleist.; Martine à Domme; Mam.
   (Delpech, F., et al.)   1970A
Pleist.; Montgaudier; Mam.
   (Duport, L.)   1968A
Pleist.; Montpellier; Mam.
   (Barrière, J., Michaux, J.)   1970A
   (Chaline, J., Michaux, J.)   1969A
Pleist.; Nice
   (Lumley, H. de)   1967B
   (Rage, J.-C.)   1969A
Pleist.; Nice; Aves
   (Bouchud, J.)   1969B
Pleist.; Nice; Mam.
   (Bonifay, M.-F.)   1969A
   (Chaline, J.)   1969A
Pleist.; Pâques Cave; Mam.
   (Ravoux, G., Bazile, F.)   1967A
Pleist.; Pégourié; Mam.
   (Seronie-Vivien, R.)   1971A
Pleist.; Petit Puymoyen; Mam.
   (Boeuf, O.)   1970A
Pleist.; Prélétang Cave; Mam.
   (Lequatre, P.)   1966A
Pleist.; Provence; Mam.
   (Gagnière, S.)   1970A
Pleist.; Rhône V.; Mam.
   (Bonnet, A., Bornand, M.)   1970A
Pleist.; Rhuis; Mam.
   (Prat, F.)   1968A
Pleist.; Roc de Marsal; Mam.
   (Bouchud, J.)   1962B

GEOCHRONOLOGY - cont.
  Biostratigraphy
    Europe; Miocene mammals
      (Cicha, I.)   1970A
      (Cicha, I., et al.)   1972A
    Europe; Neogene mammals
      (Van Couvering, J.)   1972A
    Europe; Pleist. mammals
      (Arambourg, C.)   1969A,B
      (Bout, P.)   1972A
      (Cooke, H. B. S.)   1972A
      (Pasa, A.)   1969A
    Europe; Pleist. vertebrates
      (Bout, P.)   1970A
    Europe; Plio-Pleistocene mammals
      (Tobien, H.)   1970A, 1972A
    Europe; Plio-Pleistocene rodents
      (Michaux, J.)   1970A
    Europe; Villafranchian mammals
      (Savage, D. E., Curtis, G. H.)   1970A
    Europe, western; Villafranchian mammals
      (Bout, P.)   1968A
    Fossil hominids
      (Gromov, V. I.)   1967A
      (Ivanova, I. K.)   1968A,B
    France; Aquitanian rodents
      (Ringeade, M.)   1967A
    France; Eocene mammals
      (Jaeger, J.-J.)   1971B
    France; Paleogene rodents
      (Ringeade, M.)   1967B,D
    France; Pleist. mammal cave faunas
      (Cavaillé, A.)   1970A
    France; Pleist. mammals
      (Dewolf, Y.)   1970A
    France; Pleist. rodents
      (Chaline, J.)   1972A
    France; Riss elephants
      (Théobald, N.)   1970A
    France; Tert. mammals
      (Rey, R.)   1968A,B
    France; Villafranchian mammals
      (Dubar, M.)   1969A
    General
      (Davitashvili, L. Sh.)   1967A
      (Durham, J. W.)   1971A
    Germany; Eocene mammals
      (Wirth, E.)   1969A
    Germany, Graisbach; Neogene
      proboscideans
      (Gall, H.)   1971A
    Germany; Miocene Lagomorpha
      (Tobien, H.)   1970C
    Germany; Paleogene mammals
      (Ritzkowski, S.)   1969A
    Gondwanaland; vertebrates
      (Anderson, H. M., Anderson, J. M.)   1970A
    Greece; Pleist. vertebrates
      (Kahlke, H. D.)   1968A,B
    Greece; Pliocene vertebrates
      (Kahlke, H. D.)   1968A,B
    Hipparion
      (Koenigswald, G. H. R. von)   1970A
      (Meladze, G. K.)   1967B
    Hungary; Pleist. mammals
      (Jánossy, D.)   1969D, 1970A, 1972B

GEOCHRONOLOGY - cont.
  Biostratigraphy
    Italy, central; Plio-Pleistocene mammals
      (Ambrosetti, P., et al.)   1972A
    Kenya; Pleist. mammals
      (Maglio, V. J.)   1972A
    Mammoth
      (Shcheglova, V. V.)   1964A
    Mediterranean region; Miocene mammals
      (Van Couvering, J. A.)   1972B
    Mongolia; Cret. vertebrates
      (Martinson, G. G., Sochava, A. V.,
        Barsbold, R.)   1969A, 1970A
    Mongolia; dinosaurs
      (Rozhdestvenskiĭ, A. K.)   1971B
    Neogene mammals
      (Gabuniﬁa, L. K.)   1970B
      (Gromov, V. I., Nikiforova, K. V.)
                                                  1968A,B,C
    New Mexico; Mesozoic reptiles
      (Galton, P. M.)   1971C
    New Mexico; Tertiary mammals
      (Galusha, T., Blick, J. C.)   1971A
    No. America; Cenozoic mammals
      (Gabuniﬁa, L. K., Rubinshteĭn, M. M.)
                                      1965A, 1967A, 1968A,B,C
    No. America; Cenozoic vertebrates
      (Rubinshteĭn, M. M.,
        Gabuniﬁa, L. K.)   1972A
    No. America; dinosaurs
      (Folinsbee, R. E., Baadsgaard, H.,
        Cumming, G. L.)   1970A
    No. America; Pleist. mammals
      (Cooke, H. B. S.)   1972A
    Pisces, value
      (Dmitriev, G. A., Skoblo, V. M.)   1966A
    Pleist. mammals
      (Gaĭduk, I. M.)   1967A
      (Gromov, V. I., Krasnov, I. I.,
        Nikiforova, K. V., Shanﬁser, E. V.)   1969A
      (Gromov, V. I.,
        Nikiforova, K. V.)   1968A,B,C
      (Gromov, V. I., Vangengeĭm, E. A.,
        Nikiforova, K. V.)   1965B
      (Menner, V. V.)   1968B
      (Zubakov, V. A.)   1966B
    Plio-Pleistocene mammals
      (Grichuk, V. P., Hey, R. W.,
        Venzo, S.)   1964A
    Portugal; Miocene mammals
      (Telles Antunes, M.)   1970B
      (Telles Antunes, M.,
        Torquato, J. R.)   1970A
    Portugal; Pleist. mammals
      (Aguado, M. M.)   1968A
    Reptiles, value
      (Dmitriev, G. A., Skoblo, V. M.)   1966A
    Rodentia
      (Shevchenko, A. I.)   1964A
    Rumania; Neogene mammals
      (Mihăilă, N.)   1969A
    Rumania; Pleist. vertebrate fauna
      (Alimen, H., Radulesco, C.,
        Samson, P.)   1968B
    Siberia; Neogene mammals
      (Aubekerov, B. Zh., et al.)   1970A

GEOCHRONOLOGY - cont.
  Methods
    Paleomagnetic correlation, biostratigraphic
    subdivisions
      (Menner, V. V., et al.)   1972A
    Stratigraphic nomenclature; So. Africa
      (Truswell, J. F.)   1967A
    Stratigraphy, documentation
      (Shaw, A. B.)   1971A
  Time Scales
    Nomenclature
      (Wilson, R. W.)   1953A
    Paleolithic; Siberia
      (Abramova, Z. A.)   1968B
GEORGIA
  Paleontology
    Mam.; Eocene; Twiggs Co.
      (Voorhies, M. R.)   1969A
  Vertebrate Faunas
    Pleist.; Ladds
      (Holman, J. A.) (Wetmore, A.)   1967B
    Pleist., upper; Glynn Co.; Mam.
      (Voorhies, M. R.)   1971B
    Pliocene; Taylor Co.; Mam.
      (Voorhies, M. R.)   1970A
GEOGRAPHY. See Paleogeography.
GERMANY
  Paleoanthropology
    Bocksteinschmiede; Paleolithic art
      (Wetzel, R., Bosinski, G.)   1969A
    Hohlenstein; Paleolithic art
      (Hahn, J.)   1970A, 1971A
    Neander V.; fossil hominids
      (Lyell, C.)   1972A
      (Schaaffhausen, D.)   1971A
    Rees; fossil hominids
      (Erdbrink, D.-P., Tacoma, J.)   1968A
  Paleontology
    Amph.; Permian, lower; Saar
      (Boy, J. A.)   1971B
    Amph.; Tert.; Wartenberg
      (Westphal, F.)   1970A
    Aves; Eocene; Halle
      (Fischer, K.-H.)   1967C
    Aves; Jurassic; Solenhofen
      (Vogt, H.-H.)   1971A
    Aves; Miocene; Eichstätt, Wintershof West
      (Ballmann, P.)   1969B
    Aves; Oligocene; Gaimersheim
      (Ballmann, P.)   1970A
    Aves; Tert.; Mainz Basin
      (Rothausen, K.)   1966A
    Mam.; Cenozoic; Bavaria, Sandelzhausen
      (Schmidt-Kittler, N.)   1971A
    Mam.; Eocene; Geiseltal
      (Matthes, H. W.)   1969A, 1972A
    Mam.; Eocene; Messel bei Darmstadt
      (Russell, D. E., Sigé, B.)   1970A
      (Tobien, H.)   1969A
    Mam.; Miocene; Bavaria
      (Fahlbusch, V.)   1970C
    Mam.; Miocene, lower; Mainz Basin
      (Tobien, H.)   1970C
    Mam.; Miocene, upper; Reisensburg
      (Wellnhofer, P.)   1969A

GERMANY - cont.
  Paleontology
    Mam.; Miocene; Weissenburg
      (Fahlbusch, V.)   1968A
    Mam.; Oligocene; Gaimersheim
      (Fahlbusch, V.)   1969B
      (Heissig, K.)   1969A
    Mam.; Oligocene; Gunzenheim
      (Ginsburg, L.)   1969C
    Mam.; Oligocene, lower; Hessen, northern
      (Tobien, H.)   1971A
    Mam.; Oligocene, lower;
    Württemberg, Ehrenstein
      (Schmidt-Kittler, N.)   1971B
    Mam.; Oligocene, upper;
    Düsseldorf-Kaiserswerth
      (Rothausen, K.)   1971A
    Mam.; Oligocene; Wiesbaden
      (Tobien, H.)   1971B
    Mam.; Paleogene
      (Bosma, A., Schmidt-Kittler, N.)   1972A
    Mam.; Paleogene; Ehrenstein
      (Schmidt-Kittler, N.)   1970A
    Mam.; Pleist.; Berlin
      (Pohle, H.)   1959A
    Mam.; Pleist.; Kärlich
      (Nobis, G.)   1970A
      (Rothausen, K.)   1970B
    Mam.; Pleist.; Lindhöft
      (Guenther, E. W.)   1969B
    Mam.; Pleist., lower; Oberrhein
      (Adam, K. D.)   1965C
    Mam.; Pleist., lower; Süssenborn
      (Schaefer, H.)   1969A
    Mam.; Pleist.; Mannheim-Käfertal
      (Jörg, E.)   1971A
    Mam.; Pleist.; Mauer an der Elsenz
      (Schütt, G.)   1969B
    Mam.; Pleist., middle; Harz
      (Koenigswald, W. v.)   1972A
    Mam.; Pleist., middle; Wiesbaden
      (Bahlo, E.)   1971A
    Mam.; Pleist.; Mosbach
      (Guenther, E. W.)   1969C
      (Hemmer, H., Schütt, G.)   1969A
    Mam.; Pleist.; Rheinland
      (Lehmann, E. von)   1968A
    Mam.; Pleist.; Scharzfeld
      (Schütt, G.)   1968A
    Mam.; Pleist.; Schleswig-Holstein
      (Guenther, E. W.)   1967B
    Mam.; Pleist.; Stammheim
      (Hemmer, H., Jaeger, R.)   1969A
    Mam.; Pleist., upper; Bad Frankenhausen
      (Teichert, M.)   1971A
    Mam.; Pleist., upper; Bärenkeller
      (Feustel, R., et al.)   1971A
    Mam.; Pleist., upper; Meitze
      (Sickenberg, O.)   1968B
    Mam.; Pleist.; Wiesbaden
      (Bahlo, E., Malec, F.)   1971A
      (Schütt, G.)   1970A,B
    Mam.; Pliocene; Kaltensundheim/Rhön
      (Böhme, G.)   1963A
    Mam.; Pliocene; Rheinhessen
      (Hünermann, K. A.)   1968A

GERMANY - cont.
Vertebrate Faunas
Pleist.; Wiesbaden; Mam.
(Tobien, H.) 1968I
Pleist.; Wurzacher Becken
(German, R., et al.) 1968A
Pleist.; Würzburg-Schalksberg
(Rutte, E.) 1970A
Pliocene; Rheinland; Mam.
(Gliese, J., Strauch, F.) 1969A
Tert.; Nördlinger Ries
(Bolten, R., Müller, D.) 1969A
Tert.; Pisces
(Kruckow, T.) 1964A
Triassic; Bavaria, northern; Pisces
(Stahl, G.) 1971A
Triassic; Karlsruhe-Durlach; Pisces
(Jörg, E.) 1969A, 1970A
Triassic, middle; Karlstadt
(Rutte, E.) 1971A
Triassic, upper; northwest; Pisces
(Will, H.-J.) 1969A
Triassic; western
(Ortlam, D.) 1967A, 1968A
GILBRALTAR
Vertebrate Faunas
Pleist.; Gorham's Cave; Aves
(Eastham, A.) 1968A
GONDWANALAND
Paleogeography
Continental drift
(Anon.) 1970BL, 1971BR
(Colbert, E. H.) 1971C
(Corro, G. del) 1968A, 1971A
(Romer, A. S.) 1968E
Paleontology
General
(Gosh, P. K., Sastry, M. V. A.) 1967A
Vertebrate Faunas
General
(Bigarella, J. J., Salamuni, R.) 1967A
GREAT BRITAIN
Paleontology
Aves; Eocene
(Harrison, C. J. O.) 1971A
(Harrison, C. J. O., Walker, C. A.) 1971A
Vertebrate Faunas
Pleist.; Cefn Cave; Mam.
(Valdemar, A. E.) 1970A
GREECE
Absolute Age
Samos Is.; vertebrates
(Van Couvering, J. A., Miller, J. A.) 1971A
Paleoanthropology
Petralona; fossil hominids
(Poulianos, A. N.) 1967A, 1971A
Paleontology
Mam.; Miocene; Kalimeriani
(Melentis, J. K.) 1966N
Mam.; Miocene; Serrae
(Melentis, J. K.) 1966Q, 1967E
Mam.; Miocene, upper; Crete
(Bruijn, H. de, Meulenkamp, J. E.) 1972A
Mam.; Pleist., lower; Volaks
(Sickenberg, O.) 1967A, 1970A
Mam.; Pleist.; Megalopolis
(Melentis, J. K.) 1963A, 1966F,G,H,I,J

GREECE - cont.
Paleontology
Mam.; Pleist.; Ptolemais
(Mitzopoulos, M. K.) 1967B
Mam.; Pliocene
(Mitzopoulos, M. K.) 1966A
Mam.; Pliocene; Attika
(Melentis, J. K.) 1969A
Mam.; Pliocene; Halmyropotamos
(Melentis, J. K.) 1966L
Mam.; Pliocene; Pikermi
(Melentis, J. K.) 1966L,O
Mam.; Pliocene; Rhodes
(Bruijn, H. de, Dawson, M. R.,
Mein, P.) 1970A
Mam.; Pliocene; Samos Is.
(Beaumont, G. de)1968B, 1969A,B, 1970A,B
(Gentry, A. W.) 1971A
(Sondaar, P. Y.) 1971A
Mam.; Plio-Pleistocene; Drama
(Melentis, J. K.) 1966M
Pisces; Cret.; Lindos
(Melentis, J. K.) 1967D
Rept.; Pleist.; Megalopolis
(Melentis, J. K.) 1966K
Rept.; Pleist.; Pikermi
(Bachmayer, F.) 1967B
Vertebrate Faunas
Miocene; Chios Is.
(Tobien, H.) 1968H, 1969B
Miocene; Chios Is.; Mam.
(Melentis, J. K., Tobien, H.) 1970A
Miocene; Pikermi; Mam.
(Guernet, C., Sauvage, J.) 1971A
Pleist.; Cos Is.; Mam.
(Charrier, G., Giglio, A.) 1969A
Pleist.; Haliakmon; Mam.
(Melentis, J. K.) 1966P
Pleist.; Kasos Is.; Mam.
(Kuss, S. E.) 1969B
Pleist.; Petralona Cave; Mam.
(Sickenberg, O.) 1964B
Pleist.; Thessalia; Mam.
(Schneider, H. E.) 1968A
Pliocene; Halmyropotamos; Mam.
(Melentis, J. K.) 1966L, 1967F, 1970A
Pliocene; Strimon Basin
(Gramann, F., Kockel, F.) 1969A
Pliocene; Thessalia; Mam.
(Melentis, J. K., Schneider, H.) 1966A
Tert.; Thracia; Mam.
(Kopp, K.-O., Pavoni, N.,
Schindler, C.) 1969A
GREENLAND
Vertebrate Faunas
Cret.; western; Pisces
(Bendix-Almgreen, S. E.) 1969A
(Rosenkrantz, A.) 1970A
Tert.; western; Pisces
(Bendix-Almgreen, S. E.) 1969A
(Rosenkrantz, A.) 1970A
GROWTH. See Paleobiology under class term,
Vertebrate.
GUATEMALA
Paleontology
Mam.; Pleist.; Santa Amelia
(Woodburne, M. O.) 1969B

HISTORY - cont.
  Paleontology
    Hungarian Geological Institut
      (Kretzoi, M.)   1969E
    Nineteenth century
      (Gerstner, P. A.)   1970A
    North America
      (Tedford, R. H.)   1970A
    Rhodesia
      (Bond, G.)   1972A
    Süssenborn bei Weimar
      (Nolte, H., Wolfram, H.-J.,
      Wöllner, H.)   1969A
    Trends
      (Moore, R. C., et al.)   1968A
    United States, southwest,
      Plateau Province
      (Welles, S. P.)   1969A
    University of Calif., Berkeley
      (Camp, C. L.)   1969A
  Paleontology Department
    University of Calif.
      (Wagner, C. D.)   1969A
  Peabody Museum, Harvard
    Anthropology
      (Brew, J. O.)   1968A,B
  Peale's Museum
    Philadelphia
      (Ellis, R. P.)   1966A
  Peking Man
    Original specimens
      (Shapiro, H. L.)   1971A
  Piltdown Man
    General
      (Oakley, K. P.)   1968B
  Prehistory
    Research
      (Prudhommeau, M.)   1964A, 1966A
  Radiocarbon Dating
    General
      (Vogt, H.-H.)   1971B
  Rancho La Brea
    Excavations
      (Miller, G. J.)   1970A
    General
      (Heric, T. M.)   1969A
    Oil exploration
      (Myers, D. P.)   1970A
  Royal Institution Library of Science
    Friday evening discourses, 1851–1937
      (Runcorn, S. K.)   1971A
  Sharktooth Hill
    California
      (Powell, C. L.)   1971A
  Smithsonian Institution
    General
      (Karp, W.)   1965A
      (Oehser, P. H.)   1970A
  "Snow-man"
    Critique
      (Pidoplichko, I. G., et al.)   1969A
  Solnhofen
    Paleontology
      (Mundlos, R.)   1967A

HISTORY - cont.
  Species
    Concept development
      (Skvortsov, A. K.)   1967A
  Staatliches Museum für Naturkunde
    Stuttgart
      (Schüz, E.)   1966A
  Uganda Museum
    Exhibitions
      (Deming, L. M.)   1966A
  Ukrainian Academy of Sciences
    Research
      (Pidoplichko, I. G.)   1969A
  University of California Expedition
    John Day beds, 1899
      (Miller, L.)   1972A
  University of New Mexico
    Department of Geology
      (Northrop, S. A.)   1966A
  Verein für Vaterländische Naturkunde
    Württemberg   (Schüz, E.)   1970A
  Whitney Geological Survey
    California
      (Holton, C. P.)   1969A
HONDURAS
  Vertebrate Faunas
    Pleist.; Comayagua V.; Mam.
      (Webb, S. D.)   1970A
HUNGARY
  Paleoanthropology
    Vértesszöllös; fossil hominids
      (Martí Jusmet, F.)   1970A
      (Matiukhin, A. E.)   1972A
      (Roginskiĭ, Iа. Iа.)   1969B
      (Thoma, A.)   1969B, 1972A,B
      (Vértes, L.)   1969B
      (Wolpoff, M. H.)   1971B,E
  Paleontology
    Mam.; Pleist., lower. Mt. Osztramos
      (Jánossy, D.)   1969C, 1970B
  Vertebrate Faunas
    Miocene; Mecsek Mts.
      (Hámor, G.)   1970A
    Miocene; Szurdokpüspöki; Mam.
      (Kretzoi, M., Pálfalvy, I.)   1969A
    Pleist.; Budapest
      (Csánk, V. G.)   1968A
    Pleist.; Csarnóta
      (Kretzoi, M.)   1962D
    Pleist.; Érd; Mam.
      (Kretzoi, M.)   1968C
    Pleist.; Komárom Co.; Mam.
      (Jánossy, D.)   1970-71A
    Pleist.; Mam.
      (Jánossy, D.)   1972B
    Pleist.; Subalyuk Cave; Mam.
      (Jánossy, D.)   1960A
    Pleist.; Uppony
      (Jánossy, D., Krolopp, E.,
      Brunnacker, K.)   1968A
ICHNOLOGY. See Tracks and Traces.
IDAHO
  Paleontology
    Amph.; Pliocene; Glenns Ferry Fm.
      (Chantell, C. J.)   1970A

INDIA - cont.
  Vertebrate Faunas
    Pleist.; Chirki-on-Pravara; Mam.
      (Corvinus, G. K.)   1968-69A
    Pleist.; Deccan; Mam.
      (Rajaguru, S. N.)   1969A
    Pleist.; Maharashtra; Mam.
      (Tripathi, C.)   1967A
    Pleist.; Narmada R.; Mam.
      (Khatri, A. P.)   1966A
    Pleist.; Susunia; Mam.
      (Sastry, M. V. A.)   1966A
    Pliocene; Siwaliks; Mam.
      (Sahni, M. R., Mathur, L. P.)   1964A
    Plio-Pleistocene; Pinjaurs, Tatrots
      (Sahni, M. R., Khan, E.)   1968A
    Tert.; Ladakh
      (Dixit, P. C., Kachroo, R. K.,
      Rai, H., Sharma, N. L.)   1971A
    Tert.; Mayurbhanj; Pisces
      (Sahni, A., Mehrotra, D. K.,
      Jauhari, A. K.)   1971A
    Tert.; Siwaliks
      (Satsangi, P. P.)   1964B
    Tert.; Siwaliks; Mam.
      (Sastry, M. V. A.)   1969A
    Triassic; Pranhita-Godavari V.
      (Chatterjee, S.)   1967B
      (Chatterjee, S., et al.)   1969A
INDONESIA
  Paleoanthropology
    Fossil hominids
      (Jacob, T.)   1965A
  Paleontology
    Mam.; Pleist.
      (Hooijer, D. A.)   1969C, 1970A
    Mam.; Pleist.; Flores, Timor
      (Hooijer, D. A.)   1972A,B
    Mam.; Pleist.; Timor
      (Sartono, S.)   1969A
    Rept.; Pleist., lower; Timor
      (Hooijer, D. A.)   1971A,B
INSTITUTIONS. See Museums.
INTEGUMENTARY STRUCTURES. See Anatomy under
  class name.
IOWA
  Paleontology
    Pisces; Devonian, middle; Vogel Quarry
      (Straka, J. J., Semken, H. A.)   1969A,B
  Vertebrate Faunas
    Pleist.; Turin; Mam.
      (Frankforter, W. D.)   1971A
IRAN
  Paleoanthropology
    Fossil hominids
      (Bacon, E.)   1971A
  Paleontology
    Pisces; Eocene; Ilam
      (Haghipour, A., Brants, A.)   1971A
    Pisces; Oligocene; Ilam, Istehbanat
      (Arambourg, C.)   1966A
  Vertebrate Faunas
    Cenozoic; Mam.
      (Boné, E. L.)   1971A
    Pleist.; Ali Tappeh
      (McBurney, C. B. M.)   1968B

IRAN - cont.
  Vertebrate Faunas
    Pliocene; Maragheh
      (Tobien, H.)   1968H
IRAQ
  Paleoanthropology
    Fossil hominids
      (Bacon, E.)   1971A
    Shanidar Cave; fossil hominids
      (Leroi-Gourhan, Arlette)   1968A
      (Solecki, R. S.)   1968A, 1971A,B
      (Sullivan, W.)   1968A
      (Suzuki, H.)   1969A
IRELAND
  Paleontology
    Mam.; Pleist.; Larne
      (Doughty, P. S.)   1969A
ISRAEL
  Absolute Age
    Amud Cave; vertebrates
      (Sakanoue, M., Yoshioka, M.)   1970A
      (Suzuki, M.)   1970A
  Paleoanthropology
    Amud Cave; fossil hominids
      (Endo, B., Kimura, T.)   1970A
      (Ogawa, T., et al.)   1969A
      (Ogawa, T., Hosokawa, H.)   1969A
      (Sakura, H.)   1969A, 1970A,B
      (Suzuki, H.)   1969A, 1970A,B,C
      (Suzuki, H., Takai, F.)   1970A
    Fossil hominids
      (Asmus, G.)   1967B
    Hazorea; fossil hominids
      (Anati, E., Haas, N.)   1967B
      (Avnimelech, M. A.)   1967A
    Mt. Carmel; fossil hominids
      (Garrod, D. A. E., et al.)   1971A
      (McCown, T. D., Keith, A.)   1972A
      (Wreschner, E.)   1967A
    Qafzeh; fossil hominids
      (Vandermeersch, B.)   1969C, 1970B
    'Ubeidiya; fossil hominids
      (Bay, R.)   1966B
      (Stekelis, M.)   1966A
  Paleontology
    Amph.; Cret., lower
      (Nevo, E.)   1968A
    Amph.; Cret., lower; Makhtesh Ramon
      (Nevo, E., Estes, R.)   1969A
    Mam.; Pleist.
      (Haas, G.)   1970B
      (Tchernov, E.)   1968B
    Mam.; Pleist.; Geula Cave
      (Frenkel, H.)   1970A
    Pisces; Cret.; Jericho
      (Raab, M.)   1967A
    Rept.; Triassic; Wadi Ramon
      (Haas, G.)   1969A, 1970A
  Vertebrate Faunas
    Miocene; Mam.
      (Savage, R. J. G., Tchernov, E.)   1968A
    Pleist.; Amud Cave; Mam.
      (Takai, F.)   1970A
    Pleist.; Djebel Qafze Cave; Mam.
      (Haas, G.)   1972A
    Pleist.; 'Evron; Mam.
      (Issar, A., Kafri, U.)   1969A

ITALY - cont.
Vertebrate Faunas
Pleist.; Imola; Mam.
   (Azzaroli, A., Berzi, A.)   1970A
Pleist.; Mam.
   (Azzaroli, A., Ambrosetti, P.) 1970A, 1972A
Pleist.; Marina di Camerota; Mam.
   (Palma di Cesnola, A.,
    Vigliardi, A.)   1967A
Pleist.; Mario Bernardini Cave; Mam.
   (Borzatti von Löwenstern, E.)   1970A,B
Pleist.; Mèrcure R.; Mam.
   (Vezzani, L.)   1967A
Pleist.; Messina Strait; Mam.
   (Bonfiglio, L., Berdar, A.)   1969A
Pleist.; Nasino; Mam.
   (Anon.)   1969BL
Pleist.; Paglicci Cave; Mam.
   (Palma di Cesnola, A.)   1970A
Pleist.; Poggio Cave; Mam.
   (Palma di Cesnola, A.)   1969B
Pleist.; Prazziche; Mam.
   (Borzatti von Löwenstern, E.)   1966A
Pleist.; Rigoli; Mam.
   (Borzatti von Löwenstern, E.,
    Dani, A.)   1968A
Pleist.; Rome; Mam.
   (Ambrosetti, P.)   1967A
Pleist.; Sabatini Mt.; Mam.
   (Camponeschi, B.)   1970A
Pleist.; St. Agostino Cave; Mam.
   (Tozzi, C.)   1970A
Pleist.; St. Teodoro Cave; Mam.
   (Vigliardi, A.)   1968A
Pleist.; Salento; Mam.
   (Borzatti von Löwenstern, E.)   1966C
Pleist.; Santa Caterina; Mam.
   (Borzatti von Löwenstern, E.)   1966B
Pleist.; Sardinia
   (Comaschi Caria, I.)   1968A
Pleist.; Sardinia; Aves
   (Malatesta, A., Suriano, F.)   1971A
Pleist.; Spagnoli Cave; Mam.
   (Guerri, M.)   1970A
Pleist.; Spinagallo Cave; Mam.
   (Petronio, C.)   1970B
Pleist.; Tagliente; Mam.
   (Leonardi, P., Ruffo, S.)   1969A
Pleist.; Uluzzo Bay
   (Borzatti von Löwenstern, E.)   1965C
Pleist.; Valdemino Cave
   (Tozzi, C.)   1969A
Pleist.; Veneri Cave; Mam.
   (Radmilli, A.)   1967A
JAMAICA
Paleontology
Rept.; Eocene, middle
   (Berg, D. E.)   1969B
JAPAN
Absolute Age
Pleist. verts.
   (Chard, C. S., Morlan, R. E.)   1970A
Paleoanthropology
Hamakita; fossil hominids
   (Suzuki, H., et al.)   1966A
   (Vallois, H. V.)   1969A

JAPAN - cont.
Paleontology
Mam.; Miocene, middle; Iwaki
   (Shikama, T., Yanagisawa, I.)   1971A
Mam.; Miocene; Naka-niikawa district
   (Fujii, S.)   1970A
Mam.; Neogene; northern
   (Hatai, K., Hayasaka, S.,
    Masuda, K.)   1963A
Mam.; Neogene; Sendai
   (Hatai, K., Masuda, K.)   1966A
Mam.; Oligocene; Kita-kyushu
   (Hasegawa, Y., Hojo, Y.)   1965A
Mam.; Pleist.
   (Hasegawa, Y.)   1968C
   (Iwamoto, M., Hasegawa, Y.)   1972A
   (Nagasawa, J.)   1968A
   (Onodera, S.)   1970B
Mam.; Pleist.; Akashi Fm.
   (Otsuka, H.)   1972A
Mam.; Pleist.; central
   (Chinji, M.)   1971A,B,C,D,E
Mam.; Pleist.; Hamamatsu
   (Kobayashi, K.)   1963B
Mam.; Pleist.; Iwanoshita
   (Onodera, S.)   1970A
Mam.; Pleist.; Kyushu
   (Otsuka, H.)   1970B
Mam.; Pleist., lower; Oga Peninsula
   (Shikama, T., Takayasu, Y.)   1971A
Mam.; Pleist.; Ojika-do
   (Hasegawa, Y.)   1964C
Mam.; Pleist.; Shizu shell bed
   (Nagasawa, J.)   1971A
Mam.; Pleist.; Shizukuishi-machi
   (Onodera, S., et al.)   1967A
Mam.; Pleist.; Shodoshima Is.
   (Hasegawa, Y.)   1972A
   (Ozaki, H., Hasegawa, Y.)   1969A
Mam.; Pleist.; Tokyo
   (Shikama, T., Kanno, S.)   1970A
Mam.; Pleist.; Yokosuka
   (Hasegawa, Y., Kanie, Y.)   1971A
Mam.; Pliocene
   (Shikama, T., Domning, D.)   1970A
Mam.; Plio-Pleistocene; Nakijin
   (Takamiya, H.)   1967A
Pisces; Cret., upper; Aman-cho
   (Hasegawa, Y., Ueno, T.)   1967A
Pisces; Pleist.; Boso, Miura Peninsulas
   (Aoki, N.)   1968A
Pisces; Pliocene; Aomori
   (Hatai, K.)   1965C
Rept.
   (Hasegawa, Y., Obata, I.)   1972A
Rept.; Cret., upper; Obisagawa R.
   (Obata, I., Hasegawa, Y.,
    Suzuki, T.)   1970A
Rept.; Jurassic; Miyama-cho
   (Shikama, T.)   1967A, 1969A
Rept.; Miocene; Kyushu
   (Otsuka, H.)   1970A
Rept.; Pleist.; central
   (Kamei, T.)   1971A
Rept.; Triassic; Utatsu
   (Murata, M.)   1971A

KENYA - cont.
Paleoanthropology
Lake Rudolf; fossil hominids
  (Behrensmeyer, A. K.) 1970A
  (Isaac, G. L., Leakey, R. E. F.,
  Behrensmeyer, A. K.) 1971A
  (Leakey, R. E. F.) 1970B, 1971A
  (Leakey, R. E. F., Mungai, J. M.,
  Walker, A. C.) 1971A, 1972A
  (Robinson, J. T.) 1972B
  (T., L.) 1971A
  (Vandermeersch, B.) 1972A
Rudolf Basin; fossil hominids
  (Vondra, C. F.) 1971A
Paleontology
Mam.; Miocene; Fort Ternan
  (Churcher, C. S.) 1970B
  (Gentry, A. W.) 1970A
Mam.; Miocene, middle; Kabarsero
  (Crusafont Pairó, M., Aguirre, E.) 1971B
Mam.; Miocene; northwestern
  (Maglio, V. J.) 1969A
Mam.; Miocene; Rusinga, Songhor
  (Andrews, P.) 1970A
Mam.; Miocene, upper; Loperot
  (Hooijer, D. A.) 1971C
Mam.; Pleist.; Lake Baringo
  (Leakey, R. E. F.) 1969A
Mam.; Pliocene; Ft. Ternan
  (Leakey, L. S. B.) 1971E,F
Mam.; Pliocene; Kanapoi, Lothagam
  (Cooke, H. B. S., Ewer, R. F.) 1972A
Mam.; Pliocene; Kayadibi
  (Tekkaya, I.) 1969A
Mam.; Pliocene; northwestern
  (Hooijer, D. A., Patterson, B.) 1972A
Mam.; Plio-Pleistocene; northwestern
  (Maglio, V. J.) 1970B
Rept.; Mesozoic; Lake Rudolf
  (Arambourg, C., Wolff, R. G.) 1969A
Vertebrate Faunas
Cenozoic; Rift V.
  (Bishop, W. W., et al.) 1971A
Miocene; Lake Rudolf; Mam.
  (Arambourg, C., Wolff, R. G.) 1969A
Miocene; Muruarot Hill; Mam.
  (Madden, C. T.) 1972A
Miocene; Rusinga Is.
  (Van Couvering, J.) 1972A
Pleist.; East Rudolf
  (Maglio, V. J.) 1971A, 1972A
Pleist.; Lake Rudolf
  (Leakey, R. E. F.) 1970A
Pliocene; East Rudolf
  (Maglio, V. J.) 1971A
Pliocene; Lothagam Hill
  (Patterson, B., Behrensmeyer, A. K.,
  Sill, W. D.) 1970A
Pliocene; Rift V.; Mam.
  (Bishop, W. W., Chapman, G. R.) 1970A
Plio-Pleistocene; Lake Rudolf
  (Poplin, F.) 1971A
LEBANON
Paleontology
Pisces; Cret.; Hajula
  (Goody, P. C.) 1969A

LEBANON - cont.
Paleontology
Pisces; Cret., upper
  (Gaudant, M.) 1969A
  (Patterson, C.) 1970A
Vertebrate Faunas
Cret.; Pisces
  (Hückel, U.) 1970A
Pleist.; Joub Jannine; Mam.
  (Besançon, J., Copeland, L.,
  Hours, F.) 1970A
Pleist.; Masloukh
  (Gautier, A.) 1970A
LEGISLATION. See under Evolution, Paleontology.
LESOTHO
Paleontology
Rept.; Karroo system
  (Turner, B. R.) 1972A
Rept.; Triassic, upper
  (Thulborn, R. A.) 1970A, 1971B, 1972A
LIBYA
Vertebrate Faunas
Tert., lower; Dor el Talha
  (Savage, R. J. G.) 1969A
LIFE (evolution in general). See under Evolution.
LOUISIANA
Paleontology
Mam.
  (Rivière, A. E. A.) 1837B
MADAGASCAR
Paleontology
Rept.; Triassic
  (Westphal, F.) 1970B
Vertebrate Faunas
Paleozoic; Gondwana Fm.
  (Besairie, H.) 1967A
Triassic; northwest; Pisces
  (Beltan, L.) 1968A
MALAYSIA
Absolute Age
Sarawak, Niah Cave; verts.
  (Harrisson, T.) 1967A
MALTA
Paleontology
Mam.; Pleist.; Ghar Dalam Cave
  (Malec, F., Storch, G.) 1970A
MAMMALIA
Absarokius abbotti
Dentition
  (Bown, T. M., Gingerich, P. D.) 1972A
Acanthion
Pleist.; Java, Sangiran; dental pattern
  (Bosma, A. A.) 1968A
Aceratherium
Oligocene; France, Saverdun; limbs
  (Bergounioux, F. M., Crouzel, F.) 1971A
Acinonyx
Pleist., lower; Germany, Wiesbaden
  (Schütt, G.) 1970B
Adapidae
Morphology; systematics
  (Szalay, F. S.) 1971B
Adapis
Tert.; England, southern; limbs
  (Day, M. H., Walker, A. C.) 1969A

MAMMALIA - cont.

Aegyptopithecus
Endocranial cast
(Radinsky, L.) 1972A
Oligocene; Egypt; skull
(Anon.) 1967CE,CG, 1968BJ, 1971BT
Agriotherium
Pliocene; So. Afr., Langebaanweg; jaw,
teeth; n. sp.
(Hendey, Q. B.) 1972B
Ailurus
Pleist.; China
(Anon.) 1972BB
Akodon
Pliocene; Argentina, Chapadmalal; jaws, teeth
(Reig, O. A., Linares, O. J.) 1969A
Alactaginae
Pliocene, upper; USSR, Odessa Prov.;
distribution; evolution; tooth; n. gen.
(Topachevs'kyĭ, V. O.) 1971C
Pliocene, upper; USSR, Ukraine; dentition;
metatarsal; n. gen.
(Topachevs'kyĭ, V. A., Skoryk, O. F.) 1971A
Alces
Morphology; systematics; phylogeny
(Heptner, W. G.,
Nasimowitsch, A. A.) 1967A
Pleist.; England, Lancashire,
Poulton-le-Fylde
(Barnes, B., et al.) 1971A
Pleist.; Rumania, Transylvania;
skull, limbs
(Rădulescu, C., Hermann, W.) 1969A
Allacerops
Oligocene; Mongolia, Ulan Ganga;
jaw, teeth
(Borsuk-Białynicka, M.) 1968A
Allactaga jaculus
Pleist., middle; Siberia, western; limb
(Erbaeva, M. A.) 1972A
Allocricetus
Pleist.; France, Arago Cave; teeth; n. subsp.
(Chaline, J.) 1971A
Allodesmus
Miocene; Calif., Kern Co., Round
Mountain silt; jaws; nomenclature
(Barnes, L. G.) 1970A
Allohippus
Pleist.; USSR, Tadzhik Basin; phalanx
(Mavlïanov, G. A.,
Kambariddinov, R. K.,
Mirzabaev, Kh.) 1968A
Alphadon
Cret., upper; Peru, Vilquechico Fm.;
teeth, maxillary
(Sigé, B.) 1971B
Alticonodon
Cret.; Alberta; jaw, teeth; n. gen.
(Fox, R. C.) 1969A
Amphicyon
Systematics
(Bonis, L. de) 1969B
Amphicyonidae
Miocene; Nebraska, Agate Springs;
jaws, limbs
(Hunt, R. M.) 1972A

MAMMALIA - cont.

Amphicyonidae
North America; morphology
(Hunt, R. M.) 1971A
Amphilagus
Miocene; France, Anjou; teeth; phylogeny
(Janvier, P.) 1969A
Amphipithecus
Evolution
(Szalay, F. S.) 1970A
Amynodontidae
Eocene; USSR, Kazakhstan, n. taxa
(Belîaeva, E. I.) 1971B
Oligocene, middle; USSR, Kazakhstan,
Teniz Lake; tooth
(Belîaeva, E. I.) 1970A
Anagalida
Paleocene. Mongolia, Gashato; morphology;
n. taxa
(Szalay, F. S., McKenna, M. C.) 1971A
Anatomy
Brain evolution
(Gabuniâ, L. K.) 1967B
(Radinsky, L. B.) 1968B, 1970A, 1971A
(Repérant, J.) 1970A
Circulatory system; Rodentia
(Guthrie, D. A.) 1969A
Dentition; collogen fibrils
(Sato, T.) 1969A
Digestive system; Rodentia
(Voronîsov, N. N.) 1967A
Electron microscopy; teeth; Rodentia
(Chaline, J.) 1968A
Endonasals; ethmoids
(Vilar Fiol, R.) 1967A
Functional, arboreal; Primates
(Cartmill, M.) 1972A
Functional, brachiating; Hominoidea
(Lewis, O. J.) 1969A, 1971A
Functional, carnivorous
(Van Valen, L.) 1969C
Functional, cursorial; pelvis
(Dalzell, B. B.) 1969A
Functional; dentition
(Butler, P. M.) 1972A
Functional; dentition; selenodont ungulates
(Friant, M.) 1971B
Functional, feeding system
(Crompton, A. W., Hiiemäe, K.) 1969A
(Turnbull, W. D.) 1970A
Functional, feeding system; *Adapis*
(Gingerich, P. D.) 1972B
Functional, feeding system; Elephantidae
(Maglio, V. J.) 1972B
Functional, feeding system; *Hyaenodon*
(Mellett, J. S.) 1969A
Functional, feeding system;
Merycoidodontidae
(Greaves, W. S.) 1972B
Functional, feeding system;
Mesonychidae
(Szalay, F. S.) 1969D
Functional, feeding system; Primates
(Szalay, F. S.) 1972C
Functional, feeding system; *Smilodon*
(Miller, G. J.) 1969B

MAMMALIA - cont.
Anatomy
Functional, jaw joint, evolution
(Kermack, K. A.)   1972A
Functional, limbs
(Manzii, S. F.)   1968A
Functional, locomotor system
(Gambarian, P. P.)   1967A
Functional, locomotor system; Camelidae
(Webb, S. D.)   1972A
Functional, locomotor system; Pongidae
(Conroy, G. C., Fleagle, J. G.)   1972A
(Tuttle, R. H.)   1969A,B
(Tuttle, R. H., Oxnard, C. E.)   1969A
Functional, locomotor system; Primates
(Napier, J. R.)   1967A
(Oxnard, C., Tuttle, R.)   1969A
(Szalay, F. S.)   1972C
Functional, musculature system; Felidae
(Torre, D.)   1967B
Functional, wing; Plecotus
(Norberg, U. M.)   1970A
Hand; evolution
(Astanin, L. P.)   1968A
Histology; teeth; Palaeotheriidae, Equidae
(Remy, J. A.)   1972B
Histology; tissues; Equus
(Kokurichev, P. I., Dobin, M. A.)   1972A
Integumentary system; Coelodonta
(Kubiak, H.)   1969A
Muscular system, mastication; Didelphis
(Hiiemäe, K., Jenkins, F. A.)   1969A
Nervous system
(Dechaseaux, C.)   1969B, 1970C
Nervous system; Primates
(Ozhigova, A. P.)   1968A
Osteology, Atlas
(Pales, L.)   1972A
(Schmid, E.)   1972A
Palate and choanae,
adaptive radiation
(Flerov, K. K.)   1969A
Petrosal, systematic value
(MacIntyre, G. T.)   1972A
Sensory system, ear; Insectivora,
Marsupialia
(Segall, W.)   1970A
Sensory system; sound perception
(Zvorykin, V. P.)   1968A
Skeletal system, braincase
(Kermack, K. A.,
Kielan-Jaworowska, Z.)   1971A
Skeletal system, forelimb; Tadarida
(Sigé, B.)   1971A
Skull; Catarrhini
(Vogel, C.)   1968B
Skull, evolution
(Jollie, M.)   1968B
Skull; primates
(Vogel, C.)   1969A
Teeth; Cercopithecoidea
(Voruz, C.)   1970A
Teeth, evolution and homologies
(Hershkovitz, P.)   1971A
Teeth and hair, correlation
(Schriefer, A.)   1970A

MAMMALIA - cont.
Anatomy
Tribosphenic molar
(Vandebroek, G.)   1967A
X-ray photography; teeth;
Palaeotheriidae
(Remy, J. A.)   1972B
Andegameryx
Miocene; France; morphology; n. gen.
(Ginsburg, L.)   1970B
Ankarapithecus
Cenozoic; Turkey; jaw, teeth
(Ozansoy, F.)   1966A
Pliocene; Turkey, Ankara; jaw, teeth
(Ozansoy, F.)   1970A
Anomalomyidae
Phylogeny; n. taxa
(Kretzoi, M.)   1970-71A
Anomalomys
Miocene; Czech.; Cheb basin;
phylogeny; teeth; n. sp.
(Fejfar, O.)   1972A
Antiacodon
Eocene; Utah, Green River; jaw
(Burke, J. J.)   1969A
Anthracotheriidae
Oligocene; Germany, Wiesbaden; limb
(Tobien, H.)   1971B
Apatemyidae
Eocene; No. America; systematics; ecology
(West, R. M.)   1972C
Eocene, upper; Calif., Utah
(West, R. M.)   1971A
Evolution
(Szalay, F. S.)   1968C
Archaeoceti
Eocene, upper; England, Hampshire;
vertebrae
(Halstead, L. B., Middleton, J.)   1972A
Archaeocetus
Miocene; Rumania, Avrameni and
Dragușenii; vertebrae
(Macarovici, N., Zaharia, N.)   1968A
Archaeolambda
Paleocene; Mongolia, Naran Bulak;
morphology
(Kielan-Jaworowska, Z.)   1968C
Archaeolemurinae
Skull, teeth
(Tattersall, I.)   1972A
Archaeotherium
Oligocene; Oregon, John Day Basin; jaw
(Coleman, R. G.)   1951A
Archidiskodon
Evolution
(Garutt, V. E., Alekseeva, L. I.)   1964A
Pleist.; Greece, Ptolemais; teeth
(Mitzopoulos, M. K.)   1967B
Pleist.; Siberia, Chelkar; jaw, skeleton
(Zhylkibaev, K. Zh.)   1969A
Plio-Pleistocene; Siberia, Enisei R.;
skull frag., teeth
(Lavrent'ev, A. I.)   1968A
Archidiskodon exoptatus
Nomenclature; systematics
(Maglio, V. J.)   1969B

MAMMALIA - cont.
Biogeography
Marsupials
(Hoffstetter, R.) 1970B
(Hoffstetter, R.) 1972A
(Tedford, R. H.) 1971A
(Thenius, E.) 1971B
Muroidea
(Vorontsov, N. N.) 1968A
Oligocene; Asia
(Flerov, K. K., Ianovskaia, N. M.) 1971A
Placentals; origin; distribution
(Hoffstetter, R.) 1972A
(Thenius, E.) 1971B
Pleist.; Tibet
(Shen-Sjao-Chzhou) 1963A
Plio-Pleistocene; Asia, northern
(Sher, A. V.) 1968B
Plio-Pleistocene; No. America
(Sher, A. V.) 1968B
Southern continents
(Keast, A.) 1968A, 1972A
Southern continents; distribution;
phylogeny; Mes., Cen.
(Hoffstetter, R.) 1971A
Tertiary
(Kurtén, B.) 1972D
Tert., lower; Europe
(McKenna, M. C.) 1972F
Tert., lower; No. America
(McKenna, M. C.) 1972F
Bison
Cenozoic; Eurasia; evolution;
systematics; distribution
(Flerow, C. C.) 1971A
Cenozoic; No. America; evolution;
systematics; distribution
(Flerow, C. C.) 1971A
Distribution; evolution
(Gunderson, H. L.) 1969A
(Guthrie, R. D.) 1970A
Morphology, variation; systematics
(Hillerud, J. M.) 1972A
Pleist.; Colorado; morphology
(Lewis, G. E.) 1970A
Pleist.; East Germany, Süssenborn;
morphology; n. taxa
(Flerov, K. K.) 1969B
Pleist.; Europe; morphology
(Flerov, K. K.) 1969C
Pleist.; Florida; morphology; distribution
(Robertson, J. S.) 1969A
Pleist.; Germany, Teufels Cave;
morphology; ecology
(Lehmann, U.) 1966B
Pleist.; Idaho, Snake Co.; origin
(Butler, B. R.) 1971A
Pleist.; Iowa; skeleton
(Anon.) 1969BO
Pleist.; Rumania, Fumureni; skull;
distribution
(Ionete, L.) 1964A
Pleist.; Texas, Randall Co.; skull;
paleoecology
(Schultz, G. E., Cheatum, E. P.) 1969A,
1970A

MAMMALIA - cont.
Bison
Pleist.; USSR, Fergana; skull
(Khudaiberdiev, T. N.) 1971A
Pleist.; Wyoming, Casper; morphology;
systematics
(Wilson, M.) 1972B
Skeleton
(Reshetov, V. Iu.) 1969A
Bison antiquus
Pleist.; Northwest Territories; skull
(Gordon, B. C.) 1970A
Bison latifrons
Pleist.; Texas, Sand Creek; skull
(Schultz, G. E.) 1972B
Blarina brevicauda
Systematics
(Graham, R. W.) 1972A
Boötherium
Morphology
(Kraege, H.) 1970A
Pleist.; Kentucky, Big Bone Lick
(Anon.) 1966BZ
Borhyaenidae
Eocene; Argentina, Chubut; morphology;
n. taxa
(Simpson, G. G.) 1970D
Borophagus
Pliocene; Texas, Blanco Fm.;
skull, skeleton
(Dalquest, W. W.) 1968A
Bos
Domestication
(Jarman, M. R.) 1969A
Pleist.; Denmark; morphology
(Degerbøl, M., Fredskild, B.) 1970A
Pleist.; India, Haritalyangar; hoof
(Prasad, K. N., Satsangi, P. P.) 1962B
Pleist., middle; USSR, Georgia;
skull, skeleton
(Vekua, A. K.,
Matskhonashvili, K. G.) 1970A
Bos primigenius
Pleist.; France, Cornerives;
skull, skeleton
(David, E., Frachon, J.-C.,
Sattonnet, R.) 1968A
Skulls, horns
(Chrzanowska, W.) 1971A
Bovidae
Distribution; adaptations
(Burchak-Abramovich, N. I.) 1966F,
1970A
Miocene; Kenya, Ft. Ternan; morphology;
systematics; n. taxa
(Gentry, A. W.) 1970A
Pleist.; Germany, Schleswig-Holstein;
horn sheaths
(Guenther, E. W.) 1967B
Pleist.; USSR, Nogaïsk; horn cores; n. gen.
(Vereshchagin, N. K.) 1969A
Pleist.; USSR, Smolensk district;
musk ox, skull
(Salov, I. N.) 1963A
Pliocene; China, Tsaidam; systematics
(Gentry, A. W.) 1968B

MAMMALIA - cont.

Carnivora

Pleist.; Nebraska, Brown Co.; jaws, teeth; n. sp.
(Hibbard, C. W.)   1972A

Pleist.; Rumania; morphology
(Samson, P., Radulesco, C., Kisgyörgy, Z.)   1971A

Pleist.; Spain, Aitzbitarte; jaws, teeth, limbs
(Altuna, J.)   1970A

Pleist.; USSR, Iakutia; morphology
(Rusanov, B. S.)   1968B

Pleist.; Yugoslavia, Macedonia; morphology
(Garevski, R.)   1969A

Pliocene; Idaho, Hagerman; morphology; systematics; n. taxa
(Bjork, P. R.)   1970A

Pliocene; Oregon, southeastern; morphology; n. sp.
(Shotwell, J. A.)   1970A

Pliocene; Texas, Coffee Ranch; morphology; n. sp.
(Dalquest, W. W.)   1969A

Pliocene; USSR, Azov Sea; morphology
(Baĭgusheva, V. S.)   1971A

Plio-Pleistocene; China, Shansi; morphology
(Erdbrink, D.-P.)   1968A

Carterodon

Morphology
(Friant, M.)   1969A

Castor

Pleist.; USSR, Moldavia; distribution
(David, A. I.)   1966C

Castoridae

Cenozoic; USSR, Kazakhstan; n. gen.
(Lychev, G. F., Aubekerova, P. A.)   1971A

Dentition
(Friant, M.)   1965C

Morphology; evolution
(Djoshkin, W. W., Safonow, W. G.)   1972A

Pleist.; East Germany, Süssenborn; teeth
(Kretzoi, M.)   1969A

Pleist.; Rumania, Braşov; teeth, limbs; n. gen.
(Radulesco, C., Samson, P.)   1972A

Tert.; Montana, No. Dakota; correlation
(Stout, T. M., Stone, W. J.)   1971A

Castoroides

Pleist.; Florida, Santa Fe R.; morphology; systematics
(Martin, R. A.)   1969A

Pleist.; Wisconsin, Hope; skull, jaw
(Dallman, J. E.)   1969A

Catalogs

Mexico; taxonomic
(Alvarez, T.)   1965A

Catarrhini

Evolution
(Napier, J. R.)   1970B

Maxillary incisors, evolution
(Swindler, D. R.)   1968A

Morphology; phylogeny
(Szalay, F. S.)   1972A

Morphology; systematics
(Simons, E. L.)   1971A,C

MAMMALIA - cont.

Catarrhini

Old World; checklist
(Hill, W. C. O.)   1968A

Caviomorpha

Evolution; distribution
(Hoffstetter, R.)   1972C

Oligocene; Bolivia, Salla-Luribay Basin; skulls, teeth; n. taxa
(Hoffstetter, R., Lavocat, R.)   1970A

Phylogeny
(Lavocat, R.)   1971B

Ceboidea

Evolution; distribution
(Hoffstetter, R.)   1972C

Cenolestoidea

Evolution
(Hayman, D. L., et al.)   1971A

Cenozoic

Taxonomic diversity
(Lillegraven, J. A.)   1972A

Cercopithecidae

Evolution
(Simons, E. L.)   1970A

Evolution; systematics
(Napier, J. R., Napier, P. H.)   1970A

Miocene; East Africa; morphology; n. taxa
(Koenigswald, G. H. R. von)   1969A

Morphology; adaptations
(Jolly, C. J.)   1970D

Pliocene; Spain, Gavá; jaw, teeth
(Delson, E.)   1971A

Cercopithecoidea

Pleist.; Kenya, Lake Baringo; skulls, skeletons; n. taxa
(Leakey, R. E. R.)   1969A

Pleist.; South Africa, Kromdraai; jaws, teeth
(Freedman, L., Brain, C. K.)   1972A

Pleist.; South Africa, Makapansgat; morphology
(Maier, W.)   1970B

Pleist.; Spain; Soria & Teruel
(Crusafont Pairó, M., Golpe Posse, J. M.)   1969A

South Africa; checklist
(Freedman, L.)   1970A

Systematics; phylogeny
(Maier, W.)   1970A

Cervalces

Pleist.; Ohio, Ansonia; vertebrae
(Mills, R. S., Guilday, J. E.)   1972A

Cervidae

Neogene, upper; USSR, Black Sea region; systematics; phylogeny
(Korotkevich, E. L.)   1970B

Pleist.; antler
(Anon.)   1961DA

Pleist.; Austria, Eggenburg; morphology; systematics
(Thenius, E.)   1966G

Pleist.; East Germany, Süssenborn; skulls, limbs; distribution
(Kahlke, H.-D.)   1969D

Pleist.; France; morphology
(Heintz, E.)   1970A

MAMMALIA - cont.
Chonecetus
Oligocene; British Columbia, Vancouver Is.;
  skull, vertebrae; n. gen.
    (Russell, L. S.)   1968B
Chrysemys
Evolution; systematics
    (Rose, F. L.)   1969A
Clethrionomys
Pleist., upper; Kansas, Ellis Co., jaw
    (Zakrzewski, R. J., Maxfield, J. L.)   1971A
Coelodonta
Pleist.; Germany, Hannover; skull
    (Lang, H. D.)   1969A
Pleist.; Rumania, Chişcani; skull, teeth
    (Apostol, L.)   1970A
Pleist.; Rumania; skull, jaw
    (Apostol, L., Vicoveanu, D.)   1970A
Coelodonta antiquitatis
Habits, food
    (Garutt, V. E., Metel'fseva, E. P.,
     Tikhomirov, B. A.)   1970A
Pleist.; France, Ain, Villereversure;
  teeth, limbs; ecology
    (Guérin, C.)   1970A
Pleist.; Germany, Mannheim-Käfertal;
  skull, teeth
    (Jörg, E.)   1971A
Colodon
Oligocene; So. Dakota; teeth; distribution
    (Bjork, P. R.)   1968A
Condylarthra
Dentition
    (Friant, M.)   1967B
Paleocene; Belgium, Brabant; tooth
    (Quinet, G. E., Verlinden, W.,
     Coupatez, P.)   1971A
Creodonta
Paleocene; Belgium, Dormaal; systematics;
  n. taxa
    (Quinet, G. E.)   1969B
Cretaceous
England, Wealden Fm.; morphology; n. sp.
    (Clemens, W. A., Lees, P. M.)   1971A
Evolution
    (Clemens, W. A.)   1970B, 1971B
General
    (Sahni, A.)   1969A
Texas
    (Slaughter, B. H.)   1970C
Cricetidae
Dentition; phylogeny
    (Koby, F.-E.)   1965A
Miocene; Germany, Bavaria; phylogeny;
  stratigraphic significance
    (Fahlbusch, V.)   1970C
Neogene, middle; France, Vieux-
  Collonges; teeth; n. sp.
    (Mein, P., Freudenthal, M.)   1971B
Oligocene; Europe; phylogeny
    (Vianey-Liaud, M.)   1971A
Oligocene; Europe, western; distribution;
  phylogeny; dentition; n. sp.
    (Vianey-Liaud, M.)   1972B
Oligocene; Spain, Montalban;
  morphology; n. taxa
    (Thaler, L.)   1969A

MAMMALIA - cont.
Cricetidae
Pleist.; China, Chen-chia-ou; n. gen.
    (Chow, M-c., Li, C-k.)   1965B
Pleist.; Florida, Reddick; systematics
    (Pinkham, C. F. A.)   1971A
Plio-Pleistocene; Czechoslovakia,
  Hajnácka, Ivanovce; jaws, teeth
    (Fejfar, O.)   1970A
Systematics
    (Kretzoi, M.)   1967A
Tert.; Europe. systematics; evolution;
  n. taxa
    (Mein, P., Freudenthal, M.)   1971A
Cricetinae
Molar evolution
    (Hershkovitz, P.)   1967A
Pleist.; Poland; morphology; n. taxa
    (Fahlbusch, V.)   1969A
Pliocene; Austria, Vienna Basin;
  teeth; n. taxa
    (Daxner-Höck, G.)   1972A
Pliocene; Poland; morphology; n. taxa
    (Fahlbusch, V.)   1969A
Cricetodon
Nomenclature
    (Freudenthal, M., Fahlbusch, V.)   1969A
    (Mein, P.)   1969B
Cricetus
Pleist.; Austria, Schlenkendurchgang's
  Cave; morphology
    (Ehrenberg, K., Mais, K.)   1968A
Crocuta
Pleist.; Great Britain; distribution;
  adaptations
    (Sutcliffe, A. J.)   1969A
Pleist.; Greece, *Megalopolis*; jaw, teeth
    (Melentis, J. K.)   1966H
Pleist.; Spain, Pedraza de la Sierra; teeth
    (Torres Perezhidalgo, T. J. de)   1969A
Crocuta spelaea
Pleist., upper; Netherlands; mandible; teeth
    (Erdbrink, D. P.)   1972A
Systematics
    (Ehrenberg, K.)   1966G
Cryptotis
Systematics; phylogeny; biogeography
    (Choate, J. R.)   1970A
Cuvieronius
Pleist.; Mexico, Oaxaca; tusks; n. sp.
    (Ochoterena F., H.,
     Silva-Barcenas, A.)   1970A
Cylindrodontidae
Eocene, upper; Wyoming, Badwater
  Creek; teeth; n. sp.
    (Black, C. C.)   1970B
Oligocene; Colorado, northeastern;
  morphology
    (Galbreath, E. C.)   1969A
Oligocene; Mongolia; morphology;
  distribution
    (Wood, A. E.)   1970A
Oligocene; Montana; morphology;
  distribution
    (Wood, A. E.)   1970A

MAMMALIA - cont.
Dinotherium
  Feet
    (Danilova, E. I., Svistun, V. I.)   1969A
  Pliocene; USSR, Ukraine; jaws, teeth, limbs
    (Vinokur, I. S.)   1969A
Dipodidae
  Pliocene; USSR, Kazakhstan; morphology;
    evolution; phylogeny; systematics; n. taxa
    (Savinov, P. F.)   1970A
Diprotodontidae
  Skeleton, specializations
    (Waters, B. T., Savage, D. E.)   1969A
Dissacus
  Eocene; Spain, Corsá; tooth; n. sp.
    (Crusafont Pairó, M.,
      Golpe Posse, J. M.)   1968B
Docodon
  Dentition
    (Jenkins, F. A.)   1969A
Docodonta
  Jur., upper; Portugal, Guimarota;
    mandible; n. gen.
    (Kühne, W. G., Krusat, G.)   1972A
Docodontidae
  Jur., middle; Scotland, Skye;
    mandible; n. gen.
    (Waldman, M., Savage, R. J. G.)   1972A
Dolicopithecus
  Restoration
    (Battetta, J.)   1969A
Dolomys
  Pleist.; Italy, Venetia & Corso; teeth;
    statistics; distribution; ecology; n. subsp.
    (Bartolomei, G.)   1970B
Domestic
  Africa; origin; phylogeny
    (Epstein, H.)   1971A
  Evolution
    (Zeuner, F. E.)   1967A
Dryolestidae
  Cret., lower; Spain, Uña; jaws; n. gen.
    (Henkel, S., Krebs, B.)   1969A
  Jaw; dentition
    (Krebs, B.)   1970A
  Jaw, evolution
    (Krebs, B.)   1971A
Dryopithecinae
  Systematics
    (Prasad, K. N.)   1971A
Dryopithecus
  Miocene; France, St. Gaudens; humerus
    (Pilbeam, D., Simons, E. L.)   1971A
  Miocene; India; morphology; systematics
    (Simons, E. L., Pilbeam, D.)   1971A
  Miocene; Kenya; tali
    (Pilbeam, D.)   1969C
  Systematics
    (Eckhardt, R. B.)   1972A
Dryopithecus africanus
  Carpus
    (Lewis, O. J.)   1972A
Echimyidae
  Oligocene; Argentina, Patagonia;
    systematics; morphology; n. taxa
    (Patterson, B., Pascual, R.)   1968B

MAMMALIA - cont.
Elaphurus shikamai
  Pleist.; Japan, Akashi Fm.; antlers;
    systematics
    (Otsuka, H.)   1972A
Elephantidae
  Ceylon
    (Deraniyagala, P. E. P.)   1970A
  Phylogeny; nomenclature; n. subsp.
    (Aguirre, E. E.)   1969B
  Phylogeny; systematics
    (Garutt, V. E.)   1971A
  Phylogeny; systematics; dentition,
    variation
    (Aguirre, E. E.)   1968B
  Pleist.; England, Powderstock; tusk
    (Cope, J. C. W.)   1972A
  Pleist.; Germany, Mosbach; teeth
    (Guenther, E. W.)   1969C
  Pleist.; Italy; endocranial casts
    (Accordi, F. S., Palombo, M. R.)   1971A
  Pleist.; Japan, central; skulls, jaws
    (Chinji, M.)   1971A,B,C,D,E
  Pleist.; USSR, Moldavia
    (David, A. I.)   1964B
  Plio-Pleistocene; Kenya, northwestern;
    morphology; n. taxa
    (Maglio, V. J.)   1970B
  Systematics; nomenclature
    (Aguirre, E. E.)   1969A
  Teeth; biometry; phylogeny
    (Nicolussi, C. M.)   1971A
  Tert.; Africa; evolution
    (Maglio, V. J.)   1970A
Elephas
  Dentition, skeleton
    (Bouchud, J.)   1961D
  Japan
    (Anon.)   1967BV
  Pleist.; France, Bas-Rhin; teeth
    (Théobald, N.)   1970A
  Pleist.; France, Palaminy; jaw
    (Méroc, L.)   1967A
  Pleist.; France Pas-de-Calais; molar
    (Bouchud, J.)   1964B
  Pleist.; France, Praz-Rodet; skeleton,
    skull
    (Weidmann, M.)   1969A, 1970A
  Pleist.; France, Vaulx-en-Velin; teeth
    (Jeannet, M.)   1971A
  Pleist.; Italy, Grotta dei Puntali; skull
    (Piccoli, G., et al.)   1970A
  Pleist.; Rumania; distribution
    (Isă, Gh. I.)   1967A
  Pleist.; Spain, Salamanca; humerus
    (Sos Baynat, V.)   1969A
  Pleist.; Turkey, Çakil Kaya; tusks
    (Erdbrink, D. P.,
      Van Asch, T. W. J.)   1972A
  Pleist.; USSR, Turkmenia; skeleton
    (Fedorovich, B. A.)   1957A
  Skeleton; n. subsp.
    (Ambrosetti, P., et al.)   1972A
  Tooth, microstructure
    (Kobayashi, I.)   1971A
    (Kobayashi, I., Suga, S.)   1971A

MAMMALIA - cont.

Elephas antiquus
Pleist.; Italy, Perugia; skull, teeth
(Bartolomei, G.) 1969B
Elephas meridionalis
Pleist.; Spain, Granada; skulls
(Vidarte, C. F.) 1966A
Elephas primigenius
Pleist., upper; Austria, Eggenburg; dentition
(Adam, K. D.) 1966D
Elephas trogontherii
Pleist.; USSR, Azov; skeleton
(Anon.) 1972AZ
Entelodon
Oligocene; France, Villebramar; skull, teeth
(Brunet, M.) 1972A
Oligocene; Saskatchewan; skull, jaws
(Anon.) 1969BP
Entelodontidae
Miocene, early; Kazakhstan, Sary-Ozek;
n. gen.
(Aubekerova, P. A.) 1969A
Tert., lower; Texas, Trans-Pecos; skull,
teeth, jaws
(Wilson, J. A.) 1971B
Entoptychinae
Miocene; Oregon, John Day Fm.;
morphology; systematics; n. taxa
(Rensberger, J. M.) 1971A
Eomyidae
Miocene; Germany, Weissenburg;
morphology; n. gen.
(Fahlbusch, V.) 1968A
Neogene; France, Lyonnaise;
morphology; n. taxa
(Hugueney, M., Mein, P.) 1969A
Oligocene; Texas, Ash Spring; morphology;
phylogeny; n. gen.
(Harris, J. M., Wood, A. E.) 1969A
Pleist., lower; Hungary, Mt. Osztramos;
skull, jaw; n. gen.
(Jánossy, D.) 1969C
Tert.; Europe; morphology; n. sp.
(Fahlbusch, V.) 1970A
Eotragus
Miocene; France, Artenay; jaw, teeth; n. sp.
(Ginsburg, L., Heintz, E.) 1968A
Epihippus
Eocene; Texas, Presidio Co.; teeth
(Forstén, A.-M.) 1971A
Equidae
Cave art, species represented
(Blanchard, J.) 1964B
Cenozoic; Florida; evolution; morphology
(Waldrop, J.) 1969A
Cenozoic; Siberia
(Kornutova, E. I.) 1968A
Evolution; distribution
(Skorkowski, E.) 1969A
Evolution, Przewalski's horse
(Skorkowski, E.) 1967B
North America
(Haines, F.) 1971A
Phylogeny and ontogeny
(Gabuniia, L. K.) 1968A
Pleist.; East Germany, Süssenborn;
teeth, limbs
(Musil, R.) 1969A

MAMMALIA - cont.

Equidae
Pleist.; Eurasia; phylogeny
(Nobis, G.) 1967A
Pleist.; Ireland, Larne; teeth
(Doughty, P. S.) 1969A
Pleist.; Italy, Vald'Arno;
nomenclature; systematics
(Gromova, V. I.) 1972A
Pleist., lower; Nebraska, Brown Co.;
nomenclature
(Skinner, M. F.) 1972A
Pleist., lower; USSR, northeastern;
skull; restoration
(Lazarev, P. A.) 1971A
Pleist., upper; So. America; holotypes
(Souza Cunha, F. L. de) 1971A
Pleist.; USSR, Tiraspol
(Gromova, V. I., Dubrovo, I. A.) 1969A
Pliocene; Mexico, La Carreta;
morphology; n. taxa
(Mooser, O.) 1968A
Skull, brain; systematics
(Trumler, E.) 1969A
So. Africa, Krugersdorp Caves; teeth, limbs
(Churcher, C. S.) 1970A
Systematics; evolution; n. taxa
(Sondaar, P. Y.) 1969A
Tert., upper; Alberta, Hand Hills;
astragalus
(Atkinson, T.) 1969A
Equoidea
Eocene; Spain, Pyrenees Mts.; jaws,
teeth; n. sp.
(Crusafont Pairó, M., Remy, J. A.) 1970A
Equus
Pleist.; Alberta, Bindloss; tooth, limb
(Churcher, C. S.) 1972B
Pleist.; Alberta, Pashley; feet
(Churcher, C. S., Stalker, A. Mac S.) 1970A
Pleist.; Czechoslovakia, Pekárna Cave;
teeth, variation
(Musil, R.) 1969C
Pleist.; France, Solutré
(Friese, F.) 1971A
Pleist.; Germany, Kärlich; jaws, teeth
(Nobis, G.) 1970A
Pleist.; India, Ariyalur; tooth
(Khan, E.) 1971A
Pleist.; Nebraska, Broadwater; teeth,
metapodials, variation
(Howe, J. A.) 1970A
Pleist.; Rumania; teeth
(Macarovici, N., Semaka, A.) 1969A
Pleist., upper; Germany, Bad
Frankenhausen; dentition
(Teichert, M.) 1971A
Pleist., upper; Germany, Bärenkeller;
teeth, limbs
(Feustel, R., Kerkmann, K.,
Schmid, E., Musil, R., Jacob, H.) 1971A
Pleist.; USSR, Kara Tau Mts.; phalanx
(Kambariddinov, R. K.) 1969A
Equus abeli
Pleist.; Greece, megalopolis;
morphology
(Melentis, J. K.) 1966J

MAMMALIA - cont.
Equus caballus gallicus
  Pleist.; France, Solutré; systematics
    (Prat, F.)   1969A
Equus francisci
  Morphology; nomenclature
    (Lundelius, E. L., Stevens, M. S.)   1970A
Eremotherium
  Pleist.; Brazil; tooth, rib, vertebra
    (Moreira, L. E.,
      Gomes de Melo, S. M.)   1971A
  Pleist.; Georgia, Brunswick; skeletons
    (Voorhies, M.)   1972A
Erethizon
  Pleist.; United States; distribution
    (Ray, C. E., Lipps, L.)   1970A
Erethizontidae
  Cenozoic, upper; No. America; skull,
  teeth; n. sp.
    (White, J. A.)   1970A
Erinaceidae
  Tert.; Europe; dentition
    (Friant, M.)   1971C
Esthonychinae
  Eocene, lower; Wyoming, Bighorn Basin;
  systematics; mandible, teeth; n. gen.
    (Rose, K. D.)   1972A
Estramomys
  Pleist.; Hungary, Osztramos; teeth
    (Jánossy, D.)   1970B
Eucosmodontidae
  Eocene; England, Abbey Wood; n. gen.
    (Kühne, W. G.)   1969A
Euctenoceros
  Pleist.; France, southeast; n. sp.
    (Bonifay, M.-F.)   1968C
Eumegamys
  Pliocene; Venezuela, Campo El Mamon;
  jaw, teeth
    (Pascual, R.,
      Díaz de Gamero, M. L.)   1969A
Eumys exiguus
  Systematics
    (Dawson, M. R., Black, C. C.)   1970A
Euryboas
  Pleist.; Italy, Olivola; jaw
    (Ficcarelli, G., Torre, D.)   1967B
Eurymylidae
  Paleocene; Mongolia, Naran Bulak;
  jaws, teeth; phylogeny; n. order
    (Sych, L.)   1971A
Eutheria
  Cret.; Alberta, Edmonton Fm.; teeth,
  jaws; phylogeny; evolution; n. sp.
    (Lillegraven, J. A.)   1969B
  Cret.; Alberta; tooth
    (Fox, R. C.)   1970A
  Evolution; biogeography
    (Hoffstetter, R.)   1970A
  Tribosphenic molar; origin
    (Quinet, G. E.)   1966D, 1967A
Evolution
  Climatic correlation
    (Binge, H. G.)   1964A
  Dental enamel
    (Moss, M. L.)   1969A
  Dentition
    (Friant, M.)   1965C

MAMMALIA - cont.
Evolution
  Half-life concept
    (Kurtén, B.)   1972C
  Ontogenetic types
    (Müller, F.)   1968B
  Rates
    (Mezhzherin, V. A.)   1969A
  Social behavior; population density
    (Christian, J. J.)   1970A
  South America
    (Patterson, B., Pascual, R.)   1968A
  Southern continents
    (Keast, A.)   1972B
    (Keast, A., Erk, F. C., Glass, B.)   1972A
Felidae
  Miocene; Spain, Piera; skull, teeth; n. taxa
    (Crusafont-Pairó, M., Aguirre, E.)   1972A
  Oligocene; No. America; anatomical study
    (Brunet, M.)   1967A
  Pleist., lower; Nebraska, Broadwater,
  Lisco; morphology; n. sp.
    (Schultz, C. B., Martin, L. D.)   1970A
  Pleist.; Missouri, Perry Co.; skull, jaw
    (Oesch, R. D.)   1969B
  Pleist.; Pennsylvania, Bone Cave; jaw
    (Anon.)   1971AC
Felis
  Pleist.; France, La Chaise; tooth
    (Suire, C.)   1968A
Felis leo
  Pleist.; Spain, Oñate-Guipúzcoa;
  Arrikrutz Cave; skeleton
    (Altuna, J.)   1967A
Felis spelaea
  Pleist.; France; dentition
    (Suire, C.)   1970A
  Pleist., middle; USSR, Vishnia R.; jaw,
  teeth; paleoecology
    (Tatarinov, K. A.)   1969A
Gargantuodon
  Miocene; France, Pontigné; teeth; n. gen.
    (Ginsburg, L.)   1969A
Gazella
  Horns; sexual dimorphism; phylogeny
    (Heintz, E.)   1969C
  Neogene; Mongolia, western
    (Dmitrieva, E. L.)   1971B
  Nomenclature
    (Heintz, E.)   1971A
  Pleist.; France; stratigraphic occurrence
    (Heintz, E.)   1969A
  Pliocene; France, Mont Lubéron; dentition,
  skull, horn cores, variation; teeth,
  biometry
    (Heintz, E.)   1971B
  Pliocene; Greece, Pikermi; braincast
    (Melentis, J. K.)   1966O
  Pliocene; Turkey, Sinap; horn core
    (Tekkaya, I.)   1970A
  Pliocene; USSR, Kazakhstan; teeth,
  limbs; evolution
    (Dmitrieva, E. L.)   1969A
  Systematics
    (Dmitrieva, E. L.)   1970A
  Systematics; phylogeny
    (Dmitrieva, E. L.)   1971A

MAMMALIA - cont.
Heterocricetodon
Oligocene; Hungary; n. sp.
  (Jámbor, A., et al.)   1971A
Hipparion
Evolution
  (Macarovici, N., Jeanrenaud, P.)   1968A
Miocene, middle; France, Vaucluse,
Vaison-la-Romaine; teeth
  (Guérin, C., et al.)   1972A
Miocene; USSR, Chimishliia; skull,
teeth, skeleton; n. sp.
  (Tarabukin, B. A.)   1968B
Miocene, upper; USSR, Nikolaev Prov.,
Starokondakovo; systematics; teeth, limbs
  (Korotkevich, O. L.)   1971C
Neogene; Mongolia; evolution;
distribution; n. sp.
  (Zhegallo, V. I.)   1971A
Neogene; Rumania; morphology; n. sp.
  (Macarovici, N.)   1967A
Pleist.; Europe
  (Koenigswald, G. H. R. von)   1970B
Pleist.; Europe; systematics; distribution
  (Koenigswald, G. H.)   1972A
Pliocene; Asia; morphology; systematics
  (Hussain, S. T.)   1971A,B
Pliocene; Greece, Samos Is.; skulls, limbs
  (Sondaar, P. Y.)   1971A
Pliocene; Rumania, Derşida; teeth
  (Macarovici, N., Jurcsák, T.)   1968A
Pliocene; Spain, Layna; morphology; n. sp.
  (Crusafont Pairó, M., Sondaar, P.)   1971A
Pliocene, upper; Kvabebi; skull, jaws, teeth
  (Vekua, A. K.)   1967A
Tert.; Bulgaria; skulls, dentition; n. sp.
  (Nikolov, Iv.)   1971A
Tert.; India, Siwaliks; distribution
  (Simons, E. L., Pilbeam, D.,
    Boyer, S. J.)   1971A
Hipparion primigenium
Miocene, upper; Tunisia, Bled Douarah;
dentition; feet
  (Forsten, A.-M.)   1972A
Hippopotamidae
Pleist.; Cyprus
  (Steele, N.)   1972A
Hippopotamus
Pleist.; Spain, Banyoles
  (Bech Borrás, J.)   1970A
Variation; evolution
  (Coryndon, S. C.)   1970A
Hippopotamus amphibius
Pleist., lower; Germany, Oberrhein; jaw
frag., teeth
  (Adam, K. D.)   1965C
Holoclemensia
Nomenclature
  (Slaughter, B. H.)   1968D
Hominoidea
Behavior, evolution
  (Washburn, S. L., Harding, R. S.)   1972A
Cenozoic, upper; East Africa; evolution
  (Bishop, W. W.)   1971A
Dentition, evolution
  (Pilbeam, D.)   1972C

MAMMALIA - cont.
Hominoidea
Foot bones
  (Oxnard, C. E.)   1972A
Hallucial tarsometatarsal joint, evolution
  (Lewis, O. J.)   1972B
Jaw
  (Anon.)   1971AV
Miocene; forelimb
  (Morbeck, M. E.)   1972A
Morphology; systematics
  (Simons, E. L., Pilbeam, D. R.)   1972A
Phylogeny; divergence dates
  (Read, D. W., Lestrel, P.)   1972A
Homotherium
Pleist.; France, Senèze; morphology
  (Ballesio, R.)   1964A
Pleist., lower; Germany, Wiesbaden;
metacarpal
  (Schütt, G.)   1970A
Hyaena
Pliocene; Greece, Samos Is.; dentition, jaw
  (Beaumont, G. de)   1968B
Pliocene; Greece, Samos Is.; dentition,
skull
  (Beaumont, G. de)   1969A
Hyaenidae
Cenozoic; systematics; phylogeny
  (Ficarelli, G., Torre, D.)   1970A
Pliocene; Spain, Layna; teeth
  (Crusafont, M., Aguirre, E.)   1971A
Skulls, vertebrae
  (Buckland-Wright, J. C.)   1969A
Hyaenodon
Origin
  (Lange-Badré, B.)   1972A
Hyaenodontidae
Oligocene; Saskatchewan; morphology
  (Russell, L. S.)   1972B
Hydrodamalis
Pleist.; Alaska, Amchitka Is.; skeleton
  (Gard, L. M., Lewis, G. E.,
    Whitmore, F. C.)   1972A
Pliocene; Japan; rib
  (Shikama, T.)   1971A
Pliocene; Japan; rib
  (Shikama, T., Domning, D.)   1970A
Hydrodamalis gigas
Extinction
  (Domning, D. P.)   1972B
Hylobates
Systematics
  (Groves, C. P.)   1969A
Hylobatinae
Phylogeny
  (Koenigswald, G. H. R. von)   1968C
Hypolagus
Miocene; Calif., Barstow Fm.; jaw
  (Lindsay, E. H.)   1972B
Hypselephas
Pleist.; India, Tirunelveli; skull
  (Prasad, K. N., Daniel, J. A.)   1968A
Hypsohipparion
Pleist.; Rumania, Bureşti; tooth;
nomenclature
  (Ivan'ev, L. N.)   1971A

MAMMALIA - cont.

Kenyapithecus
Pliocene; Kenya, Ft. Ternan
(Leakey, L. S. B.) 1971E,F
Systematics
(Greenfield, L. O.) 1971A
(Leakey, L. S. B.) 1971A

Kenyapithecus africanus
Jaw
(Zwell, M.) 1972A

Kopidodon
Eocene; Germany, Messel; skull, jaw, teeth
(Tobien, H.) 1969A

Kryptobaatar
Prepubic bone
(Kielan-Jaworowska, Z.) 1969B

Kyzylkakhippus
Systematics
(Thenius, E.) 1968A

Labidolemur
Paleocene; Wyoming, Bison Basin;
jaw, teeth; n. sp.
(West, R. M.) 1972A

Lagomeryx
Miocene, upper; USSR, Moldavia;
systematics; evolution; n. sp.
(Lungu, A. N.) 1972A

Lagomorpha
Miocene; France, La Romieu; teeth
(Baudelot, S.) 1969A
Miocene, lower; Germany, Mainz Basin;
evolution
(Tobien, H.) 1970C
Miocene; Portugal, Lisbon; teeth
(Janvier, Ph.) 1971C
Miocene; So. Dakota, Black Bear Quarry II;
morphology; paleoecology; n. gen.
(Green, M.) 1972A
Miocene; Texas, Big Bend; morphology; n. sp.
(Stevens, M. S., Stevens, J. B.,
Dawson, M. R.) 1969A
Morphology; systematics
(Wood, A. E.) 1971A
Pleist.; Alaska, Cape Deceit;
dentition; n. sp.
(Guthrie, R. D., Matthews, J. V.) 1971A
Pleist.; Italy, Villafranca d'Asti;
jaws, teeth; n. sp.
(Berzi, A.) 1970A
Pleist.; Siberia, Selenga R.; morphology;
systematics; evolution
(Erbaeva, M. A.) 1970A
Pliocene; Greece, Isle of Rhodes;
morphology; n. sp.
(Bruijn, H. de, Dawson, M. R.,
Mein, P.) 1970A
Pliocene; limbs, comparison
(Campbell, K. E.) 1969A
Pliocene; Oregon, southeastern; morphology
(Shotwell, J. A.) 1970A

Lagurus
Pleist.; Rumania; morphology;
distribution; phylogeny
(Terzea, E.) 1968A

Lagurus lagurus
Pleist., upper; Siberia, Tura R.; teeth
(Maleeva, A. G., Vorob'eva, T. D.) 1970A

MAMMALIA - cont.

Lemmus
Pleist.; Rumania, Betfia; teeth
(Terzea, E.) 1972A

Lemuroidea
Evolution
(Charles-Dominique, P.,
Martin, R. D.) 1970A

Leontinia
Oligocene; Brazil, São Paulo; ecology;
skull frag.
(Paula Couto, C. de,
Mezzalira, S.) 1971A

Leporidae
Miocene; Spain, La Alberca; teeth;
n. gen.
(Janvier, P., Montenat, C.) 1970A
Oligocene; Saskatchewan; morphology
(Russell, L. S.) 1972B
Pleist.; Arizona, San Pedro V.; teeth; n. sp.
(Downey, J. S.) 1970A
Pleist.; Java, Sangiran; teeth
(Dawson, M. R.) 1971A
Pleist.; Nebraska, Brown Co.;
jaw, teeth
(Hibbard, C. W.) 1972A
Pliocene; Arizona, Benson; teeth; n. gen.
(Downey, J. S.) 1968A
Pliocene; Idaho, Hagerman; skulls, teeth
(Hibbard, C. W.) 1969A

Leptictidae
Oligocene; Saskatchewan; morphology
(Russell, L. S.) 1972B

Leptictis acutidens
Dentition, deciduous
(West, R. M.) 1972D

Leptictoidea
Cret.; Mongolia, Bayn Dzak;
Mongolia; n. gen.
(Kielan-Jaworowska, Z.) 1968B

Leptomeryx
Population dynamics
(Clark, J., Guensburg, T. E.) 1970A

Lepus
Pleist.; Spain, Aitzbitarte; jaw, teeth
(Altuna, J.) 1970A
Pleist.; Spain, Urtiaga; teeth
(Altuna, J.) 1970B

Litopterna
Dentition
(Friant, M.) 1967B

Lophiodon
Dentition, variation
(Sudre, J.) 1971A

Lophiomeryx
Oligocene; China; morphology
(Chiu, Cs.) 1965A

Lorisidae
Miocene, early; East Africa;
skeleton; phylogeny
(Walker, A.) 1970A

Lutra
Pleist.; Japan, Ojika-do; jaw
(Hasegawa, Y.) 1964C

Lutrinae
Endocranial casts; brain evolution
(Radinsky, L. B.) 1968A

MAMMALIA - cont.
Marsupialia
Cret.; Mexico, Baja California;
morphology
(Lillegraven, J. A.)   1972B
Distribution
(Jardine, N., McKenzie, D.)   1972A
Evolution, rates; divergence from Eutheria
(Air, G. M., et al.)   1971A
Oligocene; Germany, Hessen; teeth
(Tobien, H.)   1971A
Origin; dispersal
(Tedford, R. H.)   1971A
Paleocene; Brazil, São José de Itaboraí;
morphology; n. taxa
(Paula Couto, C. de)   1970A
Pliocene; Australia, Grange Burn;
morphology; n. taxa
(Turnbull, W. D., Lundelius, E. L.)   1970A
So. America; evolution
(Simpson, G. G.)   1971F
Systematics
(Stirton, R. A.)   1965C
Martes
Evolution
(Anderson, E.)   1970A
Mastodon
Miocene; Yugoslavia, Bosnia; teeth
(Soklić, I., Malez, M.)   1969A
Neogene; USSR, Aruktau Ridge
(Burachek, A. R.,
Chikhachev, P. K.)   1959A
Mastodontidae
Miocene, upper; Germany, Reisensburg;
skeleton
(Wellnhofer, P.)   1969A
Maurimontia
Eocene; Europe; morphology; systematics
(Friant, M.)   1968A
Megaceros kinryuensis
Pleist.; Japan; jaw
(Onodera, S.)   1970B
Megaloceros giganteus
Distribution; habitat
(Møhl, U.)   1972A
Reconstructions
(Van Bemmel, A. C. U.)   1971A
Megalocnus
Pleist.; Cuba, Vaho Cave; skull; n. sp.
(Mayo, N. A.)   1969A
Megalonychidae
Distribution; phylogeny
(Hirschfeld, S. E.)   1969A
Pleist.; Cuba, Pio-Domingo; skull; skeleton
(Fischer, K.)   1971A
Megalonyx
Pleist.; Minnesota, Ramsey Co.; phalanx
(Erickson, B. R.)   1968A
Pleist.; Virginia, Lane Cave; skeleton
(Holsinger, J. R.)   1967A
Pliocene; Oregon, southeastern; morphology
(Shotwell, J. A.)   1970A
Megalonyx jeffersoni
Pleist.; Tennessee, Big Bone Cave; skull,
skeleton
(Barr, T. C.)   1957A

MAMMALIA - cont.
Megantereon
Pleist.; So. Africa, Makapansgat; skull,
jaw; n. sp.
(Collings, G. E.)   1972A
Meles
Pleist.; France, Clain R.; humerus
(Beden, M.)   1970A
Meliakrouniomys
Oligocene; Wyoming, Natrona Co.;
skull, jaws; n. sp.
(Emry, R. J.)   1972A
Menoceras
Miocene, middle; Nebraska, Morrill Co.,
Bridgeport; skull; n. sp.
(Tanner, L. G.)   1972A
Miocene; Nebraska, Hemingford; skull;
phylogeny; n. sp.
(Tanner, L. G.)   1969A
Merychyus
Miocene; Nebraska, Running Water Fm.;
skull, skeleton; n. sp.
(Stevens, M. S.)   1970A
Merycoidodontidae
Morphology; evolution
(Friant, M.)   1969B
Oligocene; Arizona, central; morphology
(Lindsay, E. H., Lundin, R. F.)   1972A
Temporal fossae
(Greaves, W. S.)   1972A
Tert., lower; Texas, Trans-Pecos; morphology;
statistical study; n. sp.
(Wilson, J. A.)   1971A
Mesatirhinus
Eocene; Utah, Green R. Fm.; skeleton
(Parker, L. R.)   1970A
Mesocetus
Miocene; Poland, Pińczów; skull frag.
(Ryziewicz, Z.)   1969A
Mesohippus
Oligocene; So. Dakota, Big Badlands;
teeth
(Forstén, A.-M.)   1970C
Oligocene; Texas, Presidio Co.; jaws,
teeth; n. sp.
(McGrew, P. O.)   1971A
Teeth, variation
(Forstén, A.-M.)   1971B
Mesohippus bairdii
Oligocene; So. Dakota, Big Badlands;
teeth, variation
(Forstén, A.-M.)   1970A
Mesonychidae
Morphology; phylogeny
(Szalay, F. S.)   1969A
Paleocene; Mongolia, Gashato; morphology
(Szalay, F. S., McKenna, M. C.)   1971A
Mesozoic
Evolution
(Clemens, W. A.)   1970A, 1971A
(Gabuniia, L. K.)   1966D
General
(Kermack, D. M., Kermack, K. A.)   1971A
Systematics; n. taxa
(Turnbull, W. D.)   1971A

MAMMALIA - cont.
  Multituberculata
    Oligocene; Wyoming, Jackson Hole; tooth
      (Sutton, J. F.)   1972A
    Skull; phylogeny
      (Kielan-Jaworowska, Z.)   1971A
    Variation
      (Fox, R. C.)   1968D
  Muridae
    Neogene; Europe, southwest; evolution
      (Michaux, J.)   1971A
    Pleist.; Canary Is.; skull, teeth; n. gen.
      (Crusafont Pairó, M., Petter, F.)   1964A
    Pleist., upper; Australia, Broom Cave;
      dentition, variation
      (Schram, F. R., Turnbull, W. D.)   1970A
    Pliocene; Spain, France; morphology;
      n. taxa
      (Michaux, J.)   1969B
    So. America; evolution
      (Hershkovitz, P.)   1962A
  Muroidea
    Systematics; origin
      (Dieterlen, F.)   1969A
  Mustela
    Pleist., upper; Germany, Meitze; skull;
      paleoclimatology
      (Sickenberg, O.)   1968B
    Systematics; morphology
      (Anderson, E.)   1972A
  Mustelidae
    Miocene; France; morphology;
      systematics; n. taxa
      (Ginsburg, L.)   1968C
    Pliocene; Spain, Teruel; dentition
      (Adrover, R.)   1966B
    Systematics; evolution
      (Sokolov, I. I.)   1968A
  Mustelinae
    Oligocene; France, Quercy; skull,
      teeth; n. gen.
      (Lange, B.)   1969A, 1970A
  Mylagaulidae
    Miocene; USSR, Zaĭsan basin;
      teeth; n. gen.
      (Shevyreva, N. S.)   1971B
  Mylodon
    Distribution
      (Quaintance, C. W.)   1969A
  Mylodontidae
    Pleist.; Nebraska, Brown Co.; metacarpal
      (Hibbard, C. W.)   1972A
  Myotis
    Pleist.; Spain, Aitzbitarte; jaw, skeletal frags.
      (Altuna, J.)   1970A
  Myotragus
    Pleist.; Spain, Mallorca; Genova Cave;
      skull frags.; jaw; variation
      (Adrover, R.)   1967A
    Pleist.; Spain, Mallorca; skeleton
      (Waldren, W., Kopper, J. S.)   1968A
    Pleist.; Spain, Menorca; distribution
      (Mercadal, B.)   1967A
    Pleist., upper; Spain, Baleares; dentition
      (Adrover, R., Cuerda Barceló, J.)   1969B

MAMMALIA - cont.
  Myotragus
    Pleist., upper; Spain, Mallorca, Es Bufador
      Cave; dentition
      (Adrover, R., Cuerda Barceló, J.)   1969A
    Teeth
      (Merrilees, D.)   1971A
  Myotragus balearicus
    Pleist.; Spain, Mallorca; Can Sion Cave;
      skeleton; biometry
      (Adrover, R., Angel, B.)   1967A
  Mytonolagus
    Eocene, upper; Wyoming, Badwater
      Creek; teeth
      (Dawson, M. R.)   1970A
  Nanomys
    Oligocene; Wyoming, Natrona Co.;
      jaw; n. gen.
      (Emry, R. J., Dawson, M. R.)   1972A
  Nebraskomys
    Pliocene; Kansas, Meade Co.; teeth; n. sp.
      (Hibbard, C. W.)   1970B
  Neohipparion
    Pliocene; Montana, Flaxville Gravels; teeth
      (Storer, J. E.)   1969A
  Neophoca
    Pleist.; Australia, Melbourne
      (Gill, E. D.)   1968B
  Nesophontes
    Dentition
      (Gould, S. J., Garwood, R. A.)   1969A
  Niptomomys doreenae
    Dentition
      (Bown, T. M., Gingerich, P. D.)   1972A
  Notharctus
    Eocene; No. America; morphology
      (Robinson, P.)   1957C
  Nothrotheriinae
    Pleist.; Brazil, São Paulo; phylogeny
      (Paula Couto, C. de)   1971A
  Nyanzachoerus
    Pleist.; Tunisia, Hamada Damous; jaw,
      teeth; n. sp.
      (Coppens, Y.)   1971A
  Nyctalus
    Pleist.; France, Nice; tooth
      (Jullien, R., Pillard, B.)   1969B
  Nyctereutes
    Pleist.; France, Saint-Vallier; morphology
      (Martin, R.)   1971A
  Nyctitheriidae
    Eocene; Wyoming, Bridger Fm.;
      systematics; morphology
      (Robinson, P.)   1968C
  Ochotona
    Pleist.; Europe, southwest; distribution
      (Malez, M.)   1969B
    Pleist.; Yugoslavia, northern; jaws, teeth
      (Malez, M.)   1968C
  Ochotonidae
    Miocene; Switzerland, Anwil; morphology;
      systematics
      (Engesser, B.)   1972A
    Miocene, upper; Saskatchewan, southern;
      teeth; n. taxa
      (Storer, J. E.)   1970A

MAMMALIA - cont.

Ochotonoides
Pleist.; USSR, Georgia; jaw, teeth; n. sp.
(Vekua, A. K.) 1967B

Odobenia
Plio-Pleistocene; Netherlands, Scheldt R.;
skull
(Van der Feen, P. J.) 1968A

Odobenus
Pleist.; Virginia, Chincoteague; jaw, teeth
(Manville, R. H., Wilson, J. J.) 1970A
Skull; phylogeny
(Kaiser, H. E.) 1970A

Ondatra
Dentition; paleoecology
(Nelson, R. S., Semken, H. A.) 1969A
Pleist.; So. Dakota
(Harksen, J. C.) 1968A
Pleist.; U.S.; biogeography; teeth
(Nelson, R. S., Semken, H. A.) 1970A

Oreamnos
Pleist.; British Columbia, Quesnel Forks;
skull frag.; dispersal
(Harington, C. R.) 1971B

Oreopithecoidea
Miocene; East Africa; n. gen.
(Koenigswald, G. H. R. von) 1969A

Oreopithecus
Morphology; phylogeny
(Ozaki, H., Obata, I.) 1963B

Orthogonoceros
Pleist.; Greece, Haliakmon; skull, antlers
(Melentis, J. K.) 1967C

Orycteropus
Pliocene; Greece, Samos Is.; auditory region,
teeth
(Beaumont, G. de) 1970B

Oryctolagus
Pleist.; France, Nice; skull, skeleton
(Jullien, R., Pillard, B.) 1969A

Otariidae
Evolution
(Lipps, J. H.) 1969A
New Zealand
(Fleming, C. A.) 1968A

Ovibos
Pleist.; Alaska, Nome; skull frag.
(Harington, C. R.) 1970A
Pleist.; East Germany, Süssenborn;
skull, teeth
(Kahlke, H.-D.) 1969B
Pleist.; Germany, Rheinland; horn core
(Lehmann, E. von) 1968A
Pleist.; Illinois; morphology
(Ray, C. E., Wills, D. L.,
Palmquist, J. C.) 1968A
Pleist.; Manitoba, Grandview; skull frag.;
biogeography
(Harington, C. R.) 1970B
Pleist., middle; USSR, Moscow; skull
(Sukachev, V. N.,
Sokolovskaia, V. T.) 1965A, 1966A
Pleist.; Northwest Territories, Banks Is.;
Metacarpal
(Maher, W. J.) 1966A

MAMMALIA - cont.

Ovis
Pleist.; U.S., Great Basin; phylogeny
(Stock, A. D., Stokes, W. L.) 1969A

Pachynolophus
Paleogene; France, Quercy; systematics,
phylogeny, evolution; skull,
dentition; n. sp.
(Remy, J.-A.) 1972A

Paciculus
Miocene, lower; Nebraska; teeth; n. sp.
(Alker, J.) 1969A

Paenungulata
Paleogene; Africa, northern; systematics;
phylogeny
(Tobien, H.) 1971C

Palaeoamasia
Eocene; Turkey, Boyabat; jaw, teeth
(Ozansoy, F.) 1969A

Palaeoloxodon
Limbs
(Beden, M.) 1969A
Pleist.; East Germany, Orlishausen; skeleton
(Kahlke, H.-D.) 1971A
Pleist.; Japan, Hamamatsu
(Kobayashi, K.) 1963B
Pleist.; Japan, Shodoshima Is.; skull, skeleton
(Hasegawa, Y.) 1972A
Pleist.; Japan, Shodo-shima; morphology
(Ozaki, H., Hasegawa, Y.) 1969A
Pleist.; Japan, Tokyo; jaws, teeth, humerus
(Shikama, T., Kanno, S.) 1970A
Pleist.; Japan, Yokosuka; scapula, humerus
(Hasegawa, Y., Kanie, Y.) 1971A
Pleist.; Poland, Sokolka; jaw, teeth
(Ruprecht, A. L.) 1971A
Pleist.; Poland, Warsaw; skeleton
(Jakubowski, G., Krysiak, K.,
Roskosz, T.) 1968A
Pleist.; Spain, Jarama; teeth, humerus
(Pérez González, A., Fuentes
Vidarte, C., Aguirre, E.) 1970A
Pleist., upper; Siberia, Irkutsk Prov.; tooth
(Ivan'ev, L. N.) 1969A

Palaeopropithecus
Habits
(Mahé, J.) 1968A

Palaeosyops
Eocene; Wyoming, Emblem; teeth
(Guthrie, D. A.) 1971A

Palaeotherium
Systematics; morphology; n. taxa
(Franzen, J. L.) 1968A

Palaeotraginae
Neogene; USSR, Kazakhstan &
Kirgizia; morphology
(Godina, A. Ia.) 1971A
Pleist., lower; Greece, Volaks; skull,
skeleton; n. gen.
(Sickenberg, O.) 1967A

Palaeotragus
Miocene; East Africa; jaw; reconstruction
(Churcher, C. S.) 1972A
Neogene; Mongolia, western; distribution;
systematics; evolution
(Godina, A. Ia.) 1971B

MAMMALIA - cont.
Paleoparadoxia
  Morphology
    (Zuidema, H. P.) 1970B
  Morphology; paleoecology; reconstruction
    (Zuidema, H. P.) 1970A
  Skeleton
    (Anon.) 1965CX
Panochthini
  Pleist., upper; Brazil, northeastern;
    systematics; caudal tubes, variation; n. gen.
    (Moreira, L. E.) 1971A
Panthera
  Dentition
    (Schütt, G.) 1969A
  Pleist.; Czechoslovakia, Brno; jaws,
    teeth; distribution
    (Thenius, E.) 1969B
  Pleist.; Europe, central; jaws
    (Hemmer, H.) 1971A
  Pleist.; Europe; systematics; dentition,
    skull; variation; biometry; phylogeny
    (Hemmer, H.) 1971C
  Pleist.; France, L'Escale & Lunel-Viel;
    systematics
    (Hemmer, H.) 1972A
  Pleist.; Germany, Mauer an der Elsenz;
    jaw teeth; n. subsp.
    (Schütt, G.) 1969B
  Pleist.; Italy, Tuscany; skull, teeth
    (Ficcarelli, G., Torre, D.) 1968A
  Pleist.; Java; jaws, teeth
    (Hemmer, H.) 1971B
  Pleist.; Tennessee; skull, skeleton
    (Guilday, J. E.) 1961F
  Systematics
    (Hemmer, H., Schütt, G.) 1970A
Panthera atrox
  Pleist.; Alberta; skull frag.
    (Harington, C. R.) 1971A
  Pleist.; Yukon Territory; skull, limb
    (Harington, C. R.) 1969A
Panthera gombaszoegensis
  Pleist.; Germany, Mosbach Sands; jaw
    (Hemmer, H., Schütt, G.) 1969A
Panthera onca
  Pleist.; Tennessee, Big Bone Cave; skeleton
    (Guilday, J. E., McGinnes, H.) 1972A
Panthera pardus
  Pleist.; Yugoslavia, Vjetrenica Cave; skeleton
    (Malez, M., Pepeonik, Z.) 1969A
Panthera spelaea
  Morphology; phylogeny; distribution;
    habits; nomenclature
    (Vereshchagin, N. K.) 1971B
  Pleist.; Yugoslavia, Lesno brdo; teeth
    (Rakovec, I.) 1969A
Pantolestidae
  Eocene; France, Bouxwiller; jaws,
    teeth; n. gen.
    (Jaeger, J.-J.) 1970B
Pantotheria
  Jurassic; Portugal, Guimarota; jaws
    (Krebs, B.) 1969B
  Jurassic; Portugal, Porto Pinheiro; tooth
    (Krusat, G.) 1969A

MAMMALIA - cont.
Paraentelodon
  Oligocene; Bulgaria, Razlog; tooth
    (Nikolov, Iv., Velichkov, V.) 1969A
Paraethomys
  Pleist.; France, Philippeville; jaw,
    teeth; n. gen.
    (Petter, F.) 1968A
Paraleporillus
  Pleist.; Australia, Wellington Caves;
    skull, jaw; n. gen.
    (Martinez R., C., Lidicker, W. Z.) 1971A
Paramys
  Paleocene; Belgium, Dormaal; systematics;
    n. sp.
    (Quinet, G. E.) 1969B
Paramys wyomingensis
  Nomenclature
    (West, R. M.) 1969A
Parapapio
  Pleist.; Angola, Leba; skull
    (Minkoff, E. C.) 1972A
  Pleist.; So. Africa, Sterkfontein; dentition
    (Freedman, L., Stenhouse, N. S.) 1972A
  Pleist.; So. Africa, Taung; skull
    (Maier, W.) 1971A
Paraphenacodus
  Eocene; USSR, Zaĭsan Basin; tooth;
    n. gen.
    (Gabuniia, L. K.) 1971A
Pararhizomys
  Pliocene; Mongolia, Altan Teli; skull,
    jaws; systematics
    (Kowalski, K.) 1968A
Parastrepsiceros
  Pliocene; USSR, Georgia; skull,
    teeth, limbs
    (Vekua, A. K.) 1970A
Parelephas
  Pleist.; East Germany; Süssenborn;
    teeth, variation
    (Guenther, E. W.) 1969A
Parendotherium
  Cret.; Spain, Galve; tooth;
    systematics; n. gen.
    (Crusafont Pairó, M.,
      Adrover, R.) 1965A, 1966A
Pareumys
  Eocene; Utah, Uintah Co.; jaw,
    teeth; n. sp.
    (Black, C. C.) 1970A
Parictis
  Oligocene; United States; systematics;
    dentition, skull; n. sp.
    (Clark, J., Guensburg, T. E.) 1972A
Paromomyidae
  Paleocene, middle; New Mexico,
    San Juan Co.; mandible, teeth; n. sp.
    (Wilson, R. W., Szalay, F. S.) 1972A
Paschatherium
  Paleocene; Belgium, Dormaal;
    systematics; n. sp.
    (Quinet, G. E.) 1969B
Patriocetus
  Oligocene; Japan, Kita-kyushu; vertebra
    (Hasegawa, Y., Hojo, Y.) 1965A

MAMMALIA - cont.
Pinnepedia
Polygony, evolution
(Bartholomew, G. A.)   1970A
Pitymys
Pleist.; Malta, Ghar Dalam Cave;
teeth, skeleton
(Malec, F., Storch, G.)   1970A
Platybelodon
Miocene; Kenya, northwestern; tooth
(Maglio, V. J.)   1969A
Miocene; Mongolia, western, Oshi;
teeth; n. sp.
(Alekseeva, L. I.)   1971A
Platychaerops
Evolution
(Gingerich, P. D.)   1972A
Platygonus
Pleist.; Colorado; morphology
(Lewis, G. E.)   1970A
Pleist.; Mexico, Valsequillo; jaw, teeth
(Thenius, E.)   1970C
Pleist.; Pennsylvania, Mosherville; skeleton
(Ray, C. E., Denny, C. S., Rubin, M.) 1970A
Platyrhini
Morphology; distribution; n. taxa
(Hershkovitz, P.)   1970B
Plesiadapis
Evolution
(Gingerich, P. D.)   1972A
Skull, reconstruction
(Gingerich, P. D.)   1971A
(Szalay, F. S.)   1971A
Plesiarctomys
Eocene; Europe; skull frags., jaws   .
(Wood, A. E.)   1970B
Plesiogale
Skulls, endocranial cast
(Beaumont, G. de)   1968C
Plesiogulo
Systematics; phylogeny; n. sp.
(Kurtén, B.)   1970A
Pliocervus
Pliocene; Greece, Attika; antlers
(Melentis, J. K.)   1969A
Pliohippus
Pliocene; Calif., Los Angeles; teeth
(Mount, J. D.)   1970A
Pliohyrax
Pleist.; Greece, Pikermi & Halmyropotamos;
morphology; systematics
(Melentis, J. K.)   1966L
Pliometanastes
Pliocene; Calif., Knight's Ferry;
skull, skeleton
(Anon.)   1972AN
(Moore, W.)   1972A
Pliomys
Pleist.; Spain, Lezetxiki Cave; dentition;
distribution
(Chaline, J.)   1970A
Pliophenacomys
Pleist.; Kansas, Fox Canyon; jaw,
palate; n. sp.
(Hibbard, C. W.,
Zakrzewski, R. J.)   1972A

MAMMALIA - cont.
Plioviverrops
Pliocene; Greece, Samos Is.; skull,
teeth; systematics
(Beaumont, G. de)   1969B, 1970A
Polymorphinae
Systematics; morphology
(Rivas, O. E. O.)   1969A
Pongidae
Dentition, evolution
(Skaryd, S. M.)   1971A,B
Habits, hand use
(Kortlandt, A.)   1968A
Miocene; Kenya; Rusinga Is.; Songhor
(Andrews, P.)   1970A
Pleist.; Uganda, Lake Edward; incisor
(Bartheld, F. v., Erdbrink, D. P.,
Krommenhoek, W.)   1970A,B
Spain
(Crusafont Pairó, M., Hürzeler, J.) 1969A
Tert.; East Africa; systematics; habits
(Pilbeam, D. R.)   1968C, 1969A
Pongo pygmaeus
Dentition, biometry
(Marcus, L. F.)   1969A
Pontolis
Tert.; Oregon, Fossil Point; jaw
(Shotwell, J. A.)   1951A
Postpalerinaceus
Pleist.; Spain, Puebla de Valverde;
jaw, teeth
(Crochet, J. Y., Heintz, E.)   1970A
Potamotherium
Miocene, middle; Switzerland, Elgg;
mandible, teeth; reconstruction
(Hünermann, K. A.)   1971B
Praemegaceros
Pleist.; Germany, Kärlich/Neuwieder
Basin; horn cores; stratigraphic
importance
(Rothausen, K.)   1970B
Primates
Adaptations
(Jay, P. C.)   1968A
Adaptive radiation, New World
(Erikson, G. E.)   1962A
Brain evolution
(Hofer, H. O.)   1969B
(Radinsky, L.)   1972B
Cenozoic; Germany, Württemberg,
Ehrenstein; teeth; evolution;
taxonomy; n. sp.
(Schmidt-Kittler, N.)   1971B
Chins; restorations
(Hershkovitz, P.)   1970A
Cortex, evolution
(Shevchenko, Iu. G.)   1970A
Dentition, evolution
(Every, R. G.)   1970A
Dentition, variation
(Frisch, J.)   1969A
Ethmoid bone
(Cartmill, M.)   1971A
Evolution
(Clark, W. E Le Gros   1971A, 1972A
(Gray, R.)   1969A

MAMMALIA - cont.
 Proboscidea
  Pliocene; USSR, Azov Sea;
   morphology; n. sp.
    (Baïgusheva, V. S.)   1971A
  Plio-Pleistocene; Greece, Drama; morphology
    (Melentis, J. K.)   1966M
  Tert.; Kansas, Manhattan; tusk
    (O'Brien, P. J.)   1968A
  Tert.; systematics; teeth, biometry
    (Alberdi, M. T., Aguirre, E.)   1970A
  U.S., Atlantic Coast; teeth
    (Drummond, A. H.)   1970B
  USSR; distribution
    (Sherstiukov, N. M.)   1971A
 Procamelus
  Neogene; U.S.; endocranial casts
    (Repérant, J.)   1970A
 Procapra
  Systematics; phylogeny
    (Dmitriyeva, Y. L.)   1971C
 Procetus
  Eocene; India, Kutch; skull, jaws; n. sp.
    (Sahni, A., Mishra, V. P.)   1972A
 Procoptodon
  Pleist.; Australia, Darling Downs; jaw,
   dentition
    (Bartholomai, A.)   1970A
 Procynocephalus
  Pleist., lower; India, Pinjor; jaw, teeth; n. sp.
    (Verma, B. C.)   1969A
 Prodipodomys
  Pliocene; Kansas, southwestern; jaws,
   teeth; n. sp.
    (Zakrzewski, R. J.)   1970A
 Prodissopsalis
  Eocene; France, Issel; jaw, teeth; n. sp.
    (Calas, G.)   1969A
  Eocene; Germany, Geiseltal; morphology
    (Matthes, H. W.)   1967E
 Prohylobates
  Morphology, nomenclature
    (Simons, E. L.)   1969B
 Prolagus
  Pliocene; Austria, Kohfidisch fissures;
   jaws, teeth
    (Bachmayer, F., Wilson, R. W.)   1970A
  Pliocene; Italy, Montagnola; jaw,
   teeth; systematics
    (Fondi, R.)   1970A
  Reconstruction
    (Dawson, M. R.)   1969A
  Skeleton; adaptations
    (Dawson, M. R.)   1969C
  Skeleton; reconstruction
    (Dawson, M. R.)   1969B
 Propalaeocastor
  Oligocene; USSR, Agyspe; skull, teeth; n. sp.
    (Lychev, G. F.)   1970A
 Propalaeotherium
  Eocene; Germany, Geiseltal; jaws, teeth
    (Matthes, H. W.)   1972A
 Propleopus oscillans
  Pleist.; Australia, Darling Downs; dentition
    (Bartholomai, A.)   1972A

MAMMALIA - cont.
 Propotto
  Systematics
    (Walker, A.)   1969A
 Prosimii
  Brain evolution
    (Radinsky, L. B.)   1970A
 Prosiphneus
  Tert.; USSR, Bashkiria; morphology;
   systematics
    (Sukhov, V. P.)   1968A
 Prospalax priscus
  Pliocene, upper; Poland, Węże;
   distribution; teeth
    (Kowalski, K.)   1960C
 Protadelomys
  Eocene; Europe, central; morphology;
   evolution; n. sp.
    (Hartenberger, J.-L.)   1969A
 Protemnodon
  Pliocene; Australia, Lake Tyers; morphology
    (Plane, M.)   1971A
  Pliocene; New Guinea; morphology
    (Plane, M.)   1965B
 Prothryptacodon
  Paleocene; Alberta, Balzac; jaw; n. sp.
    (Fox, R. C.)   1968C
 Protolabis
  Miocene; Calif., Barstow Fm.; skull,
   skeleton; n. sp.
    (Lewis, G. E.)   1968A
  Systematics
    (Frick, C., Taylor, B. E.)   1971A
 Protomomys
  Nomenclature
    (McKenna, M. C., Russell, D. E.,
     Savage, D. E.)   1969A
    (Melville, R. V.)   1971A
 Prototheria
  Evolution; systematics
    (Griffiths, M.)   1968A
  Origin; evolution
    (Hopson, J. A.)   1969A
  Systematics
    (Hopson, J. A.)   1970A
 Pseudictops
  Paleocene; Mongolia; morphology;
   systematics; n. taxa
    (Sulimski, A.)   1968B
 Pseudocricetodon
  Oligocene; France, Saint-Martin-de-Castillon;
   teeth; n. sp.
    (Hugueney, M.)   1971A
 Pseudoplohophorus
  Pliocene; Uruguay, Barrancas de
   San Gregorio; n. sp.
    (Mones, A.)   1970A
 Pseudosciuridae
  Dentition
    (Schmidt-Kittler, N.)   1972A
  Paleogene; Europe; distribution;
   systematics; phylogeny; dentition; n. gen.
    (Schmidt-Kittler, N.)   1971C
  Paleogene; Germany, Ehrenstein; teeth;
   n. gen.
    (Schmidt-Kittler, N.)   1970A

MAMMALIA - cont.
  Rodentia
    Miocene; Spain, Calatayud; morphology;
      systematics, n. taxa
      (Bruijn, H. de)   1967A
    Miocene, upper; Crete; teeth; n. subsp.
      (Bruijn, H. de, Meulenkamp, J. E.)   1972A
    Miocene, upper; Switzerland, Anwil;
      systematics; teeth; n. gen.
      (Engesser, B.)   1972A
    Miocene; Wyoming, Bighorn Mts.; morphology
      (McKenna, M. C., Love, J. D.)   1972A
    Mio-Pliocene; Nebraska, Norden Bridge; n. sp.
      (Klingener, D.)   1968A
    Neogene; India, Pakistan; Siwaliks
      (Black, C. C.)   1972A
    Oligocene; France, Coderet-Bransat;
      morphology; systematics; n. taxa
      (Hugueney, M.)   1969A
    Oligocene; Mexico, Rancho Gaitan;
      morphology; n. taxa
      (Ferrusquia-Villafranca, I.,
      Wood, A. E.)   1969A
    Oligocene, middle; France, Quercy; morphology
      (Vianey-Liaud, M.)   1969A
    Oligocene; Mongolia; distribution;
      systematics; phylogeny; n. taxa
      (Shevyreva, N. S.)   1971C
    Oligocene; Saskatchewan; morphology; n. taxa
      (Russell, L. S.)   1972B
    Oligocene; USSR, Kazakhstan; distribution;
      systematics; phylogeny; n. taxa
      (Shevyreva, N. S.)   1971C
    Paleogene; Mongolia; morphology; n. taxa
      (Shevyreva, N. S.)   1972A
    Paleogene; No. America; evolution
      (Wilson, R. W.)   1972A,C
    Paleogene; USSR, Kazakhstan;
      morphology; n. taxa
      (Shevyreva, N. S.)   1972A
    Phylogeny
      (Wood, A. E.)   1972B
    Pleist.; Alaska, Cape Deceit; dentition;
      n. taxa
      (Guthrie, R. D., Matthews, J. V.)   1971A
    Pleist.; Algeria, Ternifine; morphology;
      biogeography
      (Jaeger, J.-J.)   1969A
    Pleist.; East Germany, Süssenborn; teeth
      (Fejfar, O.)   1969A
    Pleist.; France; distribution; evolution
      (Chaline, J.)   1970B
    Pleist.; France; systematics; evolution
      (Chaline, J.)   1972A
    Pleist.; France, Nice; teeth
      (Chaline, J.)   1969A
    Pleist.; Germany, Harz; morphology
      (Koenigswald, W. v.)   1972A
    Pleist.; Germany, Wiesbaden
      (Bahlo, E., Malec, F.)   1971A
    Pleist.; Israel, Djebel Qafze Cave; n. sp.
      (Haas, G.)   1972A
    Pleist.; Israel, Jerusalem; morphology; n. taxa
      (Tchernov, E.)   1968C
    Pleist.; Israel; morphology;
      systematics; n. taxa
      (Tchernov, E.)   1968B

MAMMALIA - cont.
  Rodentia
    Pleist.; Israel, 'Ubeidiya; n. taxa
      (Haas, G.)   1966A
    Pleist.; Italy; teeth, skeleton
      (Bartolomei, G., Pasa, A.)   1969A
    Pleist.; Kansas; morphology;
      paleoecology
      (Schultz, G. E.)   1969A
    Pleist.; Nebraska, Brown Co.; skulls,
      jaws, teeth; n. taxa
      (Hibbard, C. W.)   1972A
    Pleist.; Poland, Nietoperzowa Cave;
      morphology
      (Kowalski, K.)   1964C
    Pleist.; Rumania, Betfia; morphology
      (Terzea, E., Jurcsák, T.)   1967A
    Pleist.; Rumania; morphology
      (Samson, P., Radulesco, C.,
      Kisgyörgy, Z.)   1971A
    Pleist.; Siberia, Selenga R.; morphology;
      systematics; evolution
      (Erbaeva, M. A.)   1970A
    Pleist.; Sicily, Spinagallo Cave; skull, limbs
      (Ambrosetti, P.)   1969A
    Pleist.; Spain, Aitzbitarte; skulls, jaws
      (Altuna, J.)   1970A
    Pleist., upper; Siberia, Irtysh V.
      (Agadzhanian, A. K.,
      Motuzko, A. N.)   1972A
    Pleist., upper; USSR, Azov Sea &
      Don region
      (Agadzhanian, A. K.)   1972A
    Pleist.; Uruguay; skulls, jaws, teeth
      (Calcaterra, A.)   1972A
    Pleist.; USSR, Íakutia; morphology
      (Rusanov, B. S.)   1968B
    Pliocene; Austria, Kohfidisch fissures;
      morphology; n. taxa
      (Bachmayer, F., Wilson, R. W.)   1970A
    Pliocene; Europe; morphology; n. taxa
      (Mein, P., Michaux, J.)   1970A
    Pliocene; Greece, Isle of Rhodes;
      morphology; n. taxa
      (Bruijn, H. de, Dawson, M. R.,
      Mein, P.)   1970A
    Pliocene, lower; Austria, Mödling; teeth
      (Daxner-Höck, G.)   1970A
    Pliocene; Oregon, southeastern;
      morphology; n. taxa
      (Shotwell, J. A.)   1970A
    Pliocene, upper; Idaho, Hagerman;
      morphology; n. sp.
      (Zakrzewski, R. J.)   1969A
    Pliocene, upper; USSR, Bashkiria;
      morphology; n. taxa
      (Sukhov, V. P.)   1970A
    Pliocene; Uruguay; skulls, jaws, teeth
      (Calcaterra, A.)   1972A
    Plio-Pleistocene; Villafranca d'Asti,
      Arondelli; teeth
      (Michaux, J.)   1970A
    Skull anatomy
      (Lavocat, R.)   1971A
  Ruscinomys
    Pliocene; Spain; dentition; biometry; n. sp.
      (Adrover, R.)   1969A

MAMMALIA - cont.
Stegodon
Pleist.; Indonesia, Flores and Timor; teeth
  (Hooijer, D. A.)   1972A,B
Pleist.; Indonesia; morphology
  (Hooijer, D. A.)   1969C, 1970A
Pleist.; Indonesia, Timor; tooth; n. sp.
  (Sartono, S.)   1969A
Stegolophodon
Miocene; Japan, Naka-niikawa district;
  morphology
  (Fujii, S.)   1970A
Miocene, middle; Japan, Iwaki; tooth
  (Shikama, T., Yanagisawa, I.)   1971A
Stegomastodon
Pleist.; Nebraska, Brown Co.; skull frags.,
  jaw, teeth
  (Hibbard, C. W.)   1972A
Pliocene; Oregon, southeastern; morphology
  (Shotwell, J. A.)   1970A
Stegotetrabelodontinae
Pliocene; Tchad, Menilla; evolution;
  mandible, teeth; n. gen.
  (Coppens, Y.)   1972B
Steneofiber
Evolution; systematics
  (Ginsburg, L.)   1971A
Miocene; Greece, Serrae; teeth;
  systematics; distribution
  (Melentis, J. K.)   1966Q, 1967E
Strongyloceros spelaeus
Pleist.; England, Devon; antlers, limbs;
  nomenclature
  (Friant, M.)   1971A
Suidae
Cenozoic; Germany, Sandelzhausen; skull,
  dentition; evolution; phylogeny;
  systematics; n. gen.
  (Schmidt-Kittler, N.)   1971A
Miocene; Moravia, Dolní Nětčice; teeth
  (Čtyroký, P., Fejfar, O.)   1963A
Neogene; Europe; teeth; distribution
  (Hünermann, K. A.)   1969A
Pliocene; Germany, Rheinhessen;
  morphology; phylogeny
  (Hünermann, K. A.)   1968A
Pliocene; Kenya, Kanapoi and Lothagam;
  skull, teeth; n. sp.
  (Cooke, H. B. S., Ewer, R. F.)   1972A
Systematics; evolution; dispersal
  (Thenius, E.)   1970D
Suiformes
Tert.; Spain; n. gen.
  (Golpe Posse, J. M.)   1971C
Tert.; Spain; systematics; n. taxa
  (Golpe Posse, J. M.)   1972A
Suncus
Pleist.; So. Africa; skull, jaws
  (Meester, J., Meyer, I. J.)   1972A
Sus
No. America; distribution
  (Quinn, J. H.)   1970A
Pleist.; Celebes; skull, teeth
  (Hooijer, D. A.)   1969A
Pleist.; East Germany, Süssenborn;
  teeth; distribution
  (Hünermann, K. A.)   1969B

MAMMALIA - cont.
Sus
Plio-Pleistocene; Czechoslovakia; teeth
  (Hünermann, K. A.)   1971A
Sus scrofa
Pleist.; Greece, Megalopolis; morphology;
  systematics
  (Melentis, J. K.)   1966H
Symbos
Morphology
  (Kraege, H.)   1970A
Pleist.; British Colombia, Dease Lake;
  skull frag.
  (Harington, C. R.)   1968A
Symmetrodonta
Cret., upper; Alberta; teeth
  (Fox, R. C.)   1972B
Symphalangus
Dentition, evolution
  (Kitahara, J.)   1971A
Synthetoceratinae
Morphology; systematics; n. taxa
  (Patton, T. H., Taylor, B. E.)   1971A
Tachyoryctoides
Oligocene, middle; Mongolia,
  Tatal-Gol; n. sp.
  (Dashzeveg, D.)   1971A
Talpidae
Miocene; France, Sansan; n. gen.
  (Baudelot, S.)   1968A
Pleist.; France, Nice; teeth
  (Jullien, R., Pillard, B.)   1969B
Tert.; France, Allier; evolution;
  dentition; n. subsp.
  (Hugueney, M.)   1972A
Tapiridae
Manus
  (Klaits, B. G.)   1972A
Tapiroidea
Tert.; USSR, Kazakhstan
  (Biriukov, M. D.)   1971A
Tert.; USSR, Kazakhstan, Turgai,
  Zaisan; distribution
  (Biriukov, M. D.)   1962A
Tapirus
Pleist.; Brazil, Tremembe; skeleton
  (Silva Santos, R. da)   1970A
Tayassu
Pleist.; Mississippi; Metapodials
  (Kaye, J. M.)   1971A
Tayassuidae
Cenozoic; Florida; morphology
  (Webb, S. W.)   1972B
Morphology; systematics; biogeography;
  n. sp.
  (Woodburne, M. O.)   1969A
Pleist.; Kentucky, Welsh Cave; adaptation;
  distribution; phylogeny
  (Guilday, J. E., et al.)   1971A
Teleoceras
Pliocene; Mexico
  (Brunet, J.)   1969A
Tetonius homunculus
Eocene; Wyoming, Bighorn Basin;
  endocranial cast
  (Radinsky, L. B.)   1967D

MAMMALIA - cont.

Ursus spelaeus
Pleist.; Rumania, Dimboviţa V.; skull, limbs
(Bera, Al.)   1968A
Pleist.; Yugoslavia, Mokrica Cave; biometry
(Rakovec, I.)   1967B
Pleist.; Yugoslavia, Veternica Cave; skulls
(Malez, M.)   1956A
Systematics; biometry
(Cordy, J.-M.)   1972A

Vespertilionidae
Miocene; France, Sansan; jaw, teeth; n. sp.
(Baudelot, S.)   1970A
Pleist.; Calif., Anza-Borrego Desert; n. gen.
(White, J. A.)   1969A

Villanyia
Pleist.; USSR; teeth; systematics
(Skorik, A. F.)   1972A

Vombatus
Pleist.; Australia, Dunolly; jaw
(Gill, E. D.)   1972A

Vulpes
Pleist.; Europe. distribution; phylogeny
(Beneš, J.)   1972A

Wombatidae
Dentition, variation
(Merrilees, D.)   1967C

Xenarthra
Pleist.; Florida; morphology
(Webb, S. D.)   1970B
Skulls, endocranial casts; systematics;
evolution
(Dechaseaux, C.)   1971A
Systematics; phylogeny
(Hoffstetter, R.)   1969A

Zalophus
Pleist.; Japan, Shizu shell bed; radius
(Nagasawa, J.)   1971A
Pleist.; Oregon, Cape Blanco; radius
(Packard, E. L.)   1949B

Zapodidae
Evolution; n. sp.
(Shevyreva, N. S.)   1970A
Miocene; Wyoming, Split Rock; jaw, teeth
(Sutton, J. F.)   1972B

Ziphiidae
Miocene; Peru; endocranial cast
(Spillmann, F.)   1970A

Zygolophodon
Miocene; China, Inner Mongolia; teeth; n. sp.
(Dubrovo, I. A.)   1970A

Zygomaturus
Pleist.; Australia, western; jaws
(Merrilees, D.)   1970A
Tert.; Australia, Beaumaris; jaw, dentition
(Woodburne, M. O.)   1969C

MAN, FOSSIL. See Paleoanthropology.

MANITOBA
Paleontology
Mam.; Pleist.; Grandview
(Harington, C. R.)   1970B
Vertebrate Faunas
Pleist.; Lake Agassiz; Mam.
(Pettipas, L.)   1966A

MARYLAND
Vertebrate Faunas
Miocene; Calvert Cliffs; Mam.
(Whitmore, F. C.)   1971A

MAURITANIA
Vertebrate Faunas
Pleist.; Adrar; Mam.
(Biberson, P.)   1969B

MESOZOIC
Correlation
Mongolia; dinosaurs
(Rozhdestvenskiĭ, A. K.)   1971B
Geochronology
Mongolia; dinosaurs
(Rozhdestvenskiĭ, A. K.)   1971B
New Mexico; reptiles
(Galton, P. M.)   1971C
No. America; dinosaurs
(Folinsbee, R. E., Baadsgaard, H.,
Cumming, G. L.)   1970A
Spain; dinosaur egg
(Plaziat, J.-C.)   1972A
USSR; reptiles
(Kirina, T. I.)   1964A, 1965A

MEXICO
Paleoanthropology
Sonora; fossil hominids
(Johnson, A. E.)   1966A
Tehuacán V.; fossil hominids
(MacNeish, R. S.)   1966A
Tepexpan; fossil hominids
(Soustelle, J.)   1967A
Valley of Mexico; fossil hominids
(Heizer, R. F., Cook, S. F.)   1966A
Paleontology
Mam.; catalogue
(Alvarez, T.)   1965A
Mam.; Cret., upper; Baja California
(Lillegraven, J. A.)   1972B
Mam.; Oligocene; Rancho Gaitan
(Ferrusquia-Villafranca, I.,
Wood, A. E.)   1969A
Mam.; Paleogene; Baja California
(Morris, W. J.)   1968B
Mam.; Pleist.; Oaxaca
(Ochoterena F., H.,
Silva-Barcenas, A.)   1970A
Mam.; Pleist.; Valsequillo
(Thenius, E.)   1970C
Mam.; Pliocene; La Carreta
(Mooser, O.)   1968A
Pisces; Pleist.; Chapala, Zacoalco
(Alvarez, J.)   1966A
Pisces; Pliocene; Jalisco, Barranca de Santa
Rosa
(Alvarez, J., Arreola, J.)   1972A
Rept.; Cret., upper; Baja California
(Morris, W. J.)   1969A, 1972A
Rept.; Pleist.; Aguascalientes
(Mooser, O.)   1972A
Vert.; Perm.-Quat.; catalog
(Silva-Barcenas, A.)   1969B
Vertebrate Faunas
Cret.; Baja California; Mam.
(Anon.)   1969BS

MONGOLIA - cont.
  Paleontology
    Pisces; Neogene; Bol'shie Ozera Basin
      (Sychevskaia, E. K., Lebedev, V. D.)   1971A
    Rept.; Cret.; Gobi Desert
      (Khosatzky, L. I.,
        Młynarski, M.)   1971A
      (Kolesnikov, Ch. M., Sochava, A. V.)   1972A
      (Martinson, G. G., Sochava, A. V.,
        Kolesnikov, Ch. M.)   1971A
      (Sochava, A. V.)   1972A
    Rept.; Cret.; Nemegt Basin
      (Gradziński, R.)   1970A
      (Maryańska, T.)   1970A
    Rept.; Cret., upper
      (Sulimski, A.)   1972A
    Rept.; Cret., upper; Bayn Dzak
      (Maryańska, T.)   1971A
      (Osmólska, H.)   1972A
    Rept.; Cret., upper; Gobi Desert
      (Młynarski, M.)   1972A
      (Młynarski, M., Narmandach, P.)   1972A
      (Osmólska, H., Roniewicz, E.)   1970A
      (Osmólska, H., Roniewicz, E.,
        Barsbold, R.)   1972A
    Rept.; Cret., upper; Nemegt Basin
      (Nowiński, A.)   1971A
    Rept.; Paleogene
      (Młynarski, M.)   1968B
    Rept.; Tert.
      (Chkhikvadze, V. M.)   1971B
  Vertebrate Faunas
    Cenozoic
      (Barsbold, R., Voronin, Iu. I.,
        Zhegallo, V. I.)   1971A
      (Trofimov, B. A.)   1971A
    Cretaceous
      (Barsbold, R., Voronin, Iu. I.,
        Zhegallo, V. I.)   1971A
    Cret.; Bayn Dzak
      (Lefeld, J.)   1971A
    Cret.; Gobi Desert
      (Kalandadze, N. N., Reshetov, V. Iu.)   1971A
    Eocene; Gobi Desert
      (Kalandadze, N. N., Reshetov, V. Iu.)   1971A
    General
      (Trofimov, B. A., Chudinov, P. K.)   1970A
    Jurassic, upper; Pisces
      (Shuvalov, V. F.)   1969A, 1970A
    Mesozoic
      (Trofimov, B. A.)   1971A
    Oligocene; Hsanda Gol Fm.; Mam.
      (Mellett, J. S.)   1967A
    Oligocene; Mam.
      (Dashzeveg, D.)   1970A
    Paleocene; Gashato; Mam.
      (Szalay, F. S., McKenna, M. C.)   1971A
    Paleocene; Nemebeta Basin; Mam.
      (Dashzeveg, D.)   1969A
    Pleist.; Mam.
      (Deviatkin, E. V., Strelkov, S. A.)   1968A
    Pleist.; Tsagan-Nur Lake; Mam.
      (Spirkin, A. I.)   1970A
    Pliocene; Mam.
      (Deviatkin, E. V., Strelkov, S. A.)   1968A
      (Deviatkin, E. V., Zazhigin, V. S.,
        Liskun, I. G.)   1969A

MONGOLIA - cont.
  Vertebrate Faunas
    Tertiary
      (Deviatkin, E. V.)   1970B
MONTANA
  Paleoecology
    Cret.; Bug Creek Anthills
      (Estes, R., Berberian, P.)   1970A
  Paleontology
    Mam.; Pliocene; Flaxville Gravels
      (Storer, J. E.)   1969A
    Pisces; Cret.
      (Estes, R., Berberian, P.)   1969A
    Pisces; Penn.; Becket
      (Melton, W. G.)   1969B
    Rept.; Cret.; Hell Creek Fm.
      (Gaffney, E. S., Hiatt, R.)   1971A
      (Tabrum, A. R.)   1970A
    Rept.; Cret., lower; Cloverly Fm.
      (Ostrom, J. H.)   1969A,G
    Rept.; Cret.; McCone Co.
      (Estes, R.)   1969D
  Vertebrate Faunas
    Carb.; Bear Gulch; Pisces
      (Lund, R.)   1972A
    Cret.; Bug Creek Anthills
      (Estes, R., Berberian, P.,
        Meszoely, C. A. M.)   1969A
    Cret., lower; Cloverly Fm.
      (Ostrom, J. H.)   1970C
    Cret., upper; Judith R. Fm.
      (Sahni, A.)   1969C, 1972A
    Eocene; Burnt Hills; Mam.
      (Petkewich, R. M., Fields, R. W.)   1971A
    Miocene; Anceney; Mam.
      (Tate, R. B.)   1969A
    Penn.; Bear Gulch; Pisces
      (Melton, W. G.)   1971A
    Penn.; Big Snowy Mts.; Pisces
      (Melton, W. G.)   1969A
    Tert.; Beaverhead R. Basin; Mam.
      (Hoffman, D. S.)   1972A
    Tert.; Jefferson Basin
      (Kuenzi, W. D., Fields, R. W.)   1971A
MOROCCO
  Paleoanthropology
    Casablanca; fossil hominids
      (Ennouchi, E.)   1970A
      (Vallois, H. V.)   1969F
    Jebel Irhoud; fossil hominids
      (Ennouchi, E.)   1969A
    Tangiers; fossil hominids
      (Briggs, L. C.)   1967A
    Thomas Quarry; fossil hominids
      (Ennouchi, E.)   1969B, 1972A
  Paleontology
    Rept.; Triassic; Azendoh
      (Dutuit, J.-M.)   1972B
    Rept.; Triassic, upper; Atlas Mts., Imi
    N'Tanoute
      (Dutuit, J.-M.)   1972A
  Vertebrate Faunas
    Pleist.; Jebel Irhoud; Mam.
      (Jaeger, J.-J.)   1970A
    Pleist.; Mam.
      (Biberson, P.)   1966B, 1970A

MUSEUMS - cont.
Institute of Geological Sciences
Paleontological data, archives
(Anon.) 1969BE
Instituto Provincial de Paleontología de Sabadell
Activities
(Berengueras Alsina, M. T.) 1969A, 1971A
(Golpe Posse, J. M.) 1971D, 1972B
La Brea Tar Pits
Exhibits
(Anon.) 1966BU
Menton Museum
Exhibits
(Octobon, F. C. E.) 1965B
Moravian Museum
Exhibits
(Jelínek, J.) 1969B
Musée de Saint-Germain
Paleolithic art
(Rousseau, M.) 1969B
Museo Paleontologico, Rome University
Mammal skeletons
(Petronio, C.) 1970A
Muséum National d'Histoire Naturelle
Exhibit, vertebrate paleontology
(Anon.) 1972BA
Museum of Comparative Zoology, Harvard
Annual report
(Mayr, E.) 1968B, 1969E, 1970B
Museum of Geology and Paleontology, Padova
History; guide
(Dal Piaz, G.) 1971A
Museum of Paleontology, Berkeley
Illustrators
(Anon.) 1971AB
Nairobi National Museum
Annual report
(Leakey, M. D.) 1968A
National Museum, Prague
Exhibits
(Neústupný, J.) 1969A
National Museums of Kenya
History
(Leakey, L. S. B.) 1971B
National Science Museum, Japan
Exhibits
(Ozaki, H.) 1970A
(Tezuka, H., Ishibashi, I.) 1971A
90th Anniversary
(Sugie, T., et al.) 1967A
Natural History Museums
Organization
(Meyer, K. O.) 1970A
Naturforschende Gesellschafts Museum
Report
(Schaefer, H.) 1967A
Naturhistorische Museum, Mainz
Annual report
(Brüning, H.) 1970A
Nebraska State Museum
History
(Schultz, C. B.) 1971A, 1972A
History; activities
(Schultz, C. B., Gunderson, H. L.) 1972A
New York State Museum
Exhibits
(Sifton, D. W.) 1969A

MUSEUMS - cont.
Paläontologische Institut und Museum der
Universität Zürich
Activities
(Kuhn-Schnyder, E.) 1971B
Peale's Museum, Philadelphia
History
(Ellis, R. P.) 1966A
Pengelly Cave Studies Center
Exhibits
(Halliday, W. R.) 1969A
Ray Alf Museum and Science Center
Dedication
(Downs, T.) 1969A
Royal Ontario Museum
Exhibits
(Anon.) 1971BG
Samuel Bonfman Biblical and
Archaeological Museum
Exhibits
(Kahane, P. P.) 1967A
Santa Barbara Museum of Natural History
Annual report
(Morres, N. K.) 1967A, 1968A
Senckenberg Museum
Diplodocus mount
(Klausewitz, W.) 1970A
Exhibits
(Schäfer, W.) 1969A,C
(Schäfer, W., et al.) 1970C
Smithsonian Institution
Annual report
(Anon.) 1967CF, 1968BG, 1969BZ
(Cowan, R. S.) 1966A
South African Museum
Exhibits
(Anon.) 1967CC
Rock art center
(Anon.) 1967CB
Staatliches Museum für Naturkunde
History
(Schüz, E.) 1966A
Uganda Museum
History
(Deming, L. M.) 1966A
United States National Museum
Publications
(Anon.) 1971BX
Urmensch Museum, Steinheim am Murr.
Dedication
(Schopf, M.) 1969A
Exhibits
(Adam, K. D.) 1969A
(Schopf, M.) 1969B
Vaterländische Naturkunde Museum
History
(Schüz, E.) 1970A
Yale Peabody Museum
Activities
(Anon.) 1969AH
Exhibits
(Anon.) 1968AS
(Drew, L. C.) 1968A
(Remington, J. E.) 1968A
Report
(Anon.) 1968AR

NEW MEXICO
Absolute Age
Blackwater Draw; artifacts
(Agogino, G. A., Rovner, I.)   1969A
Paleontology
Amph.; Permian, early; Arroyo de Agua
(Vaughn, P. P.)   1969A
Mam.; Paleocene, middle; San Juan Co.
(Wilson, R. W., Szalay, F. S.)   1972A
Vertebrate Faunas
Cret.; San Juan Basin
(Fassett, J. E., Hinds, J. S.)   1971A
Cret.; San Juan Basin; Rept.
(Powell, J. S.)   1969A
Eocene; Baca Fm.; Mam.
(Snyder, D. O.)   1970A
Miss.; Datil Plateau; Pisces
(Armstrong, A. K.)   1959A
Permian; Chama Basin
(Budding, A. J., Pitrat, C. W.,
Smith, C. T.)   1960A
Permian; Kaibab Fm. and Toroweap Fm.;
Pisces
(McKee, E. D., Breed, W. J.)   1969A
Permian, lower; Otero Co.
(Vaughn, P. P.)   1969C
Pleist.; Albuquerque; Mam.
(Lambert, P. W.)   1969A, 1970A
Pleist.; Blackwater Draw; Mam.
(Agogino, G. A.)   1969A
Pleist.; Dark Canyon Cave; Aves
(Howard, H.)   1971B
Pleist.; Dry Cave
(Holman, J. A.)   1970B
Pleist.; Dry Cave; Mam.
(Harris, A. H.)   1970A
Pleist.; Gypsum Cave; Mam.
(Dunn, D.)   1968A
Pleist.; southcentral
(Kottlowski, F. E.)   1955A
Pleist.; southern
(Ruhe, R. V.)   1961A
Pleist., upper; Harding Co.
(McMullen, T. L.,
Zakrzewski, R. J.)   1972A
Tert., lower; San Juan Basin; Mam.
(Simpson, G. G.)   1950S
Triassic; Dockum group
(Gregory, J. T.)   1972A
NEW YORK
Paleoanthropology
Fossil hominids
(Ritchie, W. A.)   1969A
NEW ZEALAND
Paleontology
Aves; Miocene; North Canterbury
(Scarlett, R. J.)   1972A
Aves; Pleist.
(Scarlett, R. J.)   1970A
Aves; Pleist., upper; Te Waka
(Scarlett, R. J.)   1970B
Aves; Pliocene; Motunau Beach
(Howard, H., Warter, S. L.)   1969A
Aves; Tert.
(Simpson, G. G.)   1971C

NEW ZEALAND - cont.
Paleontology
Mam.; Pliocene; Cape Kidnappers
(Berry, J. A., King, J. E.)   1970A
Pisces; Oligocene; Fossil Point
(Climo, F. M., Baker, A. N.)   1972A
Pisces; Tert.
(Keyes, I. W.)   1972A
Rept.; Cret., upper; Marine
(Welles, S. P., Gregg, D. R.)   1971A
Rept.; Mesozoic
(Fleming, C. A., Gregg, D. R.,
Welles, S. P.)   1971A
NICARAGUA
Vertebrate Faunas
Pleist.; Mam.
(Howell, T. R.)   1969A
NIGER
Paleontology
Pisces; Cret.; Iullemmeden
(Cappetta, H.)   1972B
Pisces; Tert.; Iullemmeden
(Cappetta, H.)   1972B
Rept.; Cret.
(Bergounioux, F. M., Crouzel, F.)   1968A
Rept.; Eocene
(Bergounioux, F. M., Crouzel, F.)   1968A
Rept.; Permian; Agadès
(Ricqlès, A. de)   1969B
Rept.; Permian, upper; Tchimozenog
(Taquet, P.)   1969A
Vertebrate Faunas
Cret., lower; Gadoufaoua
(Taquet, P.)   1970A
Cret.; Pisces
(Cappetta, H.)   1970B
Tert.; Pisces
(Cappetta, H.)   1970B
NIGERIA
Paleogeography
Eocene
(Adegoke, O. S.)   1969A
Vertebrate Faunas
Cret., upper; Sokoto Basin
(De Giuli, C., Ficcarelli, G.,
Torre, D.)   1970A
Eocene; Pisces
(Adegoke, O. S.)   1969A
Mesozoic; Mali-Nigerian Basin
(Gatinskiĭ, Iu. G., Gerus, E. A.,
Klochko, V. P., Trofimov, D. M.)   1967A
Paleogene; Sokoto Basin
(De Giuli, C., Ficcarelli, G.,
Torre, D.)   1970A
Tert.; Pisces
(White, E. I.)   1955C
NOMENCLATURE. See appropriate taxon under
class name.
NORTH AFRICA
Paleoanthropology
Fossil hominids
(Blanc, A. C.)   1964A
(Cadenat, P.)   1966A
Fossil hominids; C-14 dates
(Camps, G., et al.)   1968A

OBITUARIES - cont.

Angel V. Borrello
  Biography; portrait
    (Cuerda, A.)   1971A
Edouard Bourdelle
  Portrait
    (Bouchud, J.)   1961B
Jean Bouyssonie
    (Anon.)   1966BS
Henri Breuil
  Biography; portrait
    (Anon.)   1962CP
  Portrait
    (Anon.)   1961DF
André Cheynier
    (Barandiarán, I.)   1968A
    (Vilaseca, S.)   1969-70A
  Portrait
    (Delporte, H.)   1969A
W. E. Le Gros Clark
    (Anon.)   1971AP
  Portrait
    (Weddell, G.)   1972A
Margaret C. Cook
    (McKenna, M. C.)   1969B
Pierre David
  Biography; portrait
    (Pintaud, R. C.)   1964A
Georgiĭ F. Debets
    (Okladnikov, A. P., et al.)   1969A
  Portrait
    (Anon.)   1969CA
    (Bader, O. N.)   1969C
    (Editorial Board)   1970A
    (Uryson, M. I.)   1969B
Petr Petrovich Efimenko
  Biography; portrait
    (Editors)   1972A
  Portrait
    (Tret'iakov, P. N.)   1970A
Ian Martynovich Eglon
  Biography; portrait
    (Rozhdestvenskiĭ, A. K.)   1971A,D
James Maxwell McConnell Fisher
  Portrait
    (B., W. R. P.)   1971A
Miguel Fusté
  Portrait
    (Ripoll Perelló, E.)   1966B
Dorothy Garrod
    (Anon.)   1969AM
    (Daniel, G.)   1969A
Mikhail M. Gerasimov
    (Okladnikov, A. P., Larichev, V. E.)   1971A
  Portrait
    (Alekseeva, T. I.)   1971A
    (Anon.)   1970BM
    (Matiushin, G. N.)   1971A
André Glory
    (Kühn, H.)   1969A
    (Ripoll Perelló, E.)   1966A
  Biography; portrait
    (Bergounioux, F. M.)   1967A
William King Gregory
    (Anon.)   1969AW
    (Crusafont Pairó, M.)   1972C

OBITUARIES - cont.

William King Gregory
  Biography; portrait
    (Simpson, G. G.)   1971G, 1972C
  Portrait
    (Schaeffer, B.)   1971B
H. James Gut
    (Brodkorb, P.)   1969B
Hugo Otto Gross
    (Frenzel, B.)   1969A
Richard Hagen
  Biography; portrait
    (Matthes, H. W.)   1969A
A. C. Hoffman
    (Anon.)   1969BR
A. Tindell Hopwood
    (Anon.)   1970AI
    (Simpson, G. G.)   1970H
Friedrich F. von Huene
    (Gross, W.)   1969B
  Portrait
    (Seilacher, A.)   1969A
    (Seilacher, A., Westphal, F.)   1969A
Giuseppe Isetti
    (Martinelli Coco, T.)   1965A
    (Ripoll Perelló, E.)   1967A
Werner Janensch
    (Gross, W.)   1970A
Daniel W. Josselyn
    (Anon.)   1970AL
J. LeRoy Kay
    (Guilday, J. E., Dawson, M.)   1971A
Remington Kellogg
    (Wetmore, A.)   1969A
F. E. Koby
    (Barandiarán, I.)   1969-70A
    (Nougier, L.-R.)   1969B
Veronika I. Kochetkova
  Biography; portrait
    (Anon.)   1971CB
M. S. Krishnan
  Portrait
    (R., S. K.)   1970A
Othmar Kühn
    (Bogsch, L.)   1969A
    (Thenius, E.)   1969A
  Biography
    (Steininger, F.)   1970A
L. S. B. Leakey
    (Anon.)   1972AJ,BD,BP
  Portrait
    (Anon.)   1972BL
A. Lémozi
    (Lorblanchet, M.)   1970A
D. N. Lev
  Portrait
    (Boriskovskiĭ, P. I.,
      Okladnikov, A. P.)   1970A
Theodore Doney McCown
  Biography
    (Brooks, S.)   1970A
  Portrait
    (Hammel, E. A.)   1969A, 1970A
Kurt W. Marek
    (Anon.)   1972AH
Louis Méroc
    (Clottes, J.)   1970A

OBITUARIES - cont.
  Lothar F. Zotz
      (Ripoll Perelló, E.)   1967C
    Portrait
      (Brodar, S.)   1967A
OHIO
  Paleontology
    Amph.; Penn., upper
      (Vaughn, P. P.)   1971A
    Amph.; Permian; Marietta
      (Olson, E. C.)   1970B
    Pisces; Devonian; Cleveland Shale
      (Hlavin, W. J.)   1972A
    Pisces; Devonian; Silica Fm.
      (Mitchell, S. W.)   1971A
    Pisces; Penn.; Portage Co.
      (Murphy, J. L.)   1971B
  Vertebrate Faunas
    Pleist.; Ansonia; Mam.
      (Mills, R. S.; Guilday, J. E.)   1972A
    Pleist., upper; Mam.
      (Mills, R. S.)   1972A
OKLAHOMA
  Absolute Age
    Domebo; vertebrates
      (Bell, R. E.)   1968A
  Paleontology
    Amph.; Permian; Chickasha Fm.
      (Olson, E. C.)   1972C
    Amph.; Permian; Cleveland Co.
      (Olson, E. C.)   1971B
    Amph.; Permian, lower; Comanche Co.
      (Bolt, J. R.)   1969A
    Amph.; Permian, upper; Blaine Co.
      (Olson, E. C.)   1972A
    Pisces; Permian; Hennessey Fm.
      (Olson, E. C., Daly, E.)   1972A
    Pisces; Permian; north-central
      (Carlson, K. J.)   1968A
    Rept.; Permian; Logan Co.
      (MacLean, W. P.)   1970A
    Rept.; Permian, lower; Logan Co.
      (Zídek, J.)   1971A
    Rept.; Permian, lower; Tillman Co.,
    Grandfield
      (Daly, E.)   1969A
    Vert.; Permian, lower
      (Olson, E. C.)   1970A
  Vertebrate Faunas
    Permian; Chickasha Fm.
      (Olson, E. C.)   1972D
ONTARIO
  Paleontology
    Pisces; Pleist.
      (Harington, C. R.)   1971C
ORANGE FREE STATE
  Paleontology
    Rept.; Permian; Edenville
      (Cluver, M. A.)   1969A
OREGON
  Paleontology
    Mam.; Eocene; Clarno Fm.
      (Mellett, J. S.)   1969B
    Mam.; Miocene; John Day Fm.
      (Rensberger, J. M.)   1971A

OREGON - cont.
  Paleontology
    Mam.; Oligocene; John Day Basin
      (Coleman, R. G.)   1951A
    Mam.; Pleist.; Cape Blanco
      (Packard, E. L.)   1949B
    Mam.; Pleist., upper; Malheur Co.
      (Allison, I. S., Boyd, H. A.)   1954A
    Mam.; Pliocene; southeast
      (Shotwell, J. A.)   1970A
    Mam.; Tert.; Fossil Point
      (Shotwell, J. A.)   1951A
    Pisces
      (Welton, B. J.)   1972A
    Pisces; Eocene; Yamhill Fm.
      (Applegate, S. P.)   1968A
    Pisces; Oligocene; Wheeler Co.
      (Cavender, T. M.)   1969A
    Pisces; Pliocene; Gateway
      (Cavender, T. M., Miller, R. R.)   1972A
  Vertebrate Faunas
    Eocene; northcentral; Pisces
      (Cavender, T. M.)   1968A
    Miocene; Pendleton
      (Sargent, S., Shotwell, J. A.)   1951A
    Oligocene; northcentral; Pisces
      (Cavender, T. M.)   1968A
    Pleist.; southern; Mam.
      (Arment, H. L.)   1961A
    Pleist., upper; Fort Rock Lake; Mam.
      (Bedwell, S. F., Cressman, L. S.)   1971A
    Pliocene; McKay Reservoir
      (Shotwell, J. A.)   1954B
OTOLITHS. See under Pisces.
PACIFIC OCEAN
  Paleoclimatology
    Quaternary
      (Blumenstock, D. I.)   1966A
  Paleontology
    Pisces; Cenozoic
      (Beliaev, G. M., Glikman, L. S.)   1970B
PAKISTAN
  Paleontology
    Mam.; Neogene; Siwalik
      (Black, C. C.)   1972A
    Mam.; Tert.
      (Heissig, K.)   1972A
    Mam.; Tert.; Siwalik
      (Heissig, K.)   1972A
PALEOANTHROPOLOGY
  Evolution
    Africa
      (Wells, L. H.)   1971A
    Aggression
      (Alland, A.)   1972A
      (Bigelow, R.)   1970A
      (Lewis, J., Towers, B.)   1969A
      (McBroom, P.)   1971A
    Allometric growth of skull
      (Hemmer, H.)   1969A, 1970A
    Alpine race, origin
      (Ferembach, D.)   1967A
    Antiquity of man
      (Weber, T. J.)   1968A
    Area of origin
      (Nesturkh, M. F.)   1964D

PALEOANTHROPOLOGY - cont.
  Evolution
    General
      (Uryson, M. I.)   1966D, 1970B
      (Uspenskiĭ, S. I.)   1964A
      (Wallace, A. R.)   1972A
      (Washburn, S. L.)   1969B
      (Washburn, S. L., Shirek, J.)   1967A
      (Westenhöfer, M.)   1953A
      (Wilder, H. H.)   1972A
    Habiline phase
      (Schott, L.)   1970A
    Hand
      (Campbell, B. G.)   1968C
      (Marzhe, M. W.)   1971A
      (Napier, J. R.)   1965A
    Hominization
      (Sicard, H.)   1957A, 1965A
    Homo sapiens
      (Grigor'ev, G. P.)   1968A
    Homo sapiens, origin
      (Semenov, Iu. I.)   1971A
    Hunting
      (Washburn, S. L.,
        Lancaster, C. S.)   1968A, 1971A
    Intelligence
      (Sicard, H.)   1967A
    Interpretations
      (Ryan, B.)   1965A
    Juvenile book
      (May, J.)   1968A
    Lineages
      (Kleemann, G.)   1971A
    Mandible
      (Clermont, N.)   1965A
      (Stewart, T. D.)   1969B
    Naked ape concept
      (Pilbeam, D.)   1972B
    North Africa
      (Briggs, L. C.)   1968A
    Origin of man
      (Brace, C. L.)   1970A
      (Carter, C. O.)   1968A
      (Eckhardt, R. B.)   1972A
      (Hübner, P.)   1969A
      (Nesturkh, M. F.)   1970A
      (Uryson, M. I.)   1969A
      (Vandebosch, A.)   1957A
      (Vandermeersch, B.)   1969D, 1970A
      (Washburn, S. L.)   1969A
    Paleoclimatic effects
      (Emiliani, C.)   1968A
    Philosophical anthropology,
      Teilhard de Chardin
      (Gosztonyi, A.)   1968A
    Phylogeny
      (Dauvillier, A.)   1971A
    Phylogeny, systematics
      (Schultz, A. H.)   1966A
      (Vandermeersch, B.)   1971B
    Popular article
      (Eiseley, L.)   1970A
    Popular book
      (Alekseev, V. P.)   1969A
      (Ardrey, R.)   1967A
      (Kurtén, B.)   1972A

PALEOANTHROPOLOGY - cont.
  Evolution
    Popular book
      (Leakey, L. S. B., Goodall, V. M.)   1969A
      (McKern, S. S., McKern, T. W.)   1970A
      (Montagu, A.)   1964D
      (Morgan, E.)   1972A
      (Morris, D.)   1968A
      (Pilbeam, D.)   1970A
      (Place, R.)   1968A
      (Simak, C. D.)   1971A
    Prehistory
      (Barral, L.)   1968A
    Primate ancestry of man
      (Genet-Varcin, E.)   1969B
    Problems
      (Roginskiĭ, Iͣa. Iͣa.)   1972A
    Psychic constancy
      (Frolov, B. A.)   1969A
    Races
      (Alekseev, V. P.)   1969B,C
      (Benoist, J.)   1968A
      (Coon, C. S.)   1972A
      (Harris, M.)   1971A
      (Iͣakimov, V. P.)   1965A
      (Kennedy, K. A. R.)   1972A
      (Saller, K.)   1968A
      (Van Valen, L.)   1968B
    Relation to diet
      (Watson, L.)   1971A
    Sexual selection
      (Aĭzenberg, D. M.,
        Roginskiĭ, Iͣa. Iͣa.)   1970A
    Shoulder
      (Oxnard, C. E.)   1968D, 1969A
    Skull morphology
      (Uryson, M. I.)   1968A
    Social role of fire
      (Semenov, S. A.)   1970A
    Stages
      (Jullien, R.)   1966A
      (Kozłowski, J. K.)   1970A
      (Thoma, A.)   1969A
      (Uryson, M. I.)   1964C
    Stratigraphy
      (Straus, W. L.)   1968A
    Survey
      (Kuhn-Schnyder, E.)   1971C
    Systematics
      (Lipták, P.)   1969A
    Textbook
      (Adams, F. T.)   1968A
      (Alimen, M.-H., Steve, M.-J.)   1966A
      (Altner, G.)   1969A
      (Barnett, S. A.)   1971A
      (Beals, R. L., Hoijer, H.)   1971A
      (Birdsell, J. B.)   1972A
      (Braidwood, R. J.)   1967B
      (Chard, C. S.)   1969A
      (Clark, G.)   1969A
      (Clark, J. D.)   1970A
      (Clark, W. E. Le Gros)   1971A
      (Clegg, E. J.)   1968A
      (Comas, J.)   1971A
      (Daniel, G.)   1968C

PALEOANTHROPOLOGY - cont.
  Fossil Hominids
    Archeological interpretation
      (Armelagos, G. J.)   1968A
    Arcy-sur-Cure; Paleolithic
      (Movius, H. L.)   1969A
    Artifacts, paleobiological importance
      (Ehrenberg, K.)   1968A
    Asia; Paleolithic; skeletons, coprolites
      (Bacon, E.)   1971A
    Atlas
      (Day, M. H.)   1967B
    Australia
      (Anon.)   1970AQ
      (Mulvaney, D. J.)   1969A, 1972A
      (Thorne, A. G.)   1972A
    Australia; origins
      (Abbie, A. A.)   1969A
    Australia, Tasmania
      (Jones, R.)   1968A
    Australopithecine bone accumulation
      (Brain, C. K.)   1970A
      (Hillaby, J.)   1967C
    Australopithecine height
      (Burns, P. E.)   1971A
    Australopithecine skeleton
      (Genet-Varcin, E.)   1969A
    Australopithecine tooth size
      (Keene, H. J.)   1967A
    Australopithecines
      (Brace, C. L.)   1964B
      (Howell, F. C.)   1971A
    Australopithecines; adaptive radiation
      (Robinson, J. T.)   1968A, 1972C
    Australopithecines; artifacts; brain structure
      (Matiukhin, A. E.)   1972B
    Australopithecines; behavior; locomotion
      (Schott, L.)   1970B
    Australopithecines, canine size
      (Mamak, A.)   1970A
    Australopithecines; dentition; diet
      (Groves, C. P., Napier, J. R.)   1968A
    Australopithecines, endocranial volumes
      (Holloway, R. L.)   1970A,B
    Australopithecines, morphology
      (Clark, W. E. Le Gros)   1971B
    Australopithecines; morphology; evolution
      (Iakimov, V. P.)   1964B
    Australopithecines; morphology, systematics
      (Ferembach, D.)   1964B
    Australopithecines; morphology; systematics;
      ecology; adaptive radiation
      (Robinson, J. T.)   1966B
    Australopithecines, morphologic variation
      (Wolpoff, M. H.)   1969C
    Australopithecines, osteodontokeratic culture
      (Koenigswald, G. H. R. von)   1968E
    Australopithecus
      (Wolpoff, M. H.)   1969A
    Australopithecus, culture
      (Holloway, R. L.)   1969A,B
      (Wescott, R. W.)   1970A
    Australopithecus, cranial capacity
      (Holloway, R. L.)   1972B
    Australopithecus, diet
      (Butzer, K. W.)   1971B

PALEOANTHROPOLOGY - cont.
  Fossil Hominids
    Australopithecus; distribution,
      population structure
      (Tobias, P. V.)   1972B
    Australopithecus, femoral anatomy
      (Heiple, K. G., Lovejoy, C. O.)   1971A
      (Lovejoy, C. O.)   1971A
      (Lovejoy, C. O., Heiple, K. G.)   1972A
    Australopithecus; femur, reconstruction
      (Lovejoy, C. O., Heiple, K. G.)   1970A
    Australopithecus, gait
      (Jenkins, F.)   1972A
    Australopithecus, habits
      (Schaller, G. B.)   1972A
      (Schaller, G. B., Lowther, G. R.)   1969A
    Australopithecus; habits; systematics
      (Rose, B.)   1966A
    Australopithecus, limb proportions
      (Hamilton, M. E.)   1972A
    Australopithecus, locomotion
      (Zihlman, A. L.)   1971A
    Australopithecus; morphology; systematics
      (Broom, R.)   1972A
    Australopithicus; morphologic variation
      (Brace, C. L.)   1969A
    Australopithecus, paleo-obstetrics
      (Malinas, Y.)   1970A
    Australopithecus, sexual dimorphism
      (Brace, C. L.)   1969B
    Australopithecus, systematics
      (Greene, D. L.)   1970B
    Australopithecus, systematics; culture
      (Givens, R. D.)   1970A
      (Robinson, J. T.)   1970B
    Australopithecus; systematics, phylogeny
      (Tobias, P. V.)   1968D
    Australopithecus, tool use
      (Rosiński, F.)   1970A
    Australopithecus, tooth eruption
      (Mann, A.)   1968A
    Australopithecus; venous sinus grooves
      (Tobias, P. V.)   1968E
    Auvergne; skull; engravings
      (Delporte, H.)   1970A
    Balkan Penninsula; Paleolithic
      (Menghin, O.)   1968A
    Barma Grande; Paleolithic burials
      (Pales, L.)   1970B
    Basura Cave; footprints
      (Molleson, T. I., Oakley, K. P.,
      Vogel, J. C.)   1972A
    Bears, interactions
      (Herrero, S.)   1970A
    Beegden; femur
      (Erdbrink, D.-P., Tacoma, J.)   1967A
    Behavior
      (Eisenberg, J. F., Dillon, W. S.)   1971A
      (Jay, P.)   1968B
      (Kurth, G.)   1967B
    Behavioral adaptation, arctic winter
      (Watanabe, H.)   1969A
    Belgium
      (Lyell, C.)   1972A
    Bergerac; Paleolithic
      (Marsac, M.)   1970A

PALEOANTHROPOLOGY - cont.
  Fossil Hominids
    Dentition
      (Bailit, H. L., Friedlaender, J. S.)   1967A
      (Kipp, F. A.)   1966A
      (Vandebroek, G.)   1966B
      (Wolpoff, M. H.)   1972A
    Dentition; diet
      (Robinson, J. T.)   1969A, 1970A
    Dentition, evolution
      (Petit-Maire, N., Charon, M.)   1972A
    Dentition, relation to environment
      (Brace, C. L.)   1967B
    Dentition, variation
      (Eckhardt, R. B.)   1972B
    Dictionary
      (Bray, W., Trump, D.)   1970A
      (Brézillon, M.)   1969A
    Diet
      (Bouchud, J.)   1967B
      (Brothwell, D. R., Brothwell, P.)   1969A
      (Delcourt, A. A.)   1967A
      (Harris, M.)   1972A
      (Jude, P. E.)   1961A
    Diet; cooking
      (Leopold, C. A., Ardrey, R.)   1972A
    Diet; food gathering
      (Ullrich, W.)   1970A
    Discoveries
      (Prost, J. H.)   1971A
    Distribution; abundance
      (Livingstone, D. A.)   1971A
    Djetis; jaws
      (Lovejoy, C. O.)   1970A
    Don R.; skulls
      (Klein, R. G.)   1969C
    Dordogne; Paleolithic, upper; skeleton
      (Billy, G.)   1969A
    Dordogne; skulls
      (Bouchud, J.)   1966G
    Duport Cave; Aurignacian; skull
      (David, P., Duport, L.)   1955A
    Duport Cave; femur, occipital
      (Bouvier, J. M., et al.)   1969A
    East Africa
      (Isaac, G. L.)   1969A
      (Leakey, R. E.)   1971B
      (Tobias, P. V.)   1969B
    East Africa; chronology
      (Howell, F. C.)   1972A
    East Africa; ecology
      (Leakey, L. S. B.)   1966D
    East Africa; feet
      (Day, M. H., Wood, B. A.)   1969A
    East Castaigne Cave; Mousterian;
      skull frags., teeth
      (Duport, L.)   1966A
    East Rudolf
      (Anon.)   1971AO, 1972AR
    East Rudolf; australopithecines;
      skulls, limbs
      (Leakey, R. E. F., Mungai, J. M.,
       Walker, A. C.)   1971A, 1972A
    East Rudolf; skull
      (Anon.)   1972AL,BF,BG,BM
    East Rudolf; systematics
      (Robinson, J. T.)   1972B

PALEOANTHROPOLOGY - cont.
  Fossil Hominids
    Easter Island; skulls
      (Radwanski, P. A.)   1969A
    Egypt
      (Hayes, W. C.)   1965A
    El Centro; skeleton
      (Anon.)   1972AK,BE
    Elandsfontein; skull
      (Singer, R.)   1971A
    Endocranial casts
      (Stęślicka-Mydlarska, W.)   1971A
    Endocranium
      (Kochetkova, V. I.)   1960B
    Endocranium, reconstruction
      (Kochetkova, V. I.)   1968B, 1969B
    Eniseĭ V., migrations
      (Astakhov, S. N.)   1966C
    Ethnography
      (Howell, F. C., et al.)   1968A
    Eurasia, northern; origin, migration
      (Ivanova, I. K.)   1969C
    Eurasia; Paleolithic; migrations
      (Gaĭduk, I. M.)   1969A
    Europe
      (Coles, J. M.)   1968A
      (Coles, J. M., Simpson, D. D. A.)   1968A
    Europe; catalog
      (Oakley, K. P., Campbell, B. G.,
       Molleson, T. I.)   1971A
    Europe, central, eastern; Paleolithic;
      civilizations
      (Bárta, J.)   1965E
    Europe, north-east; Paleolithic;
      migration
      (Bader, O. N.)   1968D
    Europe, northern; Paleolithic;
      distribution
      (Bader, O. N.)   1971B
    Europe; Paleolithic
      (Laet, S. J. de)   1967A
    Europe; Paleolithic; dentition,
      variability
      (Bailit, H. L.)   1966A
    Europe; Paleolithic, upper
      (Ferembach, D.)   1963B
      (Valoch, K.)   1969A,B
    Exploitation of animals
      (Vereshchagin, N. K.)   1970A
    Facial skeleton, taxonomic value
      (Guseva, I. S.)   1969A
    First man
      (Simon, K. H.)   1971A
    Fishing
      (Anon.)   1967CA
    Foot bones
      (Oxnard, C. E.)   1972A
    Fort Ternan; jaw
      (Leakey, L. S. B.)   1970D
    Fort Ternan; Miocene, upper; morphology
      (Simons, E. L.)   1969A
    Fort Ternan; nomenclature
      (Leakey, L. S. B.)   1969A
    France; Paleolithic, lower
      (Tieghem, A. G.)   1969A
    General
      (Anon.)   1969BY,CC

PALEOANTHROPOLOGY - cont.
Fossil Hominids
Israel
(Anon.) 1968AL
Israel; Paleolithic, lower
(Asmus, G.) 1967B
Istria; skull frag., skeleton bones
(Malez, M.) 1972A
Italy, southern; Neanderthal; jaw
(Ascenzi, A., Segre, A. G.) 1971A
Java
(Koenigswald, G. H. R. von) 1969B
(Sartono, S.) 1971B
Java; dating
(Jacob, T., Curtiss, G. H.) 1971A
Jebel Irhoud; Mousterian; jaw, teeth, skulls
(Ennouchi, E.) 1969A
Jebel Sahaba; Paleolithic, upper; burial
(Wendorf, F.) 1968F
Kamchatka; Paleolithic burials
(Dikov, N. N.) 1969A
Kanapoi, Lothagam
(Robbins, L. H.) 1972A
Kenya
(Leakey, L. S. B.) 1970E
(Simons, H.) 1967A
Kiik-Koba Cave; Mousterian
(Liubin, V. P.) 1969A
Kenyapithecus; habits
(Anon.) 1968AQ
Koobi Fora, Ileret
(Leakey, R. E. F.) 1972A
Kow Swamp; skeletons
(Anon.) 1972AI,AS,BH
(Thorne, A. G., Macumber, P. G.) 1972A
Kow Swamp; skull, jaw
(Bickel, L.) 1970A
Krapina; Neanderthal
(Čanadjija, S.) 1970A
Krapina; Neanderthal; cannibalism
(Tomić-Karović, K.) 1970B
Krapina; Neanderthal; jaw
(Kallay, J.) 1970C
Krapina; Neanderthal; jaws, teeth
(Kallay, J.) 1969A, 1970A
Krapina; Neanderthal; morphology
(Kallay, J.) 1970E
Krapina; Neanderthal; morphology; pathology
(Tomić-Karović, K.) 1970A
Krapina; Neanderthal; skull, reconstruction
(Smith, F. H.) 1972A
Krapina; Neanderthal; teeth
(Kallay, J.) 1970D
Krasnoiarsk Water Reservoir; Paleolithic,
upper; jaw frag.
(Abramova, Z. A.) 1969A
Kůlna Cave; Neanderthal; jaw, teeth
(Jelínek, J.) 1967A
La Adam Cave; tooth, juvenile
(Necrasov, O.) 1962-63A
La Chaise
(Debenath, A.) 1968A, 1969A, 1970A
La Chaise, Fontéchevade; skulls
(Delarai, J.) 1957A
La Chaise; skull, arteries
(David, P., Piveteau, J.) 1953A

PALEOANTHROPOLOGY - cont.
Fossil Hominids
La Chaise; skull frags.
(Piveteau, J.) 1970A
La Chaise; skull, jaw
(Debénath, A., Piveteau, J.) 1969A
La Chapelle-aux-Saints; Mousterian;
skeleton
(Boule, M.) 1971A
(Bouyssonie, A., Bouyssonie, J.,
Bardon, L.) 1971A
La Ferrassie; endocranial cast
(Anthony, J., Heim, J.-L.) 1970A
La Quina; jaw
(Piveteau, J.) 1972B
La Quina; Neanderthal; temporal bone
(Vallois, H. V.) 1969D
Lake Baringo; Acheulean; jaw, teeth
(Leakey, M., et al.) 1969A
Lake Mungo; skeleton
(Barbetti, M., Allen, H.) 1972A
(Bowler, J. M., et al.) 1970A
(Bowler, J. M., Thorne, A. G.,
Polach, H. A.) 1972A
Lake Rudolf
(Anon.) 1971BS
(Behrensmeyer, A. K.) 1970A
(Isaac, G. L., Leakey, R. E. F.,
Behrensmeyer, A. K.) 1971A
(Leakey, R. E. F.) 1970A,B, 1971A
(T., L.) 1971A
(Vandermeersch, B.) 1972A
Lake Rudolf; Australopithecus; jaw
(Anon.) 1971BQ
Lake Rudolf; jaw
(Anon.) 1971AH
Lake Rudolf; Pliocene; dating
(Kurth, G.) 1972A
Lantian; jaw
(Lisowski, F. P.) 1965A
Lantian; skull, teeth
(Larichev, V. E.) 1970A
Lazaret Cave
(Lumley, H. de) 1969B, 1970A
Lazaret Cave; skull frag.
(Piveteau, J.) 1972A
Lazaret Cave; skull frag., teeth
(Gagnière, S.) 1970A
Lazaret Cave; teeth, parietal
(Lumley, M.-A. de, Piveteau, J.) 1969A
Les Eyzies; Cro-Magnon man
(Baker, J.) 1969A
Life span
(Acsádi, Gy., Nemeskéri, J.) 1970A
Ligurie-Provence; teeth, footprints
(Lumley-Woodyear, H. de) 1969D
Liukiang, Tung-tien-yen Cave; skull,
skeleton
(Woo, J-k.) 1959F
Locomotion
(Napier, J.) 1967B
Lothagam Hill; Australopithecus
(Patterson, B., Behrensmeyer, A. K.,
Sill, W. D.) 1970A
Makapansgat; bone accumulations
(Brain, C. K.) 1968A

PALEOANTHROPOLOGY - cont.
  Fossil Hominids
    Nomenclature
      (Campbell, B. G.)   1968B
      (Garn, S. M.)   1971A
      (Nesturkh, M. F.)   1972B
    North Africa
      (Cadenat, P.)   1966A
    North Africa; migrations
      (Blanc, A. C.)   1964A
    North America
      (Anon.)   1970BJ, 1971BO
      (Bosch-Gimpera, P.)   1971A
      (Haynes, C. V.)   1969A, 1972A
      (Jennings, J. D.)   1969A
      (Lindig, W.)   1970A
    North America; antiquity of man
      (Graham, J. A., Heizer, R. F.)   1967A
    North America; dating early man
      (Willey, G. R.)   1968A
    North America; habits
      (Wheat, J. B.)   1971A
    North America, migrations
      (Bandi, H.-G.)   1968A
      (Bosch y Gimpera, P.)   1967A
    North America; Paleo-Indian
      (Wormington, H. M.)   1967A
    North America; Paleo-Indian, hunting
    economy
      (Farb, P.)   1968A
    North America; settlement
      (Safronov, F. G.)   1971A
    Nubia; Paleolithic, upper; skeleton
      (Anderson, J. E.)   1968A
    Occipital bone, rate of growth
      (Petit-Maire Heintz, N., Dricot, J.-M.,
      d'Ans, C.)   1970A
    Ohaba Ponor Cave; Neanderthal; phalanges
      (Berciu, D.)   1967A
    Oldman R.; frags.
      (Forbis, R. G.)   1970A
    Olduvai Gorge
      (Anon.)   1967BL
      (Bonnefille, R., Chavaillon, J.,
      Coppens, Y.)   1970A
      (Leakey, L. S. B.)   1971C,D
      (Leakey, L. S. B., Leakey, M. D.)   1968A
      (Leakey, M. D.)   1971B
      (Robinson, J. T.)   1972A
      (Simons, H.)   1965C
      (Tobias, P. V.)   1972A
    Olduvai Gorge; Acheulean; skeleton
      (Leakey, M. D.)   1971A
    Olduvai Gorge; clavicle
      (Oxnard, C. E.)   1968C
    Olduvai Gorge; craniometry; taxonomy
      (Wolpoff, M. H.)   1969B, 1970A
    Olduvai Gorge; dentition, evolutionary rate
      (Bilsborough, A.)   1969A
    Olduvai Gorge; femur
      (Day, M. H.)   1969B
    Olduvai Gorge; femur, pelvis
      (Day, M. H.)   1971A
    Olduvai Gorge; foot
      (Day, M. H., Wood, B. A.)   1968A
    Olduvai Gorge; footprints
      (Anon.)   1972BC

  Fossil Hominids
    Olduvai Gorge; Homo habilis
      (Leakey, L. S. B., Tobias, P. V.,
      Napier, J. R.)   1971A
    Olduvai Gorge, Lake Natron; jaws, skull
    fragments
      (Leakey, L. S. B., Leakey, M. D.)   1971A
    Olduvai Gorge; skull
      (Anon.)   1961DH
      (Leakey, M. D., Clarke, R. J.,
      Leakey, L. S. B.)   1971A
    Olduvai Gorge; skull, teeth
      (Leakey, L. S. B.)   1960F, 1967H
      (Leakey, M. D.)   1969A
    Omo V.
      (Anfray, F.)   1968A
      (Anon.)   1969BA,BC
      (Butzer, K. W.)   1971A
      (Butzer, K. W., Brown, F. H.,
      Thurber, D. L.)   1969A
      (Coppens, Y.)   1970B, 1971C
      (Howell, F. C.)   1968A
      (Howell, F. C., Butzer, K. W.)   1968A
      (Thaler, L.)   1971B
    Omo V.; Homo sapiens, geochronology
      (Butzer, K. W.)   1969B
    Omo V.; jaws, teeth
      (Coppens, Y.)   1970A
      (Howell, F. C.)   1969C
      (Vallois, H. V.)   1969G
    Omo V.; skull, skeleton
      (Day, M. H.)   1969C
      (Leakey, L. S. B.)   1969B
    Omo V.; stratigraphy
      (Butzer, K. W.)   1969A
    Omo V.; teeth
      (Howell, F. C.)   1969A,B
    Ophir Mine; skull
      (Reichlen, P., Heizer, R. F.)   1966A
    Origin; diet
      (Eisenberg, L.)   1971A
    Origin; radiation
      (Alekseev, V. P.)   1970A
    Osteodontokeratic culture
      (Feustel, R.)   1969B
      (Wolberg, D. L.)   1970B,C
    Otjiseva; skull, jaw
      (Sydow, W.)   1969A
    Pacific areas
      (Shutler, R.)   1967D
    Paleo-Indian, habits
      (Kunz, M.)   1969A
    Paleolithic, uses of mammoth
      (Kupsch, W. O.)   1969A
    Paviland; environment
      (Bowen, D. Q.)   1970A
    Paviland; Paleolithic; skeleton; age
      (Oakley, K. P.)   1968A
    Paviland; skeleton
      (Anon.)   1969AR
      (Hillaby, J.)   1968A
      (John, B. S.)   1971A
    Pavlov; endocranial cast
      (Kochetkova, V. I.)   1967B
    Pech-de-l'Azé; Mousterian skull
      (Fenart, R.)   1969A

PALEOANTHROPOLOGY - cont.
Fossil Hominids
Schmerling Cave; Neanderthals
  (Vandebosch, A.)   1955A
Serbia; tooth
  (Gavela, B.)   1957A
Sexual dimorphism, cranial characteristics
  (Goździewski, S.)   1967A
Shanidar Cave; Neanderthal; burial
  (Leroi-Gourhan, Arlette)   1968A
Shanidar Cave; Neanderthal; skeletons
  (Anon.)   1961DJ, 1968BF
  (Solecki, R. S.)   1968A, 1971B
  (Sullivan, W.)   1968A
Shanidar Cave; Neanderthal; skeletons;
  habits
  (Solecki, R. S.)   1971A
Shensi; skull
  (Hoyanagi, M.)   1969A
Siberia; distribution
  (Amaré, R. F.)   1965A
Siberia, Indigirka; Paleolithic, upper;
  distribution
  (Vereshchagin, N. K.,
    Mochanov, Iu. A.)   1972A
Siberia, Maiorych; Paleolithic, upper;
  migration; art
  (Mochanov, Iu. A.)   1972A
Siberia, Volch'ia Griva; Paleolithic, upper;
  mammoth hunters
  (Alekseeva, E. V.,
    Vereshchagin, N. K.)   1970A
  (Alekseeva, E. V., Volkov, I. A.)   1969A
Sinanthropus, Mongoloid race derivation
  (Olivier, G.)   1967C
Skeletal biology
  (Brothwell, D. R.)   1968A
Skeleton
  (Khrisanfova, E. N.)   1967B,C, 1969A
Skull
  (Oakley, K. P.)   1965C
Skull crest; function
  (Angst, R.)   1970A
Skull, cultural significance
  (Henschen, F.)   1965A, 1966C
Skull, jaw; evolutionary trends
  (Petit-Maire, N.)   1972A
Skull morphology
  (Uryson, M. I.)   1970A
Skull, occipital cap
  (Petit-Maire-Heintz, N., Dricot, J.-M.)   1970A
Skull, x-ray
  (Brothwell, D. R., Molleson, T.,
    Metreweli, C.)   1968A
Sonora; skull
  (Johnson, A. E.)   1966A
South Africa
  (Anon.)   1970AV
  (Campbell, B. G.)   1969A
  (Klein, R. G.)   1970B
South Africa; Paleolithic
  (Inskeep, R. R.)   1969B
South America
  (Schobinger, J.)   1969A
Southeast Asia
  (Solheim, W. G.)   1969A

PALEOANTHROPOLOGY - cont.
Fossil Hominids
Steinheim man; skull
  (Adam, K. D.)   1969A
Sterkfontein
  (Bilsborough, A.)   1971A
  (Cooke, H. B. S.)   1968B
Sterkfontein; Australopithecus;
  skull, jaw
  (Broom, R.)   1971A
Sterkfontein; scapula
  (Oxnard, C. E.)   1968A
Suard Cave; Mousterian; skull, skeleton
  (David, P.)   1952A
Sungir'; Paleolithic burial
  (Anon.)   1971BY
  (Bader, O. N.)   1966D, 1970A
  (Sergin, V. Ia.)   1970A
Sungir'; Paleolithic burial; reconstruction
  (Bader, O. N.)   1970B, 1971A
Svitavka; skull, skeleton
  (Vlček, E.)   1967B
Swanscombe; skull frag.
  (Anon.)   1970AR
  (Marston, A. T.)   1971A
  (Wymer, J.)   1971A
Swartkrans
  (Bilsborough, A.)   1971A
Swartkrans; Australopithecine endocasts
  (Holloway, R. L.)   1972A
Swartkrans; Australopithecines, predation
  (Brain, C. K.)   1969A
Swartkrans; bone accumulations
  (Brain, C. K.)   1968B
Swartkrans; multiple species hypothesis
  (Wolpoff, M. H.)   1970B
Swartkrans; Paranthropus; metacarpal;
  biometry
  (Rightmire, G. P.)   1972A
Swartkrans; skull
  (Clarke, R. J., Howell, F. C.)   1972A
  (Wolpoff, M. H.)   1971A
Systematics
  (Collins, D.)   1969A
  (Coon, C. S.)   1966A, 1968A
  (Grigor'ev, G. P.)   1972B
  (Kharitonov, V. M.)   1972A
  (Khrisanfova, E. N.)   1972A
  (Reshetov, Iu. G.)   1972A
  (Simons, E. L., Pilbeam, D.,
    Ettel, P. C.)   1969A
  (Uryson, M. I.)   1972B
  (Zubov, A. A.)   1972A
Systematics; distribution; population
  structure
  (Kurth, G.)   1967A
Systematics; nomenclature
  (Jelínek, J.)   1966A
Taber; skeleton
  (Stalker, A. M.)   1969A
Talgai; skull
  (Anon.)   1969AN
  (Macintosh, N. W. G.)   1969A
Tangiers; jaw, tooth
  (Briggs, L. C.)   1967A

PALEOANTHROPOLOGY - cont.
Paleolithic Art
Rock art; Spain; Levante
(Pericot García, L.)   1964A
Rock engravings; USSR, Kostenki
(Fradkin, E. E.)   1969A
Rock paintings; falsification
(Weiss, J.)   1963A
Rock paintings; South Africa
(Lee, D. N., Woodhouse, H. C.)   1970A
Rock paintings; USSR, Zaraut-Kamar
(Formozov, A. A.)   1965C
Rock relief
(Barrière, C.)   1962A
Scimitar cat; France, Isturitz cave
(Mazak, V.)   1970A
Sculpture; USSR, Gagarino
(Tarasov, L. M.)   1972A
Shamanism
(Lommel, A.)   1967A
Statuette; France, Monpazier
(Clottes, J.)   1971A
Symposium
(Ripoll Perelló, E.)   1968A
Venus statues
(Pales, L.)   1968A
Paleopathology
Actinomycosis
(Dastugue, J.)   1967B
Bibliography
(Armelagos, G. J., Mielke, J. H.,
Winter, J.)   1971A
Bone lesions
(Dastugue, J.)   1969A
(Soriano, M.)   1970A
Dental caries
(Verger-Pratoucy, J.)   1967A
Dietary factors
(Brothwell, D. R., Brothwell, P.)   1969A
Enterobius vermicularis
(Fry, G. F., Moore, J. G.)   1969A
Evolutionary response
(Armelagos, G. J., Dewey, J. R.)   1970A
General
(Inskeep, R. R.)   1969A
Neanderthal
(Wright, D. J. M.)   1971A
Neanderthals; rickets
(Anon.)   1971AU
(Ivanhoe, F.)   1970A
(Wunderlich, M. D.)   1971A
Recent literature
(Goldstein, M. S.)   1969A
Textbook
(Janssens, P. A.)   1970A
PALEOBIOLOGY. See under Vertebrate.
PALEOCLIMATOLOGY
Cenozoic
Siberia; upper Irtysh Basin
(Bazhanov, V. S., Erofeev, V. S.)   1971A
Indicators
Cetacea
(Rothausen, K.)   1967A
Mesozoic fishes
(Schaeffer, B.)   1970A
Mesozoic terrestrial vertebrates
(Ostrom, J. H.)   1969F

PALEOCLIMATOLOGY - cont.
Indicators
Permian; No. America; vertebrates
(Olson, E. C., Vaughn, P. P.)   1970A
Pleist.; Australia; fossil sea lion
(Gill, E. D.)   1968B
Pleist. mammals
(Ryziewicz, Z.)   1964A
Permian
U.S., Four Corners; vertebrates
(Vaughn, P. P.)   1970B
Quaternary
Africa
(Heinzelin de Braucourt, J. de)   1966A
(Moreau, R. E.)   1963A
Asia; Tian-Shan
(Alešinskaja, Z. V., Bondarev, L. G.) 1969A
Canada; mammal fauna
(Christiansen, E. A.)   1972A
East Africa
(Gautier, A.)   1964A
Eurasia
(Markov, C. C.)   1968A
Europe
(Bonifay, M.-F.)   1969B
(Hesemann, J.)   1970A
(Kaiser, K.)   1967A
(Pasa, A.)   1969A
France
(Simard, S.)   1968A
France, Pyrenees
(Chaline, J.)   1971A
General
(Bouchud, J.)   1965C
(Mörner, N.-A.)   1970A
(Velichko, A. A.)   1968A
Hungary
(Kriván, P.)   1968A
Kenya
(Leakey, L. S. B.)   1970E
Libya
(Hey, R. W.)   1968A
Nubia
(Heinzelin de Braucourt, J. de)   1968A
Pacific area
(Blumenstock, D. I.)   1966A
Rumania, Brașov depression
(Alimen, H., Radulesco, C.,
Samson, P.)   1968B
Sarawak
(Petersen, R. M.)   1969A
Siberia
(Ravskiǐ, E. I.)   1969A
Temperature
Thermal coefficients
(Fabre, F.)   1970A
Tertiary
Argentina
(Volkheimer, W.)   1971A
Australia
(Stonehouse, B.)   1969A
Nebraska
(Voorhies, M. R.)   1971A
Saskatchewan; Miocene
(Holman, J. A.)   1971A
USSR, Kazakhstan
(Kosminskiǐ, V. V.)   1970A

PALEOECOLOGY - cont.
  Protohominids
    Plio-Pleistocene; Africa, Asia
      (Bartholomew, G. A., Birdsell, J. B.)   1969A
  Quaternary
    Africa
      (Moreau, R. E.)   1963A
    Africa, Sahara
      (Monod, T.)   1966A
    Africa, southern
      (Bond, G.)   1966A
    Glacial; USSR
      (Gromov, V. I., Nikiforova, K. V.)   1969A
    Japan
      (Kotani, Y.)   1969A
    Lake; Texas
      (Anderson, R. Y., Kirkland, D. W.)   1969A
    Littoral; France
      (Lumley, H. de, Gagnières, S.,
        Fournier, A.)   1969A
    Marine; Canada
      (Wagner, J. E.)   1970A
    Mexico, Tehuácan V.
      (MacNeish, R. S., Byers, D. S., et al.)   1967A
    Periglacial; USSR
      (Erbaeva, M. A.)   1969A
    Postglacial; No. America, eastern
      (Fitting, J. E.)   1968A
    So. America
      (Vuilleumier, B. S.)   1971A
    Steppe; Israel
      (Haas, G.)   1966A
    Subpluvial; U.S., Llano Estacado
      (Wendorf, F.)   1970A
    Terrestrial; Calif.
      (Gordon, W. D.)   1969A
    U.S., central plains
      (Cross, F. B.)   1970A
      (Dort, W., Jones, J. K.)   1970A
      (Kapp, R. O.)   1970B
    USSR, northern Ural Mts.
      (Kuz'mina, I. E.)   1970A
  Ramapithecus
    Miocene; India
      (Leakey, L. S. B.)   1969B
    North India
      (Tattersall, I.)   1969A,B
  Rodentia
    Pleist., upper; USSR, lower Aldan R.
      (Agadzhanían, A. K.,
        Boíarskaía, T. D.)   1969A
    Pleist.; USSR, Azov Sea
      (Agadzhanían, A. K.)   1970A
  Sarcopterygii
    Paleozoic; aquatic
      (Thomson, K. S.)   1969A
  Sauropoda
    Mesozoic; terrestrial
      (Thaler, L.)   1970A
  Teleostei
    Tert.; Serbia; fresh, brackish water
      (Anđelković, J.)   1970A
  Tertiary
    Germany, Mainz Basin
      (Rothausen, K.)   1969A
    Lacustrine; North America
      (Gregory, J. T.)   1969A

PALEOECOLOGY - cont.
  Tertiary
    Limnetic; Germany; Pliocene
      (Remane, J.)   1970A
  Triassic
    Humid-arid cycle; Argentina
      (Bonaparte, J. F.)   1969E
    Littoral; France
      (Gall, J.-Cl.)   1971A
  Vertebrates
    Cenozoic; U.S., Atlantic coastal
      plain; subtropical
      (Whitmore, F. C.)   1969A
    Deltaic swamps
      (Westoll, T. S.)   1968A
    Eocene; Utah, central
      (Baer, J. L.)   1969A
    Permo-Triassic; faunal replacement
      (Robinson, P. L.)   1971A
    Pleist., upper; Iowa, Mud Creek; forest
      (Kramer, T. L.)   1972A
    Pliocene; Kansas, Trego Co.
      (Wilson, R. L.)   1968B
    Triassic; Argentina; food niche distribution
      (Reig, O. A.)   1969A
    Triassic; faunal succession
      (Romer, A. S.)   1969H
PALEOGEOGRAPHY
  Bering Land Bridge
    Tert.-Quat.
      (Hopkins, D. M.)   1961A
  Cenozoic
    Arctic
      (Strelkov, S. A.)   1970A
    Beringia
      (Flerov, K. K.)   1964A
      (Portenko, L. A.)   1970A
      (Shtegman, B. K.)   1967A
    Colombia
      (Porta, J. de)   1969A
  Continental Drift
    Biological consequences
      (McKenna, M. C.)   1972E
    Evidence, Antarctic amphibians
      (Baranov, A. S.)   1969A
    Evidence, Antarctica Triassic tetrapods
      (Elliot, D. H., et al.)   1970A
    Evidence, fossil record
      (Hallam, A.)   1972A
    Evidence, Gondwanaland fossils
      (Romer, A. S.)   1968E
    Evidence, Gondwanaland reptile faunas
      (Corro, G. del)   1968A, 1971A
    Evidence, herpetofaunas
      (Estes, R.)   1971A
    Evidence, Lystrosaurus
      (Franzen, J. L.)   1970A
    Evidence, Lystrosaurus fauna
      (Colbert, E. H.)   1972C
    Evidence, mammal faunas
      (Fooden, J.)   1972A
    Evidence, paleozoogeographic
      (Smith, A. G., Hallam, A.)   1970A
    Evidence, tetrapods
      (Colbert, E. H.)   1971B
      (Gaffney, E. S.)   1971A
      (Romer, A. S.)   1972J

PALEONTOLOGY - cont.
  General
    Textbook
      (Thenius, E.)   1970A, 1972B
    Textbook, Australia
      (Laseron, C.)   1969A
    Textbook, Dolomite Mts.
      (Leonardi, P., et al.)   1967A
    Textbook; Michigan
      (Dorr, J. A., Eschman, D. F.)   1970A
    Textbook, Tert. faunas
      (Davies, A. M.)   1971A
    Trends
      (Haughton, S. H.)   1970A
    Vocational activities
      (Churcher, C. S.)   1968C
  Laboratory Techniques
    Age determination, fossil bone
      (Wysoczański-Minkowicz, T.)   1969A,B
    Age determination, teeth and bone layers
      (Klevezal, G., Kleinenberg, S.) 1969A
    Airbrasive
      (Kuhn-Schnyder, E.)   1969B
    Bone formation rates, determination
      (Frost, H. M., Wu, K.)   1967A
    Casting
      (Rennie, G. S.)   1969A
    Casting, plastics
      (Parsons, K. C.)   1968A
    Casts, Solnhofen vertebrates
      (Keller, R.)   1971A
    Collagen extraction
      (Longin, R.)   1970A, 1971A
    Color coding
      (Chartkoff, J. L.)   1966A
    Computer simulation
      (Harbaugh, J. W.)   1967A
    Computer usage
      (Olson, E. C.)   1970C
      (Squires, D. F.)   1966A
    Contamination treatment
      (Lefevre, M., Laporte, G. S.)   1968A
    Craniological series, study of contours
      (Gokhman, I. I.)   1967A
    Craniometry
      (Anderson, S.)   1968A
    Drawing technique
      (Souza Cunha, F. L. de, Jain, S. L.) 1968A
    Faunal analysis
      (Daly, P.)   1969A
    Faunal analysis, quantification
      (Bekeni, Sh.)   1969A
      (Krantz, G. S.)   1968A
      (Thomas, D. H.)   1969A
    General
      (Rudner, I.)   1970A
    Identification, cataloging
      (Guilday, J. E.)   1959A
    Megafossil study
      (Hayami, I., Obata, I.)   1966A,B
    Microvertebrates, recovery with acetic acid
      (Green, M.)   1970A
    Model making
      (Wade, R. E., et al.)   1969A
    Molds, skull cavities
      (Lecacheux, B.)   1967A

PALEONTOLOGY - cont.
  Laboratory Techniques
    Molds, vinyl
      (Kampa, E.)   1971A
    Paleoengineering
      (Whitfield, G., Bramwell, C.)   1971A
    Photoelectric separation
      (Kühne, W. G.)   1971A
    Photography
      (Imperatori, L.)   1967A
      (Wells, C.)   1967A
    Preparation
      (Fonin, V. D.)   1966A
      (Guilday, J. E.)   1959A
      (Sacchi Vialli, G.)   1967A
    Preparation, acid, gypsum encrusted
      material
      (Harris, J. M.)   1971A
    Preparation, bone tissue, frozen sections
      (Gashev, N. S., Bakhmutov, V. A.) 1968A
    Preparation, chemical
      (Lund, R.)   1970A
    Preparation, cleaning fossils
      (Anon.)   1969BN
    Preparation, Pleist. mammals
      (Keller, B.)   1968A
    Preparation, polyurethane
      (Carreck, J. N., Adams, S. J.)   1969A
    Preservation of bone
      (White, T.)   1971A
    Reproductions
      (Kuznetsov, V. V.,
       Birûkov, M. D.)   1969A,B
    Serial sectioning
      (Kermack, D. M.)   1970A
      (Poplin, C. M., Ricqlès, A. J. de) 1970A
    Silicon rubber prints
      (Brezinová, D., Losos, L.,
       Majzner, Z.)   1968A
    Specimens, treatment
      (Ambrose, W. R.)   1968A
    Storage
      (Yochelson, E. L.)   1969A
    Tags for specimens
      (Aish, P. J., et al.)   1968A
    Vestibular method
      (Fenart, R.)   1969B
      (Fenart, R., Empereur-Buisson, R.) 1970A
PALEOPATHOLOGY. See under Paleoanthropology,
  Vertebrate.
PALEOZOIC
  Correlation
    No. America, Appalachian-Caledonian
      orogeny; fishes
      (Turner, S.)   1970A
    USSR; fishes
      (Obruchev, D. V.,
       Karatajute-Talimaa, V.)   1968A
PENNSYLVANIA
  Paleontology
    Mam.; Pleist.; Mosherville
      (Ray, C. E., Denny, C. S.,
       Rubin, M.)   1970A
    Mam.; Pleist.; New Paris Sinkholes
      (Guilday, J. E.)   1961E

PISCES - cont.

Actinopterygii

Cret., upper; Bolivia; skull frags.,
fin spines
(Wenz, S.)   1969A,B

Mesozoic; Siberia; morphology; n. taxa
(Iakovlev, V. N.)   1968A

Miocene; Yugoslavia, Belgrad
(Andelković, J. S.)   1969A

Oligocene; Iran, Elam, Istehbanat; n. taxa
(Arambourg, C.)   1966A

Paleocene; Niger, Iullemmeden basin;
morphology; ecology
(Cappetta, H.)   1972B

Triassic; Germany, Karlsruhe-Durlach;
skeletons; n. taxa
(Jörg, E.)   1969A, 1970A

Triassic; Madagascar; neurocrania; n. taxa
(Beltan, L.)   1968A

Aeoliscus heinrichi

Oligocene, middle; Germany, Wiesloch;
evolution; skull, fins
(Weiler, W.)   1971C

Albulidae

Cret.; Montana; skull frags., tooth plates;
n. taxa
(Estes, R.)   1969E

Cret.; Wyoming; skull frags., tooth plates;
n. taxa
(Estes, R.)   1969E

Allenypterus

Penn.; Montana, Becket; morphology; n. gen.
(Melton, W. G.)   1969B

Amblypterus

Habitat
(Kapoor, H. M.)   1965A

Permian; Poland, intra-Sudetic basin;
morphology
(Dziedzic, K.)   1961A

Amia fragosa

Cret.; Montana; morphology; systematics
(Estes, R., Berberian, P.)   1969A

Amiidae

Systematics; taphonomy
(Boreske, J. R. A.)   1972A

Amphiaspidiformes

Dev.; Siberia; morphology; phylogeny;
systematics; n. taxa
(Novitskaia, L. I.)   1968A, 1971B

Anacoracidae

Cret., upper; USSR; systematics;
evolution; teeth; n. gen.
(Glikman, L. S., Shvazhaite, R. A.)   1971A

Anaethalion

Jurassic; France, Verdun
(Gaudant, J., Maubeuge, P.)   1971A

Morphology; systematics; n. sp.
(Gaudant, J.)   1968B

Anatomy

Functional, feeding system; Acanthodes
(Miles, R. S.)   1968A

Functional, feeding system; Arthrodira
(Miles, R. S.)   1969A

Functional, fins; Xenacanthidae
(Zídek, J.)   1965A

PISCES - cont.

Anatomy

Functional, locomotor system; Latimeria
(Wahlert, G. von; Wahlert, H. von)   1967A

Functional, muscular system;
Eusthenopteron
(Andrews, S. M., Westoll, T. S.)   1970A

Functional; Sarcopterygii
(Thomson, K. S.)   1969B

Functional, sensory system; Rhipidistia
(Van Bergijk, W. A.)   1966A

Functional; skeletal system;
Eusthenopteron
(Andrews, S. M., Westoll, T. S.)   1970A

Functional, swimming
(Lighthill, M. J.)   1970A

Functional; tail, heterocercal
(Iakovlev, V. N.)   1968B

Functional, tail; Heterostraci
(Denison, R. H.)   1971B

Histology; integument
(Ørvig, T.)   1972A

Histology; skull; Janassa bituminosa
(Malzahn, E.)   1972A

Histology; vertebrae; Dipnoi
(Schultze, H.-P.)   1970A

Jaw, dentition; Homalacanthus
(Schultze, H.-P.)   1972A

Lateral line system; Arthrodira; n. gen.
(Ørvig, T.)   1971A

Locomotor system
(Simons, J. R.)   1971A

Muscular system; Actinopterigii
(Jessen, H.)   1972A

Nervous system; Coelacanthiformes
(Bjerring, H. C.)   1972B

Skeletal system; Actinopterigii
(Jessen, H.)   1972A

Skeletal system, dermal bone
(Kapoor, A. S.)   1970A

Skeletal system; Dolichothoraci
(Goujet, D.)   1972A

Skull; Dipnorhynchus süssmilchi;
evolution
(Thomson, K. S.,
Campbell, K. S. W.)   1971A

Teeth; Rhipidistia
(Schultze, H.-P.)   1970D

Aplodinotus

Pleist.; Ontario; pharyngeals
(Harington, C. R.)   1971C

Archaeomaenidae

Jur., lower; Antarctica, Queen Alexandra
Range; skull, skeleton; n. gen.
(Schaeffer, B.)   1972A

Archegonaspis

Sil., upper; USSR, Vaigach Is.
(Novitskaia, L. I.)   1970B

Sil.; USSR, Vaigach Is.; morphology;
n. sp.
(Novitskaia, L. I.)   1970A

Arctolepidae

Devonian; Persian Gulf; n. taxa
(White, E, I.)   1969A

PISCES - cont.
Chondrichthyes
Paleocene; Bulgaria, Plevna region
(Dachev, D.)   1967A
Cimolichthys
Morphology; reconstruction
(Goody, P. C.)   1970B
Clupavus
Cret., upper; Congo, Vonso;
morphology; n. sp.
(Taverne, L.)   1969C
Cret.; Wyoming, Cody; skull,
skeleton; reconstruction
(Dunkle, D. H.)   1971A
Nomenclature; n. sp.
(Arambourg, C.)   1967B
Clupeidae
Miocene; Yugoslavia. Belgrade; n. sp.
(Anđelković, J. S.)   1967A
Oligocene; USSR, Caucasus
(Klebanova, N. I.)   1971A
Tert.; Asia, southwestern; evolution;
phylogeny
(Danil'chenko, V. P.)   1972A
Clupeiformes
Cret.; Australia, Victoria; morphology;
n. taxa
(Waldman, M.)   1971B
Cret., lower; England, Folkestone;
skull; n. gen.
(Patterson, C.)   1970B
Coccosteiformes
Devonian; USSR; morphology; distribution;
evolution; n. gen.
(Obrucheva, O. P.)   1962C
Coelodus
Cret.; Greece, Lindos; teeth; phylogeny
(Melentis, J. K.)   1967D
Coelolepiddae
Devonian; USSR, Podolia; morphology;
n. taxa
(Karatajute-Talimaa, V. N.)   1968B
Colobodus
Triassic; East Germany, Bechstedt-Wagd;
skull, jaws
(Müller, A. H.)   1970D
Conchopoma
Penn.; Illinois; morphology; n. sp.
(Denison, R. H.)   1969A
Coryphaenoides
Oligocene, upper; USSR, Kamchatka,
eastern
(Grechina, N. I.)   1971A
Cottidae
Plio-Pleistocene; Idaho, Glenns Ferry Fm.
(Linder, A. D.)   1970A
Texas; coelomic cavity casts
(Gillette, D. D.)   1972A
Crossopterygii
Dev.; USSR, Latvia; taphonomy
(Lyarskaya, L., Mark-Kurik, E.)   1972A
Ctenacanthus
Permian, upper; Germany, Richelsdorfer
Gebirge; skeleton
(Bendix-Almgreen, S. E.,
Malzahn, E.)   1969A

PISCES - cont.
Ctenacanthus
Permian, upper; India, Kashmir;
tooth; n. sp.
(Kapoor, H. M., Sahni, A.)   1971A
Ctenodontidae
Carb., lower; Siberia, Iakutia; skull;
n. gen.
(Vorob'eva, E. I.)   1972A
Cyclostomata
Morphology; systematics; phylogeny
(Stensiö, E.)   1968A
Origin
(Obruchev, D. V.)   1971A
Origin; evolution
(Obruchev, D. V.)   1971A
Cylindracanthus
Cret., upper; Spain
(Bauzá Rullán, J.)   1971C
Cyprinidae
Pleist.; Czechoslovakia; morphology
(Obrhelová, N.)   1970A
Tert.; Czechoslovakia; morphology;
n. taxa
(Obrhelová, N.)   1969A, 1970B
Dalatias
Triassic; England, Barnstone; n. sp.
(Sykes, J. H.)   1971A
Dasybatus
Pliocene; Japan, Aomori; spine; n. sp.
(Hatai, K.)   1965C
Devonian
Antarctica, Victoria Land; n. taxa
(White, E. I.)   1968A
Dinichthyidae
Devonian, middle; Iowa, Vogel
Quarry; jaw
(Straka, J. J., Semken, H. A.)   1969A,B
Diodontidae
Miocene; Calif.; dentition
(Bacskai, J.)   1969A
Diplomystus
Cret.; Tunisia, south; n. sp.
(Gaudant, M., Gaudant, J.)   1971A
Dipnoi
Cret.; Niger; Iullemmeden basin;
morphology; ecology
(Cappetta, H.)   1972B
Dev.; Germany, Bergisch-Gladbach;
skull, skeleton; reconstruction; n. sp.
(Schultze, H.-P.)   1969A
Dev.; Pennsylvania, northeastern;
aestivation cylinders
(Woodrow, D. L., Fletcher, F. W.)   1969A
Origin, freshwater
(Dasch, E. J., Campbell, K. S. W.)   1970A
Paleocene; Niger, Iullemmeden basin;
morphology; ecology
(Cappetta, H.)   1972B
Penn.; Pennsylvania, Pittsburgh; skull,
skeleton; n. taxa
(Lund, R.)   1970B
Phylogeny; anatomy, skull
(Bertmar, G.)   1968A
Phylogeny; evolution
(Bertmar, G.)   1968B

PISCES - cont.
General
Systematics; evolution
 (Kuhn, O.)   1967D
Gnathorhiza
Perm.; Oklahoma, Hennessey Fm.;
skeleton, teeth; n. sp.
 (Olson, E. C., Daly, E.) 1972A
Perm.; Oklahoma, northcentral;
skull, burrows; phylogeny
 (Carlson, K. J.)   1968A
Gnathostomata
Evolution; phylogeny
 (Wahlert, G. von)   1968A
Goodeidae
Pliocene; Mexico, Jalisco,
Barranca de Santa Rosa; n. taxa
 (Alvarez, J., Arreola, J.) 1972A
Gyracanthus
Carb.; USSR, Donefs basin; spine
 (Karlov, N. N.)   1968A
Gyroptychius
Devonian; British Colombia, Wokkpash
Creek; n. sp.
 (Jessen, H.)   1968A
Helicoprion
Permian; Canada, Ellesmere Is.; morphology
 (Nassichuk, W. W., Spinosa, C.) 1970A
Permian; Canada, Sverdrup Basin;
morphology
 (Nassichuk, W. W.)   1971A
Permian; Spitzbergen; skeleton; n. sp.
 (Siedlecki, S.)   1970A
Heterostraci
Devonian; USSR, Podolia; morphology;
n. taxa
 (Karatajute-Talimaa, V. N.) 1968B
Evolution; phylogeny
 (Obruchev, D. V.)   1968C
Spiracle
 (Halstead, L. B.)   1971A
Holocephali
Morphology; systematics
 (Patterson, C.)   1969A
Holonema
Devonian; Idaho, Lemhi Mts.;
morphology; n. sp.
 (Denison, R. H.)   1968B
Devonian; Ohio, Silica Fm.; cranial
shield plate
 (Mitchell, S. W.)   1971A
Holonematidae
Dev.; systematics; anatomy; n. sp.
 (Miles, R. S.)   1971B
Holostei
Pleist.; Nebraska, Sand Draw; morphology
 (Smith, G. R., Lundberg, J. G.) 1972A
Hybodontidae
Cret., upper; No. America, western;
morphology; stratigraphy
 (Wilson, M.)   1972A
Hybodus
Carb., upper; Czechoslovakia, Kounov;
tooth; systematics
 (Zídek, J.)   1969A

PISCES - cont.
Hypoprion
Miocene; India, Baiwa; tooth
 (Singh, G.)   1971A
Hypospondylus
Systematics; nomenclature
 (Zídek, J.)   1967A
Ictaluridae
Eocene; Wyoming, Green River Fm.;
systematics; n. gen.
 (Lundberg, J. G., Case, G. R.) 1970A
Ictalurus
Pleist.; Mexico, Chapala & Zacoalco;
skull, skeleton
 (Alvarez, J.)   1966A
Pleist.; Texas; fin spines
 (Douglas, C. L.)   1969A
Ischyodus
Cret., lower; Poland, Annopol; morphology
 (Radwański, A.)   1968A
Ischyrhiza
Cret.; Alberta; teeth
 (Storer, J. E.)   1972B
Isurus
Miocene; Calif., Topanga Fm.; tooth
 (Totten, D. K.)   1969A
Jamoytius
Morphology
 (Durham, J. W.)   1971C
Labrodon
Miocene; Portugal; tooth plates
 (Jonet, S.)   1968A
Lamna
Miocene; Angola; teeth; distribution;
n. taxa
 (Telles Antunes, M.) 1970A
Lamnidae
Pliocene; Italy, Punta Ristola;
morphology
 (Menesini, E.)   1968A
Lepidorhombus
Oligocene; East Germany, Malliss;
morphology
 (Heinrich, W.-D.)   1970A
Lepidotes
Cret., lower; Brazil, Bahia; scales; n. sp.
 (Silva Santos, R. da) 1969A
Cret., lower; Texas, northcentral;
morphology
 (Bilelo, M. M.)   1969A
Lepomis
Pleist.; Texas, Randall Co.;
premaxillary; paleoecology
 (Schultz, G. E., Cheatum, E. P.) 1970A
Leuciscus
Tert.; Czechoslovakia; skull, skeleton;
reconstruction
 (Obrhelová, N.)   1971A
Lophosteus
Silurian; USSR, Estonia; morphology;
systematics; n. taxa
 (Gross, W.)   1969A
Systematics
 (Gross, W.)   1971B

PISCES - cont.
  Otoliths
    Miocene; Rumania, Buituri
      (Rado, G.)   1969A
    Miocene; Rumania, Copăcel-Chijic
      (Rado, G.)   1968A
    Miocene; Rumania, Coşteiul de Sus
      (Rado, G.)   1965A
    Miocene; Switzerland, Boudry; n. taxa
      (Stinton, F. C., Kissling, D.)   1968A
    Miocene; Switzerland, Entlebuch
      (Salis, K. von)   1967A
    Miocene; USSR, Azerbaĭdzhan
      (Voroshilova, A. G.)   1971A
    Oligocene; Czechoslovakia, Pouzdřany
      (Brzobohatý, R.)   1966A
    Oligo-Miocene; Germany, north
      (Boekschoten, G. J.)   1969A
    Pleist.; Calif., San Fedro
      (Fitch, J. E.)   1968A
    Pleist.; Japan
      (Aoki, N.)   1968A
    Pleist., upper; Calif., Arcata and
      Palos Verdes Sand
      (Fitch, J. E.)   1970A
    Pliocene; Italy, Sicily; n. sp.
      (Weiler, W.)   1971B
    Pliocene; Sardinia, Orosei
      (Dieni, I.)   1968A
    Significance
      (Gaemers, P. A. M.)   1968A
    Tert.; Germany, Mayence Basin;
      nomenclature; n. sp.
      (Schwarzhans, W., Weiler, W.)   1971A
    Tert.; Germany, northern
      (Martini, E.)   1968A
    Tert.; Rumania, Socenci
      (Stancu, J.)   1970A
  Pachyrhizodus
    Cret., lower; morphology; reconstruction
      (Bartholomai, A.)   1969A
  Palaeogadus
    Oligocene; USSR, Belaĩa R.,
      skeleton; n. sp.
      (Fedotov, V. F.)   1970A
  Palaeolabridae
    Cret.; Montana; skull frags.,
      tooth plates; n. taxa
      (Estes, R.)   1969E
    Cret.; Wyoming; skull frags.,
      tooth plates; n. taxa
      (Estes, R.)   1969E
  Palaeonisciformes
    Carb.; So. Africa, Willowmore;
      morphology; n. taxa
      (Gardiner, B. G.)   1969A
    Cret.; Australia, Victoria; morphology; n. sp.
      (Waldman, M.)   1971B
    Systematics; n. fam.
      (Kazanĩseva, A. A.)   1971A
  Palaeoniscoidea
    Carb.; USSR, Bystraĩà Fm.; morphology;
      n. taxa
      (Kazanĩseva, A. A.)   1968A
    Cret., lower; Germany, Stadthagen;
      skull, skeleton; n. gen.
      (Schultze, H.-P.)   1970B

PISCES - cont.
  Palaeospondylus
    Morphology; systematics
      (Lehman, J.-P.)   1969A
  Palealbula
    Cret.; Germany, Engelbostel bei Hannover;
      otoliths; n. sp.
      (Weiler, W.)   1971A
  Paleozoic
    Evolution
      (Piveteau, J.)   1969A
    Morphology; evolution
      (Thomson, K. S.)   1971A
    Textbook
      (Moy-Thomas, J. A.)   1971A
  Panderichthys
    Skull anatomy
      (Vorob'eva, E. I.)   1971B
  Paracanthopterygii
    Morphology; systematics; n. taxa
      (Rosen, D. E., Patterson, C.)   1969A
  Paraceratodus
    Triassic; Madagascar; neurocranium
      (Beltan, L.)   1968A
  Paramblypterus
    Perm., lower; France, Surmoulin;
      skull, girdle
      (Heyler, D.)   1971A
  Parasilurus
    Pleist.; Czechoslovakia; pectoral ray
      (Obrhelová, N.)   1970A
  Paratrisopterus
    Miocene; USSR, Moldavia; skeleton;
      n. gen.
      (Fedotov, V. F.)   1971B
  Perca
    Variation
      (Lebedev, V. D., Fedotov, V. F.)   1969A
  Perciformes
    Eocene; Italy, Bolca; morphology;
      systematics; n. taxa
      (Blot, J.)   1969B
  Permian
    France; morphology; systematics;
      n. taxa
      (Heyler, D.)   1969A
  Petromyzontidae
    Evolution
      (Hubbs, C. L., Potter, I. C.)   1971A
  Phlebolepis
    Silurian; USSR, Oesel; morphology
      (Ritchie, A.)   1968B
  Pholidophoriformes
    Cret.; Australia, Victoria;
      morphology; n. taxa
      (Waldman, M.)   1971B
    Jurassic, lower; Antarctica, Queen
      Alexandra Range; morphology
      (Schaeffer, B.)   1971C
  Phyllodontidae
    Morphology; systematics; evolution;
      n. taxa
      (Estes, R.)   1969G
  Phylogeny
    Criteria; Agnatha, Pisces
      (Obruchev, D. V.)   1972A

PISCES - cont.
 Selachii
  Cret.; Niger, Iullemmeden basin;
   morphology; ecology; n. taxa
   (Cappetta, H.)   1972B
  Cret.; USSR, Kazakhstan, western;
   teeth; n. taxa
   (Zhelezko, V. I., Glikman, L. S.) 1971A
  Miocene; France, Montpellier; morphology;
   n. taxa
   (Cappetta, H.)   1969B, 1970A
  Miocene, lower; Austria, Plesching; morphology
   (Schultz, O.)   1968A
  Miocene, lower; France, Hérault; teeth; n. sp.
   (Cappetta, H.)   1972A
  Miocene; Netherlands; Delden
   (Bosch, M. v. d.)   1969A
  Miocene; Portugal, Lisbon; morphology;
   n. taxa
   (Telles Antunes, M., Jonet, S.)   1970A
  Miocene; USSR, Ciscarpathia; teeth
   (Skvortsova, K. V.)   1972A
  Paleocene; Niger, Iullemmeden basin;
   morphology; ecology; n. taxa
   (Cappetta, H.)   1972B
  Penn.; Illinois, Will Co.; n. taxa
   (Zangerl, R.)   1969A
 Serranidae
  Cenozoic; northern Bohemia; Bílina;
   morphology; reconstruction; n. gen.
   (Obrhelová, N.)   1971B
  Tert.; Rumania, Bretçu-Tg. Secuiesc
   depression
   (Bucur, I.)   1971A
 Silurus
  Pleist.; Belgium; pectoral spines
   (Casier, E.)   1957C
 Sparidae
  Pliocene; Italy, Punta Ristola; morphology
   (Menesini, E.)   1968A
 Sphyraenidae
  Miocene, middle; USSR, Pirekeshkíul';
   morphology; systematics
   (Svichenskaîa, A. A.)   1968A
 Squalicorax
  Cret., upper; Texas, northcentral;
   teeth; systematics
   (Bilelo, M. A. M.)   1969B
 Squalodon
  Miocene; North Carolina; taphonomy
   (Boreske, J. R., Goldberg, L.,
    Cameron, B.)   1972A
   (Cameron, B., Boreske, J. R.)   1972A
 Squalodontidae
  Oligocene; New Zealand, Fossil Point; jaws
   (Climo, F. M., Baker, A. N.)   1972A
 Strobilodus
  Jurassic; Germany, Solnhofen;
   skull, skeleton
   (Janicke, V.)   1970A
 Syngnathidae
  Oligocene; USSR, Azerbaïdzhan; n. sp.
   (Sergienko, N. I.)   1971A
 Synorichthys
  Triassic; No. America; morphology
   (Schaeffer, B., Mangus, M.)   1970A

PISCES - cont.
 Teleostei
  Cenozoic; California; history
   (Fitch, J. E., Lavenberg, R. J.) 1971A
  Cret.; Northwest Territories, Lac de Bois;
   skeleton, skull, scales
   (Waldman, M.)   1969B
  Eocene; Belgium; otoliths; n. sp.
   (Nolf, D.)   1970C
  Eocene; Iran, Ilam; morphology
   (Haghipour, A., Brants, A.)   1971A
  Miocene; Brazil, Pará; morphology
   (Silva Santos, R.,
    Sardenberg Salgado, M.)   1971A
  Miocene; Japan, Shizukuishi;
   morphology; n. taxa
   (Sato, J.)   1962A
  Morphology; systematics
   (Gosline, W. A.)   1971A
  Neogene; Mongolia, Bol'shie Ozera
   Basin; biogeography; n. sp.
   (Sychevskaîa, E. K.,
    Lebedev, V. D.)   1971A
  Oligocene; Rumania, Piatra-Neamţ; n. taxa
   (Ciobanu, M.)   1969A
  Paleocene; USSR, Turkmenia;
   morphology; n. taxa
   (Danil'chenko, P. G.)   1968B
  Phylogeny
   (Nelson, G. J.)   1969C
  Pleist.; Nebraska, Sand Draw;
   morphology; n. sp.
   (Smith, G. R., Lundberg, J. G.)   1972A
  Tert.; Yugoslavia, Serbia; distribution;
   paleoecology; systematics
   (Anđelković, J.)   1970A
 Thelodonti
  Dev., lower; Norway, Spitsbergen; n. taxa
   (Heintz, N.)   1972A
 Thelodontidae
  Silurian, lower; Northwest Territories,
   Prince of Wales Is.; morphology
   (Turner, S., Dixon, J.)   1971A
 Thrissops
  Systematics
   (Nybelin, O.)   1964A
 Thursius
  Devonian, middle; USSR, Latvia;
   skull; n. sp.
   (Vorob'eva, E. I.)   1971C
 Thymallus
  Pleist.; Canada, Yukon Territory; scales
   (McAllister, D. E., Harington, C. R.) 1969A
 Triacanthoidea
  Morphology; evolution; phylogeny
   (Tyler, J. C.)   1968A
 Turinia
  Devonian; Australia, Wilson Cliffs;
   scales; n. sp.
   (Gross, W.)   1971C
 Umbridae
  Oligocene; Siberia, western; morphology;
   phylogeny; distribution; n. taxa
   (Sychevskaîa, E. K.)   1968A
 Uranolophus
  Morphology
   (Denison, R. H.)   1968C

POPULAR WORKS - cont.
  Dinosaurs
    Colorado; Australia
      (Anon.)   1972BN
    Connecticut
      (Ostrom, J. H.)   1969D
    Duck-bills
      (Ostrom, J. H.)   1965B
    Evolution; habits
      (Pringle, L.)   1968A
    France
      (Lapparent, A. F. de)   1967A
    General
      (Anon.)   1966BT
      (Colbert, E. H.)   1964F
      (Jackson, K.)   1972A
      (McGowen, T.)   1972A
    Habits
      (Wernert, S.)   1969A
    Montana
      (Ostrom, J. H.)   1969B,C
    Morphology; evolution
      (Russell, L. S.)   1971A
    Tracks
      (Anon.)   1967BR
  Earth History
    General
      (Matthews, W. H.)   1968B
  Evolution
    Processes; vertebrate phylogeny
      (Wallace, C.)   1969A
  Extinct Fauna
    North America
      (McClung, R. M.)   1969A
  Fossil Horses
    North America
      (Haines, F.)   1971A
  Fossil Mammals
    Morphology; reconstructions
      (Markman, H. C.)   1952A
  Fossil Man
    Cultural evolution
      (Galbraith, H.)   1963A
    Origin
      (Innes, H.)   1971A
    Paleolithic hunters
      (Elting, M., Folsom, F.)   1971A
    Ramapithecus; antiquity of Homo sapiens
      (Chedd, G., Stubbs, P.)   1969A
  Fossils
    Amateur collecting
      (Macdonald, J. R.)   1968B
    Antarctica
      (Frazier, K.)   1970B,C
      (Lear, J.)   1970A
      (Tweedie, M.)   1970B
    Arizona, Rampart Cave
      (Harington, C. R.)   1972A
    Arizona, Ventana Cave
      (Johnston, B.)   1969A
    California
      (Stinson, M. C.)   1964A
      (Stinson, M. C.)   1971A
    Calif., Barstow
      (Davenport, L. C.,
        Goldbrandsen, J.)   1963A

POPULAR WORKS - cont.
  Fossils
    Calif., Knight's Ferry
      (Moore, W.)   1972A
    Calif., Mojave Desert
      (Belden, L. B.)   1968A
    Calif.; state fossil
      (Welter, J.)   1972A
    Catastrophic deaths
      (Casson, M.)   1972A
    Collecting, ethic
      (Fisher, D. W.)   1972A
    Collecting, guide
      (Casanova, R.)   1970A
    Collecting, methods
      (Chedd, G., Stubbs, P., Wick, G.)   1970A
    Collection; preparation
      (Schuberth, C. J.)   1965A
    Dinosaur National Monument
      (Berman, D. S.)   1971A
    Fieldtrip, Jr. California Academy of
      Sciences
      (Firby, J., Lucas, K.)   1970A
    Fish and its prey
      (Muralidhara, V.)   1969B
    Florida
      (Pyles, G.)   1969A
    General
      (Kirkaldy, J. F.)   1967A
      (Matthews, W. H.)   1968A
    Germany
      (Stöhr, M.)   1968A
    Germany, Augsburg
      (Roeck, B.)   1968A
    Iowa
      (Brenner, P.)   1969A
    Localities
      (Schroeder, D.)   1969A,B,C, 1970A,B,C,D
    Mammals
      (Kurtén, B.)   1969D, 1971A
      (McKenna, M. C.)   1971B
    Nevada, Gypsum Cave
      (Lawlor, F.)   1970A
    New Jersey
      (Anon.)   1965DA
    New Mexico
      (Northrop, S. A.)   1962A
    Oregon, John Day Basin
      (Ouellette, C., Ouellette, E.)   1970A
    Pennsylvania
      (Guilday, J. E.)   1970A
    Pleistocene mammals
      (Cohen, D.)   1969A
    Preparation
      (Rudner, I.)   1970A
    Rancho la Brea
      (Gerster, G.)   1971A
      (Holliday, K.)   1972A
      (Miller, G. J.)   1971A, 1972A
      (Welch, D.)   1965A
    Saskatchewan
      (Johnson, H.)   1969A
    Teeth
      (Ørvig, T.)   1968A
    Vertebrates
      (Anon.)   1965CZ

QUATERNARY - cont.
  Correlation
    East Africa; methods
      (Bishop, W. W.)   1968A
    Ethiopia, Omo V.; vertebrates
      (Heinzelin de Braucourt, J. de)   1969A
    Europe, eastern; mammals
      (Vangengeĭm, E. A., Zazhigin, V. S.)   1969A
    Europe, eastern; microtines
      (Zazhigin, V. S.)   1969A
    Europe; mammals
      (Arambourg, C.)   1969A,B
      (Moskvitin, A. I.)   1970A
      (Nikiforova, K. V.)   1968A
      (Nikiforova, K. V., et al.)   1971A
      (Nikiforova, K. V., Ivanova, I. K.,
        Konstantinova, N. A.)   1969A, 1970A
    Europe; vertebrates
      (Biberson, P.)   1969A
    Europe; Villafranchian; mammals
      (Azzaroli, A.)   1970A
    Siberia; microtines
      (Zazhigin, V. S.)   1969A
    Siberia; mammals
      (Vangengeĭm, E. A., Zazhigin, V. S.)   1969A
    So. Africa; Australopithecines, elephants
      (Wright, G. A., Skaryd, S.)   1972A
    Turkey; mammals
      (Vita-Finzi, C.)   1970A
    U.S., Great Plains; mammals
      (Hibbard, C. W.)   1972B
    U.S.; mammals
      (Birkeland, P. W., Crandell, D. R.,
        Richmond, G. M.)   1971A
    USSR; mammals
      (Kostenko, N. N.,
        Kozhamkulova, B. S.)   1964A
      (Lebedeva, N. A.)   1968A, 1971A
    USSR, Transcaucasia; mammals
      (Lebedeva, N. A.)   1972A
    Vietnam; vertebrates
      (Boriskovskiĭ, P. I.)   1966B
  Geochronology
    Africa; mammals
      (Arambourg, C.)   1969A,B
      (Coppens, Y.)   1972A
    Africa, Nyasa-Rukwa Rift; vertebrates
      (Haynes, C. V.)   1968C
    Asia, eastern; mammals
      (Alekseev, M. N.)   1969A
    Asia; Villafranchian; mammals
      (Ravskiĭ, E. I.)   1968A,B
    Austria; mammals
      (Mottl, M.)   1960B
    Bering Strait; mammals
      (Sher, A. V.)   1971C
    East Africa; mammals
      (Anon.)   1972AV
      (Bishop, W. W.)   1972A
    East Africa; Plio-Pleistocene; mammals
      (Cooke, H. B. S., Maglio, V. J.)   1972A
    Ethiopia, Omo Basin; vertebrates
      (Brown, F. H.)   1969A
      (Brown, F. H., Heinzelin, J.,
        Howell, F. C.)   1970A

QUATERNARY - cont.
  Geochronology
    Ethiopia, Omo V.; mammals
      (Arambourg, C.)   1969C
    Eurasia; mammals
      (Nikiforova, K. V.)   1969A
    Europe; mammals
      (Arambourg, C.)   1969A,B
      (Bout, P.)   1972A
      (Cooke, H. B. S.)   1972A
      (Pasa, A.)   1969A
    Europe; Plio-Pleistocene; mammals
      (Tobien, H.)   1970A, 1972A
    Europe; Plio-Pleistocene; rodents
      (Michaux, J.)   1970A
    Europe; vertebrates
      (Bout, P.)   1970A
    Europe; Villafranchian; mammals
      (Savage, D. E., Curtiss, G. H.)   1970A
    Europe, western; Villafranchian;
      mammals
      (Bout, P.)   1968A
    Fossil hominids
      (Gromov, V. I.)   1969A
      (Ivanova, I. K.)   1968A,B
    France; mammal cave faunas
      (Cavaillé, A.)   1970A
    France; mammals
      (Dewolf, Y.)   1970A
    France; Riss; elephants
      (Théobald, N.)   1970A
    France; rodents
      (Chaline, J.)   1972A
    France; Villafranchian; mammals
      (Dubar, M.)   1969A
    Greece; vertebrates
      (Kahlke, H. D.)   1968A,B
    Hungary; mammals
      (Jánossy, D.)   1969D, 1970A, 1972B
    Italy, central; Plio-Pleistocene; mammals
      (Ambrosetti, P., et al.)   1972A
    Kenya; mammals
      (Maglio, V. J.)   1972A
    Mammals
      (Gaĭduk, I. M.)   1967A
      (Gromov, V. I., Krasnov, I. I.,
        Nikiforova, K. V., Shanĉer, E. V.) 1969A
      (Gromov, V. I.,
        Nikiforova, K. V.)   1968A,B,C
      (Gromov, V. I., Vangengeĭm, E. A.,
        Nikiforova, K. V.)   1965B
      (Menner, V. V.)   1968B
      (Zubakov, V. A.)   1966B
    No. America; mammals
      (Cooke, H. B. S.)   1972A
    Plio-Pleistocene; mammals
      (Grichuk, V. P., Hey, R. W.,
        Venzo, S.)   1964A
    Portugal; mammals
      (Aguado, M. M.)   1968A
    Rumania; vertebrate fauna
      (Alimen, H., Radulesco, C.,
        Samson, P.)   1968B
    Siberia; mammals
      (Alekseev, M. N.)   1970A
      (Kaz'mina, T. A.)   1969A

REPTILIA - cont.
Anguidae
  Systematics; morphology; n. taxa
    (Meszoely, C. A. M.)   1970A
Ankylosauria
  Morphology; systematics
    (Coombs, W. P.)   1971A
Anomodontia
  Morphology; systematics
    (Keyser, A. W.)   1972A
Antarctosaurus
  Maestrichtian; Argentina, Arroyo del
  Morterito; skeleton
    (Bonaparte, J. F., Bossi, G.)   1967A
Archosauria
  Cret.; Alberta, Dinosaur Provincial
  Park; taphonomy
    (Dodson, P.)   1971A
  Cret.; Alberta; preservation
    (Sternberg, C. M.)   1970A
  Cret.; India; distribution
    (Prasad, K. N.)   1968A
  Cret.; Mongolia, Nemegt Basin
    (Gradziński, R.)   1970A
  Cret.; Spain, central; skeletons
    (Lapparent, A. F. de, et al.)   1969A
  Cret., upper; France, southern; eggs
    (Caillaud, P.)   1968A
  Cret., upper; Mongolia, Gobi Desert; eggs
    (Sochava, A. V.)   1969A,B, 1970A,B,C
  Cret.; Utah; eggs
    (Jensen, J. A.)   1969A, 1970A
  Cret.; Utah, Wasatch Plateau; eggs
    (Jensen, J. A.)   1966A
  Cret.; Wyoming; preservation
    (Sternberg, C. M.)   1970A
  Eggs, microstructure
    (Sochava, A. V.)   1971A,B
  Evolution
    (Anon.)   1970AU
  Evolution; systematics; tracks; n. taxa
    (Haubold, H.)   1969B
  General
    (Swinton, W. E.)   1970A
  Habits, bipedalism
    (Charig, A. J.)   1966B
  Phylogeny
    (Demathieu, G.)   1969A, 1970A
  Phylogeny; evolution
    (Reig, O. A.)   1970A
  Reconstructions
    (Bakker, R. T.)   1968A
Azendohsaurus
  Triassic; Morocco, Azendoh; jaw,
  teeth; n. gen.
    (Dutuit, J.-M.)   1972B
Baenidae
  Cret., Tert.; No. America; systematics;
  phylogeny; skull, shell; n. taxa
    (Gaffney, E. S.)   1972A
Baenoidea
  Phylogeny
    (Gaffney, E. S.)   1970A
Biogeography
  Carboniferous
    (Panchen, A. L.)   1972C

REPTILIA - cont.
Biogeography
  Diversification factors
    (Kurtén, B.)   1967C, 1969B
  Paleozoic
    (Brown, D. A.)   1968A
  Permian
    (Romer, A. S.)   1972H
  Tert.; U.S., western; Chelonia
    (Bramble, D. M., Hutchison, J. H.)   1971A
  Tert.; U.S., western; Crocodilia
    (Bramble, D. M., Hutchison, J. H.)   1971A
  Triassic
    (Brown, D. A.)   1968A
Bothremys
  Morphology; diagnosis
    (Zangerl, R.)   1968A
Brachiosauridae
  Skull, jaws, episternal
    (Marsh, O. C.)   1879J
Brachyopidae
  Systematics
    (Welles, S. P., Estes, R.)   1969A
Brazilosaurus
  Restoration
    (Zullo, V. A.)   1969A
Camptosaurus browni
  Reconstruction
    (Pinna, G.)   1969A
Captorhinidae
  Morphology
    (Heaton, M. J.)   1972B
Captorhinomorpha
  Permian; East Germany, Freital;
  skull, skeleton; systematics; n. gen.
    (Carroll, R. L., Gaskill, P.)   1971A
  Permian, upper; Niger, Tchimozenog;
  skull; n. gen.
    (Taquet, P.)   1969A
Captorhinus
  Neural spines, variation
    (Vaughn, P. P.)   1970A
Carnosauria
  Claws
    (Rozhdestvenskiĭ, A. K.)   1970A,B
Catalogs
  Germany, Bavaria; taxonomic
    (Kuhn, O.)   1967E
  Taxonomic
    (Kuhn, O.)   1968B,D
Ceratopsia
  Evolution
    (Colbert, E. H.)   1969B
Champsosauridae
  Cret.-Tert.; No. America; aquatic;
  distribution; phylogeny; nomenclature;
  restoration
    (Erickson, B. R.)   1972A
Champsosaurus
  Braincase
    (Fox, R. C.)   1968A
Chanaresuchus
  Tri., middle; Argentina, Chañares;
  systematics; skeleton; restoration
    (Romer, A. S.)   1972A

REPTILIA - cont.

Charactosuchus
Eocene, middle; Jamaica; jaw; n. sp.
  (Berg, D. E.)   1969B
Chelidae
Tertiary, middle; Tasmania; skeleton
  (Warren, J. W.)   1969A
Chelonia
Cret., lower; Australia, Victoria, Carapook;
  skeleton; n. taxa
  (Warren, J. W.)   1969B
Cret.; Mongolia, Gobi Desert; skulls,
  skeleton; n. taxa
  (Khosatzky, L. I.,
  Młynarski, M.)   1971A
Cret., upper; Mongolia; morphology
  (Młynarski, M., Narmandach, P.)   1972A
Eocene; USSR, Zaĭsan Basin; plastron;
  n. taxa
  (Chkhikvadze, V. M.)   1970B
Mesozoic, Cenozoic; USSR, Kazakhstan
  (Kuznetŝov, V. V.)   1964A
Miocene; Japan, Kyushu; morphology
  (Otsuka, H.)   1970A
Miocene; Yugoslavia, Blaca; eggs
  (Miloševič, V. M.)   1967A
Morphology, ancestral turtle
  (Holman, J. A.)   1969F
Paleogene; USSR, Kazakhstan; n. taxa
  (Chkhikvadze, V. M.)   1969A
Phylogeny; systematics
  (Gaffney, E. S.)   1971B
Pliocene; USSR, Moldavia & Ukraine
  (Telepneva, V. P.)   1964A
Plio-Pleistocene; Europe
  (Młynarski, M.)   1968A
Systematics
  (Auffenberg, W.)   1972A
Systematics; morphology
  (Młynarski, M.)   1969A
Tert.; Mongolia; systematics
  (Chkhikvadze, V. M.)   1971B
Chelydridae
Cret.; Africa; skull; systematics; n. gen.
  (Bergounioux, F. M., Crouzel, F.)   1968A
Tert.; USSR, Zaĭsan Basin; plastron;
  systematics; n. taxa
  (Chkhikvadze, V. M.)   1971A
Chiniquodontidae
Triassic; Brazil; skull
  (Romer, A. S.)   1969C
Chroniosuchidae
Permian; USSR, Donguz R.; skull,
  limbs; n. taxa
  (Tverdokhlebova, G. I.)   1972A,B
Triassic; USSR, Donguz; taphonomy
  (Tverdokhlebova, G. I.)   1969A
Chroniosuchus
Permian, upper; USSR, Blĭumental'; jaw;
  nomenclature
  (Tverdokhlebova, G. I.)   1968A
Vertebrae
  (Borkhvardt, V. G.)   1969A,B
Clemmys
Pleist.; Greece, Megalopolis; plastron
  (Melentis, J. K.)   1966K

REPTILIA - cont.

Coeluridae
Nomenclature, n. gen.
  (Welles, S. P.)   1970A
Coluber
Pliocene; Nevada, Truckee Fm.; skeleton
  (Anon.)   1972AC
Pliocene; Nevada, west-central; morphology
  (Ruben, J. A.)   1971A
Compressidens
Nomenclature
  (Thurmond, J. T.)   1969A
Compsognathus
Jurassic; France, Canjuers; skull, skeleton
  (Bidar, A., Demay, L., Thomel, G.)   1972B
Jurassic; France, Petit Plan de
  Canjuers; skeleton; n. sp.
  (Bidar, A., Demay, L., Thomel, G.)   1972A
Morphology
  (Anon.)   1972BQ
Contogenys
Cret.; Montana, McCone Co.; jaw; n. gen.
  (Estes, R.)   1969D
Coprolites
Cret., upper; Alberta
  (Waldman, M., Hopkins, W. S.)   1970A
Tert.; Czech., Bechlejovice
  (Štamberg, S.)   1970A
Cotylosauria
Classification
  (Kuhn, O.)   1972A
Morphology; evolution; systematics;
  n. taxa
  (Kuhn, O.)   1969C
Triassic; Connecticut; skull
  (Anon.)   1969AG
Cretaceous
Germany
  (Kuhn, O.)   1971F
Crocodilia
Cret.; Alberta; coprolite
  (Waldman, M.)   1970B
Cret., lower; Algeria, Gara Samanie, skull
  (Broin, F., Grenot, C., Vernet, R.)   1971A
Eocene; Spain, Pyrenees; jaw,
  skull frag., teeth
  (Berg, D. E., Crusafont, M.)   1970A
Evolution
  (Guggisberg, C. A. W.)   1972A
Jurassic; France, Haudainville Quarry;
  jaw, teeth; systematics
  (Maubeuge, P. L.)   1968A
Miocene; Germany, Wiesbaden-Biebrich
  (Berg, D. E.)   1967A
Paleogene; Europe; morphology;
  distribution
  (Berg, D. E.)   1969A
Phylogeny; morphology
  (Walker, A. D.)   1972A
Systematics
  (Romer, A. S.)   1972F
  (Walker, A. D.)   1970A
Systematics; phylogeny; n. taxa
  (Kuhn, O.)   1968C
Crocodylidae
Distribution; evolution
  (Neill, W. T.)   1971A

REPTILIA - cont.
Crocodylus
Pleist.; Cuba; skull; n. sp.
    (Varona, L. S.)   1966A
Cryptodira
Oligocene; USSR, Kazakhstan; skull,
plastron; n. taxa
    (Chkhikvadze, V. M.)   1971B
Ctenochasma
Jur.; France, Haute-Marne; skull
    (Taquet, Ph.)   1972A
Ctenosauriscus
Triassic; Germany, Göttingen; vertebrae
    (Krebs, B.)   1969A
Cynodontia
Classification
    (Hopson, J. A., Kitching, J. W.)   1972A
Jaw articulation, evolution
    (Crompton, A. W.)   1972A
Lesotho, Karoo system; stratigraphic position
    (Turner, B. R.)   1972A
Origin; morphology
    (Kemp, T. S.)   1972B
Skeleton
    (Jenkins, F. A.)   1970A, 1971A
Triassic; Argentina, Chañares; skulls; n. taxa
    (Romer, A. S.)   1972G
Triassic; India, Pranhita-Godavari V.;
teeth
    (Chatterjee, S., et al.)   1969A
Cynognathus
Triassic; Argentina, Las Malvinas;
skull, jaw; n. sp.
    (Bonaparte, J. F.)   1969A
Cyrbasiodon
Morphology; tooth replacement
    (Mendrez, C. H.)   1972E
Deinocephalia
Permian; USSR, Ezhovo; skull, teeth;
n. taxa
    (Chudinov, P. K.)   1968C
Deinocheirus
Cret., upper; Mongolia, Gobi Desert;
morphology; n. taxa
    (Osmolska, H., Roniewicz, E.)   1970A
Deinonychus
Cret., lower; Montana, Cloverly Fm.;
skull, skeleton; habits
    (Ostrom, J. H.)   1969A,G
Restoration
    (Anon.)   1970AS
Dermatemydidae
Cret., upper; Mongolia; carapace,
plastron; n. taxa
    (Młynarski, M.)   1972A
Desmatodon
Penn., upper; Colorado, Fremont Co.;
systematics; skull
    (Vaughn, P. P.)   1972A
Diadectes
Permian, lower; West Virginia, Reedy; skull
    (Berman, D. S.)   1971B
Diadectidae
Penn., upper; Colorado, central; n. taxa
    (Vaughn, P. P.)   1969B

REPTILIA - cont.
Diademodon
Tooth replacement
    (Hopson, J. A.)   1970B, 1971A
    (Ziegler, A. C.)   1969A
Dicynodon
Mandible, palate
    (Cluver, M. A.)   1970A
Dicynodontia
Permian; So. Africa, Zwartskraal; skulls
    (Barry, T. H.)   1972A
Triassic; India, Pranhita-Godavari V.;
skulls; n. taxa
    (Chowdhury, T. R.)   1970B
Triassic; USSR, Cisuralia; morphology;
n. taxa
    (V'iushkov, B. P.)   1969A,
Triassic; Zambia, N'tawere Fm.;
morphology; n. sp.
    (Crozier, E. A.)   1970A
Triassic; Zambia, Sitwe; morphology;
n. taxa
    (Cox, C. B.)   1969A
Dilophosaurus
Jur., Arizona, Kayenta Fm., reconstruction
    (Welles, S. P.)   1972A
Dinilysia patagonica
Cranial morphology; systematics
    (Estes, R., Frazzetta, T. H.,
    Williams, E. E.)   1970A
Dinosauria
Cret.; Mongolia, Gobi Desert; eggs
    (Martinson, G. G., Sochava, A. V.,
    Kolesnikov, Ch. M.)   1971A
Cret.; Mongolia, Gobi Desert; eggs,
embryo
    (Sochava, A. V.)   1972A
Cret.; Mongolia, Gobi Desert; eggs;
histology, biochemistry
    (Kolesnikov, C. M., Sochava, A. V.) 1972A
Cret., upper; Mexico, Baja Calif.
    (Morris, W. J.)   1969A
Dictionary
    (Glut, D. F.)   1972A
Endothermy
    (Bakker, R. T.)   1972A
France, Mongolia; eggs
    (Stel, J. H.)   1970A
Habits
    (Anon.)   1971BN, 1972AX
Morphology; evolution
    (Steel, R.)   1970B
Ontogeny
    (Dodson, P.)   1972A
Diplocynodon
Miocene, upper; France, Aquitania
    (Jehenne, Y.)   1970A
Oligocene; Marseille and Kassel;
mandibles
    (Berg, D. E.)   1971A
Diplodocus
Mesozoic; Kenya, Lake Rudolf
    (Arambourg, C., Wolff, R. G.)   1969A
Dromaeosaurus
Cret.; Alberta, Red Deer R.; morphology;
systematics; n. fam.
    (Colbert, E. H., Russell, D. A.)   1969A

REPTILIA - cont.
Gopherus
Pleist.; Mexico, Aguascalientes; shell; n. sp.
  (Mooser, O.)   1972A
Gorgonopsidae
Systematics; morphology; n. taxa
  (Sigogneau, D.)   1970A
Hadrokkosaurus
Triassic; Arizona, Moenkopi Fm.;
  skull, skeleton
  (Welles, S. P., Estes, R.)   1969A
Hadrosauridae
Anatomy, skull
  (Heaton, M. J.)   1972A
Cret.; California, La Jolla
  (Kennedy, L.)   1970A
Cret.; Mexico, Baja California
  (Anon.)   1971BP
Cret.; Mexico, El Rosario
  (Anon.)   1971BD
Cret.; USSR, Kazakhstan; morphology;
  n. taxa
  (Rozhdestvenskiĭ, A. K.)   1968C
Habitat
  (Anon.)   1971AM
Habits, bipedalism
  (Galton, P. M.)   1970A
Hallopus
Jurassic, upper; Colorado, Garden Park;
  skeleton; restoration
  (Walker, A. D.)   1970A
Halticosaurus
Triassic; France, Airel; tooth, vertebrae
  (Sarsonneur, C., Lapparent, F. de)   1966A
Hemiprotosuchus
Triassic; Argentina; skull, skeleton
  (Bonaparte, J. F.)   1971B
Hoplitosaurus
Cret., lower; Utah, eastern; morphology
  (Bodily, N. M.)   1969A
Hydrotherosaurus
Japan; skeleton
  (Hasegawa, Y., Obata, I.)   1972A
Icarosaurus
Morphology; habits; systematics
  (Colbert, E. H.)   1970D
Ichthyosauria
Jurassic; England, Lyme Regis; visceral
  contents
  (Pollard, J. E.)   1968A
Jurassic; England, Swanage; feet, vertebrae
  (Delair, J. B.)   1969B
Mesozoic; New Zealand; morphology
  (Fleming, C. A., Gregg, D. R.,
  Welles, S. P.)   1971A
Skull, forefin
  (McGowan, C.)   1972B
Skulls, forefins; phylogeny
  (McGowan, C.)   1972A
Tri.; USSR, Omolon' R. basin;
  vertebrae; n. sp.
  (Poloubotko, I. V., Ochev, V. G.)   1972A
Ictidorhinidae
Permian; So. Africa, Bultfontein; skull,
  jaw, teeth; systematics
  (Sigogneau, D.)   1970B

REPTILIA - cont.
Jurassic
Germany
  (Kuhn, O.)   1971C
Kannemeyeria
Systematics
  (Cruickshank, A. R. I.)   1970A
Kannemeyeridae
Triassic; USSR, Karagachka R.;
  skull; n. gen., n. sp.
  (Danilov, A. I.)   1971A
Triassic; USSR, Ural Mts.; morphology;
  n. taxa
  (Kalandadze, N. N.)   1969A, 1970A
Kawingasaurus
Permian; Tanzania, Kawinga Fm.;
  skull, limbs
  (Cox, C. B.)   1972A
Kinosternon
Distribution
  (Fichter, L. S.)   1969A
Kritosaurus
Cret.; Alberta, Sand Creek; skeleton
  (Waldman, M.)   1969A
Labidosaurikos
Permian, lower; Oklahoma, Logan Co.; skull
  (Zídek, J.)   1971A
Permian; Oklahoma, Logan Co.;
  braincase
  (MacLean, W. P.)   1970A
Lacerta goliath
Vertebrae
  (Gasc, J.-P.)   1971A
Lacertilia
Jurassic, upper; China, Chingning;
  skull, skeleton; n. gen.
  (Young, C.-c.)   1959K
Lambeosaurus
Cret., upper; Mexico, Baja Calif.;
  humerus
  (Morris, W. J.)   1972A
Leidyosuchus
Morphology; systematics
  (Langston, W.)   1972A
Leptoceratops
Cret.; Alberta, Edmonton Fm.;
  reconstruction
  (Russell, D. A.)   1970A
Cret.; Wyoming, northwestern; morphology
  (McKenna, M. C., Love, J. D.)   1970A
Liopleurodon rossicus
Jur., upper; USSR, Moscow Basin;
  mandible; vertebrae
  (Halstead, L. B.)   1971B
Longisquama
Morphology
  (Anon.)   1971BE
Tri.; Fergana; n. taxa
  (Sharov, A. G.)   1970A,1
Luperosuchus
Triassic; Argentina, Chañares; skull; n. gen.
  (Romer, A. S.)   1971B
Lycorhinus angustidens
Tri., upper; So. Africa; Cape Prov.;
  systematics; skull; dentition
  (Thulborn, R. A.)   1970B

REPTILIA - cont.
Ornithischia
Palpebral bone, phylogeny
(Coombs, W. P.)   1972A
Ornithocheiridae
Cret., lower; Brazil, Pernambuco;
limbs; n. taxa
(Price, L. I.)   1971A
Ornithomimidae
Cret., upper; Alberta; systematics;
skeleton reconstruction; myology;
adaptation; n. gen.
(Russell, D. A.)   1972A
Cret., upper; Mongolia, Gobi Desert;
skull, skeleton; n. taxa
(Osmólska, H., Roniewicz, E.,
Barsbold, R.)   1972A
Ornithopoda
Systematics; evolution
(Galton, P. M.)   1972A
Pachycephalosauridae
Skull, function
(Galton, P. M.)   1970C, 1971A
Paleozoic
Amphibian-reptile transition
(Carroll, R. L.)   1970C
Pareiasauria
Skin structures
(Findlay, G. H.)   1970B
Pelomedusidae
Cenozoic; Asia; morphology; n. sp.
(Wood, R. C.)   1970A
Pelusios
Pleist., lower; Tchad, Ouadi Derdemi;
shell, legbone
(Broin, F.)   1969A,B
Permian
Germany
(Kuhn, O.)   1970D
Oklahoma; morphology;
systematics; n. taxa
(Olson, E. C.)   1970A
So. Africa, Karoo; systematics
(Boonstra, L. D.)   1969A
Petrolacosaurus
Morphology; systematics
(Reisz, R.)   1972A
Phylogeny
Evolution; origin
(Bellairs, A.)   1969A
General
(Olson, E. C.)   1968C
Ornithischia, sauropods; origin
(Attridge, J., Charig, A. J.)   1967A
Phytosauria
Evolution; morphology
(Gregory, J. T.)   1969B
Triassic; Europe; systematics
(Gregory, J. T., Westphal, F.)   1969A
Triassic; Madagascar; dermal scutes
(Westphal, F.)   1970B
Pinacosaurus
Cret., upper; Mongolia, Bayn Dzak;
skull, skeleton
(Maryańska, T.)   1971A

REPTILIA - cont.
Placodontia
Triassic; Germany; skull, teeth;
reconstruction
(Westphal, F., Westphal, I.)   1967A
Plateosaurus
Jurassic; France, Salins; skeleton
(Théobald, N., Blanc, M.,
David, E.)   s.d.
Platysternidae
Oligocene; USSR, Khazakhstan;
plastron; n. gen.
(Čkhikvadze, V. M.)   1971C,
Plesiosauria
Cret.; New Zealand; morphology
(Welles, S. P., Gregg, D. R.)   1971A
Jur.; Germany, Bavaria; localities
(Wellnhofer, P.)   1971B
Jurassic; Switzerland, Baden; humerus
(Wild, R.)   1968A
Plesiosauridae
Jurassic, middle; Germany, Amberg;
skeleton; systematics
(Wellnhofer, P.)   1970B
Plesiosaurus
Jurassic; Germany; morphology
(Müller, H.)   1960A
Podocnemis
Eocene; Spain, Teso de la Flecha;
carapace, plastron; n. sp.
(Jiménez Fuentes, E.)   1971A
Pliocene; Venezuela; morphology;
fossil record; n. sp.
(Wood, R., Gamero, M. L. D., de)   1971A
Pristerognathidae
Snout anatomy; systematics
(Mendrez, C. H.)   1972A
Probainognathus
Jaw articulation
(Romer, A. S.)   1969G
Triassic; Argentina, Chañares; skull,
jaw; n. gen.
(Romer, A. S.)   1970A
Probelesodon
Triassic; Argentina, Chañares; skull; n. gen.
(Romer, A. S.)   1969A
Procolophonia
Permian, lower; Oklahoma, Tillman Co.,
Grandfield; skull, jaw; n. taxa
(Daly, E.)   1969A
Procynosuchidae
Systematics
(Battail, B.)   1972A
Proplacerias
Morphology; nomenclature
(Cruickshank, A. R. I.)   1972B
Proterochampsidae
Triassic; Argentina, Chañares;
morphology; n. taxa
(Romer, A. S.)   1971E
Proterosuchia
Morphology; evolution
(Reig, O. A.)   1970A
Systematics
(Charig, A. J., Reig, O. A.)   1970A

REPTILIA - cont.
Scelidosaurus
  Jurassic; England; skeleton, juvenile
    (Rixon, A. E.)   1968A
Sebecosuchia
  Cret.; Argentina; morphology; systematics
    (Gasparini, Z. B. de)   1972A
  Eocene; Argentina; morphology; systematics
    (Gasparini, Z. B. de)   1972A
Solenodonsauridae
  Morphology; systematics
    (Carroll, R. L.)   1972A
Sordes pilosus
  Jur.; USSR, Kazakhstan
    (Abelin, P. G.)   1972A
Sphenodon
  Skull, kinetic mobility
    (Ostrom, J. H.)   1962C
Squamata
  Jurassic; Japan, Miyama-cho; skull,
    skeleton; n. gen.
    (Shikama, T.)   1967A
  Miocene; Saskatchewan; morphology; n. taxa
    (Holman, J. A.)   1970A
  Pleist.; Nebraska, Brown Co; morphology
    (Holman, J. A.)   1972A
  Systematics
    (Tarlo, L. B. H.)   1968A
Stahleckeriidae
  Triassic; Argentina, Chañares; skulls,
    jaw; n. taxa
    (Cox, C. B.)   1968A
Steneosaurus
  Jurassic; England, Dorset; skull frag.
    (Cope, J. C. W.)   1971A
  Jurassic; France, Sansac; skull frags.,
    vertebrae
    (Dechaseaux, C.)   1966A
Stenopelix
  Cret.; Germany, north; morphology,
    latex mold
    (Schmidt, H.)   1969A
Stereogenys
  Eocene; Spain, Teso de la Flecha;
    plastron; n. sp.
    (Jiménez Fuentes, E.)   1968A, 1970A
Stereognathus
  Jur., middle; Scotland, Skye Is.; teeth; n. sp.
    (Waldman, M., Savage, R. J. G.)   1972A
Stygiochelys
  Cret.; Montana, Hell Cr. Fm.; skull; n. gen.
    (Gaffney, E. S., Hiatt, R.)   1971A
Stylemys
  Statistical study
    (Auffenberg, W.)   1969A
Syntarsus
  Triassic, upper; Rhodesia, Southcote;
    skeleton; n. gen.
    (Raath, M. A.)   1969A
Tanystropheus
  Triassic; Israel, Wadi Ramon; interclavicle
    (Haas, G.)   1970A
Taphrosphys
  New Jersey
    (Anon.)   1970AH

REPTILIA - cont.
Tedorosaurus
  Jurassic; Japan, Miyama-cho; skull,
    skeleton; restoration; systematics
    (Shikama, T.)   1969A
Teiidae
  Cret.; Alberta; jaw, teeth
    (Waldman, M.)   1970A
  Cret.; morphology; systematics; n. taxa
    (Estes, R.)   1969A
Teleorhinus
  Cret.; Minnesota, Itasca Co.; snout; n. sp.
    (Erickson, B. R.)   1969A
Tertiary
  Germany
    (Kuhn, O.)   1971E
Testudines
  Pleist.; Nebraska, Brown Co.;
    morphology; n. sp.
    (Holman, J. A.)   1972A
Testudinidae
  Evolution; phylogeny; n. sp.
    (Auffenberg, W.)   1971A
  Origin; n. gen.
    (Chkhikvadze, V. M.)   1970A
  Paleogene; Mongolia; morphology;
    systematics; n. sp.
    (Młynarski, M.)   1968B
  Phylogeny
    (Chkhikvadze, V. M.)   1968C
  Pliocene; nomenclature
    (Adler, K.)   1968A
  Pliocene, upper; Idaho, Hagerman;
    morphology
    (Zug, G. R.)   1969A
  Tert.; Palearctic; systematics; n. taxa
    (Chkhikvadze, V. M.)   1972A
  Tert.; USSR, Kazakhstan, Zaĭsan basin; n. sp.
    (Chkhikvadze, V. M.)   1971D
Testudo
  Miocene, middle; USSR, Kazakhstan;
    systematics; n. sp.
    (Kuznetsov, V. V.)   1972A
  Miocene; Spain, Arévalo; morphology
    (García, J., Alberdi, M. T.)   1968A
  Neogene; USSR, Tadzhikistan
    (Kuznetsov, V. V.)   1970A
  Pleist.; Greece, Pikermi; carapace, skeleton
    (Bachmayer, F.)   1967B
  Pliocene, middle; USSR, Kirgizia;
    armor; n. sp.
    (Kuznetsov, V. V., et al.)   1964A
Testudo canetoniana
  Miocene, middle; France, Sansan; taphonomy
    (Crouzel, F.)   1971B
Thalassemydidae
  Jurassic, upper; Germany, Schernfeld;
    girdle, limbs
    (Wellnhofer, P.)   1967A
Thalassomedon
  Restoration; discovery
    (Welles, S. P.)   1970B
Thecodontia
  Systematics
    (Romer, A. S.)   1972F

RUMANIA - cont.
Paleontology
Mam.; Neogene
  (Macarovici, N.)   1967A
Mam.; Paleogene; Albeşti-Muscel
  (Grigorescu, D.)   1967A
Mam.; Pleist.
  (Apostol, L.)   1968A
  (Isă, Gh. I.)   1967A
  (Macarovici, N., Semaka, A.)   1969A
  (Rădulescu, C.)   1969A
  (Terzea, E.)   1968A
Mam.; Pleist.; Betfia
  (Terzea, E.)   1972A
Mam.; Pleist.; Bîrlad
  (Apostol, L., Vicoveanu, D.)   1970A
Mam.; Pleist.; Braĭla
  (Popescu, A.)   1964A
Mam.; Pleist.; Braşov
  (Rădulesco, C., Samson, P.)   1972A
  (Samson, P., Radulesco, C.,
    Kisgyörgy, Z.)   1971A
Mam.; Pleist.; Brateiu
  (Samson, P., Hermann, W.)   1968A
Mam.; Pleist.; Buciumeni
  (Apostol, L.)   1960A
Mam.; Pleist.; Bugiulesti
  (Rădulescu, C., Samson, P.)   1965B
Mam.; Pleist.; Chişcani
  (Apostol, L.)   1970A
Mam.; Pleist.; Dimboviţa V.
  (Bera, Al.)   1968A
Mam.; Pleist.; Fumureni
  (Ionete, L.)   1964A
Mam.; Pleist., middle; Codreni
  (Apostol, L.)   1971A
Mam.; Pleist.; Moldova Nouă
  (Mârza, J.)   1971A
Mam.; Pleist.; Transylvania
  (Rădulescu, C., Hermann, W.) 1969A
Mam.; Pliocene; Derşida
  (Macarovici, N., Jurcsàk, T.)   1968A
Pisces; Cret., upper; Dobrogea
  (Grigorescu, D., Marin, I.)   1971A
Pisces; Eocene; Cluj
  (Fuchs, H.)   1963A
Pisces; Miocene
  (Florei, N.)   1970A
Pisces; Miocene; Buituri
  (Rado, G.)   1969A
Pisces; Miocene; Copăcel-Chijic
  (Rado, G.)   1968A
Pisces; Miocene; Coşteiul de Sus
  (Rado, G.)   1965A
Pisces; Oligocene; Piatra-Neamt.
  (Ciobanu, M.)   1969A
Pisces; Paleogene; Breţcu-Tg. Secuiesc
  depression
  (Bucur, I.)   1971A
Pisces; Tert.; Soceni
  (Stancu, J.)   1970A
Vertebrate Faunas
Cenozoic; Mam.
  (Macarovici, N.)   1972A

RUMANIA - cont.
Vertebrate Faunas
Devonian; Moesia; Pisces
  (Patrulius, D., Iordan, M.) 1969A, 1970A
Miocene; Carpathians, southern; Pisces
  (Stancu, J., et al.)   1971A
Miocene; Mehadia Basin; Pisces
  (Grossu, A. V., Voicu, G.)   1971A
Miocene; Paun-Jassy; Mam.
  (Macarovici, N., Paghida, N.)   1966A
Oligocene; Piatra Neamt; Pisces
  (Cosmovici, N. L., Şova, C.,
    Tărăbuţă, C.)   1964A
Pleist.; Baraolt Basin; Mam.
  (Rădulescu, C., Kovács, A.)   1968A
Pleist.; Betfia
  (Terzea, E., Jurcsák, T.)   1967A
Pleist.; Betfia; Mam.
  (Terzea, E., Jurcsák, T.) 1968A, 1969A
Pleist.; Braşov depression; Mam.
  (Alimen, H., Radulesco, C.,
    Samson, P.)   1968B
Pleist.; Dacia; Mam.
  (Ghenea, C.)   1969A, 1970A, 1972A
Pleist.; Harghita district; Mam.
  (Samson, P., Rădulescu, C.)   1969A
Pleist.; "La Adam" Cave; Mam.
  (Dumitrescu, M., et al.)   1962-63A
Pleist.; Mam.
  (Macarovici, N.)   1972C
Pleist., middle; Mam.
  (Samson, P., Rădulescu, C.)   1968A
Pleist.; Moldavian Plateau; Mam.
  (Ghenea, C.)   1968A
Pleist.; Valachian depression; Mam.
  (Ghenea, C., Bandrabur, T.,
    Mihăilă, N.)   1967A
Pleist.; Vîrghis Gorge; Mam.
  (Orghidan, T., Dumitrescu, M.) 1962-63A
Pliocene; Dacia; Mam.
  (Ghenea, C.)   1972A
Pliocene; Mam.
  (Macarovici, N.)   1972C
Pliocene; Moldavian Plateau; Mam.
  (Ghenea, C.)   1968A
Plio-Pleistocene; Mam.
  (Mihăilă, N.)   1971A
SARDINIA
Paleontology
Mam.; Pleist.; Is Oreris
  (Comaschi Caria, I.)   1970B
Pisces; Miocene
  (Comaschi Caria, I.)   1970A
Pisces; Pliocene; Orosei
  (Dieni, I.)   1968A
SASKATCHEWAN
Paleoclimatology
Pleistocene
  (Christiansen, E. A.)   1972A
Paleontology
Amph; Oligocene
  (Holman, J. A.)   1968B
Mam.; Miocene; southern
  (Storer, J. E.)   1970A
Mam.; Oligocene
  (Russell, L. S.)   1972B

SIBERIA - cont.
  Vertebrate Faunas
    Neogene; western
      (Antypko, B. E.)   1964A
      (Martynov, V. A., Nikitin, V. P.)   1968A
    Oligocene; west; Mam.
      (Zal'ĭsman, I. G.)   1964A, 1967B
    Paleogene; western; Pisces
      (Rudkevich, M. Ĭa.)   1964A
    Permian; Kuznetsk Basin
      (Fomichev, V. D.)   1967A
    Pleist.; Aldan R., Mamontova Gora; Mam.
      (Bojarskaja, T. D.)   1969A
    Pleist.; Baĭkal; Mam.
      (Bazarov, D. B., Antoshchenko-Olenev,
        I. V., Gurulev, S. A.)   1969A
      (Pokatilov, A. G.)   1968A
    Pleist.; Beregovaĭa; Mam.
      (Vangengeĭm, E. A., et al.)   1968A
    Pleist.; Beringia; Mam.
      (Sher, A. V.)   1970A
    Pleist.; Biĭsk-Barnaul depression; Mam.
      (Shchukina, E. N.)   1967A
    Pleist.; Eniseĭ, Baĭkal, Transbaĭkalia
      (Abramova, E. A.)   1966B
    Pleist.; Eniseĭ; Mam.
      (Arkhipov, S. A., Matveeva, O. V.)   1964A
    Pleist.; Gornaĭa Shorifa, Kuznetskiĭ
      Alatau; Mam.
      (Shchukina, E. N.)   1967B
    Pleist.; Gornyĭ Altaĭ; Mam.
      (Shchukina, E. N.)   1967D
    Pleist.; Ĭana-Indigirka; Mam.
      (Timashev, I. E.)   1972A
    Pleist.; Kalistratikha; Mam.
      (Zudin, A. N., Panychev, V. A.)   1968A
    Pleist.; Kokorevo; Mam.
      (Ermolova, N. M.)   1971A
    Pleist.; Kolyma Lowlands; Mam.
      (Sher, A. V.)   1969A, 1971A
    Pleist.; Kuznetsk Basin; Mam.
      (Alekseeva, E. V.)   1970A
      (Fomichev, V. D.)   1967B
    Pleist.; Mam.
      (Nikolaev, V. A.)   1964A
      (Vangengeĭm, E. A., Sher, A. V.)   1972A
      (Vangengeĭm, E. A.,
        Zazhigin, V. S.)   1969A
    Pleist.; Minusinsk; Mam.
      (Puminov, A. P.)   1964A
    Pleist.; Muĭa R.; Mam.
      (Muzis, A. I.)   1968A
    Pleist.; Novokuznetsk; Mam.
      (Rĭabchikova, E. D.)   1970A
    Pleist.; Salair; Mam.
      (Shchukina, E. N.)   1967C
    Pleist.; Selenga Mts.
      (Bazarov, D. B.)   1968A
    Pleist.; Selenga Mts.; Mam.
      (Bazarov, D. B.)   1964A
    Pleist.; Selenga R. basin; Mam.
      (Erbaeva, M. A.)   1970A
    Pleist.; Transbaĭkal; Mam.
      (Pokatilov, A. G.)   1968A
      (Ravskiĭ, E. I., Gerbova, V. G.)   1970A
      (Vangengeĭm, E. A., Pĭatakov, V. V.,
        Shevchenko, V. K.)   1969A,B

SIBERIA - cont.
  Vertebrate Faunas
    Pleist.; Transbaĭkal, western; Mam.
      (Bazarov, D. B.)   1970A
      (Bazarov, D. B., Antoshchenko-Olenev,
        I. V., Gurulev, S. A.)   1969A
    Pleist., upper; Aldan R.; Mam.
      (Mochanov, Ĭu. A.)   1970A
    Pleist.; Vilĭuĭ R.; Mam.
      (Alekseev, M. N.)   1970B
      (Alekseev, M. N., Giterman, R. E.,
        Dubrovo, I. A.)   1972A
    Pleist.; western
      (Feniksova, V. V.)   1970A
    Pleist.; western; Mam.
      (Adamenko, O. M.)   1968A
      (Krasnov, I. I., Zarrina, E. P.)   1964A
      (Lazukov, G. I.)   1970A
      (Martynov, V. A.)   1967A
    Pliocene; Turgaĭ depression; Mam.
      (Boboedova, A. A.)   1968A
    Pliocene; western
      (Feniksova, V. V.)   1970A
    Plio-Pleistocene; western; Mam.
      (Martynov, V. A.)   1968A
    Silurian; Nizhnĭaĭa Chunku R.; Pisces
      (Moskalenko, T. A.)   1968A
    Tert.; western; Mam.
      (Zal'ĭsman, I. G.)   1968A
SKELETON. See appropriate taxon under class name.
SKULL. See appropriate taxon under class name.
SOUTH AFRICA
  Absolute Age
    Fossil hominids
      (Vogel, J. C., Beaumont, P. B.)   1972A
  Paleoanthropology
    Elandsfontein; fossil hominids
      (Singer, R.)   1971A
    Fossil hominids
      (Campbell, B. G.)   1969A
      (Klein, R. G.)   1970B
      (Inskeep, R. R.)   1969B
    Otjiseva; fossil hominids
      (Sydow, W.)   1969A
    Paleolithic art
      (Lee, D. N., Woodhouse, H. C.)   1970A
    Sterkfontein; fossil hominids
      (Bilsborough, A.)   1971A
      (Broom, R.)   1971A
      (Cooke, H. B. S.)   1968B
      (Oxnard, C. E.)   1968A
    Swartkrans; fossil hominids
      (Bilsborough, A.)   1971A
      (Brain, C. K.)   1969A
      (Clarke, R. J., Howell, F. C.)   1972A
      (Holloway, R. L.)   1972A
      (Rightmire, G. P.)   1972A
      (Wolpoff, M. H.)   1970B, 1971A
    Taungs; fossil hominids
      (Dart, R. A.)   1971A
  Paleontology
    Aves; Pliocene; Cape Province
      (Simpson, G. G.)   1971A
    Mam.; Krugersdorp Caves
      (Churcher, C. S.)   1970A
    Mam.; Pleist.
      (Meester, J., Meyer, I. J.)   1972A

SPAIN - cont.
  Paleoanthropology
    Cantábrica; Paleolithic art
      (Jordá Cerdá, F.)   1964D
    Chimeneas Cave; Paleolithic art
      (González Echegaray, J.)   1962A
    Chora Cave; fossil hominids
      (González Echegaray, P. J., García
       Guinea, M. A., Begines Ramírez, A.) 1963A
    Eastern; Paleolithic art
      (Lantier, R.)   1964A
    Ekain Cave; Paleolithic art
      (Barandiarán, J. M., Altuna, J.)   1969A
    El Ramu Cave; Paleolithic art
      (Mallo Viesca, M., Pérez Pérez, M.) 1969A
    Guipúzcoa, Vizcaya; fossil hominids
      (Basabe, J. M.)   1969A
    Levante; Paleolithic art
      (Pericot García, L.)   1964A
    Maestrazgo; Paleolithic art
      (Porcar, J. B.)   1964A
    Mondragón; fossil hominids
      (Basabe, J. M.)   1970A
    Negra Cave; fossil hominids
      (Lumley, M.-A. de)   1970A
    Paleolithic art
      (Ripoll Perelló, E.)   1964B,C
    Pasiega; Paleolithic art
      (Glory, A.)   1965C
  Paleontology
    Amph.; Jurassic, upper
      (Hecht, M. K.)   1970A
    Amph.; Mesozoic; Lerida
      (Seiffert, J.)   1972A
    Mam.; Cret.; Galve
      (Crusafont Pairó, M., Adrover, R.)   1965A,
                                           1966A
    Mam.; Cret., lower; Uña
      (Henkel, S., Krebs, B.)   1969A
    Mam.; Eocene; Corsá
      (Crusafont Pairó, M.,
       Golpe Posse, J. M.)   1968B
    Mam.; Eocene; Pyrenees Mts.
      (Crusafont Pairó, M., Remy, J. A.)   1970A
    Mam.; Mallorca; Can Sion Cave
      (Adrover, R., Angel, B.)   1967A
    Mam.; Mallorca, Génova Cave
      (Adrover, R.)   1967A
    Mam.; Miocene; Calatayud
      (Bruijn, H. de)   1967A
    Mam.; Miocene; Can Llobateres
      (Crusafont Pairó, M.)   1972A
    Mam.; Miocene; La Alberca
      (Janvier, P., Montenat, C.)   1970A
    Mam.; Miocene; Piera
      (Crusafont Pairó, M.,
       Aguirre, E.)   1972A
    Mam.; Miocene; Polinyá
      (Alberdi, M. T.)   1971A
    Mam.; Oligocene; Montalban
      (Thaler, L.)   1969A
    Mam.; Pleist.
      (Heintz, E.)   1970A
    Mam.; Pleist.; Ambrona
      (Imperatori, L.)   1971A
    Mam.; Pleist.; Banyoles
      (Bech Borrás, J.)   1970A

SPAIN - cont.
  Paleontology
    Mam.; Pleist.; Granada
      (Vidarte, C. F.)   1966A
    Mam.; Pleist.; Guipúscoa, Aitzbitarte
      (Altuna, J.)   1970A
    Mam.; Pleist.; Jarama
      (Pérez González, A., Fuentes Vidarte, C.,
       Aguirre, E.)   1970A
    Mam.; Pleist.; Mallorca
      (Waldren, W., Kopper, J. S.)   1968A
    Mam.; Pleist.; Menorca
      (Mercadal, B.)   1967A
    Mam.; Pleist.; Oñate-Guipúzcoa,
     Arrikrutz Cave
      (Altuna, J.)   1967A
    Mam.; Pleist.; Pedraza de la Sierra
      (Torres Perezhidalgo, T. J. de)   1969A
    Mam.; Pleist.; Puebla de Valverde
      (Crochet, J. Y., Heintz, E.)   1970A
    Mam.; Pleist.; Salamanca
      (Sos Baynat, V.)   1969A
    Mam.; Pleist.; Teruel and Soria
      (Crusafont Pairó, M.,
       Golpe Posse, J. M.)   1969A
    Mam.; Pleist., upper; Baleares
      (Adrover, R., Cuerda Barceló, J.)   1969B
    Mam.; Pleist., upper; Guipúscoa,
     Urtiaga
      (Altuna, J.)   1970B
    Mam.; Pleist., upper; Mallorca,
     Es Bufador Cave
      (Adrover, R., Cuerda Barceló, J.)   1969A
    Mam.; Pliocene
      (Michaux, J.)   1969B
    Mam.; Pliocene; Cuenca
      (Crouzel, F., Viallard, P.)   1968A
    Mam.; Pliocene; Gavá
      (Delson, E.)   1971A
    Mam.; Pliocene; Layna
      (Crusafont, M., Aguirre, E.)   1971A
    Mam.; Pliocene; Layna
      (Crusafont Pairó, M., Sondaar, P.)   1971A
    Mam.; Pliocene; Los Mansuetos
      (Adrover, R.)   1969B
    Mam.; Pliocene; Teruel
      (Adrover, R.)   1966B
    Mam.; Plio-Pleistocene
      (Michaux, J.)   1971B
    Mam.; Tert.
      (Alberdi, M. T., Aguirre, E.)   1970A
      (Golpe Posse, J. M.)   1971C, 1972A
    Pisces; Cret., upper
      (Bauzá Rullán, J.)   1971C
    Pisces; Jurassic, upper; Montsech
      (Wenz, S.)   1971A
    Pisces; Miocene; Can Mayol
      (Bauzá R., J.)   1971A
    Pisces; Neogene; Menorca
      (Bauzá R., J.)   1967A
    Rept.; Cret.; central
      (Lapparent, A. F. de, et al.)   1969A
    Rept.; Eocene; Corrales
      (Jiménez Fuentes, E.)   1971B
    Rept.; Eocene; Pyrenees
      (Berg, D. E., Crusafont, M.)   1970A

STATISTICAL METHODS - cont.
  Paleontology
    Allometric analysis, mammal teeth
      (Kurtén, B.)   1967D
SUDAN
  Paleoanthropology
    Jebel Sahaba; fossil hominids
      (Wendorf, F.)   1968F
  Vertebrate Faunas
    Pleist.; Mam.
      (Gautier, A.)   1968A
    Pleist.; Nubia; Pisces
      (Greenwood, P. H.)   1968B
    Pleist.; Saggai
      (Cloudsley-Thompson, J. L.)   1966A
SWEDEN
  Vertebrate Faunas
    Pleist.; Aves
      (Mascher, J. W.)   1970A
    Silurian; Gotland, Gogs; Pisces
      (Janvier, Ph.)   1971B
    Silurian; Gotland; Pisces
      (Gross, W.)   1968E
SWITZERLAND
  Paleoanthropology
    Birse R. V.; fossil hominids
      (Bay, R.)   1969A
  Paleolithic art
      (Bandi, H.-G.)   1969C
  Paleontology
    Mam.; Miocene, middle; Elgg
      (Hünermann, K. A.)   1971B
    Mam.; Miocene, upper; Anwil
      (Engesser, B.)   1972A
    Pisces; Miocene; Boudry
      (Stinton, F. C., Kissling, D.)   1968A
    Pisces; Triassic; Monte San Giorgio
      (Schwarz, W.)   1970A
    Rept.; Jurassic; Baden
      (Wild, R.)   1968A
    Rept.; Triassic, middle; Monte
      San Giorgio
      (Kuhn-Schnyder, E.)   1971A
  Vertebrate Faunas
    Eocene; Egerkingen; Mam.
      (Hartenberger, J.-L.)   1970A,B
    Miocene; Entlebuch; Pisces
      (Salis, K. von)   1967A
    Oligocene, upper; western; Mam.
      (Hugueney, M., Kissling, D.)   1972A
SYRIA
  Vertebrate Faunas
    Pleist.; Latamne; Mam.
      (Clark, J. D.)   1967D
    Pleist.; Yabroud; Mam.
      (Perkins, D.)   1968A
      (Solecki, R. S.)   1968B
SYSTEMATICS. See under Vertebrates.
TAIWAN
  Paleontology
    Rept.; Pleist.; Tsochin
      (Shikama, T.)   1972A

TANZANIA
  Paleoanthropology
    Lake Natron; fossil hominids
      (Leakey, L. S. B., Leakey, M. D.)   1971A
    Olduvai Gorge; fossil hominids
      (Bilsborough, A.)   1969A
      (Bishop, W. W.)   1966B
      (Bonnefille, R., Chavaillon, J.,
      Coppens, Y.)   1970A
      (Day, M. H.)   1969B, 1971A
      (Leakey, L. S. B.)   1960F,
                                        1967H, 1971C,D
      (Leakey, L. S. B.,
      Leakey, M. D.)   1968A, 1971A
      (Leakey, L. S. B., Tobias, P. V.,
      Napier, J. R.)   1971A
      (Leakey, M. D.)   1969A, 1971A,B
      (Leakey, M. D., Clarke, R. J.,
      Leakey, L. S. B.)   1971A
      (Oxnard, C. E.)   1968C
      (Wolpoff, M. H.)   1969B, 1970A
  Paleontology
    Amph.; Triassic; Manda Fm.
      (Howie, A. A.)   1970A
    Mam.; Pleist.; Olduvai Gorge
      (Leakey, L. S. B.)   1970C
    Rept.; Permian, upper; Kawinga Fm.
      (Cox, C. B.)   1972A
  Vertebrate Faunas
    Pleist.; Isimila; Mam.
      (Coryndon, S. C., et al.)   1972A
    Pleist.; Mam.
      (Leakey, L. S. B.)   1969D
    Pleist.; Olduvai Gorge; Pisces
      (Greenwood, P. H., Todd, E. J.)   1970A
TAPHONOMY. See under Vertebrates.
TASMANIA
  Paleontology
    Rept.; Tert., middle
      (Warren, J. W.)   1969A
TCHAD
  Paleontology
    Mam.; Pliocene; Menalla
      (Coppens, Y.)   1972B
    Rept.; Pleist.; Ouadi Derdemi
      (Broin, F.)   1969A,B
TENNESSEE
  Paleontology
    Mam.; Pleist.
      (Guilday, J. E.)   1961F
    Mam.; Pleist.; Big Bone Cave
      (Guilday, J. E., McGinnes, H.)   1972A
  Vertebrate Faunas
    Pleist.; Big Bone Cave; Mam.
      (Barr, T. C.)   1957A
    Pleist.; Robinson Cave; Mam.
      (Guilday, J. E., Hamilton, H. W.,
      McCrady, A. D.)   1969A
TERTIARY
  Correlation
    Africa; elephants
      (Maglio, V. J.)   1970A

TEXAS - cont.
　Paleontology
　　Aves; Pliocene, upper; Scurry Co.;
　　　Beck Ranch
　　　　(Brodkorb, P.)　　　　　　1970B
　　Mam.; Eocene; Big Bend
　　　　(Wood, A. E.)　　　　　　1972A
　　Mam.; Cret.
　　　　(Slaughter, B. H.)　　　　1969A
　　Mam.; Cret., lower; Trinity Fm.
　　　　(Turnbull, W. D.)　　　　1971A
　　Mam.; Eocene; Presidio Co.
　　　　(Forstén, A.-M.)　　　　　1971A
　　Mam.; Neogene
　　　　(Patton, T. H.)　　　1967C, 1969B
　　Mam.; Oligocene; Ash Spring
　　　　(Harris, J. M., Wood, A. E.)　1969A
　　Mam.; Oligocene; Presidio Co.
　　　　(McGrew, P. O.)　　　　　1971A
　　Mam.; Pleist.; Friesenhahn Cave
　　　　(Martin, R. A.)　　　　　1968C
　　Mam.; Pleist.; Sand Creek
　　　　(Schultz, G. E.)　　　　　1972B
　　Mam.; Pliocene; Blanco Fm.
　　　　(Dalquest, W. W.)　　　　1968A
　　Mam.; Pliocene; Coffee Ranch
　　　　(Dalquest, W. W.)　　　　1969A
　　Mam.; Pliocene, upper; Scurry Co.
　　　　(Dalquest, W. W.)　　　　1972A
　　Pisces; Cret.; Dallas Co.
　　　　(Goody, P. C.)　　　　　1970A
　　　　(McNulty, C. L., Kienzlen, G.)　1970A
　　Pisces; Cret.; Eulogy
　　　　(Johnson, G. D.)　　　　1972A
　　Pisces; Cret., lower; north-central
　　　　(Bilelo, M. M.)　　　　　1969A
　　　　(Thurmond, J. T.)　　　　1971B
　　Pisces; Cret., lower; Wise Co.
　　　　(Schaeffer, B.)　　　　　1971A
　　Pisces; Cret., upper; northcentral
　　　　(Bilelo, M. A. M.)　　　　1969B
　　Pisces; Pleist.; Rita Blanca Lake
　　　　(Koster, W. J.)　　　　　1969A
　　Rept.; Pleist.; Kendall Co.
　　　　(Hill, W. H.)　　　　　　1971A
　　Vert.; Pleist.; Randall Co.
　　　　(Schultz, G. E.,
　　　　　Cheatum, E. P.)　　1969A, 1970A
　Vertebrate Faunas
　　Cret., lower; northcentral; Pisces
　　　　(Thurmond, J. T.)　　1970A, 1971A
　　Cret., middle; Butler Farm; Mam.
　　　　(Slaughter, B. H.)　　　　1971A
　　Cret.; Tarrant Co.
　　　　(McNulty, C. L., Slaughter, B. H.)　1969A
　　Miocene; Big Bend
　　　　(Stevens, M. S., Stevens, J. B.,
　　　　　Dawson, M. R.)　　　　1969A
　　Miocene; Newton Co.
　　　　(Floyd, D. N., Miller, T. H.,
　　　　　Berry, W. B. N.)　　　　1958A
　　Permian, lower; northcentral
　　　　(Berman, D. S.)　　　1969A, 1970A
　　Pleist.; Cave Without a Name; Mam.
　　　　(Semkin, H. A.)　　　　　1959B

TEXAS - cont.
　Vertebrate Faunas
　　Pleist.; Edwards Co., Schulze Cave; Mam.
　　　　(Dalquest, W. W., Roth, E.,
　　　　　Judd, F.)　　　　　　1969A
　　Pleist.; Houston
　　　　(DuBar, J. R., Clopine, G.)　1961A
　　Pleist.; Kendall Co.
　　　　(Holman, J. A.)　　　　　1968A
　　Pleist.; Klein Cave; Aves
　　　　(Feduccia, A.)　　　　　1972A
　　Pleist.; Laubach Cave; Mam.
　　　　(Slaughter, B. H.)　　　　1964C
　　Pleist.; Longhorn Cavern
　　　　(Lundelius, E.)　　　　　1958A
　　Pleist.; Love Fm.
　　　　(Akersten, W. A.)　　　　1972A
　　Pleist.; Lubbock Co., Slaton quarry
　　　　(Dalquest, W. W.)　　　　1967A
　　Pleist.; Miller's Cave
　　　　(Holman, J. A.)　　　　　1972E
　　Pleist.; Rattlesnake Cave; Mam.
　　　　(Semken, H. A.)　　　　　1972B
　　Pleist.; San Pedro Springs; Mam.
　　　　(Warnock, F. B.)　　　　1972A
　　Pleist.; Schultze Cave; Amph.
　　　　(Holman, J. A.)　　　　　1969D
　　Pleist.; Slaton quarry
　　　　(Holman, J. A.)　　　　　1969E
　　Pleist.; Tedford Quarry
　　　　(Price, W. A.)　　　　　1958A
　　Pleist.; Trinity R.; Mam.
　　　　(Slaughter, B. H.)　　　　1969B
　　　　(Willimon, E. L.)　　　　1972A
　　Pleist., upper; Klein Cave; Mam.
　　　　(Roth, E. L.)　　　　　　1972A
　　Pleist., upper; Val Verde Co.; Mam.
　　　　(Lundelius, E.)　　　　　1972A
　　Tert., lower; Trans-Pecos; Mam.
　　　　(Wilson, J. A.)　　　　　1971A,B
　　Triassic; Dockum group
　　　　(Gregory, J. T.)　　　　1972A
TEXTBOOKS. See under Evolution, Paleoanthropology,
　Paleontology.
THEOLOGICAL INTERPRETATION. See under
　Evolution.
TRACKS AND TRACES
　Amphibia
　　Carboniferous
　　　　(Haubold, H.)　　　　　1970A
　　Carboniferous, upper; France; n. gen.,
　　　n. sp.
　　　　(Dollé, P., et al.)　　　　1970A
　　Devonian; Australia, Genoa R.
　　　　(Anon.)　　　　　　1972BJ,BK
　　Devonian; Australia, Victoria
　　　　(Warren, J. W., Wakefield, N. A.)　1972A
　　Permian
　　　　(Haubold, H.)　　　　　1970A
　　Perm., upper; Australia, Queensland
　　　　(Warren, A.)　　　　　1972A
　　Triassic; Australia, Hawkesbury
　　　　(Sherwin, L.)　　　　　1969A
　　Triassic; Germany, western
　　　　(Ortlam, D.)　　　　　1968A

TRACKS AND TRACES - cont.
Vertebrata
Geological Museum, Bohum
(Hahne, C.)   1966A
Italy, Florence
(Parea, G. C.)   1964A
Jur.; Afghanistan, Band-e-Turkestan
(Lapparent, A. F. de, Stöcklin, J.)   1971A
Mesozoic; Germany, Hassberge
(Welzel, E.)   1968A
Miocene; Rumania, Carpathian Mts.
(Panin, N.)   1964A, 1965A
Permian; East Germany, Morungen bei Wippra
(Müller, A. H.)   1970C
Permian; England, Mansfield
(Sarjeant, W. A. S.)   1966A
Permian; Texas, Castle Peak
(Sarjeant, W. A. S.)   1971A
Pleistocene; Hungary, Vértesszölös
(Vértes, L.)   1968A
Pleistocene; New Mexico, Sante Fe
(Lamb, S. H.)   1970A
Pleistocene; Syria, Yabroud
(Solecki, R. S.)   1968B
Pliocene; Argentina, Quebrada del Yeso
(Bonaparte, J. F.)   1965A
Triassic; England
(Sarjeant, W. A. S.)   1967A
Triassic; France, Autunois
(Demathieu, G.)   1967A
Triassic; Germany
(Haubold, H.)   1971A
Triassic; Scotland, Dumfriesshire
(Delair, J. B.)   1970A
Triassic; France; n. gen., n. sp.
(Demathieu, G.)   1970B
TRIASSIC
Correlation
Capitosauroids
(Ochev, V. G.)   1968B
Eurasia; amphibians
(Belousova, Z. D.,
Riabukhina, S. G.)   1971A
Germany; phytosaurs
(Gregory, J. T.)   1969B
Labyrinthodonts
(Vavilov, M. N., Lozovskiĭ, V. R.)   1970A
So. Africa; Morganucodontidae
(Attridge, J., Charig, A. J.)   1967B
So. America; vertebrates
(Sill, W. D.)   1969B
USSR; amphibians
(Ochev, V. G.,
Tverdokhlebova, G. I.)   1970A
Vertebrate footprints
(Haubold, H.)   1969A
Geochronology
Argentina; reptiles
(Romer, A. S.)   1971C
Argentina; vertebrates
(Bonaparte, J. F.)   1966F
Capitosauroids
(Ochev, V. G.)   1968B
Eurasia; amphibians
(Belousova, Z. D.,
Riabukhina, S. G.)   1971A

TRIASSIC - cont.
Geochronology
Labyrinthodonts
(Vavilov, M. N., Lozovskiĭ, V. R.)   1970A
USSR; amphibians
(Lipatova, V. V., et al.)   1972A
(Ochev, V. G., Shishkin, M. A.,
Gariainov, V. A.,
Tverdokhlebov, V. P.)   1964A, 1965A
USSR; labyrinthodonts
(Tverdokhlebov, V. P.)   1970A
USSR; lungfish
(Minikh, M. G.)   1969A
USSR, Pechora; vertebrates
(Chalyshev, V. I.,
Variukhina, L. M.)   1966A
USSR; vertebrates
(Ochev, V. G., Lozovskiĭ, V. R.,
Dubeĭkovskiĭ, S. G.)   1972A
TUNISIA
Paleontology
Aves; Miocene, upper; Bled Douarah
(Rich, P. V.)   1972A
Mam.; Miocene, upper; Bled Douarah
(Forstén, A.-M.)   1972A
Mam.; Pleist.; Hamada Damous
(Coppens, Y.)   1971A
Vertebrate Faunas
Miocene; central; Mam.
(Robinson, P.)   1972A
Miocene, middle; Bled Douarah; Mam.
(Robinson, P., Black, C. C.)   1969A
Pleistocene
(Coppens, Y.)   1971B
Pleist.; Ichkeul; Mam.
(Jaeger, J.-J.)   1971A
Pleist.; Mam.
(Tchoumakov, I. S., Alexeeva, L. I.) 1971A
Tertiary
(Black, C. C.)   1969A
Triassic; southern; Rept.
(Halstead, L. B., Stewart, A. D.)   1970A
TURKEY
Paleoanthropology
Anatolia; fossil hominids
(Erdbrink, D.-P., Tacoma, J.,
Visser, H.)   1966A
Fossil hominids
(Ozansoy, F.)   1969C
(Vallois, H. V.)   1968D
Paleontology
Mam.; Eocene; Boyabat
(Ozansoy, F.)   1969A
Mam.; Pleist.; Çakil Kaya
(Erdbrink, D.-P.,
Van Asch, T. W. J.)   1972A
Mam.; Pliocene; Ankara
(Ozansoy, F.)   1970A
Mam.; Pliocene; Sinap
(Tekkaya, I.)   1970A
Pisces; Eocene; Thala
(Gaudant, M., Gaudant, J.)   1969A
Vertebrate Faunas
Cenozoic; Mam.
(Ozansoy, F.)   1966A
(Sickenberg, O., Tobien, H.)   1971A

USSR - cont.
Paleoanthropology
  Altaĭ; fossil hominids
    (Gaĭduk, I. M.)   1969A
  Black Sea; fossil hominids
    (Kleĭn, R. G.)   1967C
  Caucasus; fossil hominids
    (Liubin, V. P.)   1972A
    (Vekilova, E. A., Zubov, A. A.)   1972A
  Crimea; fossil hominids
    (Bibikov, S. N.)   1971A
  Crimea; Paleolithic shelters
    (Vekilova, E. A., Muratov, V. M.,
      Fridenberg, E. O.)   1969A
  Don R.; fossil hominids
    (Kleĭn, R. G.)   1969C
  Eniseĭ V.; fossil hominids
    (Astakhov, S. N.)   1966C
  Fossil hominids
    (Bacon, E.)   1971A
    (Iakimov, V. P.)   1969B
  Gagarino; Paleolithic art
    (Tarasov, L. M.)   1969A, 1971A, 1972A
  Kamchatka; fossil hominids
    (Dikov, N. N.)   1969A
  Kostenki; Paleolithic art
    (Fradkin, E. E.)   1969A
    (Korobkova, G. F.)   1969B
  Pechora R. basin; fossil hominids
    (Beznosikov, Ia. N.)   1970A
  Samarkand; fossil hominids
    (Lev, D. N.)   1965A
  Sungir'; Paleolithic burial
    (Bader, O. N.)   1966D, 1970A,B, 1971A
    (Sergin, V. Ia.)   1970A
  Ukraine; mammoth bone dwelling
    (Pidoplichko, I. G.)   1969B
  Ural Mts., Kapovaja Cave; cave paintings
    (Bader, O. N.)   1966E
  Ural Mts.; Paleolithic migrations
    (Bader, O. N.)   1970C
  Uzbekistan, Zaraut-Kamar; Paleolithic art
    (Formozov, A. A.)   1965C
Paleoecology
  Neogene; Black Sea region; *Hipparion* faunas
    (Korotkevich, E. L.)   1972A
Paleontology
  Amph.; Perm., upper; Donguz R.
    (Tverdokhlebova, G. I.)   1972A
  Amph.; Perm., upper; Isheevo
    (Tatarinov, L. P.)   1968B
  Amph.; Triassic, lower; Tikhvino
    (Ivakhnenko, M. F.)   1971A, 1972A
  Aves; Eocene; Zaĭsan
    (Bendukidze, O. G.)   1971A
  Aves; Miocene, upper; Moldavia
    (Kurochkin, E. N., Ganĭa, I. M.)   1972A
  Aves; Oligocene; Azerbaĭdzhan,
    Perekishkĭul'
    (Aslanova, S. M., Burczak-Abramowicz,
      N. I.)   1968A
  Aves; Pleist.; Azerbaĭdzhan, Binagady
    (Burchak-Abramovich, N. I.)   1968A
  Aves; Pleist., middle; Kuĭbyshev Prov.,
    S''ezzhaĭa R.
    (Pidoplichko, I. G., Goldin, G. K.)   1964A

USSR - cont.
Paleontology
  Aves; Pleist.; Moldavia
    (Ganĭa, I. M.)   1969A,B
  Aves; Pliocene; Georgia
    (Burchak-Abramovich, N. I.,
      Vekua, A. K.)   1971A
  Mam.; Bering Is.
    (Chelnokov, F. G.)   1969A
  Mam.; Cenozoic; Kazakhstan
    (Lychev, G. F., Aubekerova, P. A.) 1971A
  Mam.; Eocene; Kazakhstan, Andarak,
    Zaĭsan
    (Beliaeva, E. I.)   1971B
  Mam.; Eocene-Miocene; Kazakhstan
    (Biriukov, M. D.)   1962A
    (Musakulova, L. T.)   1966A, 1971A
  Mam.; Eocene; Zaĭsan Basin
    (Gabuniĭa, L. K.)   1970A, 1971A
    (Shevyreva, N. S.)   1971A
  Mam.; Miocene; Andreevka
    (Topachevskiĭ, V. A.)   1971A
  Mam.; Miocene; Chimishliĭa
    (Tarabukin, B. A.)   1968B
  Mam.; Miocene; Kamchatka
    (Dubrovo, I. A.,
      Sinel'nikova, V. N.)   1971A
  Mam.; Miocene, lower; Kazakhstan,
    Sary-Ozek.
    (Aubekerova, P. A.)   1969A
  Mam.; Miocene; Odessa
    (Korotkevich, E. L.)   1972C
  Mam.; Miocene; Sakhalin Is.
    (Siryk, I. M., Dubrovo, I. A.)   1970A
  Mam.; Miocene, upper; Moldavia
    (Lungu, A. N.)   1972A
  Mam.; Miocene, upper; Nikolaev Prov.
    (Korotkevich, E. L.)   1971C
  Mam.; Miocene, upper; Odessa Prov.
    (Korotkevich, E. L.)   1971B
    (Topachevs'kyĭ, V. O.)   1971B
  Mam.; Miocene; Zaĭsan Basin
    (Shevyreva, N. S.)   1971B
  Mam.; Neogene; Kazakhstan, Kirgizia
    (Godina, A. Ia.)   1971A
  Mam.; Neogene, upper; Black Sea region
    (Korotkevich, E. L.)   1970B
  Mam.; Oligocene; Kazakhstan
    (Shevyreva, N. S.)   1971C
  Mam.; Oligocene; Kazakhstan, Agyspe
    (Lychev, G. F.)   1970A
  Mam.; Oligocene; Kazakhstan, Bolatam
    (Reshetov, V. Iu.)   1971A
  Mam.; Oligocene; Kazakhstan
    (Ianovskaĭa, N. M.)   1970A
  Mam.; Oligocene; Mangyshlak
    (Dubrovo, I. A., Sharkov, A. A.)   1971A
  Mam.; Oligocene, middle; Kazakhstan,
    Teniz Lake
    (Beliaeva, E. I.)   1970A
  Mam.; Pleist.
    (Vereshchagin, N. K.)   1971B
  Mam.; Pleist.; Azerbaĭdzhan, Azykh Cave
    (Gadzhiev, D. V., Aliev, S. D.)   1966B,
                        1971A

USSR - cont.
  Paleontology
    Pisces; Pliocene; Gvada
      (Gabelaia, Ts. D.)   1971A
    Pisces; Silurian; Estonia
      (Gross, W.)   1969A
    Pisces; Silurian; Oesel
      (Ritchie, A.)   1968B
    Pisces; Silurian, upper; Vaĭgach Is.
      (Novitskaia, L. I.)   1970A,B
    Pisces; Triassic; Mt. Bogdo
      (Rykov, S. P., Minikh, M. G.)   1969A, 1970A
    Rept.; Cenozoic; Kazakhstan
      (Kuznetsov, V. V.)   1964A
    Rept.; Cenozoic; Kazakhstan, Kyzyl-Kaz
      (Chkhikvadze, V. M.)   1971C
    Rept.; Cenozoic; Ukraine
      (Tarashchuk, V. I.)   1971B
    Rept.; Cret.; Kazakhstan
      (Rozhdestvenskiĭ, A. K.)   1968C
    Rept.; Jur.; Kazakhstan, Karatau
      (Abelin, P. G.)   1972A
    Rept.; Jur., upper; Moscow Basin
      (Halstead, L. B.)   1971B
    Rept.; Mesozoic; Kazakhstan
      (Kuznetsov, V. V.)   1964A
    Rept.; Mesozoic; Kazakhstan, Kirgizia
      (Sharov, A. G.)   1971A
    Rept.; Miocene, middle; Kazakhstan
      (Kuznetsov, V. V.)   1972A
    Rept.; Neogene; Tadzhikistan
      (Kuznetsov, V. V.)   1970A
    Rept.; Oligocene; Dzhungarian Alatau
      (Khozatskiĭ, L. I., Kuznetsov, V. V.)   1971A
    Rept.; Oligocene; Kazakhstan
      (Chkhikvadze, V. M.)   1971B,E
    Rept.; Paleogene; Kazakhstan
      (Chkhikvadze, V. M.)   1969A
    Rept.; Permian; Donguz R.
      (Tverdokhlebova, G. I.)   1972B
    Rept.; Permian; Ezhovo
      (Chudinov, P. K.)   1968C
    Rept.; Permian; North Dvina R.
      (Tatarinov, L. P.)   1971A
    Rept.; Permian, upper
      (Tatarinov, L. P.)   1968C
    Rept.; Permian, upper; Bliumental'
      (Tverdokhlebova, G. I.)   1968A
    Rept.; Permian; western
      (Sigogneau, D., Tchudinov, P. K.)   1972A
    Rept.; Pleist.; Azerbaĭdzhan, Fat'mai
      (Khozatskiĭ, L. I.)   1967B
    Rept.; Pliocene; Crimea
      (Tarashchuk, V. I.)   1971A
    Rept.; Pliocene, middle, Kirgizia,
        Dzhety-Oguz R.
      (Kuznetsov, V. V., et al.)   1964A
    Rept.; Pliocene; Moldavia, Ukraine
      (Telepneva, V. P.)   1964A
    Rept.; Tert.; Kazakhstan
      (Chkhikvadze, V. M.)   1972A
    Rept.; Tert.; Kazakhstan, Zaĭsan basin
      (Chkhikvadze, V. M.)   1970B,C, 1971A,D
    Rept.; Triassic; Cisuralia
      (V'iushkov, B. P.)   1969A,B
    Rept.; Triassic; Karagachka R.
      (Danilov, A. I.)   1971A,B

USSR - cont.
  Paleontology
    Rept.; Triassic, lower; Madygen
      (Sharov, A. G.)   1970A,B
    Rept.; Triassic; Omolon' R. basin
      (Polubotko, I. V., Ochev, V. G.)   1972A
    Rept.; Triassic; Orenburg Prov.
      (Danilov, A. I., Kalandadze, N. N.)   1970A
    Rept.; Triassic; Ural Mts.
      (Kalandadze, N. N.)   1969A, 1970A
    Vert.; Kazakhstan
      (Orlovskaia, E. R., Savinov, P. F.)   1971A
    Vert.; Silurian; Vaĭgach Is.
      (Cherkesov, S. V.)   1970A
  Vertebrate Faunas
    Carb.; Saĭan-Altaĭ; Pisces
      (Graĭzer, M. I.)   1967A
    Cenozoic
      (Rozhdestvenskiĭ, A. K.)   1970C
    Cenozoic; Azerbaĭdzhan
      (Alizade, K. A., Gadzhiev, D. V.)   1970A
    Cenozoic; Beringia; Mam.
      (Cherniavskiĭ, F. B.)   1970A
    Cenozoic; Caucasus; Aves
      (Burchak-Abramovich, N. I.)   1965C
    Cenozoic; Kazakhstan
      (Kozhamkulova, B. S.,
        Orlovskaia, E. R.)   1971A
    Cenozoic; Kazakhstan; Aves
      (Aubekerova, P. A.)   1965A
    Cenozoic; Kazakhstan, central; Mam.
      (Malinovskiĭ, V. Iu.)   1967A
      (Shantser, E. V., Mikulina, T. M.)   1967A
    Cenozoic; Kuznetsk Basin; Mam.
      (Alekseeva, E. V.)   1970A
    Cenozoic; Moldavia; Rept.
      (Khozatskiĭ, L. I., Tofan, V. E.)   1970A
    Cenozoic; Ob' R.; Mam.
      (Zudin, A. N., Pospelova, G. A.)   1970A
    Cenozoic; Tadzhikistan, southern; Mam.
      (Nikonov, A. A., et al.)   1971A
    Cenozoic; Ural Mts.; Mam.
      (Iakhimovich, N. N.)   1965A,B
    Cret.; Kazakhstan
      (Kostenko, N. N., Nikitin, E. A.,
        Polumiskova, L. A.)   1971A
      (Kozhamkulova, B. G.,
        Orlovskaia, E. R.)   1971A
    Cret.; Kazakhstan; Pisces
      (Kostenko, N. N., et al.)   1971A
    Cret.; Kazakhstan; Rept.
      (Kovrizhnykh, Iu. B.)   1971A
    Cret.; Kyzylkumy
      (Martinson, G. G.)   1969A
    Cret.; Pisces
      (Danilevich, A. M., Vasil'ev, V. I.)   1966A
    Cret.; Rept.
      (Sigov, A. P.)   1969A
    Cret., upper; Amu-Dar'ia; Pisces
      (Sokolov, M. I.)   1957A
    Cret., upper; Kazakhstan; Rept.
      (Bazhanov, O. V., Kostenko, N. N.)   1971A
    Cret.; Urals
      (Sharfman, V. S., Tsetlin, V. P.,
        Skripko, K. A.)   1965A
    Cret.; Zeia-Bureia depression; Rept.
      (Krasnyĭ, L. I.)   1966A

USSR - cont.
Vertebrate Faunas
Oligocene; Caucasus; Pisces
  (Somov, V. D.) 1970A
Oligocene; Chernye Mts.; Pisces
  (Somov, V. D.) 1969A
Oligocene; Fergana; Mam.
  (Eroshkin, A. F., Savinov, P. F.) 1971A
Oligocene; Georgia
  (Laliev, A. G.) 1964A
Oligocene; Little Caucasus, eastern; Pisces
  (Alizade, K. A.) 1968A
Oligocene; Mardachaĭ; Pisces
  (Tatieva, K. G.) 1960A
Oligocene; Turgaĭ; Mam.
  (Sakharov, V. A.) 1971A
Oligocene; Turgaĭ; Pisces
  (Udris, K. P.) 1971A
Paleocene; Kirgizia; Mam.
  (Zhukov, Ĭu. V.) 1970A
Paleogene; Kazakhstan
  (Kostenko, N. N., Nikitin, E. A.,
  Lĭadzhina, K. A.) 1971A
Paleogene; Kazakhstan; Mam.
  (Bazhanov, O. V., et al.) 1971A
Paleogene; Maritime Prov.; Mam.
  (Bersenev, I. I., et al.) 1969A
Paleogene; Pisces
  (Fedorenko, E. N.) 1970A
Paleogene; Povolzh'e, Prikam'e; Pisces
  (Leonov, G. P.) 1967A
Paleogene; Saur Zone
  (Borisov, B. A., Kleĭman, G. P.) 1967A
Paleogene; Ukrainia; Pisces
  (Klĭushnikov, M. N.) 1958A
Paleogene; Ural Mts.; Pisces
  (Sigov, A. P.) 1969B
Paleogene; Zaĭsan trough; Mam.
  (Shevyreva, N. S.) 1969A
Paleozoic; Dnestr; Pisces
  (Tsegel'nĭuk, P. D.) 1969A
Permian
  (Nalivkin, V. D., Larionova, E. N.,
  Shershnev, K. S.) 1969A
Permian; Povolzh'e, Prikam'e
  (Ignat'ev, V. I.) 1967A
  (Tikhvinskaĭa, E. I.) 1967A
Permian; Russian Platform
  (Zoricheva, A. I.) 1963A
Permian; southern
  (Lĭutkevich, E. M.) 1969A
Permian, upper; Maritime Prov.; Pisces
  (Zimina, V. G.) 1969A, 1970A
Permian, upper; Transcaucasia; Pisces
  (Barskov, I. S., Koroleva, N. V.) 1969A
Permian; western
  (Rotaĭ, A. P.) 1963A
Pleistocene
  (Zamoriĭ, P. K.) 1958A
Pleist.; Abkhazia
  (Burchak-Abramovich, N. I.) 1965D
Pleist.; Aksaĭtaĭ R.; Mam.
  (Kambariddinov, R. K.,
  Sharakhmedov, Sh. Sh.) 1971A
Pleist.; Altaĭ; Mam.
  (Matsuĭ, V. M., Mos'kina, O. D.) 1968A

USSR - cont.
Vertebrate Faunas
Pleist.; Altaĭ, Ust'-Kanskaĭa Cave
  (Anisĭutkin, N. K., Astakhov, S. N.) 1970A
Pleist.; Amur, Khabarovsk; Mam.
  (Chemekov, Ĭu. F.) 1966A
Pleist.; Armenia, Erevan; Mam.
  (Eritsĭan, B. G., Semenov, S. A.) 1971A
Pleist.; Armenia; Mam.
  (Aslanĭan, A. T.) 1970A
  (Gudilin, I. S.) 1966A
  (Saĭadĭan, Ĭu. V.) 1970A
Pleist.; Armenia, Pambak V.; Mam.
  (Davtĭan, A. R.) 1970A
Pleist.; Armenia, western
  (Avakĭan, L. A., Davtĭan, A. R.) 1970A
Pleist.; Aves
  (Burchak-Abramovich, N. I.) 1966G
  (Dementiev, G. P.) 1960A
Pleist.; Azerbaĭdzhan, Azykh Cave; Mam.
  (Gadzhiev, D. V., Aliev, S. D.) 1966B,
  1969A
Pleist.; Bashkirian Predural'e; Mam.
  (Sukhov, V. P.) 1967B
  (Varlamov, I. P.) 1959A
Pleist.; Caucasus
  (Burchak-Abramovich, N. I.) 1969A
Pleist.; Caucasus; Aves
  (Burchak-Abramovich, N. I.) 1966H
Pleist.; Caucasus, Kepsha; Mam.
  (Lĭubin, V. P., et al.) 1971A
Pleist.; Chikoĭ R.; Mam.
  (Erbaeva, M. A.) 1968B
Pleist.; Cis-Altaĭ plain; Mam.
  (Adamenko, O. M.) 1971A
Pleist.; Crimea
  (Bibikov, S. N.) 1969A
Pleist.; Crimea; Aves
  (Voinstvenskiĭ, M. A.) 1963A, 1965A
Pleist.; Crimea; Mam.
  (Bachinskiĭ, G. A.,
  Dublĭanskiĭ, V. N.) 1963A
  (Shchepinskiĭ, A. A.) 1971A
Pleist.; Crimea, Sinĭakhov,
  Tarkhankut Caves
  (Bachyn'skyĭ, G. O.) 1965A
Pleist.; Dobranichev; Mam.
  (Shovkoplĭas, I. G.) 1969A
Pleist.; Don R. basin; Mam.
  (Krasnenkov, R. V., et al.) 1970A
  (Vasil'ev, Ĭu. M.) 1969A
Pleist.; Dnestr; Mam.
  (Negadaev-Nikonov, K. N.,
  Bukatchuk, P. D.) 1969A
Pleist.; Kirgizia, Dzhargalan R.; Mam.
  (Kambariddinova, T. K.,
  Talipov, M. A.) 1969A
  (Talipov, M. A.) 1968A
  (Talipov, M. A., Korolev, V. G.) 1970A
Pleist.; eastern; Mam.
  (Mokrousov, V. P., Sadovskiĭ, N. D.)1964A
  (Vangengeĭm, E. A., Sher, A. V.) 1969A,
  1970A
Pleist.; European part
  (Breslav, S. L.) 1971A

USSR - cont.
  Vertebrate Faunas
    Pleist.; Transcaucasia; Mam.
      (Lebedeva, N. A.)   1972A
      (Saĭadĭan, Ĭu. V.)   1969A
    Pleist.; Turgaĭ; Mam.
      (Boboedova, A. A.)   1971B
    Pleist.; Ukraine; Mam.
      (Tatarinov, K. A.,
        Bachyns'kyĭ, G. O.)   1968A
    Pleist.; Ukraine, western; Aves
      (Marisova, I. V., Tatarinov, K. A.)   1965A
      (Tatarinov, K. A., Marisova, I. V.)   1971A
    Pleist.; Ulalinka R.; Mam.
      (Adamenko, O. M.)   1970A
    Pleist., upper; Azov Sea region; Mam.
      (Agadzhanĭan, A. K.)   1972A
    Pleist., upper; lower Aldan R.; Mamontova
      Gora; Mam.
      (Agadzhanĭan, A. K.,
        Boĭarskaĭa, T. D.)   1969A
    Pleist., upper; North Urals; Mam.
      (Kuz'mina, I. E.)   1971A
    Pleist., upper; Ukraine, Kremenetś; Amph.
      (Tatarinov, K. A., Marisova, I. V.)   1962A
    Pleist., upper; Ukraine, Kremenetś; Mam.
      (Tatarinov, K. A.)   1962A
    Pleist.; Ural Mts.; Mam.
      (Stefanovskiĭ, V. V.)   1970A
      (Sukhorukov, A. M.)   1964A
    Pleist.; Ural Mts., Zhiguli; Mam.
      (Bader, O. N.)   1969A
    Pleist.; Volchiĭ Cave; Mam.
      (Bader, O. N.)   1969D
    Pleist.; Volyn'
      (Tatarinov, K. A.)   1971A
    Pleist.; West Kalba; Mam.
      (Sevrĭugin, N. A.)   1967A
    Pleist.; western; Mam.
      (Lider, V. A.)   1969A
      (Popov, G. I.)   1970A
    Pleist.; Yakutia; Mam.
      (Okladnikov, A. P.)   1970A
    Pliocene; Aksaĭtaĭ R.; Mam.
      (Kambariddinov, R. K.,
        Sharakhmedov, Sh. Sh.)   1971A
    Pliocene; Aves
      (Burchak-Abramovich, N. I.)   1966G
    Pliocene; Caucasus, northern; Mam.
      (Zhizhchenko, B. P., Serezhenko, V. A.,
        Churilova, E. V.)   1968A
    Pliocene; Don basin; Mam.
      (Krasnenkov, R. V.,
        Aleksandrova, L. P.)   1967A
    Pliocene; East Georgia; Mam.
      (Vekua, A. K.)   1972A
    Pliocene; Georgia, Bazaleti series; Mam.
      (Adamiĭa, Sh. A., et al.)   1965A
    Pliocene; Georgia, Gvda; Pisces
      (Gabelaĭa, Ťs. D.)   1971B
      (Gabelaĭa, Ťs. D., Ramishvili, I. Sh.,
        Maĭsuradze, L. S.)   1970A
    Pliocene; Georgia, Kisatibi; Pisces
      (Gabelaĭa, Ťs. D.)   1970A
    Pliocene; Georgia; Mam.
      (Buleĭshvili, D. A.)   1964B

USSR - cont.
  Vertebrate Faunas
    Pliocene; Kazakhstan; Mam.
      (Aubekerova, P. A.)   1968A
    Pliocene; Kopet-Dagh
      (Birman, A. S.,
        Rasťsvetaev, L. M.)   1967A, 1969A
      (Birman, A. S.,
        Zhegallo, V. I., et al.)   1971A
    Pliocene; Kvabebi; Mam.
      (Gabuniĭa, L. K., Vekua, A. K.)   1968A,B,C
    Pliocene, lower; Moldavia; Mam.
      (Bukatchuk, P. D., et al.)   1968A,B
    Pliocene; Moldavia
      (Sinegub, V. V.)   1969A
    Pliocene; Odessa
      (Odintśov, I. A.)   1969A
    Pliocene; Pechora, Vychegda; Mam.
      (Timofeev, E. M., Steklov, A. A.,
        Alekseeva, L. I.)   1970A
    Pliocene; Rudnyĭ Altaĭ
      (Borisov, B. A., Chumakov, I. S.)   1967A
    Pliocene; southern; desert
      (Karlov, N. N.)   1971A
    Pliocene; southern; Mam.
      (Shevchenko, A. I.)   1968A
    Pliocene; Tadzhikistan; Mam.
      (Nikonov, A. A.)   1971A
    Pliocene; Ukrainia, Morskoĭ farm; Mam.
      (Skorik, A. F.)   1969A
    Pliocene, upper; Azov Sea area; Mam.
      (Baĭgusheva, V. S.)   1971A
    Pliocene, upper; Bashkiria; Mam.
      (Sukhov, V. P.)   1970A
    Pliocene, upper; Kazakhstan, central; Mam.
      (Gus'kova, A. I., et al.)   1971A
    Pliocene, upper; Moldavia,
      Chishmikioĭ; Mam.
      (Khubka, A. N., Shushpanov, K. I.) 1971A
    Pliocene, upper; Sev. Donetś,
      Buzinnaĭa; Mam.
      (Prokhodskiĭ, S. I.)   1963A
    Pliocene, upper; Volga region; Pisces
      (Kirsanov, N. V.)   1971A
    Silurian; Baltic region; Pisces
      (Karatajute-Talimaa, V. N.)   1968A,C
                                                     1970A
    Silurian; Estonia; Pisces
      (Mark-Kurik, E.)   1969A
      (Mark-Kurik, E., Noppel, T.)   1970A
    Silurian; Pisces
      (Vladimirskaĭa, E. V.,
        Blagonravov, V. A.)   1966A
    Silurian; Timan; Pisces
      (Varsanoṕeva, V. A.)   1963A
    Silurian; western; Pisces
      (Obruchev, D. V.,
        Karatajute-Talimaa, V. N.)   1968A
    Tert.; Don R.; Pisces
      (Fedorov, A. V.)   1970A
    Tert.; European part, center
      (Iosifova, Ĭu. I.)   1971A
    Tert.; Issyk-Kul'; Mam.
      (Tarasov, S. A.)   1970A
    Tert.; Kazakhstan
      (Timush, A. V.)   1965A

VERTEBRATE - cont.
  Systematics
    Numerical taxonomy
      (Pokorný, V.)   1969A
      (Sokal, R. R.)   1968A
      (Vaĭnshteĭn, B. A.)   1968A
    Paratypes
      (Smith, C. L., Buerkli, M.)   1969A
    Phenetic classification
      (Jardine, N.)   1971A
    Phylogenetic classification
      (Ponomarenko, A. G.,
        Rasnitsyn, A. P.)   1971A
      (Schindewolf, O. H.)   1968A, 1969A
    Principles
      (Mayr, E.)   1969D
      (Michener, C. D.)   1970A
    Principles, Simpson's
      (Kiriakoff, S. G.)   1961A
    Problems
      (George, T. N.)   1971A
      (Liubishchev, A. A.)   1968A
      (Lukin, E. I.)   1968A
    Systematic biology
      (Ghiselin, M. T.)   1969B
    Taxonomy, evolutionary patterns
      (Weller, J. M.)   1965C
  Taphonomy
    Cenozoic; Ukraine; principles
      (Bachyns'kyĭ, G. O.)   1967A
    Devonian; USSR, Latvia
      (Lyarskaya, L.)   1972A
    Eocene; Wyoming, Allen quarry
      (Turnbull, W. D.)   1972B
    Fossilization processes
      (Kräusel, W.)   1968A
    Permian; USSR, Priural'e
      (Chudinov, P. K.)   1968D
    Pleistocene; Japan, Tsubami
      (Otsuka, H.)   1971A
    Pleistocene; USSR, Crimea
      (Bachinskiĭ, G. A.,
        Dublianskiĭ, V. N.)   1963A
    Pleistocene; USSR, Siniakhov,
      Tarkhankut Caves
      (Bachyns'kyĭ, G. O.)   1965A
    Pleistocene; USSR, Tadzhikistan
      (Nikonov, A. A.)   1971A
    Pleistocene; USSR, Tologoĭ
      (Erbaeva, M. A.)   1964A
    Pleistocene; USSR, western Transbaĭkalia
      (Erbaeva, M. A.)   1968A
    Pliocene; Nebraska, Verdigre Quarry
      (Voorhies, M. R.)   1969B, 1971C
    Pliocene; USSR, Tadzhikistan
      (Nikonov, A. A.)   1971A
    Rhaetic; Germany
      (Büchner, M.)   1967A
    Tertiary; Uganda
      (Hill, A., Walker, A.)   1972A
    Triassic; Germany, southwest
      (Reif, W.-E.)   1971A
  X-Ray Photography
    Diffraction studies
      (Fujiwara, T.)   1967A

VERTEBRATE - cont.
  X-Ray Photography
    Dinosaur bone
      (Ozaki, H., Kato, A., Obata, I.)   1965A
    France, Lazaret
      (Périnet, G.)   1969A,B
    Functional studies
      (Crompton, A. W.)   1968B
    Methods
      (Stürmer, W.)   1970A, 1971A
VERTEBRATE FAUNAS
  Carboniferous
    England, Monmouthshire; Pisces
      (Hall, I. H. S., Squirrell, H. C.)   1972A
    France, Ronchamp Basin; Stephanian;
      Pisces
      (Mathieu, G.)   1970A
    Montana, Bear Gulch; Pisces
      (Lund, R.)   1972A
    Siberia; Pisces
      (Makarenko, G. F.)   1971A
    USSR, Saĭan-Altaĭ; Pisces
      (Graĭzer, M. I.)   1967A
    West Virginia, Greer; Amph.
      (Anon.)   1970BG
  Cenozoic
    Africa; faunal history
      (Furon, R.)   1970A
    Africa; Mam.
      (Cooke, H. B. S.)   1972B
      (Coryndon, S. C., Savage, R. J. G.) 1972A
    Argentina, Buenos Aires Prov.
      (Pascual, R., et al.)   1966A
    Argentina, Corrientes
      (Herbst, R.)   1971A
    Arizona, San Pedro V.
      (Lindsay, E. H.)   1972A
    Asia, Europe; upper; Mam.
      (Flerow, C. C.)   1971B
    Asia; Mam.
      (Bazhanov, V. S., et al.)   1971A
    Asia, northern; Mam.; faunal history
      (Vangengeĭm, E. A., Zhegallo, V. I.,
        Zazhigin, V. S.)   1972A
    Asia, southeast; Mam.; Rept.
      (Kudriavtsev, G. A., et al.)   1969A
    Australia; Aves
      (Mayr, E.)   1972A
    Australia, Murrey Basin; Pisces
      (Pels, S.)   1969A
    Ceylon
      (Cooray, P. G.)   1967A
    Colombia
      (Porta, J. de)   1969A
    Czechoslovakia; Mam.
      (Fejfar, O.)   1966D, 1968A
    Ethiopia, Awash valley; Mam.; Rept.
      (Taieb, M., et al.)   1972A
    Florida
      (Olsen, S. J.)   1965A
      (Patton, T. H., Webb, S. D.)   1970A
    Florida; Mam.
      (Olsen, S. J.)   1959F
    France, central; Mam.
      (Allain, J.)   1970A

VERTEBRATE FAUNAS - cont.
Cretaceous
Montana, Judith R. Fm.; Mam., Rept.
  (Sahni, A.)   1969C
New Mexico, Big Burro Mts.; Rept.
  (Cunningham, J. E.)   1966A
New Mexico, San Juan Basin
  (Fassett, J. E., Hinds, J. S.)   1971A
New Mexico, San Juan Basin; Rept.
  (Powell, J. S.)   1969A
Niger, Gadoufaoua; Pisces, Rept.
  (Taquet, P.)   1970A
Niger; Pisces
  (Cappetta, H.)   1970B
Nigeria, Sokoto B.; upper; Pisces, Rept.
  (De Giuli, C., Ficcarelli, G.,
    Torre, D.)   1970A
Poland, Holy Cross Mts.; Pisces, Rept.
  (Hakenberg, M.)   1969A
Portugal, Lisbon; Pisces, Rept.
  (Jonet, S.)   1971A
Siberia, western; Rept.
  (Kazarinov, V. P.)   1967A
South Africa, Needs Camp; upper;
  Pisces, Rept.
  (McGowran, B., Moore, A. C.) 1971A
Spain, Galve; Amph., Mam.,
  Pisces, Rept.
  (Kühne, W. G.)   1966A
Spain; Mam.
  (Crusafont Pairó, M.)   1971D
Spain, Uña; Mam., Rept.
  (Kühne, W. G.,
    Crusafont-Pairó, M.)   1968A
Texas, Butler Farm; Mam.
  (Slaughter, B. H.)   1971A
Texas, northcentral; Pisces
  (Thurmond, J. T.)   1970A, 1971A
Texas, Tarrant Co.; Mam., Pisces; Rept.
  (McNulty, C. L., Slaughter, B. H.) 1969A
USSR, Amu-Dar'ia; Pisces
  (Sokolov, M. I.)   1957A
USSR, Kazakhstan; Pisces, Rept.
  (Kostenko, N. N., et al.)   1971A
USSR, Kazakhstan; Rept.
  (Kozhamkulova, B. S.,
    Orlovskaîa, E. R.)   1971A
USSR, Kazakhstan; Senonian; Pisces, Rept.
  (Kostenko, N. N., Nikitin, E. A.,
    Polumiskova, L. A.)   1971A
USSR, Kazakhstan; Senonian; Rept.
  (Bazhanov, O. V., Kostenko, N. N.) 1971A
  (Kovrizhnykh, Iu. B.)   1971A
USSR, Kyzylkumy; Pisces, Rept.
  (Martinson, G. G.)   1969A
USSR; Pisces
  (Danilevich, A. M., Vasil'ev, V. I.) 1966A
USSR, Rept.
  (Sigov, A. P.)   1969A
USSR, Urals; Pisces, Rept.
  (Sharfman, V. S., Tsetlin, V. P.,
    Skripko, K. A.)   1965A
USSR, Zeîa-Bureîa depression; Rept.
  (Krasnyĭ, L. I.)   1966A
Wyoming, Pierre Shale; Pisces, Rept.
  (Gill, J. R., Cobban, W. A.)   1966A

VERTEBRATE FAUNAS - cont.
Cretaceous
Yugoslavia, Bileća; Rept.
  (Slišković, T.)   1970A
Devonian
Antarctica; Pisces
  (Ritchie, A.)   1969A
Antarctica, Victoria Land; Pisces
  (McKelvey, B. C., et al.)   1970A
  (White, E. I.)   1968A
Arctic, Axel Heiberg I.; Pisces
  (Trettin, H. P.)   1969A
Arizona, central; Pisces
  (Teichert, C.)   1965A
Australia, Gogo; Pisces
  (Anon.)   1969BD, 1972AP
Australia, New South Wales; Pisces
  (Conolly, J. R., Hall, L. R.,
    Rose, G.)   1969A
Australia; Pisces
  (Ritchie, A.)   1969A
Australia, western; Pisces
  (Miles, R. S.)   1971A
Calif., Lost Burro Gap; Pisces
  (Dunkle, D. H., Lane, N. G.) 1971A
Canada, Somerset Is.; Pisces
  (Dineley, D. L., Rust, B. R.) 1968A
Colorado, central; Pisces
  (Pampe, W. R.)   1969A
England, Breconshire; Pisces
  (Taylor, K.)   1972A
Europe, eastern; Pisces
  (Obruchev, D.,
    Karatajute-Talimaa, V.)   1967A
Germany, Hünsruck Island; Pisces
  (Solle, G.)   1970A
India, Kashmir; Pisces
  (Gupta, V. J.)   1969B,C
Nepal; Pisces
  (Fuchs, G., Mostler, H.)   1969A
Norway, Spitsbergen; Pisces
  (Birkenmajer, K.)   1964A
  (Ørvig, T.)   1969A,D,E
Prince of Wales Is.; Pisces
  (Broad, D. S., Dineley, D. L.,
    Miall, A. D.)   1968A
Quebec, Gaspé; Pisces
  (Pageau, Y.)   1968A, 1969A,B
Quebec, Miguasha; Pisces
  (Schultze, H.-P.)   1972B
Rumania, Moesia; Pisces
  (Patrulius, D., Iordan, M.) 1969A, 1970A
Scotland, Caithness, Orkney; Pisces
  (Saxon, J.)   1967A
Siberia, Gornyĭ Altaĭ; Pisces
  (Gintsinger, A. V.)   1967A
Siberia, Kuznetsk basin; Frasnian,
  Famennian; Pisces
  (Bel'skaîa, T. N.)   1960A
Siberia, Noril'sk; Pisces
  (Glushnitskiĭ, O. T.,
    Menner, V. V.)   1970A
Siberia, Siberian Platform; Pisces
  (Menner, V. V.. et al.)   1970A

VERTEBRATE FAUNAS - cont.
Paleozoic
France, Blanzy-Montceau; Pisces
  (Anon.)   1969AV
India, Gondwana Fm.
  (Robinson, P. L.)   1967C
Madagascar, Gondwana Fm.; Amph., Rept.
  (Besairie, H.)   1967A
USSR, Baltic region; Pisces
  (Karatajūte-Talimaa, V. N.) 1968A,C, 1970A
USSR, Dnestr; Pisces
  (Tsegel'niuk, P. D.)   1969A
Pennsylvanian
Colorado, Fremont Co.; Stephanian;
  Amph., Pisces, Rept.
  (Vaughn, P. P.)   1972A
Illinois, Mazon Creek; Pisces
  (Johnson, R. G.)   1969A
  (Richardson, E. S., Johnson, R. G.) 1971A
Kansas, Hamilton quarry
  (Bridge, T. E., Leisman, G. A.,
    Lockard, W.)   1972A
Kansas, Nebraska; Amph., Pisces, Rept.
  (Rasmussen, D. L., et al.)   1971A
Montana, Bear Gulch; Pisces
  (Melton, W. G.)   1971A
Montana, Big Snowy Mts.; Pisces
  (Melton, W. G.)   1969A
Permian
Brazil, São Paulo; Rept.
  (Amaral, S. E. de)   1971A
Colorado, Cutler Fm.; Amph., Pisces, Rept.
  (Kirkland, P. L.)   1963A
France; Amph., Pisces, Rept.
  (Heyler, D.)   1969A
Germany, Kusel; Amph., Pisces
  (Boy, J. A.)   1971C
Germany, Red Beds
  (Staesche, K.)   1969A
Germany, Richelsdorfer Mts.; Pisces
  (Schaumberg, G.)   1970A
India, Pranhita-Godavari V., Rept.
  (Kutty, T. S.)   1972A
India, Risin-Zewan; Amph., Pisces
  (Chakravarti, D. K.)   1968A
Kansas; Amph., Pisces, Rept.
  (Rasmussen, D. L.)   1971A
Nebraska; Amph., Pisces, Rept.
  (Rasmussen, D. L.)   1971A
Nebraska, Nemaha Co., Peru; Amph., Pisces
  (Martin, L. D.)   1969A
Nebraska, Nemaha Co., Peru; Amph., Rept.
  (Martin, L. D.)   1971B
New Mexico; Chama Basin
  (Budding, A. J., Pitrat, C. W.,
    Smith, C. T.)   1960A
New Mexico; Kaibab Fm. & Toroweap Fm.;
  Pisces
  (McKee, E. D., Breed, W. J.)   1969A
New Mexico, Otero Co.; Amph.,
  Pisces, Rept.
  (Vaughn, P. P.)   1969C
Oklahoma, Chickasha Fm.; Amph., Rept.
  (Olson, E. C.)   1972D
Siberia, Kuznetsk Basin; Pisces, Rept.
  (Fomichev, V. D.)   1967A

VERTEBRATE FAUNAS - cont.
Permian
South Africa, Karroo; Rept.
  (Barry, T. H.)   1972A
  (Boonstra, L. D.)   1969A,I
Texas, northcentral; Pisces, Amph., Rept.
  (Berman, D. S.)   1969A, 1970A
USSR, Maritime Province; Pisces
  (Zimina, V. G.)   1969A, 1970A
USSR; Pisces, Rept.
  (Nalivkin, V. D., Larionova, E. N.,
    Shershnev, K. S.)   1969A
USSR, Povolzh'e, Prikam'e; Amph.,
  Pisces, Rept.
  (Tikhvinskaia, E. I.)   1967A
USSR, Povolzh'e, Prikam'e; Amph., Rept.
  (Ignat'ev, V. I.)   1967A
USSR, Russian Platform; Amph., Pisces, Rept.
  (Zoricheva, A. I.)   1963A
USSR, southern; Amph., Rept.
  (Liutkevich, E. M.)   1969A
USSR, Transcaucasia; Dzhul'fa; Pisces
  (Barskov, I. S., Koroleva, N. V.) 1969A
USSR, western; Amph., Rept.
  (Rotai, A. P.)   1963A
Permo-Triassic
West Pakistan; Pisces
  (Kummel, B., Teichert, C.)   1970B
Quaternary
Africa, central; Mam., Pisces; Rept.
  (Mawby, J. E.)   1969A, 1970A
Africa, Lake Victoria; Pisces
  (Temple, P. H.)   1969A
Africa, Malawi Rift; Mam.
  (Clark, J. D.)   1968C
Africa; Mam.
  (Cooke, H. B. S.)   1966A
  (Coppens, Y.)   1972A
Africa, sub-Sahara; Mam.
  (Cartmill, M.)   1967A
Alaska, Amchitka Is.; Mam.
  (Gard, L. M., Szabo, B. J.)   1971A
Alaska, Cape Deceit; Mam.
  (Guthrie, R. D., Matthews, J. V.) 1971A
Alaska, Mam.
  (Guthrie, R. D.)   1972A
Alaska, Pribilof Is.; Mam.
  (Ray, C. E.)   1971A
Alaska, Seward Peninsula; Mam.
  (Larsen, H.)   1968A
Alberta, Cochrane; Mam.
  (Churcher, C. S.)   1968B
Alberta; Mam.
  (Stalker, A. M., Churcher, C. S.) 1972A
Arctic; Mam.
  (Sher, A. V.)   1971B
Argentina, Malacara; Mam.
  (Kraglievich, J. L.)   1959C
Arkansas, Conard Fissure; Mam.
  (Quinn, J. H.)   1972A
Australia, Lara; Mam.
  (Wilkinson, H. E.)   1971A
Australia; Mam.
  (Calaby, J. H.)   1971A
  (Mulvaney, D. J.)   1969A
Austria, Eichkogels; lower
  (Daxner-Höck, G., Rabeder, G.) 1971A

VERTEBRATE FAUNAS - cont.
Quaternary
Europe; Mam.
  (Negadaev-Nikonov, K. N.,
    David, A. I., Khubka, A. N.)   1970A
  (Tobien, H.)   1972A
Europe, northeastern; Makarikha R.; Mam.
  (Zarkhidze, V. S.)   1970A
Europe, western; Villafranchian; Mam.
  (Bout, P.)   1968A
Europe, western; Würm; Mam.; migrations
  (Koby, F.-E.)   1960B
Florida
  (DuBar, J. R.)   1958B
Florida, Alachua Co.
  (Dolan, E. M., Allen, G. T.)   1961A
Florida, Arredondo; Aves
  (Frailey, C. D.)   1972A
Florida, Coleman II A; Mam.
  (Martin, R. A.)   1970B
Florida, Dale Co.; Mam., Rept.
  (Weaver, W. G., Ober, L. D.)   1971A
Florida, Haile XV A; Blancan; Mam.
  (Robertson, J. S.)   1971A
Florida, southern
  (Ober, L. D., Weaver, W. G.)   1971A
Florida, Vero Beach
  (Weigel, R. D.)   1962C
France
  (Bonifay, M. F.)   1969C
  (Bouchud, J.)   1957A
France, Achenheimer loess; Mam.
  (Wernert, P.)   1968A
France, Allier
  (Bouchud, J.)   1959B
France, Auvergue and Velay;
  Villafranchian; Mam.
  (Bout, P.)   1967A
France, Basses-Alpes, Puimoisson;
  Villafranchian; Mam.
  (Dubar, M.)   1969A
France, Blassac-La Girondie;
  Villafranchian; Mam.
  (Beden, M., Guth, C.)   1970B
France, central; Mam.
  (Bout, P.)   1972A
France, Chagny; Villafranchian; Mam.
  (Chaline, J., Clair, A.,
    Puissegur, J. J.)   1970A
France; Châtillon-St.-Jean; Mam.
  (Bonnet, A.)   1970A
France, Chilhac; Villafranchian; Mam.
  (Beden, M., Guth, C.)   1970A
France, Eure V.; Riss, Würm; Mam.
  (Dewolf, Y.)   1970A
France, Hermolsheim; Mam.
  (Wernert, P., Wolf, M.)   1970A
France, La Canéda; Mam.
  (Delpech, F.)   1970A
France, La Fage à Noailles; Würm;
  Aves, Mam.
  (Couchard, J.)   1963A
France, Landes, Duruthy; Würm;
  Aves, Mam.
  (Delpech, F.)   1970B

VERTEBRATE FAUNAS - cont.
Quaternary
France, Landes, Duruthy; Würm; Aves,
  Mam., Pisces
  (Delpech, F.)   1968A
France, Landes Fm.; Würm; Mam.
  (Legigan, P.)   1970A
France, Ligurie-Provence
  (Lumley-Woodyear, H. de)   1969D
France, Lille; Mam.
  (Waterlot, G.)   1969A
France, Montpellier; Mam.
  (Chaline, J., Michaux, J.)   1969A
France, Montpellier; Villafranchian;
  rodents; faunal history
  (Barrière, J., Michaux, J.)   1970A
France, Petit Puymoyen; Mam.
  (Boeuf, O.)   1970A
France, Rhone V.; Mam.
  (Bonnet, A., Bornand, M.)   1970A
France, Rhuis; Mam.
  (Prat, F.)   1968A
France, Saône V., Dijon;
  Villafranchian; Mam.
  (Clair, A., Puisségur, J.-J.)   1969A
France, Seine R.; Mam.
  (Michel, J. P., Carite, D.)   1971A
France, Seine-et-Marne, Val-d'Oise;
  Aves, Mam.
  (Bailloud, M. G.)   1969A
France, Solutré; Mam.
  (Joly, J.)   1970A
France, southeast; Mam.
  (Bonifay, M.-F.)   1968C
France, Villefranche-sur-Saône; Mam.
  (Monjuvent, G.)   1968A
France, Villereversure; Mam.
  (Martin, R.)   1968A
General
  (Bouchud, J.)   1962D, 1965C
  (Vereshchagin, N. K.)   1963A
Georgia, Glynn Co.; Mam.
  (Voorhies, M. R.)   1971B
Georgia, Ladds; Amph., Rept.
  (Holman, J. A.)   1967B
Georgia, Ladds; Aves
  (Wetmore, A.)   1967B
Germany, Bensheim; Mam.
  (Homann, W.)   1968A
Germany, Lehringen; Mam.
  (Sickenberg, O.)   1969A
Germany, Mecklenburg; Amph.,
  Mam., Pisces, Rept.
  (Diebel, K., Heinrich, W.-D.)   1970A
Germany, Mosbach Sands; Mam.
  (Bahlo, E., Malec, F.)   1969A
Germany, Neuwieder Becken;
  Würmian; Aves, Mam.
  (Boecker, M., Lehmann, E. v.,
    Remy, H.)   1972A
Germany, northern; Mam.
  (Hollaus, E.)   1969A
Germany, southern
  (Müller-Beck, H.)   1969A
Germany, Wiesbaden; Mam.
  (Tobien, H.)   1968I

VERTEBRATE FAUNAS - cont.
  Quaternary
    Kenya, Lake Baringo; Aves, Mam., Rept.
      (Bishop, W. W.)   1972A
    Kenya, Lake Baringo; Mam.
      (Leakey, M., et al.)   1969A
    Kenya, Lake Rudolf; Mam., Pisces, Rept.
      (Leakey, R. E. F.)   1970A
    Lebanon, Joub Jannine; Mam.
      (Besançon, J., Copeland, L.,
      Hours, F.)   1970A
    Lebanon, Masloukh; Aves, Mam., Rept.
      (Gautier, A.)   1970A
    Mam.
      (Cornwall, I.)   1970A
    Manitoba, Lake Agassiz; Mam.
      (Pettipas, L.)   1966A
    Mauritania, Adrar; Mam.
      (Biberson, P.)   1969B
    Mexico, Baja California; Mam.
      (Massey, W. C.)   1966A
    Mexico, central; Aves
      (Howard, H.)   1969B
    Mexico, Mexican Plateau; Mam.
      (Silva-Barcenas, A.)   1969A
    Mexico, Santa Isabel Iztapan; Mam.
      (Aveleyra Arroyo de Anda, L.)   1966A
    Mexico, Tlapacoya; upper; Mam.
      (Alvarez, T.)   1969A
    Michigan; Mam.
      (Blodgett, R. H.)   1971A
    Missouri, Ozark Mts.
      (Mehringer, P. J., King, J. E.,
      Lindsay, E. H.)   1970A
    Missouri, Pomme de Terre R. Basin;
    Würmian-Recent; Mam.
      (McMillan, R. B.)   1972A
    Mongolia; Mam.
      (Devîatkin, E. V., Strelkov, S. A.)   1968A
    Mongolia, Tsagan-Nur Lake; Mam.
      (Spirkin, A. I.)   1970A
    Morocco; Mam.
      (Biberson, P.)   1966B, 1970A
    Morocco, Tangier
      (Howe, B.)   1967A
    Nebraska, Angus; Mam.
      (Martin, L. D., Schultz, C. B.)   1971A
    Nebraska, Brown Co.; lower; Amph.,
    Aves, Mam., Pisces, Rept.
      (Skinner, M. F., Hibbard, C. W.)   1972A
    Nebraska, Brown Co.; Mam.
      (Hibbard, C. W.)   1972A
    Nebraska, Dawson Co.; upper; Aves, Mam.
      (Tate, J., Martin, L. D.)   1968A
    Nebraska, Milburn; Mam.
      (Hillerud, J. M.)   1970A
    Nebraska, Sand Draw; Aftonian; Aves
      (Feduccia, J. A.)   1970A
    Netherlands, Beegden; Mam.
      (Erdbrink, D.-P., Tacoma, J.)   1967A
    Netherlands, Bunde
      (Erdbrink, D.-P.)   1968B
    New Mexico, Albuquerque; Mam.
      (Lambert, P. W.)   1969A, 1970A
    New Mexico, Blackwater Draw; Mam.
      (Agogino, G. A.)   1968B, 1969A

VERTEBRATE FAUNAS - cont.
  Quaternary
    New Mexico, Harding Co.; Amph., Aves,
    Mam.
      (McMullen, T. L.,
      Zakrzewski, R. J.)   1972A
    New Mexico, southcentral
      (Kottlowski, F. E.)   1955A
    New Mexico, southern
      (Ruhe, R. V.)   1961A
    Nicaragua; Mam.
      (Howell, T. R.)   1969A
    North America; Mam.
      (Sher, A. V.)   1970B
    Ohio, Ansonia; Mam.
      (Mills, R. S., Guilday, J. E.)   1972A
    Ohio; Wisconsinian; Mam.
      (Mills, R. S.)   1972A
    Oregon, Fort Rock Lake; Mam.
      (Bedwell, S. F., Cressman, L. S.)   1971A
    Oregon, south; Mam.
      (Arment, H. L.)   1961A
    Peru, Tulara Tar Seeps; Aves
      (Campbell, K. E.)   1972A
    Phillipines, Anda; Mam.
      (Saurin, E.)   1966A
    Portugal, Estremadura; Würm; Aves,
    Mam., Pisces, Rept.
      (Roche, J.)   1972A
    Portugal; Tagus R., Mam.
      (Aguado, M. M.)   1968A
    Rumania; Baraolt Basin; Mam.
      (Rădulescu, C., Kovács, A.)   1968A
    Rumania, Betfia; Aves, Mam., Rept.
      (Terzea, E., Jurcsák, T.)   1967A
    Rumania, Betfia; Mam.
      (Terzea, E.)   1972A
      (Terzea, E., Jurcsák, T.)   1968A, 1969A
    Rumania, Brașov depression; Mam.
      (Alimen, H., Radulesco, C.,
      Samson, P.)   1968B
    Rumania, Dacic Basin; Mam.
      (Ghenea, C.)   1969A, 1970A
    Rumania, Harghita district; Mam.
      (Samson, P., Rădulescu, C.)   1969A
    Rumania; Mam.
      (Samson, P., Rădulescu, C.)   1968A
    Rumania, Moldavian Plateau; Mam.
      (Ghenea, C.)   1968A
    Rumania, Valachian depression; Mam.
      (Ghenea, C., Bandrabur, T.,
      Mihăilă, N.)   1967A
    Rumania, Villafranchian; Mam.
      (Macarovici, N.)   1972C
    Rumania, Vîrghiș Gorge; Mam.
      (Orghidan, T., Dumitrescu, M.)   1962-63A
    Saskatchewan; Mam.
      (Stalker, A. M., Churcher, C. S.)   1972A
    Saskatchewan, Qu' Appelle; Mam.
      (Khan, E.)   1970A
    Saskatchewan, Saskatoon
      (Lammers, G. E.)   1968B
    Scotland; Mam.
      (Delair, J. B.)   1969A
    Siberia, Aldan R.; Würm; Mam.
      (Mochanov, Iû. A.)   1970A

VERTEBRATE FAUNAS - cont.
  Quaternary
    Sudan, Nubia; Pisces
      (Greenwood, P. H.)   1968B
    Sudan, Saggai; Mam., Pisces, Rept.
      (Cloudsley-Thompson, J. L.)   1966A
    Sweden; Aves
      (Mascher, J. W.)   1970A
    Syria, Latamne; Mam.
      (Clark, J. D.)   1967D
    Tanzania, Isimila; upper; Mam.
      (Coryndon, S. C., et al.)   1972A
    Tanzania; Mam.
      (Leakey, L. S. B.)   1969D
    Tanzania, Olduvai Gorge
      (Leakey, M. D.)   1971B
    Tanzania, Olduvai Gorge; Pisces
      (Greenwood, P. H., Todd, E. J.)   1970A
    Texas, Houston
      (DuBar, J. R., Clopine, G.)   1961A
    Texas, Love Fm.; Blancan; Amph., Aves,
      Pisces, Mam., Rept.
      (Akersten, W. A.)   1972A
    Texas, Lubbock Co., Slaton quarry; Amph., Rept.
      (Holman, J. A.)   1969E
    Texas, Lubbock Co., Slaton quarry; Mam.
      (Dalquest, W. W.)   1967A
    Texas, San Pedro Springs; Mam.
      (Warnock, F. B.)   1972A
    Texas, Tedford Quarry
      (Price, W. A.)   1958A
    Texas, Trinity R.; Mam.
      (Slaughter, B. H.)   1969B
      (Willimon, E. L.)   1972A
    Texas, Val Verde Co.; Mam.
      (Lundelius, E.)   1972A
    Tunisia, Ichkeul; Villafranchian; Mam.
      (Jaeger, J.-J.)   1971A
    Tunisia; Villafranchian; Aves, Mam., Rept.
      (Coppens, Y.)   1971B
    Tunisia; Villafranchian; Mam.
      (Tchoumakov, I. S., Alexeeva, L. I.)   1971A
    Turkey, Eskişehir; Mam.
      (Becker-Platen, J. D.,
        Sickenberg, O.)   1968A
    Turkey; Mam.
      (Sickenberg, O., Tobien, H.)   1971A
    Uganda, Kaiso Fm.; Mam.
      (Cooke, H. B. S., Coryndon, S. C.)   1970A
    United States
      (Wright, H. E., Frey, D. G.)   1969A
    United States, Central Great Plains; Mam.
      (Schultz, C. B., Martin, L. D.)   1970B
    United States, central; Mam.
      (Hibbard, C. W.)   1970C
    United States, Great Plains; Mam.
      (Hoffmann, R. S., Jones, J. K.)   1970A
    United States, Midwest; upper; Mam.
      (Brown, J., Cleland, C.)   1968A
    USSR
      (Zamorii, P. K.)   1958A
    USSR, Aksaitai R.; Mam.
      (Kambariddinov, R. K.,
        Sharakhmedov, Sh. Sh.)   1971A
    USSR; Aldan R., Mamontova Gora; Mam.
      (Agadzhanian, A. K.,
        Boiarskaia, T. D.)   1969A

VERTEBRATE FAUNAS - cont.
  Quaternary
    USSR, Altaĭ; Mam.
      (Matsuĭ, V. M., Mos'kina, O. D.)   1968A
    USSR, Altaĭ; Paleolithic; Mam.
      (Adamenko, O. M., Gaĭduk, I. M.)   1967A
      (Gaĭduk, I. M.)   1969A
    USSR, Amur, Khabarovsk; Mam.
      (Chemekov, Iu. F.)   1966A
    USSR, Armenia; Mam.
      (Aslanian, A. T.)   1970A
      (Gudilin, I. S.)   1966A
      (Saiadian, Iu. V.)   1970A
    USSR, Armenia; Mam., Pisces
      (Avakian, L. A., Davtian, A. R.)   1970A
    USSR, Armenia, Pambak V.; Würm; Mam.
      (Davtian, A. R.)   1970A
    USSR; Aves
      (Dementiev, G. P.)   1960A
    USSR, Azov Sea region; Mam.
      (Agadzhanian, A. K., et al.)   1972A
    USSR, Azov Sea, Taganrog Bay; Mam.
      (Agadzhanian, A. K.)   1970A
    USSR, Bashkirian Predural'e; Mam.
      (Sukhov, V. P.)   1967B
      (Varlamov, I. P.)   1959A
    USSR, Beregovaia; Villafranchian; Mam.
      (Vangengeim, E. A., et al.)   1968A
    USSR, Buruktal; Mam.
      (Iakhimovich, V. L.,
        Nemkova, V. K.)   1969A
    USSR, Chikoĭ R.; Mam.
      (Erbaeva, M. A.)   1968B
    USSR, Cis-Altaĭ plain; lower; Mam.
      (Adamenko, O. M.)   1971A
    USSR, Crimea; Aves
      (Voinstvenskiĭ, M. A.)   1963A
    USSR, Crimea; Aves; faunal history
      (Voinstvenskiĭ, M. A.)   1965A
    USSR, Crimea; Mam.
      (Shchepinskiĭ, A. A.)   1971A
    USSR, Crimea; Mousterian; Mam.
      (Shchepinskiĭ, A. A.)   1971A
    USSR, Dnestr; Mam.
      (Negadaev-Nikonov, K. N.,
        Bukatchuk, P. D.)   1969A
    USSR, Dobranichev; Mam.
      (Shovkoplias, I. G.)   1969A
    USSR, Don R. basin; Mam.
      (Krasnenkov, R. V., et al.)   1970A
      (Vasil'ev, Iu. M.)   1969A
    USSR, Kirgizia, Dzhargalan R.; Mam.
      (Kambariddinova, T. K.,
        Talipov, M. A.)   1969A
      (Talipov, M. A.)   1968A
      (Talipov, M. A., Korolev, V. G.)   1970A
    USSR, eastern; Mam.
      (Mokrousov, V. P., Sadovskiĭ, N. D.)   1964A
    USSR, eastern; Mindel; Mam.
      (Vangengeim, E. A., Sher, A. V.)   1969A,
                                                  1970A
    USSR, European part, center; Mam.,
      Pisces
      (Breslav, S. L.)   1971A
    USSR, European part; Mam.
      (Bader, O. N.)   1971B
      (Gromov, V. I.)   1972A

VERTEBRATE FAUNAS - cont.
  Quaternary
    USSR, Ukraine, Kremenefs; Mam.
      (Tatarinov, K. A.)   1962A
    USSR, Ukraine, Medzhibozh; Mam.
      (Gozhik, P. F.)   1969A
    USSR, Ukraine, western; Aves
      (Marisova, I. V., Tatarinov, K. A.) 1965A
      (Tatarinov, K. A., Marisova, I. V.) 1971A
    USSR; Ulalinka R.; Mam.
      (Adamenko, O. M.)   1970A
    USSR, Ural Mts.; Mam.
      (Stefanovskiĭ, V. V.)   1970A
      (Sukhorukov, A. M.)   1964A
    USSR, Volyn'; Aves, Mam.
      (Tatarinov, K. A.)   1971A
    USSR, West Kalba; Mam.
      (Sevrĭugin, N. A.)   1967A
    USSR, western; Mam.
      (Lider, V. A.)   1969A
      (Popov, G. I.)   1970A
    USSR, western; Mam.
      (Alekseeva, L. I.)   1968A
    USSR, Yakutia; Mam.
      (Okladnikov, A. P.)   1970A
    Utah, Salt Lake City; Mam.
      (Miller, W. E.)   1972A
    Virginia, coast; Mam.
      (Drummond, A. H.)   1970A
    Virginia, Saltville; Mam.
      (Bottoms, E.)   1969A
    Virginia, southeastern; Aves, Mam., Pisces
      (Ray, C. E., Wetmore, A.,
        Dunkle, D. H., Drez, P.)   1968A
    Washington, Horse Heaven Hills; Mam.
      (Fry, W. E.)   1969A
    Washington, White Bluffs; Blancan; Mam.
      (Gustafson, E. P.)   1972A
    Wyoming, Hell Gap; Mam.
      (Roberts, M. F.)   1970A
    Wyoming; Mam.
      (Duguid, J., Bedish, G.)   1968A
    Yugoslavia, Dubci; Aves, Mam., Rept.
      (Malez, M.)   1967C
    Yugoslavia; Mam.
      (Marković-Marjanović, J.)   1972A
      (Rakovec, I.)   1968A
    Yugoslavia; Mam., Rept.
      (Marković-Marjanović, J.)   1970A
    Yugoslavia, Slovenia
      (Osole, F.)   1964-65D
    Yugoslavia, Slovenia; Mam.
      (Rakovec, I.)   1967A
  Quaternary Caves
    Alabama, New Fern Cave; Mam.
      (Hale, D.)   1970A
    Alaska, Seward Peninsula; Mam.
      (Larsen, H.)   1968B
    Algeria, Algiers; Mam.
      (Brahimi, C.)   1968A
    Algeria, Filfila; Amph., Aves, Mam., Rept.
      (Ginsburg, L., Hilly, J.,
        Taquet, P.)   1968A
    Antilles; Mam., Rept.
      (Hooijer, D. A.)   1972C
    Arizona, Rampart Cave; Mam.
      (Harington, C. R.)   1972A

VERTEBRATE FAUNAS - cont.
  Quaternary Caves
    Arkansas, Peccary Cave; Amph., Mam.,
      Rept.
      (Davis, L. C.)   1972A
    Arkansas, Peccary Cave; Mam.
      (Davis, L. C.)   1969A
      (Quinn, J. H.)   1972B
      (Semken, H. A.)   1972A
    Australia, Labyrinth Cave; Aves, Mam.
      (Merrilees, D.)   1969A
    Australia, Mabel, Pyramid Caves; Mam.
      (Wakefield, N. A.)   1967A
    Australia, McEachern's Cave; Mam.
      (Wakefield, N. A.)   1967B
    Australia, Victoria Cave; Mam.
      (Smith, M. J.)   1971A
    Austria, Schlenkendurchgang's Cave;
      Aves, Mam.
      (Ehrenberg, K., Mais, K.)   1968A,
                                          1970A,B
    Austria, Teufels, Fuchsen Caves
      (Ehrenberg, K.)   1966F,G,H
      (Wettstein-Westersheimb, O.)   1966B
    Austria, Teufels, Fuchsen Caves; Aves
      (Soergel, E.)   1966B
    Austria, Teufels, Fuchsen Caves; Mam.
      (Zapfe, H.)   1966D,E,F
    Belgium, Le Trou Dubois; Würm; Mam.
      (Destexhe Jamotte, J.)   1970A
    Bulgaria; Magourata Cave; Mam.
      (Anati, E.)   1969A
    Bulgaria, Peshketo Cave; Mam.
      (Dzhambazov, N.)   1970A
    China, Kwangsi; Mam.
      (Pei, W.-c.)   1957K
    Cuba, Pio-Domingo Cave; Aves
      (Fischer, K., Stephan, B.)   1971B
    Czechoslovakia, Bohemia; Mam.
      (Mostecký, V.)   1969A
    Czechoslovakia, Chlum Cave; Mam.
      (Beneš, J.)   1970A
    Czechoslovakia, Kůlna Cave; Mam.
      (Valoch, K.)   1970A
      (Valoch, K., et al.)   1969A
    Czechoslovakia, Pod Hradem Cave;
      Würm; Mam.
      (Musil, R., Valoch, K.)   1966A
    Czechoslovakia, Žernavă; Mam.
      (Musil, R.)   1969D
    England, King Arthur's Cave; Mam.
      (Hart, C.)   1967A
    France, Angles-sur-l'Anglin;
      Würm; Mam.
      (Pradel, L.)   1965E
    France, Aquitaine; Mam.
      (Bordes, F.)   1970A
    France, Arago Cave; Mam.
      (Chaline, J.)   1971A
    France, Arago Cave; Mam., Rept.
      (Lumley, H. de, Lumley, M.-A. de)   1971A
    France, Balme-d'Épy; Mam.
      (Guérin, C.)   1971A
    France, Baume; Mam.
      (Bouchud, J.)   1966I, 1968D
    France, Bédeilhac Cave
      (Beltran, A., Robert, R., Gailli, R.) 1967A

VERTEBRATE FAUNAS - cont.
Quaternary Caves
Israel, Djebel Qafze Cave; Mousterian; Mam.
  (Haas, G.)   1972A
Israel, Geula Caves; Amph., Mam., Rept.
  (Haas, G.)   1967B
Israel, Geula Cave; Mam.
  (Heller, J.)   1970A
  (Petter, G., Heintz, E.)   1969A
Italy, Alto Cave
  (Borzatti von Löwenstern, E.,
    Magaldi, D.)   1967A
Italy, Arboschio Cave; Mam.
  (Pavia, G.)   1970A
Italy, Ciota Ciara Cave; Mam.
  (Fedele, F., Chiarelli, B., Masali, M.) 1966A
Italy, Colombo Cave; Mam.
  (Tozzi, C.)   1965B
Italy, Grimaldi; Mam.
  (Barral, L.)   1965C, 1970A
Italy, Grimaldi, Prince Cave; Mam.
  (Barral, L., Simone, S.)   1968B,C,
    1969A, 1970A
  (Simone, S.)   1969A
Italy, Grotta del Cavallo; Mam.
  (Palma di Cesnola, A.) 1966A,B, 1969A
Italy, Grotta Sepolcrale; Mam.
  (Palma di Cesnola, A.)   1965C, 1966C
Italy, Marina di Camerota; Mam.
  (Palma di Cesnola, A.,
    Vigliardi, A.)   1967A
Italy, Mario Bernardini Cave; Mam.
  (Borzatti von Löwenstern, E.)   1970A,B
Italy, Paglicci Cave; Mam.
  (Palma di Cesnola, A.)   1970A
Italy, Poggio Cave; Mam.
  (Palma di Cesnola, A.)   1969B
Italy, Prazziche; Mam.
  (Borzatti von Löwenstern, E.)   1966A
Italy, Rigoli; Würm; Mam.
  (Borzatti von Löwenstern, E.,
    Dani, A.)   1968A
Italy, Salento; Mam.
  (Borzatti von Löwenstern, E.)   1966C
Italy, Sardinia; Würmian; Aves
  (Malatesta, A., Suriano, F.)   1971A
Italy, Spagnoli Cave; Mam.
  (Guerri, M.)   1970A
Italy, Spinagallo Cave; Mam.
  (Petronio, C.)   1970B
Italy, St. Agostino; Mam.
  (Tozzi, C.)   1970A
Italy, St. Teodoro Cave; Mam.
  (Vigliardi, A.)   1968A
Italy, Uluzzo Bay; Aves, Mam.
  (Borzatti von Löwenstern, E.)   1965C
Italy, Valdemino Cave; Amph., Mam., Rept.
  (Tozzi, C.)   1969A
Italy, Veneri Cave; Mam.
  (Radmilli, A.)   1967A
Kentucky, Welsh Cave; Mam.
  (Guilday, J. E., et al.)   1971A
Mexico, Tamaulipas; Amph., Rept.
  (Holman, J. A.)   1969B
Mexico, Tamaulipas, Cueva de Abra; Mam.
  (Dalquest, W. W., Roth, E.)   1970A

VERTEBRATE FAUNAS - cont.
Quaternary Caves
Missouri, Bat Cave; Mam.
  (Foley, R.)   1969A
Missouri, Crankshaft Cave
  (Oesch, R. D.)   1969A
  (Parmalee, P. W., Oesch, R. D.,
    Guilday, J. E.)   1969A
Missouri, Ozark Highlands; Mam.
  (Parmalee, P. W.)   1971A
Monaco, Balauzière; Würm; Mam.
  (Bonifay, M.-F.)   1967A
Monaco, l'Observatoire Cave; Mam.
  (Barral, L.)   1965A
Morocco, Jebel Irhoud; Mam.
  (Jaeger, J.-J.)   1970A
Nevada, Lincoln City; Mam.
  (Jefferson, G. T.)   1969A
New Mexico, Dark Canyon Cave; Aves
  (Howard, H.)   1971B
New Mexico, Dry Cave; Amph., Rept.
  (Holman, J. A.)   1970B
New Mexico, Dry Cave; Mam.
  (Harris, A. H.)   1970A
New Mexico, Gypsum Cave; Mam.
  (Dunn, D.)   1968A
Pennsylvania, New Paris Sinkholes
  (Guilday, J. E.)   1956A
Pennsylvania, New Paris Sinkholes;
  Amph., Mam., Rept.
  (McCrady, A. D.)   1958A
Poland, Bear Cave; Mam.
  (Pulina, M.)   1969A
Poland, Cracow Uplands; Mam.
  (Madeyska-Niklewska, T.)   1969A
Poland; Mam.
  (Kowalski, K.)   1970B
Poland, Nietoperzowa Cave; Mam.
  (Ivanova, I. K.)   1964A
Poland, Nietoperzowa Cave; Würm
  (Wójcik, M.)   1971A
Poland, Tatra Caves; Würm; Amph.,
  Aves, Mam.
  (Wójcik, Z.)   1966A
Portugal, Salemas Cave; Mam.
  (Roche, J.,
    Veiga Ferreira, O. da)   1970A
Rumania, "La Adam" Cave; Würm; Mam.
  (Dumitrescu, M., et al.)   1962-63A
Sicily, Addaura and Lévanzo Caves
  (Guido, M.)   1967A
South Africa, Swartklip; Mam.
  (Hendey, Q. B., Hendey, H.)   1968A
Spain, Aitzbitarte; Würm; Mam.
  (Altuna, J.)   1970A
Spain, Cantabria, Cueva del Otero; Mam.
  (González Echegaray, J., et al.)   1966A
Spain, Carigüela Cave
  (Lumley, H. de)   1969A
Spain, Carigüela Cave; Mam.
  (Bouchud, J.)   1969A
Spain, Chora Cave; Aves, Mam.
  (Madariaga de la Campa, B.)   1963A
Spain, Guipúscoa, Lezetxiki;
  Würm; Mam.
  (Chaline, J.)   1970A

VERTEBRATE FAUNAS - cont.
  Silurian
    Sweden, Gotland; Pisces
      (Gross, W.)   1968E
      (Janvier, Ph.)   1971B
    USSR, Estonia; Pisces
      (Mark-Kurik, E.)   1969A
      (Mark-Kurik, E., Noppel, T.)   1970A
    USSR; Pisces
      (Vladimirskaĭa, E. V.,
        Blagonravov, V. A.)   1966A
    USSR, Timan; Pisces
      (Varsanof'eva, V. A.)   1963A
    USSR, western; Pisces
      (Obruchev, D. V.,
        Karatajute-Talimaa, V. N.)   1968A
  Tertiary
    Africa; Pliocene; Mam.
      (Coppens, Y.)   1972A
    Argentina, northwestern; upper; Mam.
      (Castellanos, A.)   1969A
    Argentina, Paraná; Pliocene; Pisces
      (Scartascini, G.)   1959A
    Arizona, north-central; Pliocene; Mam.
      (McKee, E. D., Anderson, C. A.)   1971A
    Arizona, San Pedro V.; Plio-Pleistocene; Mam.
      (Lammers, G. E.)   1969A
    Australia, Alcoota; Miocene
      (Woodburne, M. O.)   1969D
    Australia, Grange Burn; Pliocene; Mam.
      (Turnbull, W. D.,
        Lundelius, E. L.)   1970A
    Australia; Mam.
      (Tedford, R. H.)   1961B
    Australia; Neogene; Mam.; faunal history
      (Ride, W. D. L.)   1968A
    Australia, Victoria; Pliocene; Mam.
      (Turnbull, W. D.)   1969A
    Austria; early
      (Zapfe, H.)   1969A
    Austria, Eibiswald; Miocene; Mam.
      (Flugel, H., Maurin, V.)   1959A
    Austria, Kohfidisch; Pliocene
      (Bachmayer, F., Zapfe, H.)   1969A
    Austria, Mödling; Pliocene, lower; Mam.
      (Rabeder, G.)   1970A
    Austria; Neogene; Mam.
      (Kollmann, K.)   1964A
    Austria, Plesching; Miocene, lower; Pisces
      (Schultz, O.)   1968A
    Austria, Plesching; Oligo-Miocene; Pisces
      (Steininger, F.)   1966A
    Austria, Salzburg; Eocene; Pisces
      (Vogeltanz, R.)   1968A
    Austria, Salzburg; Eocene; Pisces, Rept.
      (Vogeltanz, R.)   1970A
    Austria, St. Oswald b. Gratwein; Mam.
      (Mottl, M.)   1969B
    Austria, Steiermark; Miocene; Mam.
      (Mottl, M.)   1970A
    Austria, Vienna Basin; Miocene; Pisces
      (Schultz, O.)   1972A
    Belgium, Aalter; Eocene; Pisces
      (Nolf, D.)   1969A
    Belgium, Dormaal; Paleocene; Pisces
      (Casier, E.)   1967B

VERTEBRATE FAUNAS - cont.
  Tertiary
    Belgium; Eocene; Pisces
      (Nolf, D.)   1966A
    Belgium, Merelbeke; Eocene; Pisces
      (Casier, E., et al.)   1966A
      (Nolf, D.)   1970B
    Belgium, Montroel-au-Bois; Eocene; Pisces
      (Quinet, G. E., Coupatez, P.,
        Wouters, G.)   1970A
    Belgium; Pisces
      (Nolf, D.)   1970A
    Belgium, Zeebrugge; Paleogene; Pisces
      (Nolf, D.)   1967A
    Bolivia, Altiplano; Neogene; Mam.
      (Hoffstetter, R., Martinez, C.,
        Tomasi, P.)   1972A
    Bolivia, Lacayani; Oligocene, lower; Mam.
      (Hoffstetter, R., Martinez, C.,
        Mattauer, M., Tomasi, P.)   1971A
    Brazil; Paleocene; Amph., Rept.
      (Estes, R.)   1972A
    Brazil, Taubaté; Neogene; Pisces
      (Moncharmont Zei, M.)   1970A
    Bulgaria, northeast; Pliocene; Mam.
      (Khalvadzhiev, M.)   1969A
    Calif., Barstow Fm.; Miocene; Mam.
      (Lewis, G. E.)   1968A
      (Lindsay, E. H.)   1972B
    Calif., Cajon V.; Miocene; Mam.
      (Woodburne, M. O., Golz, D. J.)   1972A
    Calif., Coalinga region; Neogene; Mam.
      (Adegoke, O. S.)   1969B
    Calif., Hungry V.; Pliocene; Mam., Rept.
      (Miller, W. E., Downs, T.)   1971A
    Calif., Kern Co.; Miocene; Pisces
      (Bishop, R. C.)   1969A
    Calif., Las Trampas Park; Mam.
      (Anon.)   1972AA
    Calif., Los Angeles Basin; Pisces
      (Pugh, W.)   1969A
    Calif.; Miocene, Pliocene; Mam.
      (Williams, C. T.)   1971A
    Calif., Mojave Desert; Miocene,
      Pliocene; Rept.
      (Whistler, D. P.)   1969A
    Calif., Monterey Co.; Miocene; Mam.
      (Pierson, P., Kendall, B. D.)   1969A
    Calif., Newport Bay; Pliocene; Pisces
      (Mount, J. D.)   1969A
    Calif., Newport Beach; Pliocene; Pisces
      (Zinsmeister, W. J.)   1971A
    Calif., Oceanside; Pliocene;
      Aves, Mam., Pisces
      (Frazier, K.)   1970A
    Calif.; Pliocene
      (Downs, T., White, J. A.)   1968B
    Calif., San Diego; Eocene; Aves,
      Mam., Rept.
      (Kennedy, M. P.)   1971A
    Calif., Sharktooth Hill; Miocene;
      Mam., Pisces
      (Powell, C. L.)   1971A
    Ceylon, Arna Kallu; Miocene; Mam.,
      Pisces, Rept.
      (Deraniyagala, P. E. P.)   1969C

VERTEBRATE FAUNAS - cont.
Tertiary
France, Montpellier; Pliocene; Aves,
Mam., Pisces, Rept.
(Michaux, J.)   1969A
France, Noyant-sous-le-Lude; Miocene;
Mam., Pisces, Rept.
(Ginsburg, L., Janvier, P.)   1970A
France, Paris Basin; Eocene; Mam.
(Rich, T. H. V.)   1971A
France, Perpignan; Pliocene; Mam.
(Leinders, J., Michaux, J.)   1969A
France, Pont-Pourquey; Miocene;
Aves, Pisces
(Moyes, J.)   1966A
France, Priay; Mam.
(Combémorel, R., et al.)   1970A
France, Provence; Oligocene; Mam.
(Helmer, D., Vianey-Liaud, M.)   1970A
France, Rhine Valley; Eocene; Mam.
(Sittler, C.)   1969A
France, Rhone R.; Miocene; Mam., Pisces
(Demarcq, G.)   1970A
France, Rhone region; Neogene; Mam.
(Guérin, C., Mein, P.)   1971A
France, Rians; Eocene; Mam., Rept.
(Ginsburg, L., Mennessier, G.,
Russell, D.)   1967A
France, Robiac; Eocene; Amph., Mam., Rept.
(Sudre, J.)   1969B
France, Robiac; Eocene; Mam.
(Sudre, J.)   1969A
France, Saint-Capraise d'Eymet; Oligocene;
Mam.
(Jehenne, Y.)   1969A
France, Serre de Vergès; Miocene; Amph.,
Aves, Mam., Rept.
(Meurisse, M., Michaux, J., Sigé, B.)   1969A
France, St. Martin-de-Casselvi; Stampian; Mam.
(Bergounioux, F. M., Crouzel, F.)   1968B
France, Tarn-et-Garonne; Oligocene,
upper; Amph., Aves, Mam., Rept.
(Crochet, J.-Y.)   1971A
France, Valence; Miocene; Mam.
(Martin, R.)   1970A
France, Valensole; Pliocene; Mam.
(Guérin, C., Mein, P., Truc, G.)   1970A
(Guillemot, J., Ünalan, G.)   1970A
France, Var; Oligocene
(Touraine, F.)   1968A
France, Vaucluse; Miocene; Mam.
(Mein, P., Truc, G., Demarcq, G.)   1971A
France, Vaucluse; Oligocene; Mam.
(Hugueney, M., Truc, G.,
Philippe, M.)   1971A
France, Villefranche-sur-Saône; Pliocene;
Mam.
(Monjuvent, G.)   1968A
General
(Davies, A. M.)   1971A
Georgia, Taylor Co.; Pliocene; Mam.
(Voorhies, M. R.)   1970A
Germany, Bavaria, Sandelzhausen; Miocene,
upper; Aves, Mam., Rept.
(Fahlbusch, V., et al.)   1972A
Germany, Darmstadt; Eocene
(Kuster-Wendenburg, E.)   1969A

VERTEBRATE FAUNAS - cont.
Tertiary
Germany, Ehrenstein; Paleogene; Mam.,
Rept.
(Schmidt, N.)   1969A
Germany, Frankfurt a. M.; Miocene; Pisces
(Kümmerle, E.)   1971A
(Wiesner, E.)   1971A
Germany, Geiseltal; Eocene; Aves,
Mam., Rept.
(Matthes, H. W.)   1967D
Germany, Geiseltal
(Matthes, H. W.)   1970A
Germany, Harburg; Oligocene; Mam., Rept.
(Trischler, J., Winkler, H.)   1968A
Germany, Mainburg; Miocene
(Fahlbusch, V., Gall, H.)   1970A
Germany, Messel bei Darmstadt; Eocene;
Amph., Aves, Mam., Pisces, Rept.
(Tobien, H.)   1969C, 1970D
Germany, Monheim; Neogene; Mam.
(Gall, H., Müller, D.)   1970A
Germany, Murnau; Chattian; Mam., Rept.
(Behrens, M., et al.)   1970A
Germany, Nördlinger Ries
(Bolten, R., Müller, D.)   1969A
Germany; Pisces
(Kruckow, T.)   1964A
Germany, Rheinland; Pliocene; Mam.
(Gliese, J., Strauch, F.)   1969A
Germany, southwest; Oligocene
(Heissig, K.)   1970A
Germany, Wartenberg; Neogene; Mam.
(Westphal, F.)   1970A
Germany, Weissenburg; Oligocene; Mam.
(Fahlbusch, V., Schmidt, N.)   1969A
Greece, Chios Is.; Miocene; Mam.
(Melentis, J. K., Tobien, H.)   1970A
Greece, Chios Is.; Miocene; Mam.,
Pisces, Rept.
(Tobien, H.)   1968H, 1969B
Greece, Halmyropotamos; Pliocene; Mam.
(Melentis, J. K.)   1967F, 1970A
Greece, Macedonia, Strimon Basin;
Pliocene; Mam., Rept.
(Gramann, F., Kockel, F.)   1969A
Greece, Pikermi; Miocene; Mam.
(Guernet, C., Sauvage, J.)   1971A
Greece, Thessalia; Pliocene; Mam.
(Melentis, J. K., Schneider, H.)   1966A
Greece, Thracia; Mam.
(Kopp, K.-O., Pavoni, N.,
Schindler, C.)   1969A
Greenland, west; lower; Pisces
(Bendix-Almgreen, S. E.)   1969A
Greenland, western; Pisces
(Rosenkrantz, A.)   1970A
Hungary, Mecsek Mts.; Miocene;
Mam., Pisces
(Hámor, G.)   1970A
Hungary, Szurdokpüspöki;
Miocene; Mam.
(Kretzoi, M., Pálfalvy, I.)   1969A
Idaho, Glens Ferry Fm.; Pliocene; Pisces
(Smith, G. R.)   1972A
Idaho, Hagerman; Blancan; Mam.
(Bjork, P. R.)   1969A, 1970A

VERTEBRATE FAUNAS - cont.
Tertiary
Nebraska; Oligocene
(Guthrie, D. A.)   1972A
Nebraska; Oligocene; Mam.
(Wood, A. E.)   1969A
Nebraska, Verdigre Quarry; Pliocene; Amph.,
Mam., Pisces, Rept.
(Voorhies, M. R.)   1969B, 1971C
Netherlands, Overijssel; Oligocene; Pisces
(Bosch, M. van den)   1964D
Nevada; Miocene, lower; Mam.
(Anon.)   1966CA
Nevada, Stewert and Ione V.; Pliocene
(Mawby, J. E.)   1968D
New Mexico, Baca Fm.; Eocene; Mam.
(Snyder, D. O.)   1970A
New Mexico, San Juan Basin; Eocene; Mam.
(Simpson, G. G.)   1950S
New Mexico, San Juan Basin; Paleocene; Mam.
(Simpson, G. G.)   1950S
Niger; Pisces
(Cappetta, H.)   1970B
Nigeria; Eocene; Pisces
(White, E. I.)   1955C
Nigeria, Sokoto B.; Paleogene; Pisces, Rept.
(De Giuli, C., Ficcarelli, G.,
Torre, D.)   1970A
Nigeria, southern; Eocene; Pisces
(Adegoke, O. S.)   1969A
North Africa
(Arambourg, C.)   1966C
North America; Paleocene; Mam.
(Russell, D. E.)   1967B
North America; Wasatchian; Mam.
(Savage, D. E.)   1971B
Norway, Spitzbergen; Pisces
(Vonderbank, K.)   1970A
Oregon, McKay Reservoir; Hemphillian
(Shotwell, J. A.)   1954B
Oregon, northcentral; Eocene; Pisces
(Cavender, T. M.)   1968A
Oregon, northcentral; Oligocene; Pisces
(Cavender, T. M.)   1968A
Oregon, Pendelton; Miocene
(Sargent, S., Shotwell, J. A.)   1951A
Poland, Carpathian Mts.; Oligocene; Pisces
(Jerzmańska, A.)   1968A
Poland, central; Paleocene; Pisces
(Liszkowski, J.)   1970A
Poland, Niskowa; Tortonian; Pisces
(Bałuk, W.)   1970A
Poland, Przeworno; Miocene; Mam.
(Głazek, J., Oberc, J., Sulimski, A.)   1971A
Poland, Silesia; Miocene; Mam.
(Głazek, J., et al.)   1972A
Portugal, Lisbon; Helvetian; Mam.
(Telles Antunes, M.)   1966E
Rumania, Carpathians; Miocene; Pisces
(Stancu, J., et al.)   1971A
Rumania, Mehadia Basin; Miocene; Pisces
(Grossu, A. V., Voicu, G.)   1971A
Rumania, Moldavian Plateau; Pliocene;
Mam.
(Ghenea, C.)   1968A
Rumania, Paun-Jassy; Miocene; Mam.
(Macarovici, N., Paghida, N.)   1966A

VERTEBRATE FAUNAS - cont.
Tertiary
Rumania, Piatra Neamt; Oligocene; Pisces
(Cosmovici, N. L., Şova, C.,
Tărăbuţă, C.)   1964A
Rumania; Plio-Pleistocene; Mam.
(Mihăilă, N.)   1971A
Saskatchewan, Pine Cree Park; Paleocene;
Mam., Pisces, Rept.
(Edmund, A. G.)   1972A
(Russell, L. S.)   1972A
Saskatchewan; Wood Mountain Fm.;
Miocene; Amph., Rept.
(Holman, J. A.)   1970A
Saskatchewan, Wood Mt.; Miocene; Mam.
(Storer, J. E.)   1972A
Siberia, Baikal; Neogene; Amph., Rept.
(Ivan'ev, L. N.,
Khozafskiĭ, L. I.)   1970A
Siberia, Irtysh R. area; Neogene; Mam.
(Aubekerov, B. Zh.)   1970A
Siberia, Turgaĭ depression; Pliocene;
Mam.
(Boboedova, A. A.)   1968A
Siberia, western; Mam.
(Zal'tsman, I. G.)   1968A
Siberia, western; Miocene; Mam.
(Zal'tsman, I. G.)   1967B
Siberia, western; Miocene, Pliocene;
Mam., Rept.
(Antypko, B. E.)   1964A
Siberia, western; Neogene; Mam., Pisces
(Martynov, V. A., Nikitin, V. P.)   1968A
Siberia, western; Oligocene; Mam.
(Zal'tsman, I. G.)   1964A
Siberia, western; Paleogene; Pisces
(Rudkevich, M. Ia.)   1964A
Siberia, western; Pliocene; Aves, Mam.
(Feniksova, V. V.)   1970A
Siberia, western; Pliocene; Mam.
(Antypko, B. E., Krasnov, I. I.)   1964A
Siberia, western; Plio-Pleistocene; Mam.
(Martynov, V. A.)   1968A
South Africa, Bogenfels; Miocene; Pisces
(Taverne, L.)   1969D
South Dakota, Badlands; Oligocene
(Lemley, R. E.)   1971A
South Dakota, Batesland Fm.; Miocene
(Harksen, J. C., Macdonald, J. R.)   1967A
South Dakota, Big Badlands; Oligocene;
Amph., Mam., Pisces, Rept.
(Harksen, J. C., Macdonald, J. R.)   1969B
South Dakota, Mission; Pliocene; Mam.
(Green, M.)   1971A
South Dakota, Rosebud Fm.; Miocene
(Macdonald, J. R., Harksen, J. C.)   1968A
South Dakota, Slim Buttes; Oligocene;
Aves, Mam., Rept.
(Lillegraven, J. A.)   1969A
South Dakota, Thin Elk Fm.; Pliocene;
Mam.
(Harksen, J. C., Green, M.)   1971A
South Dakota, White River Group;
Oligocene; Mam.
(Wilson, R. W.)   1971A
South Dakota, Wounded Knee; Miocene
(Macdonald, J. R.)   1970A

VERTEBRATE FAUNAS - cont.
Tertiary
USSR, Georgia, Kisatibi; Pliocene; Pisces
  (Gabelaia, Ts. D.)   1970A
USSR, Georgia, Kvabebi; Pliocene; Mam.
  (Gabuniia, L. K., Vekua, A. K.)   1968A,B,C
USSR, Georgia, Mardachai; Oligocene;
  Pisces
  (Tatieva, K. G.)   1960A
USSR, Georgia; Miocene; Mam., Rept.
  (Bulershvili, D. A.)   1964A
USSR, Georgia; Neogene; Mam.
  (Gabashvili, E. G.)   1970A
  (Gabuniia, L. K.)   1970C
USSR, Georgia; Oligocene; Mam., Pisces,
  Rept.
  (Laliev, A. G.)   1964A
USSR, Georgia; Pliocene; Mam.
  (Bulershvili, D. A.)   1964B
USSR, Issyk-Kul'; Mam.
  (Tarasov, S. A.)   1970A
USSR, Karakumy, Sarykamysh, Ustiurt;
  Eocene; Pisces
  (Balakhmatova, V. T.)   1957A
USSR, Kazakhstan, Aiaguz R.
  (Men'shikov, S. F.)   1971A
USSR, Kazakhstan, Aiaguz R. Basin
  (Tolochko, V. V.,
  Aubekerova, P. A.)   1971A
USSR, Kazakhstan, central; Pliocene,
  upper; Mam.
  (Gus'kova, A. I., et al.)   1971A
USSR, Kazakhstan; Eocene; Mam.
  (Kosminskii, V. V.)   1970A
USSR, Kazakhstan; Eocene; Pisces
  (Bliakhova, S. M.,
  Martynova, M. Ia.)   1971A
USSR, Kazakhstan; Mam., Rept.
  (Timush, A. V.)   1965A
USSR, Kazakhstan; Miocene; Mam.
  (Kosminskii, V. V.)   1970A
USSR, Kazakhstan, Mugodzhary;
  Neogene; Mam.
  (Tapalov, E. D.)   1971A
USSR, Kazakhstan; Neogene; Aves,
  Mam., Pisces
  (Bazhanov, O. V.,
  Bocharova, N. I., et al.)   1971A
USSR, Kazakhstan; Neogene; Mam.
  (Kostenko, N. N., Savinova, A. P.)   1971A
USSR, Kazakhstan; Neogene;
  Mam., Rept.
  (Kostenko, N. N., Nikitin, E. A.,
  Savinova, A. P.)   1971A
USSR, Kazakhstan; Paleogene;
  Mam., Pisces
  (Kostenko, N. N., Nikitin, E. A.,
  Liadzhina, K. A.)   1971A
USSR, Kazakhstan; Paleogene; Mam.,
  Rept.
  (Bazhanov, O. V., et al.)   1971A
USSR, Kazakhstan; Pliocene; Mam.
  (Aubekerova, P. A.)   1968A
USSR, Kazakhstan, Saur zone; Paleogene;
  Mam., Pisces, Rept.
  (Borisov, B. A., Kleiman, G. P.)   1967A

VERTEBRATE FAUNAS - cont.
Tertiary
USSR, Kazakhstan, West Kalba; Neogene;
  Mam., Rept.
  (Borisov, B. A., Sevriugin, N. A.)   1967A
USSR, Kirgizia; Paleocene; Mam.
  (Zhukov, Iu. V.)   1970A
USSR, Kopet-Dagh; Pliocene; Mam., Rept.
  (Birman, A. S.,
  Rastsvetaev, L. M.)   1967A, 1969A
  (Birman, A. S.,
  Zhegallo, V. I., et al.)   1971A
USSR, Kuial'nik; Neogene; Mam.
  (Alekseev, L. I.)   1969C
USSR, Little Caucasus; Oligocene; Pisces
  (Alizade, K. A.)   1968A
USSR, Maritime Province; Paleocene;
  Mam.
  (Bersenev, I. I., et al.)   1969A
USSR, Moldavia, Kalfa; Miocene; Mam.
  (Lungu, A. N.)   1964A
USSR, Moldavia; Miocene; Aves,
  Mam., Rept.
  (Lungu, A. N.)   1966A,B
USSR, Moldavia; Miocene; Mam.,
  Pisces, Rept.
  (Roshka, V. K.)   1969A
USSR, Moldavia, Naslavcha; Miocene;
  Pisces
  (Ivanchenko, V. I.)   1969A
USSR, Moldavia; Neogene; Mam.
  (David, A. I., Shushpanov, K. I.)   1972A
USSR, Moldavia; Neogene; Mam., Pisces
  (Didkovskii, V. Ia.)   1958A
USSR, Moldavia; Pliocene; Mam.
  (Sinegub, V. V.)   1969A
USSR, Moldavia; Pliocene, lower; Mam.
  (Bukatchuk, P. D., et al.)   1968A,B
USSR, Moldavia; Pliocene, upper; Mam.
  (Khubka, A. N., Shushpanov, K. I.)   1971A
USSR, Ob' R.; Pliocene; Mam.
  (Zudin, A. N., Pospelova, G. A.)   1970A
USSR, Odessa; Pliocene
  (Odintsov, I. A.)   1969A
USSR; Paleogene; Pisces
  (Fedorenko, E. N.)   1970A
USSR, Pechora, Vychegda; Pliocene;
  Mam.
  (Timofeev, E. M., Steklov, A. A.,
  Alekseeva, L. I.)   1970A
USSR, Povolzh'e, Prikam'e; Neogene;
  Mam.
  (Moskvitin, A. I., Morozov, V. A.)   1967A
USSR, Povolzh'e, Prikam'e; Paleogene;
  Pisces
  (Leonov, G. P.)   1967A
USSR, Rudnyi Altai; Pliocene;
  Mam., Pisces
  (Borisov, B. A., Chumakov, I. S.)   1967A
USSR, Sakhalin; Miocene; Pisces
  (Grechina, N. I.)   1971B
USSR, Sev. Donets, Buzinnaia;
  Pliocene, upper; Mam.
  (Prokhodskii, S. I.)   1963A
USSR, southern; Pliocene; Aves, Mam.
  (Karlov, N. N.)   1971A

VERTEBRATE FAUNAS - cont.
Triassic
Antarctica; Amph., Rept.
  (Colbert, E. H.)   1970A,C, 1972A,B
  (Elliot, D. H., et al.)   1970A
  (Steinert, H.)   1972A
  (Stubbs, P., Wick, G.)   1969C
Antarctica, Coalsack Bluff; Amph., Rept.
  (Colbert, E. H.)   1970B,E,G
Antarctica; McGregor Glacier;
Amph., Rept.
  (Colbert, E. H.)   1971A
  (Kitching, J. W.)   1971A
Argentina; Rept.
  (Anon.)   1969BG
  (Bonaparte, J. F.)   1969C
Argentina, San Juan-La Rioja; Amph., Rept.
  (Bonaparte, J. F.)   1969E
Arizona, Chinle Fm.
  (Repenning, C. A., Cooley, M. E.,
    Akers, J. P.)   1969A
Australia
  (Bartholomai, A., Howie, A.)   1970A
Australia, Sydney Basin; Amph.,
Pisces, Rept.
  (Lovering, J. F., McElroy, C. T.)   1969A
  (McElroy, C. T., et al.)   1969A
Australia, Sydney Basin; Pisces, Rept.
  (Standard, J. C.)   1969A
Australia, western
  (Cosgriff, J. W.)   1967B
Austria, Wiestal; Pisces
  (Vogeltanz, R.)   1969A
British Isles; Amph., Pisces, Rept.
  (Audley-Charles, M. G.)   1970A
Canada, eastern; Rept.
  (Carroll, R. L., et al.)   1972A
China, Wuhsiang; Rept.
  (Young, C.-c.)   1957E
Colorado, Colorado Plateau; Amph., Rept.
  (Stewart, J. H.)   1969A
Connecticut; Pisces
  (McKenna, M. C.)   1972B
England, Mendip; Rept.
  (Halstead, L. B., Nicoll, P. G.)   1971A
England, Midlands; Amph., Rept.
  (Warrington, G.)   1970A
England; Rept.
  (Walker, A. D.)   1969A
Europe, Tethys; middle; Pisces, Rept.
  (Wild, R.)   1972A
Germany, Bavaria; Keuper; Pisces, Rept.
  (Stahl, G.)   1971A
Germany, Karlsruhe-Durlach; Pisces
  (Jörg, E.)   1969A, 1970A
Germany, Karlstadt; middle; Pisces, Rept.
  (Rutte, E.)   1971A
Germany, northwest; Pisces
  (Will, H.-J.)   1969A
Germany, western; Amph., Rept.
  (Ortlam, D.)   1968A
Germany, western; Pisces, Rept.
  (Ortlam, D.)   1967A
India, Pranhita-Godavari V.; Amph.,
Pisces, Rept.
  (Chatterjee, S., et al.)   1969A

VERTEBRATE FAUNAS - cont.
Triassic
India, Pranhita-Godavari V.; Pisces, Rept.
  (Chatterjee, S.)   1967B
Madagascar, northwest; Pisces
  (Beltan, L.)   1968A
Morocco, Atlas western; Amph., Pisces,
Rept.
  (Dutuit, J.-M.)   1971A
New Mexico, Chama Basin
  (Budding, A. J., Pitrat, C. W.,
    Smith, C. T.)   1960A
New Mexico, Texas, Dockum group;
Amph., Pisces, Rept.
  (Gregory, J. T.)   1972A
North America; Pisces
  (Schaeffer, B., Mangus, M.)   1970A
South Africa; Mam., Rept.
  (Crompton, A. W.)   1969A
Tunisia, southern; Rept.
  (Halstead, L. B., Stewart, A. D.)   1970A
United States, Colorado Plateau;
Amph., Pisces, Rept.
  (Stewart, J. H., Poole, F. G.,
    Wilson, R. F.)   1972A
USSR, Cisuralia; lower; Amph.
  (Tverdokhlebov, V. P.)   1970B
USSR, European part, center; Amph.,
Pisces, Rept.
  (Gorbatkina, T. E., Lozovskiĭ, V. R.,
    Strok, N. I.)   1971A
USSR, Moscow; Amph., Pisces, Rept.
  (Lozovskiĭ, V. P.)   1967A
  (Lozovskiĭ, V. R., Rozanov, V. I.) 1969A
USSR, Pechora Basin; Pisces
  (Gorskiĭ, V. P.)   1963A
USSR, Povolzh'e, Prikam'e; Amph.,
Pisces, Rept.
  (Blom, G. I.)   1967A
USSR, Povolzh'e, Prikam'e; Amph.,
Rept.
  (Blom, G. I.)   1968A
USSR, Pricaspian, Aralsorsk; Pisces
  (Bogacheva, M. I., et al.)   1965A
USSR, Russian Platform; Amph.,
Pisces, Rept.
  (Zoricheva, A. I.)   1963B
USSR, southern Urals, Obshchiĭ Syrt;
Indian; Amph.
  (Tverdokhlebov, V. P.)   1970A
USSR, Volgograd
  (Movshovich, E. V.)   1970A
VIETNAM
Vertebrate Faunas
Pleist.; Mam.
  (Saurin, E.)   1968A
VIRGINIA
Paleontology
Mam.; Pleist.; Chincoteague
  (Manville, R. H., Wilson, J. J.)   1970A
Mam.; Pleist.; Lane Cave
  (Holsinger, J. R.)   1967A
Vertebrate Faunas
Pleist.; coast; Mam.
  (Drummond, A. H.)   1970A

WYOMING - cont.
Vertebrate Faunas
  Eocene; Pass Peak Fm.; Mam.
    (Dorr, J. A.) 1969A
  Eocene; Washakie Fm.; Mam.
    (Turnbull, W. D.) 1972A
  Eocene; western; Mam.
    (Dorr, J. A., Steidtmann, J. R.) 1970A
  Eocene; Wind R. Fm.; Mam.
    (Guthrie, D. A.) 1971B
  Miocene; Colter Fm.; Mam.
    (Black, C. C.) 1968C
  Miocene; Jackson Hole; Mam.
    (Sutton, J. F., Black, C. C.) 1972A
  Miocene; Middle Park; Mam.
    (Robinson, P.) 1968E
  Miocene; Split Rock; Mam.
    (Robinson, P.) 1968D
  Miocene; Teton Co.; Mam.
    (McKenna, M. C.) 1972D
  Miocene; Trail Creek; Mam.
    (Forstén, A.-M.) 1970B
  Oligocene; Cedar Ridge; Mam.
    (Black, C. C.) 1968D
  Oligocene; Flagstaff Rim
    (Emry, R. J.) 1971A
  Oligocene; Jackson Hole; Mam.
    (Sutton, J. F., Black, C. C.) 1972A
  Paleocene; Little Muddy Creek; Mam.
    (Gazin, C. L.) 1969A
  Pleist.; Hell Gap; Mam.
    (Roberts, M. F.) 1970A
  Pleist.; Little Box Elder Cave; Mam.
    (Long, C. A.) 1971A
  Pleist.; Mam.
    (Duguid, J., Bedish, G.) 1968A
  Tertiary
    (McGrew, P. O.) 1971C
  Tertiary; Fossil Basin
    (Oriel, S. S., Tracey, J. I.) 1970A
  Tert.; Granite Mts.; Mam.
    (Love, J. D.) 1970A
  Tert.; Togwotee Pass
    (McKenna, M. C.) 1972A
X-RAY PHOTOGRAPHY. See under Vertebrate.
YUGOSLAVIA
Paleoanthropology
  Istria; fossil hominids
    (Malez, M.) 1972A
  Krapina; fossil hominids
    (Čanadjija, S.) 1970A
    (Kallay, J.) 1969A, 1970A,C,D,E
    (Smith, F. H.) 1972A
    (Tomić-Karović, K.) 1970A,B
  Slovenia; colloquium
    (Broglio, A.) 1965B
  Veternica Cave; fossil hominids
    (Malez, M.) 1956A
Paleontology
  Mam.; Miocene; Bosnia
    (Soklić, I., Malez, M.) 1969A
  Mam.; Pleist.; Lesno brdo
    (Rakovec, I.) 1969A
  Mam.; Pleist., lower; Dalmatia
    (Malez, M.) 1960E
  Mam.; Pleist.; Mokrica Cave
    (Rakovec, I.) 1967B

YUGOSLAVIA - cont.
Paleontology
  Mam.; Pleist.; northern
    (Malez, M.) 1968C
  Mam.; Pleist.; Šalek V.
    (Rakovec, I.) 1968B
  Mam.; Pleist.; Vjetrenica Cave
    (Malez, M., Pepeonik, Z.) 1969A
  Mam.; Pliocene; Škale
    (Drobne, K.) 1967A
  Pisces; Miocene; Belgrad
    (Anđelković, J. S.) 1967A, 1969B
  Pisces; Tert.; Serbia
    (Anđelković, J. S.) 1970A
Vertebrate Faunas
  Cret., upper; Bileća; Rept.
    (Slišković, T.) 1970A
  Miocene; Belgrad; Pisces
    (Anđelković, J. S.) 1969A
  Neogene; Toplica Basin; Mam.
    (Pavlović, M. B.) 1967A, 1969A
  Pleistocene
    (Malez, M.) 1965L, 1967D
    (Marković-Marjanović, J.) 1970A
  Pleist.; Croatia; Mam.
    (Malez, M.) 1956B, 1967A
  Pleist.; Crvena
    (Malez, M.) 1967B
  Pleist.; Dinar Karsts; Mam.
    (Malez, M.) 1968B
  Pleist.; Dubci
    (Malez, M.) 1967C
  Pleist.; Krapina
    (Malez, M.) 1970A
  Pleist.; Mam.
    (Malez, M.) 1966B, 1969A
    (Marković-Marjanović, J.) 1972A
    (Rakovec, I.) 1968A
  Pleist.; Risovaca; Mam.
    (Rakovec, I.) 1965C
  Pleist.; Serbia; Mam.
    (Gavela, B.) 1955A, 1957A
  Pleist.; Slovenia
    (Osole, F.) 1964-65D
  Pleist.; Slovenia; Mam.
    (Rakovec, I.) 1967A
  Pleist.; Triestine Karst
    (Leben, F.) 1967A
  Pleist., upper; Macedonia; Mam.
    (Garevski, R.) 1969A
  Pleist., upper; Slovenia; Mam.
    (Brodar, M.) 1964-65A
  Pleist.; Velika Pećina; Mam.
    (Malez, M., Vogel, J. C.) 1970A
  Pleist.; Zakajeni Spodmol; Mam.
    (Osole, F.) 1967A
  Tert.; Sinj; Mam.
    (Takšić, A.) 1968A
YUKON TERRITORY
Paleontology
  Mam.; Pleist.
    (Harington, C. R.) 1969A
  Pisces; Pleist.
    (McAllister, D. E.,
    Harington, C. R.) 1969A
  Pisces; Silurian; Beaver R., Snake R.
    (Broad, D. S., Lenz, A. C.) 1972A

SYSTEMATIC INDEX

SYSTEMATIC INDEX

Several changes in indexing procedure from that followed in previous volumes have been introduced in this index.

The Synopsis of Classification has been omitted, and the organization of the systematic index, with few exceptions, follows the classification in the third edition of A. S. Romer, Vertebrate Paleontology (1966), and shows how authors deviate from it. Although some major systematic revisions have been incorporated (i.e., Aves: Brodkorb, Catalogue of fossil birds, 1963, 1964, 1967, 1971; Gorgonopsia: Sigogneau 1970A; Felidae (and some other mammals): Simpson 1945 Elephantidae: Aguirre 1969B), the purpose of this index is to place each entry in a taxonomic context and refer the reade to the published source of information rather than to summarize current opinion. No attempt was made to evaluate the systematic validity of the entries, or to emend or correct usage which appeared improper, even though mere typographical errors were responsible. Nevertheless, numerous arbitrary allocations were required to provide a consistent index to the diverse nomenclature applied to cats, elephants, ostracoderms and some other groups of fossils. In all cases the systematic assignment by each author is also indicated.

Authors' names appear here as printed on the publication, and some differ from the Author Catalogue, where publications by authors who use several names or whose names are spelled in more than one way have often been brought together. A list of names which have not been cross-referenced is printed at the beginning of the Author Catalogue.

The basic entry in the Systematic Index is the genus, under which each included species is listed in alphabetical order, followed by the name of the author and year of publication, these items providing a reference to the appropriate title in the Author Catalogue. Generic and specific nomina are not italicized in this index.

The names of the authors of newly proposed taxa are printed in italics. As all authors who discuss each taxon are listed in alphabetical order, the name of the original describer may not follow the name of the taxon directly.

The primary index term is followed by the name of the next higher taxon (e.g., family, order, etc.) to which it belongs. All genera which are dealt with in publications included in this volume are listed after the name of the family to which they are assigned. For more complete indication of the generic content of families, reference must be made to Romer (1966) or other comprehensive treatises.

Higher taxonomic categories are indexed where warranted by publications dealing with a broad subject. Supra-generic taxa without bibliographic reference are entered to show systematic relationships.

Species names also appear in alphabetical sequence and are followed in parenthesis by names of the genera to which they pertain. It is necessary to refer to the generic listing to find references to pertinent publications.

Parentheses ( ) following the author's name and date enclose comments, either regarding classification (i.e., differing from the standard) or other pertinent information (cf., subgen., n. comb., otol., ichn., restor.), or subject matter, especially when dealing with a large group.

Brackets [ ] always indicate synonymies, but they are used in two distinctly different ways: A bracketed term immediately following the prime systematic entry means that the author proposes a new synonymy, suppressing the bracketed term, and including it within or giving priority to the term preceeding the brackets. Example: *Albertosaurus libratus* [*Gorgosaurus, G. sternbergi*] Russell, D. A. 1970C (n. comb.). Here the author proposes that *Gorgosaurus libratus* should be referred to the genus *Albertosaurus,* and that *G. sternbergi* is a junior synonym of *Albertosaurus libratus* and should be included in that species.

Brackets at the end of a reference, following the author and year, enclose the author's usage of a name in his publication which differs from the standard adopted for this Index. Example: *Amia fragosa* Sahni, A. 1972A [*Kindleia*]. In this case the brackets indicate that Sahni uses the name *Kindleia fragosa,* assigning this species to a genus included (in Romer's classification) in *Amia.*

Extensive cross-references, with special emphasis on terms in parentheses and brackets, have been attempted to aid the reader.

ABBREVIATIONS USED IN SYSTEMATIC INDEX

aff.	related to	phylog.	phylogeny
cf. & cfr.	compare	reconstr.	reconstruction
classif.	classification	restor.	restoration
comb.	combination	s.d.	no date
evol.	evolution	sens	sense
gen.	genus	sp.	species
gr.	group	subcl.	subclass
ichn.	ichnites	subfam.	subfamily
incl.	including	subgen.	subgenus
infraord.	infraorder	subord.	suborder
mut.	mutant	subsp.	subspecies
n.	new	subtr.	subtribe
nom.	nomen.	superfam.	superfamily
nr.	near	syst.	systematics
ord.	order	var.	variety
otol.	otolith	w.	with

acutidens (Esthonix, Ictops, Leptictis)
acutipes (Microsauropus)
acutirostratus (Aceratherium)
acutissima (Odontaspis)
acutorostrata (Balaenoptera)
acutum (Peristedion)
acutus (Deltoptychius, Procolophonipus, Trachinus)
Adaetontherium see Dryopithecus
Adamisaurus ? Agamidae *Sulimski, A.* 1972A
    magnidentatus *Sulimski, A.* 1972A
adamsi (Blarina, Cryptotis, Salichnium)
Adapidae [Notharctidae] Primates — Lemuroidea
    Adapis, Agerina, Gesneropithex, Lantianius,
        Notharctus, Pelycodus, Pronycticebus,
        Protoadapis, Smilodectes
Adapis Adapidae
    magnus Day, M. H., Walker, A. C. 1969A;
        Gingerich, P. D. 1972B; Schmidt-Kittler, N.
        1971B
    parisiensis Sudre, J. 1969B (aff.)
    ulmensis *Schmidt-Kittler, N.* 1971B
Adapisorex Adapisoricidae Quinet, G. E. 1969B (invalid)
Adapisoricidae Insectivora — Erinaceoidea
    Adapisorex, Centetodon, Clinopternodus, Entomolestes,
        Geolabis, Gypsonictops, Hyracolestes, Ictopidium,
        Leptacodon, Myolestes, Nycticonodon,
        Nyctitherium, Praolestes, Scenopagus, Talpavus
Adapisoriculus Tupaiidae Quinet, G. E. 1969B (invalid,
        see Nycticonodon)
adaurora (Loxodonta)
Adeloblarina Soricidae
    berklandi Gureev, A. A. 1971A
Adelomyarion Cricetidae — Cricetodontinae
        Hugueney, M. 1969A
    vireti *Hugueney, M.* 1969A
Adelomys see Sciuroides
Adelpharctos Ursidae *Bonis, L.* 1971A
    mirus *Bonis, L.* 1971A
Adelphomyinae Echimyidae *Patterson, B., Pascual, R.*
        1968B
Adenota Bovidae
    kob Gautier, A. 1968A (?)
Adjidaumo Eomyidae
    hansonorum *Russell, L. S.* 1972B
    minutus Wood, A. E. 1969A
    russelli *Storer, J. E.* 1970A
    stewarti *Russell, L. S.* 1972B
admixtus (Lewisuchus)
Adocus Dermatemydidae Powell, J. S. 1969A
adriani (Nothosaurus)
Adroichthys Chirodontidae *Gardiner, B. G.* 1969A
        (in Amphicentridae)
    tuberculatus *Gardiner, B. G.* 1969A
adroveri (Baranogale, Ictitherium)
aduncus (Galeocerdo)
advena (Blastomeryx)
Aedua
    gaudryi see Paramblypterus
Aeduella Aeduellidae
    blainvillei Heyler, D. 1969A (reconstr.)
    primigenius *Heyler, D.* 1969A (?)
Aeduellidae Palaeonisciformes — Palaeoniscoidei
    Aeduella, Bourbonnella, Decazella, Igornella,
        Igornichthys

Aegialodon Dryolestidae Turnbull, W. D. 1971A
        (in Eutheria — Tribosphena)
    dawsoni Clemens, W. A., Lees, P. M. 1971A
        (in Aegialodontidae); Crompton, A. W. 1971A
Aegialodontidae see Dryolestidae
Aegialornis Aegialornithidae
    leenhardti [A. leenhardti] Brodkorb, P. 1971A
Aegialornithidae Caprimulgiformes
    Aegialornis
Aegolius Strigidae
    funereus Jánossy, D. 1972A (aff.)
Aegypius Accipitridae
    monachus Ganiã, I. M. 1969A
aegyptiacus (Asteracanthus)
Aegyptopithecus Pongidae Andrews, P. 1970A;
        Radinsky, L. 1972A
    zeuxis Simons, E. L. 1971C; Simons, E. L.,
        Pilbeam, D. R. 1972A
Aelurodon Canidae
    haydeni Webb, S. D. 1969C (cf.)
    saevus Green, M. 1971A
    taxoides Webb, S. D. 1969C
Aelurognathus Gorgonopsidae — Gorgonopsinae
    haughtoni see Leontocephalus
    microdon see Lycaenops
    minor see Arctops kitchingi, Lycaenops minor
    nyassaensis see A. tigriceps
    parringtoni Ricqlès, A. 1969A [Scymnognathus];
        [Scymnognathus] Sigogneau, D. 1970A
        (?, n. comb.)
    quadratus Ricqlès, A. 1969A [Dixeya]; [Dixeya]
        Sigogneau, D. 1970A (n. comb.);
    serratidens [Lycaenoides angusticeps] Sigogneau, D.
        1970A
    sollasi [Scymnognathus holmesi] Sigogneau, D. 1970A
    tigriceps Ricqlès, A. 1969A (?); [A. nyassaensis]
        Sigogneau, D. 1970A
Aelurosauridae see Gorgonopsidae — Gorgonopsinae
Aelurosauroides see Aelurosaurus
Aelurosauropsidae see Gorgonopsidae — Gorgonopsinae
Aelurosauropsis see Aelurosaurus
Aelurosaurus Gorgonopsidae — Gorgonopsinae
    breviceps Sigogneau, D. 1970A
    curvimola see Arctognathus
    felinus [A. striatidens, Aelurosauroides watsoni]
        Sigogneau, D. 1970A; [A. tenuirostris]
        Sigogneau, D. 1970A (cf.)
    polyodon [Galerhinus] Sigogneau, D. 1970A
        (n. comb.)
    striatidens see A. felinus
    tenuirostris see A. cf. felinus
    watermeyeri [Nanogorgon gracilis]
        Sigogneau, D. 1970A (cf.);
        [Scylacocephalus, Cyniscops
        broomianus] Sigogneau, D. 1970A
        (?, n. comb.)
    whaitsi Sigogneau, D. 1970A
    wilmanae [Aelurosauropsis] Sigogneau, D. 1970A
aemulus (Anaptomorphus, Myotis)
aenigma (Geranodornis)
aenigmaticum (Belonochasma)
Aenocyon Canis
Aeoliscus Macrorhamphidae
    heinrichi Weiler, W. 1971C (in Centriscidae)

Albertochampsa   Crocodylidae–Alligatorinae
    Erickson, B. R. 1972B,C
    langstoni *Erickson, B. R.* 1972C
Albertosaurus   Tyrannosauridae
    arctunguis see A. sarcophagus
    lancensis Russell, D. A. 1970C
    libratus [Gorgosaurus, G. sternbergi] Russell, D. A.
        1970C (n. comb.)
    sarcophagus [A. arctunguis, Dryptosaurus
        incrassatus, Laelaps incrassatus] Russell,
        D. A. 1970C
albidens (Astrohippus)
albifrons (Anser)
albigula (Neotoma)
Albula   Albulidae
    dunklei *Applegate, S. P.* 1970A
    oweni Casier, E. 1967B
Albulidae   Elopiformes–Albuloidei Weiler, W. 1969A
        (in Clupeiformes)
    Albula, Casierius, Coriops, Palealbula, Paralbula,
        Pterothrissidarum, Pterothrissus
    See also Otolithus
Alburnus   Cyprinidae Salis, K. 1967A
albyi (Bregmaceros)
Alca   Alcidae
    impennis Ascenzi, A., Segre, A. 1971B
Alcelaphus   Bovidae Clutton-Brock, J. 1970A
    buselaphus Churcher, C. S. 1972C; Gautier, A. 1968A
alces (Alces)
Alces   Cervidae Baǐgusheva, V. S. 1971A [Libralces];
        Schmidt, Z., Halouzka, R. 1970A
    alces Barnes, B., Edwards, B. J. N., Hallam, J. S.,
        Stuart, A. J. 1971A; Heptner, W. G.,
        Nasimowitsch, A. A. 1967A; Melentis, J. K.
        1966P; Rǎdulescu, C., Hermann, W. 1969A;
        Samson, P., Hermann, W. 1968A; Torres
        Perezhidalgo, T. 1971A; Vangengeǐm, E. A.
        1963A
    brevirostris Jánossy, D. 1969B
    latifrons David, A. I. 1969A; Kahlke, H.-D. 1969D;
        Motuzko, A. N. 1970A
Alcidae   Charadriiformes–Alcae
    Alca, Cerorhinca, Endomychura, Mancalla
aldeni (Miortyx)
aldingeri (Birgeria)
Alectoris   Phasianidae
    bavarica *Ballmann, P.* 1969B
    kakelik Aubekerova, P. A. 1965A
alemanii (Platygonus compressus)
alexanderi (Scaphiopus)
alexandrae (Mojavemys, Thalattosaurus)
alexeevae (Anancus)
alfa (Bathygenys)
alfi (Microsyops)
algarensis (Megaloceros)
algirus (Erinaceus)
alienus (Palaeorallus)
alipioi (Mirandatherium)
Allacerops see Epiaceratherium [Allocerops]
Allactaga   Dipodidae
    elater Sukhov, V. P. 1970A (ex gr.)
    jaculus Erbaeva, M. A. 1972A
    saltator
        transbaicalicus Erbaeva, M. A. 1970A
Allaeochelys   Carettochelyidae
    casasecai *Jimenez Fuentes, E.* 1971B

allegheniensis (Hybodus)
alleni (Bison)
Allenypterus   Dorypteridae *Melton, W. G.* 1969B
    montanus *Melton, W. G.* 1969B
Alligatorellus   Atoposauridae
    beaumonti
        bavaricus *Wellnhofer, P.* 1971A (n. subsp.)
        beaumonti Wellnhofer, P. 1971A
Alligatorium   Atoposauridae
    depereti Wellnhofer, P. 1971A
    franconicum Wellnhofer, P. 1971A
    meyeri Wellnhofer, P. 1971A
    paintenense Wellnhofer, P. 1971A
allmanni (Loxomma)
Alloberyx   Holocentridae *Gaudant, M.* 1969A
    syriacus [Beryx] Gaudant, M. 1969A
Allocerops see Epiaceratherium
Allocricetulus   Cricetidae Sukhov, V. P. 1970A
Allocricetus   Cricetidae
    bursae Chaline, J. 1971A; Fahlbusch, V. 1969A;
        Fejfar, O. 1970A (cf.); Jánossy, D. 1969B;
        Koenigswald, W. 1971A; Malez, M. 1967C
        (cf.); Terzea, E., Jurcsák, T. 1967A;
        Tchernov, E. 1968C
    bursae
        pyrenaicus *Chaline, J.* 1971A (n. subsp.)
    ehiki Fahlbusch, V. 1969A
    jesreelicus Tchernov, E. 1968B
    magnus *Tchernov, E.* 1968B
Allodesmus   Otariidae
    courseni [Atopotarus] Barnes, L. G. 1969A, 1972A
    kelloggi see A. kernensis
    kernensis [A. kelloggi] Barnes, L. G. 1969A, 1970A,
        1972A
    packardi *Barnes, L. G.* 1972A
Allognathosuchus   Crocodylidae Berg, D. E. 1969A
    polyodon Mook, C. C. 1961A
Allohippus see Equus
Allomys   Aplodontidae
    ernii Hugueney, M. 1969A
    harkseni Macdonald, J. R. 1970A
    sharpi *Macdonald, J. R.* 1970A
    stirtoni *Klingener, D.* 1968A
Allophaiomys   Cricetidae Agadzhanian, A. K.,
        Motuzko, A. N. 1972A; Erbaeva, M. A. 1970A
    pliocaenicus Chaline, J. 1968A; Chaline, J.,
        Matthey, R. 1971A (in Arvicolidae);
        Malez, M. 1967C (cf.); Sukhov, V. P. 1970A
        (cf.); Terzea, E., Jurcsák, T. 1967A
        (in Arvicolidae)
Allopus   Ichnites see Baropezia, Limnopus
Allosaurus   Megalosauridae Miller, R. C. 1972A;
        Ozaki, H., Obata, I. 1963A
    fragilis Welles, S. P. 1972A
Alloscapanus   Talpidae *Baudelot, S.* 1968A
    auscitanensis *Baudelot, S.* 1968A
Allosiphneus see Myospalax
Allosorex   Soricidae
    stenodus Fejfar, O. 1966D; Gureev, A. A. 1971A
Allosoricina   Soricidae–Soricinae *Gureev, A. A.* 1971A
        (n. subtr., in Blarinini)
Allospalax   Anomalomyidae *Kretzoi, M.* 1970-71A
    plenus *Kretzoi, M.* 1970-71A
Allotheria   Mammalia–Prototheria Hopson, J. A. 1970A
        (infracl., n. rank, incl. Multituberculata)

Amiidae   Amiiformes–Amioidei Boreske, J. R. A., Jr.
      1972A
   Amia, Pseudamiatus, Urocles
Amiiformes   Holostei
   Incl. subord. Parasemionotoidei, Amioidei
amissadomus (Paeneprolimnocyon)
Amiurus   Ictalurus
Ammodytes   Ammodytidae
   antipai Jerzmańska, A. 1968A
   obliquus Heinrich, W.-D. 1969B (otol.); Robba, E.
      1970A (otol.)
Ammodytidae   Perciformes–Ammodytoidei
   Ammodytes
ammon (Ovis)
ammon–polii (Ovis)
ammoni (Anurognathus)
Ammosaurus   Theropoda incertae sedis Galton, P. M.
      1971C
Ammotragus see Ovis
amnicolus (Coriops)
amoenus (Grayemys)
amouraensis (Columbosauripus)
Amphechinus   Erinaceidae Telles Antunes, M.,
      Mein, P. 1971A
   acridens Sulimski, A. 1970A (subgen.
      Palaeoscaptor)
   horncloudi Macdonald, J. R. 1970A
      [Palaeoerinaceus]
   minimus Sulimski, A. 1970A (cf., subgen.
      Palaeoerinaceus)
   rectus Sulimski, A. 1970A (cf., subgen.
      Palaeoscaptor)
   rusingensis Butler, P. M. 1969A
Ampheristus see Hoplobrotula
Amphiaspididae   Heterostraci (incl. Amphiaspida,
      Hibernaspida of Stensiö)
   Amphiaspis, Eglonaspis, Hibernaspis, Pelurgaspis
   See also Eglonaspididae, Hibernaspididae
Amphiaspidiformes   Heterostraci Novitskaia, L. I.
      1968A, 1971B (incl. Olbiaspididae,
      Edaphaspididae, Gabreyaspididae,
      Amphiaspididae, Siberiaspididae,
      Tuxeraspididae, Eglonaspididae,
      Hibernaspididae, Aphataspididae)
Amphiaspis   Amphiaspididae
   argos Novitskaia, L. I. 1971B
Amphibia
   Incl. subcl. Labyrinthodontia, Lepospondyli,
      Lissamphibia Frazzetta, T. H. 1968A;
      Kuhn, O. 1970B (classif.), 1971E, 1972A;
      Lebedkina, N. S. 1968A; Lehman, J.-P.
      1968B; Medvedeva, I. M. 1961A, 1965A;
      Panchen, A. L. 1972B; Schultze, H.-P.
      1969B (teeth)
amphibius (Hippopotamus)
Amphicentridae see Chirodontidae
Amphicyon   Canidae Bonis, L. de 1969B
   major Telles Antunes, M. 1960C
Amphicyonidae see Canidae
Amphidyromys
   pusillus see Glirulus
Amphilagus   Ochotonidae
   antiquus Tobien, H. 1970C
   fontannesi Engesser, B. 1972A
   ulmensis Janvier, P. 1969A

Amphilestidae   Triconodonta see Triconodontidae
Amphimerycidae   Artiodactyla–Anoplotheroidea
   Pseudamphimeryx
Amphipithecus   Pongidae Simons, E. L. 1971A;
      Szalay, F. S. 1970A (in ? Lemuroidea),
      1972A
   mogoungensis Szalay, F. S. 1970A
Amphiplaga   Aphredoderidae
   brachyptera Rosen, D. E., Patterson, C. 1969A
      (in Percopsidae)
Amphisauroides   Ichnites Haubold, H. 1970A
   conrectus Haubold, H. 1970A
   discessus Haubold, H. 1970A
   minor [Auxipes] Haubold, H. 1970A
Amphisauropus   Ichnites Haubold, H. 1970A
      (in Seymouriamorpha)
   imminutus Haubold, H. 1970A
   latus Haubold, H. 1970A
Amphisbaenidae   Squamata–Lacertilia
   Macrorhineura
Amphiserpentarius   Sagittariidae
   robustus see Amynoptilon
   schlosseri Cracraft, J., Rich, P. V. 1972A
      (in Cathartidae)
Amphisorex   Soricidae
   primaevus Gureev, A. A. 1971A
Amphistiidae see Ephippidae
Amphistium   Ephippidae
   paradoxum Blot, J. 1969B (in Amphistiidae)
Amphitheriidae   Pantotheria
   Amphitherium, ?Peramus
Amphitherium   Amphitheriidae Crompton, A. W. 1971A
Amphiuma   Amphiumidae
   jepseni Estes, R. 1969B
Amphiumidae   Urodela
   Amphiuma, Proamphiuma
ampla (Oreaspis)
amurensis (Mandschurosaurus)
Amynodon   Amynodontidae Zhegallo, V. I.,
      Borisov, B. A. 1968A
Amynodontidae   Perissodactyla–Rhinocerotoidea
   Amynodon, Cadurcodon, Lushiamynodon,
      Procadurcodon, Zaisanamynodon
Amynoptilon   Sagittariidae Cracraft, J., Rich, P. V.
      1972A
   robustum [Amphiserpentarius] Cracraft, J.,
      Rich, P. V. 1972A
Amyzon   Catostomidae Cavender, T. M. 1968A (cf.)
Anabernicula   Anatidae
   robusta Short, L. L. 1970A
anacingularis (Paramys, Paramys nanus)
Anacoracidae see Isuridae
Anacorax see Squalicorax
Anaethalion   Anaethalionidae Gaudant, J.,
      Maubeuge, P. 1971A
   affinis Gaudant, J. 1968B
   cirinensis Gaudant, J. 1968B
   knorri Gaudant, J. 1968B
   subovatus Gaudant, J. 1968B (cf.)
Anaethalionidae   Leptolepidiformes Gaudant, J.
      1968B (incl. Anaethalion, Anaethalionopsis,
      Manchurichthys)
   Anaethalion
Anagalida   Mammalia Szalay, F. S., McKenna, M. C.
      1971A (n. order, incl. Zalambdalestidae,
      Pseudictopidae, Anagalidae, Eurymylidae)

Anagalidae Insectivora—Leptictoidea Szalay, F. S.,
  McKenna, M. C. 1971A (in Anagalida)
  Khashanagale
analensis (Dwykia)
Anancus Gomphotheriidae
  alexeevae Baïgusheva, V. S. 1971A
  arvernensis Apostol, L. 1968A; Beden, M. 1970B;
    Heintz, E. 1969B; Khalvadzhiev, M. 1969A;
    Mihăilă, N. 1971A; Mitzopoulos, M. K. 1966A
    (subgen. Bunolophodon); Pavia, G. 1970A;
    Rădulescu, C., Kovács, A. 1968A; Rakovec, I.
    1968B [Bunolophodon, subgen. Anancus];
    Samson, P. et al. 1971A; Schmidt, Z.,
    Halouzka, R. 1970A; Tobien, H. 1968I
  kazachstanicus Kozhamkulova, B. S., Orlovskaïa,
    E. R. 1971A
  kenyensis Cooke, H. B. S., Coryndon, S. C. 1970A
  osiris Arambourg, C. 1970A; Tchoumakov, I. S.,
    Alekseeva, L. I. 1971A (cf.)
Anaptomorphidae Primates—Tarsioidei
  Absarokius, Anaptomorphus, Tetonius, Uintanius,
  Uintasorex
Anaptomorphus Anaptomorphidae
  aemulus McGrew, P. O., Sullivan, R. 1970A
Anarthraspis Phlyctaenaspidae Stensiö, E. 1969B,
    1971A (in Spinothoracidi—Dolichothoraci)
Anas Anatidae Feduccia, J. A., Rich, P. V. 1972A;
    Koenigswald, W. 1972A
  acuta Churcher, C. S. 1972C; Jánossy, D. 1972A (cf.)
  crecca Churcher, C. S. 1972C
  leucophrys Tonni, E. P. 1969A
  penelope Churcher, C. S. 1972C; Jánossy, D. 1972A
    (cf.)
  platyrhynchos Churcher, C. S. 1972C; Jánossy, D.
    1972A (cf.)
  querquedula Jánossy, D. 1972A (cf.)
  strepera Jánossy, D. 1972A (cf.)
anas (Anatipeda)
Anaspida Agnatha—Monorhina Whiting, H. P. 1972A
Anatidae Anseriformes
  Anabernicula, Anas, Anser, ? Anserobranta, Aythya,
    Biziura, Branta, Bucephala, Cygnus, Guguschia,
    Mergus, Oxyura, ? Paracygnus, Romainvillia,
    Spatula, Tadorna
Anatipeda Anatipedidae
  anas Panin, N. 1964A, 1965A
Anatipedae see Anatipedidae
Anatipedidae [Anatipedae] Avipedia
  Anatipeda
Anatosaurus Hadrosauridae
  annectens Morris, W. J. 1970A (bill mold; reconstr.)
anceps (Liodon)
ancestralis (Paralligator)
Anchiblarinella [Limnoecus] Soricidae Hibbard, C. W.,
    Jammot, D. 1971A
  wakeeneyensis Hibbard, C. W., Jammot, D. 1971A
Anchilophus Equidae
  radegondensis Bessonnat, G., Dughi, R., Sirugue, F.
    1969A (ichn.)
Anchisauridae Saurischia—Sauropodomorpha
    Steel, R. 1970A
Anchisauripodidae Ichnites Haubold, H. 1969B
  (in Saurischia—Coelurosauria, incl.
    Anchisauripus, Grallator, Coelurosaurichnus,
    Stenonyx, Saltopoides, Talmontopus)

Anchisauripus Ichnites Haubold, H. 1969B
  (in Anchisauripodidae)
  bibractensis Demathieu, G. 1971A
  sillimani Ostrom, J. H. 1968A; Peoples, J. W.
    1967A (coelurosaur)
Anchitherium Equidae
  aurelianense Engesser, B. 1972A; Pavlović, M. B.
    1969A
Anchoa Engraulidae
  weileri Cappetta, H. C. 1969B (otol.)
Ancylotherium Chalicotheriidae
  hennigi Cooke, H. B. S., Coryndon, S. C. 1970A
    (cf.)
  pentelicum Telles Antunes, M. 1966E
Andegameryx Hypertragulidae Ginsburg, L. 1970B
  andegaviensis Ginsburg, L. 1970B
  serum [Bachitherium] Ginsburg, L. 1970B
andegaviensis (Andegameryx)
andersontau (Hitonkala)
anderssoni (Chilotherium, Martes)
Andescynodon Traversodontidae Bonaparte, J. F.
    1969B
  mendozensis Bonaparte, J. F. 1969B, 1972A
andina (Vinceria)
Andreolepis Lophosteidae Gross, W. 1969A
  hedei Janvier, P. 1971B
andrewsi (Phacochoerus)
Andrias Cryptobranchidae Westphal, F. 1970A
Androsorex Leptictidae Quinet, G. E. 1969B
Angaraspis Olbiaspididae
  urvantzevi Novitskaïa, L. I. 1971B; Stensiö, E.
    1968A
Angarichthys Homostiidae, Stensiö, E. 1969B, 1971A
Angelocabrerus Borhyaenidae Simpson, G. G. 1970D
  daptes Simpson, G. G. 1970D
Angistorhinus Phytosauridae Gregory, J. T. 1969B
Anglaspis Cyathaspididae Turner, S., Dixon, J. 1971A
  heintzi Denison, R. H. 1971B (restor.)
anglica (Heightingtonaspis)
anglicus (Parailurus)
angressi (Hystrix)
Anguidae Squamata—Lacertilia Meszoely, C. A. M.
    1970A
  Anguis, Arpadosaurus, Melanosaurus, Ophisaurus,
    Pancelosaurus, Peltosaurus, Xestops
Anguilla Anguillidae
  rectangularis Stinton, F. C., Nolf, D. 1969A (otol.)
anguillaris (Clarias)
Anguillidae Anguilliformes—Anguilloidei
  Anguilla
Anguilliformes Teleostei
  Incl. subord. Anguilloidei, Saccopharyngoidei
Anguis Anguidae Koenigswald, W. 1971A
  fragilis Koenigswald, W. 1972A
angularis (Alacodon)
angulatus (Mylagaulodon, Pterothrissus)
angusta (Antigonia)
angusticeps (Lycaenops, Rubidgina)
angustidens (Gomphotherium, Hyracotherium, Isurus,
    Lycorhinus, Microsyops, Plesiogale,
    Plesispermophilus, Quercygale, Triakis)
Angustidens Soricidae
  vireti Gureev, A. A. 1971A
angustidentatus (Labrodon)
angustifrons (Plesiogale)

angustipes (Bucephala)
angustirostris (Mirounga, Saurolophus)
Anhinga Anhingidae
　　pannonica Rich, P. V. 1972A
Anhingidae Pelecaniformes
　　Anhinga
anitae (Lonchidion)
Ankarapithecus see Dryopithecus
Ankylosauria Ornithischia Coombs, W. P. 1971A
annanensis (Delairichnus)
annectens (Anatosaurus, Doleserpeton, Microsyops)
annulatus (Crossotelos)
Anomalichthys Holonematidae Stensiö, E. 1969B
　　(in ? Holonemida)
Anomalomyidae Rodentia–Muroidea Kretzoi, M.
　　1970-71A (incl. Anomalomys, Miospalax,
　　Allospalax, Pterospalax, Prospalax)
　　Allospalax, Pterospalax
　　See also Cricetidae
Anomalomyini Spalacidae Fejfar, O. 1972A
Anomalomys Cricetidae
　　gaillardi Kretzoi, M. 1970-71A
　　(in Anomalomyidae)
　　gaudryi Engesser, B. 1972A; Kretzoi, M. 1970-
　　71A (in Anomalomyidae)
　　minor Fejfar, O. 1972A (in Spalacidae)
anomalus (Occitanomys, Paraethomys, Sciurus)
Anomegodus Pseudotheridomys Jámbor, A.,
　　Korpás, L., Kretzoi, M., Pálfalvy, I.,
　　Rákosi, L. 1971A (n. subgen.)
Anomoepodidae Ichnites Haubold, H. 1969B
　　(in Saurischia–Prosauropoda, incl.
　　Anomoepus, Apatichnus)
Anomoepus Ichnites Haubold, H. 1969B
　　(in Anomoepodidae)
Anomoiodon Procolophonidae
　　krejcii Ortlam, D. 1967A
Anoplosuchus Estemmenosuchidae Chudinov,
　　P. K. 1968C
　　tenuirostris Chudinov, P. K. 1968C
Anoplotheriidae Artiodactyla–Anoplotheroidea
　　Anoplotherium, Catodontherium, Dacrytherium,
　　Diplobune, Robiacina, Tapirulus
Anoplotherium Anoplotheriidae Jehenne, Y. 1969A
　　commune Bessonnat, G., Dughi, R., Sirugue, F.
　　1969A (ichn.)
　　latipes Bessonnat, G., Dughi, R., Sirugue, F.
　　1969A (ichn.)
Anoplotheroidea Artiodactyla–Ruminantia Sudre, J.
　　1969A
Anourosorex Soricidae Rabeder, G. 1970A
　　densicingulatus Gureev, A. A. 1971A
　　[Shikamainosorex]
　　inexpectatus Gureev, A. A. 1971A
　　japonicus Gureev, A. A. 1971A
　　kormosi Bachmayer, F., Wilson, R. W. 1970A
　　mariae Kretzoi, M. 1962D [Shikamainosorex]
Anourosoricodon Soricidae
　　pidoplichkoi Gureev, A. A. 1971A
Anser Anatidae
　　albifrons Churcher, C. S. 1972C; Jánossy, D.
　　1972A (aff.)
　　anser Jánossy, D. 1972A (aff.)
　　devjatkini Kurochkin, E. N. 1971A
　　fabalis Churcher, C. S. 1972C
anser (Anser)

Anseriformes Aves
　　Incertae sedis: Heterochen
Anserobranta Anatidae Kurochkin, E. N., Ganîa, I. M.
　　1972A
　　tarabukini Kurochkin, E. N., Ganîa, I. M. 1972A
Antarctaspidae Arthrodira–Arctolepida White, E. I.
　　1968A
　　Antarctaspis
Antarctaspis Antarctaspidae White, E. I. 1968A
　　mcmurdoensis White, E. I. 1968A
antarctica (Bothriolepis)
Antarctichnus Ichnites Covacevich C., V.,
　　Lamperein R., C. 1970A (in Rallidae)
　　fuenzalidae Covacevich C., V., Lamperein R., C.
　　1970A
antarcticus (Gyroptychius, Palaeeudyptes)
Antarctolepis Phlyctaenaspidae White, E. I. 1968A
　　gunni White, E. I. 1968A
Antarctonchus Acanthodii incertae sedis
　　White, E. I. 1968A
　　glacialis White, E. I. 1968A
Antarctosaurus Titanosauridae Bonaparte, J. F.,
　　Bossi, G. 1967A
　　wichmannianus Casamiquela, R. M., Corvalán, J.,
　　Franquesa, F. 1969A (cf.)
Anteosauridae Therapsida–Dinocephalia Boonstra,
　　L. D. 1969A
　　Anteosaurus, Paranteosaurus
Anteosaurus Anteosauridae Boonstra, L. D. 1968B;
　　Ricqlès, A. 1972B
　　magnificus Boonstra, L. D. 1969A
Anthichnium Ichnites Haubold, H. 1970A
　　(in Dendrerpetontidae)
　　obtusum [Nanopus] Haubold, H. 1970A
　　quadratum [Nanopus] Haubold, H. 1970A
　　salamandroides [Saurichnites] Haubold, H. 1970A
anthracinus (Eopelobates)
Anthracodromeus Romeriidae Carroll, R. L.,
　　Baird, D. 1972A
　　longipes Carroll, R. L., Baird, D. 1972A
Anthracomys Muridae
　　meini Michaux, J. 1969B
Anthracopus Ichnites Haubold, H. 1970A
　　(in Amphibia)
　　ellangowensis Haubold, H. 1970A
　　saxoniae [Cursipes] Haubold, H. 1970A
Anthracosauria Amphibia–Labyrinthodontia
　　Incl. subord. Schizomeri, Diplomeri, Embolomeri,
　　Seymouriamorpha Anon. 1971AS; Kuhn, O.
　　1969A; Panchen, A. L. 1970A (subord.,
　　incl. Anthracosauridae, Eogyrinidae,
　　Archeriidae); Schultze, H.-P. 1969B
Anthracotheriidae Artiodactyla–Hippopotamoidea
　　Tobien, H. 1971B
　　Anthracotherium, Arretotherium, Brachyodus,
　　Elomeryx, Haplobunodon, Lophiobunodon
Anthracotherium Anthracotheriidae
　　alsaticum Brunet, M. 1970A
　　kalimerianum Melentis, J. K. 1966N (nomen nudum)
　　magnum Bergounioux, F. M., Crouzel, F. 1968B
Anthropoidea Primates Van Valen, L. 1969A (incl.
　　superfam. Ceboidea, Cercopithecoidea,
　　Hominoidea)
Anthus Motacillidae Jánossy, D. 1972A
Antiacodon Homacodontidae
　　pygmaeus Burke, J. J. 1969A (in Dichobunidae)
　　vanvaleni Guthrie, D. A. 1971B (in Dichobunidae)

Antiarchi Placodermi Stensiö, E. 1971A (syst.)
Antidorcas Bovidae
marsupialis
australis Hendey, Q. B., Hendey, H. 1968A
Antigonia Antigoniidae
angusta Stinton, F. C., Nolf, D. 1969A (otol.)
Antigoniidae Beryciformes–Berycoidei
Antigonia
antillensis (Crocodylus)
Antilocapridae Artiodactyla–Bovoidea
Capromeryx, Merycodus, Ramoceros, Sphenophalos,
Tetrameryx
antilopinum (Hipparion)
Antilospira Bovidae
incarinatus Tekkaya, I. 1969A
antipai (Ammodytes)
antiqua (Myxomygale, Paracrax, Plesiobaena,
Promacrauchenia, Prosybris, Tringa, Tyto)
antiquior (Palaeosauropus)
antiquitatis (Coelodonta)
antiquorum (Phoenicopterus)
antiquum (Peratherium)
antiquus (Agriochoerus, Amphilagus, Beatragus, Bison,
Cimexomys, Cryptornis, Hippopotamus
amphibius, Ligerimys, Microchoerus,
Oligosorex, Palaeoloxodon, Papio, Percichthys,
Pliolemmus, Prototomus, Pterodactylus,
Steneofiber castorinus, Sus, Tridentinosaurus)
antirrhopus (Deinonychus)
Antrozous Vespertilionidae
pallidus Miller, W. E. 1971A
antunesi (Rhinobatos)
antverpiensis (Odobenus)
antwerpiensis (Trisopterus)
Anura [Salientia] Amphibia–Lissamphibia
Incl. subord. Proanura, Archaeobatrachia,
Neobatrachia Seiffert, J. 1969B; Severtsov,
A. S. 1969A; Špinar, Z. V. 1970A
Incertae sedis: Quinquevertebron
Anurognathidae Pterosauria–Rhamphorhynchoidea
Anurognathus
Anurognathus Anurognathidae
ammoni Wellnhofer, P. 1970A
anwilensis (Keramidomys)
anzaensis (Synaptomys)
Anzanycteris Vespertilionidae–Nyctophylinae
White, J. A. 1969A
anzensis White, J. A. 1969A
anzensis (Anzanycteris)
aomoriensis (Palaeoloxodon)
aonychoides (Aonyx)
Aonyx Mustelidae
aonychoides Radinsky, L. B. 1968A
Apalolepis Thelodontidae Karatajūtė-Talimaa, V. N.
1968B (in Coelolepididae)
obruchevi Karatajūtė-Talimaa, V. N. 1968B;
Obruchev, D., Karatajūtė-Talimaa, V. N.
1967A
Apatemyidae Insectivora–Apatemyoidea Sudre, J.
1969B; Szalay, F. S. 1968C; West, R. M.
1972C
Apatemys, Eochiromys, Jepsenella, Labidolemur,
Stehlinella
Apatemyoidea Insectivora–Proteutheria
Apatemys Apatemyidae West, R. M., Atkins, E. G.
1971A
bellus Guthrie, D. A. 1971B (cf.)

Apatemys - cont.
downsi West, R. M. 1971A
whitakeri Guthrie, D. A. 1971B
Apateodus Enchodontidae
striatus Goody, P. C. 1969A (in Ichthyotringoidei
incertae sedis)
Apateopholidae Salmoniformes–Ichthyotringoidei
Goody, P. C. 1969B (incl. Apateopholis)
See also Dercetidae
Apateopholis Dercetidae
laniatus [Prionolepis] Goody, P. C. 1969B
(in Apateopholidae)
Apatichnus Ichnites Haubold, H. 1969B
(in Anomoepodidae)
Apatopodidae Ichnites Haubold, H. 1969B
(in Parasuchia; incl. Apatopus)
Apatopus Ichnites Haubold, H. 1969B
(in Apatopodidae)
Apatosaurus Brachiosauridae
ajax Marsh, O. C. 1879J(?)
apenninicus (Lampanyctus)
Apeomys Eomyidae Fahlbusch, V. 1968A
tuerkheimae Fahlbusch, V. 1968A
apertus (Hyracodon)
Aphaneramma Trematosauridae Schultze, H.-P. 1969B
aphanistus (Machairodus)
Aphanius Cyprinodontidae
germaniae Salis, K. 1967A (cf., otol.)
moraviae Brzobohatý, R. 1969A (otol.)
aphantus (Dracontolestes)
Aphataspididae Heterostraci Novitskaia, L. I. 1971B
(in Amphiaspidiformes–Hibernaspidoidei,
incl. Aphataspis, Putoranaspis)
See also Cyathaspididae
Aphataspis Cyathaspididae
kiaeri Novitskaia, L. I. 1971B (in Aphataspididae)
Aphelops Rhinocerotidae Tanner, L. G. 1970A;
Webb, S. D. 1969C
Aphelosaurus Younginiidae
lutevensis Heyler, D. 1969A (in Araeoscelidae)
Aphredoderidae Amblyopsiformes–Aphredoderoidei
Amphiplaga, Asineops, Erismatopterus, Trichophanes
Aphronorus Pentacodontidae
orieli Gazin, C. L. 1969A (in Pantolestidae)
apicalis (Potorous, Stratodus)
apicatus (Coelorhyncus ornatus, Malacocephalus ornatus)
Apidium Parapithecidae Simons, E. L. 1968C
phiomense Simons, E. L. 1971C (reconst.)
apivorus (Pernis)
Aplodinotus Sciaenidae
grunniens Harington, C. R. 1971C; Smith, G. R.,
Lundberg, J. G. 1972A
Aplodontia Aplodontidae
rufa Guthrie, D. A. 1969A
Aplodontidae Rodentia–Aplodontoidea
Allomys, Aplodontia, Haplomys, Meniscomys,
Niglarodon, Tardontia
Aplodontoidea Rodentia
Apoda [Gymnophiona] Amphibia–Lissamphibia
Apodemus Muridae Altuna, J. 1970A; Bartolomei, G.,
Pasa, A. 1970A
alsomyoides Michaux, J. 1970A (cf.)
caesareanus Tchernov, E. 1968B,C
dominans Bruijn, H., Dawson, M. R., Mein, P.
1970A; Kretzoi, M. 1962D
flavicollis Tchernov, E. 1968B
jeanteti Bruijn, H., Dawson, M. R., Mein, P. 1970A

Apodemus - cont.
   levantinus Heller, J. 1970A; Tchernov, E. 1968B,C
   maximus *Thaler, L.* 1972A
   mystacinus Heller, J. 1970A; Malez, M. 1967C (cf.);
      Tchernov, E. 1968B,C
   sylvaticus Boecker, M. et al. 1972A; Chaline, J.
      1969A; Jánossy, D. 1969B; Koenigswald, W.
      1970A, 1972A; Sukhov, V. P. 1970A (cf.);
      Tchernov, E. 1968B
Apodidae   Apodiformes
   Apus
Apodiformes   Aves
Apodops   Caeciliidae *Estes, R., Wake, M. H.* 1972A
   pricei *Estes, R., Wake, M. H.* 1972A
apodus (Ophisaurus)
apogerontus (Paratarpon)
Apogon   Apogonidae
   arambourgi *Stinton, F. C., Nolf, D.* 1969A (otol.)
Apogonidae   Perciformes–Percoidei Svichenskaïa,
      A. A. 1968A
   Apogon
Apopempsinae   Musophagidae *Brodkorb, P.* 1971A
Apopempsis   Musophagidae–Apopempsinae
      Brodkorb, P. 1971A
   meini [Musophaga] Brodkorb, P. 1971A
appendiculata (Lamna)
applanatus (Mugil)
approximata (Solea)
Aprionodon   Carcharhinidae
   acuarius Cappetta, H. C. 1969B, 1970A;
      Telles Antunes, M., Jonet, S. 1970A
Aprionodon
   amekiensis see Negaprion
Aprionodon
   caunnellensis *Cappetta, H. C.* 1969B, 1970A
apsheronica (Parasphyraena)
Apus   Apodidae
   apus Jánossy, D. 1972A (aff.)
   melba Ballmann, P., Adrover, R. 1970A
   submelba *Jánossy, D.* 1972A
apus (Apus)
aquaticus (Scalopus)
aquatilis (Isoptychus)
Aquila   Accipitridae Jánossy, D. 1972A
   chrysaetos Churcher, C. S. 1972C
   fulva Delpech, F. 1968A
   nipalensis Aubekerova, A. P. 1965A (cf.)
   rapax Gania, I. M. 1969A
Aquiladelphis   Pediomyidae *Fox, R. C.* 1970C,
      1971B
   incus *Fox, R. C.* 1971B
   minor *Fox, R. C.* 1971B
aquilensis (Potamotelses)
aquilonius (Baiomys, Peneteius)
aquitanicum (Cricetodon)
aquitanicus (Pristis)
Araeoscelidae   Araeoscelidia
   Tridentinosaurus
   See also Younginiidae
Araeoscelidia   Reptilia–Euryapsida Kuhn, O.
      1969D [Araeoscelomorpha,
      Protorosauria]
   Incertae sedis: Dictybolos
Araeosceloidea see Araeoscelidia

aragonensis (Armantomys, Armantomys aragonensis)
aralensis (Jaxartosaurus)
Aralosaurus   Hadrosauridae–Hadrosaurinae
      Rozhdestvenskiĭ, A. K. 1968C
   tuberiferus *Rozhdestvenskiĭ, A. K.* 1968C
aramaeus (Mesocricetus)
arambourgi (Apogon, Lissoberyx, Sphyrna, Trigla)
araneus (Sorex)
arankae (Lagurus)
Araripesaurus   Ornithocheiridae *Price, L. I.* 1971A
   castilhoi *Price, L. I.* 1971A
Araripesuchus   Notosuchidae Gasparini, Z. B. 1971A
   (in Uruguaysuchidae)
arboraptus (Prosciurus)
arborea (Ardeagrandis, Hyla)
arcadensis (Alluvisorex)
arcanus (Asarotus, Terrarboreus)
Archaeoceti   Cetacea
   Incertae sedis: Chonecetus
Archaeocetus   Balaenopteridae
   fockii Macarovici, N., Zaharia, N. 1968B
      major *Macarovici, N., Zaharia, N.* 1968A
      (n. subsp.)
      minor *Macarovici, N., Zaharia, N.* 1968A
      (n. subsp.)
Archaeolagus   Leporidae
   acaricolus Stevens, M. S., Stevens, J. B., Dawson,
      M. R. 1969A (cf.)
   buangulus Stevens, M. S., Stevens, J. B., *Dawson,
      M. R.* 1969A
   ennisianus Macdonald, J. R. 1970A (cf.)
   macrocephalus Green, M. 1972A (cf.); Macdonald,
      J. R. 1970A
   primigenius Green, M. 1972A; Macdonald, J. R.
      1970A
Archaeolambda   Archaeolambdidae
   planicanina Kielan-Jaworowska, Z. 1968C
Archaeolambdidae   Pantodonta
   Archaeolambda
Archaeolemur   Lemuridae Jolly, C. J. 1970C
Archaeolemurinae   Lemuridae Tattersall, I. 1972A
Archaeolepidotus   Semionotidae
   leonardii Leonardi, P., et al. 1967A
Archaeomaenidae   Pholidophoriformes
   Oreochima, Wadeichthys
Archaeomys   Theridomyidae
   laurillardi Hugueney, M. 1969A
Archaeonycteridae   Chiroptera–Microchiroptera
   Archaeonycteris
Archaeonycteris   Archaeonycteridae Russell, D. E.,
      Sigé, B. 1970A (in Palaeochyropterygidae–
      Archaeonycteridinae)
   revilliodi *Russell, D. E., Sigé, B.* 1970A
   trigonodon Russell, D. E., Sigé, B. 1970A
Archaeopteropus   Pteropodidae Russell, D. E.,
      Sigé, B. 1970A (in ? Microchiroptera–
      Icaronycteridae)
   transiens Jepsen, G. L. 1970A
Archaeopterygidae   Archaeopterygiformes
   Archaeopteryx
Archaeopterygiformes   Aves
Archaeopteryx   Archaeopterygidae Barthel, K. W.
      1970A; Bramwell, C. D. 1971A;
      Brodkorb, P. 1971B; Carey, D. J. 1972A;

argos (Amphiaspis)
argutus (Dinematichthys)
Argyriaspis Siberiaspididae *Novitskaia, L. I.* 1971B
tcherkesovae *Novitskaia, L. I.* 1971B
Argyrolagidae [Microtragulidae] Marsupialia–
Polyprotodonta
Argyrolagus, Microtragulus
Argyrolagus Argyrolagidae
palmeri Simpson, G. G. 1970E,F
parodii Simpson, G. G. 1970E,F
scagliai *Simpson, G. G.* 1970E,F
See also Microtragulus
Argyrolambda Didolodontidae Friant, M. 1967B
Argyropelecus Sternoptychidae
cosmovicii Jerzmańska, J. 1968A
argyropuloi (Lagurus)
aries (Ovis)
Ariidae Siluriformes
Arius
arikarense (Menoceras)
Arikarornis Accipitridae
macdonaldi Macdonald, J. R. 1970A
Ariosoma Congridae
pantanelli Brzobohatý, R. 1967C [Congermuraena,
otol.]
Arius Ariidae
iheringi Moncharmont Zei, M. 1970A (cfr.)
vangionis Rado, G. 1969A (otol.)
arizonae (Baropezia)
Armantomys Gliridae
aragonensis
aragonensis Bruijn, H. 1967A
giganteus *Bruijn, H.* 1967A
armata (Menaspis)
armatum (Diceratherium)
armatus (Dercetis)
armeniacus (Mammuthus)
armigerus (Deltoptychius)
Arminiheringia Borhyaenidae
auceta Simpson, G. G. 1970D
contigua Simpson, G. G. 1970D
Arpadosaurus Anguidae *Meszoely, C. A. M.* 1970A
gazinorum *Meszoely, C. A. M.* 1970A
arquatus (Numenius)
arredondoi (Pulsatrix)
Arretotherium Anthracotheriidae
leptodus Macdonald, J. R. 1970A
Arsinoitheriidae Embrithopoda
Arsinoitherium
Arsinoitherium Arsinoitheriidae
zitteli Remington, J. E. 1968A (reconstr.)
artenensis (Eotragus, Mionictis)
arthritus (Thinocetus)
Arthrodira Placodermi
Incl. subord. Arctolepida, Brachythoraci
Miles, R. S. 1969A; Stensiö, E. 1969A,B,
1971A,B (in Placodermi, incl.
Euarthrodira, Antiarchi)
Incertae sedis: Batteraspis, Cartieraspis, Gaspeaspis,
Kolpaspis, Laurentaspis
Arthrodytes Spheniscidae Simpson, G. G. 1972B
articeps (Rhynchosauroides)
Artiodactyla Mammalia
Incl. subord. Palaeodonta, Suina, Ruminantia
Dechaseaux, C. 1969A
Artiodactypedae see Artiodactypedidae

Artiodactypedidae [Artiodactypedae] Mammalipedia
Panin, N. 1964A
Pecoripeda
arvalidens (Pitymys)
arvalinus (Microtus)
arvalis (Microtus)
arvalis-agrestis (Microtus)
arvaloides (Pitymys)
arvensis (Alauda)
arvernense (Peratherium)
arvernensis (Anancus, Dolichopithecus, Mygatalpa,
Paratyto, Tapirus)
Arvicanthis Muridae Jaeger, J.-J. 1969A
ectos Haas, G. 1972A (cf.); Tchernov, E. 1968B
Arvicola Cricetidae Bouchud, J. 1961C; Chaline, J.
1969A (in Arvicolidae); Heller, J. 1970A;
Koby, F.-E. 1965A
cantiana Koenigswald, W. 1970A, 1972A
greeni-praeceptor Jánossy, D. 1969B (group, in
Arvicolidae)
jordanica *Haas, G.* 1966A(?)
terrestris Altuna, J. 1970A; Boecker, M. 1972A;
Boeuf, O. 1970A; Martin, R. 1968A;
Tchernov, E. 1968B (in Microtidae)
Arvicolidae see Cricetidae
Arvicolinae Cricetidae Anon. 1968BI (origin);
Repenning, C. A. 1968A
arvicolinus (Myospalax)
Asarotidae Asarotiformes *Schaeffer, B.* 1968B
Asarotus
Asarotiformes Actinopterygii–Chondrostei? or
Holostei? *Schaeffer, B.* 1968B
Asarotus Asarotidae *Schaeffer, B.* 1968B
arcanus *Schaeffer, B.* 1968B
Asiacastor Castoridae *Lychev, G. F.,* Aubekerova,
P. A. 1971A
baschanovi *Lychev, G. F.,* Aubekerova, P. A. 1971A
major *Lychev, G. F.,* Aubekerova, P. A. 1971A
asiaticus (Cryptomys, Palaeotragus)
Asiatosuchus Crocodylidae Berg, D. E. 1969A;
Berg, D. E., Crusafont, M. 1970A
germanicus Tobien, H. 1969C
Asineopidae see Aphredoderidae
Asineops Aphredoderidae
squamifrons Rosen, D., Patterson, C. 1969A
(in Asineopidae inc. sed.)
Asinus Equus
asinus (Equus)
Asio Strigidae–Striginae Ballmann, P. 1969B
flammeus Frailey, C. D. 1972A; Gania, I. M. 1969A;
Jánossy, D. 1972A (aff.)
Askeptosauridae see Thalattosauridae
Askeptosauroidea Eosuchia *Kuhn-Schnyder, E.* 1971A
(n. subord., incl. Askeptosauridae)
Askeptosaurus Thalattosauridae
italicus Kuhn-Schnyder, E. 1971A (in
Askeptosauroidea–Askeptosauridae)
Asmithwoodwardia Hyopsodontidae
subtrigona Friant, M. 1967B (in Didolodontidae)
asodes (Uintacyon)
Asoriculus Soricidae
gibberodon [Crocidura, Soriculus kubinyi]
Kretzoi, M. 1962D
aspalax (Myospalax)
asper (Archaephippus)
asperoides (Trigla)

Australopithecinae - cont.
    Leakey, R. E. F., Mungai, J. M., Walker,
        A. C. 1971A, 1972A (E. Rudolf); Mamak, A.
    1970A; Marcozzi, V. 1966A; Robinson, J. T.
    1966B, 1968A, 1972C; Schott, L. 1970B;
    Tobias, P. V. 1968D; Wolpoff, M. H. 1969C,
    1970B, 1971A
Australopithecus   Hominidae Broom, R. 1972A;
    Carney, J., Hill, A., Miller, J. A., Walker, A.
    1971A; Day, M. H. 1969B [Australopithecine];
    Genet-Varcin, E. 1969A; Givens, R. D. 1970A;
    Greene, D. L. 1970B; Groves, C. P., Napier,
    J. R. 1968A; Heiple, K. G., Lovejoy, C. O.
    1971A; Howell, F. C. 1969A; Howell, F. C.,
    Tattersall, I. M. 1971A; Jay, P. 1968B;
    Kochetkova, V. I. 1970A; Khrisanfova, E. N.
    1972A; Leakey, R. E. F. 1971A, 1972A;
    Lovejoy, C. O., Heiple, K. G. 1972A;
    Mann, A. 1968A, 1970A; Minkoff, E. C.
    1972A; Robinson, J. T. 1969A, 1970A,B,
    1971A, 1972A; Rose, B. 1966A; Rosiński, F.
    1970A; Schaller, G. B. 1972A; Thaler, L.
    1971B; Vallois, H. V. 1969G; Wolpoff, M. H.
    1969A; Zihlman, A. L. 1971A
    africanus Butzer, K. W. 1971A,B; Dart, R. A. 1971A;
        Howell, F. C. 1969B (cf.); Jenkins, F. 1972A;
        Lovejoy, C. O. 1971A; Lovejoy, C. O., Heiple,
        K. G. 1970A (reconstr.); Tobias, P. V. 1972B
    boisei Butzer, K. W. 1971A (cf.); Leakey, L. S. B.
        1960F, 1967H, 1971C [Zinjanthropus];
        Leakey, R. E. F. 1970A,B; Tobias, P. V. 1968E
    habilis see Homo
    prometheus Malinas, Y. 1970A
    robustus Butzer, K. W. 1971B; Jenkins, F. 1972A;
        Lovejoy, C. O. 1971A; Tobias, P. V. 1972B
    transvaalensis Broom, R. 1971A
Australosomus   Pholidopleuridae
    longirostris Beltan, L. 1968A
    merlei Beltan, L. 1968A
austriaca (Atherina)
austriacus (Muscardinus pliocaenicus, Myctophum debilis)
austrinum (Alphadon)
Austrosqualodon   Squalodontidae Climo, F. M.,
        Baker, A. N. 1972A
    trirhizodonta Climo, F. M., Baker, A. N. 1972A
autunensis (Charleuxia)
Auxipes see Amphisauroides
Auxis   Scombridae
    minor Anđelković, J. S. 1969A
avellanarius (Muscardinus)
Avenantia   Tapinocephalidae Boonstra, L. D. 1969A
Aves Brodkorb, P. 1971B; Burchak-Abramovich, N. I.
    1967B; Dechaseaux, C. 1969B; Eastham, A.
    1968A; Galton, P. M. 1970B (origin);
    Howard, H. 1972A (type specimens); Iudin,
    K. A. 1970A,B; Kuhn, O. 1971A; Ricqlès, A.
    1971A
avidus (Ptomalestes)
avinoffi (Eryops)
Avipedia   Vertebratichnia
avita (Coturnicops)
avus (Eobrycon, Paratrisopterus)
Aythya   Anatidae
    ferina Churcher, C. S. 1972C
    fuligula Jánossy, D. 1972D (cf.)
    nyroca Jánossy, D. 1972A (cf.)

Azendohsaurus   Ornithischia incertae sedis Dutuit,
        J.-M. 1972B
    laaroussii Dutuit, J.-M. 1972B (comparable to
        Fabrosaurus australis)
aztecus (Nannipus)
babai Otolithus (Sparidarum)
Bachitherium
    serum see Andegameryx
baconicus (Pseudotheridomys)
Baena   Baenidae
    antiqua see Plesiobaena
    arenosa Gaffney, E. S. 1972A (in Baeninae)
Baenidae   Chelonia–Amphichelydia Gaffney, E. S.
        1972A (in Testudines–Cryptodira, incl.
        Trinitichelyinae, Hayemydinae, Eubaeninae,
        Palatobaeninae, Baeninae)
    Baena, Chisternon, Hayemys, Palatobaena,
        Plesiobaena, Stygiochelys, Trinitichelys
    See also Dermatemydidae, Eubaenidae, Neurankylidae
Baenoidea   Chelonia–Amphichelydia Gaffney, E. S.
        1970A
bagajevi (Sicista)
Bagre   Bagridae Greenwood, P. H. 1968B [Bagrus]
Bagridae   Siluriformes
    Bagre, Chrysichthys, Eomacrones
Bagrus see Bagre
bahiai (Sparassocynus)
Bahomys   Cricetidae Chow, M.-ch., Li, Ch.-k. 1965B
    hypsodonta Chow, M.-ch., Li, Ch.-k. 1965B
bai (Madtsoia)
baini (Oudenodon)
Baiomys   Cricetidae
    aquilonius Zakrzewski, R. J. 1969A
bairdi (Lisserpeton, Palatobaena)
bairdii (Mesohippus)
Balaena   Balaenidae
    belgica Plisnier-Ladame, F., Quinet, G. E. 1969A
Balaenidae   Cetacea–Mysticeti
    Balaena, Balaenula
Balaenoptera   Balaenopteridae
    acutorostrata
        cuvierii Caretto, P. G. 1970A
        taiwanica Chiu, H. T. 1972A
Balaenopteridae   Cetacea–Mysticeti
    Archaeocetus, Balaenoptera
Balaenula   Balaenidae Cuscani Politi, P. 1960-61A
balearicus (Myotragus)
Baleiichthys see Pholidophorus
Balistes   Balistidae Cappetta, H. C. 1969B
    capriscus Bauzá Rullán, J. 1967A
    lerichei Bauzá Rullán, J. 1967A
Balistidae   Tetraodontiformes–Balistoidei
    Balistes, Marosichthys
balius (Nectosaurus)
ballesioi (Rhagapodemus)
baltica (Glyptolepis)
bambolii (Oreopithecus)
Bananogmiidae   Elopiformes–Plethodoidea Applegate,
        S. P. 1970A (incl. Bananogmius,
        Paranogmius, Moorevillea)
    Moorevillia
Bananogmius   Thryptodontidae Applegate, S. P. 1970A
        (in Bananogmiidae)
    crieleyi Applegate, S. P. 1970A
    polymicrodus Applegate, S. P. 1970A (cf.)
    zitteli Applegate, S. P. 1970A (cf.)

Bandringa Bandringidae *Zangerl, R.* 1969A
 rayi *Zangerl, R.* 1969A
Bandringidae Cladoselachii *Zangerl, R.* 1969A
 (in Selachii—Ctenacanthoidea)
 Bandringa
Baptanodon see Ophthalmosaurus
barabensis (Cricetulus)
Baranogale Mustelidae
 adroveri Adrover, R. 1966B
Baranomys [Microtodon] Cricetidae Fejfar, O. 1970A
 kowalskii *Kretzoi, M.* 1962D
 loczyi Kretzoi, M. 1962D
Barbastella Vespertilionidae
 barbastellus Koenigswald, W. 1972A
barbastellus (Barbastella)
barberi (Bothremys, Edaphodon)
barbouri (Candelaria, Paenemarmota, Promerycochoerus)
Barbourofelini Felidae—Machairodontinae *Schultz,*
 C. B., Schultz, M. R., Martin, L. D. 1970A
 (n. tribe, incl. Barbourofelis,
 ?Sansanosmilus)
Barbourofelis Felidae—Machairodontinae *Schultz,*
 C. B., Schultz, M. R., Martin, L. D. 1970A
 fricki *Schultz, C. B., Schultz, M. R., Martin, L. D.*
 1970A
 morrisi *Schultz, C. B., Schultz, M. R., Martin, L. D.*
 1970A
 osborni [Ischyrosmilus, Sansanosmilus] Schultz,
 C. B., Schultz, M. R., Martin, L. D. 1970A
 piveteaui [Megantereon] Schultz, C. B., Schultz,
 M. R., Martin, L. D. 1970A(?)
 whitfordi [Eusmilus, Sansanosmilus], Schultz, C. B.,
 Schultz, M. R., Martin, L. D. 1970A(?)
Barbouromeryx Palaeomerycidae
 submilleri Patton, T. H. 1969B (subgen.
 Bouromeryx; in Cervidae—Dromomerycinae)
Barbus Cyprinidae
 bynni Churcher, C. S. 1972C; Greenwood, P. H.
 1968B (cf.)
 orientalis Gabelaia, Ts. D. 1970A
 rudeli Touraine, F. 1971A,B
Barillopus Ichnites
 arctus Haubold, H. 1970A (in Microsauria)
 confusus Haubold, H. 1970A
 ungifer Haubold, H. 1970A
baringensis (Papio)
barnstonensis (Dalatias)
Baropezia Ichnites
 arizonae [Allopus] Haubold, H. 1970A
 eakini Haubold, H. 1970A
 sydnensis [Sauropus] Haubold, H. 1970A
Baropus see Limnopus
Barosaurus Titanosauridae Bakker, R. T. 1968A
 (restor.)
barrierei (Cricetus)
barrionuevoi (Proterochampsa)
barroisi (Amia)
barstowensis (Copemys, Protolabis)
barthassadensis (Sciaena)
barthii (Chirotherium)
bartholomaii (Changpeipus)
Barysoma Kannemeyeriidae
 lenzii Bonaparte, J. F. 1972A
Barytheriidae Proboscidea—?Barytherioidea
 Barytherium
Barytherium Barytheriidae Savage, R. J. G. 1969A

baschanovi (Asiacastor)
baschkirica (Mimomys)
basilaris (Entoptychus)
Basilemys Dermatemydidae Sahni, A. 1972A
basilii (Martes)
Basilosauridae [Zeuglodontidae] Cetacea—Archaeoceti
 Mchedlidze, G. A. 1970B [Zeuglodontidae;
 incl. Basilosaurus, Prozeuglodon,
 Microzeuglodon, Platyosphys?]
 Basilosaurus
Basilosaurus Basilosauridae Halstead, L. B.,
 Middleton, J. 1972A
 cetoides Applegate, S. P. 1969-70B
bassa (Mauchchunkia)
bassanianus (Scophthalmus)
bassanii (Macrocnemus)
Bassariscus Procyonidae Graham, R. E. 1960B
 astutus Beaumont, G. de 1968D
 parvus Webb, S. D. 1969C
 sumichrasti Beaumont, G. de 1968D
bassleri (Podocnemis)
bataar (Tarbosaurus)
Bataguridae Chelonia
 Grayemys
batei (Myotragus, Rattus)
Bathornis Cariamidae Cracraft, J. 1968B, 1971A
 (in Bathornithidae)
 celeripes Cracraft, J. 1968B
 cursor Cracraft, J. 1968B
 fricki *Cracraft, J.* 1968B
 geographicus Cracraft, J. 1968B, 1971A
 minor *Cracraft, J.* 1971A
 veredus Cracraft, J. 1971A
Bathornithidae Ralliformes Cracraft, J. 1968B, 1971A
 (incl. Bathornis, Paracrax, Eutreptornis)
 See also Cariamidae
Bathyergidae Rodentia—Thryonomyoidea
 Cryptomys
Bathygenys Merycoidodontidae
 alfa Ferrusquia-Villafranca, I. 1969A
 reevesi *Wilson, J. A.* 1971A
bathygnathum (Erethizon)
Bathylagidae Salmoniformes—Argentinoidei
 Bathylagus
Bathylagus Bathylagidae
 obesa *Satō, J.* 1962A
 sencta *Satō, J.* 1962A, 1968A
Bathyopsis Uintatheriidae
 fissidens Guthrie, D. A. 1971B
Bathysoma ?Veliferidae Patterson, C. 1968B
Batodon Deltatheriidae
 tenuis Lillegraven, J. A. 1969B (in Palaeoryctidae)
Batoidea Chondrichthyes—Elasmobranchii
 Incl. subord. Pristoidea, Rhinobatoidea,
 Torpedinoidea, Rajoidea, Myliobatoidea
 Disler, N. N. 1966A
Batrachichnidae Ichnites *Haubold, H.* 1970A
 (in Temnospondyli—Edopoidea, incl.
 Batrachichnus, Nanipes)
Batrachichnus Ichnites Haubold, H. 1970A
 (in Batrachichnidae)
 jacksonensis [Notalacerta] Haubold, H. 1970A
 obscurus Haubold, H. 1970A(?)
 parvus [Dromillopus] Haubold, H. 1970A(?)
 plainvillensis Haubold, H. 1970A
Batrachoididae Batrachoidiformes
 Porichthys

Batrachoidiformes Teleostei
Batrachopodidae Ichnites *Haubold, H.* 1969B
(in Crocodylia, incl. Batrachopus)
Batrachopus Ichnites Haubold, H. 1969B
(in Batrachopodidae); Montenat, C. 1970A
(cf.)
dispar Ostrom, J. H. 1968A; Peoples, J. W. 1967A
(thecodont)
varians *Demathieu, G.* 1970B
Batrachosauria Labyrinthodontia Panchen, A. L. 1970A
(order, incl. subord. Anthracosauria,
Gephyrostegoidea, Seymouriamorpha)
See also Seymouriamorpha
Batrachosauroides Batrachosauroididae
gotoi *Estes, R.* 1969F
Batrachosauroididae Urodela—Ambystomatoidea
Batrachosauroides
See also Plethodontidae
Batrachosuchus Brachyopidae
browni Cosgriff, J. W. 1969A; Welles, S. P.,
Estes, R. 1969A
watsoni Cosgriff, J. W. 1969A; Welles, S. P.,
Estes, R. 1969A
Batropetes [Petrobates] Captorhinomorpha incertae
sedis *Carroll, R. L., Gaskill, P.* 1971A
truncatus [Petrobates] Carroll, R. L., Gaskill, P.
1971A (n. comb.)
Batropetidae Cotylosauria—Captorhinomorpha
Kuhn, O. 1972A (in Captorhinomorpha—
Captorhinida)
Batteraspis Arthrodira incertae sedis *Pageau, Y.* 1969B
fulgens *Pageau, Y.* 1969B
Bauriamorpha Therapsida—Theriodontia Mendrez,
C. H. 1972D [Scaloposauria]
Incertae sedis: Regisaurus
Baurusuchidae Crocodilia—Sebecosuchia Walker, A. D.
1970A (in Crocodylomorpha—Paracrocodylia)
Cynodontosuchus
Bauzaia Ophidiidae
acutangula [Otol. (Gadidarum) acutangulus]
Robba, E. 1970A (otol.)
difformis [Otol. (Gadidarum) difformis] Robba, E.
1970A (otol.)
gibba [Otol. (Ophidium) gibbus] Robba, E. 1970A
(otol.)
joachimica Gaemers, P. A. M. 1969A (otol.),
1971A (otol.)
ornatissima *Robba, E.* 1970A (otol.)
tuberosa *Robba, E.* 1970A (otol.)
bavarica (Alectoris)
bavaricum (Deinotherium)
bavaricus (Alligatorellus beaumonti, Pseudarctos)
bayeri (Eopelobates, Macromerion)
baylei (Haptodus)
baylorensis (Seymouria)
bazarovi (Citellus itancinicus)
beadnelli (Palaeomastodon)
beasleyi (Rhynchosauroides)
Beatomus [Beatomys] Cylindrodontidae
Shevyreva, N. S. 1972A
bisus [Beatomys] *Shevyreva, N. S.* 1972A
Beatomys Cylindrodontidae *Shevyreva, N. S.*
1971D, 1972A (nomen nudum)
bisus *Shevyreva, N. S.* 1971D, 1972A
(nomen nudum)

Beatragus Bovidae
antiquus Cooke, H. B. S., Coryndon, S. C. 1970A
(cf.)
beaudryi (Kolpaspis)
beaumonti (Alligatorellus, Tertiariaporphyrula)
becassi (Charadriipeda)
bechsteini (Myotis)
becki (Salichnium)
Beckiasorex Soricidae *Dalquest, W. W.* 1972A
hibbardi *Dalquest, W. W.* 1972A
becklesii (Plagiaulax)
becksmanni (Triasocapsula)
beecheyi (Citellus)
Begertheriinae Rhinocerotidae *Beliaeva, E. I.* 1971A
Begertherium Rhinocerotidae—Begertheriinae
Beliaeva, E. I. 1971A
borissiaki *Beliaeva, E. I.* 1971A
beinerti (Palaeosiren)
Belemnacanthus Astrolepidae Stensiö, E. 1969B
[Grossaspis, in Antiarchi incertae sedis]
Belesodon Traversodontidae Romer, A. S. 1969A,C
(in Chiniquodontidae)
magnificus Bonaparte, J. F. 1972A
(in Chiniquodontidae); Ricqlès, A. 1969A
(in Cynognathidae)
belgica (Balaena, Teilhardina)
beliajevae (Platybelodon)
beliajevi (Teleolophus)
bellmanni (Promastodonsaurus)
bellus (Apatemys, Otolithus (Congridarum))
Belodon see Mystriosuchus
Belonochasma Pterodactylidae
aenigmaticum Wellnhofer, P. 1970A (fish)
Belonostomus Aspidorhynchiae Casier, E.,
Taverne, L. 1971A; Taverne, L. 1969B
longirostris Sahni, A. 1972A
Belosteus Trematosteidae Stensiö, E. 1969A,B
benedeni (Gadus, Isurus, Trisopterus)
Benedenius Styracopteridae Kazantseva, A. A. 1971A
benedentatus (Oxydactylus)
bengalensis (Prionailurus)
bensonensis (Aluralagus)
Bensonomys Cricetidae
meadensis Hibbard, C. W. 1972A (in Muridae—
Cricetinae)
Benthesikyme see Dercetis
Benthosuchidae Temnospondyli—Stereospondyli
Gorskii, V. P. 1963A
Benthosuchus, Thoosuchus
Benthosuchus Benthosuchidae Ivakhnenko, M. F.
1971A; Schultze, H.-P. 1969B
korobkovi *Ivakhnenko, M. F.* 1972A
sushkini Shishkin, M. A. 1968B
beogradensis (Sardinella)
beremendensis (Hypolagus)
Beremendia Soricidae
fissidens Gureev, A. A. 1971A; Jánossy, D. 1969B;
Koenigswald, W. 1971A
Beremendina Soricidae—Soricinae *Gureev, A. A.* 1971A
(n. subtr., in Blarinini)
bergi (Tungussogyrinus)
Bergisuchus Sebecosuchia incertae sedis *Kuhn, O.*
1968C
dietrichbergi *Kuhn, O.* 1968C
berislavicus (Palaeotragus)

Blarina - cont.
    simplicidens Gureev, A. A. 1971A
Blarinella   Soricidae Bruijn, H., Dawson, M. R.,
    Mein, P. 1970A
Blarinoides   Soricidae
    mariae Gureev, A. A. 1971A
blasii (Rhinolophus)
Blastomeryx   Palaeomerycidae
    advena Macdonald, J. R. 1970 (subgen.
        Pseudoblastomeryx, in Cervidae)
    elegans Patton, T. H. 1969B (in Cervidae—
        Palaeomerycinae)
    gemmifer Webb, S. D. 1969C
    primus Macdonald, J. R. 1970A
        (subgen. Problastomeryx,
        in Cervidae)
Blattoidealestes   Scaloposauridae Boonstra, L. D. 1969A
Blicca   Cyprinidae
    pliocenicus Sychevskaia, E. K., Lebedev, V. D. 1971A
blicki (Longirostromeryx)
Blinasaurus   Brachyopidae Cosgriff, J. W. 1969A
    henwoodi Cosgriff, J. W. 1969A; Welles, S. P.,
        Estes, R. 1969A
    wilkinsoni Cosgriff, J. W. 1969A
Blochiidae see Xiphiidae
bobac (Marmota)
Bobbschaefferia   Didelphidae Paula Couto, C. 1970A
    fluminensis Paula Couto, C. 1970A (n. comb.)
Bodianus see Symphodus
boeckhi (Protarctos)
bogdanovi (Dolomys)
bogerti (Paraderma)
bohemicum (Diplovertebron)
bohemicus (Hypospondylus)
bohlini (Neomys)
Boidae   Squamata—Ophidia
    Albaneryx, Bransateryx, Cadurceryx, Charina, Eryx,
        Madtsoia
boisei (Australopithecus)
boissieri (Eurypholis)
boixedatensis (Pachynolophus)
bolivari (Testudo)
boliviana (Branisella)
bolivianus (Incamys)
bolkayi (Dolomys episcopalis)
Bolodon   Paulchoffatiidae
    crassidens Hahn, G. 1969A, 1971A
    elongatus Hahn, G. 1969A
    osborni Hahn, G. 1969A, 1971A
?Bolosauridae   Cotylosauria—Captorhinomorpha
        Kuhn, O. 1969D (in Bolosauromorpha—
        Bolosauria)
    Bolosaurus
Bolosaurus   Bolosauridae
    striatus Carroll, R. L., Gaskill, P. 1971A
bombifrons (Bootherium, Scaphiopus)
bombina (Bombina)
Bombina   Discoglossidae Vergnaud-Grazzini, C. 1970A
    bombina Iskakova, K. I. 1969A (cf.)
        (in Bombinidae)
Bombinidae see Discoglossidae
bonali (Hemitragus jemlahicus)
bonapartei (Argentinosuchus, Chanaresuchus)
Bonapartia   Gonostomatidae
    spina Heinrich, W.-D. 1969B (otol.)
bonasus (Bison)

bonii (Clupea)
bonneri (Pteranodon)
bonus (Tragocerus)
boonstrai (Hipposaurus)
Boops   Sparidae
    . roulei Cappetta, H. C. 1969B (aff.)
Bootherium   Bovidae
    bombifrons Kraege, H. 1970A
boothi (Spermophilus)
Borealestes   Docodontidae Waldman, M.,
        Savage, R. J. G. 1972A
    serendipitus Waldman, M., Savage, R. J. G. 1972A
borealis (Eotitanops, Peridiomys)
Boreaspis   Cephalaspidae Janvier, P. 1971A
Boremys   Neurankylidae Powell, J. S. 1969A
    pulchra Gaffney, E. S. 1972A (in Baenidae)
Boreodon   Didelphidae
    matutinus Sahni, A. 1972A (in Stagodontidae)
Boreofiber   Castoridae Radulesco, C., Samson, P.
        1972A
    wenzensis [Steneofiber] Radulesco, C., Samson, P.
        1972A
Boreosaurus   Brachyopidae
    thorslundi Cosgriff, J. W. 1969A; Welles, S. P.,
        Estes, R. 1969A (in Stereospondyli
        incertae sedis)
Boreosomus   Acrolepidae Beltan, L. 1968A
        (in Palaeoniscidae)
    piveteaui Ørvig, T. 1968B
Borhyaenidae   Marsupialia—Polyprotodonta
    Angelocabrerus, Arminiheringia, Patene, Thylacosmilus
borisovi (Zaisanamynodon)
borissiaki (Begertherium, Eotrigonias)
bornemanni (Rhynchosauroides)
Borophagus   Canidae Akersten, W. A. 1972A;
        Bjork, P. R. 1970A; Shotwell, J. A. 1970A
    diversidens Dalquest, W. W. 1968A; Hibbard, C. W.
        1972A
borsoni (Mammut)
borysthenica (Geoemyda)
Bos   Bovidae Guenther, E. W. 1967B; Prasad, K. N.,
        Satsangi, P. P. 1962B; Torres Perezhidalgo, T.
        1971A
    brachyceros Churcher, C. S. 1972C
    latifrons Khan, E. 1970A
    namadicus Khatri, A. P. 1966A
    primigenius Ambrosetti, P. 1967A; Apostol, L.,
        Vicoveanu, D. 1970A; Biddittu, I.,
        Cassoli, P. 1968A; Boeuf, O. 1970A;
        Bonifay, M.-F. 1967A, 1968B; Bouchud, J.
        1968C; Chrzanowska, W. 1971A; Churcher,
        C. S. 1972C; David, E., Frachon, J.-C.,
        Sattonnet, R. 1968A; David, L., et al. 1972A;
        Degerbøl, M., Fredskild, B. 1970A; Delpech, F.
        1968A, 1969A; Gautier, A. 1968A; Martin, R.
        1968A; Melentis, J. K. 1966I,P; Petronio, C.
        1970A; Prat, F. 1968A
    trochoceros David, A. I., Lungu, A. N. 1972A;
        Vekua, A. K., Mafskhonashvili, K. G. 1970A
Bosdagius   Ursidae Sickenberg, O. 1970A
    felinus Sickenberg, O. 1970A
Boselaphus   Bovidae Clutton-Brock, J. 1970A
Bothidae   Pleuronectiformes—Pleuronectoidei
    Lepidorhombus

Bothremys Pelomedusidae
  barberi [Podocnemis, P. alabamae]
    Zangerl, R. 1968A
  cooki Zangerl, R. 1968A
Bothriceps Brachyopidae
  australis Cosgriff, J. W. 1969A; Welles, S. P.,
    Estes, R. 1969A
  major Welles, S. P., Estes, R. 1969A
Bothriolepis [Bothryolepis] Astrolepidae
  Bel'skaïa, T. N. 1960A; Gilbert-Tomlinson, J.
    1968A; Ïavorskiĩ, V. I., Rzhonsnitskaïa, M. A.
    1967A; Stensiö, E. 1969B (in Bothriolepididae);
    Taylor, K. 1972A
  antarctica White, E. I. 1968B
  canadensis Ørvig, T. 1968B
  coloradensis Pampe, W. R. 1969A
  prima Garkusha, M. P. et al. 1971A (cf.)
Bothryolepis see Bothriolepis
bottae (Nematonotus, Thomomys)
botti (Scomberomorus)
boulei (Oioceros)
Bourbonnella Aeduellidae Heyler, D. 1969A
  guilloti Heyler, D. 1969A (reconstr.)
Bouromeryx Barbouromeryx
Bovidae Artiodactyla—Bovoidea Burchak-
    Abramovich, N. I. 1970A
  Adenota, Aepyceros, Alcelaphus, Antidorcas,
    Antilospira, Beatragus, Bison, Bootherium,
    Bos, Boselaphus, Bubalus, Capra,
    Damaliscus, Eotragus, Gazella, Gazellospira,
    Helicotragus, Hemibos, Hemitragus,
    Hippotragus, Homoioceras, Hypsodontus,
    Ioribos, Kobus, Leptobos, Makapania,
    Megalovis, Menelikia, Myotragus,
    Nemorhoedus, Oioceros, Oreamnos, Oryx,
    Ovibos, Ovis, Pachytragus, Palaeoreas,
    Palaeoryx, Parabos, Parastrepsiceros,
    Parmularius, Pontoceros, Proamphibos,
    Probison, Prostrepsiceros, Protoryx,
    Protragelaphus, Protragoceros, Pultiphagonides,
    Qurliqnoria, Redunca, Rupicapra, Saiga,
    Soergelia, Sporadotragus, Strepsiceros, Symbos,
    Syncerus, Tragocerus, Ugandax
bowleri (Sminthosinis)
boycei (Cyrbasiodon)
boylii (Peromyscus)
brabantica (Eochelone)
brabanticus (Polyacrodus)
brachycephalus (Brontops)
Brachychampsa Crocodylidae
  montana Sahni, A. 1972A
Brachiosauridae Saurischia—Sauropodomorpha
    Apatosaurus, Camarasaurus
Brachiscirtetes see Brachyscirtetes
brachyceps (Capatanka)
brachyceros (Bos)
Brachychirotherium Ichnites Freyberg, B. 1965B
  circaparvum Demathieu, G. 1971A
  coburgense Sarjeant, W. A. S. 1967A
  hassfurtense Welzel, E. 1968A
  tintanti Demathieu, G. 1971A
brachycoelous (Pleuristion)
brachydactylum (Ichnium)
Brachydeiridae Arthrodira—Brachythoraci
  (Incl. Brachydiridae, Oxyosteidae, Synaucheniidae
    of Stensiö) Stensiö, E. 1969A,B
    [Brachydiridae, in Pachyosteomorphi—
    ?Parapachyostei]

Brachydeiridae - cont.
  Brachydeirus, ?Kiangyosteus, Oxyosteus,
    Synauchenia
Brachydeirus Brachydeiridae Stensiö, E. 1969A,B
    [Brachydirus, in Brachydiridae]
brachydens (Cricotillus, Pliopygerethmus)
Brachydiridae see Brachydeiridae
Brachydirus see Brachydeirus
Brachyerix Erinaceidae
  incertis [Talpa incerta, Metechinus fergusoni]
    Rich, T. H. V., Rich, P. V. 1971A (n. comb.)
  macrotis [Metechinus marslandensis] Rich, T. H. V.,
    Rich, P. V. 1971A
brachygnathum (Coendou)
brachygnathus (Hypolagus, Macroneomys, Plesiogulo)
Brachyhyops Choeropotamidae
  wyomingensis Wilson, J. A. 1971B
    (in Entelodontidae)
Brachylophosaurus Hadrosauridae
  canadensis Heaton, M. J. 1972A
Brachyodon see Gobielodon
brachyodon (Megalagus)
brachyodonta (Didelphis)
Brachyodus Anthracotheriidae Bergounioux, F. M.,
    Crouzel, F. 1968B
  manchharensis Prasad, K. N. 1964C, 1967A
  onoideus Melentis, J. K. 1966N
Brachyopidae Temnospondyli—Brachyopoidea
    Batrachosuchus, Blinasaurus, Boreosaurus,
    Bothriceps, Brachyops, Enosuchus,
    ?Hadrokkosaurus, Indobrachyops,
    Pelorocephalus, Phrynosuchus, Plagiorophus,
    Trucheosaurus, ?Tungussogyrinus,
    ?Tupilakosaurus
Brachyopoidea Temnospondyli—Stereospondyli
Brachyops Brachyopidae
  laticeps Cosgriff, J. W. 1969A; Welles, S. P.,
    Estes, R. 1969A
brachyops (Nimravus)
Brachyostreus Trematosteidae Stensiö, E. 1969A,B
Brachypotherium Rhinocerotidae Bonis, L. de 1969A,
    1970A; Gand, G. 1971A (ichn.)
  heinzelini Heissig, K. 1971A
  lewisi Hooijer, D. A., Patterson, B. 1972A
Brachypsalini Mustelidae Webb, S. D. 1969C
    (n. name, tribe, incl. Paroligobunis,
    Brachypsalis, Brachypsaloides, Sthenictis)
Brachypsalis Mustelidae
  pristinus Webb, S. D. 1969C
Brachypsaloides Mustelidae Webb, S. D. 1969C
  modicus Webb, S. D. 1969C (n. comb.)
brachyptera (Amphiplaga)
brachypternus (Phenacodus)
brachypterygius (Sphenocephalus)
Brachyrhynchocyon Canidae
  douglasi Macdonald, J. R. 1970A
Brachyscirtetes Dipodidae
  robustus Savinov, P. F. 1970A [Brachiscirtetes;
    in Allactaginae]
Brachytherium Proterotheriidae Friant, M. 1967B
    [Epitherium]
Brachythoraci Arthrodira (incl. Pachyosteomorphi,
    Coccosteomorphi of Stensiö)
brachyurus (Acanthion)
bradyi (Hadrokkosaurus, Rotodactylus)
? Bradyodonti Elasmobranchii incertae sedis
    Bendix-Almgreen, S. E. 1968A

Bradysaurus   Pareiasauridae Boonstra, L. D. 1969 A
brailloni (Occitanomys)
brama (Notelops)
Bramapithecus   Hominidae Pilbeam, D. R. 1969A
Branchierpeton   Micromelerpetontidae Boy, J. A. 1972B
    amblystomus [Branchiosaurus]Boy, J. A. 1972B
Branchiosauridae   Amphibia—Dissorophoidea Boy, J. A.
        1971A, 1972B
    Branchiosaurus, Leptorophus
Branchiosaurus   Branchiosauridae
    amblystomus see Branchierpeton
    caducus Boy, J. A. 1972B
    petrolei Boy, J. A. 1972B (subgen. Protriton
        n. rank)
    salamandroides Boy, J. A. 1972B (n. subgen.
        Branchiosaurus)
Branchiosaurus   Branchiosaurus
brandti (Microtus)
branisai (Gasteroclupea)
Branisamys   Caviomorpha incertae sedis Hoffstetter, R.,
        Lavocat, R. 1970A
    luribayensis Hoffstetter, R., Lavocat, R. 1970A
Branisella   Primates incertae sedis Hoffstetter, R.
        1969B (in ?Omomyidae)
    boliviana Hoffstetter, R. 1969B
branneri (Eobrycon)
Brannerion   Elopidae
    vestitum Silva Santos, R. 1971A
Bransateryx   Boidae—Erycinae Hoffstetter, R.,
        Rage, J.-C. 1972A
    vireti Hoffstetter, R., Rage, J.-C. 1972A
Bransatoglis [Branssatoglis] Gliridae
    concavidens Hugueney, M. 1969A
branssatensis (Piezodus)
Branssatoglis see Bransatoglis
Branta   Anatidae Churcher, C. S. 1972C
    canadensis Feduccia, J. A., Rich, P. V. 1972A;
        Tate, J., Martin, D. 1969A
brasiliensis (Gomphodontosuchus, Mesosaurus,
        Podocnemis)
Braunosteidae see Trematosteidae
Braunosteus   Trematosteidae Stensiö, E. 1969A,B
        (in Braunosteidae)
bravoi (Canariomys)
Brazilosaurus   Reptilia incertae sedis
    sanpauloensis Zullo, V. A. 1969A
brecciensis (Microtus)
bredai (Sciurus, Spermophilinus)
Bregmaceros   Gadidae
    albyi Anđelković, J. S. 1969A
        (in Bregmacerotidae); Anfossi, G.,
        Mosna, S. 1971A (otol.); Weiler, W. 1971B
        (otol.)
    catulus Anfossi, G., Mosna, S. 1969A (otol.);
        Brzobohatý, R. 1967C (otol., in
        Bregmacerotidae)
    filamentosus Arambourg, C. 1966A; Haghipour, A.,
        Brants, A. 1971A
Bregmacerotidae see Gadidae
bressana (Pliopetaurista)
bressanus (Equus)
brevicauda (Blarina)
breviceps (Aelurosaurus, Arctognathus, Enosuchus,
        Kritosaurus, Petaurus)
brevicostatus (Hybodus)
brevicranius (Miodugong)

brevidens (Steneosaurus)
breviramus (Buisnictis)
brevirhinus (Ursavus)
brevirostre (Ronzotherium)
brevirostris (Alces, Dinodontosaurus, Eozanclus, Hyaena,
        Ramapithecus)
brevirostrus   (Hyaenodon)
brevis (Carangopsis, Cryptobalistes, Democricetodon
        minor, Lepidocottus, Strix, Varhostichthys)
brevitertius (Dromiceiomimus)
briatextensis (Entelodon depereti)
bridgeri (Sciuravus)
brilli (Coloraderpeton)
brinki (Hipposaurus, Prorubidgea)
brodiei (Prorubidgea, Sycosaurus)
brodkorbi (Paraptenodytes)
broggii (Incacetus)
broili (Lunaspis)
Broiliana   Mustelidae
    nobilis Beaumont, G. 1968D
Broilina   Gemuendinidae Stensiö, E. 1969B, 1971A
        (in Rhenanida)
    heroldi Stensiö, E. 1971A
bronni (Acanthodes)
Brontops   Brontotheriidae
    brachycephalus Ferrusquía-Villafranca, I. 1969A (cf.)
Brontotheriidae   Perissodactyla—Brontotherioidea
        Friant, M. 1970B [Titanotheriidae];
        Gabuniĭa, L. K. 1970A
    Brontops, Brontotherium, Eotitanops,
        Lambdotherium, Mesatirhinus, Palaeosyops,
        Rhinotitan
Brontotherium   Brontotheriidae Crockett, C. T. 1970B
broomi (Elephas, Makapania, Papio)
Broomicephalus   Gorgonopsidae—Rubidgeinae
    laticeps [Dinogorgon, Rubidgea] Sigogneau, D. 1970A
Broomichnium   Ichnites
    permianum Haubold, H. 1970A (in Dissorophidae)
Broomisauridae see Gorgonopsidae—Gorgonopsinae
Broomisaurus   Gorgonopsidae—Gorgonopsinae
    planiceps [Scymnorhinus] Sigogneau, D. 1970A
    rubidgei see Leontocephalus
Brosmius   Gadidae
    fuchsianus Anđelković, J. S. 1969A
    murdjadjensis Anđelković, J. S. 1969A
Brotulidae see Ophidiidae
Brouffia   Romeriidae Carroll, R. L., Baird, D. 1972A
    orientalis Carroll, R. L., Baird, D. 1972A
Broughia   Parasemionotidae Beltan, L. 1968A
browni (Batrachosuchus, Camptosaurus, Ceratodus,
        Delahomeryx)
bruijni (Gliravus)
brumpti (Euthecodon)
brunensis (Palaeosauropus)
brunonis (Neocometes)
brunswickii (Rhynchosauroides)
brusinai (Sparus)
bruxelliensis (Rhinobatos)
bryanti (Litoptychus)
Bryantolepis   Phlyctaenaspidae Stensiö, E. 1969B,
        1971A (in Spinothoracidi—Dolichothoraci)
Brychaetus see Brychetus
Brychetus   Osteoglossidae
    caheni Taverne, L. 1969A [Brychaetus]
    muelleri Cappetta, H. C. 1972B [aff.; Brychaetus]
buangulus (Archaeolagus)

Bubalus Bovidae
 palaeindicus Khatri, A. P. 1966A
bubalus (Leuciscus)
Bubo see Paratyto
Bucconidae Piciformes
 Primobucco
Bucephala Anatidae
 albeola Feduccia, J. A., Rich, P. V. 1972A
 angustipes Jánossy, D. 1972A
 clangula Boecker, M., et al. 1972A
Bucerotidae Coraciiformes
 Cryptornis
Buchanosteus Coccosteidae Miles, R. S. 1971B;
  Stensiö, E. 1969B, 1971A
  (in ? Spinothoracidi)
bucheri (Protaspis)
budensis (Serranus)
Buettneria see Metoposaurus
bufo (Bufo)
Bufo Bufonidae Chantell, C. J. 1970A (?);
  Holman, J. A. 1967B; Malez, M. 1967C;
  Vergnaud-Grazzini, C., Młynarski, M. 1969A
  [Pliobatrachus; in Palaeobatrachidae]
 bufo Iskakova, K. I. 1969A (cf.); Vergnaud-
  Grazzini, C. 1970A (cf.)
 hibbardi Chantell, C. J. 1971A (cf.)
 marinus
  horribilis Vergnaud-Grazzini, C. 1968B (cf.)
 paracnemis Vergnaud-Grazzini, C. 1968B (cf.)
 valentinensis Chantell, C. J. 1971A; Holman,
  J. A. 1970A
 viridis Iskakova, K. I. 1969A (cf.); Vergnaud-
  Grazzini, C. 1970A (cf.)
 woodhousei
  bexarensis Holman, J. A. 1969D
Bufonidae Anura–Neobatrachia
 Bufo
Buginbaatar ?Cimolomyidae Kielan-Jaworowska, Z.,
  Sochava, A. V. 1969A
 transaltaiensis Kielan-Jaworowska, Z.,
  Sochava, A. V. 1969A
Buisnictis Mustelidae
 breviramus Bjork, P. R. 1970A
 burrowsi Hibbard, C. W. 1972A
bullatus (Gallimimus)
bumpi (Proheteromys)
Bungartius Dinichthyidae Stensiö, E. 1969A,B
  (in Pachyostei incertae sedis)
Bunolophodon Anancus
Bunolophodon Gomphotherium
Bunophorus Diacodectidae [Wasatchia] Van Valen, L.
  1971C
 etsagicus Guthrie, D. A. 1971B (in Dichobunidae)
 gazini Guthrie, D. A. 1971B (in Dichobunidae)
burchelli (Equus)
Burhinidae Charadriiformes
 Milnea
burkemorani (Greererpeton)
Burnetidae see Burnetiidae
Burnetiidae [Burnetidae] Therapsida–Gorgonopsia
 Proburnetia, Styracocephalus
Burramyidae see Phalangeridae
Burramys Phalangeridae Imaizumi, Y. 1968A;
  Turnbull, W. D., Lundelius, E. L. 1970A
 parvus Anon. 1966BW
burrowsi (Buisnictis)
bursae (Allocricetus)

bursarius (Geomys)
bursauxi (Enchodus)
buselaphus (Alcelaphus)
bussoni (Wellesaurus)
Buteo Accipitridae
 buteo Ganîa, I. M. 1969A
 circoides Kurochkin, E. N. 1968C
 lagopus Ganîa, I. M. 1969A
 pusillus Ballmann, P. 1969A
buteo (Buteo)
butleri (Hybodus)
buxgovianum (Catodontherium)
Buxolestes Pantolestidae Jaeger, J.-J. 1970B
 hammeli Jaeger, J.-J. 1970B
bynni (Barbus)
Byssacanthoides Ischnacanthidae
 debenhami White, E. I. 1968A
Byssacanthus Astrolepidae Stensiö, E. 1969B
  (in Antiarchi incertae sedis)
bystrowi (Edaphaspis)
caballus (Equus)
cabindensis (Scyliorhinus)
cabrerai (Didelphopsis)
cadlei (Leontocephalus)
caducus (Branchiosaurus)
Cadurceryx Boidae–Erycinae Hoffstetter, R.,
  Rage, J.-C. 1972A
 filholi Hoffstetter, R., Rage, J.-C. 1972A
Cadurcodon Amynodontidae Beliaeva, E. I. 1970A
caeca (Talpa)
Caeciliidae Apoda Taylor, E. H. 1968A
 Apodops, Ichthyophis, Prohypogeophis
Caenagnathidae ?Saurischia–Theropoda Cracraft, J.
  1971B (in Aves–Caenagnathiformes)
 Caenagnathus
Caenagnathus Caenagnathidae
 collinsi Cracraft, J. 1971B
Caenolestidae Marsupialia–Caenolestoidia Hayman,
  D. L., et al. 1971A
caesareanus (Apodemus)
caheni (Brychetus)
cahirinus (Acomys)
Cainotheriidae Artiodactyla–Cainotheroidea
 Cainotherium
Cainotherium Cainotheriidae
 miocaenicum Telles Antunes, M. 1961F
caledoniae (Acherontiscus)
Calidris Scolopacidae Jánossy, D. 1972A
calidus Otolithus (Crangidarum)
californianus (Zalophus)
californicus (Castor, Ichthyosaurus, Lepus, Microtus,
  Smilodon)
californiensis (Mancalla)
caliodorensis (Steneofiber depereti)
Calippus Equidae Waldrop, J. 1969A
 placidus Webb, S. D. 1969C
Callibrachion see Haptodus
calobatus (Equus)
Calomyscus Cricetidae
 minor Bruijn, H., Dawson, M. R., Mein, P. 1970A
Camarasauridae Saurischia–Sauropodomorpha
  Steel, R. 1970A
Camarasaurus Brachiosauridae
 grandis Marsh, O. C. 1879J [Morosaurus]
Camelidae Artiodactyla–Cameloidea Gentry, A. W.,
  Gentry, A. 1969A; Jerison, H. J. 1971A;

Camelidae - cont.
  Loring, S. E., Wood, A. E. 1969A (deciduous
    premolars); Patton, T. H. 1967C; Webb, S. D.
    1972A
  Aepycamelus, Alticamelus, Australocamelus, Camelops,
    Camelus, ?Delahomeryx, Gigantocamelus,
    Megatylopus, Michenia, Miotylopus, Nothokemas,
    Nothotylopus, Oxydactylus, Paracamelus,
    Poebrotherium, Priscocamelus, Procamelus,
    Protolabis, Stenomylus, Tanupolama,
    Titanotylopus
  See also Hypertragulidae
Camelops Camelidae Akersten, W. A. 1972A; Allison,
    I. S., Boyd, H. A. 1954A; Hibbard, C. W.
    1972A
  hesternus Herre, W., Kaup, L. 1969A; Khan, E.
    1970A; Miller, W. E. 1971A (cf.)
  kansanus Schultz, G. E. 1969A
  minidokae Herre, W., Kaup, L. 1969A
  sulcatus Dalquest, W. W. 1967A
Camelus Camelidae Howell, F. C., Fichter, L. S.,
    Wolff, R. 1969A
  dromedarius Clutton-Brock, J. 1970A
  knoblochi Alekseeva, L. I. 1969A
cameronense (Chirotherium)
campanensis (Eptesicus)
campbelltonensis (Cephalaspis)
Campephilus Picidae
  dalquesti Brodkorb, P. 1970B
campestris (Gerbillus, Martes)
campi (Syrrhophus, Tseajaia)
campivagus (Eogeranoides)
camptognathus (Nothotylopus)
Camptosaurichnus Ichnites Casamiquela, R. M.,
    Fasola, A. 1968A (in Iguanodontidae)
  fasolae Casamiquela, R. M., Fasola, A. 1968A
Camptosaurus Iguanodontidae
  browni Pinna, G. 1969A (reconstr.)
Campylocynodon Parictis
canadensis (Bothriolepis, Brachylophosaurus, Branta,
    Castor, Cervus, Daphoenus, Leidyosuchus,
    Lutra, Melanognathus, Ophisaurus, Ovis,
    Rhinophrynus)
Canariomys Muridae Crusafont Pairó, M.,
    Petter, F. 1964A
  bravoi Crusafont Pairó, M., Petter, F. 1964A
canavus (Vulpavus)
cancellata (Epinnula)
Candelaria Procolophonidae
  barbouri Bonaparte, J. F. 1972A
canetotiana (Testudo)
Canidae Carnivora—Arctoidea (incl. Amphicyonidae)
    Beneš, J. 1972A; Hunt, R. M. 1971A;
    Radinsky, L. B. 1969B (brain evol.)
  Aelurodon, Alopex, Amphicyon, Borophagus,
    Brachyrhynchocyon, Canis, Carpocyon,
    Cuon, Cynelos, Cynodesmus, Cynodictis,
    Cynogulo, Cynotherium, Daphoenocyon,
    Daphoenus, Enhydrocyon, Gobicyon,
    Goupilictis, Harpagophagus, Hesperocyon,
    Ischyrocyon, Leptocyon, Mammacyon,
    Mesocyon, Neocynodesmus, Nothocyon,
    Nyctereutes, Osteoborus, Parictis,
    Pseudarctos, Simamphicyon, Simocyon,
    Strobodon, Sunkahetanka, Temnocyon,
    Tomarctus, Urocyon, Vulpes, Ysengrinia

caninus (Pachyrhizodus)
Canis Canidae Alvarez, T. 1969A; Baïgusheva, V. S.
    1971A; Churcher, C. S. 1972C; Guthrie,
    R. D., Matthews, J. V. 1971A; Heller, J.
    1970A; Kermack, K. A., Kielan-Jaworowska,
    Z. 1971A (braincase); Khan, E. 1970A;
    Leinders, J., Michaux, J. 1969A
  aureus
    sondaicus Gautier, A. 1968A (cf.)
  davisi Shotwell, J. A. 1970A
  dirus Guilday, J. E., Hamilton, H. W., McCrady,
    A. D. 1971A; Miller, W. E. 1971A (cf.);
    Schultz, G. E. 1969A (subgen. Aenocyon);
    Thenius, E. 1970C (subgen. Aenocyon)
  etruscus Bonifay, M.-F. 1971A
  latrans Gill, D. 1970A; Miller, W. E. 1971A (cf.)
  lepophagus Akersten, W. A. 1972A (cf.); Bjork,
    P. R. 1970A; Hibbard, C. W. 1972A
  lupaster Petter, G., Heintz, E. 1969A (cf.)
  lupus Altuna, J. 1970A; Boeuf, O. 1970A;
    Bonifay, M.-F. 1967A, 1969A, 1971A;
    Bouchud, J. 1969A; Delpech, F. 1968A;
    Delpech, F., et al. 1970A; Erdbrink, D. P.
    1968A (cf.); Garevski, R. 1969A;
    Jánossy, D. 1969B; Kuz'mina, I. E. 1971A;
    Martin, R. 1968A; Mostecký, V. 1969A;
    Schütt, G. 1969C; Zapfe, H. 1966E
    lunellensis Bonifay, M.-F. 1971A
    mosbachensis Kurtén, B. 1969A; Schaefer, H.
      1969A
  mesomelas Gautier, A. 1968A
  mosbachensis Feustel, R., et al. 1971B; Jánossy, D.
    1969B; Koenigswald, W. 1972A
  rufus Hale, D. 1970A
cankpeopi (Capatanka)
cannabina (Carduelis)
Canobiidae Palaeonisciformes—Palaeoniscoidei
  Canobius, Charleuxia, Sundayichthys, Whiteichthys
Canobius Canobiidae Kazantseva, A. A. 1971A
canorus (Cuculus)
cansouni (Estellomys)
cantabrigiensis (Rhinochelys)
Cantharus see Spondyliosoma
cantiana (Arvicola)
canus (Larus, Picus)
Capacikala Castoridae
  gradatus Macdonald, J. R. 1970A
  sciuroides Macdonald, J. R. 1970A(?)
caparti (Nycticonodon)
Capatanka Castoridae
  brachyceps Macdonald, J. R. 1970A
  cankpeopi Macdonald, J. R. 1970A
capeki (Francolinus, Surnia)
Capella Scolopacidae
  gallinago Jánossy, D. 1972A (cf.)
  media Jánossy, D. 1972A (cf.)
capellinii (Kyrtogymnodon)
Capellirallus Rallidae
  hodgeni [Rallus] Scarlett, R. J. 1970A
  karamu Scarlett, R. J. 1970A
capeniensis (Romanocastor)
capensis (Equus, Lepus, Moschops, Phacochoerus,
    Prionodelphis, Scylacops)
Capitonidae Piciformes—Picoidea Ballmann, P. 1969A,B
  Capitonides

Carcharodon megalodon - cont.
　　　　Keyes, I. W. 1972A; Menesini, E. 1969A;
　　　　Silva Santos, R., Sardenberg Salgado, M.
　　　　1971A; Telles Antunes, M., Jonet, S. 1970A
　　　　[Procarcharodon. in Lamnidae]
　　　chubutensis Schultz, O. 1968A
　　　megalodon Schultz, O. 1968A
Cardharidae see Carcharhinidae
Cardipeltidae Heterostraci
　　Cardipeltis
Cardipeltis Cardipeltidae
　　richardsoni Denison, R. H. 1971B
carduelis (Carduelis)
Carduelis Ploceidae
　　cannabina Ballmann, P., Adrover, R. 1970A
　　　　(in Fringilidae)
　　carduelis Jánossy, D. 1972A (aff., in Sturnidae)
Carettochelyidae Chelonia–Cryptodira
　　Allaeochelys
Cariamidae Ralliformes–Cariamae
　　Bathornis, Eutreptornis, Paracrax
carinatus (Dapalis)
Carinodens [Compressidens] Mosasauridae
　　　　Thurmond, J. T. 1969A (n. name)
carinthiacus (Gobius)
carlylensis (Oolithes)
carnegiei (Diplodocus)
Carnivora Mammalia
　　Incl. Miacoidea, Aeluroidea, Arctoidea, Pinnipedia
Carnivoripedae see Carnivoripedidae
Carnivoripedidae [Carnivoripedae]Mammalipedia
　　Felipeda
carnutense (Steneofiber depereti)
carolinae (Protoryx)
caroloameghinoi (Coelostylodon)
carpathicus (Pseudotheridomys)
carpathorum (Capra ibex)
carpaticus Otolithus (Myctophidarum)
carpiromanica (Idrissia)
Carpocyon Canidae–Caninae Webb, S. D. 1969A
　　limosus Webb, S. D. 1969A
Carpodaptes Carpolestidae Gazin, C. L. 1971A
Carpolestidae Primates–Plesiadapoidea Szalay, F. S.
　　　　1969C, 1972C
　　Carpodaptes, Elphidotarsius
carrikeri (Promerycochoerus)
cartailhaci (Plagiolophus)
cartei (Leithia)
Carteremys Pelomedusidae
　　leithii Wood, R. C. 1970A
carteri (Omomys)
Carterodon Echimyidae
　　sulcidens Friant, M. 1969A
Cartieraspis Arthrodira incertae sedis Pageau, Y. 1969B
　　nigra Pageau, Y. 1969B
cartieri (Chasmotherium, Protadelomys)
casasecai (Allaeochelys)
casca (Danatinia)
cascoensis (Coendou)
casei (Paralbula)
casieri (Aglyptorhynchus, Ceratodus, Clupavus,
　　　　Dollochelys, Oxyaena, Rhomboplites)
Casierius Albulidae Estes, R. 1969H
　　heckelii Estes, R. 1969H; Johnson, G. D. 1972A
caspica (Clemmys)
caspius (Paratrisopterus)

Cassandra Myctophidae Patterson, C. 1968B
　　See also Sardinioides
cassivii (Gaspeaspis)
castilhoi (Araripesaurus)
Castillomys Muridae Michaux, J. 1969B
　　crusafonti Bruijn, H., Dawson, M. R., Mein, P.
　　　　1970A; Michaux, J. 1969B
Castor Castoridae
　　accessor Shotwell, J. A. 1970A
　　californicus Zakrzewski, R. J. 1969A (cf.)
　　canadensis Schultz, G. E. 1969A
　　fiber David, A. I. 1966C; Feustel, R., et al. 1971B(?);
　　　　Jánossy, D. 1969B; Kretzoi, M. 1969A;
　　　　Kuz'mina, I. E. 1971A; Lychev, G. F.,
　　　　Aubekerova, P. A. 1971A (aff.);
　　　　Mostecký, V. 1969A
　　praefiber Samson, P., et al. 1971A
Castoridae Rodentia–Castoroidea
　　Incl. subfam. Castorinae, Castoroidinae Djoshkin,
　　　　W. W., Safonow, W. G. 1972A
　　Amblycastor, Asiacastor, Boreofiber, Capacikala,
　　　　Capatanka, Castor, Castoroides, Dipoides,
　　　　Eucastor, Monosaulax, Palaeocastor,
　　　　Palaeomys, Procastoroides, Propalaeocastor,
　　　　Romanocastor, Steneofiber, Trogontherium
castorinus (Steneofiber, Steneofiber castorinus)
Castoroidea Rodentia
Castoroides Castoridae
　　ohioensis Dallman, J. E. 1969A
　　　　dilophidus Martin, R. A. 1970A
castoroides (Palaeomys)
castrense (Palaeotherium, Xiphodon)
Casuariformes Aves
catalaunicus (Iberovaranus, Leptodontomys)
catalunica (Vidalamia)
catamarcensis (Microtragulus)
cataphractus (Prionolepis)
Catarrhini Primates Simons, E. L. 1971C
catclawensis (Ovis)
catesbiana (Rana)
cathalai (Progonomys)
Cathartidae see Vulturidae, Sagittariidae
catocopsis (Machairodus)
Catodontherium Anoplotheriidae
　　argentonicum see Haplobunodon mulleri
　　buxgovianum Sudre, J. 1972A
　　fallax Sudre, J. 1972A
　　robiacense Sudre, J. 1969B
Catostomidae Cypriniformes–Cyprinoidei
　　Amyzon
　　See also Cyprinidae
cattica (Lamna, Lamna cattica)
cattoi (Ischisaurus)
catulus (Bregmaceros)
Caturidae Amiiformes–Amioidei
　　Caturus, Macrepistius, ?Paraliodesmus
Caturus Caturidae Janicke, V. 1970A [Strobilodus];
　　　　Schlomm, W. 1970A
caucasicum (Elasmotherium)
caudatus (Nanopus)
Caudochelys Geochelone
caunnellensis (Aprionodon)
cavernosa (Dasyatis)
cavifrons (Entoptychus, Struthiocephaloides, Symbos)
Caviidae Rodentia–Caviomorpha
　　Dolichotis

Cervidae   Artiodactyla–Cervoidea Crouzel, F. 1971A;
 Dobroruka, L. J. 1971A; Fry, W. E.,
 Gustafson, E. P. 1972A; Heintz, E. 1970A;
 Pohle, H. 1959A (antler)
 Alces, Capreolus, Cervalces, Cervocerus, Cervus,
 Ctenocerus, Ctenocervus, Dama, Dicrocerus,
 Elaphurus, Eucladoceros, Euctenoceros,
 Longirostromeryx, Megaloceros, Micromeryx,
 Muntiacus, Neomegaloceros, Odocoileus,
 Praedama, Praemegaceros, Procapreolus,
 Rangifer, Strongyloceros
 See also Palaeomerycidae
cervinum (Dichodon)
Cervocerus   Cervidae Bukatchuk, P. D., Burdenko,
 B. V., Voloshin, V. E. 1968A,B [Procervus]
Cervodama see Cervus
Cervus   Cervidae Bahlo, E. 1971A; Baigusheva, V. S.
 1971A (subgen. Rusa); Khatri, A. P. 1966A;
 Otsuka, H. 1970B; Samson, P., et al. 1971A;
 Schmidt, Z., Halouzka, R. 1970A; Shotwell,
 J. A. 1970A
 acoronatus David, A. I. 1969A; Jánossy, D. 1969B;
 Kahlke, H.-D. 1969D
 canadensis Churcher, C. S. 1968B
 cretensis [Megaceros] Kuss, S. E. 1969A,B
 dicranios see Eucladoceros
 elaphoides Kahlke, H.-D. 1969D
 elaphus Baigusheva, V. S. 1971A (cf.);
 Biddittu, I., Cassoli, P. 1968A; Boecker, M.,
 et al. 1972A; Bonifay, M.-F. 1967A, 1969A;
 Bouchud, J. 1968C, 1969A; Delpech, F.
 1968A, 1969A; Erdbrink, D. P. 1964B;
 Guthrie, R. D., Matthews, J. V. 1971A (cf.);
 Jánossy, D. 1969B; Kambariddinov, R. K.,
 et al. 1971A (cf.); Malez, M. 1967C;
 Martin, R. 1968A; Melentis, J. K. 1966F,P;
 Mostecký, V. 1969A; Petronio, C. 1970A;
 Plusquellec, Y. 1968A; Prat, F. 1968A;
 Schütt, G. 1969C; Seronie-Vivien, R. 1971A;
 Torres Perezhidalgo, T. 1971A; Tozzi, C.
 1969A; Vekua, A. K., Khukhia, N. V. 1972A
 primigenius Thenius, E. 1966G
 philisi Baigusheva, V. S. 1971A (cf.); Beden, M.1970B
 pontoborealis Baigusheva, V. S. 1971A [Cervodama]
 praenipponicus Onodera, S. 1970A (subgen.
 Depereta)
 somonensis Melentis, J. K. 1966F (subgen. Dama)
 warthae Czyżewska, T. 1968A
Cestracion
 duponti see Dasyatis
 priscus see Sphyrna
Cetacea   Mammalia
 Incl. subord. Archaeoceti, Odontoceti, Mysticeti
 Hasegawa, Y., et al. 1972A; Hatai, K. et al.
 1963A (fossil tympanic bones; classif.);
 Iablokov, A. V. 1966A; Mchedlidze, G. A.
 1966A, 1967B, 1968A, 1970A,B
 See also Mizuhoptera
cetoides (Basilosaurus)
Cetorhinidae   Selachii-Galeoidea
 Cetorhinus
Cetorhinus   Cetorhinidae
 maximus Bosch, M. van den 1969A

Cetotheriidae   Cetacea–Mysticeti
 Cetotheriopsis, Cetotherium, Halicetus, Isocetus,
 Mesocetus, Mioceta, Thinocetus
Cetotheriopsis   Cetotheriidae
 tobieni Rothausen, K. 1971A
Cetotherium   Cetotheriidae Mchedlidze, G. A. 1970B
 priscum Macarovici, N., Zaharia, N. 1968B
chadwicki (Downsimus)
Chaenobryttus   Centrarchidae
 serratus Smith, G. R., Lundberg, J. G. 1972A
Chaenohyus see Perchoerus
chalaniati (Lophiomeryx)
chalchis (Saykanomys)
Chalicomys see Palaeomys
Chalicotheriidae   Perissodactyla–Chalicotherioidea
 Ancylotherium, Chalicotherium, Palaeoamasia,
 Phyllotillon
Chalicotherium   Chalicotheriidae
 goldfussi Friant, M. 1970B; Schaefer, H., Zapfe, H.
 1971A
 grande Schaefer, H., Zapfe, H. 1971A; Telles
 Antunes, M. 1966E
chamerpes (Erythrozootes)
Champos   Teiidae Waldman, M. 1970A
 segnis Sahni, A. 1972A
Champsodelphis   Acrodelphidae
 fuchsii Macarovici, N., Zaharia, N. 1968B (cf.)
Champsosauridae   Eosuchia–Choristodera
 Champsosaurus
Champsosaurus   Champsosauridae Fox, R. C. 1968A;
 Sahni, A. 1972A
 albertensis Erickson, B. R. 1972A
 ambulator Erickson, B. R. 1972A
 gigas Erickson, B. R. 1972A
 laramiensis [C. australis; C. puercensis; ?C. saponensis]
 Erickson, B. R. 1972A
 natator [?C. annectens; ?C. profundus;
 ?C. brevicollis; C. inflatus; C. inelegens]
 Erickson, B. R. 1972A
 vaccinsulensis Erickson, B. R. 1972A (nom. vanum)
chanarensis (Lagerpeton)
Chanaresuchus   Proterochampsidae Romer, A. S. 1971E
 bonapartei Romer, A. S. 1971E, 1972A
Chanaria   Stahleckeriidae Cox, C. B. 1968A
 platyceps Bonaparte, J. F. 1972A; Cox, C. B. 1968A
chandoni (Microparamys)
chaneyi (Bison)
Changisaurus   Thalassemyidae Young, C.-c. 1959K
 (in Lacertilia–Gekkonidae)
 microrhinus Young, C.-c. 1959K
Changpeipus   Ichnites
 bartholomaii Haubold, H. 1971B (in Carnosauria)
Changyonophyton   Arctolepida incertae sedis
 Stensiö, E. 1969B, 1971A (in Spinothoracidi–
 Dolichothoraci incertae sedis)
Chanidae   Gonorhynchiformes–Chanoidei
 Chanos, Parachanos
Chanos   Chanidae
 torosus Danil'chenko, P. G. 1968B
chantrei (Plesiodimylus)
Chaohusaurus   Omphalosauridae Young, C.-c.,
 Dong, Z.-m. 1972A
 geishanensis Young, C.-c., Dong, Z.-m. 1972A
chapalmalensis (Thylophorops)

chirobates (Aeolopithecus)
Chirocentridae   Clupeiformes–Clupeoidei
    Allothrissops, Opsithrissops, Pachythrissops,
        Platinx, Thrissops
    See also Ichthyodectidae
Chirocentrites   Icthyodectidae
    guinensis Casier, E., Taverne, L. 1971A
        (in Chirocentridae)
Chirocentroidea   Clupeiformes–Clupeoidei
    Applegate, S. P. 1970A (n. superfam.,
        incl. Ichthyodectidae, Saurodontidae,
        Chirocentridae)
Chirodipterus   Dipteridae Schaeffer, B. 1968C
    wildungensis Bertmar, G. 1968B; Jarvik, E. 1968A
Chirodontidae [Amphicentridae] Palaeonisciformes–
        Platysomoidei
    Adroichthys
Chiroptera   Mammalia Jepsen, G. L. 1970A; Jones,
        J. K., Genoways, H. H. 1970A; Koopman,
        K. F. 1970A; Koopman, K. F., Jones, J. K.
        1970A; Martin, R. A. 1972A; Slaughter,
        B. H., Walton, D. W. (eds.) 1970A
Chirosaurus see Chirotherium
Chirotheriidae   Ichnites Haubold, H. 1969B, 1971A
        (in Pseudosuchia, incl. Chirotherium)
Chirotherium   Ichnites Buffard, R., Demathieu, G.,
        Demathieu, P. 1969A; Ellenberger, F.,
        Ellenberger, P., Ginsburg, L. 1970A;
        Haubold, H. 1971A (in Chirotheriidae);
        [Chirosaurus] Haubold, H. 1969B
        (in Chirotheriidae); Montenat, C. 1970A;
        Rehnelt, K. 1959A; Ritzkowski, S. 1965A
    barthii Demathieu, G. 1970B; Demathieu, G.,
        Samama, J. C. 1970A; Haubold, H. 1969A,C,
        1971A; Kupfahl, H.-G. 1961A
    bipedale Haubold, H. 1971A (?)
    cameronense Haubold, H. 1971A
    coltoni Haubold, H. 1971A
    coureli Demathieu, G. 1970B
    demathieui Haubold, H. 1971A
    diabloense Haubold, H. 1971A
    eyermani Haubold, H. 1971A
    geinitzi see Dicynodontipus
    harrasense Haubold, H. 1971A
    herculis Haubold, H. 1969C, 1971A
    hessbergense Haubold, H. 1971A
    hessei Haubold, H. 1971A
    hildburghausense Haubold, H. 1971A
    jenense Haubold, H. 1971A
    lomasi Haubold, H. 1971A
    lulli Haubold, H. 1971A
    marshalli Haubold, H. 1971A
    moquinense Haubold, H. 1971A
    parvum Demathieu, G. 1970B; Demathieu, G.,
        Samama, J. C. 1970A; Haubold, H. 1971A
    praeparvum Haubold, H. 1971A
    pseudosuchoides Haubold, H. 1971A
    rex Haubold, H. 1971A
    sickleri Haubold, H. 1969A,C, 1971A
    soergeli Haubold, H. 1971A
        See also Isochirotherium
    thuringiacum Haubold, H. 1971A
    wondrai Haubold, H. 1971A
Chisternon   Baenidae
    undatum Gaffney, E. S. 1972A (in Baeninae)
Chiwetsaurus see Gorgonops

Chleuastochoerus   Suidae
    stehlini Schmidt-Kittler, N. 1971A
Chlidonias   Laridae
    nigra Jánossy, D. 1972A (aff.)
Chloephaga
    picta see Foetopterus ambiguus
choeroides (Sus)
Choerolophodon see Gomphotherium
Choeromorus   Tayassuidae
    pygmaeus Engesser, B. 1972A [Taucanamo]
    See also Taucanamo
Choeropotamidae   Artiodactyla–Entelodontoidea
    ?Brachyhyops, Choeropotamus, ?Indohyus
Choeropotamus   Choeropotamidae
    lautricensis Sudre, J. 1969B
    parisiensis Jehenne, Y. 1969A
Choeropsis   Hippopotamidae Steele, N. 1972A
        [pigmy hippos]
    liberiensis Cooke, H. B. S., Coryndon, S. C. 1970A
Choerotherium
    sansaniense see Taucanamo
cholmicus (Sachalinocetus)
Chondrenchelyidae   Bradyodonti
    Chondrenchelys
Chondrenchelys   Chondrenchelyidae Bendix-Almgreen,
        S. E. 1968A
Chondrichthyes
    Incl. subcl. Elasmobranchii, Holocephali
        Budker, P. 1971A; Lineaweaver, T. H.,
        Backus, R. H. 1970A; Patterson, C. 1969A
Chondrichthyes or Placodermi incertae sedis–
        Ichthyodorulites
    Stethacanthus
Chondropterygii Wahlert, G. 1968A (= Chondrichthyes)
Chondrostoma   Cyprinidae
    elongata Anđelković, J. 1970A
    stephani Anđelković, J. 1970A
Chonecetus   Archaeoceti incertae sedis Russell, L. S.
        1968B
    sookensis Russell, L. S. 1968B
chosaricus (Equus, Mammuthus)
chozaensis (Captorhinikos)
Chriacus   Arctocyonidae
    europaeus Quinet, G. E. 1966F(?), 1969B(?)
    pelvidens Gazin, C. L. 1969A (cf.)
    truncatus Gazin, C. L. 1969A (cf.)
Chromis   Pomacentridae
    savornini Anđelković, J. 1969A (in Cichlidae)
Chroniosaurus   Chroniosuchidae Tverdokhlebova, G. I.
        1972A,B
    dongusensis Tverdokhlebova, G. I. 1972A,B
Chroniosuchida   Seymouriamorpha Tatarinov, L. P.
        1972B (n. subord., in Batrachosauria,
        incl. Chroniosuchidae)
Chroniosuchidae   Anthracosauria–Seymouriamorpha
        Tverdokhlebova, G. I. 1969A
    Chroniosaurus, Chroniosuchus
Chroniosuchus   Chroniosuchidae [Jugosuchus]
        Tverdokhlebova, G. I. 1968A
    mirabilis Borkhvardt, V. G. 1969A,B;
        Tverdokhlebova, G. I. 1968A
    paradoxus Shishkin, M. A. 1968B
chrysaetos (Aquila)
Chrysemys   Testudinidae Rose, F. L. 1969A
        (incl. Pseudemys)
    idahoensis Zug, G. R. 1969A

Clethrionomys - cont.
  glareolus Boecker, M., et al. 1972A; Chaline, J.
    1969A (in Arvicolidae); Jánossy, D. 1969B
    (group; in Arvicolidae); Koenigswald, W.
    1970A (subgen. Myodes), 1972A (cf.);
    Sukhov, V. P. 1970A (ex gr.)
  rufocanus Erbaeva, M. A. 1970A
Clevosaurus Sphenodontidae Halstead, L. B.,
    Nicoll, P. G. 1971A
Clidastes Mosasauridae Thurmond, J. T. 1969B
  propython Russell, D. A. 1970B
Climatiformes Osteichthyes—Acanthodii
Climatiidae Climatiformes
  Climatius, Nostolepis
Climatius Climatiidae
  latispinosus Pageau, Y. 1969A
Clinopternodus Adapisoricidae Robinson, P. 1968C
    (in Nyctitheriidae—Micropternodontinae)
cluae (Elomeryx)
Clupavidae see Leptolepididae
Clupavus Leptolepididae Casier, E., Taverne, L.
    1971A; Dunkle, D. H. 1971A
  casieri Taverne, L. 1969C, 1970A (in Clupavidae)
  maroccanus Arambourg, C. 1967B
Clupea Clupeidae Anfossi, G., Mosna, S. 1969A
    (otol.); Cappetta, H. C. 1969B (otol.);
    Gaemers, P. A. M. 1969A (otol.)
  bonii Anfossi, G., Mosna, S. 1971A (otol.)
  gaudryi see Gaudryella
  humilis Anđelković, J. 1970A; Brzobohatý, R.
    1969A (aff., otol.)
  inflata Anđelković, J. S. 1969A
  lanceolata Anđelković, J. S. 1969A
  sardinites Jerzmańska, A. 1968A
  spinosa Anđelković, J. S. 1969A
  testis Heinrich, W.-D. 1969B (otol.); Rado, G.
    1965A, 1969A (otol.)
  voinovi Anđelković, J. S. 1969A
Clupeidae Clupeiformes—Clupeoidei (incl.
    ? Engraulidae) Danil'chenko, V. P. 1972A
    Alosa, Clupea, Clupeidarum, Diplomystus,
    Etrumeus, Gasteroclupea, Opisthonema,
    Pateroperca, Pomolobus, Primisardinella,
    ? Sardina, Sardinella, Stolephorus, Xyne
  See also Otolithus
Clupeidarum see Otolithus
Clupeiformes Teleostei
  Incl. subord. Denticipitoidei, Clupeoidei
  Incertae sedis: Spratticeps
clypeata (Spatula)
Cnemidophorus Teiidae
  gularis Holman, J. A. 1969B
  sexlineatus Holman, J. A. 1972A (cf.)
coalescens (Olbiaspis)
cobbi (Cincosaurus)
coburgense (Brachychirotherium)
Coccolepididae Palaeonisciformes—Palaeoniscoidei
  Coccolepis
  See also Birgeriidae
Coccolepis Coccolepididae
  woodwardi Waldman, M. 1971B
Coccosteidae Arthrodira—Brachythoraci (incl.
    Coccosteidae, Millerosteidae,
    Rhachiosteidae of Stensiö) Stensiö, E.
    1969A,B (in Spinothoracidi—
    Coccosteomorphi)

Coccosteidae - cont.
    Buchanosteus, Clarkosteus, Coccosteus, Dickosteus,
    Eldenosteus, ? Hussakofia, Livosteus,
    ? Machaerognathus, Millerosteus, Plourdosteus,
    Protitanichthys, Rhachiosteus, Taemasosteus,
    ? Trachosteus, Watsonosteus
  See also Dinichthyidae
Coccosteomorphi Arthrodira Stensiö, E. 1969A,B,
    1971A (in Spinothoracidi)
Coccosteus Coccosteidae Miles, R. S. 1971B;
    Stensiö, E. 1969A,B
  cuspidatus Goujet, D. 1972A (reconstr.)
  decipiens Obrucheva, O. P. 1962C
  grandis see Livosteus
  grossi Obrucheva, O. P. 1962C
  markae Obrucheva, O. P. 1962C
  mironovi see Plourdosteus
  orvikui Obrucheva, O. P. 1962C
coccothraustes (Coccothraustes)
Coccothraustes Ploceidae
  coccothraustes Ballmann, P., Adrover, R. 1970A
    (in Fringilidae); Jánossy, D. 1972A (cf.,
    in Sturnidae)
Cochleosauridae Temnospondyli—Edopoidea
  Cochleosaurus, Gaudrya
Cochleosaurus Cochleosauridae Schultze, H.-P. 1969B;
    Schultze, H.-P. 1969B [Nyrania]
Cochliodontidae Chimaeriformes—Cochliodontoidei
  Cochliodus, Deltoptychius, Menaspis, Psephodus
Cochliodontoidei Chimaeriformes Patterson, C. 1968C
Cochliodus Cochliodontidae
  contortus Patterson, C. 1968C
Coelacanthidae Crossopterygii—Coelacanthini
  Mawsonia, Spermatodus, Whiteia
Coelacanthini Crossopterygii Bjerring, H. C. 1972B
    [coelacanthiforms]; Wahlert, G. 1968A
    [Actinistia]; Wahlert, G., Wahlert, H. 1967A
Coelodonta Rhinocerotidae Kahlke, H.-D. 1969E
    antiquitatis Apostol, L. 1970A; Apostol, L.,
    Vicoveanu, D. 1970A; Bouchud, J. 1968C;
    David, A. I. 1966B; Flerov, K. K. 1970A
    (restor.); Garutt, V. E., Metel'ĉeva, E. P.,
    Tikhomirov, B. A. 1970A; Guérin, C. 1970A;
    Jörg, E. 1971A; Kubiak, H. 1969A;
    Kuz'mina, I. E. 1971A; Lang, H. D. 1969A;
    Melentis, J. K. 1966G; Mihăilă, N. 1971A;
    Mostecký, V. 1969A; Rădulescu, C.,
    Hermann, W. 1969A; Samson, P.,
    Hermann, W. 1968A; Schütt, G. 1969C(?);
    Thenius, E. 1966G; Vereĭskiĭ, N. G.,
    Ivanova, I. K., Neĭshtadt, M. I. 1964A
coelodus (Mimomys)
Coelodus Pycnodontidae Cappetta, H. C. 1972B
    (in Gyrodontidae); Wenz, S. 1969A(?)
  munsteri Melentis, J. K. 1967D
? Coelolepida Agnatha—Diplorhina (incl. Thelodonti-
    Phlebolepida and Thelodontia of Stensiö)
Coelolepididae see Thelodontidae
Coelophrys (Palaeotragus)
Coelophysis Procompsognathidae Peoples, J. W. 1969A
    (reconst.)
Coelorhynchus Xiphiidae Bauzá Rullán, J. 1971C
    [Cylindracanthus, in Blochiidae]
  ellipticus Dieni, I. 1968A [Glyptorhynchus; in
    Macrouridae; otol.]

Coelorhynchus - cont.
  ornatus
    apicatus Anfossi, G., Mosna, S. 1969B (otol.,
      in Macrouridae); Dieni, I. 1968A
      [Glyptorhynchus; in Macrouridae; otol.]
    rectus Nolf, D. 1970A [Cylindracanthus; in
      Blochiidae, otol.]
    toulai Anfossi, G., Mosna, S. 1969A (otol., in
      Macrouridae); Brzobohatý, R. 1967C (otol.,
      in Macrouridae)
    See also Glyptorhynchus
Coelostegus Romeriidae Carroll, R. L., Baird, D.
      1972A
    prothales Carroll, R. L., Baird, D. 1972A
Coelostylodon Isotemnidae Simpson, G. G. 1970D
    caroloameghinoi Simpson, G. G. 1970D
    florentinoameghinoi Simpson, G. G. 1970D
Coeluridae Saurischia—Theropoda
    Compsognathus, Dilophosaurus, Dromaeosaurus,
      ?Hallopus, Microvenator, Paronychodon,
      Saurornithoides, Velociraptor
    See also Dromaeosauridae
Coelurosaurichnus Ichnites Haubold, H. 1969B
      (in Anchisauripodidae); [Dinosauripus]
      Rehnelt, K. 1959A; Sarjeant, W. A. S.
      1967A
    kehli Welzel, E. 1968A
    kronbergeri Rehnelt, K. 1959A
    schlehenbergensis [Dinosaurichnium] Rehnelt, K.
      1959A
    ziegelangernensis Wills, L. J., Sarjeant, W. A. S.
      1970A (cf.)
Coendou Erethizontidae
    brachygnathum White, J. A. 1970A
    cascoensis White, J. A. 1970A
    cumberlandicus White, J. A. 1970A
    stirtoni White, J. A. 1970A
coeruleus (Parus)
cognatus (Merlangius, Parahippus)
cognitus (Platinx)
colberti (Rattus)
Colbertosaurus Cynognathidae
    muralis Bonaparte, J. F. 1972A
colchicus (Phasianus)
colchidica (Atherina)
colei (Leuciscus)
colgatei (Didymoconus)
Coliidae Coliiformes
    Colius
Coliiformes Aves
Colius Coliidae [Limnatornis; Necrornis;
      Palaeopicus] Ballmann, P. 1969A
    palustris Ballmann, P. 1969A (cf.)
collaris (Prunella)
collatum (Eucricetodon)
Collimys Cricetidae—Cricetinae Daxner-Höck, G.
      1972A
    primus Daxner-Höck, G. 1972A
collinsi (Caenagnathus)
collinus (Cylindrodon)
collongensis (Democricetodon minor, Hipposideros)
Collongomys Megacricetodon Mein, P.,
      Freudenthal, M. 1971A (n. subgen.)
Colobidae see Cercopithecidae
Colobodus Perleididae Rutte, E. 1971A
    maximus Müller, A. H. 1970D

Colodon Helaletidae Bjork, P. R. 1968A
    orientalis Biriukov, M. D. 1962A
Coloeus Corvidae
    monedula Jánossy, D. 1972A (cf.)
Colombitheriidae Pyrotheria? Hoffstetter, R. 1970D
    Colombitherium
Colombitherium Colombitheriidae Hoffstetter, R.
      1970D
    tolimense Hoffstetter, R. 1970D
coloradense (Neohipparion)
coloradensis (Bipedopus, Bothriolepis, Parabaropus,
      Parahippus)
Coloraderpeton Ophiderpetontidae Vaughn, P. P.
      1969B
    brilli Vaughn, P. P. 1969B
colorata (Jachaleria)
Colosteidae Temnospondyli—Rhachitomi
    Greererpeton
coltoni (Chirotherium)
Coluber Colubridae Malez, M. 1967C; Ruben, J. A.
      1971A
Colubridae Squamata—Ophidia
    Coluber, Elaphe, Heterodon, Lampropeltis, Natrix,
      Paracoluber, Thamnophis
Columba Columbidae
    palumbus Jánossy, D. 1972A (aff.)
columbi (Mammuthus)
Columbidae Columbiformes
    Columba, Zenaidura
Columbiformes Aves
Columbomyinae Theridomyidae Hartenberger, J.-L.
      1971B (incl. Columbomys, Sciuromys)
Columbosauripus Ichnites
    amouraensis Haubold, H. 1971B (in Coelurosauria)
columnae (Myctophum)
comblei (Igornella, Paramblypterus)
Commentrya Commentryidae Mathieu, G. 1970A
    [Elaveria]
Commentryidae Palaeonisciformes—Palaeoniscoidei
      (incl. Paramblypteridae)
    Commentrya, Paramblypterus
commune (Anoplotherium)
communis (Gelocus, Glyptorhynchus, Macrourus)
complicatus (Microdyromys, Sivacanthion)
compositus (Peridyromys)
Compressidens Mosasauridae Quinet, G. E. 1970B
    See also Carinodens
compressus (Platygonus, Sorex, Xenacanthus)
Compsemys Dermatemydidae
    victa Gaffney, E. S. 1972A (in Baenidae)
Compsognathus Coeluridae
    corallestris Bidar, A., Demay, L., Thomel, G.
      1972A,B
comstocki (Peratherium)
concavidens (Bransatoglis)
Conchopoma Conchopomidae
    edesi Denison, R. H. 1969A
Conchopomidae Dipnoi
    Conchopoma
concinnus (Homalacanthus)
concisa (Petenyia)
concolor (Felis)
Condylarthra Mammalia Quinet, G. E., et al. 1971A;
      Szalay, F. S. 1969D
confusus (Barillopus)

Conger Congridae
durus *Aoki, N.* 1968A (otol.)
magnus [Otol. (Ophidium) magnus] Robba, E.
1970A (otol.)
Congermuraena see Ariosoma
congolensis (Leptolepis)
Congridae Anguilliformes—Anguilloidei
Ariosoma, Conger, Congridarum, Paraconger,
Uroconger
See also Otolithus
Congridarum Congridae see Otolithus
connectens (Megapaloelodus, Mergus)
conodon (Mosasaurus)
Conodontes see Trogontherium
Conohyus Suidae
simorrensis Engesser, B. 1972A;
Hünermann, K. A.
1968A
conrectus (Amphisauroides)
constans (Peratherium)
contigua (Arminiheringia)
Contogenys Scincidae? *Estes, R.* 1969D
sloani *Estes, R.* 1969D
contortidens (Odontaspis)
contortus (Cochliodus)
conversidens (Equus)
convincens (Procheneosaurus)
cooki (Arctognathus, Bothremys, Cynodesmus,
Diceratherium, Plesiadapis, Syndyoceras,
Trigonictis)
cooperi (Shoshonius, Synaptomys)
Copanagnathus see Hussakofia
copei (Hybodus, Paramys, Prodesmodon)
Copemys Cricetidae Fahlbusch, V. 1969A
(subgen. Democricetodon)
barstowensis *Lindsay, E. H.* 1972B
esmeraldensis Lindsay, E. H. 1972B
kelloggae Klingener, D. 1968A (in Muridae)
longidens Lindsay, E. H. 1972B
pagei Lindsay, E. H. 1972B
russelli Lindsay, E. H. 1972B
tenuis *Lindsay, E. H.* 1972B
copiosus (Gobius)
Copodontidae Bradyodonti
Copodus
Copodus Copodontidae
spatulatus Patterson, C. 1968C
cor (Dromimomys)
Coraciiformes Aves
Coragyps Vulturidae
occidentalis Frailey, C. D. 1972A
corallestris (Compsognathus)
corax (Corvus)
Corax Isuridae see Palaeoanacorax
cordatus (Pantylus)
Cordicephalus Pipidae *Nevo, E.* 1968A
gracilis *Nevo, E.* 1968A
longicostatus *Nevo, E.* 1968A
cordicingularis (Paramys)
cordieri (Sardinius)
Coriops Albulidae *Estes, R.* 1969E
amnicolus *Estes, R.* 1969E
cornfeldi (Crocidura)
cornix (Corvus corone)
cornutum (Phrynosoma)
corone (Corvus)

coronensis (Dolomys, Parapodemus)
corrugatus (Orodus)
Corvaspididae Heterostraci
Corvaspis
Corvaspis Corvaspididae Turner, S., Dixon, J. 1971A
Corvidae Passeriformes—Passeres
Coloeus, Corvus, Garrulus, Miocitta, Pica, Protocitta,
Pyrrhocorax
Corvina Sciaenidae Brzobohatý, R. 1969A (?, otol.)
speciosa Gaemers, P. A. M. 1971A (otol.);
Heinrich, W.-D. 1969B (otol.); Stancu, J.
1970A (cf., otol., in Serranidae)
Corvus Corvidae
corax Jánossy, D. 1972A (cf.)
corone
cornix Jánossy, D. 1972A (group)
Coryphaenoides see Macrourus
coryphaeus (Platecarpus)
Corythosaurus Hadrosauridae
excavatus Heaton, M. J. 1972A; Morris, W. J. 1970A
intermedius Morris, W. J. 1970A
Cosmacanthus Acanthodii incertae sedis White, E. I.
1968A
Cosmaspis Protaspis *Denison, R. H.* 1970B
(n. subgen.)
Cosmoptychiidae Palaeonisciformes—Palaeoniscoidei
Grassator
cosmovicii (Argyropelecus)
Cosomys see Mimomys
Cosoryx see Merycodus
costatus (Palaeoscincus)
costellatus (Cheiracanthus)
Cotimus Cricetidae Bruijn, H., Meulenkamp, J. E.
1972A
latior Engesser, B. 1972A (cf.)
Cottidae Scorpaeniformes—Cottoidei
Cottopsis, Cottus, Lepidocottus
Cottopsis Cottidae
gaudryi Arambourg, C. 1966A (in Serranidae—
Apogoninae)
Cottus Cottidae
cryptotremus see C. divaricatus
divaricatus [C. cryptotremus] Linder, A. D. 1970A
germanicus Rado, G. 1965A, 1969A (otol.)
pontifex Linder, A. D. 1970A
Coturnicops Rallidae
avita *Feduccia, J. A.* 1968A
coturnix (Coturnix)
Coturnix Phasianidae
coturnix Boecker, M., et al. 1972A; Jánossy, D.
1972A (cf.)
Cotylosauria Reptilia—Anapsida
Incl. subord. Captorhinomorpha, Procolophonia
Kuhn, O. 1969A,C
coureli (Chirotherium)
courseni (Allodesmus)
cozlae (Eomyctophum)
Cracidae Galliformes
Palaeortyx, Taoperdix
Cramauchenia Macraucheniidae
insolita Friant, M. 1967B
Crangidarum see Otolithus
cranibrevis (Procheneosaurus)
Cranioceras Palaeomerycidae
clarendonensis Patton, T. H. 1969B (in Cervidae—
Dromomerycinae)
unicornis Webb, S. D. 1969C

Criocephalus   Tapinocephalidae Boonstra, L. D. 1969A
   gunyankaensis Boonstra, L. D. 1968B
cristata (Sus)
cristatum (Pseudholocentrum, Thylatheridium)
cristatus (Ctenodus, Pterodactylus, Rabidosaurus)
critinus (Peromyscus)
croaticus (Lates, Priacanthus)
Crocidosorex   Soricidae
   piveteaui Gureev, A. A. 1971A
Crocidura   Soricidae Altuna, J. 1970A; Rzebik, B.
      1968A
   cornfeldi Gureev, A. A. 1971A
   gibberodon see Asoriculus
   leucodon Gureev, A. A. 1971A
   obtusa Gureev, A. A. 1971A; Jánossy, D. 1969B;
      Koenigswald, W. 1971A
   pavlodarica Gureev, A. A. 1971A
   russula Malec, F., Storch, G. 1970A (cf.)
   suaveolens Heller, J. 1970A; Jánossy, D. 1969B
      (group)
   zorzii Bartolomei, G., Pasa, A. 1970A; Gureev,
      A. A. 1971A
Crocodylia   Reptilia–Archosauria
   Incl. subord. Protosuchia, Archaeosuchia,
      Mesosuchia, Sebecosuchia, Eusuchia
      Berg, D. E. 1967A; Guggisberg, C. A. W.
      1972A; Kuhn, O. 1968C (classif.);
      Romer, A. S. 1972F (classif.); Walker,
      A. D. 1970A (subord., in Crocodylomorpha,
      incl. infraord. Protosuchia)
   Incertae sedis: Macelognathus
Crocodylidae   Crocodylia–Eosuchia Neill, W. T.
      1971A
   Albertochampsa, Allognathosuchus, Asiatosuchus,
      Brachychampsa, Charactosuchus,
      Crocodylus, Diplocynodon, Euthecodon,
      Leidyosuchus, Pristichampsus, Tomistoma
Crocodylomorpha   Reptilia Walker, A. D. 1970A
      (order, incl. subord. Crocodylia,
      Paracrocodylia)
Crocodylus   Crocodylidae
   antillensis Varona, L. S. 1966A
crocuta (Crocuta)
Crocuta   Hyaenidae Baigusheva, V. S. 1971A
   crocuta Bonifay, M.-F. 1967A; Buckland-
      Wright, J. C. 1969A; Kurtén, B. 1969A;
      Melentis, J. K. 1966H; Sutcliffe, A. J.
      1969A
   dorotheae Petter, G., Heintz, E. 1969A
   spelaea Erdbrink, D. P. 1972A; Martin, R. 1968A
   eximia Melentis, J. K. 1970A
   miocenica Pavlović, B. 1969A
   perrieri Torres Perezhidalgo, T. J. 1969A (cf.)
   spelaea Bonifay, M.-F. 1971A; Bouchud, J. 1969A;
      Delpech, F., et al. 1970A; Ehrenberg, K.
      1966G; Garevski, R. 1969A; Melentis, J. K.
      1966P; Mostecký, V. 1969A; Rădulescu, C.,
      Kovács, A. 1968A; Schütt, G. 1969C
   intermedia Bonifay, M.-F. 1971A
cromerensis (Mammuthus meridionalis)
cromptoni (Soetendalichthys)
Crossopterygii   Osteichthyes–Sarcopterygii
   Incl. subord. Rhipidistia, Coelacanthini
      Schultze, H.-P. 1969B (teeth)
Crossotelos   Urocordylidae
   annulatus Berman, D. S. 1970A
crucians (Hyaenodon)

crucifer (Hyla)
cruciger (Edaphosaurus)
crucigera (Vulpes vulpes)
cruentus (Hyaenodon)
crusafonti (Castillomys, Cryptopterus, Hipparion,
      Hispanolagus, Ischyrosmilus, Praearmantomys,
      Theridomys)
Crusafontia   Dryolestidae Henkel, S., Krebs, B. 1969A
   cuencana Henkel, S. 1970A; Henkel, S., Krebs, B.
      1969A; Krebs, B. 1971A
Cryptobalistes   Triacanthidae–Cryptacanthodinae
      Tyler, J. C. 1968A
   brevis [Acanthopleurus] Tyler, J. C. 1968A
Cryptobranchidae   Urodela
   Andrias, Piceoerpeton
Cryptodontidae see Dicynodontidae
Cryptomys   ?Bathyergidae
   asiaticus Tchernov, E. 1968C
Cryptopterus   Sciuridae Mein, P. 1970A
   crusafonti Mein, P. 1970A
   gaillardi Engesser, B. 1972A; Mein, P. 1970A
   lappi [Sciuropterus] Mein, P. 1970A
   neogrivensis Mein, P. 1970A
   thaleri Mein, P. 1970A
   tobieni Mein, P. 1970A
Cryptornis   Bucerotidae
   antiquus Brunet, J. 1970A (in Piciformes–Picidae)
Cryptotis   Soricidae
   adamsi Choate, J. R. 1970A
   kansasensis Choate, J. R. 1970A; Gureev, A. A.
      1971A
   meadensis Choate, J. R. 1970A; Gureev, A. A.
      1971A(?)
crystarhynchus (Rechnisaurus)
Csakvaromys   Sciurotamias
csarnotanus (Ochotonoides)
Cseria   Villanyia
   See also Mimomys
Ctenacanthidae   Cladoselachii
   Ctenacanthus
Ctenacanthus   Ctenacanthidae Bel'skaia, T. N.
      1960A(?); Bendix-Almgreen, S. E.,
      Malzahn, E. 1969A
   amblyxiphias Berman, D. S. 1970A (cf.)
   ishii Kapoor, H. M., Sahni, A. 1971A
   ornatus Pageau, Y. 1969A(?)
Ctenacodon   Plagiaulacidae Hahn, G. 1969A, 1971A
Ctenocephalichthys   Holocentridae Gaudant, M. 1969A
   longispinnus Gaudant, M. 1969A
   lorteti Gaudant, M. 1969A
Ctenocerus   Cervidae Bukatchuk, P. D., Burdenko,
      B. V., Voloshin, V. E. 1968A,B [Pliocervus]
   pentelici Melentis, J. K. 1969A, 1970A [Pliocervus]
   See also Ctenocervus
Ctenocervus   [Ctenocerus] Cervidae Kretzoi, M. 1968B
      (nov. nom.)
Ctenochasma   Pterodactylidae Taquet, P. 1972A
      (in Ctenochasmidae)
   gracile Wellnhofer, P. 1970A (in Ctenochasmatidae)
Ctenochasmatidae see Pterodactylidae
Ctenodactylidae   Rodentia
   Pectinator, ?Pellegrinia, Sayimys, Woodomys
ctenodon (Ichthyodectes)
Ctenodontidae   Dipnoi
   Ctenodus, Parasagenodus
   See also Sagenodontidae

Ctenodus Ctenodontidae
   cristatus Bertmar, T. 1968B
Ctenoptychius Petalodontidae Berman, D. S. 1970A
Ctenosauriscidae Sphenacodontia Krebs, B. 1969A
   (in Pseudosuchia; incl. Ctenosauriscus,
   Hypselorhachis)
Ctenosauriscus Sphenacodontidae
   koeneni Krebs, B. 1969A (in Ctenosauriscidae)
Ctenothrissa Ctenothrissidae Patterson, C. 1968B
Ctenothrissidae Ctenothrissiformes
   Ctenothrissa
Ctenothrissiformes Teleostei
Ctenurella Ptyctodontidae Stensiö, E. 1969B
Cubanocnus [Microcnus] Megalonychidae
   Kretzoi, M. 1968B (nov. nom.)
cubensis (Grus)
Cuculidae Cuculiformes
   Chrysococcyx, Cuculus, Saurothera
Cuculiformes Aves
Cuculus Cuculidae
   canorus Jánossy, D. 1972A (aff.)
cudahyensis (Sorex)
cuencana (Crusafontia)
cultripes (Pelobates)
cumberlandicus (Coendou)
cumminsi (Equus)
cuneata (Logania)
cuneatus (Grallator)
cuneiformis (Spinacanthus)
cunicularia (Speotyto)
cunicularius (Sylvilagus)
cuniculus (Oryctolagus, Oryctolagus cuniculus)
Cuon Canidae Erdbrink, D. P. 1968A
   alpinus Bonifay, M.-F. 1971A
      sardus see Cynotherium sardus
   dubius see Cynotherium
   priscus Bonifay, M.-F. 1971A
   sardus Comaschi Caria, I. 1968A (subgen.
      Cynotherium)
   stehlini Bonifay, M.-F. 1971A (cf.)
Cupidinimus Heteromyidae Green, M. 1971A
   nebraskensis Klingener, D. 1968A;
      Lindsay, E. H. 1972B
Cursipes Ichnites
   dawsoni Haubold, H. 1970A (in Dissorophidae)
   See also Anthracopus, Quadropedia
cursor (Bathornis)
cursorius (Rotodactylus)
curta (Scaumenacia)
curtirostris (Platecarpus)
curtisi (Sigmodon)
curtum (Palaeotherium)
curtus (Gregorymys, Oreodontoides, Pomolobus)
curvicuspidens (Protoadapis)
curvidactylus (Varanopus)
curvidens (Desmatochoerus, Equus)
curvimola (Arctognathus)
curvirostra (Loxia)
curvirostris (Dapalis)
cuspidata (Eudaemonema, Odontaspis)
cuspidatus (Coccosteus, Dichodon)
cutlerensis (Ecolsonia, Limnopus)
cuvieri (Galeocerdo, Gypsornis, Palaegithalus,
      Palaeocircus, Peratherium,
      Protopelicanus, Trogontherium)
cuvierii (Balaenoptera acutorostrata)

Cuvieronius Gomphotheriidae
   arellanoi [C. chinangoensis] Ochoterena, F. H.,
      Silva-Barcenas, A. 1970A
   chinangoensis Ochoterena, F. H., Silva-Barcenas, A.
      1970A (nomen nudum, see C. arellanoi)
cuyamensis (Perognathus)
Cuyosuchus Erythrosuchidae
   huenei Bonaparte, J. F. 1972A (in ?Proterosuchidae)
cyanellus (Lepomis)
Cyathaspididae Heterostraci (in Cyathaspiformes–
      Cyathaspida, Stensiö)
   Anglaspis, Aphataspis, Archegonaspis, Dykenaspis,
      Poraspis, Putoranaspis, Vernonaspis
   See also Aphataspididae, Poraspididae
Cybium see Scomberomorus
cybium (Muraenesox)
cyclomorpha (Argentina)
Cyclopidius Merycoidodontidae
   schucherti Macdonald, J. R. 1970A
   simus Macdonald, J. R. 1970A
Cycloptychius
   bidens see Grassator
Cyclostomata Agnatha–Monorhina (incl.
      Petromyzontida and Myxinoidea of
      Stensiö) Obruchev, D. V. 1971A
Cyclotosaurus Capitosauridae Ortlam, D. 1967A;
      Schultze, H.-P. 1969B
   mechernichensis Müller, E. M., et al. 1960A
Cygnus Anatidae
   pristinus Kurochkin, E. N. 1971A
Cylindracanthus see Coelorhynchus
cylindrifer (Stylinodon)
Cylindrodon Cylindrodontidae
   collinus Russell, L. S. 1972B
   fontis Galbreath, E. C. 1969A
Cylindrodontidae Rodentia–Ischyromyoidea
   Ardynomys, Beatomus, Beatomys, Cylindrodon,
      Jaywilsonomys, Morosomys, Pareumys,
      Pseudocylindrodon, Pseudotsaganomys,
      Sepulkomys, Tsaganomys
Cymaprimadon Cymaprimadontidae Clark, J. 1968A,
      1969A
   kenni Clark, J. 1968A
Cymaprimadontidae Insectivora Clark, J. 1968A
   Cymaprimadon
Cymathoriza Gymnarthridae Schultze, H.-P. 1969B
Cymbospondylidae see Shastasauridae
Cymbospondylus Shastasauridae Polubotko, I. V.,
      Ochev, V. G. 1972A (?, in Cymbospondylidae);
      Schultze, H.-P. 1969B
Cynarioides see Aloposaurus, Scylacognathus
Cynariops see Scylacognathus
Cynariopsidae see Gorgonopsidae–Gorgonopsinae
Cynelos Canidae Hunt, R. M. 1972A
      (in Amphicyonidae)
Cyniscopoides see Cyonosaurus
Cyniscops see Aelurosaurus, Arctognathus, Cyonosaurus
cynocephalus (Thylacinus)
Cynodesmus Canidae
   cooki Macdonald, J. R. 1970A
   vulpinus Macdonald, J. R. 1970A
Cynodictis Canidae
   minor Ianovskaîa, N. M. 1970A
   mongoliensis Ianovskaîa, N. M. 1970A

Cynodontia   Therapsida–Theriodontia Crompton, A. W.
    1972A (jaw articulation); Hopson, J. A.,
    Kitching, J. W. 1972A (classif.); Jenkins, F. A.
    1970A, 1971A; Kemp, T. S. 1972B; Turner,
    B. R. 1972A
Cynodontomys see Microsyops
Cynodontosuchus   Baurusuchidae
    rothi Gasparini, Z. B. 1972A
Cynoglossidae   Pleuronectiformes–Pleuronectoidei
    Rhinoplagusia
Cynognathidae   Therapsida–Cynodontia
    Chiniquodon, ?Colbertosaurus, Cynognathus
    See also Chiniquodontidae, Traversodontidae
Cynognathus   Cynognathidae Jenkins, F. A. 1971A;
    Kermack, K. A., Kielan-Jaworowska, Z.
    1971A
    minor Bonaparte, J. F. 1969A, 1972A
Cynogulo [Pliogulo] Canidae Kretzoi, M. 1968B
    (nov. nom.)
Cynomys   Sciuridae
    ludovicianus Schultz, G. E. 1969A
    vetus Dalquest, W. W. 1967A
Cynopithecinae   Cercopithecidae Hill, W. C. O. 1970A
Cynorca   Tayassuidae
    hesperia Woodburne, M. O. 1969A
    occidentale Woodburne, M. O. 1969A
    proterva Woodburne, M. O. 1969A
    sociale Woodburne, M. O. 1969A
Cynotherium   Canidae
    dubius [Cuon] Malatesta, A. 1970A
    sardus [Cuon alpinus sardus] Malatesta, A. 1970A
Cynotherium   Cuon
cyonoides (Osteoborus)
Cyonosaurus   Gorgonopsidae–Gorgonopsinae
    kitchingi [Alopecorhynchus rubidgei] Sigogneau, D.
        1970A (cf.); [Cyniscops] Sigogneau, D.
        1970A (n. comb.)
    longiceps [Cyniscops] Sigogneau, D. 1970A
    rubidgei [Cyniscops] Sigogneau, D. 1970A
        (n. comb.); [Cyniscopoides broomi]
        Sigogneau, D. 1970A (cf.)
Cypholepis   Astrolepidae Stensiö, E. 1969B
    (in Antiarchi incertae sedis)
cyprinellus (Ictiobus)
Cyprinidae   Cypriniformes–Cyprinoidei Weiler, W.
    1970A
    Abramis, Alburnus, Aspius, Barbus, Blicca,
        Carassius, Chondrostoma, Cyprinus,
        Gobio, Ictiobus, Leuciscus, Palaeotinca,
        Phoxinus, Pimephales, Rodeus, Rutilus,
        Scardinius, Serrodens, Tinca,
        Varhostichthys, Varicorhinus
Cypriniformes   Teleostei
    Incl. subord. Characoidei, Gymnotoidei,
        Cyprinoidei
Cyprinodon   Cyprinodontidae
    dentifer Stinton, F. C., Kissling, D. 1968A (otol.)
    subtrigonus Stinton, F. C., Kissling, D. 1968A
        (otol.)
Cyprinodontidae   Atheriniformes–Cyprinodontoidei
    Aphanius, Cyprinodon, Cyprinodontinarum,
        Fundulus, Prolebias
    See also Otolithus
Cyprinodontinarum   Cyprinodontidae see Otolithus
cyprinoides (Megalops)

Cyprinus   Cyprinidae
    priscus Anđelković, J. 1970A
Cyrbasiodon   Ericiolacertidae
    boycei Mendrez, C. H. 1972E (in Cynodontia–
        Procynosuchidae)
Cyrtaspidichthys   Protaspis
Cyrtosteus   Trematosteidae Stensiö, E. 1969A,B
    czekanowskii (Palaeoniscinotus)
dacicus (Muscardinus)
Dacrytherium   Anoplotheriidae
    priscum Sudre, J. 1972A(?)
Dactylopteridae   Dactylopteriformes
    Dactylopterus
Dactylopteriformes   Teleostei
Dactylopterus   Dactylopteridae
    stintoni Cappetta, H. C. 1969B (otol.)
Dahutherium   Ichnites Montenat, C. 1970A
    agilis Montenat, C. 1970A
dainellii (Volcichthys)
dakotensis (Domnina, Grangerimus, Parictis, Pleurolicus)
Dalatias   Dalatiidae
    barnstonensis Sykes, J. H. 1971A
Dalatiidae [Scymnorhinidae] Selachii–Squaloidea
    Dalatias, Isistius
dalinkevichiusi (Eoanacorax)
Dallia   Umbridae Cavender, T. 1969A
dalmatinus (Dolomys)
Dalpiazia see Onchosaurus
dalquesti (Campephilus)
Dama   Cervidae Ducos, P. 1968A; Jánossy, D. 1969B;
        Torres Perezhidalgo, T. 1971A;
        Vandermeersch, B. 1970B
    dama Mostecký, V. 1969A
    See also Cervus
dama (Dama)
Damaliscus   Bovidae
    porrocornutus Vrba, E. S. 1971A, 1972A
Danatinia   Turkmenidae Danil'chenko, P. G. 1968B
    casca Danil'chenko, P. G. 1968B
Dapalis   Serranidae Salis, K. 1967A [Smerdis; otol.]
    carinatus Stinton, F. C., Kissling, D. 1968A (otol.)
    crassirostris Brzobohatý, R. 1969A [Smerdis; otol.]
    curvirostris Brzobohatý, R. 1969A [Smerdis; otol.]
    elongatus Anđelković, J. 1970A [Smerdis]
    formosus Anđelković, J. 1970A [Smerdis];
        Brzobohatý, R. 1969A [Smerdis; otol.]
    macrurus Anđelković, J. 1970A [Smerdis]
    microcanthus Anđelković, J. 1970A [Smerdis]
    minutus Anđelković, J. 1970A [Smerdis]
    rhomboidalis Stinton, F. C., Kissling, D. 1968A
        (otol.)
Daphoenocyon   Canidae Clark, J. 1969A; Russell, L. S.
        1972B(?)
Daphoenus   Canidae
    canadensis Russell, L. S. 1972B
    hartshornianus Russell, L. S. 1972B (cf.)
    lambei Russell, L. S. 1972B
    vetus Russell, L. S. 1972B (cf.)
daptes (Angelocabrerus)
Daptocephalus see Dicynodon
darewskii (Protestudo)
darocensis (Fahlbuschia)
darti (Papio)
Dartmuthiidae   Osteostraci
    Oeselaspis, Tyriaspis

deltoides (Tylodus)
Deltoptychius Cochliodontidae
  acutus Patterson, C. 1968C
  armigerus Bendix-Almgreen, S. E. 1971A;
    Patterson, C. 1968C
demathieui (Chirotherium)
dementjevi (Tutor, Venerator)
deminutus (Bison priscus)
Democricetodon Copemys
Democricetodon Cricetidae
  affinis
    cretensis Bruijn, H., Meulenkamp, J. E. 1972A
    crassus [D. minor] Mein, P., Freudenthal, M. 1971A
  gaillardi
    freisingensis Engesser, B. 1972A
    gregarius Engesser, B. 1972A [Megacricetodon]
    minor Telles Antunes, M., Mein, P. 1971A (cf.);
      Telles Antunes, M., Mein, P. 1971A
      [Megacricetodon]
    brevis Engesser, B. 1972A
    collongensis Baudelot, S. 1969A
      [Megacricetodon]
    See also D. crassus
    romiviensis Baudelot, S. 1969A
    schaubi Engesser, B. 1972A [aff., Megacricetodon]
    similis Engesser, B. 1972A [Megacricetodon]
Dendragapus Phasianidae
  gilli
    gilli Jehl, J. R. 1969A (n. subsp.)
    milleri Jehl, J. R. 1969A (n. subsp.)
    lucasi [D. nanus] Jehl, J. R. 1969A
    nanus see D. lucasi
Dendrerpeton Dendrerpetontidae Schultze, H.-P.
    1969B
Dendrerpetontidae Temnospondyli—Edopoidea
  Dendrerpeton
  See also Ichnites
dendrocerus (Megaloceros verticornis)
Dendrocopos Picidae
  major Jánossy, D. 1972A (cf.)
deningeri (Ursus, Ursus deningeri)
denisoni (Astroconodon, Hirella)
densicingulatus (Anourosorex)
dentata (Gerronaspis)
Dentex Sparidae
  elegans [otol. (Sparidarum) elegans] Robba, E.
    1970A
  gregarius Brzobohatý, R. 1967C (cf., otol.);
    Gaemers, P. A. M. 1969A (otol.), 1971A
    (otol.)
  latior Dieni, I. 1968A (otol.); Robba, E. 1970A
  nobilis
    miocenica Gaemers, P. A. M. 1969A (otol.),
      1971A (otol.); Heinrich, W.-D. 1969B (otol.)
    nota Stinton, F. C., Nolf, D. 1969A (otol.)
  subnobilis Anfossi, G., Mosna, S. 1969B (aff., otol.)
denticulatus (Leptochamops)
dentifer (Cyprinodon)
de Pauwii (Isocetus)
deperdita (Gazella)
Depereta Cervus
Deperetella Deperetellidae Zhukov, ĨU. V. 1970A
Deperetellidae Perissodactyla—Tapiroidea
  Deperetella, Teleolophus
depereti (Albaneryx, Alligatorium, Entelodon,
    Palaeortyx, Steneofiber, Steneofiber
    depereti, Tapirulus)

Deperetomys Cricetodon Mein, P., Freudenthal, M.
    1971A (n. subgen.)
depressidens (Paromomys)
depressus (Knightomys)
deprofundis (Qataraspis)
Dercetidae Salmoniformes—Myctophoidei
  Apateopholis, Dercetis, Pelargorhynchus, Prionolepis,
    Rhynchodercetis, Stratodus
dercetiformis (Pelargorhynchus)
Dercetis Dercetidae
  armatus Goody, P. C. 1969B (restor.)
  gracilis Goody, P. C. 1969B (restor.)
  linguifer see D. triqueter
  rostralis Goody, P. C. 1969B (restor.)
  triqueter [Leptotrachelus, Benthesikyme,
    D. linguifer] Goody, P. C. 1969B
Dermatemydidae Chelonia—Cryptodira Verzilin, N. N.,
    et al. 1970A
  Adocus, Basilemys, Compsemys, Hoplochelys,
    Mongolemys, Tretosternon, Tsaotanemys,
    Zangerlia
Dermochelyidae Chelonia—Cryptodira
  Psephophorus
derthonensis (Hygophus intermedius)
Desmana Talpidae
  kormosi Rabeder, G. 1970A (cf.); Topachevskii, V. A.
    1962A
  moschata Topachevskii, V. A. 1962A
    hungarica Topachevskii, V. A. 1962A
    magna Topachevskii, V. A. 1962A
    moravica Topachevskii, V. A. 1962A
    mosbachensis Bahlo, E., Malec, F. 1969A (cf.);
      Topachevskii, V. A. 1962A
    palaeoborysthenica Topachevskii, V. A. 1962A
    ternopolitana Topachevskii, V. A. 1962A
  nehringi Kretzoi, M. 1967B (cf.); Rzebik-Kowalska, B.
    1971A; Topachevskii, V. A. 1962A
  pontica Bachmayer, F., Wilson, R. W. 1970A(?);
    Topachevskii, V. A. 1962A
  semseyi Topachevskii, V. A. 1962A
  thermalis Jánossy, D. 1969B (cf.); Topachevskii, V. A.
    1962A
  verestchagini Topachevskii, V. A. 1962A
Desmanella Talpidae—Desmaninae Engesser, B. 1972A
  stehlini Engesser, B. 1972A
Desmathyus see Hesperhys
Desmatochoerus Merycoidodontidae
  curvidens
    gregoryi Macdonald, J. R. 1970A
  hatcheri
    geringensis Macdonald, J. R. 1970A
    wyomingensis Macdonald, J. R. 1970A (subgen.
      Paradesmatochoerus)
Desmatodon Diadectidae
  hesperis Vaughn, P. P. 1969B, 1972A
Desmatolagus Ochotonidae McKenna, M. C., Love,
    J. D. 1972A
Desmoporella Ptyctodontidae Ørvig, T. 1971A
  minor ["Epipetalichthys"] Ørvig, T. 1971A
Desmostylia Mammalia Domning, D. P. 1972A
Desmostylidae Desmostylia
  Desmostylus, Paleoparadoxia
Desmostylus Desmostylidae [Kronokotherium]
    Dubrovo, I. A., Sinel'nikova, V. N. 1971A;
    Mel'nikov, O. A., Shustov, L. N. 1969A;
    Strelkov, S. A. 1970A

Dicrostonyx - cont.
    torquatus Kozłowski, J. K., Kubiak, H., Welc, A.
        1970A; Kuz'mina, I. E. 1971A; Martin, R.
        1968A
Dictybolos Araeoscelidia incertae sedis *Olson, E. C.*
    1970A (in Araeosceloidea inc. sed.)
    tener *Olson, E. C.* 1970A
Dicynodon Dicynodontidae Boonstra, L. D. 1968B,
        1969A; Ricqlès, A. 1972B [Daptocephalus];
        Young, C.-c. 1957E(?)
    latifrons see Kannemeyeria simocephalus
    tener Ricqlès, A. 1972B
    testudirostris Cluver, M. A. 1970A
    turpior see Dinodontosaurus
    tylorhinus see Propelanomodon
Dicynodontia Therapsida—Anomodontia Barry, T. H.
        1972A
Dicynodontidae Therapsida—Dicynodontia
    Aulacephalodon, Dicynodon, ? Kawingasaurus,
        Kingoria, Oudenodon, Pelanomodon,
        Propelanomodon, Rhachiocephalus,
        Rhadiodromus
Dicynodontipus Ichnites
    geinitzi [Chirotherium, Chelichnus] Haubold, H.
        1971A (in Theriodontia)
didactylus (Moodieichnus)
Didelphidae Marsupialia—Polyprotodonta
    Alacodon, Albertatherium, Alphadon,
        Arctodelphis, Bobbschaefferia, Boreodon,
        Didelphis, Didelphodon, Didelphopsis,
        Eodelphis, Gaylordia, Holoclemensia,
        ?Lactemys, Lutreolina, Marmosa,
        Marmosopsis, Minusculodelphis,
        Mirandatherium, Monodelphopsis,
        Nanodelphis, Paradidelphys, Pediomys,
        Peratherium, Protodidelphis,
        Sparassocynus, Sternbergia,
        Thylatheridium, Thylophorops,
        Xenodelphis
Didelphis Didelphidae Kermack, K. A., Kielan-
        Jaworowska, Z. 1971A (braincase)
    brachyodonta [Paradidelphys] Simpson, G. G.
        1972A
    marsupialis Hiiemäe, K., Jenkins, F. 1969A
    reigi *Simpson, G. G.* 1972A
Didelphodon Didelphidae
    vorax Lillegraven, J. A. 1969B
        (in Stagodontidae)
Didelphodus Deltatheridiidae Crompton, A. W.
        1971A; Rich, T. H. V. 1971A (cf., in
        Palaeoryctidae)
    altidens Guthrie, D. A. 1971B (in
        Palaeoryctidae)
didelphoides (Palaeosinopa)
Didelphopsis Didelphidae
    cabrerai Paula Couto, C. 1970A
Didolodontidae Condylarthra
    Argyrolambda, Didolodus, Enneoconus,
        Proectocion
    See also Hyopsodontidae
Didolodus Didolodontidae Simpson, G. G.
        1970D
    lanceolatus Friant, M. 1967B [Lonchoconus]
    multicuspis Friant, M. 1967B
Didymictis Miacidae
    altidens Guthrie, D. A. 1971B

Didymoconidae Creodonta—Deltatheridia
    Didymoconus, Kennatherium
Didymoconus Didymoconidae
    colgatei Mellett, J. S., Szalay, F. S. 1968A
diegense (Mancalla)
dietrichbergi (Bergisuchus)
dietrichi (Hipparion, Kuehneodon)
difformis (Bauzaia)
digitatum (Diplovertebron)
digitatus (Dipterus)
digitipes (Mirotenthes)
Dikenaspis Cyathaspididae
    yukonensis Stensiö, E. 1968A
Dikkomys Geomyidae Munthe, J., Jr. 1971A
    matthewi Macdonald, J. R. 1970A
    woodi [Horatiomys montanus] Black, C. C. 1969B
dilatus (Habrosaurus)
dilophidus (Castoroides ohioensis)
Dilophosauripus Ichnites *Welles, S. P.* 1971A
        (in Coelurosauria, Grallatoridae)
    williamsi *Welles, S. P.* 1971A
Dilophosaurus Coeluridae *Welles, S. P.* 1970A
    wetherilli [Megalosaurus] Welles, S. P. 1970A
        (n. comb.), 1972A
diluviana (Martes)
diluvianus (Palaeobatrachus)
Dimetrodon Sphenacodontidae Berman, D. S. 1970A
Dimorphodontidae Pterosauria—Rhamphorhynchoidea
    Sordes
Dimylechinus Erinaceidae Friant, M. 1971C
Dimylidae Insectivora—Erinaceoidea
    Metacordylodon, Plesiodimylus
Dimylosorex Soricidae—Soricinae *Rabeder, G.* 1972A
    tholodus *Rabeder, G.* 1972A
Dinematichthys Ophidiidae
    argutus Robba, E. 1970A (otol., in Brotulidae)
Dinichthyidae Arthrodira—Brachythoraci (incl.
        Dunkleosteidae of Stensiö) Straka, J. J.,
        Semken, H. A. 1969A
    Bungartius, Dinichthys, Dunkleosteus, Eastmanosteus,
        Gorgonichthys, Heintzichthys, Holdenius,
        ? Tafilalichthys, ? Timanosteus
Dinichthys Dinichthyidae Stensiö, E. 1969A,B (nomen
        nudum); Stensiö, E. 1969B [Perissognathus,
        in Euarthrodira incertae sedis]
    egloni Obrucheva, O. P. 1962C
    licharevi Obrucheva, O. P. 1962C
    machlaevi Obrucheva, O. P. 1962C
Dinictis Felidae Brunet, M. 1967A; Eklund, R. R.
        1969A; Levine, W. E. 1971A
    eileenae *Macdonald, J. R.* 1970A
    felina Russell, L. S. 1972B
Dinilysia Dinilysiidae
    patagonica Estes, R., Frazzetta, T. H., Williams, E. E.
        1970A; Frazzetta, T. H. 1970A (reconstr.)
Dinilysiidae Squamata—Ophidia
    Dinilysia
Dinocephalia Therapsida—Anomodontia
Dinocerata Mammalia Flerov, K. K. 1967B (Mongolia)
Dinodontosaurus Stahleckeriidae
    brevirostris Bonaparte, J. F. 1972A; *Cox, C. B.*
        1968A
    platygnathus Bonaparte, J. F. 1972A; *Cox, C. B.*
        1968A
    turpior Bonaparte, J. F. 1972A; Ricqlès, A. 1972B
        [Dicynodon]

Dinofelis Felidae Kurtén, B. 1972E
Dinognathus Mylostomidae Stensiö, E. 1969B
(in Euarthrodira incertae sedis)
Dinogorgon Gorgonopsidae—Rubidgeinae
laticeps see Broomicephalus
Dinogorgon
oudebergensis see D. quinquemolaris
pricei [Tigrisaurus] Sigogneau, D. 1970A (n. comb.)
quinquemolaris [D. oudebergensis] Sigogneau, D.
1970A
rubidgei Sigogneau, D. 1970A
Dinohyus Entelodontidae Parris, D. C., Green, M.
1969A
Dinomyidae Rodentia—Chinchilloidea
Eumegamys
Dinomylostoma Mylostomidae Stensiö, E. 1969B
(in Euarthrodira incertae sedis)
Dinopterygidae Beryciformes—Dinopterygoidei
Dinopteryx
Dinopteryx Dinopterygidae
spinosus Patterson, C. 1968B
Dinornis Dinornithidae
queenslandiae Scarlett, R. J. 1969A [holotype =
Pachyornis elephantopus]
Dinornithidae Dinornithiformes
Dinornis
Dinornithiformes Aves
Dinosaurichnium Ichnites
postchirotherioides Rehnelt, K. 1959A
schlehenbergense see Coelurosaurichnus
Dinosauripus see Coelurosaurichnus
Dinosorex Soricidae—Heterosoricinae Engesser, B.
1972A
pachygnathus Engesser, B. 1972B
sansaniensis Engesser, B. 1972A
Dinotherium see Deinotherium
Diodon Diodontidae
scillae Menesini, E. 1969A
sinhaleyus Deraniyagala, P. E. P. 1969A
Diodontidae Tetraodontiformes—Tetraodontoidei
Bacskai, J. A. 1969A
Diodon, Kyrtogymnodon, Progymnodon
Diomedea Diomedeidae
thyridata Wilkinson, H. E. 1969A
Diomedeidae Procellariiformes
Diomedea
Diplacanthoides see Nostolepis
Diplobune Anoplotheriidae
secundarium Jehenne, Y. 1969A
Diplocaulus Keraterpetontidae Berman, D. S. 1970A
parvus Olson, E. C. 1972C
Diplocynodon [Orthosaurus] Crocodylidae Berg, D. E.
1969A; Berg, D. E., Crusafont, M.
1970A(?)
gervaisi Jehenne, Y. 1970A (aff.)
gracilis Jehenne, Y. 1970A (aff.)
hantoniensis Berg, D. E. 1971A (aff.)
rateli Berg, D. E. 1971A (aff.); Jehenne, Y.
1970A (aff.)
Diplodocus Titanosauridae
carnegiei Miller, R. C. 1972A
longus Klausewitz, W. 1970A
Diplodus see Sargus
Diplomystus Clupeidae
goodi Casier, E., Taverne, L. 1971A
solignaci Gaudant, M., Gaudant, J. 1971A

Diplorhina Agnatha (incl. Pteraspidomorphi and
Thelodonti of Stensiö)
Diplovertebron Diplovertebrontidae
bohemicum Carroll, R. L. 1970A, 1972A
[Gephyrostegus]
digitatum Carroll, R. L. 1970A, 1972A
[Eusauropleura]
punctatum Carroll, R. L. 1970A, 1972A
Diplovertebrontidae Anthracosauria—Diplomeri
Diplovertebron
Dipnoi Osteichthyes—Sarcopterygii Bertmar, G.
1968A,B; Jarvik, E. 1968A,B; Schaeffer, B.
1968C; Schultze, H.-P. 1970A (vert.)
Incertae sedis: Melanognathus
Dipnorhynchidae Dipnoi
Dipnorhynchus, Griphognathus, Uranolophus
Dipnorhynchus Dipnorhynchidae
sussmilchi Anon. 1972AQ; Bertmar, G. 1968B;
Thomson, K. S., Campbell, K. S. W. 1971A
Dipodidae Rodentia—Dipodoidea
Allactaga, Brachyscirtetes, Pliopygerethmus,
Proalactaga, Pseudoalactaga, Scirtodipus
Dipodoidea Rodentia
Dipodomys Heteromyidae Miller, W. E. 1971A
merriami Simpson, G. G. 1970E
ordii Dalquest, W. W. 1967A
Dipoides Castoridae—Castoroidinae
intermedius Zakrzewski, R. J. 1969A
problematicus Friant, M. 1965C
rexroadensis Hibbard, C. W. 1972A
vallicula Shotwell, J. A. 1970A
Diprionomys Heteromyidae
agrarius Klingener, D. 1968A
Diprotodon Diprotodontidae Waters, B. K.,
Savage, D. E. 1969A
Diprotodonta Mammalia—Marsupiata Turnbull, W. D.
1971A (order)
Diprotodontidae Marsupialia—Diprotodonta
Diprotodon, Ngakapaldia, Sceparnodon, Zygomaturus
Dipterichthyidae Perciformes—Percoidei Arambourg, C.
1966A
Dipterichthys
Dipterichthys Dipterichthyidae Arambourg, C. 1966A
leptosomus Arambourg, C. 1966A; Haghipour, A.,
Brants, A. 1971A
nematophorus Arambourg, C. 1966A; Haghipour, A.,
Brants, A. 1971A
Dipteridae Dipnoi
Chirodipterus, Dipterus, Rhinodipterus,
?Rhynchodipterus
Dipterus Dipteridae Gupta, V. J. 1969B; Perkins, P. L.
1971A
digitatus Seddon, G. 1969A (cf.)
valenciennesi Bertmar, G. 1968B; Denison, R. H.
1968C; Gupta, V. J. 1969C (cf.); Jarvik, E.
1968A
dirus (Canis)
discessus (Amphisauroides)
Discoglossidae [Bombinidae] Anura—Archaeobatrachia
Sahni, A. 1972A; Špinar, Z. V. 1972B
[Bombinidae]
Bombina, Discoglossus, Scotiophryne, Zaphrissa
See also Leiopelmatidae
Discoglossus Discoglossidae
giganteus Vergnaud-Grazzini, C. 1970A (cf.)
Discosauriscidae Anthracosauria—Seymouriamorpha
Discosauriscus

Discosauriscus   Discosauriscidae
  sacheti [Melanerpeton] Heyler, D. 1969A
  sigalovi Kalandadze, N. N., Ochev, V. G.,
      Tatarinov, L. P., Chudinov, P. K.,
      Shishkin, M. A. 1968A
discrepans (Soricella)
disjuncta (Charadriipeda)
disjunctus (Litaletes   Microtoscoptes)
dispar (Batrachopus)
Dissacus   Mesonychidae Quinet, G. E. 1969B
      (invalid); Szalay, F. S., McKenna, M. C.
      1971A(?)
  progressus Crusafont Pairó, M., Golpe Posse, J. M.
      1968B
Dissorophidae   Temnospondyli–Eryopoidea
      Bolt, J. R. 1969A (in Dissorophoidea)
  Astreptorhachis, Fayella, Tersomius
  See also Macromelerpetontidae, Ichnites
Dissorophoidea   Temnospondyli–Rhachitomi
      Bolt, J. R. 1969A (n. superfam., incl.
      Dissorophidae, Doleserpetontidae,
      Trematopsidae)
distans (Scyliorhinus)
distincta (Vinciguerria)
distinctus (Pagrus)
divaricatus (Cottus)
diversidens (Borophagus)
dividerus (Eucastor)
divisus (Thomasinotus)
Dixeya see Arctognathus, Aelurognathus
dixeyi (Gorgonops)
dixonensis (Planisorex)
dixoni (Pteraspis)
djetyogus (Testudo)
Dmitrevichthys   Palaeoniscidae Iakovlev, V. N. 1968A
  sutaiensis Iakovlev, V. N. 1968A
dobrogensis (Osmeroides)
Dobrowlania   Palaeacanthaspidae Stensiö, E. 1969B,
      1971A (in Spinothoracidi–Dolichothoraci
      incertae sedis)
Docodon   Docodontidae Jenkins, F. A. 1969A
Docodonta   Mammalia Mills, J. R. E. 1971A
Docodontidae   Docodonta
  Borealestes, Docodon, Haldanodon
doderleini (Sparus)
dodogolica (Ochotona)
doelloi (Xenodelphis)
Doleserpeton   Doleserpetontidae Bolt, J. R. 1969A
  annectens Bolt, J. R. 1969A
Doleserpetontidae   Dissorophoidea Bolt, J. R. 1969A
  Doleserpeton
Dolichohippus   Equus
Dolichonyx   Icteridae
  kruegeri Fischer, K., Stephan, B. 1971B
Dolichopithecus   Cercopithecidae
  arvernensis Battetta, J. 1969A (restor.);
      Crusafont Pairó, M., Golpe Posse, J. M.
      1969A (close to)
Dolichothoraci see Arctolepida
Dolichotis   Caviidae
  major Calcaterra, A. 1972A
Dollochelys   Toxochelyidae–Toxochelyinae
      Zangerl, R. 1971A
  casieri Zangerl, R. 1971A
dolloi (Paschatherium)

Dollopterus   Perleididae
  volitans Müller, A. H. 1970A
Dolomys   Cricetidae
  bogdanovi Bartolomei, G., Pasa, A. 1970A (ex gr.)
      pasai Bartolomei, G. 1970B
  coronensis Jánossy, D. 1969B [Pliomys; in
      Arvicolidae]
  dalmatinus Malez, M. 1967C
  deeringensis
      see Pliomys
  episcopalis Bartolomei, G. 1970A,B; Bartolomei, G.,
      Pasa, A. 1970A; Jánossy, D. 1969B [Pliomys;
      in Arvicolidae]; Koenigswald, W. 1972A
      [Pliomys]; Sukhov, V. P. 1970A [aff.;
      Pliomys]; Terzea, E., Jurcsák, T. 1967A
      [Pliomys; in Arvicolidae]
  bolkayi Malez, M. 1967C
  lenki Bartolomei, G. 1970A,B; Bartolomei, G.,
      Pasa, A. 1970A; Chaline, J. 1969A, 1970A,
      1971A [Pliomys, in Arvicolidae];
      Koenigswald, W. 1972A [Pliomys]
  nehringi Kretzoi, M. 1962D
dominans (Apodemus, Melissiodon, Stereorachis)
Domnina   Soricidae
  dakotensis Hutchison, J. H. 1972A; Macdonald,
      J. R. 1970A
  gradata Gureev, A. A. 1971A
  greeni Hutchison, J. H. 1972A; Macdonald, J. R.
      1970A
  thompsoni Gureev, A. A. 1971A
Domninoides   Talpidae Lindsay, E. H. 1972B
dongusensis (Chroniosaurus)
donnae (Protungulatum)
donnezani (Hyaena)
Dorcabune   Tragulidae
  nagrii Prasad, K. N., Satsangi, P. P. 1967A
dorcadoides (Gazella)
dorcas (Gazella)
Dorcatherium   Tragulidae Bruijn, H., Sondaar, P. Y.,
      Zachariasse, W. J. 1971A; Engesser, B. 1972A
  crassum Głazek, J., Oberc, J., Sulimski, A. 1971A
      (cf.)
Dorcopsis   Macropodidae Turnbull, W. D.,
      Lundelius, E. L. 1970A
doreenae (Niptomomys)
dorfi (Protaspis)
dormaalensis (Gypsonictops, Palaeolabrus, Prolates)
Dormaalidae   Primates–Lemuriformes Quinet, G. E.
      1966E, 1969B
  Dormaalius
Dormaalius   Dormaalidae Quinet, G. E. 1966E, 1969B
  simonsi Quinet, G. E. 1969B
  vandebroeki Quinet, G. E. 1966E, 1969B
dormitor (Cricetops)
dorotheae (Crocuta crocuta)
dorothiae (Palaeogale)
dorsalis (Carangopsis, Rhinophrynus)
dorsatum (Erethizon)
dorsifelis (Ailuracantha)
Dorsolepis   Platysomidae Jörg, E. 1969A
  virgatus Jörg, E. 1969A, 1970A
Dorudontidae   Cetacea–Archaeoceti
  Zygorhiza
Doryaspidida see Lyktaspidida
Doryaspididae see Lyktaspididae

duvernoyi (Helladotherium)
Dvinia Procynosuchidae
    prima Amalitzky [Permocynodon sushkini]
        Tatarinov, L. P. 1968D, 1971A (in
        Dviniidae)
Dviniidae Procynosuchia—Procynosuchoidea
    Tatarinov, L. P. 1971A (incl. Dvinia)
Dvinosauridae Temnospondyli—Trimerorhachoidea
    Dvinosaurus
Dvinosaurus Dvinosauridae Schultze, H.-P. 1969B
    egregius Kalandadze, N. N., Ochev, V. G.,
        Tatarinov, L. P., Chudinov, P. K.,
        Shishkin, M. A. 1968A; Shishkin, M. A.
        1968B
    primus Cosgriff, J. W. 1969A; Shishkin, M. A.
        1968B; Welles, S. P., Estes, R. 1969A
    purlensis Kalandadze, N. N., Ochev, V. G.,
        Tatarinov, L. P., Chudinov, P. K.,
        Shishkin, M. A. 1968A
Dwykia Dwykiidae Gardiner, B. G. 1969A
    analensis Gardiner, B. G. 1969A
Dwykiidae Palaeonisciformes Gardiner, B. G. 1969A
    Dwykia
Dyoplosaurus Nodosauridae
    giganteus Margańska, T. 1970A (cf.)
Dyseohyus Tayassuidae
    fricki Woodburne, M. O. 1969A
    stirtoni Woodburne, M. O. 1969A
dyspelor (Liodon)
dzhafarovi (Ophisaurus)
dzhungaricus (Neoentelodon)
eaglesomei (Galeocerdo)
eakini (Baropezia)
Eastmanosteus Dinichthyidae Stensiö, E. 1969A,B
    (? Arthrodira)
eatoni (Pteranodon)
eburetus (Sepulkomys)
Echidna see Tachyglossus
Echimyidae Rodentia—Octodontoidea Patterson, B.,
        Pascual, R. 1968B (incl. Echimyinae,
        Dactylomyinae, Heteropsomyinae,
        Myocastorinae, Adelphomyinae)
    Carterodon, Echimys, Paradelphomys, Xylechimys
Echimys Echimyidae Friant, M. 1965C
    sulcidens Friant, M. 1969A
Echinerpeton Ophiacodontidae Reisz, R. 1972B
    intermedium Reisz, R. 1972B
Echinodon Stegosauridae Galton, P. M. 1972A
    (in Fabrosauridae)
Echinoprocta Erethizontidae White, J. A. 1970A
Echmatemys Testudinidae Larsen, K. 1970A
    orlovi Chkhikvadze, V. M. 1970C
    zaisanensis Chkhikvadze, V. M. 1970C
Ecolsonia Trematopsidae Vaughn, P. P. 1969A
    cutlerensis Vaughn, P. P. 1969A
Ectocion Phenacodontidae
    montanensis West, R. M. 1971B
    osbornianum West, R. M. 1971B
    wyomingensis West, R. M. 1971B
ectos (Arvicanthis)
Ectosteorhachis Osteolepidae Schaeffer, B. 1968C;
        Thomson, K. S. 1968C, 1972A; Thomson,
        K. S., Vaughn, P. P. 1968A
    nitidus Andrews, S. M., Westoll, T. S. 1970B
Ectropomys Theridomyidae—Oltinomyinae
    Bosma, A., Schmidt-Kittler, N. 1972A
    exiguus Bosma, A., Schmidt-Kittler, N. 1972A

Ectypodontidae Multituberculata—Ptilodontoidea
    Cimexomys, Ectypodus, Gobibaatar, Mesodma,
        Neoplagiaulax
Ectypodus Ectypodontidae
    powelli Gazin, C. L. 1969A (nr., in
        Neoplagiaulacidae)
Eczematolepis Ptyctodontidae Stensiö, E. 1969B
    [Palaeomylus]
Edaphaspididae Heterostraci Novitskaîa, L, I. 1968A
    (in Amphiaspidiformes—Amphiaspidoidei)
    Edaphaspis
Edaphaspis Edaphaspididae Novitskaîa, L, I. 1968A
    bystrowi Novitskaîa, L. I. 1968A, 1971B
Edaphodon Chimaeridae
    barberi Applegate, S. P. 1970A (in Edaphodontidae)
    mirificus Applegate, S. P. 1970A (in Edaphodontidae
Edaphodontidae see Chimaeridae
Edaphosauridae Pelycosauria—Edaphosauria
    Edaphosaurus
Edaphosaurus Edaphosauridae
    cruciger Berman, D. S. 1970A (aff.)
edax (Gobihierax)
Edentata Mammalia
    Incl. subord. Palaeanodonta, Dasypodoidea,
        Palaeopeltoidea, Glyptodontoidea,
        Megalonychoidea, Mylodontoidea,
        Vermilingua
    See also Tubulidentata
edentatus (Sangusaurus)
edesi (Conchopoma)
Edestidae Selachii—Hybodontoidea
    Erikodus, Fadenia, Helicoprion, Orodus, Physonemus,
        Sarcoprion
edingerae (Nothosaurus)
Edmontonia Nodosauridae
    longiceps Sahni, A. 1972A
edmontonicus (Ornithomimus)
Edmontosaurus Hadrosauridae
    regalis Heaton, M. J. 1972A
Edopoidea Temnospondyli—Rhachitomi
edwardsi (Microchoerus erinaceus, Palaeocryptonyx,
        Palaeoerinaceus, Sauropelta, Scaptonyx, Tyto)
egeriana (Palaeotinca)
egertoni (Carcharhinus, Prionodon)
Egertonia Labridae
    isodonta Casier, E. 1967B (cf., in Phyllodontidae);
        Estes, R. 1969G (in Phyllodontidae—
        Phyllodontinae)
    stromeri see Paralbula
Eggysodon Rhinocerotidae Bonis, L. 1969C(?)
Eglonaspididae Heterostraci Novitskaîa, L. I. 1968A,
        1971B (in Amphiaspidiformes—
        Hibernaspidoidei, incl. Eglonaspis,
        Pelurgaspis)
    Empedaspis, Gerronaspis, Lecaniaspis
    See also Amphiaspididae
Eglonaspis Amphiaspididae
    rostrata Novitskaîa, L. I. 1971B
        (in Eglonaspididae); Stensiö, E. 1968A
egloni (Dinichthys)
egregius (Dvinosaurus)
ehiki (Allocricetus)
ehingensis (Suevosciurus)
ehrenbergi (Spalax)
ehrensteinensis (Sciuroides)
eibiswaldensis (Leuciscus)
eileenae (Dinictis)

Ekbainacanthus see Pessosaurus
Ekgmoiteptecela Felidae
  olsontau Macdonald, J. R. 1970A
    (in Machaerodontidae)
Ekgmowechashala Omomyidae
  philotau Macdonald, J. R. 1970A
ekorensis (Elephas)
elami (Dussumieria, Protolophotus)
Elaphe Colubridae
  nebraskensis Holman, J. A. 1970A
  vulpina Holman, J. A. 1972A
elaphoides (Cervus)
Elaphrosuchus see Proterosuchus
Elaphuroides Elaphurus
Elaphurus Cervidae
  shikamai Otsuka, H. 1972A (n. subgen.
    Elaphuroides)
elaphus (Cervus)
Elasmobranchii Chondrichthyes Blot, J. 1969A
    (syst.); Saint-Seine, P.,
    Devillers, Ch. 1969A
Elasmodus Rhinochimaeridae
  hunteri Casier, E. 1967B (in Chimaeridae)
Elasmosauridae Sauropterygia—Plesiosauria Obata, I.,
    Hasegawa, Y., Suzuki, T. 1970A
  Hydrotherosaurus, Mauisaurus, Thalassomedon
Elasmotherium Rhinocerotidae Īakhimovich, V. L.,
    Nemkova, V. K. 1969A; Motuzko, A. N.
    1970A
  caucasicum Baĭgusheva, V. S. 1971A
  sibiricum Flerov, K. K. (1970A (restor.);
    Varlamov, 1959A
elater (Allactaga)
Elaveria see Commentrya
Eldenosteus Coccosteidae Stensiö, E. 1969A,B
electilis (Ambassis)
electus (Cimolodon)
elegans (Blastomeryx, Dentex, Elpidophorus,
    Enchodus, Eumys, Gadus, Gobius, Marsis,
    Microsyops, Mongolemys, Pediomys,
    Phlebolepis, Podocnemis, Pterodactylus,
    Rhinochelys, Seretolepis, Stichocentrus)
elegans-longirostris (Rallus)
Elegantaspis Phlyctaenaspidae Stensiö, E. 1969B,
    1971A (in Spinothoracidi—Dolichothoraci)
elegantulus (Sundayichthys)
Elephantidae Proboscidea—Euelephantoidea
    Aguirre Enríquez, E. 1968B, 1969A,B,C
    (= Elephantinae in Simpson, G. G. 1945);
    Deraniyagala, P. E. P. 1970A; Maglio, V. J.
    1970A (incl. Elephas, Mammuthus,
    Loxodonta and Stegotetrabelodon), 1972B
    (mastication); Schmidt, Z. 1969B
  Elephas, Loxodonta, Mammuthus, Palaeoloxodon,
    Primelephas, Stegodibelodon, Stegodon,
    Stegolophodon, Stegotetrabelodon
elephantopus (Pachyornis)
Elephantosaurus ?Stahleckeriidae V'iushkov, B. P.
    1969A,B
  jachimovitschi V'iushkov, B. P. 1969A,B
Elephas Elephantidae Alberti, G. 1968-1969A (s.l.);
    Maglio, V. J. 1971A; Malez, M. 1967C
  africanavus see Loxodonta
  africanus see Loxodonta
  antiquus see Palaeoloxodon
    recki see Palaeoloxodon recki

Elephas - cont.
  armeniacus (subgen. Euelephas) see Mammuthus
  atlanticus see Loxodonta
  broomi Aguirre, Enríquez, E. 1969B (in
    Elephantidae incertae sedis)
  celebensis Aguirre Enríquez, E. 1969B
  columbi see Mammuthus
  ekorensis Maglio, V. J. 1970B
  falconeri see Palaeoloxodon
  gortynius Melentis, J. K. 1963A (nomen nudum)
  hysudricus Aguirre Enríquez, E. 1969B; Prasad,
    K. N., Daniel, J. A. 1968A [Hypselephas];
    Saxena, M. N. 1968A [Hypselephas];
  hysudrindicus Aguirre Enríquez, E. 1969B
  imperator see Mammuthus
  indicus Aguirre Enríquez, E. 1969B; Khatri, A. P.
    1966A; Nicolussi, C. M. 1971A
  intermedius see Mammuthus
  iolensis see Palaeoloxodon
  mammontoides Aguirre Enríquez, E. 1969B(?)
  melitensis see Palaeoloxodon
  meridionalis
    vestinus Ambrosetti, P., Azzaroli, A.,
      Bonadonna, F. P., Follieri, M.
      1972A
    See also Mammuthus
  mnaidriensis see Loxodonta
  moghrebiensis Arambourg, C. 1970A
  namadicus see Palaeoloxodon
  planifrons Aguirre Enríquez, E. 1969B; Maglio,
    V. J. 1970B; Schmidt, Z., Halouzka, R.
    1970A [Archidiskodon]
  praeplanifrons Aguirre Enríquez, E. 1969B
  primigenius see Mammuthus
  recki see Palaeoloxodon
  shigensis Chiji, M. 1971B
  subplanifrons Aguirre Enríquez, E. 1969B
    (in Elephantidae incertae sedis); Cooke,
    H. B. S., Coryndon, S. C. 1970A
    [Mammuthus, subgen. Archidiskodon];
    Maglio, V. J., Hendey, Q. B. 1970A
    [Mammuthus]
  trogontherii see Mammuthus armeniacus
  wusti see Mammuthus
  zulu (subgen. Loxodon) see Loxodonta africana zulu
Eleutherornithidae Struthioniformes
  ? Saurornis
Elfomys Theridomyidae—Issiodoromyinae
    Hartenberger, J.-L. 1971B
  parvulus Hartenberger, J.-L. 1971B
elginensis (Rhynchodipterus)
elinorae (Prosiren)
eliomyoides (Myomimus)
Eliomys Gliridae Tchernov, E. 1968B
  intermedius Bruijn, H., Dawson, M. R., Mein, P.
    1970A
  quercinus Bouchud, J. 1961C; Chaline, J. 1969A,
    1971A; Jánossy, D. 1969B; Koenigswald, W.
    1972A
  truci Mein, P., Michaux, J. 1970A
elisabethae (Soergelia)
ellangowensis (Anthracopus)
ellenbergeri (Opisthopus)
ellenbergi (Valerymys)
ellioti (Diatropornis, Oreochima)

ellipticus (Coelorhynchus, Macrourus, Otolithus
    (Cyprinodontinarum), Otolithus
    (Sciaenidarum))
Ellobius   Cricetidae Sukhov, V. P. 1970A(?)
    fuscocapillus Jaeger, J.-J. 1969A (aff., in
        Arvicolidae)
    pedorhychus Tchernov, E. 1968B
        (in Microtidae)
    primigenius Kozhamkulova, B. S., Orlovskaia, E. R.
        1971A
    tancrei Erbaeva, M. A. 1970A
Ellopetalichthys   Macropetalichthyidae Stensiö, E.
    1969B
Elomeryx   Anthracotheriidae
    cluae Golpe-Posse, J.-M. 1971A
    garbanii Macdonald, J. R. 1970A
elongata (Alosa, Chondrostoma, Palaeochelys)
elongatum (Ronzotherium filholi)
elongatus (Bolodon, Dapalis, Morone, Onobrosmius,
    Otolithus (Sciaenidarum), Urophycis
    simplex)
Elonichthyidae   Palaeonisciformes–Palaeoniscoidei
    Ganolepis
Elopidae   Elopiformes–Elopoidei
    Brannerion, Elops, Megalops, Notelops,
        Osmeroides, Palelops, Paraelops,
        Paratarpon
    See also Chirocentridae
Elopiformes   Teleostei
    Incl. subord. Elopoidei, Albuloidei
Elops   Elopidae
    machnata Goody, P. C. 1969A
    saurus Goody, P. C. 1969A
Elornis   Phoenicopteridae Harrison, C. J. O. 1971A
Elotheriidae see Entelodontidae
Elphidotarsius   Carpolestidae
    shotgunensis Gazin, C. L. 1971A
Elpidophorus   Mixodectidae
    elegans Szalay, F. S. 1969C
    minor Szalay, F. S. 1969C
emarginatus (Myotis, Palaeogadus)
Emballonuridae   Chiroptera Butler, P. M. 1969A
Emberiza   Fringillidae
    citrinella Jánossy, D. 1972A (cf.,
        in Sturnidae)
Embrithopoda   Mammalia
Embrithosaurus   Pareiasauridae Boonstra, L. D. 1969A
Emeidae   Dinornithiformes
    Pachyornis
Empedaspis   Eglonaspididae Novitskaia, L. I. 1971B
    inermis Novitskaia, L. I. 1971B
emryi (Neodiacodexis)
Emydidae see Testudinidae
Emydoidea   Testudinidae
    blandingi [Emys twentei] Preston, R. E., McCoy,
        C. J. 1971A
Emydops   Endothiodontidae Cluver, M. A. 1970A
Emydura   Chelyidae Warren, J. W. 1969A
    macquari see Chelycarapookus arcuatus
Emys   Testudinidae
    orbicularis Ciesarik, M. 1970A; Tarashchuk, V. I.
        1971B
    twentei see Emydoidea blandingi
Enchodontidae   Salmoniformes–Myctophoidei
    Goody, P. C. 1969B, 1970A (in
        Enchodontoidei, incl. Enchodus,
        Palaeolycus)

Enchodontidae - cont.
    Apateodus, Cimolichthys, Enchodus, Eurypholis,
        Halec, Palaeolycus, Phylactocephalus,
        Saurorhamphus, Volcichthys
Enchodontoidei   Salmoniformes Goody, P. C. 1969B
    (n. subord., incl. Enchodontidae,
        Eurypholidae)
Enchodus   Enchodontidae Casier, E., Taverne, L.
    1971A
    bursauxi Taverne, L. 1970A
    crenulatus Taverne, L. 1970A
    elegans Cappetta, H. C. 1972B; Raab, M. 1967A;
        Taverne, L. 1970A
    lamberti Cappetta, H. C. 1972B (aff.)
    lewesiensis Goody, P. C. 1969B; McNulty, C. L.,
        Kienzlen, G. 1970A
    longipectoralis Silva Santos, R., Sardenberg
        Salgado, M. 1969A
    marchesettii Goody, P. C. 1969B (restor.)
    petrosus Applegate, S. P. 1970A
    saevus Applegate, S. P. 1970A (cf.)
Endolithes   Endolithidae Vialov, O. S. 1970A
    lengedensis Vialov, O. S. 1970A
    ursensis Vialov, O. S. 1970A
Endolithidae   Form taxon for calculi Vialov, O. S.
    1970A
Endolithes
    See also Coprolites in Subject Index
Endomychura   Alcidae Howard, H. 1971C(?)
Endothiodon   Endothiodontidae Kermack, D. M.
    1970A
Endothiodontidae   Therapsida–Dicynodontia
    Boonstra, L. D. 1969A
    Emydops, Endothiodon
engaeus (Neoaetosauroides)
Engraulidae   Clupeiformes–Clupeoidei
    Anchoa, Engraulis
    See also Clupeidae
Engraulis   Engraulidae
    japonica Aoki, N. 1968A (cf., otol.)
    lerichei Cappetta, H. C. 1969B (otol.)
Enhydra   Mustelidae
    lutris Miller, W. E. 1971A
Enhydrictis   Mustelidae
    galictoides Comaschi Caria, I. 1968A
Enhydrocyon   Canidae
    crassidens Macdonald, J. R. 1970A
enigmatica (Numidiopleura)
Enneoconus   Didolodontidae Friant, M. 1967B
ennisianus (Archaeolagus)
ennouchii (Erolia)
Enosuchus   Brachyopidae
    breviceps Welles, S. P., Estes, R. 1969A
        (in Stereospondyli incertae sedis)
Enseosteus   Pachyosteidae Stensiö, E. 1969A,B
    ensis (Heimenia)
Entelodon   Entelodontidae
    deguilhemi Brunet, M. 1970A
    depereti
        briatextensis Bergounioux, F. M., Crouzel, F.
            1968B (mut.)
Entelodontidae   [Elotheriidae] Artiodactyla–
        Entelodontoidea Brunet, M. 1972A
    Archaeotherium, Dinohyus, Entelodon,
        Gobielodon, Neoentelodon, Paraentelodon
Entomolestes   Adapisoricidae
    nitens Guthrie, D. A. 1971B

Eotragus - cont.
　martiniana see E. sansaniensis
　sansaniensis [E. clavata, E. martiniana] Ginsburg, L.,
　　Heintz, E. 1968A
Eotrigonias　Rhinocerotidae
　borissiaki Bersenev, I. I., et al. 1969A [Eotrigonius]
Eotrigonodon　Trigonodontidae
　serratus Nolf, D. 1970A
Eotrigonodontidae see Trigonodontidae
Eozanclus　Zanclidae Blot, J., Voruz, C. 1970A
　brevirostris [Zanclus] Blot, J., Voruz, C. 1970A
Eozostrodon　Morganucodontidae
　parvus Mills, J. R. E. 1971A; [E. problematicus,
　　Morganucodon watsoni] Parrington, F. R.
　　1971A
　problematicus Mills, J. R. E. 1971A (in
　　?Sinoconodontidae)
　See also E. parvus
Eozostrodontidae see Triconodontidae
Ephippidae [Platacidae] Perciformes—Percoidei
　Amphistium, Archaephippus, Eoplatax, Exellia
　See also Exelliidae
Epiaceratherium　Rhinocerotidae
　minor [E. turgaica minor] Borsuk-Białynicka, M.
　　1968A [Allacerops]
　turgaica
　　minor see E. minor
Epidolops　Polydolopidae
　ameghinoi Paula Couto, C. 1970A
Epihippus　Equidae
　gracilis Forstén, A.-M. 1971A (cf.)
Epinnula　Gempylidae
　cancellata Arambourg, C. 1966A
Epipetalichthys　Macropetalichthyidae Stensiö, E.
　　1969B
　minor see Desmoporella
episcopalis (Dolomys)
Episiphneus see Prosiphneus
Episoriculus　Soricidae
　gibberodon Bruijn, H., Dawson, M. R., Mein, P.
　　1970A
epitegosa (Vernonaspis)
Epitherium see Brachytherium
Eptesicus　Vespertilionidae
　campanensis Baudelot, S. 1970A
　nilssoni Koenigswald, W. 1972A (cf.)
equiceps (Miohippus)
Equidae　Perissodactyla—Equoidea Blanchard, J.
　　1964B; Doughty, P. S. 1969A;
　　Friese, F. 1971A; Gabuniĩa, L.K. 1968A;
　　Gromova, V. I. 1972A; Haines, F. 1971A;
　　Nobis, G. 1967A; Skorkowski, E. 1969A;
　　Sondaar, P. Y. 1969A; Teichert, M. 1971A
　Anchilophus, Anchitherium, Astrohippus, Calippus,
　　Epihippus, Equus, Griphippus, Hipparion,
　　Hippidion, Hypohippus, Hypsohipparion,
　　Hyracotherium, Kyzylkakhippus, Merychippus,
　　Mesohippus, Miohippus, Nannipus,
　　Neohipparion, Orohippus, Pachynolophus,
　　Parahippus, Pliohippus, Propachynolophus,
　　Propalaeotherium, Pseudhipparion
equinanus (Miohippus)
equinum (Rhinolophus ferrum)
Equus　Equidae Cooke, H. B. S., Coryndon, S. C.
　　1970A; Crockett, C. T. 1970B (subgen.
　　Plesippus); Espejo, J. A., Torres, T. 1969A;
　　Feustel, R., et al. 1971A; Guthrie, R. D.,

Equus - cont.
　Matthews, J. V. 1971A; Lazarev, P. A.
　　1971A (restor.); Miller, W. E. 1971A;
　　Musil, R. 1969C; Prat, F. 1968A; Schütt, G.
　　1969C (subgen. Equus); Waldrop, J. 1969A
　abeli Melentis, J. K. 1966J
　altidens Musil, R. 1969A
　asinus Patte, E. 1968B (subgen. Asinus)
　africanus Churcher, C. S. 1972C (cf.);
　　Gautier, A. 1968A (cf.)
　bressanus Baĭgusheva, V. S. 1971A (cf.)
　burchelli Churcher, C. S. 1970A
　caballus Biddittu, I., Cassoli, P. 1968A; Boeuf, O.
　　1970A; Bonifay, M.-F. 1967A, 1968B, 1969A;
　　Bouchud, J. 1969A; Bourdelle, E. 1955A-;
　　Delpech, F. 1968A, 1969A; Delpech, F.,
　　et al. 1970A; Garevski, R. 1969A; Martin, R.
　　1968A; Patte, E. 1968B(?); Torres
　　Perezhidalgo, T. 1971A; Vangengeĭm, E. A.
　　1963A
　fossilis Kuz'mina, I. E. 1971A
　gallicus Beden, M. 1970A (cf.); Prat, F. 1969A
　germanicus Beden, M. 1970A (cf.); Bouchud, J.
　　1968C
　calobatus Dalquest, W. W. 1967A; Schultz, G. E.
　　1971A (cf., subgen. Hemionus); Skinner,
　　M. F. 1972A (subgen. Hemionus)
　capensis Churcher, C. S. 1970A
　chosaricus Thenius, E. 1966G (cf., subgen. Equus)
　conversidens Churcher, C. S. 1968B, 1972B (subgen.
　　Asinus); Churcher, C. S., Stalker, A. MacS.
　　(1970A(?); Dalquest, W. W. 1967A; Skinner,
　　M. F. 1972A (cf., subgen. Hemionus)
　cumminsi Akersten, W. A. 1972A (subgen. Asinus)
　curvidens Souza Cunha, F. L. 1971A (subgen.
　　Amerhippus)
　francisi [E. quinni, Onager zoyatalis] Lundelius,
　　E. L., Stevens, M. S. 1970A
　germanicus Macarovici, N., Semaka, A. 1969A;
　　Mostecký, V. 1969A; Musil, R. 1969C;
　　Rădulescu, C., Hermann, W. 1969A;
　　Samson, P., Hermann, W. 1968A
　grevyi Skinner, M. F. 1972A (subgen.
　　Dolichohippus)
　hemionus Clutton-Brock, J. 1970A; Mostecký, V.
　　1969A (cf.); Skinner, M. F. 1972A (subgen.
　　Hemionus)
　hydruntinus Beden, M. 1970A (subgen. Asinus);
　　Boeuf, O. 1970A (subgen. Asinus); Bonifay,
　　M.-F. 1967A, 1968B; Bouchud, J. 1968C;
　　Clutton-Brock, J. 1970A; David, A. I.
　　1969A (cf.); Delpech, F. 1969A; Garevski, R.
　　1969A (subgen. Asinus); Hemmer, H.,
　　Jaeger, R. 1969A [cf., Asinus]; Macarovici, N.,
　　Semaka, A. 1969A (subgen. Asinus); Martin, R.
　　1968A; Patte, E. 1968B (subgen. Asinus);
　　Thenius, E. 1960C (subgen. Asinus), 1966G
　　(subgen. ?Asinus); Torres Perezhidalgo, T.
　　1971A
　idahoensis Shotwell, J. A. 1970A [Plesippus]
　marxi Musil, R. 1969A
　mosbachensis David, A. I. 1969A; Gromova, V. I.,
　　Dubrovo, I. A. 1971A; Jánossy, D. 1969B;
　　Nobis, G. 1970A
　mosbachensis-abeli Macarovici, N., Semaka, A.
　　1969A; Mostecký, V. 1969A

Equus - cont.
  namadicus Khatri, A. P. 1966A
  neogaeus Souza Cunha, F. L. 1971A (subgen.
    Amerhippus)
  niobrarensis Dalquest, W. W. 1967A
  numidicus Arambourg, C. 1970A
  orientalis Miller, W. E. 1971A (nomen dubium)
  przewalskii Burchak-Abramovich, N. I.,
    Bendukidze, O. G. 1969A (cf.); Musil, R.
    1969C
  quagga Churcher, C. S. 1970A
  quinni see E. francisi
  sanmeniensis Kambariddinov, R. K. 1969A (cf.);
    Mavlianov, G. A., et al. 1968A [cf.,
    Allohippus]; Vas'kovskii, A. P. 1963A
  scotti Akersten, W. A. 1972A (cf.); Khan, E.
    1970A; Schultz, G. E. 1969A (cf.);
    Skorkowski, E. 1969A
  scythicus Macarovici, N., Semaka, A. 1969A
  simplicidens Akersten, W. A. 1972A (cf., subgen.
    Plesippus); Howe, J. A. 1970A (subgen.
    Plesippus); [E. simplicidens, E. (Plesippus)
    simplicidens] Skinner, M. F. 1972A
    (subgen. Dolichohippus, n. comb.);
    Skorkowski, E. 1969A
  stenonis Azzaroli, A., Berzi, A. 1970A(?);
    Baĭgusheva, V. S. 1971A (cf.); Beden, M.
    1970B; Macarovici, N., Semaka, A. 1969A;
    Mihăilă, N. 1971A [Hippotigris]; Nobis, G.
    1970A
  sussenbornensis Gromova, V. I., Dubrovo, I. A.
    1969A [Allohippus]; Macarovici, N.,
    Semaka, A. 1969A; Musil, R. 1969A
  tabeti Arambourg, C. 1970A (subgen. Asinus)
Equus   Equus
erectus (Homo)
eremicus (Peromyscus)
Eremopezus   Aepyornithidae
  eocaenus Sauer, E. G. F. 1969A
Eremophila   Alaudidae
  alpestris Tate, J., Martin, L. D. 1968A
Eremotherium   Megatheriidae Lins Rolim, J. 1971A;
    Moreira, L. E., Gomes de Melo, S. M.
    1971A; Voorhies, M. 1972A; Webb, S. D.
    1970B
Erethizon   Erethizontidae
  bathygnathum Shotwell, J. A. 1970A
  dorsatum Parmalee, P. W. 1971A; Ray, C. E.,
    Lipps, L. 1970A; White, J. A. 1970A
Erethizontidae   Rodentia—Erethizontoidea
  Coendou, Echinoprocta, Erethizon
Erethizontoidea   Rodentia
Ergilemys   Testudinidae Chkhikvadze, V. M. 1972A
  insolitus [Testudo] Chkhikvadze, V. M. 1972A
  saikanensis Chkhikvadze, V. M. 1972A
  lunanensis [Testudo] Chkhikvadze, V. M. 1972A
  meschethica [Testudo] Chkhikvadze, V. M. 1972A
  perpiniana [Testudo] Chkhikvadze, V. M. 1972A
  yunnanensis [Testudo] Chkhikvadze, V. M. 1972A
Ergilia see Ardynia
Ericiolacertidae   Therapsida—Bauriamorpha
  Cyrbasiodon
Erikodus   Edestidae Bendix-Almgreen, S. E. 1968A
Erinaceidae   Insectivora—Erinaceoidea
  Amphechinus, Brachyerix, Deinogalerix,
    Dimylechinus, Erinaceus, Galerix,

Erinaceidae - cont.
  Gymnurechinus, Lantanotherium, Metechinus,
    Neurogymnurus, Ocajila, Palaeoerinaceus,
    Postpalerinaceus, Pseudogalerix, Quadrodens
  See also Adapisoricidae
Erinaceoidea   Insectivora—Lipotyphla
Erinaceus   Erinaceidae Bachmayer, F., Wilson, R. W.
    1970A(?)
  algirus Friant, M. 1971C (subgen. Aethechinus)
  carmelitus see E. europaeus
  europaeus Bouchud, J. 1961C; [E. carmelitus,
    E. sharonis] Heller, J. 1970A; Rzebik, B.
    1968A
  intermedius Friant, M. 1971C
  praeglacialis Jánossy, D. 1969B
  samsonowiczi Rzebik-Kowalska, B. 1971A
  sharonis see E. europaeus
erinaceus (Microchoerus, Necrolemur)
Eriptychiidae   Heterostraci
  Strosipherus
Erismatopterus   Aphredoderidae
  levatus Rosen, D. E., Patterson, C. 1969A
    (in Percopsidae)
erkertshofense (Peratherium frequens)
erlita (Pseudokoala)
erminea (Mustela)
ermineus (Hyracolestes)
ernii (Allomys)
Erolia   Scolopacidae
  ennouchii Ballmann, P. 1969A
Erpetopus   Ichnites
  willistoni Sarjeant, W. A. S. 1971A
Erpetosuchidae   Thecodontia—Pseudosuchia
  Cerritosaurus, Hesperosuchus, ? Rhadinosuchus,
    Saltoposuchus, Stegomosuchus
Erquelinnesia   Toxochelyidae
  gosseleti Zangerl, R. 1971A (in Osteopyginae)
erroli (Protaspis)
Erromenosteus   Pachyosteidae Stensiö, E. 1969A,B
    (in Leiosteidae)
Eryopidae   Temnospondyli—Eryopoidea
  Actinodon, Chelyderpeton, Eryops, Onchiodon,
    Sclerocephalus
  See also Branchiosauridae, Micromelerpetontidae
Eryopoidea   Temnospondyli—Rhachitomi
Eryops   Eryopidae Schultze, H.-P. 1969B
  avinoffi [Glaukerpeton] Murphy, J. L. 1971A
  megacephalus Berman, D. S. 1970A
Erythrochampsa   Notochampsidae Walker, A. D. 1970A
    (in Stegomosuchidae)
erythrophthalmus (Scardinius)
erythropus (Tringa)
Erythrosuchidae   Thecodontia—Proterosuchia
  Cruickshank, A. R. I. 1972A (incl.
    Erythrosuchus, Euparkeria, Shansisuchus)
  Cuyosuchus, Hoplitosuchus, ?Rauisuchus,
    ?Saurosuchus
Erythrotherium   Morganucodontidae Crompton, A. W.
    1968A (reconstr.)
  parringtoni Mills, J. R. E. 1971A
Erythrozootes   Tenrecidae
  chamerpes Butler, P. M. 1969A (cf.)
Eryx   Boidae Hoffstetter, R., Rage, J.-C. 1972A (cf.)
escheri (Isurus, Onychichnium)
esculenta (Rana)
eseri (Steneofiber)

esmeraldensis (Copemys)
Esocidae   Salmoniformes—Esocoidei
    Esox
Esox   Esocidae Cavender, T. M., Lundberg, J. G.,
        Wilson, R. L. 1970A; Obrhelová, N.
        1970A; Sychevskaîa, E. K., Lebedev,
        V. D. 1971A
    destructus Nelson, G. J. 1972A
    lepidotus Nelson, G. J. 1972A
    lucius Crossman, E. J., Harington, C. R. 1970A
    otto Nelson, G. J. 1972A
    papyraceus Nelson, G. J. 1972A
    robustus Nelson, G. J. 1972A
    waltschanus Nelson, G. J. 1972A
Estellomys   Theridomyidae—Oltinomyinae
        Hartenberger, J.-L. 1971B
    cansouni Hartenberger, J.-L. 1971B
Estemmenosuchidae   Therapsida—Dinocephalia
    Anoplosuchus, Estemmenosuchus
Estemmenosuchus   Estemmenosuchidae
    mirabilis Chudinov, P. K. 1968C
    uralensis Chudinov, P. K. 1970A; Ricqlès, A.
        1972B
estesi (Stygiochelys)
Esthonychidae   Tillodontia
    Esthonyx, Megalesthonix, Trogosus
Esthonyx   Esthonychidae
    acutidens Guthrie, D. A. 1971B
Estramomys   Eomyidae Jánossy, D. 1969C
    simplex Jánossy, D. 1969C, 1970B
Etrumeus   Clupeidae
    hafizi Arambourg, C. 1966A (in Dussumieriidae)
etruscus (Canis, Dicerorhinus, Rhynchosauroides,
        Suncus, Ursus)
etsagicus (Bunophorus)
Eubaena   Eubaenidae
    cephalica Gaffney, E. S. 1972A (in Baenidae—
        Eubaeninae)
    latifrons see Hayemys
Eubaenidae   Chelonia—Amphichelydia
    Eubaena
Eubrontes   Ichnites Haubold, H. 1969B
        (in Eubrontidae)
    giganteus Ostrom, J. H. 1968A; Peoples, J. W.
        1967A (coelurosaur)
Eubrontidae   Ichnites Haubold, H. 1969B
        (in Saurischia—Carnosauria, incl. Eubrontes)
Eucastor   Castoridae Green, M. 1971A
    dividerus Webb, S. D. 1969C (aff.)
    planus Webb, S. D. 1969C (cf.)
Eucladoceros   Cervidae
    dicranios Azzaroli, A., Berzi, A. 1970A [Cervus
        (Euclodoceros) cf. dicranios]; Baĭgusheva,
        V. S. 1971A
Eucosmodontidae   Multituberculata—Taeniolaboidea
    Charlesmooria, Kryptobaatar, Sloanbaatar, Stygimys
Eucricetodon   Cricetidae Vianey-Liaud, M. 1971A,
        1972B
    atavus Vianey-Liaud, M. 1972B
    collatum Vianey-Liaud, M. 1972B
    collatus
        longidens Hugueney, M. 1969A
    huberi Vianey-Liaud, M. 1969A (aff.), 1972B
    huerzeleri Vianey-Liaud, M. 1972B
    infralactorensis Telles Antunes, M., Mein, P. 1971A
    praecursor Vianey-Liaud, M. 1972B

Eucricetodon - cont.
    quercyi Vianey-Liaud, M. 1972B
    thaleri Hugueney, M. 1969A(?)
Eucricetodon   Cricetodon
Eucricetodontinae   Cricetidae Mein, P., Freudenthal, M.
        1971A (incl. Eucricetodon, Pseudocricetodon,
        ?Heterocricetodon)
Euctenoceros   Cervidae
    mediterraneus Bonifay, M.-F. 1968C
Eucyclaspis   Protaspis Denison, R. H. 1970B
        (n. subgen.)
Eudaemonema   Mixodectidae
    cuspidata Szalay, F. S. 1969C
Eudocimus   Plataleidae
    paganus [?Milnea gracilis] Cracraft, J. 1972A
        (in Threskiornithidae)
eugenei (Ischyrotomus)
eugnathoides (Watsonulus)
Euhhominidae   Hominidae Woo, Ju-kang 1962D
euilus (Phacochoerus)
Euleptaspididae see Gemuendenaspididae, Homostiidae
Euleptaspis   Gemuendenaspididae Stensiö, E. 1969B,
        1971A (in Coccosteomorphi—Euleptaspididae)
Eumeces   Scincidae
    obsoletus Holman, J. A. 1972A
Eumechichnium   Ichnites
    gampsodactylum Leonardi, P., et al. 1967A
Eumegamys   Dinomyidae Calcaterra, A. 1972A;
        Pascual, R., Díaz de Gamero, M. L. 1969A
Eumetopias   Otariidae
    jubata Gard, L. M., Szabo, B. J. 1971A (cf.)
Eumys   Cricetidae Eklund, R. R. 1969A
    blacki Macdonald, J. R. 1970A
    elegans Wood, A. E. 1969A (cf.)
    exiguus [Scottimus] Dawson, M. R., Black, C. C.
        1970A
    gloveri Macdonald, J. R. 1970A
    pritinus Russell, L. S. 1972B
    woodi Macdonald, J. R. 1970A
Eunotosauridae   Chelonia—?Eunotosauria Cox, C. B.
        1969B (in Cotylosauria—Captorhinomorpha)
    Eunotosaurus
Eunotosaurus   Eunotosauridae
    africanus Cox, C. B. 1969B
Euoplocephalus   Nodosauridae Haas, G. 1969B
    tutus Coombs, W. P. 1972A
eupachygnathus (Gorgonops)
Euparkeria   Euparkeriidae Cruickshank, A. R. I. 1972A
        (in Erythrosuchidae); Gow, C. E. 1970A
Euparkeriidae   Thecodontia—Pseudosuchia
    Euparkeria
Eupelor see Metoposaurus
Euprox see Dicrocerus
eupterygius (Halec)
eureia (Geoemyda)
eurekensis (Perognathoides)
euronensis (Metridiochoerus)
europaea (Sitta, Talpa)
europaeum (Meniscodon)
europaeus (Caprimulgus, Chriacus, Cricetinus, Erinaceus,
        Lepus, Plesiocathartes)
europeus (Capitonides, Pelomys)
Europrotaspis   Protaspis
euryale (Rhinolophus)
eurybathrodon (Negaprion)
Euryboas see Lycyaenops

falconeri (Dicerorhinus hemitoechus, Leptoptilos,
    Palaeoloxodon)
Falconidae   Accipitriformes
    Falco
    See also Accipitridae
Falconiformes see Accipitriformes
falkenbachi (Menoceras)
fallax (Catodontherium)
farsonensis (Hypsidoris)
fasolae (Camptosaurichnus)
fategadensis (Dicoryphochoerus)
faujasi (Myliobatis)
Fayella   Dissorophidae
    chickashaensis Olson, E. C. 1972A (restor.)
featherensis (Mcmurdodus)
feddeni (Carcharius)
fedti (Proheteromys)
feignouxi (Dremotherium)
Felidae   Carnivora—Aeluroidea Korotkevich, E. L.
    1969A; Radinsky, L. B. 1969B (brain
    evol.)
    Acinonyx, Barbourofelis, Dinictis, Dinofelis,
        Ekgmoiteptecela, Eusmilus, Felis,
        Homotherium, Hoplophoneus,
        Ischyrosmilus, Jansofelis, Lynx,
        Machairodus, Megantereon, Nimravus,
        Panthera, Prionailurus, Pseudaelurus,
        Sansanosmilus, Smilodon, Stenailurus
felina (Dinictis)
felinus (Aelurosaurus, Bosdagius)
Felipeda   Carnivoripedidae—Felipedinae
    felis Panin, N. 1964A, 1965A
Felis   Felidae Baïgusheva, V. S. 1971A [Lynx]
    concolor Miller, W. E. 1971A (cf.)
    issiodorensis Bonifay, M.-F. 1971A [Lynx];
        Sickenberg, O. 1970A (subgen. Lynx)
    lacustris Bjork, P. R. 1970A; Shotwell, J. A.
        1970A
    lunellensis Bonifay, M.-F. 1971A (subgen.
        Panthera?)
        See also Panthera pardus
    lynx Bonifay, M.-F. 1967A, 1971A (subgen.
        Lynx); Martin, R. 1968A (subgen. Lynx)
    magna Jánossy, D. 1969B (cf.)
    monspessulana Bonifay, M.-F. 1971A
    oxygnatha see Panthera tigris
    pardina Bonifay, M.-F. 1971A (cf., subgen. lynx)
    rexroadensis Akersten, W. A. 1972A (cf.)
    rufus Miller, W. E. 1971A [cf., Lynx]
    silvestris Bonifay, M.-F. 1971A; Delpech, F. 1969A;
        Schütt, G. 1969C
    spelaea Bonifay, M.-F. 1969A [Lynx] 1971A
        (subgen. Lynx)
    See also Lynx, Panthera, Prionailurus
felis (Felipeda)
Ferecetotherium   Patriocetidae Mchedlidze, G. A.
    1970B
    kelloggi Mchedlidze, G. A. 1970B
ferina (Aythya)
Ferinestrix   Mustelidae—Mellivorinae Bjork, P. R.
    1970A
    vorax Bjork, P. R. 1970A
ferox (Arctops, Circaetus, Megalictis, Meniscoessus,
        Sphingopus, Titanosuchus)
ferruginea (Tadorna)
ferrum (Rhinolophus)

fiber (Castor)
Fierasferidae see Carapidae
filamentosus (Bregmaceros)
filfilae (Paraethomys)
filholi (Aceratherium, Cadurceryx, Herpestes,
        Ronzotherium, Ronzotherium filholi)
finitimus (Macrorhamphus, Turkmene)
finneyi (Pliophenacomys)
firdoussii (Berycomorus)
fischeri (Scaphonyx)
fischeuri (Physodon)
fisheri (Proplegadis)
fissicaudus (Sphenocephalus)
fissidens (Bathyopsis, Beremendia)
fissura (Moringua)
fissurae (Hipparion)
fissus (Paradelphomys)
flammeus (Asio)
flavescens (Kinosternon)
flavicollis (Apodemus)
flavigula (Martes)
flerovi (Lagomeryx)
floblairi (Sphenophalos)
florancei (Ischyrictis, Ligerimys)
florensis (Archaeothyris, Stegodon trigonocephalus)
Florentiamys   Heteromyidae
    agnewi Macdonald, J. R. 1970A
florentinoameghinoi (Coelostylodon)
floridanus (Nothokemas, Peromyscus, Sylvilagus,
        Tremarctos)
Floridatragulus   Hypertragulidae Patton, T. H. 1969B
        (in Camelidae—Floridatragulinae)
    hesperus Patton, T. H. 1969B
    nanus Patton, T. H. 1969B
    texanus Patton, T. H. 1969B
flourensianus (Micromeryx)
fluminensis (Bobbschaefferia)
fluminis (Amblycastor)
fluviatilis (Hesperolagomys, Perca)
fockii (Archaeocetus)
fodiens (Neomys)
Foetopterus   Accipitridae
    ambiguus [Chloephaga picta] Tonni, E. P. 1970A
foina (Martes, Mustela)
foliarum (Trichophanes)
fontani (Dryopithecus)
fontanierii (Myospalax)
fontannesi (Amphilagus)
fontensis (Sciuroides)
fontinalis (Palaeosyops)
fontis (Cylindrodon)
foordi (Eusthenopteron)
fordi (Isoptychus)
formicarum (Procerberus)
formicorum (Mookomys)
formosa (Mesodma)
formosus (Ceratodus, Dapalis, Gregorymys, Gyracanthus,
        Thrissops, Troodon)
forstenae (Hipparion)
Forsythia   Sciuridae Bruijn, H., Meulenkamp, J. E.
        1972A(?); Mein, P. 1970A
    gaudryi Engesser, B. 1972A; [Sciuropterus]
        Mein, P. 1970A
fortis (Microtus)
fossiger (Teleoceras)

Galerix - cont.
  socialis [Parasorex] Engesser, B. 1972A
  zapfei *Bachmayer, F., Wilson, R. W.* 1970A
Galesauridae see Thrinaxodontidae
Galesaurus Thrinaxodontidae Jenkins, F. A. 1971A
Galesuchidae see Gorgonopsidae–Gorgonopsinae
Galesuchus Gorgonopsidae–Gorgonopsinae
  Boonstra, L. D. 1969A (in Galesuchidae)
  gracilis Sigogneau, D. 1970A
galictoides (Enhydrictis)
galilei (Saurosuchus)
gallicus (Equus caballus)
Galliformes Aves
Gallimimus Ornithomimidae *Osmólska, H., Roniewicz, E., Barsbold, R.* 1972A
  bullatus *Osmólska, H., Roniewicz, E., Barsbold, R.* 1972A
gallinago (Capella)
Gallinula Rallidae
  kansarum Feduccia, J. A. 1968A
Gallirallus Rallidae
  hartreei *Scarlett, R. J.* 1970B
Gallus Phasianidae Burchak-Abramovich, N. I., Bendukidze, O. G. 1971A
galushai (Osteoborus)
gambensis (Plectropterus)
gampsodactylum (Eumechichnium)
gangeticus (Carcharhinus)
Ganolepis Elonichthyidae Kazantseva, A. A. 1968A, 1971A (in Gyrolepidotidae)
  gracilis Kazantseva, A. A. 1968A
    (in Gyrolepidotidae)
  longicauda see Ministrella
Ganopristidae see Sclerorhynchus
gapperii (Clethrionomys)
garbanii (Elomeryx)
Gargantuodon Odobenidae *Ginsburg, L.* 1969A
  ligerensis *Ginsburg, L.* 1969A
Garrulus Corvidae
  glandarius Jánossy, D. 1972A (aff.)
Gaspeaspis Arthrodira incertae sedis *Pageau, Y.* 1969B
  cassivii *Pageau, Y.* 1969B
gastellarini (Neomys)
Gasteroclupea Clupeidae
  branisai Benedetto, J. L., Sanchez, T. M. 1971A; Leanza, A. F. 1969A
Gasterosteidae Gasterosteiformes–Gasterosteoidei
  Gasterosteus
Gasterosteiformes Teleostei
  Incl. subord. Gasterosteoidei, Aulostomoidei, Syngnathoidei
Gasterosteus Gasterosteidae
  doryssus Ruben, J. A. 1971A
Gaudrya Cochleosauridae Schultze, H.-P. 1969B
Gaudryella Salmoniformes incertae sedis
  Patterson, C.
  gaudryi [Clupea] Patterson, C. 1970A (n. comb.)
gaudryi (Anomalomys, Cottopsis, Forsythia, Gaudryella, Gazella, Haptodus, Leontinia, Orycteropus, Paramblypterus, Pronycticebus, Propachynolophus, Trigodon)
gaultinus (Spratticeps)
gautieri (Ugandax)
Gaylordia Didelphidae
  macrocynodonta Paula Couto, C. 1970A
  mendesi *Paula Couto, C.* 1970A

Gazella Bovidae Baïgusheva, V. S. 1971A; Dmitrieva, E. L. 1971A (subgen. Gazella, Vetagazella, Procapra); Dmitrieva, E. L. 1971C (subgen. Procapra); Ducos, P. 1968A; Gentry, A. W. 1970A; Heintz, E. 1969A; Korotkevich, E. L. 1970A; Tekkaya, I. 1969A
  deperdita Dmitrieva, E. L. 1970A (n. subgen. Vetagazella); Heintz, E. 1969C, 1971B; [G. schreuderae] Heintz, E. 1971A; Melentis, J. K. 1966O; Tekkaya, I. 1970A
  caprina Ghenea, C. 1968A (var.)
  dorcadoides Dmitrieva, E. L. 1969A
  dorcas Churcher, C. S. 1972C; Gautier, A. 1968A
  gaudryi Czyżewska, T. 1970A; Dmitrieva, E. L. 1970A (subgen. Vetagazella); Melentis, J. K. 1970A; Mihăilă, N. 1971A (cf.)
  gutturosa Dmitrieva, E. L. 1971B (subgen. Procapra)
  leptoceros Churcher, C. S. 1972C(?)
  lydekkeri Heintz, E. 1969C
  paotehensis Czyżewska, T. 1970A; Dmitrieva, E. L. 1971B (cf.)
  rufifrons Gautier, A. 1968A
  schreuderae see G. deperdita
  stehlini Heintz, E. 1969C
  wellsi Cooke, H. B. S., Coryndon, S. C. 1970A (cf.)
Gazella Gazella
gazella (Pecoripeda)
Gazellospira Bovidae
  torticornis Baïgusheva, V. S. 1971A
gazini (Bunophorus, Martes)
gazinorum (Arpadosaurus)
geinitzi (Dicynodontipus)
geishanensis (Chaohusaurus)
geismarianus (Nothocyon)
Gekkonidae Squamata–Lacertilia
  Phyllodactylus
Gelocidae Artiodactyla–Traguloidea
  Gelocus, Lophiomeryx, Prodremotherium
Gelocus Gelocidae
  communis Brunet, M. 1970A
gemma (Nibea)
gemmarosae (Miohippus, Promartes)
gemmifer (Blastomeryx)
gemmula (Glirulus)
Gempylidae Perciformes–Scombroidei
  Arambourg, C. 1966A (in Perciformes–Trichiuroidei)
  Epinnula, Thyrsitoides
Gemuendenaspididae Arthrodira–Brachythoraci (incl. Gemuendenaspididae, Euleptaspididae of Stensiö) Stensiö, E. 1969B, 1971A (in Spinothoracidi–Coccosteomorphi)
  ? Euleptaspis, Gemuendenaspis
Gemuendenaspis Gemuendenaspididae Stensiö, E. 1969B, 1971A
gemuendenensis (Drepanaspis)
Gemuendina Gemuendinidae Stensiö, E. 1969B, 1971A (in Rhenanida)
Gemuendinidae Rhenanida (incl. Radotinida, Rhenanida of Stensiö)
  Asterosteus, ? Broilina, Gemuendina, Holopetalichthys, Jagorina, Kolymaspis, Radotina, ? Tyriolepis
genetrix (Primisardinella)
Genetta Viverridae Petter, G., Heintz, E. 1969A

gentili (Raja)
gentilis (Accipiter)
Geochelone Testudinidae Holman, J. A. 1971A, 1972A
    (subgen. Caudochelys); Stevens, M. S.,
    Stevens, J. B., Dawson, M. R. 1969A(?)
    atlas Hooijer, D. A. 1971A,B
    hesterna Auffenberg, W. 1971A (subgen.
        Chelenoides)
    insolitus Młynarski, M. 1968B
    oelrichi Holman, J. A. 1972A (subgen.
        Hesperotestudo)
    oskarkuhni Młynarski, M. 1968B
Geoclemys Testudinidae [Emydidae]
    sivalensis Tewari, B. S., Badam, G. L. 1969A
        (in Emydidae)
Geoemyda Testudinidae
    borysthenica Tarashchuk, V. I. 1971B (subgen.
        Heosemys)
    eureia Tarashchuk, V. I. 1971B (subgen. Heosemys)
    malustensis Tarashchuk, V. I. 1971B (subgen.
        Spinemys)
    mossoczyi Tarashchuk, V. I. 1971B (subgen.
        Heosemys)
    pidoplickai Tarashchuk, V. I. 1971B
    pilgrimi Prasad, K. N., Satsangi, P. P. 1967B
    riabinini [Clemmys] Tarashchuk, V. I. 1971B
        (subgen. Spinemys)
    striata Deraniyagala, P. E. P. 1969A,B,C
        (in Emydidae)
geographicus (Bathornis)
Geolabis Adapisoricidae Robinson, P. 1968C
        (in Nyctitheriidae—Geolabidinae)
geologorum (Podocnemis)
Geomyidae Rodentia—Geomyoidea
    Cratogeomys, Dikkomys, Entoptychus, Geomys,
        Grangerimus, Gregorymys, ?Griphomys,
        Lignimus, Pappogeomys, Pleurolicus,
        Pliogeomys, Thomomys
Geomyoidea Rodentia
Geomys Geomyidae
    bursarius Dalquest, W. W. 1967A
    paenebursarius Akersten, W. A. 1972A
    quinni Hibbard, C. W. 1972A
georgii (Hemiramphus)
Geotrypus Talpidae
    jungi Hugueney, M. 1972A (cf.)
Gephyrostegus see Diplovertebron
Geranodornis Gruidae—Geranoidinae Cracraft, J.
        1969A (in Geranoididae)
    aenigma Cracraft, J. 1969A
Geranoides Gruidae
    jepseni Cracraft, J. 1969A (in Geranoididae)
Geranoididae Ralliformes Cracraft, J. 1969A
        (incl. Geranoides, Paragrus,
        Eogeranoides, Palaeophasianus,
        Geranodornis)
    See also Gruidae
Gerbillidae see Cricetidae
Gerbillus Cricetidae
    campestris Jaeger, J.-J. 1969A (aff., in
        Gerbillidae)
    dasyurus Tchernov, E. 1968B,C
        (in Gerbillidae)
    matthewi Bruijn, H., Dawson, M. R., Mein, P.
        1970A

Gerdalepis Astrolepidae Stensiö, E. 1969B
        (in Antiarchi incertae sedis)
gergovianus (Propalaeochoerus)
geringensis (Desmatochoerus hatcheri, Sunkahetanka)
germaniae (Aphanius)
germanicum (Hygophum, Quinquevertebron)
germanicus (Asiatosuchus, Cottus, Equus, Equus caballus,
        Palaeoloxodon antiquus)
germannorum (Entoptychus)
germanoafricanum (Ceratotherium simum)
Germanodactylidae see Pterodactylidae
Germanodactylus see Pterodactylus
Germanomys see Ungaromys
germanus (Palaeogadus)
geron Otolithus (Percidarum)
Gerronaspis Eglonaspididae Novitskaiä, L. I. 1971B
    dentata [Putoranaspis] Novitskaiä, L. I. 1971B
gervaisi (Diplocynodon)
gervaisii (Plesiarctomys)
Gesneropithex Adapidae Sudre, J. 1969A
    peyeri Szalay, F. S. 1971C
Getuloxerus Sciuridae
    blacki Baudelot, S. 1969A; Bruijn, H. 1967A
gibba (Bauzaia)
gibberodon (Asoriculus, Episoriculus)
gibberosus (Miopetaurista)
gibberula (Umbrina)
gibbi (Miotylopus)
gibbus (Leuciscus)
gidleyi (Blarina, Ischyrocyon, Paracryptotis, Thomomys)
Gigandipodidae Ichnites Haubold, H. 1969B
        (in Saurischia—Carnosauria, incl. Gigandipus,
        Hyphepus)
Gigandipus Ichnites Haubold, H. 1969B
        (in Gigandipodidae)
Gigantaspis Protaspis
gigantea (Paracrax, Potamochelys)
giganteum (Deinotherium, Hipparion)
giganteus (Armantomys, Discoglossus, Dyoplosaurus,
        Eubrontes, Holoptychus, Mastodonsaurus,
        Megaloceros, Nothosaurus, Spermophilinus)
Gigantobison Bison
Gigantocamelus Camelidae Svistun, V. I. 1971A
    spatulus Hibbard, C. W. 1972A
gigantodus (Progymnodon)
Gigantopithecus Pongidae Frayer, D. W. 1971A;
        Groves, C. P. 1970A; Iakimov, V. P. 1969A;
        Larichev, V. E. 1964D; Pei, W.-C. 1957K;
        Pilbeam, D. 1970B; Simons, E. L. 1971B;
        Simons, E. L., Ettel, P. C. 1970A; Simons,
        E. L., Pilbeam, D. R. 1972A; Woo, Ju-kang
        1963A
    bilaspurensis Simons, E. L., Chopra, S. R. K. 1969A,B
    blacki Prasad, K. N. 1969C
gigas (Bison priscus, Champsosaurus, Hexanchus,
        Hydrodamalis, Odontaspis whitei, Paracamelus,
        Phascolonus)
gilberti (Scyliorhinus)
gilli (Dendragapus, Dendragapus gilli, Zygomaturus)
Gillicus see Ichthyodectes
gilmorei (Ichniotherium)
Gilmoreichnus Ichnites Haubold, H. 1971B
        (in Ophiacodontia)
    hermitanus [Hylopus] Haubold, H. 1971B
gilpini (Parictis)

Ginglymostoma   Orectolobidae
   delfortriei Bauzá Rullán, J. 1971A; Cappetta, H. C.
      1969B, 1970A
   obliquum oshosunense *White, E. I.* 1955C (n. var.)
   sokotoense Cappetta, H. C. 1972B
ginsburgi (Praearmantomys, Prodissopsalis)
Giraffa   Giraffidae Cooke, H. B. S., Coryndon, S. C.
      1970A; Gabunia, L. K., Buachidze, T̂s. I.
      1970A; Godina, A. Iã. 1971C
   jumae Leakey, L. S. B. 1970C
Giraffidae   Artiodactyla–Cervoidea Godina, A. Iã.
      1968B; Sarkar, S. S. 1964B
      Giraffa, Giraffokeryx, Helladotherium,
         Macedonitherium, Okapia, Palaeotragus,
         Samotherium, Sivatherium
Giraffokeryx   Giraffidae
   punjabiensis Pavlović, M. B. 1969A
glacialis (Antarctonchus)
glambus (Ardynomys)
glandarius (Garrulus)
glanis (Silurus)
glareolus (Clethrionomys)
glarisianus (Lepidopus, Scopeloides)
Glaucidium   Strigidae
   passerinum Jánossy, D. 1972A (aff.)
Glaucolepis see Pteronisculus
glaucus (Gyomys, Isurus)
Glaukerpeton
   avinoffi see Eryops
Gliravinae   Gliridae *Bruijn, H.* 1967A
Gliravus   Gliridae
   bruijni Hugueney, M. 1969A
   hammeli see Eogliravus
   majori Vianey-Liaud, M. 1969A
   meridionalis *Hartenberger, J.-L.* 1971A
   priscus Hartenberger, J.-L. 1971A
   robiacensis Hartenberger, J.-L. 1971A
Gliridae   Rodentia–Glimoidea
   Armantomys, Bransatoglis, Dryomys, Eliomys,
      Eogliravus, Eomuscardinus, Gliravus,
      Glirudinus, Glirulus, Glis, Hypnomys,
      Leithia, Microdyromys, Muscardinus,
      Myoglis, Myomimus, Paraglirulus,
      Paraglis, Pentaglis, Peridyromys,
      Praearmantomys, Pseudodryomys
   See also Eomyidae
gliriformis (Microcnus)
Gliroidea   Rodentia
Glirudinus   Gliridae Bruijn, H., Meulenkamp, J. E.
      1972A; Daxner-Höck, G. 1970A
   glirulus Hugueney, M. 1968A, 1969A
   gracilis Engesser, B. 1972A (cf.)
   modestus Baudelot, S. 1969A; Bruijn, H. 1967A
   praemurinus Hugueney, M. 1968A, 1969A
Glirulinae   Gliridae *Bruijn, H.* 1967A
Glirulus   Gliridae Daxner-Höck, G. 1970A
   gemmula *Kretzoi, M.* 1962D (subgen.
      Amphidyromys?)
   lissiensis see Paraglirulus
   miocaenicus see Microdyromys
   pusillus [Amphidyromys] Michaux, J. 1970A
glirulus (Glirudinus)
Glis   Gliridae Comaschi Caria, I. 1968A [Myoxus];
      Malez, M. 1967C
   glis Bartolomei, G., Pasa, A. 1970A; Bouchud, J.
      1961C; Fejfar, O. 1969A; Jánossy, D. 1969B

Glis - cont.
   minor Chaline, J. 1968A
   sackdillingensis Jánossy, D. 1969B; Koenigswald, W.
      1971A; Terzea, E., Jurcsák, T. 1967A
glis (Glis)
Globidens   Mosasauridae
   alabamaensis Russell, D. A. 1970B; Thurmond, J. T.
      1969B
globosus Otolithus (Macrouridarum)
Glossanodon   Argentinidae
   musceli Jerzmańska, A. 1968A
Glossochelys   Toxochelyidae
   planimenta Zangerl, R. 1971A (in Osteopyginae)
Glossotherium   Mylodontidae Webb, S. D. 1970B
   lettsomi Casamiquela, R. 1968A
   robustum Dechaseaux, C. 1971A
   wegneri Dechaseaux, C. 1971A [Oreomylodon]
gloveri (Eumys)
Glyptatelus   Glyptodontidae Hoffstetter, R.,
      Martinez, C., Mattauer, M., Tomasi, P. 1971A
Glyptodontidae   Edentata–Glyptodontoidea
      Gillette, D. 1972A
   Glyptatelus, Glyptotherium, Hoplophorus,
      Panochthus, Parapanochthus, Pseudoplohophoru
Glyptolepis   Holoptychidae Schaeffer, B. 1968C;
      Schultze, H.-P. 1969B; Schultze, H.-P. 1969B
      [Hamodus]
   baltica Vorob'eva, E. I., Liârskaiâ, L. A. 1968A(?)
   paucidens Andrews, S. M., Westoll, T. S. 1970B
      (cf., in Holoptychiida–Holoptychiidae)
Glyptophidium   Ophidiidae
   litheus *Sato, J.* 1962A (in Percida–Brotulidae)
Glyptops   Pleurosternidae Verzilin, N. N., Martinson,
      G. G., Khozatskii, L. I. 1970A, 1971A
   pervicax Ostrom, J. H. 1970C (in ?Glyptopsidae)
   plicatulus Ostrom, J. H. 1970C (in ?Glyptopsidae)
Glyptopsidae see Pleurosternidae
Glyptorhynchus   Xiphiidae
   communis [Otol. (Gadus) communis, Otol.
      (Macrurus) ellipticus, Coelorhynchus]
      Robba, E. 1970A (otol.)
   toulai [Otol. (Macrurus) toulai] Robba, E. 1970A
      (otol.)
   triangulus *Robba, E.* 1970A (otol.)
   See also Coelorhynchus
Glyptotherium   Glyptodontidae
   texanum Akersten, W. A. 1972A
Gnathoberyx   Trachthyidae Patterson, C. 1968B
Gnathorhiza   Lepidosirenidae Berman, D. S. 1970A;
      Minikh, M. G. 1969A; Rykov, S. P.,
      Minikh, M. G. 1969A; Shelton, John W. 1971A
   noblensis *Olson, E. C.*, Daly, E. 1972A
   serrata Carlson, K. J. 1968A; Olson, E. C. 1970A
Gnathosaurus   Pterodactylidae
   subulatus Wellnhofer, P. 1970A (in
      Ctenochasmatidae)
Gobibaatar   Ectypodontidae *Kielan-Jaworowska, Z.*
      1970C
   parvus *Kielan-Jaworowska, Z.* 1970C
Gobicyon   Canidae
   macrognathus Pavlović, M. B. 1969A
Gobielodon [Brachyodon] Entelodontidae *Kretzoi, M.*
      1968B (n. nom., in Elotheriidae)
gobiensis (Kennalestes, Serridentinus)
Gobihierax   Accipitridae–Accipitrinae *Kurochkin, E. N.*
      1968C
   edax *Kurochkin, E. N.* 1968C

Gorgonops - cont.
  eupachygnathus [Leptotrachelus] Sigogneau, D.
    1970A (n. comb.)
  kaiseri [Pachyrhinos] Sigogneau, D. 1970A
    (n. comb.)
  longifrons [Gorgonognathus] Sigogneau, D. 1970A
    (n. comb.)
  torvus Sigogneau, D. 1970A
  whaitsi [Scymnognathus] Sigogneau, D. 1970A
    (n. comb.)
Gorgonopsia   Therapsida–Theriodontia Boonstra,
    L. D. 1969A; Kemp, T. S. 1969B;
    Sigogneau, D. 1970A
Gorgonopsidae   Gorgonopsia
  Aelurognathus, Aelurosaurus, Aloposaurus,
    Arctognathus, Arctops, Broomicephalus,
    Broomisaurus, Cerdorhinus, Clelandina,
    Cyonosaurus, Dinogorgon, Eoarctops,
    Galesuchus, "Gorgonognathus", Gorgonops,
    Leontocephalus, Lycaenops, Paragalerhinus,
    Prorubidgea, Rubidgea, Scylacognathus,
    Scylacops, Sycosaurus
Gorgonopsinae   Gorgonopsidae Sigogneau, D. 1970A
    (incl. Broomisauridae, Galesuchidae,
    Gorgonopsidae, Scymnognathidae,
    Aelurosauridae, Galerhinidae, Aelurosauropsidae,
    Scylacocephalida, Scylacopsidae, Arctognathidae,
    Cynariopsidae and part of Gorgonognathidae,
    Arctognathoididae and Rubidgeidae Romer)
Gorgonorhinus see Arctops
gorgops (Hippopotamus)
Gorgosaurus   Tyrannosauridae
  horridus Sahni, A. 1972A [Deinodon, in Deinodontidae]
  See also Albertosaurus
gorjanovici (Mullus)
gortanii (Rhynchodercetis)
gortynius (Elephas)
gosseleti (Erquelinnesia)
gossypinus (Peromyscus)
gotoi (Batrachosauroides)
Goupilictis   Canidae–Amphicyoninae Ginsburg, L.
    1969C
  minor Ginsburg, L. 1969C
gracecus (Pliopyrax)
gracile (Ctenochasma, Hipparion, Peratherium,
    Rhinodicynodon, Xiphodon)
Gracilichnium   Ichnites Haubold, H. 1970A
    (in Dissorophidae)
  jacobii Haubold, H. 1970A
gracilidens (Sorex)
gracilis (Alacodon, Aloposaurus, Caranx,
    Cimolomys, Cordicephalus, Dercetis,
    Diplocynodon, Eolates, Epihippus,
    Galesuchus, Ganolepis, Glirudinus,
    Hirella, Leptoceratops, Macrourus,
    Milnea, Mimomys, Minutipes,
    Neomegaloceros, Nerophis, Nostolepis,
    Petenyiella, Pteranodon, Rhadinosuchus,
    Saturninia, Smilodectes, Viverravus,
    Zorillodontops)
Gracilisuchus   ?Ornithosuchidae Romer, A. S.
    1972B (ornithosuchid pseudosuchian)
  stipanicicorum Romer, A. S. 1972B
graciosus (Pholidophorus)
graculus (Pyrrhocorax)
gradata (Domnina)

gradatus (Capacikala)
Grallator   Ichnites Haubold, H. 1969B
    (in Anchisauripodidae); Lapparent, A. F.,
    Davoudzadeh, M. 1972A; Montenat, C.
    1970A (cf.)
  cuneatus Ostrom, J. H. 1968A(?)
  variabilis Bassoulet, J.-P. 1971A
Grallatoridae   Ichnites Welles, S. P. 1971A
    (in Coelurosauria; incl. Dilophosauripus,
    Kayentapus)
Grammatorcynus   Scombridae
  scomberoides Arambourg, C. 1966A
grande (Chalicotherium)
grandincisivus (Tetralophodon)
grandipelvis (Pterodactylus)
grandipes (Palaeobatrachus)
grandis (Camarasaurus, Eopelobates, Hemipsalodon,
    Livosteus, Moradisaurus, Procamelus,
    Pterodactylus, Scaldicetus)
grangeri (Neoplagiaulax, Phenacodus, Pinacosaurus,
    Zalambdalestes)
Grangerimus   Geomyidae
  dakotensis Macdonald, J. R. 1970A
  harkseni Macdonald, J. R. 1970A
  oregonensis Macdonald, J. R. 1970A
granulatus (Herasmius, Myriacanthus)
granulosus (Eodiaphyodus, Peltosaurus, Pseudoegertonia)
Grassator   Cosmoptychiidae Kazanĭseva, A. A. 1968A
  bidens [Cycloptychius] Kazanĭseva, A. A. 1968A
gratum (Pseudhipparion)
gratus (Griphippus)
Grayemys   Bataguridae Chkhikvadze, V. M. 1970B
  amoenus Chkhikvadze, V. M. 1970B
Grazosteus   Groenlandaspididae Stensiö, E. 1969B
    (in Euarthrodira incertae sedis)
greeni (Domnina)
greeni-praeceptor (Arvicola)
Greererpeton   Colosteidae Romer, A. S. 1969E
  burkemorani Romer, A. S. 1969E, 1972I
gregalis (Microtus)
gregaloides (Pitymys)
gregarius (Democricetodon, Dentex, Hesperocyon)
gregorii (Diceratherium, Hesperocyon)
gregoryi (Desmatochoerus curvidens)
Gregorymys   Geomyidae Stevens, M. S., Stevens, J. B.,
    Dawson, M. R. 1969A
  curtus Macdonald, J. R. 1970A
  formosus Macdonald, J. R. 1970A
gremmelsi (Proheteromys)
greslebini (Panochthus)
gresslyi (Mixtotherium)
grevyi (Equus)
grewingki (Latvius)
griggsorum (Prodipodomys)
grimbeeki (Cynarioides)
grimmi (Miopetaurista, Nasopus)
Griphippus   Equidae
  gratus Van Valen, L. 1962A
Griphognathus   Dipnorhynchidae
  minutidens Schultze, H.-P. 1969A
  sculpta Schultze, H.-P. 1969A, 1970A
Gripholagomys   Ochotonidae Green, M. 1972A
  lavocati Green, M. 1972A
Griphomys   Geomyidae Lindsay, E. 1969A
griqua (Loxodonta)
griseigena (Podiceps)

Hadrokkosaurus - cont.
  bradyi Cosgriff, J. W. 1969A; Welles, S. P.,
    Estes, R. 1969A
Hadropithecus Lemuridae Jolly, C. J. 1970C
Hadrosauridae Ornithischia—Ornithopoda
    Galton, P. M. 1970A; Powell, J. S. 1969A
  Anatosaurus, Aralosaurus, Brachylophosaurus,
    Corythosaurus, Edmontosaurus,
    Hypacrosaurus, Jaxartosaurus, Kritosaurus,
    Mandschurosaurus, Lambeosaurus,
    Procheneosaurus, Saurolophus
Hadrosteidae Arthrodira—Brachythoraci Stensiö, E.
    1969A,B (in Pachyosteomorphi—Pachyostei)
  Hadrosteus
Hadrosteus Hadrosteidae Stensiö, E. 1969A,B
haeckeli (Propliopithecus)
hafizi (Etrumeus)
hagermanensis (Peromyscus, Sorex)
hagni (Cricetodon)
Hainosaurus Mosasauridae Quinet, G. E. 1970B
haiti (Holonema)
hakelensis (Hemisaurida, Rhynchodercetis)
Halcyornis Laridae
  toliapicus Harrison, C. J. O., Walker, C. A. 1972A
    (in Halcyornithidae)
Halcyornithidae Coraciformes Harrison, C. J. O.,
    Walker, C. A. 1972A (incl. Halcyornis)
Haldanodon Docodontidae Kühne, W. G.,
    Krusat, G. 1972A
  exspectatus Kühne, W. G., Krusat, G. 1972A
Halec Enchodontidae
  eupterygius Goody, P. C. 1969B (in Halecidae,
    restor.)
  haueri Goody, P. C. 1969B (in Halecidae, restor.)
  microlepis see Phylactocephalus
Halecidae see Enchodontidae, Myctophidae
Halecoidei Salmoniformes Goody, P. C. 1969B
    (n. subord., incl. Halecidae)
Haliaeetus Accipitridae Jánossy, D. 1972A
    [Haliaetus]
Haliaetus see Haliaeetus
haliaetus (Pandion)
Halicetus Cetotheriidae Kellogg, R. 1969A
  ignotus Kellogg, R. 1969A
Halichoerus Phocidae
  grypus Ray, C. E., Wetmore, A., et al. 1968A
Halisaurus Mosasauridae
  sternbergi Russell, D. A. 1970B
Halitherium Dugongidae Chavanon, S., Saubade,
    A. M. 1970A; Fuchs, H. 1970A(?);
    Grigorescu, D. 1967A (cf.)
  schinzi Barthel, K. W. 1966A
halleyi (Alphadon)
halli (Odocoileus, Perognathoides)
Hallopodidae Crocodylomorpha—Paracrocodylia
    Walker, A. D. 1970A (incl. Hallopus)
  See also Coeluridae
Hallopus Coeluridae
  victor Walker, A. D. 1970A (in Hallopodidae),
    1972A
Halocypselus Exocoetidae
  italicus [Otol. (Hemiramphus) italicus] Robba, E.
    1970A (otol.)
Halticosaurus Procompsognathidae Sarsonneur, C.,
    Lapparent, F. 1966A
hamadryas (Peridyromys, Pseudodryomys)

Hamatopus Ichnites Wills, L. J., Sarjeant, W. A. S.
    1970A
hammeli (Buxolestes, Eogliravus)
hammondii (Scaphiopus)
Hamodus see Glyptolepis
haningtoni (Thalassomedon)
Hanosauridae Lepidosauria? Young, C.-c., Dong,
    Z.-m. 1972A
  Hanosaurus
Hanosaurus Hanosauridae Young, C.-c., Dong, Z.-m.
    1972A
  hupehensis Young, C.-c., Dong, Z.-m. 1972A
hansonorum (Adjidaumo)
hantoniensis (Diplocynodon)
Hapalodectes Mesonychidae
  leptognathus Szalay, F. S. 1969A
  lushiensis Szalay, F. S. 1969A
  serus Szalay, F. S. 1969A
Hapalops Megatheriidae Dechaseaux, C. 1971A
  longiceps Paula Couto, C. 1971A
Haplaletes Hyopsodontidae Gazin, C. L. 1969A(?)
Haplobunodon Anthracotheriidae Sudre, J. 1969A
  mulleri [Catodontherium argentonicum] Sudre, J.
    1972A
Haplomastodon see Stegomastodon
Haplomeryx Xiphodontidae
  picteti Sudre, J. 1969B (aff.)
Haplomys Aplodontidae Rensberger, J. M. 1972A
Haptodontidae see Sphenacodontidae
Haptodus Sphenacodontidae
  baylei Heyler, D. 1969A (in Haptodontidae)
  gaudryi Heyler, D. 1969A [Callibrachion, in
    Haptodontidae]
hardi (Moorevillia)
hardingi (Hylopus)
hardwicki (Nesokia)
harkseni (Allomys, Grangerimus)
harlani (Paramylodon)
Harpagophagus Canidae Bonis, L. 1971A
    (in Amphicyonidae)
  sanguineus Bonis, L. 1971A
harrasense (Chirotherium)
harriesi (Massospondylus)
harrisi (Podocnemis)
harrisonensis (Miotapirus)
hartenbergeri (Plesiarctomys, Rotundomys)
hartreei (Gallirallus)
hartshornianus (Daphoenus)
hassfurtense (Brachychirotherium)
hassiacum (Propalaeotherium)
hastalis (Isurus)
hatcheri (Desmatochoerus, Pediomys)
Hauboldisaurus Pareiasauridae Kuhn, O. 1969C
  eopermicus Kuhn, O. 1969C
haueri (Caranx, Halec, Labrodon)
haughtoni (Leontocephalus)
haumuriensis (Tylosaurus)
haussei (Limnopus)
hautimagnensis (Rhagapodemus)
haydeni (Aelurodon, Palaeolagus)
Hayemydinae Baenidae Gaffney, E. S. 1972A
Hayemys Baenidae—Hayemydinae Gaffney, E. S.
    1972A
  latifrons [Eubaena] Gaffney, E. S. 1972A
heberti (Hyaenodon, Steneosaurus)
hebridicus (Stereognathus)

heckelii (Casierius)
hedei (Andreolepis)
Hegetotheriidae Notoungulata—Typotheria
    Prohegetotherium
heidelbergensis (Homo, Homo erectus)
Heightingtonaspis Phlyctaenaspidae *White, E. I.*
    1969A
    anglica [Phlyctaenaspis, Kujdanowiaspis]
        White, E. I. 1969A (n. comb.)
    willsi [Kujdanowiaspis] White, E. I. 1969A
heikeni (Hypertragulus)
heilmani (Tupilakosaurus)
Heimenia Porolepidae *Ørvig, T.* 1969D
    ensis *Ørvig, T.* 1969D
heinrichi (Aeoliscus, Centriscus)
heintzi (Anglaspis, Pseudamiatus)
Heintzichthys Dinichthyidae Stensiö, E. 1969A,B
        (in Pachyostei incertae sedis); Stensiö, E.
        1969B [Stenognathus] (in Pachyostei
        incertae sedis)
heinzelini (Brachypotherium, Odontaspis)
Hekatobatrachus Palaeobatrachus *Špinar, Z. V.*
    1972B (n. subgen.)
Helaletes Helaletidae
    nanus McGrew, P. O., Sullivan, R. 1970A
Helaletidae Perissodactyla—Tapiroidea
    Colodon, Helaletes, Hyrachyus, Selenaletes
    See also Hyracodontidae, Lophiodontidae
Helarctos Ursidae
    malayanus Kurtén, B. 1968D
helbingi (Heterocricetodon)
Helicoprion Edestidae Nassichuk, W. W. 1971A;
        Nassichuk, W. W., Spinosa, C. 1970A
    svalis *Siedlecki, S.* 1970A
        (in Helicoprionidae)
Helicotragus Bovidae
    rotundicornis Melentis, J. K. 1970A;
        Tekkaya, I. 1969A
Heliscomys Heteromyidae
    schlaikjeri Macdonald, J. R. 1970A
    vetus Wood, A. E. 1969A (cf.)
    woodi Macdonald, J. R. 1970A
Helladotherium Giraffidae
    duvernoyi Melentis, J. K., Schneider, H. 1966A
helmeri (Theridomys)
Helmerosteus Trematosteidae Stensiö, E. 1969A,B
Heloderma Helodermatidae Schultze, H.-P. 1969B
Helodermatidae Squamata—Lacertilia
    Heloderma
Helodontidae Bradyodonti Patterson, C. 1968C
        (in Chimaeriformes—Helodontoidei)
    Helodus
Helodontoidei [Helodontiformes] Chimaeriformes
    Patterson, C. 1968C
Helodus Helodontidae Bendix-Almgreen, S. E. 1968A
    simplex Patterson, C. 1968C
helvetiae (Gobius)
helvetica (Tadarida)
helveticus (Simamphicyon, Treposciurus mutabilis)
Hemibos Bovidae Groves, C. P. 1969A
hemicingularis (Paramys, Paramys nanus)
Hemicyclaspididae Osteostraci (in Orthobranchiata,
        Stensiö) Fraunfelter, G. H. 1970A(?)
    Aceraspis, Ateleaspis, Hemicyclaspis, Hirella
Hemicyclaspis Hemicyclaspididae Heintz, A. 1969C
    murchisoni Dineley, D. L. 1968A; Ørvig, T. 1968B

Hemicyon Ursidae Webb, S. D. 1969C
    sansaniensis Telles Antunes, M. 1960C (in Canidae)
Hemionus Equus
hemionus (Equus)
Hemipristis Carcharhinidae
    serra Cappetta, H. C. 1969B, 1970A; Deraniyagala,
        P. E. P. 1969A,B,C; Menesini, E. 1969A
        (in Galeidae); Schultz, O. 1968A; Telles
        Antunes, M., Jonet, S. 1970A
Hemiprotosuchus Protosuchidae *Bonaparte, J. F.*
    1969B
    leali *Bonaparte, J. F.* 1969B, 1971B, 1972A
Hemipsalodon Hyaenodontidae
    grandis Mellett, J. S. 1969B; Russell, L. S. 1972B
Hemiramphidae see Exocoetidae
Hemiramphus Exocoetidae
    georgii *Jerzmańska, A.* 1968A (in Hemiramphidae)
Hemisaurida Myctophidae
    hakelensis *Goody, P. C.* 1969B (in Halecidae, restor.)
hemispherica (Clemmys)
hemitoechus (Dicerorhinus)
Hemitragus Bovidae
    jemlahicus
        bonali Daxner, G. 1968A
hemmoorensis (Trigla)
hennigi (Ancylotherium)
Henodontidae Placodontia
    Henodus
Henodus Henodontidae Westphal, F., Westphal, I.
        1967A
henseli (Tyrrhenicola)
hensleighi (Mesodma)
hentscheli (Protoryx)
henwoodi (Blinasaurus)
Heosemys Geoemyda
Heptasaurus see Mastodonsaurus
Heptranchias Hexanchidae Waldman, M. 1971A
Herasmius Heterosteidae *Ørvig, T.* 1969D
    granulatus *Ørvig, T.* 1969D
herculis (Chirotherium)
heringi (Salichnium)
hermanni (Testudo)
hermitanus (Gilmoreichnus)
heroldi (Broilina)
Herpestes Viverridae
    filholi Engesser, B. 1972A
Herpetichnus Ichnites Buffard, R., Demathieu, G.,
        Demathieu, P. 1969A
herrei (Permotriturus)
Herrerasaurus Plateosauridae
    ischigualastensis Bonaparte, J. F. 1972A; Colbert,
        E. H. 1970F (in Teratosauridae)
herreroi (Parendotherium)
Hesperhys Tayassuidae
    pinensis Macdonald, J. R. 1970A [Desmathyus]
hesperia (Cynorca)
hesperides (Nannipus)
hesperis (Desmatodon)
hesperius (Nesodactylus)
Hesperocyon Canidae
    gregarius Russell, L. S. 1972B
    gregorii Macdonald, J. R. 1970A
    leptodus Macdonald, J. R. 1970A
Hesperolagomys Ochotonidae
    fluviatilis *Storer, J. E.* 1970A
    galbreathi Shotwell, J. A. 1970A (cf.)

Hesperoloxodon see Palaeoloxodon
Hesperosorex   Soricidae
    lovei Gureev, A. A. 1971A
Hesperosuchus   Erpetosuchidae Walker, A. D. 1970A
    (in Pedeticosauridae)
Hesperotestudo   Geochelone
hesperus (Desmostylus, Floridatragulus, Machairodus,
    Megantereon)
hessbergense (Chirotherium)
hessei (Chirotherium, Prosynthetoceras)
hesterna (Geochelone)
hesternus (Camelops)
Heterochen   Anseriformes incertae sedis
    pratensis Short, L. L. 1970B
Heterocricetodon   Cricetidae
    helbingi Vianey-Liaud, M. 1972B
    telonii Jámbor, A., Korpás, L., Kretzoi, M.,
        Pálfalvy, I., Rákosi, L. 1971A (n. sp.,
        n. subgen. Alsocricetodon)
heterodactylus (Limnopus)
Heterodon   Colubridae
    platyrhinos Holman, J. A. 1972A
Heterodontidae   Selachii–Heterodontoidei
    Gyropleurodus, Heterodontus, Synechodus
Heterodontosauridae   Ornithischia–Ornithopoda
    Galton, P. M. 1972A (incl.
        Heterodontosaurus, Lycorhinus,
        Geranosaurus)
    Heterodontosaurus
Heterodontosaurus   Heterodontosauridae
    tucki Thulborn, R. A. 1970B [Lycorhinus]
Heterodontus   Heterodontidae
    lerichei Casier, E. 1967B
heterodontus (Protolabis)
Heterogaspis   Phlyctaenaspidae Stensiö, E. 1969B,
        1971A (in Spinothoracidi–Dolichothoraci);
    Stensiö, E. 1969B, 1971A [Monaspis, in
        Spinothoracidi–?Dolichothoraci]
Heteroglyphis   Proterotheriidae
    dewoletzky Rivas, O. E. O. 1969A
Heteromyidae   Rodentia–Geomyoidea
    Cupidinimus, Dipodomys, Diprionomys,
        Florentiamys, Heliscomys, Hitonkala,
        Mojavemys, Mookomys,
        Parapliosaccomys, Peridiomys,
        Perognathoides, Perognathus,
        Prodipodomys, Proheteromys, Sanctimus
Heterosorex   Soricidae
    roperi see Pseudotrimylus
    sansaniensis Gureev, A. A. 1971A
Heterosoricini   Soricidae–Soricinae Gureev, A. A.
        1971A (n. tribe, incl. Heterosorex,
        Ingentisorex, Pseudotrimylus)
Heterosteidae   Arthrodira–Brachythoraci Stensiö, E.
        1969A,B [Heterostiidae, in
        ?Aspinothoracidi]
    Herasmius, Heterosteus
Heterosteus   Heterosteidae Stensiö, E. 1969A,B
        [Heterostius]
Heterostiidae see Heterosteidae
Heterostius see Heterosteus
Heterostraci   Agnatha–Diplorhina (incl. Astraspiformes,
        Pteraspiformes, Cyathaspiformes,
        Corvaspiformes, Amphiaspiformes,
        Carpideltiformes of Stensiö) Halstead, L. B.
        1971A; Karatajūte-Talimaa, V. N. 1968B
        (incl. Polymerolepidiformes);

Heterostraci - cont.
    Novitskaia, L. I. 1968A, 1971B (classif.);
    Whiting, H. P. 1972A
    See also Amphiaspidiformes
    Incertae sedis: Seretolepis
Heteroxerus   Sciuridae
    grivensis Bruijn, H. 1967A; Telles Antunes, M.,
        Mein, P. 1971A (cf.)
    lavocati Hugueney, M. 1969A
    paulhiacensis Hugueney, M. 1969A
    rubricati Bruijn, H. 1967A; Telles Antunes, M.,
        Mein, P. 1971A
    vireti Telles Antunes, M., Mein, P. 1971A
hewletti (Propenser)
Hexacodus see Protodichobune
hexagonus (Gyrodus)
Hexanchidae [Notidanidae] Selachii–Hexanchoidea
    Heptranchias, Hexanchus
Hexanchus [Notidanus] Hexanchidae
    gigas Bosch, M. 1969A [Notidanus]
    griseus Telles Antunes, M., Jonet, S. 1970A (cf.)
    loozi Casier, E. 1967B [Notidanus, subgen.
        ?Hexanchus]
    primigenius Bosch, M. 1969A [Notidanus];
        Cappetta, H. C. 1969B, 1970A; Menesini, M.
        1969A [Notidanus]; Schultz, O. 1968A
Hexanchus   Hexanchus
Hexaprotodon see Hippopotamus
hiatti (Trinitichelys)
hibbardi (Beckiasorex, Bufo, Pseudaelurus, Sorex)
hibberti (Megalichthys, Rhizodus)
Hibernaspididae   Heterostraci Novitskaia, L. I. 1968A,
        1971B (in Amphiaspidiformes–
        Hibernaspidoidei, incl. Hibernaspis)
    See also Amphiaspididae
Hibernaspis   Amphiaspididae
    macrolepis Novitskaia, L. I. 1971B
        (in Hibernaspididae); Stensiö, E. 1968A
hibernicus (Megaloceros giganteus)
hidalgensis (Nothokemas)
hildburghausense (Chirotherium)
hilgendorfi (Eotorpedo)
Hillsaspis   Astrolepidae Stensiö, E. 1969B
        (in Bothriolepididae)
Himalayasaurus   Shastasauridae Young, C.-c.,
        Dong, Z.-m. 1972A
    tibetensis Young, C.-c., Dong, Z.-m. 1972A
hinschei (Eopelobates)
hintoni (Pitymys)
Hiodon   Hiodontidae Cavender, T. M. 1968A (cf.)
    alosoides Smith, G. R., Lundberg, J. G. 1972A (cf.)
Hiodontidae   Osteoglossiformes–Notopteroidei
    Hiodon
Hipparion   Equidae Bruijn, H., Sondaar, P. Y.,
        Zachariasse, W. J. 1971A; Ghenea, C. 1968A;
        Guérin, C., et al. 1972A; Hussain, S. T. 1971B;
        Koenigswald, G. H. R. 1970A; Mihăilă, N.
        1971A; Simons, E. L., Pilbeam, D., Boyer,
        S. J. 1971A; Zhegallo, V. I. 1971A
        [Proboscidipparion]; Zhegallo, V. I.,
        Borisov, B. A. 1968A
    albertense Cooke, H. B. S., Coryndon, S. C. 1970A
        (subgen. Hipparion)
    antilopinum Hussain, S. T. 1971A
    crassum Leinders, J., Michaux, J. 1969A (cf.)
    crusafonti Koenigswald, G. H. R. 1970B, 1972A;
        Vekua, A. K. 1967A

Holocentropsis Holocentridae *Gaudant, M.* 1969A
oblongus *Gaudant, M.* 1969A
Holocentrus Holocentridae Patterson, C. 1968B
weileri *Robba, E.* 1970A (?, otol.)
Holocephali Chondrichthyes Blot, J. 1969A (syst.);
Patterson, C. 1968C (class, incl.
Chimaeriformes, Chondrenchelyiformes,
Edestiformes); Saint-Seine, P., Devilliers, Ch.
1969A
Holoclemensia Didelphidae [Clemensia] Slaughter, B. H.
1968D; Turnbull, W. D. 1971A
texana Slaughter, B. H. 1971A
Holonema Holonematidae Mitchell, S. W. 1971A;
Stensiö, E. 1969B (in Holonemida)
haiti *Denison, R. H.* 1968B
westolli *Miles, R. S.* 1971B
Holonematidae Arthrodira—Arctolepida (incl.
Holonemidae of Stensiö) Miles, R. S. 1971B
(incl. Holonema, Deirosteus, Gyroplacosteus,
Deveonema, Megaloplax, Rhenonema);
Stensiö, E. 1971B [Holonemidae, in
Euarthrodira incertae sedis]
Anomalichthys, ?Arctonema, Aspidichthys, Deirosteus,
Deveonema, Gyroplacosteus, Holonema,
Megaloplax, Rhenonema
Holonemidae see Holonematidae
Holopetalichthys Gemuendinidae Stensiö, E. 1969B,
1971A (in Spinothoracidi—Radotinida)
Holoptychidae [Holoptychiidae] Crossopterygii—
Rhipidistia
Glyptolepis, Holoptychus, Laccognathus
Holoptychius see Holoptychus
Holoptychus Holoptychidae Andrews, S. M.,
Westoll, T. S. 1970B [Holoptychius];
Schultze, H.-P. 1969B; Taylor, K. 1972A
[Holoptychius]; Vorob'eva, E. I.,
Lârskaîa, L. A. 1968A [Holoptichius]
giganteus Pampe, W. R. 1969A [Holoptychius]
holsatica (Sciaena)
Holuriidae Palaeonisciformes—Palaeoniscoidei
Australichthys
Homacodontidae Artiodactyla—Palaeodonta
Antiacodon, Microsus
Homalacanthus Acanthodidae
concinnus Schultze, H.-P. 1972A
Hominidae Primates—Catarrhini Abel, M. 1972A
(evol., females); Acsádi, Gy.,
Nemeskéri, J. 1970A (life span);
Aigner, J. S. 1972A (China); Anderson,
R. T. 1972A (evol.); Arambourg, C., et al.
1968A; Arnold, W. 1968A, 1969A (evol.);
Bilsborough, A. 1971A (S. Africa);
Birdsell, J. B. 1972A (evol.); Bowler, J. M.,
et al. 1972A (Australia); Brace, C. L.
1967B; Brace, C. L., Nelson, H., Korn, N.
1971A; Brodrick, A. H. 1971A; Campbell,
B. G. 1968B,C, 1969A; Čanadjija, S. 1970A;
Clark, J. D. 1970B; Coon, C. S. 1966A,
1968A; Coppens, Y. 1970A, 1971C;
Danilova, E. I. 1968A; Day, M. H. 1967B,
1969A,D; Day, M. H., Wood, B. A. 1968A,
1969A; Debénath, A. 1970A; DeVore, I.
1971B (evol.); Eisenberg, L. 1971A;
Endo, B., Kimura, T. 1970A; Fagg, B.
1969A (Australopithecine); Ferembach, D.
1963B (Europe), 1967A (skull); Genet-
Varcin, E. 1972A (Placard); Genet-Varcin, E.,

Hominidae - cont.
Rabischong, P. 1965A (Grimaldi); Haynes,
C. V. 1972A (N. Amer.); Heberer, G. 1969B,
1970A,B; Heintz, N. 1966C,D,E, 1967C,D;
Holloway, R. L. 1970D, 1972B (brain evol.);
Howell, F. C. 1969C (Omo V.), 1971A;
Hughes, D. R. 1967A; Huxley, T. H. 1972A;
Jakob, T. 1965A, 1967B; Jelínek, J. 1966A,
1967A, 1969A; Jolly, C. J. 1970A,B;
Jullien, R. 1966A; Kennedy, K. A. R. 1972A;
Kinzey, W. G. 1970A (canine), 1972A (brain
evol.); Klein, R. G. 1969C, 1970B (S. Africa);
Koenigswald, G. H. R. 1967E,F; Krantz, G. S.
1968B; Kurtén, B. 1971B (brain size);
Kurth, G. 1967A, 1968A; Leakey, L. S. B.
1966D, 1967G, 1971D; Leakey, L. S. B.,
Leakey, M. D. 1971A (Olduvai, Lake Natron);
Leakey, L. S. B., Prost, J., Prost, S. (eds.)
1971A; Leakey, R. E. 1971B (East Africa);
Lengyel, I. 1968A, 1969A; Lipták, P. 1969A;
Lü, Ch.-R. 1967A (China); Lyell, C. 1972A;
Marston, A. T. 1971A (Swanscombe);
Marzke, M. W. 1971A (origin of human hand);
Matîukhin, A. E. 1972A (Vertesszöllös);
Mayr, E. 1972C (taxonomy); McCown, T. D.,
Keith, A. 1972A; Napier, J. 1971A (evol.);
Nemeskéri, J., Dezsö, Gy. (eds.) 1969A;
Nesturkh, M. F. 1970A, 1972B; Oakley, K. P.,
Campbell, B. G., Molleson, T. I. (eds.) 1971A
(catalogue); Olivier, G. 1972A; Oppenheimer,
A. M. 1967A, 1968A; Oxnard, C. E. 1968A
(Sterkfontein), 1968C (Olduvai), 1968D
(shoulder evol.), 1969A (shoulder evol.),
1972A (foot bones); Ozansoy, F. 1969C
(footprints); Petit-Maire, N. 1972A (evol.);
Petit-Maire, N., Charon, M. 1972A; Petit-
Maire Heintz, N., Dricot, J. M. 1970A; Petit-
Maire Heintz, N., et al. 1970A; Pilbeam, D. R.
1967A, 1969D, 1970A,B,C, 1972A,B; Pilbeam,
D. R., Simons, E. L. 1972A (evol., classif.);
Piveteau, J. 1972A,B; Poulianos, A. N. 1967A
(Petralona), 1971A; Preuschoft, H. 1971A
(posture, locomotion); Reshetov, Iu. G. 1972A;
Ricqlès, A. 1970B; Robinson, J. T. 1972B
(E. Rudolf); Roginskiî, Ia. Ia. 1969B
(Hungary); Roper, M. K. 1969A; Rosen, S. I.,
McKern, T. W. 1971A (cranial indices);
Rossmann, D. L. 1971A; Schobinger, J. 1969A;
Schott, L. 1970A (evol.); Schwidetzky, I.
1959A, 1971A; Sergi, S. 1971A (Italy);
Sicard, H. 1957A, 1963A, 1967A; Sigmon,
B. A. 1969A (bipedalism); Simon, K. H. 1971A;
Singer, R. 1971A (Saldanha skull); Solecki,
R. S. 1971B (Shanidar); Stęślicka, W. 1968A;
Stęślicka-Mydlarska, W. 1971A; Tattersall,
I. M. 1969C; Thoma, A. 1969A; Tobias, P. V.
1971A (brain); Uryson, M. I. 1972B (syst.);
Vandebosch, A. 1957A; Vandermeersch, B.
1969A, 1971B, 1972A; Washburn, S. L.
1968B, 1971A; Washburn, S. L., Shirek, J.
1967A;Watson, L. 1971A (evol.; eating habits);
Weidenreich, F. 1972A; Westenhöfer, M.
1953A (origin); Wolpoff, M. H. 1971B,E
(Vertesszöllös); 1971C,D, 1972A (teeth);
Woo, Ju-kang 1962D, 1963A; Wymer, J. 1971A
(Swanscombe); Young, L. M. 1971A
(Australia)

Homo - cont.
1969D,I,J; Vandebosch, A. 1955A
[neandertaloids]; Vlček, E. 1968B,
1969A,B, 1970A; Wunderlich, M. D.
1971A (rickets)
Homogalax Isectolophidae
protapirinus Guthrie, D. A. 1971B
Homoioceras Bovidae
vignardi Churcher, C. S. 1972C(?)
Homonotichthys Polymixiidae Patterson, C. 1968B
Homostiidae Arthrodira—Brachythoraci (incl.
Homostiidae, Euleptaspididae of Stensiö)
Stensiö, E. 1969B, 1971A (in
Spinothoracidi—Coccosteomorphi)
Angarichthys, Homostius, ? Luetkeichthys,
Tityosteus, Tollichthys
Homostius Homostiidae Heintz, A. 1968A;
Stensiö, E. 1969B, 1971A
Homotherium Felidae Kurtén, B. 1969A; Schütt, G.
1970A
crenatidens Ballésio, R. 1964A
latidens Mazak, V. 1970A
Homunculus see Stirtonia
homunculus (Tetonius)
hookeri (Otaria)
hopei (Odontaspis)
hopii (Kayentapus)
Hopiichnus Ichnites Welles, S. P. 1971A
(in ? Ornithomimidae)
shingi Welles, S. P. 1971A
hopkinsi (Predicrostonyx)
Hoplictis Ischyrictis
Hoplitosaurus Nodosauridae Bodily, N. M.
1969A(?)
Hoplitosuchus Erythrosuchidae
raui Bonaparte, J. F. 1972A
Hoplobrotula Ophidiidae
lerichei Stinton, F. C., Nolf, D. 1969A (otol.,
in Brotulidae)
toliapicus [Ampheristus] Nolf, D. 1970A (otol.,
in Brotulidae)
Hoplocetus see Scaldicetus
Hoplochelys Dermatemydidae Chkhikvadze, V. M.
1971A (in Chelydridae)
Hoplophoneus Felidae Brunet, M. 1967A
Hoplophorini [Sclerocalyptini] Glyptodontidae—
Hoplophorinae Lins Rolim, J. 1971A
(n. nom., incl. Hoplophorus)
Hoplophorus Glyptodontidae Lins Rolim, J. 1971A
(in Hoplophorini)
Hoplopteryx Trachichthyidae Applegate, S. P.
1970A; Patterson, C. 1968B
lewisi see Stichopteryx
Hoplostethus Trachichthyidae Patterson, C. 1968B
lawleyi Robba, E. 1971A (otol.)
levis Anfossi, G., Mosna, S. 1969A (otol.);
Robba, E. 1970A (otol.)
biexcisus Robba, E. 1970A (otol.)
ostiolatus Robba, E. 1970A (otol.)
pisanus Anfossi, G., Mosna, S. 1969B (cfr., otol.);
Robba, E. 1970A (otol.)
praemediterraneus Anfossi, G., Mosna, S. 1969A
(cfr., otol.); Robba, E. 1970A (otol.)
hoppei (Gomphonchus)
hopsoni (Megalesthonix)
horai (Hypoprion)

Horatiomys Cricetidae Munthe, J., Jr. 1971A
montanus see Dikkomys woodi
horncloudi (Amphechinus, Palaeoerinaceus)
horribilis (Bufo marinus, Ursus arctos)
horridus (Gorgosaurus, Hyaenodon)
horsfieldi (Testudo)
houfenense (Hipparion)
houtumschindleri (Prostrepsiceros)
howardinus (Trihecaton)
howelli (Citellus)
huastecensis (Perognathus)
huberi (Eucricetodon)
hudsonius (Zapus)
hudspethensis (Sigmodon)
huenei (Cuyosuchus, Sphagesaurus)
huerzeleri (Eucricetodon)
hugii (Machimosaurus)
Huginaspis Phlyctaenaspidae Stensiö, E. 1969B
(in Spinothoracidi—Dolichothoraci)
huismani (Marosichthys)
Humbertia Salmoniformes incertae sedis Patterson, C.
1970A
operta Patterson, C. 1970A
humilis (Clupea, Lepomis)
humulis (Reithrodontomys)
hungarica (Desmana moschata, Petenyia)
hungaricus (Pliopetes, Propliomys, Sciurus whitei,
Villanyia)
hunteri (Elasmodus)
hupehensis (Hanosaurus)
Hupehsuchia Thecodontia Young, C.-c., Dong, Z.-m.
1972A (n. subord.)
Hupehsuchidae Thecodontia—Hupehsuchia Young,
C.-c., Dong, Z.-m. 1972A
Hupehsuchus
Hupehsuchus Hupehsuchidae Young, C.-c., Dong, Z.-m.
1972A
nanchangensis Young, C.-c., Dong, Z.-m. 1972A
hurzeleri (Plesiarctomys)
Hussakofia Coccosteidae Stensiö, E. 1969A,B
(in Pachyostei incertae sedis); Stensiö, E.
1969B [Copanagnathus, in Euarthrodira
incertae sedis]
huxleyi (Oryctolagus cuniculus, Parasuchus)
hyaena (Hyaena)
Hyaena Hyaenidae Beaumont, G. 1968B
brevirostris Kurtén, B. 1969A
licenti Erdbrink, D. P. 1968A
donnezani Crusafont Pairó, M., Aguirre, E. 1971A
dubia Beaumont, G. 1969A
hyaena Buckland-Wright, J. C. 1969A; Churcher,
C. S. 1972C
prisca Bonifay, M.-F. 1971A
robusta
progressa Jánossy, D. 1969B [cf., Pachycrocuta]
Hyaenasuchus Trochosauridae Boonstra, L. D. 1969A
(in Lycosuchidae)
Hyaenidae Carnivora—Aeluroidea Crusafont Pairó, M.,
Petter, G. 1969A; Ficcarelli, G., Torre, D.
1970A (taxonomy)
Crocuta, Hyaena, Ictitherium, Lycyaenops, Percrocuta,
Progenetta, Tungurictis
Hyaenodictis Mesonychidae Quinet, G. E. 1969B
(invalid)
Hyaenodon Hyaenodontidae Bessonnat, G., Dughi, R.,
Sirugue, F. 1969A (ichn.); Lange-Badré, B.
1972A (origin)

Hyaenodon - cont.
  brevirostrus *Macdonald, J. R.* 1970A
  crucians Mellett, J. S. 1969A
  cruentus Russell, L. S. 1972B
  heberti Sudre, J. 1969A (aff.)
  horridus Russell, L. S. 1972B(?)
  leptorhynus Bergounioux, F. M., Crouzel, F.
      1968B
  minutus Russell, L. S. 1972B (? , cf.)
  mustelinus Russell, L. S. 1972B
  requieni Jehenne, Y. 1969A (cf.)
  schlosseri see Oxyaenoides
Hyaenodontidae Creodonta—Hyaenodontia
      Macdonald, J. R. 1970A (in Carnivora);
      Matthes, H. W. 1967E
  Francotherium, Hemipsalodon, Hyaenodon,
      Imperatoria, Paeneprolimnocyon,
      Prodissopsalis, Prototomus, Pterodon,
      Tritemnodon
Hybodontidae Selachii—Hybodontoidea
      Wilson, M. 1972A
  Acrodus, Asteracanthus, Hybodus, Lonchidion,
      ? Petrodus, Polyacrodus, Pororhiza,
      Pseudoheterodontus
Hybodus Hybodontidae Lehman, J.-P. 1971A
  allegheniensis *Lund, R.* 1970B
  brevicostatus Thurmond, J. T. 1971B (cf.)
  butleri *Thurmond, J. T.* 1971B
  copei Berman, D. S. 1970A (cf.)
  parvidens Thurmond, J. T. 1971B (aff.)
  vestitus Zídek, J. 1969A
Hydrochoeridae Rodentia—Cavioidea
      Neochoerus
Hydrodamalinae Dugongidae Domning, D. P. 1971A
Hydrodamalis Dugongidae Gard, L. M., Lewis,
      G. E., Whitmore, F. C. 1972A; Shikama, T.
      1971A; Shikama, T., Domning, D. P. 1970A
  gigas Domning, D. P. 1972B; Gard, L. M., Szabo,
      B. J. 1971A
  stelleri Chelnokov, F. G. 1969A [Rhytina];
      McClung, R. M. 1969A
Hydrotherosaurus Elasmosauridae Hasegawa, Y.,
      Obata, I. 1972A
hydruntinus (Equus)
Hygophum Myctophidae
  agatense *Robba, E.* 1970A (otol.)
  germanicum *Heinrich, W.-D.* 1969B (?, otol.)
  See also Myctophum
Hygophus Myctophidae Anfossi, G., Mosna, S.
      1969A (otol.)
  intermedius
      derthonensis *Anfossi, G., Mosna, S.* 1969B
      (otol.)
Hyla Hylidae
  arborea Vergnaud-Grazzini, C. 1970A (cf.)
  cinerea Chantell, C. J. 1971A (cf.)
  crucifer Chantell, C. J. 1971A (cf.)
  regilla Chantell, C. J. 1970A (cf.)
  swanstoni *Holman, J. A.* 1968B
Hylidae Anura—Neobatrachia
  Acris, Hyla, Pseudacris
Hylobates Pongidae Groves, C. P. 1968A
Hylobatinae Pongidae Koenigswald, G. H. R. 1968C
Hylochoerus Suidae
  meinertzhageni Cooke, H. B. S., Coryndon, S. C.
      1970A

Hylopus Ichnites
  hardingi Haubold, H. 1970A
  hermitanus see Gilmoreichnus
  trifidus see Ornithoides
Hymenocephalus Macrouridae
  asymetricus Anfossi, G., Mosna, S. 1971A (otol.)
  labiatus Anfossi, G., Mosna, S. 1969A (cf., otol.);
      Brzobohatý, R. 1967C (?, otol.); Rado, G.
      1969A (?, otol.)
Hyopsodontidae Condylarthra
  Asmithwoodwardia, Haplaletes, Hyopsodus, Litaletes,
      Paschatherium, Promioclaenus, Protoselene
Hyopsodus Hyopsodontidae
  miticulus Guthrie, D. A. 1971B
  walcottianus Guthrie, D. A. 1971B
  wortmani Guthrie, D. A. 1971B
Hyotherium Suidae
  palaeocherus Hünermann, K. A. 1968A; Mihăilă, N.
      1971A
  simorrense Głazek, J., Oberc, J., Sulimski, A. 1971A
  soemmeringi Čtyroký, P., Fejfar, O. 1963A;
      Głazek, J., Oberc, J., Sulimski, A. 1971A
      (aff.); Schmidt-Kittler, N. 1971A
  See also Korynochoerus
Hypacrosaurus Hadrosauridae Schroeder, D. 1969C
hyperbates (Rhynchosauroides)
Hyperdichobune Dichobunidae
  langi [Dichobune] Sudre, J. 1972A
  nobilis [Dichobune] Sudre, J. 1972A
Hypertragulidae Artiodactyla—Traguloidea
  Andegameryx, Floridatragulus, Gobiomeryx,
      Hypertragulus, Leptomeryx, Miomeryx,
      Nanotragulus
Hypertragulus Hypertragulidae
  heikeni *Ferrusquía-Villafranca, I.* 1969A
Hyphepus Ichnites Haubold, H. 1969B
      (in Gigandipodidae)
Hypnomys Gliridae Ambrosetti, P. 1969A
hypoconus (Gypsonictops)
Hypohippus Equidae Forstén, A. 1970B
  affinis Webb, S. D. 1969C
  matthewi Webb, S. D. 1969C [Megahippus]
  osborni Crockett, C. T. 1970B
Hypolagus Leporidae Berzi, A. 1970A; Thaler, L.
      1972A
  beremendensis Feustel, R., et al. 1971B
  brachygnathus Campbell, K. E. 1969A; Chaline, J.
      1968A; Sukhov, V. P. 1970A (cf.)
  limnetus Campbell, K. E. 1969A; Downey, J. S.
      1968A (near); Hibbard, C. W. 1969A
  parviplicatus Forstén, A. 1970B; Lindsay, E. H.
      1972A
  vetus Campbell, K. E. 1969A (aff.); Hibbard, C. W.
      1969A (aff.); Shotwell, J. A. 1970A
Hypolophidae see Dasyatidae
Hypolophites Dasyatidae
  thaleri *Cappetta, H. C.* 1972B (in Mylidoatidae)
Hypolophus Dasyatidae
  mcnultyi *Thurmond, J. T.* 1971B
      (?, in Hypolophidae)
  sylvestris Casier, E. 1967B (in Hypolophidae)
Hypoprion Carcharhinidae Cappetta, H. C. 1969B;
      Silva Santos, R., Sardenberg Salgado, M.
      1971A
  acanthodon Telles Antunes, M., Jonet, S. 1970A
  horai Singh, G. 1971A

imperiale (Protobalistum)
Incacetus   Ziphiidae
    broggii Spillmann, F. 1970A
Incamys   Caviomorpha incertae sedis *Hoffstetter, R.,*
    Lavocat, R. 1970A
    bolivianus *Hoffstetter, R., Lavocat, R.* 1970A
incarinatus (Antilospira)
incertis (Brachyerix)
incertus (Microtus, Riojasaurus)
incisivum (Aceratherium)
incisus (Cimolestes)
incompletus (Palaeophasianus, Syngnathus)
incredibilis (Teratornis)
incus (Aquiladelphis)
Indaginilepis   Palaeoniscoidei incertae sedis
    Schultze, H.-P. 1970B
    rhombifera *Schultze, H.-P.* 1970B
Indarctos   Ursidae
    atticus
        lagreli Erdbrink, D. P. 1968A (cf.)
        oregonensis Dalquest, W. W. 1969A; Shotwell,
        J. A. 1970A
indentatus (Strosipherus)
index (Chrysemys, Hyracotherium, Icaronycteris)
indica (Nesokia, Podocnemis)
indicus (Dryopithecus, Elephas, Kanisamys,
    Paraulacodus, Platycephalus,
    Wadiasaurus)
indirae (Indohyus)
individens (Entoptychus)
Indobrachyops   Brachyopidae
    panchetensis Cosgriff, J. W. 1969A; Welles, S. P.,
    Estes, R. 1969A (in Stereospondyli
    incertae sedis)
Indohyus   ?Choeropotamidae *Rao, A. R.* 1971A
    indirae *Rao, A. R.* 1971A
    kalakotensis *Rao, A. R.* 1971(?)
inequalis (Stenonychosaurus)
inermis (Empedaspis)
inexpectata (Paradidelphis)
inexpectatus (Anourosorex, Megalosaurus)
infelix (Fulica)
inferus (Merluccius)
infinitesimus (Suncus)
inflata (Clupea)
infralactorensis (Eucricetodon)
ingens (Gobius, Lutra, Pteranodon)
Ingentisorex   Soricidae
    tumididens Gureev, A. A. 1971A
ingenuus (Nannipus)
Iniidae   Cetacea–Odontoceti
    Kampholophos
Inostrancevia   Inostranceviidae Fomichev, V. D.
    1967A
Inostranceviidae   Therapsida–Theriodontia
    Inostrancevia
Insectivora   Mammalia
    Incl. subord. Proteutheria, Macroscelidea,
    Dermoptera, Lipotyphla, ?Zalambdodonta
    Butler, P. M. 1972B (classif.); Hutchison,
    J. H. 1969A; Novacek, M. J. 1972A;
    Skorik, A. F. 1969A
insignis (Laterallus, Longisquama, Merychippus,
    Stegodon, Washakius)
insiliens (Thescelus)
insolita (Cramauchenia)

insolitus (Ergilemys, Geochelone, Paciculus)
insuliferus (Promimomys)
intactus (Leontocephalus)
Intasuchidae   Temnospondyli–Rhachitomi
    Intasuchus, Syndyodosuchus
Intasuchus   Intasuchidae Schultze, H.-P. 1969B
    silvicola Shishkin, M. A. 1968B
integer (Centropristis)
intergerinus (Palaeogadus)
intermedia (Crocuta spelaea, Gruipeda, Kowalskia,
    Palaeortyx, Speotyto cunicularia, Strix)
intermedium (Echinerpeton, Paraentelodon)
intermedius (Corythosaurus, Dipoides, Eliomys,
    Erinaceus, Hygophus, Mammuthus,
    Mammuthus primigenius, Megalichthys,
    Megalocnus, Mimomys, Nanotragulus,
    Nimravus, Palaeoanacorax, Phenacomys,
    Pronothodectes, Protozapus, Struthionops,
    Treposciurus)
intimus (Gobius)
intrepidus (Pseudaelurus)
Inuus   Macaca
iolensis (Palaeoloxodon)
Ioribos   Bovidae–Bovini Gabuniia, L. K., *Vekua, A. K.*
    1968C (in Ioritragini)
    aceros Gabuniia, L. K., *Vekua, A. K.* 1968C
Ioritragini   Bovidae–Bovini Gabuniia, L. K., *Vekua,*
    A. K. 1968C (n. tribe, incl. Ioribos)
iranensis (Urosphen)
Irenichthys   Lycopteridae Iakovlev, V. N. 1968A
    certus *Iakovlev, V. N.* 1968A
ironcloudi (Proheteromys)
irtyshense (Samotherium)
irtyshensis (Proumbra)
Ischignathus   Traversodontidae
    sudamericanus Bonaparte, J. F. 1972A
ischigualastensis (Herrerasaurus)
Ischigualastia   Kannemeyeriidae
    jenseni Bonaparte, J. F. 1972A
Ischirhiza   Pristidae
    nigeriensis [Markgrafia] Cappetta, H. C. 1972B
    See also Onchosaurus
Ischisaurus   Palaeosauriscidae
    cattoi Bonaparte, J. F. 1972A; Colbert, E. H. 1970F
Ischnacanthidae   Ischnacanthiformes
    ?Byssacanthoides, Gomphonchus, Poracanthodes
Ischnacanthiformes   Osteichthyes–Acanthodii
Ischyodus   Chimaeridae
    thurmanni Radwański, A 1968A
Ischyrictis   Ischyrictis
Ischyrictis   Mustelidae
    florancei Crusafont Pairó, M. 1972A (subgen.
    Hoplictis)
    petteri *Crusafont Pairó, M.* 1972A (subgen.
    Ischyrictis)
Ischyrocyon   Canidae
    gidleyi Webb, S. D. 1969C (in Amphicyonidae)
Ischyromyidae   Rodentia–Ischyromyoidea Black, C. C.
    1971A (incl. Ischyromyinae, Paramyinae,
    Reithroparamyinae, Prosciurinae)
    Downsimus, Ischyromys, Spurimus
Ischyromyoidea   Rodentia
Ischyromys   Ischyromyidae
    junctus *Russell, L. S.* 1972B
    veterior Wood, A. E. 1969A

jesreelicus (Allocricetus)
jexi (Cephalaspis)
jinglebobensis (Onychomys)
joachimica (Bauzaia)
joachimicus   Otolithus (Ophidiidarum)
joaquinensis (Plotopterum)
johnsoni (Spermophilus)
joleaudi (Scyliorhynus)
jonesi (Papio)
jonesii (Attenosaurus)
joneti (Scyliorhinus)
Jonkeria   Titanosuchidae Boonstra, L. D. 1968B,
          1969A
Jonkeriidae see Titanosuchidae
jordanica (Arvicola)
jordanicus (Parapodemus)
Jordonomys   Cricetidae Haas, G. 1966A
      haasi Tchernov, E. 1968C (in Microtidae)
      pusillus Haas, G. 1966A
jotae (Cricetodon)
jourdani (Atoposaurus)
jubata (Eumetopias)
jubbi (Mentichthys)
judaicus (Myomimus)
judithae (Cimexomys)
Jugosuchus   Melanosauridae Tverdokhlebova, G. I.
          1968A (nomen nudum, = Chroniosuchus)
jumae (Giraffa)
junctus (Ischyromys)
jungi (Geotrypus)
juradoi (Marmosopsis)
juvenilis (Nothosaurus)
kaiseni (Chasmosaurus)
kaisensis (Hippopotamus, Stegodon)
kaiseri (Gorgonops)
kakelik (Alectoris)
kalakotensis (Indohyus)
kalbica (Scirtodipus)
kalimerianum (Anthracotherium)
kalmani (Otis)
kamalii (Trilophodon)
Kampholophos   Iniidae Rensberger, J. M. 1969A
      serrulus Rensberger, J. M. 1969A
Kamptobaatar   Taeniolabididae Kielan-Jaworowska, Z.
          1970A,C
      kuczynskii Kermack, K. A., Kielan-Jaworowska, Z.
          1971A; Kielan-Jaworowska, Z. 1970A,C,
          1971A
kanamensis (Homo, Nyanzachoerus)
kanayaensis (Mizuhoptera)
Kanisamys   Cricetidae
      indicus Black, C. C. 1972A (in Rhizomyidae)
      sivalensis Black, C. C. 1972A (in Rhizomyidae)
Kannemeyeria   Kannemeyeriidae Ricqlès, A. 1972B
      argentinensis Bonaparte, J. F. 1972A;
          Cruickshank, A. R. I. 1970A
      erithrea see K. simocephalus
      latirostris Crozier, E. A. 1970A; Cruickshank,
          A. R. I. 1970A
      proboscoides see K. simocephalus
      simocephalus [K. proboscoides, K. erithrea,
          Dicynodon latifrons, Sagecephalus
          pachyrhynchus] Cruickshank, A. R. I. 1970A
      vanhoepeni [Proplacerias] Cruickshank, A. R. I.
          1972B
      See also Proplacerias
      wilsoni Cruickshank, A. R. I. 1970A

Kannemeyeriidae   Therapsida–Dicynodontia
          Kalandadze, N. N. 1969A, 1970A
      Barysoma, Ischigualastia, Jachaleria, Kannemeyeria,
          Proplacerias, Rabidosaurus, Rhinocerocephalus
          Sangusaurus, Sinokannemeyeria,
          Uralokannemeyeria, Vinceria
kansanus (Camelops)
kansarum (Gallinula)
kansasensis (Cryptotis, Peromyscus)
kansensis (Petrolacosaurus)
kansui (Palaeoamasia)
Kapurdia   Centropomidae–Chandinae Tiwari, K. K.
          1969A
      bhargavai Tiwari, K. K. 1969A
karamu (Capellirallus)
karibaensis (Vulcanodon)
kashmirensis (Amblypterus, Archegosaurus)
Katoporidae   Thelodonti–Katoporida Karatajūte-Talima
          V. N. 1970A (incl. Katoporus, Goniporus,
          Logania)
Katoporus   Thelodontidae Karatajūte-Talimaa, V. N.
          1970A (in Katoporidae)
      grossi Karatajūte-Talimaa, V. N. 1970A
      timanicus [Trimerolepis] Karatajūte-Talimaa, V. N.
          1970A
      tricavus [Trimerolepis lithuanica] Karatajūte-Talimaa,
          V. N. 1968A, 1970A
kaupi (Squalicorax)
Kawingasaurus   ?Dicynodontidae (probably) Cox, C. B.
          1972A
      fossilis Cox, C. B. 1972A
Kayentapus   Ichnites Welles, S. P. 1971A
          (in Coelurosauria, Grallatoridae)
      hopii Welles, S. P. 1971A
kayi (Opisthotriton)
kazachstanicus (Anancus, Ardynomys)
kazakhstanica (Scirtodipus)
kazakhstanika (Ardynia)
kazusensis (Trionyx)
kebarensis (Spalax)
kehli (Coelurosaurichnus)
kehreri (Amia)
kelloggae (Copemys)
kelloggi (Ferectotherium, Protospermophilus)
Kennalestes   ?Leptictoidea incertae sedis Kielan-
          Jaworowska, Z. 1968B
      gobiensis Kielan-Jaworowska, Z. 1968B
Kennatherium   Didymoconidae Mellett, J. S.,
          Szalay, F. S. 1968A
      shirensis Mellett, J. S., Szalay, F. S. 1968A
kenni (Cymaprimadon)
Kentuckia   Stegotrachelidae Kazantseva, A. A. 1971A
          (in Moythomasiidae); Schaeffer, B. 1968C
Kenyapithecus   Hominidae Day, M. H., Wood, B. A.
          1969A; Leakey, L. S. B. 1969A; Pilbeam,
          D. R. 1969A
      africanus Greenfield, L. O. 1971A; Leakey, L. S. B.
          1971A; Zwell, M. 1972A [Dryopithecus]
      wickeri Leakey, L. S. B. 1970D, 1971E,F; Simons,
          E. L. 1969A [Ramapithecus punjabicus]
      See also Ramapithecus
kenyensis (Anancus)
Keramidomys   Eomyidae
      anwilensis Engesser, B. 1972A
      mohleri Engesser, B. 1972A
      pertesunatoi Hugueney, M., Mein, P. 1968A (aff.)
      thaleri Hugueney, M., Mein, P. 1968A

Kuehneotheriidae   Pantotheria–Amphitheria
    Kuehneotherium
Kuehneotherium   Kuehneotheriidae Crompton, A. W.
    1971A; Kermack, K. A. 1972A; Mills,
    J. R. E. 1971A
    praecursoris Parrington, F. R. 1971A
kugleri (Charactosuchus)
Kujdanowiaspis   Phlyctaenaspidae Miles, R. S. 1971B;
    Stensiö, E. 1969B, 1971A (in Spinothoracidi–
    Dolichothoraci)
    anglica see Heightingtonaspis
    willsi see Heightingtonaspis
kumbulakensis (Propalaeocastor)
kummerovi (Logania)
kuntneri (Diceratherium)
Kureykaspis   Olbiaspididae Novitskaia, L. I. 1968A
    salebrosa Novitskaia, L. I. 1968A, 1971B
kurteni (Lynx issiodorensis)
Kushlukia   Kushlukiidae Danil'chenko, P. G. 1968B
    permira Danil'chenko, P. G. 1968B
Kushlukiidae   Perciformes Danil'chenko, P. G. 1968B
    Kushlukia
kwitkae (Paratrisopterus)
Kyrtogymnodon   Diodontidae
    capellinii Menesini, E. 1969A
Kyzylkakhippus   Equidae
    orlovi Thenius, E. 1968A (in Chalicotheriidae)
laaroussii (Azendohsaurus)
labialis (Leptodactylus)
labiatus (Hymenocephalus, Melursus)
Labidolemur   Apatemyidae
    major West, R. M. 1972A
Labidosaurikos   Captorhinidae
    meachami MacLean, W. P. 1970A; Zídek, J.   1971A
labidotus (Protragocerus)
labordei (Parasemionotus)
Labrax see Morone
Labridae   Perciformes–Labroidei
    Cheilinus, Egertonia, Eodiaphyodus, Labrodon,
        Palaeolabrus, ? Phyllodus,
        Pseudoegertonia, Symphodus
Labrodon   Labridae Baluk, W. 1970A; Casier, E.
    1967B [Diaphyodus, in Sciaenidae]
    africanus Jonet, S. 1968A
    angustidentatus Deraniyagala, P. E. P. 1969A,B
    haueri Jonet, S. 1968A
    multidens Jonet, S. 1968A
    pavimentatum Jonet, S. 1968A; Menesini, E. 1969A
        (in Pharyngopilidae)
    pavimentum Cappetta, H. C. 1969B
    sinhaleyus Deraniyagala, P. E. P. 1969A,B
Labyrinthodontia   Amphibia Schultze, H.-P. 1970D;
    Shishkin, M. A. 1968B
Laccognathus   Holoptychidae Schultze, H.-P. 1969B
    panderi Lyarskaya, L., Mark-Kurik, E. 1972A;
        Vorob'eva, E. I., Liarskaia, L. A. 1968A
Lacerta   Lacertidae Malez, M. 1967C
    goliath Gasc, J.-P. 1971A
Lacertidae   Squamata–Lacertilia
    Lacerta
Lacertipus   Ichnites Haubold, H. 1971B
    (in Sauria)
    navajoensis Haubold, H. 1971B
lacota (Oxydactylus)
Lactemys   ?Didelphidae Fox, R. C. 1970C
    (in ?Stagodontidae)

lacustris (Felis, Janassa, Paronychodon, Rallus, Sorex)
ladae (Leptacodon)
ladinus (Paralepidotus)
Laelaps see Albertosaurus
laevidens (Martes)
laevis (Gobius, Mylagaulus, Thelodus)
lagenocornis (Bison schoetensacki)
Lagerpeton   Pseudosuchia incertae sedis Romer, A. S.
    1971D
    chanarensis Romer, A. S. 1971D, 1972D
Lagodon   Sparidae
    pectinoides Stinton, F. C., Nolf, D. 1969A (otol.)
Lagomeryx   Palaeomerycidae Lungu, A. N. 1972A
    flerovi Lungu, A. N. 1972A
    satensis Kozhamkulova, B. S., Orlovskaia, E. R.
        1971A
Lagomorpha   Mammalia Wood, A. E. 1971A
Lagomyidae see Ochotonidae
Lagopsis see Opsolagus
lagopus (Alopex, Buteo, Lagopus, Vulpes)
Lagopus   Phasianidae Ganîa, I. M. 1969B;
        Koenigswald, W. 1972A (cf.)
    lagopus Jánossy, D. 1972A
Lagostomus   Chinchillidae Calcaterra, A. 1972A
        (subgen. Lagostomus)
Lagosuchus   Pseudosuchia incertae sedis Romer, A. S.
    1971D
    lilloensis Romer, A. S. 1972D
    talampayensis Romer, A. S. 1971D, 1972D
lagreli (Indarctos atticus)
Lagurodon   Lagurus
Lagurodon   Prolagurus
Lagurus   Cricetidae–Microtinae Zazhigin, V. S. 1969B
    arankae Terzea, E. 1968A (subgen. Lagurodon);
        Terzea, E., Jurcsák, T. 1967A (subgen.
        Lagurodon); Zazhigin, V. S. 1970A
        [Prolagurus, subgen. Lagurodon]
    argyropuloi Zazhigin, V. S. 1970A [Eolagurus]
    lagurus Jánossy, D. 1969B (cf., in Arvicolidae);
        Maleev, A. G., Vorob'eva, T. D. 1970A;
        Terzea, E. 1968A (subgen. Lagurus).
    luteus Terzea, E. 1968A (subgen. Eolagurus);
        Zazhigin, V. S. 1970A [Eolagurus]
    pannonicus Terzea, E. 1968A (subgen. Prolagurus);
        Zazhigin, V. S. 1970A [Prolagurus, subgen.
        Prolagurus]
    posterius Zazhigin, V. S. 1970A [Prolagurus, subgen.
        Prolagurus]
    praepannonicus Sukhov, V. P. 1970A (cf., subgen.
        Lagurodon)
    simplicidens Erbaeva, M. A. 1970A
        sibiricus Erbaeva, M. A. 1970A (subgen.
        Eolagurus)
        simplicidens Erbaeva, M. A. 1970A
    transiens Jánossy, D. 1969B (in Arvicolidae);
        Zazhigin, V. S. 1970A
Lagurus   Lagurus
lagurus (Lagurus)
Lambdoceras   Prosynthetoceras
Lambdotherium   Brontotheriidae
    popoagicum Guthrie, D. A. 1971B
lambei (Daphoenus, Lambeosaurus)
Lambeosaurus   Hadrosauridae Morris, W. J. 1972A
    lambei Heaton, M. J. 1972A
lamberti (Enchodus)

Lamna Isuridae Dachev, D. M. 1971A [Otodus];
 Hasegawa, Y., Ueno, T. 1967A; Hasegawa, Y.,
 Ueno, T. 1967A [Otodus]; Telles Antunes, M.,
 Jonet, S. 1970A (in Lamnidae)
 appendiculata Applegate, S. P. 1970A
 (in Lamnidae); Taverne, L. 1970A
 arcuata Thurmond, J. T. 1971B (cf.)
 biauriculata
 nigeriana *Cappetta, H. C.* 1972B (nov. subsp.)
 cattica Bosch, M. 1969A; Cappetta, H. C. 1969B,
 1970A; Schultz, O. 1968A
 cattica *Telles Antunes, M.* 1970A (n. subsp.)
 totuserrata Telles Antunes, M. 1970A
 obliqua Casier, E. 1967B
 rupeliensis Schultz, O. 1968A
 sulcata Thurmond, J. T. 1971B (aff.)
Lamnidae see Isuridae
Lampadena Myctophidae
 nanae *Satō, J.* 1962A, 1968A
Lampanyctus Myctophidae Heinrich, W.-D. 1969B
 (?, otol.)
 apenninicus *Anfossi, G., Mosna, S.* 1971A (otol.)
Lampraspis Pteraspididae–Pteraspidinae
 Denison, R. H. 1970B
 tuberculata *Denison, R. H.* 1970B, 1971B (restor.)
Lampridiformes Teleostei
 Incl. subord. Lampridoidei, Veliferoidei,
 Trachipteroidei, Styleophoroidei
Lampropeltis Colubridae
 similis Holman, J. A. 1970A
lancensis (Albertosaurus, Exostinus)
lanceolata (Clupea)
lanceolatus (Didolodus, Pristis)
lanciformes (Saurocephalus)
landenensis (Eochiromys)
Landenodon Arctocyonidae *Quinet, G. E.* 1966F,
 1969B
 luciani *Quinet, G. E.* 1966F, 1969B
 woutersi *Quinet, G. E.* 1966F, 1969B
landesi (Synaptomys)
langei (Theridomys)
langi (Hyperdichobune)
langstoni (Albertochampsa, Varanopus)
laniatus (Apateopholis)
lankae (Miocaretta)
Lanthanosuchida Seymouriamorpha *Tatarinov, L. P.*
 1972B (n. subord., in Batrachosauria, incl.
 Lanthanosuchidae)
Lantanotherium Erinaceidae Butler, P. M. 1969A;
 Friant, M. 1971C
 sansaniense Engesser, B. 1972A
 sawini Lindsay, E. H. 1972B
Lanthanotherium see Lantanotherium
lantianensis (Homo)
Lantianius Adapidae
 xiehnensis Lisowski, F. P. 1965A
lapis (Caprolagus)
lapparenti (Parotosaurus)
Lapparentichnus Ichnites *Haubold, H.* 1971B
 (in Coelurosauria)
 oleronensis *Haubold, H.* 1971B
lappi (Cryptopterus, Megacricetodon)
laramiensis (Champsosaurus)
Laridae Charadriiformes
 Chlidonias, Halcyornis, Larus, Sterna
 See also Halcyornithidae

larteti (Fahlbuschia, Myoglis)
Lartetomys Cricetidae *Mein, P., Freudenthal, M.*
 1971A (in Cricetidae incertae sedis)
 mirabilis *Mein, P., Freudenthal, M.* 1971A
 zapfei *Mein, P., Freudenthal, M.* 1971A
Larus Laridae
 canus Jánossy, D. 1972A (aff.)
 ridibundus Jánossy, D. 1972A (cf.)
lasallei (Ruscinomys)
Lasiopodomys Microtus
lasiopterus (Pipistrellus)
lata (Lecaniaspis, Sigurdia)
Lataspis see Actinolepis
latastei (Rana)
Laterallus Rallidae
 insignis *Feduccia, J. A.* 1968A
Lates Centropomidae Greenwood, P. H. 1968B
 croaticus Anđelković, J. S. 1969A
 niloticus Churcher, C. S. 1972C
laticeps (Brachyops, Broomicephalus, Eurymylus,
 Limnerpeton, Megalichthys, Pachytragus,
 Sycosaurus)
latidens (Alopias, Homotherium, Miacis, Microsyops,
 Nothocyon, Trogosus)
latifrons (Alces, Bison, Bos, Hayemys, Megalovis,
 Rhinoceros tichorhinus)
latimanus (Scapanus)
latior (Cotimus, Dentex, Solea)
latipes (Anoplotherium)
latirostratum (Myctophum)
latirostris (Actinodon, Kannemeyeria, Lystrosaurus)
latispinosus (Climatius)
latouri (Miacis)
latrans (Canis)
latus (Alacodon, Amphisauropus, Galeorhinus, Morone)
Latvius Osteolepidae
 grewingki Schultze, H.-P. 1969B
laubei (Palaeobatrachus)
Laurentaspis Arthrodira incertae sedis *Pageau, Y.*
 1969B
 splendida *Pageau, Y.* 1969B
laurillardi (Agnopterus, Archaeomys, Peratherium)
Laurillardia Sturnidae
 longirostris Brunet, J. 1970A
 munieri Brunet, J. 1970A
 parisiensis Brunet, J. 1970A
lautricense (Lophiodon)
lautricensis (Choeropotamus)
lautus (Phalacrocorax)
lavocati (Gripholagomys, Heteroxerus, Pachynolophus)
lawleyi (Hoplostethus)
leakeyi (Gymnurechinus, Homo, Homo erectus, Propotto,
 Victoriapithecus)
leali (Hemiprotosuchus)
leanus (Saurodon)
Lecaniaspis Eglonaspididae *Novitskaià, L. I.* 1971B
 lata *Novitskaià, L. I.* 1971B
lechei (Ictopidium, Polymorphis, Zalambdalestes)
lecointrae (Tetraodon)
leenhardti (Aegialornis)
lefevrei (Galeorhinus)
lehmani (Stenotosaurus)
Lehmanotus Parasemionotidae *Beltan, L.* 1968A
 markubai *Beltan, L.* 1968A
Leidyosuchus Crocodylidae Langston, W. 1972A
 canadensis Sahni, A. 1972A

Leiodon see Liodon
Leiopelmatidae   Anura–Archaeobatrachia
   ? Eodiscoglossus
Leiosteidae see Pachyosteidae, Selenosteidae
Leiosteus   Pachyosteidae Stensiö, E. 1969A,B
   (in Leiosteidae)
leiriensis (Guimarotodon)
Leithia   Gliridae Ambrosetti, P. 1969A;
   Thaler, L. 1972A
   cartei Petronio, C. 1970B
   melitensis Petronio, C. 1970B
leithii (Carteremys)
lemanense (Aceratherium)
lemanensis (Plesictis, Plesiogale)
Lemmus   Cricetidae Koenigswald, W. 1970A
   lemmus Jánossy, D. 1969B (aff., in
      Arvicolidae); Terzea, E. 1972A (aff.)
   sibericus Guthrie, R. D., Matthews, J. V.
      1971A (cf.)
lemmus (Lemmus)
lemoinei (Stolephorus)
lemur (Nothocyon)
Lemuridae   Primates–Lemuroidea
   Archaeolemur, Hadropithecus,
      Palaeopropithecus
lemuroides (Promioclaenus)
Lemurosaurus   Ictidorhinidae
   pricei Sigogneau, D. 1970A
lengedensis (Endolithes)
lenki (Dolomys)
lenzii (Barysoma)
Leo   Panthera
   See also Panthera
leo (Panthera)
leonardi (Neofiber)
leonardii (Archaeolepidotus, Palaeoloxodon antiquus)
Leontinia   Leontiniidae
   gaudryi Paula Couto, C., Mezzalira, S. 1971A (cf.)
Leontiniidae   Notoungulata–Toxodontia
   Leontinia
Leontocephalus   Gorgonopsidae–Gorgonopsinae
   cadlei Sigogneau, D. 1970A
   haughtoni [Aelurognathus] Sigogneau, D. 1970A
      (n. comb.)
   intactus Kemp, T. S. 1969B
   rubidgei [Broomisaurus] Sigogneau, D. 1970A
      (?, n. comb.)
Leontosaurus see Sycosaurus
Lepadolepis see Ceratolepis
Lepidion   Moridae
   miocenica Satō, J. 1962A, 1968A
Lepidocottus   Cottidae
   brevis Anđelković, J. 1970A (in Gobiidae)
Lepidogobius   Gobiidae
   bifidus Stinton, F. C., Kissling, D. 1968A (otol.)
Lepidophyma   Xantusiidae Holman, J. A. 1969B
Lepidopus   Trichiuridae Klebanova, N. I. 1971A
   glarisianus Jerzmańska, A. 1968A
Lepidorhombus   Bothidae
   subtriangularis Heinrich, W.-D. 1970A (otol.)
Lepidosirenidae   Dipnoi Bertmar, G. 1968A;
   Jarvik, E. 1968A
   Gnathorhiza, Monongahela
Lepidosteidae see Lepisosteidae
Lepidosteus see Lepisosteus

Lepidotes   Semionotidae Bilelo, M. M. 1969A;
   Casier, E., Taverne, L. 1971A [Lepidotus]
   oliveirai Silva Santos, R. 1969A
lepidotus (Esox)
lepidus (Promartes)
Lepisosteidae   Semionotiformes–Lepisosteidei
   Lepisosteus, ?Paralepidosteus
Lepisosteus   Lepisosteidae Schultze, H.-P. 1969B;
   Smith, G. R., Lundberg, J. G. 1972A;
   Waldman, M. 1970B
   occidentalis Sahni, A. 1972A
   strausi Tobien, H. 1969C
   suessoniensis Casier, E. 1967B [Lepidosteus]
Lepomis   Centrarchidae
   cyanellus Schultz, G. E., Cheatum, E. P. 1970A
      (cf.); Smith, G. R., Lundberg, J. G. 1972A(?)
   humilis Smith, G. R., Lundberg, J. G. 1972A (cf.)
   megalotis Koster, W. J. 1969A (cf.)
lepophagus (Canis)
Lepophidium   Ophidiidae
   aequalis Stinton, F. C., Nolf, D. 1969A (otol.)
Leporidae   Lagomorpha
   Aluralagus, Archaeolagus, Caprolagus, Hispanolagus,
      Hypolagus, Lepus, Megalagus, Mytonolagus,
      Nekrolagus, Notolagus, Oryctolagus,
      Palaeolagus, Pratilepus, Serengetilagus,
      Sylvilagus, Trischizolagus
leporinum (Hyracotherium)
Leptacodon   Adapisoricidae Robinson, P. 1968C
   (in Nyctitheriidae–Nyctitheriinae)
   ladae Gazin, C. L. 1969A (? in Nyctitheriidae)
Leptarctus   Mustelidae
   primus Webb, S. D. 1969C
Leptictidae   Insectivora–Leptictoidea
   Androsorex, Ictops, Leptictis, Metacodon,
      Palaeictops, Procerberus
   See also Adapisoricidae
Leptictis   Leptictidae
   acutidens West, R. M. 1972D
   See also Ictops
Leptictoidea   Insectivora–Proteutheria
   Incertae sedis: Kennalestes
Leptobos   Bovidae Azzaroli, A., Berzi, A. 1970A(?);
   Mihăilă, N. 1971A
Leptoceratops   Protoceratopsidae McKenna, M. C.,
   Love, J. D. 1970A
   gracilis Russell, D. A. 1970A (reconstr.)
leptoceros (Gazella)
Leptochamops   Teiidae
   denticulatus Sahni, A. 1972A
Leptochoeridae   Artiodactyla–Palaeodonta
   Van Valen, L. 1971C
   Leptochoerus
Leptochoerus   Leptochoeridae Macdonald, J. R. 1970A
Leptocyon   Canidae
   vafer Webb, S. D. 1969C
Leptodactylidae   Anura–Neobatrachia Lynch, J. D.
   1971A
   Ceratophrys, Leptodactylus, Syrrhophus
Leptodactylus   Leptodactylidae
   labialis Holman, J. A. 1969B (cf.)
   ocellatus Vergnaud-Grazzini, C. 1968B (cf.)
Leptodontomys   Eomyidae Klingener, D. 1968A(?)
   catalaunicus Engesser, B. 1972A; Hugueney, M.,
      Mein, P. 1968A

leptodus (Arretotherium, Hesperocyon)
leptognathus (Hapalodectes)
Leptolepididae   Leptolepidiformes
  Clupavus, Leptolepis, Vidalamia
  See also Anaethalionidae
Leptolepidiformes   Teleostei
Leptolepis   Leptolepididae
  congolensis Casier, E., Taverne, L. 1971A
  koonwarri *Waldman, M.* 1971B
  sprattiformis Janicke, V., Schairer, G. 1970A
Leptomerycidae see Hypertragulidae
Leptomeryx   Hypertragulidae Clark, J.,
        Guensburg, T. E. 1970A; Eklund, R. R.
        1969A; Ferrusquía-Villafranca, I. 1969A
        (cf., in Leptomerycidae); Macdonald,
        J. R. 1970
leptonyx (Megalonyx)
leptophrys (Pleurolicus)
Leptopterygius   Stenopterygiidae Schultze, H.-P.
        1969B
Leptoptilos   Ciconiidae
  falconeri Rich, P. V. 1972A (cf.)
leptorhinus (Dicerorhinus)
leptorhynus (Hyaenodon)
Leptorophus   Branchiosauridae
  tener Boy, J. A. 1972B
leptoscelos (Hypsiops)
leptosomus (Dipterichthys)
Leptosteidae   Arthrodira—Brachythoraci
        Stensiö, E. 1969A,B
        (in Pachyosteomorphi—Pachyostei)
Leptosteus
Leptosteus   Leptosteidae Stensiö, E. 1969A,B
Leptotomus   Paramyidae
  guildayi *Black, C. C.* 1971A (in Ischyromyidae—
        Paramyinae)
  parvus McGrew, P. O., Sullivan, R. 1970A
  tapensis [Ischyrotomus, Tapomys] Black, C. C.
        1971A
  See also Uintaparamys
Leptotrachelus   Dercetidae see Dercetis,
        Rhynchodercetis
Leptotrachelus   Gorgonopsidae see Gorgonops
Lepus   Leporidae Jánossy, D. 1969B; Martin, R.
        1968A
  californicus Campbell, K. E. 1969A; Dalquest,
        W. W. 1967A; Downey, J. S. 1970A (cf.)
  ∕capensis Churcher, C. S. 1972C
  europaeus Altuna, J. 1970A; Campbell, K. E.
        1969A; Tozzi, C. 1969A
  lapis see Caprolagus
  nigricollis Dawson, M. R. 1971A
  praetimidus Koenigswald, W. 1972A
  tanaiticus Kuz'mina, I. E. 1971A
  timidus Altuna, J. 1970B; Kuz'mina, I. E. 1971A;
        Mostecký, V. 1969A; Schütt, G. 1969C
lerichei (Balistes, Engraulis, Eodiaphyodus,
        Gyropleurodus, Heterodontus,
        Hoplobrotula, Sphyraenodus)
lerouxi (Taurocephalus)
lervia (Ovis)
leskevitschi (Tragocerus)
Lestodon   Mylodontidae Dechaseaux, C. 1971A
lettsomi (Glossotherium)
Leuciscus   Cyprinidae Brzobohatý, R. 1969A;
        Salis, K. 1967A

Leuciscus - cont.
  acrogaster Anđelković, J. 1970A
  brevis see Varhostichthys
  bubalus Anđelković, J. 1970A
  cephalus Sychevskaîa, E. K., Lebedev, V. D. 1971A
  colei Anđelković, J. 1970A
  eibiswaldensis Anđelković, J. 1970A
  gibbus Anđelković, J. 1970A
  idus Sychevskaîa, E. K., Lebedev, V. D. 1971A(?)
  luzicensis *Obrhelová, N.* 1969A, 1971A (subgen.
        Palaeoleuciscus)
  macrurus Anđelković, J. 1970A
  medius Anđelković, J. 1970A
  oeningensis Anđelković, J. 1970A
  papyraceus Anđelković, J. 1970A
  socoloviensis *Obrhelová, N.* 1969A, 1971A (subgen.
        Palaeoleuciscus)
leucodon (Crocidura)
leucogaster (Onychomys)
leucophrys (Anas)
leucopus (Peromyscus)
leucorodia (Platalea)
leucurus (Hystrix, Meles)
Leutkeichthys see Luetkeichthys
levantinus (Apodemus)
levatus (Erismatopterus)
levesiensis (Cimolichthys)
levis (Acrodus, Hoplostethus, Quadropedia)
levispinosus (Pycnosteroides)
levius (Deinotherium)
lewesiensis (Enchodus)
lewisi (Brachypotherium, Gypsonictops, Probelesodon,
        Sivapithecus, Stichopteryx)
Lewisuchus   Pseudosuchia incertae sedis *Romer, A. S.*
        1972C
  admixtus *Romer, A. S.* 1972C
liberiensis (Choeropsis)
Libralces see Alces
libratus (Albertosaurus)
libycum (Hipparion)
Libypithecus   Cercopithecidae Swindler, D. R. 1968A
Licaphrops   Proterotheriidae Friant, M. 1967B
licenti (Hyaena brevirostris)
licharevi (Dinichthys)
ligerensis (Gargantuodon)
Ligerimys   Eomyidae
  antiquus *Fahlbusch, V.* 1970A
  florancei Baudelot, S. 1969A (in Gliridae);
        Fahlbusch, V. 1970A; Hugueney, M.,
        Mein, P. 1968A
  lophidens Bruijn, H. 1967A; Fahlbusch, V. 1970A;
        Telles Antunes, M., Mein, P. 1971A
Lignimus   Geomyidae—Entoptychinae *Storer, J. E.*
        1970A
  montis *Storer, J. E.* 1970A
ligniticus (Eobrycon, Triportheus)
Liliaspis   Poraspididae *Novitskaîa, L. I.* 1972A
  philippovae *Novitskaîa, L. I.* 1972A
lilloensis (Lagosuchus)
limburgensis (Morone)
limicola (Eomyctophum)
Limnatornis see Colius
Limnenetes   Merycoidodontidae
  platyceps Wilson, J. A. 1971A (cf.)
Limnerpeton   Micromelerpetontidae
  laticeps Boy, J. A. 1972B

limnetes (Omochoerus)
limnetus (Hypolagus)
limnodytes (Chrysemys)
Limnoecus   Soricidae Rabeder, G. 1970A(?)
    niobrarensis Gureev, A. A. 1971A
    tricuspis Gureev, A. A. 1971A; Lindsay, E. H.
        1972B
    See also Anchiblarinella
Limnopithecus see Pliopithecus
Limnopus   Ichnites
    cutlerensis Haubold, H. 1970A
    haussei [Baropus] Haubold, H. 1970A
    heterodactylus [Thenaropus] Haubold, H. 1970A
    littoralis [Allopus] Haubold, H. 1970A
    mcnaughtoni [Thenaropus ?] Haubold, H. 1970A
    regularis [Strictipes] Haubold, H. 1970A
    vagus Haubold, H. 1970A
    waynesburgensis Haubold, H. 1970A (subgen.
        Baropus)
limosa (Limosa)
Limosa   Scolopacidae
    limosa Jánossy, D. 1972A (aff.)
limosus (Carpocyon)
lindermayeri (Palaeoreas)
lindgreni (Francotherium)
lindoei (Alticonodon)
Liodon   Mosasauridae
    anceps Taverne, L. 1970A [Leiodon]
    dyspelor Cope, E. D. 1870Y
Liomys see Prodipodomys
Liopleurodon   Pliosauridae
    rossicus [Pliosaurus] Halstead, L. B. 1971B
Lisserpeton   Scapherpetontidae
Lisserpeton
    bairdi Sahni, A. 1972A
lissiensis (Paraglirulus)
Lissoberyx   Trachichthyidae Patterson, C. 1968B
    arambourgi Gaudant, M. 1969A
Listriodon   Suidae
    michali Pavlović, M. B. 1969A
    splendens Engesser, B. 1972A; Hünermann, K. A.
        1968A
Litaletes   Hyopsodontidae
    disjunctus Gazin, C. L. 1969A (cf.)
litheus (Glyptophidium)
lithographica (Archaeopteryx)
Lithornis   Vulturidae
    vulturinus Cracraft, J., Rich, P. V. 1972A (not in
        Cathartidae)
lithuanica (Trimerolepis)
Litoptychus   Rhizodontidae
    bryanti Schultze, H.-P. 1969B
Litotaspis   Tuxeraspididae Novitskaia, L. I. 1971B
    septentrionalis Novitskaia, L. I. 1971B
littoralis (Limnopus, Phalacrocorax, Teracus)
livonicus (Plourdosteus)
Livosteus   Coccosteidae Obrucheva, O. P. 1962C
    Stensiö, E. 1969A,B
    grandis [Coccosteus] Obrucheva, O. P. 1962C
llopisi (Progenetta crassa)
lobata (Biziura)
lobatus (Zalophus)
loczyi (Baranomys)
Logania   Thelodontidae Karatajūte-Talimaa, V. N.
    1970A (in Katoporidae)

Logania - cont.
    cuneata Karatajūte-Talimaa, V. N. 1970A
    kummerovi Karatajūte-Talimaa, V. N. 1972A(?)
    ludlowiensis Karatajūte-Talimaa, V. N. 1970A(?)
    martinssoni Gross, W. 1968E; Turner, S.,
        Dickson, J. 1971A
Lohsania   Osteolepidae Thomson, K. S., Vaughn, P. P.
        1968A
    utahensis Thomson, K. S., Vaughn, P. P. 1968A
lomasi (Chirotherium)
Lonchidion   Hybodontidae
    anitae Thurmond, J. T. 1971B
Lonchoconus see Didolodus
longicauda (Ministrella)
Longicepia   Pteranodon Miller, H. W. 1972B
    (n. subgen.)
longiceps (Cyonosaurus, Edmontonia, Hapalops,
    Lycaenodon, Pteranodon)
longicollum (Pterodactylus)
longicornis (Bison priscus)
longicostatus (Cordicephalus)
longidens (Copemys, Eucricetodon collatus)
longidorsalis (Australichthys)
longifilis (Cheilinus)
longifrons (Gorgonops)
longimana (Sphyraena)
longipectoralis (Enchodus)
longipes (Anthracodromeus, Megapezia)
longipinnatus (Caranx)
longirostris (Australosomus, Belonostomus, Capros,
    Laurillardia, Riebeeckosaurus, Tetralophodon,
    Thaumatosaurus)
Longirostromeryx   Cervidae
    blicki Patton, T. H. 1969B
    vigoratus Patton, T. H. 1969B(?)
    wellsi Webb, S. D. 1969C (in Palaeomerycidae)
longispinus (Centriscus, Ramonellus)
longispinnus (Ctenocephalichthys)
Longisquama   Longisquamidae Sharov, A. G. 1970A,B
    insignis Sharov, A. G. 1970A,B; Anon. 1971BB
Longisquamidae   Thecodontia–Pseudosuchia
        Sharov, A. G. 1970A,B
    Longisquama
longobardicus (Tanystropheus)
longus (Diplodocus, Gobius)
loomisi (Nanotragulus)
loozi (Hexanchus)
lopdelli (Archaeospheniscus)
lophatus (Mojavemys)
lophidens (Cricetus, Ligerimys)
Lophiobunodon   Anthracotheriidae
    rhodanicum Sudre, J. 1972A
Lophiodon   Lophiodontidae Gottis, M. 1967A;
        Sudre, J. 1972A
    isselense Ginsburg, L., Lapierre, F., Montenat, C.
        1967A (gr.)
    lautricense Sudre, J. 1971A
    remense Ginsburg, L., Lapierre, F., Montenat, C.
        1967A
lophiodon (Pseudictops)
Lophiodontidae   Perissodactyla–Tapiroidea
    Chasmotherium, Lophiodon
Lophiomeryx   Gelocidae Chiu, Ch.-s. 1965A
    chalaniati Brunet, M. 1970A
    turgaicus Musakulova, L. T. 1971A

Lycaenops   Gorgonopsidae–Gorgonopsinae
angusticeps [Lycaenoides, Scymnognathus minor]
    Sigogneau, D. 1970A (n. comb.);
    [Scymnognathus major] Sigogneau, D.
    1970A (cf.)
kingwilli [Tigricephalus] Sigogneau, D. 1970A
    (n. comb.)
microdon [Aelurognathus] Sigogneau, D. 1971A
    (?, n. comb.)
minor Ricqlès, A. 1969A; [Aelurognathus]
    Sigogneau, D. 1970A (?, n. comb.)
ornatus Sigogneau, D. 1970A
pricei see Arctognathus cf. curvimola
tenuirostris [Tangagorgon] Sigogneau, D. 1970A
    (?, n. comb.)
See also Prorubidgea, Sycosaurus
Lycoptera   Lycopteridae Gaudant, J. 1967B
fragilis Iakovlev, V. N. 1968A
middendorffi Iakovlev, V. N. 1968A
Lycopteridae   Leptolepidiformes
Irenichthys, Lycoptera
See also Anaethalionidae
Lycorhinus   Hypsilophodontidae
angustidens Thulborn, R. A. 1970B
See also Heterodontosaurus
Lycosaurus see Arctognathus
Lychosuchidae see Trochosauridae
Lycosuchus   Trochosauridae Boonstra, L. D. 1969A
    (in Lycosuchidae)
Lycyaenops   Hyaenidae
lunensis Crusafont Pairó, M., Aguirre, E. 1971A
    [Euryboas]; Ficcarelli, G., Torre, D. 1967B
lydekkeri (Gazella)
Lyktaspidida [Doryaspidida] Heterostraci Heintz,
    Natascha 1968A (in Pteraspidomorpha)
Lyktaspididae [Doryaspididae] Heterostraci–
    Lyktaspidida Heintz, Natascha 1968A;
    Stensiö, E. 1968A (in Pteraspiformes–
    Lyktaspida)
Lyktaspis
Lyktaspis [Doryaspis] Lyktaspididae Heintz,
    Natascha 1968A
nathorsti [Scaphaspis] Heintz, Natascha 1968A
    (n. comb.); Stensiö, E. 1968A
Lynx   Felidae
issiodorensis
    kurteni Schultz, C. B., Martin, L. D. 1972A
    stouti Schultz, C. B., Martin, L. D. 1972A
    See also Felis
Lynx   Felis
lynx (Felis)
lyonsi (Moeritherium)
Lyrocephaliscus see Lyrocephalus
Lyrocephalus   Trematosauridae [Lyrocephaliscus]
    Schultze, H.-P. 1969B
lyrocera (Menelikia)
Lyrurus   Phasianidae
partium Jánossy, D. 1972A (cf.)
tetrix Boecker, M., et al. 1972A
Lysipterygium   Trimerorhachidae
deterrai Chakravarti, D. K. 1968A
Lysorophidae   Microsauria
Lysorophus
Lysorophomorpha   Amphibia Kuhn, O. 1970B
    (n. subcl.)

Lysorophus   Lysorophidae
tricarinatus Berman, D. S. 1970A (cf.); Olson,
    E. C. 1970A, 1971B
Lystrosauridae   Therapsida–Dicynodontia
Lystrosaurus
Lystrosaurus   Lystrosauridae Barry, T. H. 1968A;
    Cluver, M. A. 1970A; Colbert, E. H. 1970E,
    1972A; Crompton, A. W. 1970A; Jensen,
    J. A. 1972A; Schroeder, D. 1970C;
    Simpson, G. G. 1970B; Tweedie, M. 1970B;
    Young, C.-c. 1957E(?)
latirostris Ricqlès, A. 1972B
Mabokopithecus   Oreopithecoidea incertae sedis
    Koenigswald, G. H. R. 1969A
clarki Koenigswald, G. H. R. 1969A
Macaca   Cercopithecidae Crusafont Pairó, M., Golpe
    Posse, J. M. 1969A; Delson, E. 1971A;
    Vereshchagin, N. K. 1960C
fuscata Iwamoto, M., Hasegawa, Y. 1972A (cf.)
majori Comaschi Caria, I. 1968A [Macacus];
    Comaschi Caria, I. 1970B [Macacus, subgen.
    Inuus]
sylvanus Tozzi, C. 1969A (cf.)
Macacus see Macaca
macarovicii (Vinciguerria)
maccabei (Prorubidgea)
macdonaldi (Arikarornis)
Macedonitherium   Giraffidae Sickenberg, O. 1967C
martini Sickenberg, O. 1967A
Macelognathus   Crocodylia incertae sedis
vagans Ostrom, J. H. 1971A
macer (Phalacrocorax)
Machaeracanthus   Acanthodii incertae sedis
major Pageau, Y. 1969A(?)
Machaerodontidae see Felidae
Machaerognathus   Coccosteidae Stensiö, E. 1969B
    (in Euarthrodira incertae sedis)
Machairodus   Felidae Baigusheva, V. S. 1971A;
    Jánossy, D. 1969B; Musil, R. 1966C
aphanistus Melentis, J. K. 1970A
catocopis Dalquest, W. W. 1969A
hesperus Bjork, P. R. 1970A
machikanense (Tomistoma)
Machimosaurus   Goniopholidae
hugii Krebs, B. 1968A (in Teleosauridae);
    Maubeuge, P. L. 1968A
machlaevi (Dinichthys)
machnata (Elops)
macinnesi (Victoriapithecus)
Macracara   Cichlidae
prisca Moncharmont Zei, M. 1970A (cfr.)
macraei (Pseudaptenodytes)
Macrauchenia   Macraucheniidae
patachonica Friant, M. 1967B
Macraucheniidae   Litopterna
Cramauchenia, Macrauchenia, Paranauchenia,
    Promacrauchenia, Scalabrinitherium,
    Theosodon
See also Proterotheriidae
Macrepistius   Caturidae
arenatus Schaeffer, B. 1971A
macroactus (Merluccius)
macrocephala (Tanupolama)
Macrocephalochelys   Testudinidae
pontica Tarashchuk, V. I. 1971A (in Platysternidae)
See also Chelydropsis

macrocephalus (Archaeolagus)
Macrocnemus   Prolacertidae
  bassanii Ortlam, D. 1967A
macrocynodonta (Gaylordia)
Macrognathomys   Zapodidae–Sicistinae
  nanus Shotwell, J. A. 1970A (cf.)
macrognathus (Gobicyon, Kopidodon, Sorex araneus)
macrolepis (Hibernaspis, Psenes)
Macromerion   Sphenacodontidae
  bayeri Schultze, H.-P. 1969B
  schwarzenbergii Schultze, H.-P. 1969B
Macroneomys   Soricidae
  brachygnathus Gureev, A. A. 1971A
Macropelobates   Pelobatidae
  osborni Estes, R. 1970B
Macropetalichthyidae   Petalichthyida Patrulius, D.,
      Iordan, M. 1969A, 1970A
  Ellopetalichthys, Epipetalichthys, Lunaspis,
      Macropetalichthys, Notopetalichthys,
      Wijdeaspis
Macropetalichthys   Macropetalichthyidae Stensiö, E.
      1969B; Stensiö, E. 1969B [Physichthys]
Macropodidae   Marsupialia–Diprotodonta Frith,
      H. J., Calaby, J. H. 1969A [kangaroos];
      Ride, W. D. L. 1971A
  Bettongia, Dorcopsis, Palorchestes, Potorous,
      Procoptodon, Propleopus, Protemnodon,
      Thylogale
macropterus (Pteronisculus)
macropterygia (Paratrisopterus)
Macropterygius   Ichthyosauridae Schultze, H.-P.
      1969B
macropunctatus (Ostracion)
macropus (Pristigenys)
Macrorhamphidae [Centriscidae] Gasterosteiformes–
      Aulostomoidei
  Aeoliscus, Centriscus
Macrorhamphosidae   Syngnathiformes
  Protorhamphosus
Macrorhamphus   Scolopacidae–Charadriinae
  finitimus Kurochkin, E. N. 1971A
      (in Charadriidae)
Macrorhineura   Amphisbaenidae Macdonald, J. R.
      1970A
  skinneri Macdonald, J. R. 1970A
macrorhyncha (Pelurgaspis)
Macroscelididae   Insectivora–Macroscelidea
  Rhynchocyon
macrota (Odontaspis)
macrotis (Brachyerix)
macrotuberculata (Cephalaspis)
Macrouridae   Gadiformes–Macrouroidei
  Hymenocephalus, Macrouridarum, Macrourus,
      Malacocephalus
  See also Otolithus, Xiphiidae
Macrouridarum   Macrouridae see Otolithus
Macrourus [Macrurus] Macrouridae Grechina,
      N. I. 1971A [Coryphaenoides];
      Weiler, W. 1971B (otol.) [Macrurus]
  communis Gaemers, P. A. M. 1969A, 1971A
      [Macrurus, otol.]; Heinrich, W.-D.
      1969B (aff., otol.)
  debilis Gaemers, P. A. M. 1969A, 1971A
      [Macrurus, otol.]; Heinrich, W.-D.
      1969B (cf., otol.)
  ellipticus Anfossi, G., Mosna, S. 1969A
      [Macrurus, otol.]

Macrourus - cont.
  gracilis Anfossi, G., Mosna, S. 1969A [Macrurus,
      otol.]; Robba, E. 1970A [Macrurus, otol.]
  novus Anfossi, G., Mosna, S. 1969A [Macrurus,
      otol.]; Robba, E. 1970A [Macrurus, otol.]
  ovalis Rado, G. 1969A [Macrurus, otol.]
  rotundus Rado, G. 1969A [Macrurus, otol.]
  rumanus Rado, G. 1965A, 1969A [Macrurus, otol.]
  trolli Robba, E. 1970A [Macrurus, otol.]
Macruridarum see Otolithus Macrouridarum
Macrurus see Macrourus
macrurus (Dapalis, Leuciscus)
madagascariensis (Ambodipia, Devillersia, Saurichthys)
maderensis (Ceratoscopelus)
Madtsoia   Boidae Corro, G. 1968A
  bai Volkheimer, W. 1971A
maerurus (Ailuravus)
magilli (Ophiomys)
magister (Cimexomys)
magna (Desmana moschata, Felis, Kowalskia, Mioceta,
      Notalacerta)
magnidentatus (Adamisaurus)
magnificus (Anteosaurus, Belesodon)
magnum (Anthracotherium, Palaeotherium)
magnus (Adapis, Allocricetus, Cimexomys, Cimolestes,
      Conger, Eutypomys, Metacodon,
      Perognathus, Pontolis, Psephodus, Simidectes)
major (Amphicyon, Archaeocetus fockii, Asiacastor,
      Bothriceps, Capreolus capreolus, Citellus,
      Dendrocopos, Dolichotis, Dryopithecus,
      Eomys, Gomphotherium angustidens,
      Hippopotamus amphibius, Hipposaurus,
      Labidolemur, Machaeracanthus,
      Massetognathus, Meniscoessus, Ophiacodon,
      Palaeosyops, Paracamelus, Parictis, Parus,
      Pica pica, Plesiogulo, Prosciurus,
      Pseudaelurus, Scylacognathus, Sus,
      Traversodon, Trucheosaurus, Ustatochoerus,
      Vernonaspis)
majora (Rubidgea)
majori (Gliravus, Macaca, Palaeoryx, Totanus)
majus (Rhynchosauroides)
majusculus (Diadiaphorus)
Makapania   Bovidae
  broomi Gentry, A. W. 1970B
makpiyahe (Ocajila)
Malacocephalus   Macrouridae
  ornatus Brzobohatý, R. 1967C (?, otol.)
      apicatus [Otol. (Macrurus) ornatus var. apicatus]
      Robba, E. 1970A (otol.)
  See also Coelorhynchus
malanchinii (Placochelyanus)
malaris (Mixodectes)
malayanus (Helarctos)
maldani (Propachynolophus)
maldei (Perognathus)
maldonadoi (Peromyscus)
Malerosteus   Pholidosteidae Stensiö, E. 1969B
      (in Euarthrodira incertae sedis)
Mallotus   Osmeridae
  villosus Wagner, F. J. E. 1970A
maltha (Ciconia)
malustenense (Hipparion)
malustensis (Geoemyda)
Mamenchisauridae Young, C.-c. 1972A (incl.
      Mamenchisaurus)

Mamenchisaurus Titanosauridae
  hochuanensis Voichin, I. 1966A (restor.); Young,
    C.-c. 1972A (in Mamenchisauridae)
Mammacyon Canidae
  obtusidens Macdonald, J. R. 1970A
Mammalia
  Incl. subclass Prototheria, Allotheria, Theria
    Clemens, W. A. 1970A,B, 1971A,B
    (Mesozoic); Fox, R. C. 1968B, 1970A;
    Gabuniã, L. K. 1966D (origin);
    Hamilton, W. R. 1972A (evol., reconstr.);
    Hershkovitz, P. 1971A (teeth); Hopson,
    J. A. 1969A, 1970A (nontherian), 1972A;
    Hopson, J. A., Crompton, A. W. 1969A
    (origin); Kermack, D. M., Kermack, K. A.
    1971A (early); Kielan-Jaworowska, Z.,
    Kermack, K. A. 1970A (therian and non-
    therian); Lillegraven, J. A. 1972A
    (Cenozoic); MacIntyre, G. T. 1972A (ear
    region); Markman, H. C. 1952A (fossil);
    Mussett, F. 1967A (evol. jaw joint);
    Patterson, B., Pascual, R. 1968A
    (South America); Quinet, G. E. 1967B
    (phylog.); Simpson, G. G. 1971 (Mesozoic);
    Smith, H. M. 1972A,B (origin);
    Thenius, E. 1969D; Turnbull, W. D. 1971A
Mammalipedia Vertebratichnia
mammeatus (Ornitholithus)
mammillaris (Ptychodus)
mammillatus (Ornitholithus)
Mammonteus see Mammuthus
mammontoides (Elephas)
mammosus (Ornitholithus)
Mammut MammutidaeBurachek, A. R., Chikhachev,
    P. K. 1959A [Mastodon]; Carter, G. F.
    1968A [Mastodon]; Dreimanis, A. 1968A
    [mastodons]; Drobne, K. 1967A
    [Mastodon]; Rakovec, I. 1968A
    [mastodont]; Saunders, J. J. 1972A;
    Schmidt, Z. 1969A [Mastodonts];
    Wellnhofer, P. 1969A [Mastodon]
  americanus Coates, D. R., Landry, S. O., Lipe,
    W. D. 1971A; Miller, W. E. 1971A
  borsoni Apostol, L. 1968A [Zygolophodon];
    Ghenea, C. 1968A [Zygolophodon]
    Heintz, E. 1969B [Zygolophodon];
    Khalvadzhiev, M. 1969A [Zygolophodon];
    Mihăilă, N. 1971A [Zygolophodon];
    Mitzopoulos, M. K. 1966A [Zygolophodon];
    Rădulescu, C., Kovács, A. 1968A
    [Zygolophodon]; Rakovec, I. 1968B
    [Zygolophodon]; Samson, P., et al. 1971A
    [Zygolophodon]; Schmidt, Z., Halouzka, R.
    1970A [Zygolophodon]; Tobien, H. 1968I
  gromovae Dubrovo, I. A. 1970A [Zygolophodon,
    subgen. Zygolophodon]
  pyrenaicus Alberdi, M. T., Aguirre, E. 1970A
    [Zygolophodon]
    aurelianensis (var.) Alberdi, M. T., Aguirre, E.
    1970A [Zygolophodon]
  tapiroides Melentis, J. K. 1970A [Mastodon,
    subgen. Zygolophodon]
  turicensis Mukha, B. B. 1970A [Turicius]
Mammuthus Elephantidae Newcomb, R. C.,
    Repenning, C. A. 1970A
  africanavus see Loxodonta

Mammuthus
  armeniacus Aguirre Enríquez, E. 1969B;
    Apostol, L. 1968A, 1969A
    [M. trogontherii]; Beden, M. 1970A
    [Parelephas trogontherii]; Borsuk-
    Białynicka, B., Wysoczański-Minkowicz, T.
    1969A [M. trogontherii]; Bouchud, J. 1961D
    [Elephas trogontherii]; Coppens, Y. 1965E
    [Parelephas trogontherii]; David, A. I. 1969A
    [M. trogontherii]; Dubrovo, I. A., David,
    A. I. 1969A [M. trogontherii trogontherii];
    Guenther, E. W. 1969A,C [Parelephas
    trogontherii]; Jánossy, D. 1969B [Parelephas
    trogontherii]; Kahler, M.-L. 1969A
    [Mammonteus trogontherii]; Klein, H. 1971A
    [Parelephas trogontherii]; Kolpakov, V. V.
    1970A [M. trogontherii]; Laskowska-
    Wysoczańska, W., Niklewski, J. 1969A
    [M. trogontherii]; Méroc, L. 1967A [Elephas
    trogontherii]; Mihăilă, N. 1971A [Parelephas
    trogontherii]; Nicolussi, C. M. 1971A
    [Elephas trogontherii]; Prausnitz, M. W.
    1969A [Elephas trogontherii]; Rădulescu, C.,
    Kovács, A. 1968A [Parelephas trogontherii];
    Théobald, N. 1970A [Elephas (Mammonteus)
    trogontherii]; Vekua, A. K., Khukhia, N. V.
    1972A [M. trogontherii]
  chosaricus Garutt, V. E. 1971A
  columbi Agogino, G. A. 1969A [Elephas]; Aguirre
    Enríquez, E. 1969B; Hemmings, E. T. 1969A;
    Khan, E. 1970A (cf.); Miller, W. E. 1971A
    (cf.)
    jeffersoni Aguirre Enríquez, E. 1969B; Kapp,
    R. O. 1970A [M. jeffersoni]
  gromovi Baïgusheva, V. S. 1971A [Archidiskodon];
    Garutt, V. E., Alekseeva, L. I. 1964A
    [Archidiskodon]
  imperator Aguirre Enríquez, E. 1969B; Aveleyra
    A. de Anda, L. 1966A (subgen.
    Archidiskodon); Churcher, C. S. 1972B;
    Dalquest, W. W. 1967A [cf., Elephas]
  intermedius Aguirre Enríquez, E. 1969B
  jeffersoni see M. columbi jeffersoni
  meridionalis Aguirre Enríquez, E. 1969B; Apostol, L.
    1968A [Archidiskodon; Azzaroli, A.,
    Berzi, A. 1970A [Elephas; aff.]; Beden, M.
    1970B [Archidiskodon; Bouchud, J. 1961D
    [Elephas]; Coppens, Y. 1965E
    [Archidiskodon]; Erdbrink, D. P., Van Asch,
    Th. W. J. 1972A [Elephas, subgen.
    Archidiskodon]; Filipescu, M. G. 1968A
    [Archidiskodon]; Guenther, E. W. 1969C
    [Archidiskodon]; Lavrent'ev, A. I. 1968A
    [cf., Archidiskodon]; Maglio, V. J. 1970B;
    Melentis, J. K. 1963A, 1966P
    [Archidiskodon]; Mihăilă, N. 1971A
    [Archidiskodon]; Nicolussi, C. M. 1971A
    [Elephas]; Rădulescu, C., Kovács, A. 1968A
    [Archidiskodon]; Schneider, H. E. 1968A
    [Archidiskodon]; Vidarte, C. F. 1966A [Elephas]
    archaicus Mitzopoulos, M. K. 1967B
    [Archidiskodon]
  cromerensis (mut.) Bouchud, J. 1964B [Elephas]
  primigenius Adam, K. D. 1966D [Elephas; subgen.
    Mammonteus]; Aguirre Enríquez, E. 1969B;

Mammuthus - cont.
  Apostol, L. 1968A; Apostol, L.,
    Vicoveanu, D. 1970A; Beden, M. 1970A
    [Mammontheus]; Bonifay, M.-F. 1967A
    [Elephas]; Bouchud, J. 1961D [Elephas];
    Coppens, Y. 1965E; Delpech, F., et al.
    1970A [Elephas]; Filipescu, M. G. 1968A
    [Mamonteus]; Gillespie, J. M. 1970A (hair);
    Isă, Gh. I. 1967A [Elephas, subgen.
    Mammutus]; Jeannet, M. 1971A [Elephas];
    Korniets', N. L. 1962A [Elephas];
    KozJowski, J. K., Kubiak, H. 1972A
    (bone dwellings); KozJowski, J. K.,
    Kubiak, H., Welc, A. 1970A; Kuz'mina,
    I. E. 1971A; Martin, R. 1968A [Elephas];
    Martynov, E. G. 1969A; Mârza, I. 1971A;
    Melentis, J. K. 1963A [Mammonteus];
    Mostecký, V. 1969A [Mammonteus];
    Nicolussi, C. M. 1971A [Elephas];
    Nikolov, Iv. 1969A; Petronio, C. 1970A;
    Théobald, N. 1970A [Elephas, subgen.
    Mammonteus]; Vangengeïm, E. A. 1963A
    [Elephas]; Varlamov, I. P. 1959A
    [Elephas]; Weidmann, M. 1969A, 1970A
    [Elephas]
  intermedius Shcheglova, V. V. 1964A
  jatzkovi Golovko, V. P. 1962A [Mammonteus]
  primigenius-trogontherii Guenther, E. W. 1969B
  subplanifrons see Elephas
  transvaalensis see Palaeoloxodon recki
  trogontherii see M. armeniacus
  washingtonii Scott, W. F., Clem, R. 1967A
  wusti Fedorovich, B. A. 1957A [Elephas];
    Motuzko, A. N. 1970A [?, Archidiskodon];
    Zhylkibaev, K. Zh. 1969A [Archidiskodon]
Mammutidae Proboscidea—Euelephantoidea Alberdi,
    M. T., Aguirre, E. 1970A [Mastodontidae,
    incl. Zygolophodontidae]
Mammut
Manatidae see Trichechidae
manca (Ritteneria)
Mancalla Alcidae
  californiensis Howard, H. 1970A
  cedrosensis Howard, H. 1971C
  diegense Howard, H. 1970A, 1971C
  milleri Howard, H. 1970A, 1971C
manchharensis (Brachyodus)
Mandschurosaurus Hadrosauridae
  amurensis Krasnyĭ, L. I. 1966A
maniculatus (Peromyscus)
Manidae Pholidota Koenigswald, W. 1969A
    (Europe)
  ?Necromanis, Patriomanis, ?Teutomanis
manifrons (Koonwarria)
Manta Mobulidae
  fragilis Cappetta, H. C. 1969B, 1970A
mantelli (Iguanodon, Isurus)
mapperleyensis (Swinnertonichnus)
maquinense (Nothrotherium)
marahomensis (Chelyderpeton)
Maraisaurus Pristerognathidae
  parvus Boonstra, L. D. 1968B
maraisi (Mentzichthys)
marathonensis (Pachyrhizodus)
marchesettii (Enchodus)
mariae (Anourosorex, Blarinoides)

marinus (Bufo)
maritimus (Ursus)
maritsae (Trischizolagus)
maritsensis (Myomimus)
markae (Coccosteus)
Markgrafia see Ischirhiza
markubai (Lehmanotus)
Marmosa Didelphidae Simpson, G. G. 1972A
Marmosopsis Didelphidae
  juradoi Paula Couto, C. 1970A
marmota (Marmota)
Marmota Sciuridae
  bobac Mostecký, V. 1969A
  marmota Boecker, M., et al. 1972A; Boeuf, O.
    1970A; Chaline, J. 1969A; Martin, R. 1968A
  sibirica
    nekipelovi Erbaeva, M. A. 1970A
maroccanus (Clupavus)
Marosichthys Balistidae
  huismani Tyler, J. C. 1968A (in Triacanthodidae—
    Triacanthodinae)
marplesi (Palaeeudyptes, Platydyptes)
Marpurgichnium Ichnites
  knetschi Haubold, H. 1971A
marshalli (Chirotherium, Plesiogulo, Pseudocheirus)
marshi (Acanthodes, Alphadon, Pteranodon)
Marsis Sparidae
  elegans Dieni, I. 1968A (? , otol.)
marslandensis (Menoceras)
Marsupialia Mammalia
  Incl. subord. Polyprotodonta, Peramelida,
    Caenolestoidia, Diprotodonta Air, G. M.,
    Thompson, O. P., Richardson, B. J.,
    Sharman, G. B. 1971A; Cox, C. B. 1972B;
    Frith, H. J., Calaby, J. H. 1969A;
    Hoffstetter, R. 1970B, 1972A; Martin, P. G.
    1970A (biogeog.); Simpson, G. G. 1971F;
    Stirton, R. A. 1965C; Turnbull, W. D. 1971A
    [cohort Marsupiata]
marsupialis (Antidorcas, Didelphis)
Marsupiata Mammalia—Eutheria Turnbull, W. D.
    1971A (cohort, = Marsupialia)
Marsupicarnivora Mammalia—Marsupiata Turnbull,
    W. D. 1971A (order)
marsupium (Peratherium)
Martes Martes
martes (Martes)
Martes Mustelidae Jánossy, D. 1969B; Schütt, G.
    1969C
  americana Anderson, E. 1970A (subgen. Martes)
  anderssoni Anderson, E. 1970A (subgen. Pekania)
  basilii Adrover, R. 1966B
  campestris Anderson, E. 1970A
  diluviana Anderson, E. 1970A (subgen. Pekania)
  flavigula Anderson, E. 1970A (subgen. Charronia)
  tyrannus Anderson, E. 1970A
  foina Anderson, E. 1970A (subgen. Martes);
    Heller, J. 1970A
  gazini Anderson, E. 1970A (subgen. Tomictis)
  kinseyi Anderson, E. 1970A
  laevidens Anderson, E. 1970A
  martes Anderson, E. 1970A (subgen. Martes);
    Kuz'mina, I. E. 1971A; Zapfe, H. 1966E (cf.)
  melampus Anderson, E. 1970A (subgen. Martes)
  nobilis Anderson, E. 1970A (subgen. Martes)
  ogygia see Plionictis

Martes - cont.
  oregonensis *Shotwell, J. A.* 1970A (subgen.
      Plionictis)
  palaeosinensis Anderson, E. 1970A (subgen.
      Pekania)
  pennanti Anderson, E. 1970A (subgen. Pekania);
      Parmalee, P. W. 1971A
  pentelici
      palaeosinensis Erdbrink, D. P. 1968A
  stirtoni Anderson, E. 1970A
  vetus Anderson, E. 1970A (subgen. Martes)
  wenzensis Anderson, E. 1970A (subgen. Martes)
  zibellina Anderson, E. 1970A (subgen. Martes);
      Kuz'mina, I. E. 1971A
martini (Macedonitherium, Pliohippus)
martinsi (Ictidorhinus)
martinssoni (Logania)
marxi (Equus)
maryanus (Strepsiceros)
marylandica (Paralbula)
Massetognathus   Traversodontidae
  major *Romer, A. S.* 1972G
  pascuali Bonaparte, J. F. 1972A; Jenkins,
      F. A. 1970B
  teruggii Bonaparte, J. F. 1972A
Massospondylus   Thecodontosauridae
  harriesi Raath, M. A., et al. 1970A
Mastacomys   Muridae
  wombeyensis Schram, F. R., Turnbull, W. D.
      1970A
Mastodon
  angustidens see Gomphotherium, Trilophodon
  grandincisivus see Tetralophodon
  longirostris see Tetralophodon
  tapiroides see Mammut
Mastodonsaurus   Capitosauridae Kupfahl, H.-G.
      1961A; Schultze, H.-P. 1969B;
      Schultze, H.-P. 1969B [Diadetognathus]
  cappelensis Lehman, J.-P. 1971A
      [Heptasaurus]
  giganteus Lehman, J. P. 1971A
  platyceps Standard, J. C. 1969A
Mastodontidae see Mammutidae
Mastomys   Rattus
matthesi (Rotodactylus, Saurornis)
matthewi (Dikkomys, Gerbillus, Hipparion,
      Hypohippus, Merycochoerus,
      Nanotragulus, Proheteromys,
      Pronothodectes)
Matthewichnus   Ichnites *Haubold, H.* 1970A
      (in Amphibia)
  velox [Dromopus ?] Haubold, H. 1970A
  woodworthi [Dromopus ?] Haubold, H. 1970A
maturus (Paromomys)
matutinus (Boreodon)
Mauchchunkia   Mauchchunkiidae *Hotton, N.* 1970A
  bassa *Hotton, N.* 1970A
Mauchchunkiidae   Anthracosauria *Hotton, N.* 1970A
  Mauchchunkia
Mauisaurus   Elasmosauridae
  haasti Welles, S. P., Gregg, D. R. 1971A
Maurimontia   Paramyidae
  picteti Friant, M. 1968A
mauritanicum (Ceratotherium simum)
mauritanicus (Homo, Pagrus, Plesiosaurus)
Maurolicus   Gonostomatidae
  morgani *Arambourg, C.* 1966A

Mawsonia   Coelacanthidae
  ubangiensis Casier, E. 1969A
maximus (Agriochoerus, Apodemus,
      Carangopsis, Cetorhinus, Colobodus,
      Gorgonognathus, Melanosaurus,
      Mosasaurus)
Mayomyzon   Mayomyzonidae *Bardack, D.,*
      Zangerl, R. 1971A
  pieckoensis *Bardack, D., Zangerl, R.* 1971A
Mayomyzonidae   Cyclostomata *Bardack, D.,*
      Zangerl, R. 1971A
  Mayomyzon
mccordi (Milosaurus)
mcgregori (Paciculus)
mcgrewi (Nanodelphys, Nebraskomys, Primobucco,
      Protaspis)
mckeei (Rotodactylus)
mckennai (Navajovius)
Mcmurdodontidae   Selachii *White, E. I.* 1968A
  Mcmurdodus
Mcmurdodus   Mcmurdodontidae *White, E. I.* 1968A
  featherensis *White, E. I.* 1968A
mcmurdoensis (Antarctaspis)
mcnaughtoni (Limnopus)
mcnultyi (Hypolophus)
meachami (Labidosaurikos)
meadensis (Bensonomys, Cryptotis, Pliopotamys)
mechernichensis (Cyclotosaurus)
mecquenemi (Proserrivomer)
medasensis (Mimomys)
media (Capella)
Mediaspis   Phlyctaenaspidae Stensiö, E. 1971A
      (in Spinothoracidi–Dolichothoraci)
mediterraneum (Hipparion, Myctophum)
mediterraneus (Achirus, Euctenoceros, Otolithus
      (Myctophidarum), Ursus)
medium (Palaeotherium)
medius (Leuciscus, Miophasianus, Otolithus
      (Macrouridarum), Sigmodon, Simidectes)
meekae (Prodesmatochoerus)
meekerensis (Semibipedopus)
megacephalus (Eryops)
Megaceroides   Megaloceros
Megaceros see Megaloceros
Megacricetodon   Cricetidae
  lappi [Cricetodon lappi, C. depereti] Mein, P.,
      Freudenthal, M. 1971A (n. subgen.
      Collongomys)
  See also Democricetodon
Megacricetodontini   Cricetidae–Cricetodontinae
      Mein, P., Freudenthal, M. 1971A (n. tribe,
      incl. Megacricetodon)
Megaderma   Megadermatidae
  vireti Bachmayer, F., Wilson, R. W. 1970A
Megadermatidae   Chiroptera
  Megaderma
Megagomphodon   Traversodontidae *Romer, A. S.*
      1972G
  oligodens *Romer, A. S.* 1972G
Megahippus see Hypohippus
Megalagus   Leporidae Eklund, R. R. 1969A
  brachyodon Russell, L. S. 1972B
  primitivus Macdonald, J. R. 1970A (cf.)
Megalania   Varanidae Schultze, H.-P. 1969B

Megalesthonix Esthonychidae—Esthonychinae
Rose, K. D. 1972A
hopsoni Rose, K. D. 1972A
Megalichthys Osteolepidae Thomson, K. S. 1968C
hibberti Andrews, S. M., Westoll, T. S. 1970B
intermedius Schultze, H.-P. 1969B
laticeps Bjerring, H. C. 1972A
Megalictis Mustelidae
ferox Macdonald, J. R. 1970A
Megalocephalus Loxommatidae Schultze, H.-P.
1969B
Megaloceros Cervidae Martin, R. 1968A [Megaceros];
Prat, F. 1968A [Megaceros]; Shikama, T.,
Takayasu, Y. 1971A [?, Sinomegaceros];
Udalov, N. F. 1969A(?)
algarensis Comaschi Caria, I. 1968A [Megaceros]
cazioti Comaschi Caria, I. 1968A [Megaceros]
cretensis Kuss, S. E. 1967A [Megaceros]
See also Cervus
giganteus Beden, M. 1970A [Megaceros];
Delpech, F. 1969A [Megaceros]; Møhl, U.
1972A; Thenius, E. 1966G; Van Bemmel,
A. C. U. 1971A; Vekua, A. K., Khukhia,
N. V. 1972A
hibernicus Vlček, E. 1968B
kinryuensis Onodera, S. 1970B [Megaceros]
verticornis Comaschi Caria, I. 1968A
[Megaceros]; David, A. I. 1969A
[Orthogonoceros]; Melentis, J. K. 1967C
[Orthogonoceros]
dendrocerus Ambrosetti, P. 1967A
[Megaceros, subgen. Megaceroides]
See also Praemegaceros
yabei Hasegawa, Y. 1964C [Sinomegaceros]
Megalocnus Megalonychidae
intermedius Mayo, N. A. 1969A
rodens Fischer, K. 1971A
megalodon (Carcharodon, Carcharodon megalodon,
Mesoreodon)
Megalonychidae Edentata—Megalonychoidea
Cubanocnus, Megalocnus, Megalonyx, Mesocnus,
Microcnus, Pliometanastes
Megalonyx Megalonychidae Akersten, W. A. 1972A;
Hirschfeld, S. E. 1969A; Webb, S. D.
1970B
jeffersoni Barr, T. C. 1957A; Erickson, B. R.
1968A; Holsinger, J. R. 1967A;
Miller, W. E. 1971A (cf.)
leptonyx Shotwell, J. A. 1970A(?)
megalophylla (Mormoops)
Megaloplax Holonematidae Stensiö, E. 1969B
(in Holonemida)
Megalops Elopidae
cyprinoides Goody, P. C. 1969A
Megalosauridae Saurischia—Theropoda
Allosaurus, Ceratosaurus, Megalosaurus
Megalosaurus Megalosauridae Casanovas Cladellas,
M. L., Santafé L., J.-V. 1971A (?, Ichn.)
inexpectatus Corro, G. 1966A
wetherilli see Dilophosaurus
megalotis (Lepomis, Reithrodontomys)
Megalovis Bovidae
latifrons Gentry, A. W. 1970B
megamastoides (Nyctereutes, Nyctereutes
megamastoides)

Megantereon Felidae—Machairodontinae
hesperus Schultz, C. B., Martin, L. D. 1970A
megantereon
megantereon Sickenberg, O. 1970A
[Meganthereon]
nihowanensis Erdbrink, D. P. 1968A (cf.)
piveteaui see Barbourofelis
problematicus Collings, G. E. 1972A
megantereon (Megantereon, Megantereon megantereon)
Meganthereon see Megantereon
Meganthropus Hominidae Lovejoy, C. O. 1970A
palaeojavanicus Antak, M. 1972A; Koenigswald,
G. H. R. 1969B
Megapaloelodus Palaelodidae
connectens Howard, H. 1971C
opsigonus Howard, H. 1971C(?)
Megapezia Ichnites
coloradensis see Parabaropus
longipes Haubold, H. 1970A(?)
pineoi Haubold, H. 1970A
praesidentis see Schmidtopus
megarhinus (Dicerorhinus, Mesatirhinus)
Megaselachus see Carcharodon
Megatheriidae Edentata—Megalonychoidea
Eremotherium, Hapalops, Megatherium,
Nothrotheriops, Nothrotherium
Megatherium Megatheriidae Dechaseaux, C. 1971A
Megatylopus Camelidae
primaevus Patton, T. H. 1969B
See also Paracamelus
Megazostrodon Sinoconodontidae Mills, J. R. E.
1971A
Megoreodon Merycoidodontidae
hollandi Macdonald, J. R. 1970A
mehelyi (Mimomys)
meinertzhageni (Hylochoerus)
meini (Anthracomys, Apopempsis, Musophaga, Pentaglis)
Melamphaeidae [Melamphaidae] Beryciformes—
Stephanoberycoidei
Scopelogadus
melampus (Aepyceros, Martes)
Melanerpeton Discosauriscidae
sacheti see Discosauriscus
Melanodon Dryolestidae
hodsoni Clemens, W. A., Lees, P. M. 1971A
Melanognathus Dipnoi incertae sedis
canadensis Schultze, H.-P. 1969A
Melanorosauridae Saurischia—Sauropodomorpha
Riojasaurus, Strenusaurus, Vulcanodon
Melanosauridae Temnospondyli—Eryopoidea
Jugosuchus
Melanosaurus Anguidae
maximus Meszoely, C. A. M. 1970A
melba (Apus)
Meleagrididae see Phasianidae—Meleagrinae
Meleagris Phasianidae Bedwell, S. F. 1971A
meleagroides (Palaeophasianus)
meles (Meles, Meles meles)
Meles Mustelidae Baigusheva, V. S. 1971A; Beden, M.
1970A; Jánossy, D. 1969B
leucurus Erdbrink, D. P. 1968A
meles Altuna, J. 1970A; Boeuf, O. 1970A;
Bonifay, M.-F. 1967A; Bouchud, J. 1968C;
Martin, R. 1968A; Mostecký, V. 1969A;
Zapfe, H. 1966E
meles Bonifay, M.-F. 1971A

Meles - cont.
thorali
  spelaeus *Bonifay, M.-F.* 1971A
Meliakrouniomys Eomyidae *Harris, J. M.,*
    Wood, A. E. 1969A
  skinneri *Emry, R. J.* 1972A
  wilsoni *Harris, J. M., Wood, A. E.* 1969A
Melissiodon Cricetidae
  dominans Baudelot, S. 1969A (in Melissiodontidae)
  quercyi Hugueney, M. 1969A (aff.); Vianey-
    Liaud, M. 1972B
Melissiodontidae see Cricetidae
melitensis (Leithia, Palaeoloxodon, Pitymys)
melonii (Nemorhoedus)
meltoni (Sorex, Spermophilus)
Melursus Ursidae
  labiatus Flerov, K. K. 1970A (restor.)
membranipes (Rhynchosauroides)
Menaspis Cochliodontidae
  armata Bendix-Almgreen, S. E. 1971A;
    Patterson, C. 1968C (in Menaspoidei–
    Menaspididae)
mendesi (Gaylordia)
mendozensis (Andescynodon, Pelorocephalus)
Mene Menidae
  oblonga Blot, J. 1969B
  rhombea Blot, J. 1969B
  triangulum *Danil'chenko, P. G.* 1968B
Menelikia Bovidae
  lyrocera Cooke, H. B. S., Coryndon, S. C.
    1970A (cf.)
Menidae Perciformes–Percoidei
Mene
Meniscodon Dichobunidae
  europaeum Sudre, J. 1972A
Meniscoessus Cimolomyidae
  ferox *Fox, R. C.* 1971A
  major [Cimolomys] Sahni, A. 1972A (n. comb.)
Meniscomys Aplodontidae
  hippodus Macdonald, J. R. 1970A
  milleri *Macdonald, J. R.* 1970A
menneri (Eomyctophum)
Menoceras Rhinocerotidae
  arikarense [Diceratherium niobrarensis,
    D. cooki] Tanner, L. G. 1969A
  falkenbachi *Tanner, L. G.* 1972A
  marslandensis *Tanner, L. G.* 1969A
Mentzichthys Rhadinichthyidae
  jubbi *Gardiner, B. G.* 1969A
  maraisi *Gardiner, B. G.* 1969A
  theroni *Gardiner, B. G.* 1969A
menui (Oxyaena)
mercki (Dicerorhinus)
merganser (Mergus)
Mergus Anatidae
  albellus Churcher, C. S. 1972C
  connectens *Jánossy, D.* 1972A
  merganser Churcher, C. S. 1972C
  serrator Churcher, C. S. 1972C
meridionalis (Archidiskodon, Elephas, Gliravus,
    Mammuthus)
Meriones Cricetidae Daxner-Höck, G. 1970A(?)
  obeidiensis *Haas, G.* 1966A; Tchernov, E. 1968C
    (in Gerbillidae)
  shawi Jaeger, J.-J. 1969A (aff.) (in Gerbillidae)

Meriones - cont.
  tristrami Heller, J. 1970A; Tchernov, E. 1968B
    (in Gerbillidae)
  unguiculatus Erbaeva, M. A. 1970A (subgen.
    Pallasiomys)
Merlangius Gadidae
  cognatus Gaemers, P. A. M. 1969A (otol.), 1971A
    (otol.); Heinrich, W.-D. 1969B (otol.);
    Robba, E. 1970A (otol.)
  pseudaeglefinus Gaemers, P. A. M. 1969A (otol.),
    1971A (otol.)
  spatulatus Gaemers, P. A. M. 1969A (otol.)
    miocenicus *Heinrich, W.-D.* 1969B (otol.)
  tenuis Heinrich, W.-D. 1969B (otol.)
merlei (Australosomus)
merlini (Saurothera)
Merluccius Gadidae Cappetta, H. C. 1969B(?)
  inferus Jerzmańska, A. 1968A
  macroactus Jerzmańska, A. 1968A
  vulgaris Gaemers, P. A. M. 1969A (otol.), 1971A
    (otol.); Heinrich, W.-D. 1969B (otol.);
    Weiler, W. 1971B (cf., otol.)
  See also Otolithus
merriami (Dipodomys, Simidectes)
mertii (Pisanosaurus)
merula (Turdus)
Merychippus Equidae Forstén, A. 1970B; Tate, R. B.
    1969A; Waldrop, J. 1969A
  insignis Webb, S. D. 1969C (cf., subgen.
    Merychippus)
Merychippus Merychippus
Merychyus Merycoidodontidae Patton, T. H. 1969B;
    Stevens, M. S., Stevens, J. B., Dawson, M. R.
    1969A
  minimus Macdonald, J. R. 1970A
  verrucomalus *Stevens, M.* 1970A
Merycochoerus Merycoidodontidae
  matthewi Macdonald, J. R. 1970A
Merycodus Antilocapridae Tate, R. B. 1969A
  furcatus Webb, S. D. 1969C [Cosoryx]
  necatus Forstén, A. 1970B (cf.)
Merycoidodon Merycoidodontidae Eklund, R. R.
    1969A
  dunagani *Wilson, J. A.* 1971A
Merycoidodontidae Artiodactyla–Merycoidodontoidea
    Friant, M. 1969B; Greaves, W. S. 1972A,B;
    Lindsay, E. H., Lundin, R. F. 1972A
    [oreodont]
  Aclistomycter, Bathygenys, Cyclopidius,
    Desmatochoerus, Hypsiops, Limnenetes,
    Megoreodon, Merychyus, Merycochoerus,
    Merycoidodon, Mesoreodon, Oreodontoides,
    Phenacocoelus, Prodesmatochoerus,
    Promerycochoerus, Sespia, Ticholeptus,
    Ustatochoerus
mesabiensis (Teleorhinus)
Mesacanthida Acanthodiformes
Mesacanthus
Mesacanthus Mesacanthidae
  semistriatus Pageau, Y. 1969A
Mesaceratherium Aceratherium
Mesatirhinus Brontotheriidae
  megarhinus Parker, L. R. 1970A
meschethica (Ergilemys)
Mesocetus Cetotheriidae Ryziewicz, Z. 1969A

Mesochoerus see Omochoerus
Mesocnus Megalonychidae
 torrei Fischer, K. 1971A
Mesocricetus Cricetidae
 aramaeus Tchernov, E. 1968B
 auratus Heller, J. 1970A; Tchernov, E. 1968B
 primitivus *Bruijn, H., Dawson, M. R., Mein, P.*
  1970A
Mesocyon Canidae
 robustus Macdonald, J. R. 1970A
Mesodma Ectypodontidae
 formosa Lillegraven, J. A. 1969B, 1972B
 hensleighi *Lillegraven, J. A.* 1969B
 primaevus Sahni, A. 1972A
 senecta *Fox, R. C.* 1971A
 thompsoni Lillegraven, J. A. 1969B
mesogaster (Allothrissops)
mesogeae (Praewoodsia)
Mesohippus Equidae Eklund, R. R. 1969A
 bairdii Forstén, A.-M. 1970A,C, 1971B
 proteulophus Forstén, A. 1970C
 texanus Forstén, A.-M. 1971B; *McGrew, P. O.*
  1971A
mesomelas (Canis)
Mesonychia Condylarthra *Van Valen, L.* 1969D
 (n. name for subord. Mesonychoidea)
Mesonychidae Condylarthra Szalay, F. S. 1969A
 Dissacus, Hapalodectes, Hyaenodictis
Mesophis Simoliophidae Sliškovíc, T. 1970A
 (in Pachyophiidae)
Mesopithecus Cercopithecidae Swindler, D. R.
  1968A
Mesoreodon Merycoidodontidae
 megalodon
  sweeti Macdonald, J. R. 1970A (cf.)
Mesosauria Reptilia–Anapsida
Mesosauridae Mesosauria Kuhn, O. 1969D
 (in Proganosauromorpha–Proganosauria)
 Mesosaurus
 See also Reptilia incertae sedis
Mesosaurus Mesosauridae Beurlen, K. 1972A
 braziliensis Amaral, S. E. 1971A; Mattievich, E.,
   Danon, J. 1971A; Shikama, T. 1970A
 tumidus Amaral, S. E. 1971A
  [Stereosternum]
Mesosiphneus see Prosiphneus
Mesotheriidae see Typotheriidae
messelense (Propalaeotherium)
messelianus (Trionyx)
Metacheiromyidae Edentata–Palaeanodonta
 Palaeanodon
metacingularis (Paramys)
Metacodon Leptictidae
 magnus Russell, L. S. 1972B (cf.)
Metacodontidae see Plesiosoricidae
Metacordylodon Dimylidae
 schlosseri Engesser, B. 1972A
Metailurinae Felidae *Crusafont-Pairó, M.,*
  Aguirre, E. 1972A (incl. Metailurus,
  Therailurus, Stenailurus, Dinofelis)
Metailurus see Pseudaelurus
Metancylornis see Paraptenodytes
Metaschizotherium see Phyllotillon
Metatheria Mammalia–Theria Slaughter, B. H.
  1970C (Cret.)
Metaxomys Synaptomys *Zakrzewski, R. J.* 1972A
 (n. subgen.)

meteai (Dryopithecus)
Metechinus Erinaceidae
 fergusoni see Brachyerix incertis
 marslandensis see Brachyerix macrotis
Metopacanthus see Myriacanthus
Metoposauridae Temnospondyli–Metoposauroidea
 Metoposaurus
Metoposauroidea Temnospondyli–Stereospondyli
Metoposaurus Metoposauridae Leonardi, P., et al.
  1967A; [Buettneria] Schultze, H.-P. 1969B
  [Eupelor]
 ouazzoui Dutuit, J.-M. 1972A
Metridiochoerus Suidae
 euronensis *Haas, G.* 1970B
 See also Phacochoerus
Metriorhynchidae Crocodylia–Mesosuchia
 Metriorhynchus
Metriorhynchus Metriorhynchidae
 blainvillei Brunet, M. 1969A (cf.)
 durobrivensis Wenz, S. 1971B (cf.)
 moreli Brunet, M. 1969A (cf.)
metsiacus (Diacodexis)
mexicana (Neotoma)
mexicanus (Microtus)
meyeri (Alligatorium, Prolagus)
Miacidae Carnivora–Miacoidea MacIntyre, G. T.
  1965A
 Didymictis, Ictidopappus, Miacis, Uintacyon,
  Viverravus, Vulpavus
Miacis Miacidae Rich, T. H. V. 1971A (cf.)
 exiguus Guthrie, D. A. 1971B
 latidens Guthrie, D. A. 1971B
 latouri *Quinet, G. E.* 1966F, 1969B
mica (Neocassandra)
michali (Listriodon)
micheli (Paratalpa)
Michenia Camelidae–Protolabidini *Frick, C., Taylor,*
  B. E. 1971A
 agatensis *Frick, C., Taylor, B. E.* 1971A
Micraspis see Hirella
Microbrachius Astrolepidae Stensiö, E. 1969B (in
  Antiarchi incertae sedis)
microcanthus (Dapalis)
Microcetus Squalodontidae
 sharkovi *Dubrovo, I. A., Sharkov, A. A.* 1971A
Microchirus Soleidae
 abropteryx Anđelković, J. S. 1969A
Microchoerus Tarsiidae
 antiquus Schmidt-Kittler, N. 1971B
 erinaceus
  edwardsi [M. ornatus, Necrolemur edwardsi]
   Schmidt-Kittler, N. 1971B
  ornatus see M. erinaceus edwardsi
Microcleidus Plesiosauridae Wild, R. 1968A
Microcnus Megalonychidae
 gliriformis Fischer, K. 1971A
 See also Cubanocnus
microdon (Lycaenops)
Microdon Pycnodontidae
 penalvai *Silva Santos, R.* 1970B (in Gyrodontidae)
Microdyromys Gliridae
 complicatus Bruijn, H. 1967A
  See also M. miocaenicus
 koenigswaldi Baudelot, S. 1969A; Bruijn, H. 1967A;
   Engesser, B. 1972A (cf.)
 miocaenicus [Glirulus, M. complicatus] Engesser, B.
   1972A

microlepis (Palaeobergia, Phylactocephalus)
Micromelerpeton Micromelerpetontidae
   credneri Boy, J. A. 1972B; Malz, H. 1970A
Micromelerpetontidae   Amphibia–Dissorophoidea
   Boy, J. A. 1971A, 1972B
   Branchierpeton, Limnerpeton, Micromelerpeton
Micromeryx Cervidae
   flourensianus Engesser, B. 1972A
Micromys Muridae
   praeminutus Kretzoi, M. 1962D; Michaux, J.
      1969B
Micronothosaurus Nothosauridae
   stensioei Schultze, H.-P. 1970C
      (?Cymatosaurus)
micronyx (Pterodactylus)
Microparamys Paramyidae
   chandoni Hartenberger, J.-L. 1971A (n. sp.,
      n. subgen. Sparnacomys)
   monspeliensis Hartenberger, J.-L. 1971A
      (?, subgen. Sparnacomys)
   nanus Hartenberger, J.-L. 1971A
      See also Paramys
   parvus Hartenberger, J.-L. 1971A (subgen.
      Sparnacomys)
   russelli Hartenberger, J.-L. 1971A (n. subgen.
      Pantrogna)
   wyomingensis see Paramys
microphthalmus (Spalax)
Micropternodontidae   Creodonta–Deltatheridia
   Micropternodus
Micropternodus Micropternodontidae Robinson, P.
      1968C (in Nyctitheriidae–
      Micropternodontinae)
microrhinus (Changisaurus)
Microsauria Amphibia–Lepospondyli
   See also Ichnites
Microsauromorpha Amphibia Kuhn, O. 1970B
      (n. subcl.)
Microsauropus Ichnites
   acutipes Sarjeant, W. A. S. 1967A (aff.), 1971A
   parvus Sarjeant, W. A. S. 1971A
Microsorex Soricidae
   pratensis Gureev, A. A. 1971A
Microsteus Pachyosteidae Stensiö, E. 1969B
      (in Pachyostei incertae sedis)
Microstonyx Sus
   See also Sus
Microsus Homacodontidae McGrew, P. O.,
      Sullivan, R. 1970A
Microsyopidae   ? Primates–Tarsioidei Szalay, F. S.
      1967B, 1969B,C (in Microsyopoidea)
   Alsaticopithecus, Craseops, Microsyops,
      Navajovius
   See also Omomyidae
Microsyopoidea   ? Primates Szalay, F. S. 1969B
      (n. rank); Van Valen, L. 1969A
      (in Primates–Prosimiae)
Microsyops Microsyopidae
   alfi [Cynodontomys] Szalay, F. S. 1969C
      (n. comb.)
   angustidens [Cynodontomys] Szalay, F. S.
      1969C (n. comb.)
   annectens Szalay, F. S. 1969C; West, R. M.,
      Atkins, E. G. 1971A (cf.)
   elegans Szalay, F. S. 1969C
   kratos Szalay, F. S. 1969C

Microsyops - cont.
   latidens Guthrie, D. A. 1971B; [Cynodontomys]
      Szalay, F. S. 1969C (n. comb.)
   lundeliusi Guthrie, D. A. 1971B; Szalay, F. S. 1969C
   scottianus Guthrie, D. A. 1971B; Szalay, F. S.
      1969C
   wilsoni Szalay, F. S. 1969C
microtaton (Hipparion)
Microtidae see Cricetidae
Microtinae Cricetidae Guthrie, R. D. 1971A;
      Kowalski, K. 1970A
Microtodon see Baranomys
Microtoscoptes Cricetidae–Arvicolinae Topachevs'kyĭ,
      V. O. 1971B
   disjunctus Hibbard, C. W. 1970A; Shotwell, J. A.
      1970A
Microtragulidae see Argyrolagidae
Microtragulus Argyrolagidae
   argentinus Simpson, G. G. 1970E
   catamarcensis [Argyrolagus] Simpson, G. G. 1970E
   reigi Simpson, G. G. 1970E
Microtragus see Sporadotragus
Microtus Cricetidae Chaline, J. 1970B; Jánossy, D.
      1969B (in Arvicolidae); Martin, R. 1968A;
      Tozzi, C. 1969A
   agrestis Boecker, M., et al. 1972A
   agrestis-arvalis Altuna, J. 1970A (gr.)
   arvalinus Fejfar, O. 1969A
   arvalis Chaline, J. 1968A
   arvalis-agrestis Chaline, J. 1969A (subgen. Microtus,
      in Arvicolidae); Delpech, F. 1968A(?);
      Koenigswald, W. 1970A, 1971A, 1972A (gr.)
   brandti Erbaeva, M. A. 1970A (subgen.
      Lasiopodomys)
   brecciensis Chaline, J. 1971A
   californicus Miller, W. E. 1971A; Zakrzewski, R. J.
      1972A(?)
   deceitensis Guthrie, R. D., Matthews, J. V. 1971A
   fortis Erbaeva, M. A. 1970A (subgen. Microtus)
   gregalis Chernykh, I. I., Maleeva, A. G. 1971A
      (subgen. Stenocranius); Erbaeva, M. A.
      1970A (subgen. Stenocranius)
   guentheri Heller, J. 1970A; Tchernov, E. 1968B
      (in Microtidae)
   incertus Bartolomei, G., Pasa, A. 1970A
   mexicanus Alvarez, T. 1969A
   mongolicus Erbaeva, M. A. 1970A (subgen.
      Microtus)
   nivalis Altuna, J. 1970A
   ochrogaster Schultz, G. E. 1969A (subgen. Pedomys)
   oeconomus Boecker, M., et al. 1972A; Erbaeva,
      M. A. 1970A (subgen. Microtus)
   pennsylvanicus Martin, L. D. 1970A, 1972A;
      Schultz, G. E. 1969A
   ratticeps Altuna, J. 1970A
   subterraneus Chaline, J. 1969A (subgen. Pitymys,
      in Arvicolidae)
Microtus Microtus
Microvenator Coeluridae Ostrom, J. H. 1970C
   celer Ostrom, J. H. 1970C
micrus (Nesophontes)
middendorffi (Lycoptera)
middletoni (Aclistomycter)
mignonei (Rusconiodon)
migrans (Milvus)
migratorius (Cricetulus)

Milleretta Millerettidae
  rubidgei Gow, C. E. 1972A
Millerettidae Cotylosauria—Captorhinomorpha
  Milleretta, Milleropsis, Millerosaurus
milleri (Dendragapus gilli, Mancalla, Meniscomys)
Milleropsis Millerettidae *Gow, C. E.* 1972A
  pricei Gow, C. E. 1972A
Millerosauria Cotylosauria—Captorhinomorpha
    Kuhn, O. 1969D (in Lepidosauria, incl.
    Millerosauridae, Broomiidae,
    Mesenosauridae)
Millerosauromorpha Reptilia *Kuhn, O.* 1970B
    (n. subcl.)
Millerosaurus Millerettidae
  nuffieldi Gow, C. E. 1972A
  ornatus Gow, C. E. 1972A
Millerosteus Coccosteidae Stensiö, E. 1969A,B
    (in Millerosteidae)
milletti (Archidiskodon)
Milnea Burhinidae
  gracilis Cracraft, J. 1972A [? Eudocimus paganus]
Milosaurus Varanopsidae *De Mar, R.* 1970A
  mccordi *De Mar, R.* 1970A
Milvus Accipitridae
  korschun Aubekerova, P. A. 1965A (cf.)
  migrans Churcher, C. S. 1972C (in Falconidae)
Mimetaspis see Cephalaspis
mimica (Eostrix)
Mimomys Cricetidae Agadzhanîan, A. K.,
    Motuzko, A. N. 1972A; Chaline, J.,
    Michaux, J. 1969B (in Arvicolidae);
    Heller, F. 1969B; Koby, F.-E. 1965A
  baschkirica *Sukhov, V. P.* 1970A (subgen.
    Cheria, in Microtidae)
  cappettai *Michaux, J.* 1971B
  coelodus Sukhov, V. P. 1970A (cf., subgen.
    Mimomys, in Microtidae)
  gracilis Kretzoi, M. 1962D [Cseria]; [Cseria,
    M. proseki] Michaux, J. 1970A;
    Michaux, J. 1971B
    akkulaewae *Sukhov, V. P.* 1970A (subgen.
      Cheria, in Microtidae)
    jachimovitcii *Sukhov, V. P.* 1970A (subgen.
      Cheria, in Microtidae)
  hajnackensis see M. polonicus
  intermedius Malez, M. 1967C
    See also M. savini
    parvus *Sukhov, V. P.* 1970A (subgen.
      Mimomys, in Microtidae)
  majori see M. savini
  medasensis *Michaux, J.* 1971B
  mehelyi Kretzoi, M. 1967B (aff.)
  monahani *Martin, L. D.* 1972A
  pliocaenicus Carreck, J. N. 1966A; Kretzoi, M.
    1967B (cf.); Michaux, J. 1971B (aff.);
    Sukhov, V. P. 1970A (subgen. Mimomys,
    in Microtidae)
  polonicus Clair, A., Puisségur, J.-J. 1969A;
    [M. stehlini, M. hajnackensis] Michaux, J.
    1970A; Michaux, J. 1971B
  praehungaricus Sukhov, V. P. 1970A (subgen.
    Villanyia, in Microtidae)
  primus Zakrzewski, R. J. 1969A [Cosomys]
  proseki see M. gracilis
  pusillus Terzea, E., Jurcsák, T. 1967A
    (in Arvicolidae)

Mimomys - cont.
  reidi Clair, A., Puisségur, J.-J. 1969A; Michaux, J.
    1971B
  savini Fejfar, O. 1969A; Jánossy, D. 1969B
    (in Arvicolidae); [M. intermedius,
    M. majori] Pasquier, L. 1972A
  septimanus *Michaux, J.* 1971B
  stehlini Michaux, J. 1971B
  valeriani *Kretzoi, M.* 1967B
Mimomys Mimomys
minax (Chelydropsis)
minidokae (Camelops)
minima (Charadriipeda, Scorpaena)
minimus (Amphechinus, Capromeryx, Hyrachyus,
    Merychyus, Minusculodelphis, Nycticonodon,
    Oxypteriscus, Pachyrhizodus,
    Pericentrophorus, Protoreodon, Sardinioides,
    Sciuropterus, Suevosciurus)
Miniopterus Vespertilionidae
  schreibersi Heller, J. 1970A
Ministrella Gyrolepidotidae *Kazantseva, A. A.* 1968A,
    1971A
  longicauda [Ganolepis] Kazantseva, A. A. 1968A
minor (Amphisauroides, Anomalomys, Aquiladelphis,
    Archaeocetus fockii, Arctops, Auxis,
    Bathornis, Calomyscus, Cerorhinca,
    Charadriipeda, Cynodictis, Cynognathus,
    Democricetodon, Desmoporella,
    Elpidophorus, Entoptychus, Epiaceratherium,
    Glis, Gomphotherium angustidens, Goupilictis,
    Lycaenops, Nannipus, Nothocyon,
    Palenochta, Plagiolophus, Plesiogulo,
    Pliopotamys, Plioprion, Promerycochoerus,
    Prosciurus, Pseudaptenodytes, Sigmodon,
    Squalus, Sus, Talpa)
minshalli (Ambystoma)
minus (Cricetodon, Trogontherium)
Minusculodelphis Didelphidae
  minimus Paula Couto, C. 1970A
minusculus Otolithus (Macrouridarum)
minuta (Dasyatis, Pseudoalactaga, Robiacina, Talpa)
minutidens (Griphognathus)
Minutipes Ichnites *Demathieu, G.* 1970B
  gracilis *Demathieu, G.* 1970B
minutissimus (Scyliorhinus, Sorex)
minutum (Aceratherium)
minutus (Adjidaumo, Dapalis, Hyaenodon, Monosaulax,
    Nanipes, Nanodelphis, Perognathus, Sorex,
    Steneofiber, Trachinus)
miocaena (Taoperdix)
miocaenica (Blackia)
miocaenicum (Cainotherium)
miocaenicus (Microdyromys, Prochrysochloris,
    Rhinocdon)
Miocaretta Cheloniidae *Deraniyagala, P. E. P.* 1969A
  lankae *Deraniyagala, P. E. P.* 1967B, 1969A,B,C
miocenica (Crocuta, Dentex nobilis, Lepidion)
miocenicum (Potamotherium)
miocenicus (Merlangius spatulatus, Scarus, Trichiurus)
Mioceta Cetotheriidae *Deraniyagala, P. E. P.* 1969A
  bigelowi *Deraniyagala, P. E. P.* 1967B, 1969A,B,C
  magna *Deraniyagala, P. E. P.* 1967B, 1969A
Miocitta Corvidae *Brodkorb, P.* 1972A
  galbreathi *Brodkorb, P.* 1972A
Miodugong Dugongidae *Deraniyagala, P. E. P.* 1969A
  brevicranius *Deraniyagala, P. E. P.* 1967B, 1969A,B,C

Monachinae Phocidae Hendey, Q. B. 1972A
monachus (Aegypius)
monahani (Mimomys)
Monaspis see Heterogaspis
monedula (Coloeus)
Mongolemys Dermatemydidae Khosatzky, L. I.,
    Mlynarski, M. 1971A
    elegans Khosatzky, L. I., Mlynarski, M. 1971A;
        Mlynarski, M., Narmandach, P. 1972A
mongolicum (Chilotherium wimani, Hipparion)
mongolicus (Microtus, Pseudotsaganomys)
mongoliensis (Cynodictis, Nemegtosaurus,
    Phalacrocorax, Saurornithoides)
Monodactylidae Perciformes—Percoidei
    Pasaichthys, Psettopsis
Monodelphopsis Didelphidae
    travassosi Paula Couto, C. 1970A
monodon (Mylagaulus)
Monongahela Lepidosirenidae Lund, R. 1970B
    stenodonta Lund, R. 1970B
Monorhina Agnatha
    Incl. Cephalaspidomorphi of Stensiö
Monosaulax Castoridae Klingener, D. 1968A;
        Stout, T. M., Stone, W. J. 1971A
    minutus Friant, M. 1965C
    pansus Lindsay, E. H. 1972B; Lychev, G. F.,
        Aubekerova, P. A. 1971A
Monotremata Mammalia—Prototheria
monspeliensis (Microparamys)
monspessulana (Felis)
montadai (Progenetta)
montalbanensis (Pseudocricetodon)
montana (Brachychampsa)
montanensis (Ectocion, Entoptychus, Eutypomys,
    Palaeolabrus)
montanus (Allenypterus, Parictis, Promerycochoerus,
    Ptilodus)
Montifringilla Ploceidae
    nivalis Jánossy, D. 1972A (cf., in Sturnidae)
montis (Lignimus)
montpessulanus (Plesiogulo)
Moodieichnus Ichnites Sarjeant, W. A. S. 1971A
    didactylus [Varanopus] Sarjeant, W. A. S. 1971A
        (n. comb.)
Mookomys Heteromyidae Stevens, M. S.,
        Stevens, J. B., Dawson, M. R. 1969A(?)
    formicorum Lindsay, E. H. 1972B (cf.)
    subtilis Lindsay, E. H. 1972B
Moorevillia Bananogmiidae Applegate, S. P. 1970A
    hardi Applegate, S. P. 1970A
moquinense (Chirotherium)
Moradisaurus ?Captorhinidae Taquet, P. 1969A
    grandis Ricqlès, A. 1969B; Taquet, P. 1969A
moraviae (Aphanius)
moravica (Desmana moschata, Morone)
moreli (Metriorhynchus)
morgani (Maurolicus)
Morganucodon Morganucodontidae Kermack, K. A.
        1972A; Kermack, K. A., Kielan-
        Jaworowska, Z. 1971A; Mills, J. R. E.
        1970A; Müller, F. 1969A
    oehleri Mills, J. R. E. 1971A
    watsoni Mills, J. R. E. 1971A
    See also Eozostrodon parvus
Morganucodontidae Docodonta Attridge, J.,
        Charig, A. J. 1967B; Hillaby, J. 1967A,B;
        Kermack, K. A. 1967D; Tarlo, L. B. H. 1967E

Morganucodontidae - cont.
    Eozostrodon, Erythrotherium, Morganucodon
Moridae Gadiformes—Gadoidei
    Actuariolum, Lepidion, Onobrosmius
morinellus (Charadrius)
Moringua Moringuidae
    fissura Stinton, F. C., Nolf, D. 1969A (otol.)
Moringuidae Anguilliformes—Anguilloidei
    Moringua
moriturum (Hipparion)
Mormoops Phyllostomatidae
    megalophylla Alvarez, T. 1969A
Mormosaurus Tapinocephalidae Boonstra, L. D.
        1968B, 1969A
Morone Serranidae Salis, K. 1967A (otol.)
    aequalis Rado, G. 1969A (otol.)
    chrysops Smith, G. R., Lundberg, J. G. 1972A
        (in Perichthyidae)
    elongatus [Labrax] Andelković, J. 1970A
    latus [Labrax] Andelković, J. 1970A
    limburgensis Brzobohatý, R. 1969A (aff., otol.);
        Gaemers, P. A. M. 1969A (otol.), 1971A
        (otol.)
    moguntina Stancu, J. 1970A (otol.)
    mojsisovicsi [Labrax] Andelković, J. 1970A
    moravica Brzobohatý, R. 1969A (otol.)
    sagorensis [Labrax] Andelković, J. 1970A
Morosaurus see Camarasaurus
Morosomys Cylindrodontidae Shevyreva, N. S. 1972A
    silentiumis Shevyreva, N. S. 1972A
Morrhua see Paratrisopterus
morrisi (Barbourofelis)
mortoni (Archaeotherium, Ptychodus)
Morus Sulidae Howard, H. 1971C
Mosasauridae Squamata—Lacertilia Quinet, G. E.
        1970A,B; Russell, D. A. 1966A; Zázvorka, V.
        1965A
    Carinodens, Clidastes, Compressidens, Globidens,
        Hainosaurus, Halisaurus, Liodon, Mosasaurus,
        Platecarpus, Plioplatecarpus, Prognathodon,
        Taniwhasaurus, Tylosaurus
Mosasaurus Mosasauridae Schultze, H.-P. 1969B;
        Sigov, A. P. 1969A
    conodon Quinet, G. E. 1970B
    hoffmanni Quinet, G. E. 1970B; Plisnier-Ladame, F.,
        Coupatez, P. 1969A
    maximus Cope, E. D. 1870Y
    missouriensis Thurmond, J. T. 1969B(?)
    mokoroa Welles, S. P., Gregg, D. R. 1971A
mosbachensis (Canis, Canis lupus, Desmana moschata,
        Equus)
mosbachensis-abeli (Equus)
moschata (Desmana)
moschatus (Ovibos)
Moschoedestes Rhinocerotidae Stevens, M. S.,
        Stevens, J. B., Dawson, M. R. 1969A
    delahoensis Stevens, M. S., Stevens, J. B., Dawson,
        M. R. 1969A
Moschops Tapinocephalidae Boonstra, L. D. 1969A
    capensis Boonstra, L. D. 1968B
mosesi (Tersomius)
mossoczyi (Geoemyda)
Motacilla Motacillidae Boecker, M., et al. 1972A
Motacillidae Passeriformes—Passeres
    Anthus, Motacilla
    See also Paridae
mougeoti (Birgeria)

Moythomasia Stegotrachelidae Kazancseva, A. A.
    1971A (in Moythomasiidae)
    nitida Jessen, H. 1968B
    striata Jessen, H. 1968B (cf.)
Moythomasiidae Palaeonisciformes Kazancseva, A. A.
    1971A (incl. Moythomasia, Kentuckia)
muehlbergi (Palaeotherium)
muelleri (Brychetus, Ichthyophis, Procolophonipus)
Mugil Mugilidae
    applanatus Brzobohatý, R. 1969A (otol.)
    radobojanus Anđelković, J. S. 1969A
Mugilidae Perciformes—Mugiloidei Svichenskaîâ,
    A. A. 1968A
    mugil
mulla (Miotursiops)
mulleri (Haplobunodon)
Mullidae Perciformes—Percoidei
    Mullus
Mullus Mullidae
    gorjanovici Anđelković, J. S. 1969B
multicristatus (Ceratodus)
multicuspis (Didolodus, Palaeictops, Prototomus)
multidens (Labrodon)
multipinnatus (Gobius)
Multituberculata Mammalia—Allotheria
    Incl. suborder. Plagiaulacoidea, Ptilodontoidea,
        Taeniolaboidea Fox, R. C. 1968D;
        Mills, J. R. E. 1971A; Sutton, J. F. 1972A
munieri (Laurillardia)
munsteri (Coelodus)
Muntiacus Cervidae
    polonicus Czyžewska, T. 1968A
Muraenesocidae Anguilliformes—Anguilloidei
    Muraenesox
Muraenesox Muraenesocidae
    cybium Nolf, D. 1970A
Muraenidae Anguilliformes—Anguilloidei
    Gymnothorax
muraii (Diaphus)
muralis (Colbertosaurus)
murbani (Myctophum tenue)
murchisoni (Hemicyclaspis)
murdjadjensis (Brosmius)
Muridae Rodentia—Muroidea Hershkovitz, P. 1962A;
    Michaux, J. 1971A
    Acomys, Anthracomys, Apodemus, Arvicanthis,
        Canariomys, Castillomys, Gyomys,
        Mastacomys, Micromys, Mus, Nesokia,
        Occitanomys, Paraethomys, Paraleporillus,
        Parapodemus, Pelomys, Praomys,
        Progonomys, Pseudomys, Rattus,
        Rhagamys, Rhagapodemus, Valerymys
    See also Cricetidae
murinus (Peridyromys)
Murmur Phlyctaenaspidae Stensiö, E. 1969B,
    1971A (in Spinothoracidi—Dolichothoraci
    incertae sedis)
Muroidea Rodentia Voroncsov, N. N. 1968A
Mus Muridae Martin, R. 1968A
    musculus Heller, J. 1970A; Tchernov, E. 1968B
    synanthropus Jánossy, D. 1969B
Muscardinus Gliridae Michaux, J. 1970A
    avellanarius Chaline, J. 1968A; Jánossy, D.
        1969B; Koenigswald, W. 1972A
    dacicus Terzea, E., Jurcsák, T. 1967A
    pliocaenicus Daxner-Höck, G. 1970A
        austriacus Bachmayer, F., Wilson, R. W. 1970A
    thaleri Bruijn, H. 1967A

musceli (Glossanodon)
musculus (Mus)
Musophaga Musophagidae
    meini Ballmann, P. 1969A
    See also Apopempsis
Musophagidae Cuculiformes Ballmann, P. 1969A,
    1970A
    Apopempsis, Musophaga
Mustela Mustelidae Jánossy, D. 1969B [Putorius;
    Malez, M. 1967C; Martin, R. 1968A
    [Putorius]
    erminea Altuna, J. 1970A; Jánossy, D. 1969B (cf.);
        Schütt, G. 1969C; Zapfe, H. 1966E (cf.)
    eversmanni Anderson, E. 1972A; Kuz'mina, I. E.
        1971A (subgen. Putorius)
    soergeli Sickenberg, O. 1968B (subgen. Putorius);
        Zapfe, H. 1966E
    foina Bonifay, M.-F. 1967A
    See also Martes
    frenata Miller, W. E. 1971A; Schultz, G. E. 1969A
        (cf.)
    nigripes Anderson, E. 1972A
    nivalis Altuna, J. 1970A; Boecker, M., et al. 1972A;
        Jánossy, D. 1969B (cf.); Zapfe, H. 1966E
    palerminea Bonifay, M.-F. 1971A
    putorius Altuna, J. 1970A
    rexroadensis Bjork, P. R. 1970A
Mustelictis Mustelidae—Mustelinae Lange, B. 1969A
    piveteaui Lange, B. 1969A, 1970A
Mustelidae Carnivora—Arctoidea Eisenmann, V.
    1969A; Sokolov, I. I. 1968B (in Musteloidea)
    Aonyx, Baranogale, Brachypsalis, Brachypsaloides,
        Broiliana, Buisnictis, Enhydra, Enhydrictis,
        Eomellivora, Ferinestrix, Gulo, Ischyrictis,
        Leptarctus, Lutra, Martes, Megalictis, Meles,
        Mionictis, Mustela, Mustelictis, Palaeogale,
        Paralutra, Paroligobunis, Plesiogale,
        Plesiogulo, Plionictis, Pliotaxidea,
        Potamotherium, Promartes, Satherium,
        Sminthosinis, Stromeriella, Taxidea,
        Trigonictis, Trochotherium, Vormela
Mustelidae [Triakidae] Selachii—Galeoidea
    Mustelus, Triakis
mustelinus (Hyaenodon, Ictidopappus)
Musteloidea Carnivora Sokolov, I. I. 1968A
Mustelus Mustelidae [Triakidae] Telles Antunes, M.,
    Jonet, S. 1970A (in Carcharhinidae)
mutabilis (Trachinus, Treposciurus, Treposciurus
    mutabilis)
mutata (Semigenetta)
mutinensis Otolithus (Sparidarum)
Myctophidae [Scopelidae] Salmoniformes—Myctophoidei
    Fitch, J. E. 1969A (otol.)
    Acrognathus, Cassandra, Ceratoscopelus, Diaphus,
        Eomyctophum, Hemisaurida, Hygophum,
        Hygophus, Ichthyotringa, Lampadena,
        Lampanyctus, Myctophidarum, Myctophum,
        ?Nematonotus, Neocassandra, Sardinioides,
        Sardinius, Sedenhorstia
    See also Otolithus
Myctophidarum see Otolithus
Myctophiformes Teleostei Goody, P. C. 1969B
    (n. rank)
Myctophum Myctophidae
    columnae Anđelković, J. S. 1969A
    debile Anfossi, G., Mosna, S. 1969A (otol.);
        Brzobohatý, R. 1967C (otol.); Dieni, I. 1968A

nota (Dentex)
notabilis (Kritosaurus)
Notalacerta Ichnites Haubold, H. 1970A
    (in Dissorophidae)
    jacksonensis see Batrachichnus
    magna Haubold, H. 1970A
    missouriensis Haubold, H. 1970A
    pentadactyla Haubold, H. 1970A
Notelops Elopidae
    brama Silva Santos, R. 1971A
Notharctidae see Adapidae
Notharctus Adapidae McGrew, P. O., Sullivan, R.
        1970A (in Notharctidae); Robinson, P.
        1957C
    nunienus Guthrie, D. A. 1971B
        (in Notharctidae)
    venticolus Guthrie, D. A. 1971B
        (in Notharctidae)
Nothocyon Canidae
    geismarianus Macdonald, J. R. 1970A
    latidens Macdonald, J. R. 1970A (nr.)
    lemur Macdonald, J. R. 1970A; Stevens, M. S.,
        et al. 1969A(?)
    minor Macdonald, J. R. 1970A
    roii Macdonald, J. R. 1970A
Nothokemadidae see Camelidae
Nothokemas Camelidae
    floridanus Patton, T. H. 1969B
    hidalgensis Patton, T. H. 1969B
Nothosauridae Sauropterygia—Nothosauria
        Mayer, G. 1967A; Murata, M. 1971A(?);
        Schultze, H.-P., Wilczewski, N. 1970A
    Chinchenia, Micronothosaurus, Nothosaurus
Nothosaurus Nothosauridae Rutte, E. 1971A
    adriani Schultze, H.-P. 1970C
    chelydrops Schultze, H.-P. 1970C
    crassus see N. venustus
    edingerae Schultze, H.-P. 1970C
    giganteus Schultze, H.-P. 1970C
    juvenilis Schultze, H.-P. 1970C
    marchicus see N. venustus
    mirabilis Schultze, H.-P. 1970C
    occiduus Erickson, B. R. 1972A (nom. vanum)
    oldenburgi see N. procerus
    procerus [N. oldenburgi] Schultze, H.-P. 1970C
    raabi see N. venustus
    venustus [N. crassus, N. marchicus, N. raabi]
        Schultze, H.-P. 1970C
Nothotylopus Camelidae—Camelinae Patton, T. H.
        1969B
    camptognathus Patton, T. H. 1969B
Nothrotheriops Megatheriidae
    shastense [Nothrotherium] Paula Couto, C. 1971A
Nothrotherium Megatheriidae
    maquinense Paula Couto, C. 1971A
    shastense Miller, W. E. 1971A
        See also Nothrotheriops
Notidanidae see Hexanchidae
Notidanus see Hexanchus
notiochorinos (Protolabis)
Notiosorex Notiosorex
Notiosorex Soricidae
    crawfordi Miller, W. E. 1971A
    jacksoni Gureev, A. A. 1971A (subgen.
        Notiosorex)
Notochampsa Notochampsidae Walker, A. D. 1970A
    (in Stegomosuchidae)

Notochampsidae Crocodilia—Archaeosuchia
    Erythrochampsa, Notochampsa
Notochoerus see Phacochoerus
Notogoneus Gonorhynchidae
    osculus Perkins, P. L. 1970B
Notolagus Leporidae
    velox Downey, J. S. 1968A (cf.)
Notopetalichthys Macropetalichthyidae Stensiö, E.
        1969B
notos (Petrokozlovia)
Notosollasia Whaitsiidae Ricqlès, A. 1969A
Notosuchia Crocodilia—Mesosuchia Gasparini, Z. B.
        1971A (n. infraord., incl. Notosuchidae,
        Uruguaysuchidae)
Notosuchidae Crocodilia—Mesosuchia Gasparini, Z. B.
        1971A (in infraord. Notosuchia)
    Araripesuchus, Notosuchus, ?Sphagesaurus,
        Uruguaysuchus
Notosuchus Notosuchidae
    lepidus see N. terrestris
    terrestris [N. lepidus] Gasparini, Z. B. 1971A
Notoungulata Mammalia
    Incl. subord. Notioprogonia, Toxodontia,
        Typotheria
nova (Isurus)
novaezealandiae (Platydyptes)
novemcinctus (Dasypus)
novotnyi (Palaeobatrachus)
Novumbra Umbridae
    oregonensis Cavender, T. 1969A; Nelson, G. J.
        1972A
novus (Macrourus)
nuffieldi (Millerosaurus)
Numenius Scolopacidae
    arquatus Churcher, C. S. 1972C (?, in Charadriidae)
    gypsorum Brunet, J. 1970A; Dechaseaux, C.
        1970A,B
numidicus (Equus)
Numidiopleura Pleuronectiformes incertae sedis
        Gaudant, M., Gaudant, J. 1969A (intermediate
        between Psettodoidei and Pleuronectoidei)
    enigmatica Gaudant, M., Gaudant, J. 1969A
nunienus (Notharctus)
nuntius (Varicorhinus)
nuttalli (Ochrotomys)
Nyanzachoerus Suidae
    jaegeri Coppens, Y. 1971A
    kanamensis Cooke, H. B. S., Coryndon, S. C. 1970A;
        Cooke, H. B. S., Ewer, R. F. 1972A
    pattersoni Cooke, H. B. S., Ewer, R. F. 1972A
    plicatus Cooke, H. B. S., Ewer, R. F. 1972A
    syrticus [Sivachoerus] Cooke, H. B. S., Ewer, R. F.
        1972A
    tulotos Cooke, H. B. S., Ewer, R. F. 1972A
nyanzae (Dryopithecus)
nyassaensis (Aelurognathus)
Nyctalus see Pipistrellus
Nyctea Strigidae
    nivea Delpech, F. 1968A
Nyctereutes Canidae
    megamastoides Martin, R. 1971A
        megamastoides Sickenberg, O. 1970A
    sinensis Erdbrink, D. P. 1968A
Nycteroletorida Seymouriamorpha Tatarinov, L. P.
        1972B (n. subord., in Batrachosauria, incl.
        Nycteroletoridae)

Odontosaurus see Paracyclotosaurus
oeconomus (Microtus)
oedelemensis (Psettodes)
oehleri (Morganucodon)
oelrichi (Geochelone)
oenanthe (Oenanthe)
Oenanthe Turdidae
    oenanthe Jánossy, D. 1972A (aff.)
oeningensis (Leuciscus, Prolagus)
oervigi (Turinia)
Oeselaspis Dartmuthiidae Gross, W. 1968E
Ogilbia Ophidiidae Cappetta, H. C. 1969B (otol.)
    subregularis Stinton, F. C., Nolf, D. 1969A
      (otol., in Brotulidae)
Ogmodontomys Cricetidae
    poaphagus
      poaphagus Hibbard, C. W. 1972A
        (in Muridae—Arvicolinae)
ogygia (Plionictis)
ohioensis (Astreptorhachis, Castoroides)
Ohuus Gonostomatidae Satō, J. 1962A
    kitamurai Satō, J. 1962A, 1968A
Oioceros Bovidae
    boulei Tekkaya, I. 1969A
    tanyceras Gentry, A. W. 1970A
ojinagaensis (Jaywilsonomys)
Okapia Giraffidae
    stillei Cooke, H. B. S., Coryndon, S. C. 1970A (cf.)
Olbiaspididae Heterostraci (in Amphiaspiformes—
    Olbiaspida, Stensiö) Novitskaia, L. I.
    1968A, 1971B (in Amphiaspidiformes—
    Amphiaspidoidei)
    See also Siberiaspididae
    Angaraspis, Kureykaspis, Olbiaspis, Siberiaspis
Olbiaspis Olbiaspididae
    coalescens Novitskaia, L. I. 1971B; Stensiö, E.
      1968A
olcotti (Promartes)
Oldfieldthomasiidae Notoungulata—Toxodontia
    ? Acoelodus
oleronensis (Lapparentichnus)
oligodens (Megagomphodon)
oligoidus (Amblycoptus)
Oligokyphus Tritylodontidae Halstead, L. B.,
      Nicoll, P. G. 1971A; Ricqlès, A. 1969A
Oligopithecus Pongidae Simons, E. L. 1968C,
      1971A; Szalay, F. S. 1972A
    savagei Simons, E. L. 1971C; Simons, E. L.,
      Pilbeam, D. R. 1972A
Oligoplites Carangidae
    spinosus Arambourg, C. 1966A(?)
Oligosorex Soricidae
    antiquus Gureev, A. A. 1971A
    dehmi Gureev, A. A. 1971A
Oligosoricini Soricidae—Soricinae Gureev, A. A.
    1971A (n. tribe, incl. Amphisorex,
    Oligosorex, Crocidosorex, Alluviosorex,
    Miosorex, Domnina, Paradomnina,
    Soricella, Angustidens)
olisiponensis (Narcine, Sphyraena)
oliveirai (Lepidotes)
oliveri (Korora)
olseni (Ardynomys)
olsoni (Eotitanosuchus)
olsontau (Ekgmoiteptecela)
Oltinomyinae Theridomyidae Bosma, A.,
    Schmidt-Kittler, N. 1972A;

Oltinomyinae - cont.
    Hartenberger, J.-L. 1971B (incl. Oltinomys,
      Estellomys)
omboni (Protacanthodes)
Omochoerus Suidae
    limnetes Cooke, H. B. S., Coryndon, S. C. 1970A
      [Mesochoerus]; Maglio, V. J. 1972A
      [Mesochoerus]
Omomyidae Primates—Tarsioidei
    Ekgmowechashala, Loveina, Niptomomys, Omomys,
      Protomomys, Shoshonius, Teilhardina,
      Washakius
Omomys Omomyidae
    carteri McGrew, P. O., Sullivan, R. 1970A
Omosoma Polymixiidae Patterson, C. 1968B
Omphalosauridae Ichthyosauria
    Chaohusaurus, Omphalosaurus
Omphalosaurus Omphalosauridae Schultze, H.-P.
      1969B; Schultze, H.-P. 1969B [Tholodus]
Onager see Equus
onca (Panthera)
Onchiodon Eryopidae Schultze, H.-P. 1969B
    See also Branchiosaurus
Onchopristis Pristidae
    dunklei
      praecursor Thurmond, J. T. 1971B
Onchosaurus [Dalpiazia, Ischirhiza] Pristidae
      Storer, J. E. 1972B [Ischyrhiza]
    stromeri Cappetta, H. C. 1972B [Dalpiazia]
    See also Ischirhiza
Oncorhynchus Salmonidae Cavender, T. M., Miller,
      R. R. 1972A
Ondatra Cricetidae Harksen, J. C. 1968A; Martin,
      L. D. 1970A; Miller, W. E. 1971A; Nelson,
      R. S., Semken, H. A. 1969A, 1970A
    idahoensis Martin, L. D. 1972A
    nebrascensis Martin, L. D. 1972A
Onobrosmius Moridae
    elongatus Anđelković, J. S. 1969A
onoideus (Brachyodus)
Onychichnium Ichnites
    escheri Leonardi, P., et al. 1967A
Onychodontidae Crossopterygii-Rhipidistia
    Onychodus
Onychodus Onychodontidae Legault, J. A. 1968A;
      Vorob'eva, E. I., Liarskaia, L. A. 1968A
    sigmoides Schultze, H.-P. 1969B
Onychomys Cricetidae Akersten, W. A. 1972A;
      Hibbard, C. W. 1972A (in Muridae—
      Cricetinae)
    jinglebobensis Dalquest, W. W. 1967A (cf.)
    leucogaster Schultz, G. E. 1969A
Onychopoides Ichnites
    triadicus Haubold, H. 1971A
Oolithes [eggs, eggshell, egg capsules]
    carlylensis Jensen, J. A. 1970A
operta (Humbertia)
Ophiacodon Ophiacodontidae
    major Berman, D. S. 1970A (cf.)
Ophiacodontidae Pelycosauria—Ophiacodontia
    Archaeothyris, Echinerpeton, Ophiacodon,
      Petrolacosaurus
Ophiderpetontidae Aistopoda
    Coloraderpeton
Ophidia Squamata Bellairs, A. d'A. 1972A; Hill, W. H.
      1971A; McDowell, S. B. 1972A (origin)

Ophidiidae [Brotulidae] Gadiformes—Ophidioidei
Arambourg, C. 1966A [Brotulidae, in
Perciformes]
Bauzaia, Dinematichthys, Eolamprogrammus,
Glyptophidium, Hoplobrotula, Itatius,
Lepophidium, Neobythites, Ogilbia,
Ophidiidarum, Ophiodon, Propteridium,
Sirembo
See also Otolithus
Ophidiidarum see Otolithus
Ophiodon Ophidiidae
polli see Neobythites
Ophiomys Cricetidae
fricki *Hibbard, C. W.* 1972A (in Muridae—
Arvicolinae)
magilli *Hibbard, C. W.* 1972A (in Muridae—
Arvicolinae)
taylori Zakrzewski, R. J. 1969A
Ophisaurus Anguidae German, R., et al. 1968A
apodus
dzhafarovi *Khozatskiĭ, L. I.* 1967B
canadensis *Holman, J. A.* 1970A
Ophthalmosauridae see Ichthyosauridae
Ophthalmosaurus Ichthyosauridae Schultze, H.-P.
1969B (in Ophthalmosauridae); Schultze,
H.-P. 1969B [Baptanodon, in
Ophthalmosauridae]
opimus (Rhombomys)
opinatus Otolithus (Percidarum)
Opisthonema Clupeidae
persicum *Arambourg, C.* 1966A
vetus see Sarcodon pygmaeus
Opisthopus Ichnites
ellenbergeri Haubold, H. 1970A (in Amphibia)
Opisthotriton Plethodontidae
kayi Estes, R. 1969F (in Batrachosauroididae);
Sahni, A. 1972A
opsigonus (Megapaloelodus)
Opsithrissops Chirocentridae *Danil'chenko, P. G.*
1968B
osseus *Danil'chenko, P. G.* 1968B
Opsolagus Ochotonidae
penai Baudelot, S. 1969A [Lagopsis]; Janvier, Ph.
1971C [Lagopsis]
verus Engesser, B. 1972A [Lagopsis]
oralis (Pseudomys)
orarius (Australocamelus)
orbatus (Viridomys)
orbicularis (Emys)
orbignyi (Plioviverrops)
orbus (Stegotetrabelodon)
orc (Osteoborus)
Orchestropus Ichnites
atavus Haubold, H. 1970A (in Amphibia)
ordii (Dipodomys)
ordinatus (Nanotragulus)
Oreamnos Bovidae Harington, C. R. 1971B
Oreaspis Pteraspididae—Pteraspidinae
Denison, R. H. 1970B
ampla Denison, R. H. 1970B
dunklei *Denison, R. H.* 1970B
williamsi *Denison, R. H.* 1970B
Orectolobidae Selachii—Galeoidea
Ginglymostoma, Orectolobus
Orectolobus Orectolobidae
nigeriensis [Squatina] Cappetta, H. C. 1972B

oregonensis (Grangerimus, Indarctos, Martes, Novumbra)
orenburgensis (Scylacosuchus)
Oreochima Archaeomaenidae *Schaeffer, B.* 1972A
ellioti *Schaeffer, B.* 1972A
Oreodontoides Merycoidodontidae McKenna, M. C.,
Love, J. D. 1972A
curtus Macdonald, J. R. 1970A(?)
Oreomylodon see Glossotherium
Oreopithecidae Primates—Catarrhini
Oreopithecus
Oreopithecoidea Primates-Catarrhini
Incertae sedis: Mabokopithecus
Oreopithecus Oreopithecidae
bambolii Ozaki, H., Obata, I. 1963B
orieli (Aphronorus)
orientalis (Barbus, Brouffia, Colodon, Dicerorhinus,
Equus, Procadurcodon, Rhinotitan,
Sedenhorstia, Stegodon)
orlovi (Echmatemys, Kyzylkakhippus, Similisorex,
Struthio)
ornata (Astrolepis, Ceratophrys)
ornatissima (Bauzaia)
ornatissimus (Asteracanthus)
ornatus (Archegosaurus, Coelorhyncus, Ctenacanthus,
Lycaenops, Malacocephalus, Millerosaurus,
Rhizodus, Sorex)
Ornithischia Reptilia—Archosauria
Incl. subord. Ornithopoda, Stegosauria,
Ankylosauria, Ceratopsia Coombs, W. P.
1972A; Galton, P. M. 1970B; Steel, R. 1969A;
Thulborn, R. A. 1971A
Incertae sedis: Azendohsaurus
Ornithocheiridae Pterosauria—Pterodactyloidea
Araripesaurus, Pteranodon
Ornithodelphia Mammalia—Prototheria Hopson, J. A.
1970A (infracl., n. rank, incl. Monotremata)
Ornithoides Ichnites
trifidus [Hylopus] Haubold, H. 1970A (in
Microsauria)
See also Salichnium
Ornithoidipus Ichnites
perwangeri Leonardi, P., et al. 1967A
Ornitholithus Aves (form genus for fossil bird eggs)
arcuatus Dughi, R., Plaziat, J.-C., Sirugue, F. 1969A;
Dughi, R., Sirugue, F. 1968B
biroi Dughi, R., Sirugue, F. 1968B
mammeatus Dughi, R., Plaziat, J.-C., Sirugue, F.
1969A; Dughi, R., Sirugue, F. 1968B
mammillatus Dughi, R., Plaziat, J.-C., Sirugue, F.
1969A; Dughi, R., Sirugue, F. 1968B
mammosus Dughi, R., Plaziat, J.-C., Sirugue, F.
1969A; Dughi, R., Sirugue, F. 1968B
See also Eggs in Subject Index
Ornithomimidae Saurischia—Theropoda
Dromiceiomimus, Gallimimus, Ornithomimus
See also Ichnites
Ornithomimus Ornithomimidae Ostrom, J. H. 1970C
altus Russell, D. A. 1972A [Struthiomimus]
edmontonicus Russell, D. A. 1972A
Ornithopoda Saurischia Galton, P. M. 1972A
(classif., evol.)
Ornithorhynchidae Monotremata
Ornithorhynchus
Ornithorhynchus Ornithorhynchidae Kermack, K. A.,
Kielan-Jaworowska, Z. 1971A
Ornithosuchia Thecodontia—Pseudosuchia
Bonaparte, J. F. 1971B (?n. infraord.)

Ornithosuchidae   Saurischia–Theropoda Bonaparte, J. F.
    1971B (in Pseudosuchia–Ornithosuchia; incl.
    Venaticosuchus, Ornithosuchus, Riojasuchus);
    Romer, A. S. 1972B (? in Pseudosuchia)
  Gracilisuchus, Ornithosuchus, Riojasuchus,
    Venaticosuchus
Ornithosuchus   Ornithosuchidae Bonaparte, J. F.
    1971B
Orodus   Edestidae Hlavin, W. J. 1972A; Zangerl, R.
    1968B
  corrugatus Berman, D. S. 1970A(?)
Orohippus   Equidae
  pumilus McGrew, P. O., Sullivan, R. 1970A
oroseinum (Myctophum)
orpiensis (Eutrichiurides, Squalus)
Orthacanthus see Xenacanthus
Orthacodontidae   Selachii–Galeoidea
    Orthacodus
Orthacodus   Orthacodontidae Waldman, M. 1971A
orthodon (Rhagamys)
Orthogonoceros see Megaloceros
Orthosaurus see Diplocynodon
Orthosuchus   Protosuchidae Walker, A. D. 1970A
    (in Stegomosuchidae)
orvikui (Coccosteus)
Orycteropodidae   Tubulidentata
    Orycteropus, ?Tubulodon
Orycteropus   Orycteropodidae
  afer Beaumont, G. 1970B
  gaudryi Beaumont, G. 1970B
Oryctolagus   Leporidae
  cuniculus Boeuf, O. 1970A; Bonifay, M.-F. 1967A;
      Campbell, K. E. 1969A; Delpech, F. 1968A;
      Tozzi, C. 1969A
  cuniculus Jullien, R., Pillard, B. 1969A
  huxleyi Seronie-Vivien, R. 1971A
Oryx   Bovidae Tchoumakov, I. S., Alexeeva, L. I.
    1971A(?)
Oryzomys   Cricetidae–Cricetinae Shotwell, J. A.
    1970A(?)
osborni (Barbourofelis, Bolodon, Hypohippus,
    Macropelobates, Pliophenacomys)
osbornianum (Ectocion)
oscillans (Propleopus)
osculus (Notogoneus)
oshosunense (Ginglymostoma obliquum)
osiris (Anancus)
oskarkuhni (Geochelone)
Osmeridae   Salmoniformes–Salmonoidei
    Mallotus
Osmeroides   Elopidae Waldman, M. 1969B
    [Holcolepis]
  dobrogensis Grigorescu, D., Marin, I. 1971A
Ospia   Parasemionotidae Beltan, L. 1968A
osseticus (Gypaetus)
osseus (Opsithrissops)
Osteichthyes
  Incl. subcl. ?Acanthodii, Actinopterygii,
    Sarcopterygii Schaeffer, B. 1968C
Osteoborus   Canidae Webb, S. D. 1969C
  cyonoides Dalquest, W. W. 1969A
  dudleyi Webb, S. D. 1969A (n. comb.)
  galushai Webb, S. D. 1969A
  orc Webb, S. D. 1969A
  validus Webb, S. D. 1969A

Osteoglossidae   Osteoglossiformes–Osteoglossoidei
    Brychetus
Osteoglossiformes   Teleostei
  Incl. subord. Ichthyodectoidei, Osteoglossoidei,
    Mormyriformes, Notopteroidei
Osteolepidae   Crossopterygii–Rhipidistia
    Ectostereorhachis, Gyroptychius, Latvius, Lohsania,
    Megalichthys, Osteolepis, Panderichthys,
    Thursius
Osteolepidoidea   Crossopterygii–Rhipidistia
    Severtsov, A. S. 1969A [Osteolepiformes];
    Thomson, K. S. 1968C [Osteolepoidea]
Osteolepiformes see Osteolepidoidea
Osteolepis   Osteolepidae Schultze, H.-P. 1969B;
    Thomson, K. S. 1968C; Van Bergijk, W. A.
    1966A
  panderi Andrews, S. M., Westoll, T. S. 1970B
Osteolepoidea see Osteolepidoidea
Osteopterygii   Wahlert, G. 1968A (= Osteichthyes +
    Tetrapoda)
Osteostraci   Agnatha–Monorhina (incl. Orthobranchiata,
    Oligobranchiata, Nectaspiformes of Stensiö)
    Janvier, P. 1971A; Whiting, H. P. 1972A
    [Cephalaspida]
  Incertae sedis: Turinia
ostiolatus (Hoplostethus)
Ostracion   Ostraciontidae
  macropunctatus Nolf, D. 1970B
Ostraciontidae   Tetraodontiformes–Balistoidei
    Ostracion
oswaldi (Papio)
Otaria   Otariidae
  hookeri [Arctocephalus caninus] Berry, J. A.,
    King, J. E. 1970A [Phocarctos]
Otariidae   Carnivora–Pinnipedia Fleming, C. A. 1968A;
    Lipps, J. H. 1969A
  Allodesmus, Eumetopias, Imagotaria, Neophoca,
    Otaria, Pontolis, Zalophus
otibandus (Protemnodon)
Otididae   Ralliformes–Otides
    Otis
Otis   Otididae
  kalmani Jánossy, D. 1972A (subgen. Tetrax)
Otodus see Lamna
Otolithus   Pisces
  See also Otoliths under Pisces in Subject Index
    Fitch, J. E. 1968A, 1969A, 1970A;
    Weiler, W. 1968A
  (Berycidarum)
    tuberculatus see Myctophum
  (Chrysophris)
    doderleini see Sparus
  (Clupeidarum) Gaemers, P. A. M. 1971A
    singularis Brzobohatý, R. 1969A
  (Congridarum) Heinrich, W.-D. 1969B(?)
    bellus Aoki, N. 1968A
    pantanelli see Uroconger
  (Crangidarum)
    calidus Aoki, N. 1968A
  (Cyprinodontinarum ?) Salis, K. 1967A
    ellipticus Salis, K. 1967A
  (Gadidarum) Anfossi, G., Mosna, S. 1969A;
    Heinrich, W.-D. 1969B
    acutangulus see Bauzaia
    difformis see Bauzaia

Otolithus - cont.
(Gadus)
  communis see Glyptorhynchus
(Hemiramphus)
  italicus see Halocypselus
(Macrouridarum)
  globosus Heinrich, W.-D. 1969B
  medius Heinrich, W.-D. 1969B
  minusculus Gaemers, P. A. M. 1971A;
    Stancu, J. 1970A (in Atherinidae)
(Macrurus)
  ellipticus see Glyptorhynchus communis
  ornatus var. apicatus see Malacocephalus
  toulai see Glyptorhynchus
(Merluccius) Heinrich, W.-D. 1969B
(Myctophidarum)
  carpaticus Brzobohatý, R. 1967C
  kokeni Brzobohatý, R. 1967C
  mediterraneus Brzobohatý, R. 1967C
  obliquus Brzobohatý, R. 1967C
(Ophidiidarum) Heinrich, W.-D. 1969B
  joachimicus Rado, G. 1965A (cf.)
  obliquus Anfossi, G., Mosna, S. 1969A
  occultus Rado, G. 1965A
(Ophidium)
  gibbus see Bauzaia
  magnus see Conger
  pantanelli see Uroconger
(Percidarum) Heinrich, W.-D. 1969B
  acuminatus Rado, G. 1965A
  frequens Rado, G. 1965A, 1969A (cf.)
  geron Rado, G. 1965A
  opinatus Anfossi, G., Mosna, S. 1971A;
    Dieni, I. 1968A; Robba, E. 1970A
  transitus Weinfurter, E. 1967B
(Pterothrissidarum) Weinfurter, E. 1967B
(Sciaenidarum) Brzobohatý, R. 1969A
  ellipticus Rado, G. 1965A (aff.)
  elongatus Heinrich, W.-D. 1969B
  staringi Heinrich, W.-D. 1969B
(Sparidarum) Anfossi, G., Mosna, S. 1969A
  babai Aoki, N. 1968A
  elegans see Dentex
  mutinensis Anfossi, G., Mosna, S. 1969B;
    Dieni, I. 1968A
  voslauensis Rado, G. 1965A
(Spondyliosoma) Stancu, J. 1970A [Cantharus]
(inc. sed.)
  rzehaki Brzobohatý, R. 1969A
otomii (Neohipparion)
Otomyinae Muridae Dieterlen, F. 1969A
    (in Cricetidae)
Otospermophilus Spermophilus
Otozoidae Ichnites Haubold, H. 1969B
    (in Saurischia—Prosauropoda, incl.
    Otozoum)
Otozoum Ichnites Haubold, H. 1969B
    (in Otozoidae)
  swinnertoni Sarjeant, W. A. S. 1970A(?)
otto (Esox)
Ottonosteus Pachyost.eidae Stensiö, E. 1969A,B
Otus Strigidae—Buboninae
  scops Ballmann, P., Adrover, R. 1970A
  wintershofensis Ballmann, P. 1969B
ouazzoui (Metoposaurus)
oudebergensis (Dinogorgon)

Oudenodon Dicynodontidae Boonstra, L. D. 1969A;
    Cluver, M. A. 1970A (in Cryptodontidae);
    Keyser, A. W. 1972A
  baini Ricqlès, A. 1972B
  kolbei Ricqlès, A. 1972B
ovalis (Macrourus)
ovata (Protaspis)
Overtonaspis Phlyctaenaspidae Stensiö, E. 1969B,
    1971A (in Spinothoracidi—? Dolichothoraci)
Ovibos Bovidae
  moschatus Harington, C. R. 1970A,B; Kuz'mina,
    I. E. 1971A; Lehmann, E. 1968A; Maher,
    W. J. 1966A; Ray, C. E., Wills, D. L.,
    Palmquist, J. C. 1968A; Salov, I. N. 1963A;
    Schütt, G. 1969C; Sukachev, V. N.,
    Sokolovskaïa, V. T. 1965A, 1966A;
    Vangengeĭm, E. A. 1963A
  pallantis Kahlke, H.-D. 1969B
  sussenbornensis Kahlke, H.-D. 1969B
Ovis Bovidae
  ammon Stock, A. D., Stokes, W. L. 1969A
  ammon-polii Jánossy, D. 1969B (group)
  aries Delpech, F. 1969A
  canadensis Churcher, C. S. 1968B; Stock, A. D.,
    Stokes, W. L. 1969A
  catclawensis Stock, A. D., Stokes, W. L. 1969A
  lervia Churcher, C. S. 1972C [Ammotragus]
oweni (Albula, Taniwhasaurus)
owyheensis (Clemmys)
Oxyaena Oxyaenidae
  casieri Quinet, G. E. 1966F(?), 1969B
  menui Rich, T. H. V. 1971A
Oxyaenidae Creodonta—Hyaenodontia
  Oxyaena, Oxyaenoides, Patriofelis
Oxyaenoides Oxyaenidae
  Schlosseri [Hyaenodon] Lange-Badré, B. 1972A
Oxydactylus Camelidae
  benedentatus Patton, T. H. 1969B
  exilis Macdonald, J. R. 1970A
  gibbi see Miotylopus
  lacota Macdonald, J. R. 1970A
  wyomingensis Macdonald, J. R. 1970A (cf.)
oxygnatha (Panthera tigris)
oxyops (Wadeichthys)
Oxyosteidae see Brachydeiridae
Oxyosteus Brachydeiridae Stensiö, E. 1969A,B
    (in Oxyosteidae); Stensiö, E. 1969A
    [Platyosteus] (in Oxyosteidae)
Oxypteriscus Stegotrachelidae
  minimus Kazantseva, A. A. 1968A
Oxyrhina see Isurus
oxyrinchus (Isurus)
Oxyura Anatidae Feduccia, J. A., Rich, P. V. 1972A
Pachycephalosauridae ["Troodontidae"] Ornithischia—
    Ornithopoda Galton, P. M. 1970C, 1971A
  Pachycephalosaurus, Stegoceras, Yaverlandia
Pachycephalosaurus Pachycephalosauridae Galton, P. M.
    1971A
Pachycormidae Amiiformes—Amioidei
  Protosphyraena
Pachycrocuta see Hyaena
Pachydyptes Spheniscidae
  ponderosus Simpson, G. G. 1971C
pachygnathus (Dinosorex)

Pachynolophus Equidae
   boixedatensis Crusafont Pairó, M., Remy, J. A.
      1970A
   duvali Ginsburg, L., Lapierre, F., Montenat, C.
      1967A (aff.)
   lavocati Remy, J. A. 1972A (in Palaeotheriidae)
pachyodon (Sorex)
Pachyophis Simoliophidae Sliškovic, T. 1970A
   (in Pachyophiidae)
Pachyornis Emeidae
   elephantopus Scarlett, R. J. 1969A
Pachyosteidae Arthrodira—Brachythoraci (incl.
      Pachyosteidae, Rhinosteidae,
      Leiosteidae of Stensiö) Stensiö, E. 1969A,B
      (in Pachyosteomorphi—Pachyostei)
   Enseosteus, Erromenosteus, Leiosteus, Microsteus,
      Ottonosteus, Pachyosteus, Paraleiosteus,
      Parawalterosteus, Rhinosteus, Walterosteus
Pachyosteomorphi Arthrodira Stensiö, E. 1969A,B
   (in Aspinothoracidi)
Pachyosteus Pachyosteidae Stensiö, E. 1969A,B
Pachypleurosauridae Sauropterygia—Nothosauria
      Pachypleurosaurus
Pachypleurosaurus Pachypleurosauridae Rutte, E.
      1971A
pachypterna (Ardynia)
Pachyrhinos see Gorgonops
Pachyrhizodontidae Elopiformes—Elopoidei
      Pachyrhizodus
Pachyrhizodontoidea Elopiformes—Elopoidei
      Applegate, S. P. 1970A (n. superfam., incl.
      Pachyrhizodus, Thrissopater, Elopopsis,
      Rhacolepis)
Pachyrhizodus Pachyrhizodontidae Applegate, S. P.
      1970A (in Pachyrhizodontoidea)
   caninus Applegate, S. P. 1970A
   kingi Applegate, S. P. 1970A
   marathonensis Bartholomai, A. 1969A
   minimus Applegate, S. P. 1970A
Pachythrissops Chirocentridae
   propterus Nybelin, O. 1964A
Pachytragus Bovidae
   crassicornis Gentry, A. W. 1971A
   laticeps Gentry, A. W. 1971A
Paciculus Cricetidae
   insolitus Alker, J. 1969A
   mcgregori Macdonald, J. R. 1970A
   nebraskensis Alker, J. 1969A
packardi (Allodesmus)
paenebursarius (Geomys)
Paenemarmota Sciuridae
   barbouri Zakrzewski, R. J. 1969A
Paeneprolimnocyon Hyaenodontidae
   amissadomus Guthrie, D. A. 1971B
paganus (Eudecimus)
pagei (Copemys)
Pagrus Sparidae
   distinctus Gaemers, P. A. M. 1969A (cf., otol.),
      1971A (aff., otol.); Rado, G. 1969A
      (otol.)
   mauritanicus Menesini, E. 1969A
pahinsintewakpa (Sunkahetanka)
painei (Palorchestes)
paintenense (Alligatorium)

Palaeacanthaspidae Rhenanida (incl. Acanthothoraci
      of Stensiö)
   Dobrowlania, Kosoraspis, Palaeacanthaspis
Palaeacanthaspis Palaeacanthaspidae Stensiö, E.
      1969B, 1971A (in Spinothoracidi—
      Acanthothoraci)
Palaeanodon Metacheiromyidae
   ignavus Guthrie, D. A. 1971B
Palaechthon Phenacolemuridae Szalay, F. S. 1969C
   (in Paromomyidae)
   alticuspis Szalay, F. S. 1968B
   nacimienti Wilson, R. W., Szalay, F. S. 1972A
      (in Paromomyidae)
   woodi Gazin, C. L. 1971A (in Paromomyidae)
Palaechthonini Phenacolemuridae—Paromomyinae
      Szalay, F. S. 1969C (n. tribe, in
      Paromomyidae, incl. Palaechthon,
      Palenochtha, Plesiolestes)
Palaeeudyptes Spheniscidae
   antarcticus Simpson, G. G. 1971C
   marplesi Simpson, G. G. 1971C
Palaegithalus Paridae
   cuvieri Brunet, J. 1970A (in Motacillidae)
Palaeictops Leptictidae
   bicuspis Guthrie, D. A. 1971B
   multicuspis Guthrie, D. A. 1971B
palaeindicus (Bubalus) *
Palaelodidae Ardeiformes—Phoenicopteri
      Megapaloelodus, Palaelodus
Palaelodus Palaelodidae Harrison, C. J. O. 1971A
   ambiguus Howard, H. 1971C; Rothausen, K. 1966A
   goliath Howard, H. 1971C
Palaeoamasia Chalicotheriidae Ozansoy, F. 1966A
   kansui Ozansoy, F. 1966A, 1969A
Palaeoanacorax Isuridae Glikman, L. S., Shvazhaïte,
      R. A. 1971A (in Anacoracidae)
   intermedius Glikman, L. S., Shvazhaïte, R. A. 1971A
   obliquus [Corax] Glikman, L. S., Shvazhaïte, R. A.
      1971A
   pamiricus [Corax falcatus] Glikman, L. S.,
      Shvazhaïte, R. A. 1972A
   volgensis Glikman, L. S., Shvazhaïte, R. A. 1971A
Palaeobatrachidae Anura—Palaeobatrachina
      Vergnaud-Grazzini, C., Hoffstetter, R. 1972A
      Palaeobatrachus
Palaeobatrachus Palaeobatrachidae Špinar, Z. V. 1972B
   (incl. n. subgen. Hekatobatrachus,
      Palaeobatrachus, Suleobatrachus)
   diluvianus Špinar, Z. V. 1972A,B (subgen.
      Palaeobatrachus)
   grandipes Špinar, Z. V. 1970A; [Pelobatinopsis
      himschei] Špinar, Z. V. 1972A,B (subgen.
      Hekatobatrachus)
   laubei [Protopelobates gracilis] Špinar, Z. V. 1967C,
      1972B (subgen. Suleobatrachus)
   luedeckei Špinar, Z. V. 1972B (subgen.
      Palaeobatrachus)
   novotnyi Špinar, Z. V. 1972A,B (subgen.
      Hekatobatrachus)
   rostae Špinar, Z. V. 1972A,B (subgen.
      Palaeobatrachus)
Palaeobatrachus Palaeobatrachus
Palaeobergia Palaeobergiidae Kazantseva, A. A. 1968A,
      1971A
   microlepis Kazantseva, A. A. 1968A

Palaeomeryx   Palaeomerycidae Engesser, B. 1972A
Palaeomylus see Eczematolepis
Palaeomys   Castoridae
    castoroides Friant, M. 1965C
    jaegeri Bachmayer, F., Wilson, R. W. 1970A
        [Chalicomys; cf.]
palaeonictides (Prototomus)
Palaeoniscidae   Palaeonisciformes–Palaeoniscoidei
    Ambodipia, Dmitrevichthys, Palaeoniscinotus,
        Pteronisculus, Turgoniscus
Palaeonisciformes   Actinopterygii–Chondrostei
    Incl. subord. Palaeoniscoidei, Platysomoidei,
        Tarrasioidei, Ptycholepoidei,
        Pholidopleuroidei, Luganoioidei,
        Redfieldoidei, Perleidoidei
Palaeoniscinotus   Palaeoniscidae
    czekanowskii Iakovlev, V. N. 1968A
Palaeoniscoidei   Palaeonisciformes
    Incertae sedis: Indaginilepis
Palaeoniscus
    rohani see Paramblypterus
Palaeophasianus   Gruidae
    incompletus Cracraft, J. 1969A
        (in Geranoididae)
    meleagroides Cracraft, J. 1968C, 1969A
        (in Geranoididae)
Palaeopicus see Colius
Palaeopropithecus   Lemuridae Mahé, J. 1968A
Palaeorallus   Rallidae
    alienus Kurochkin, E. N. 1968C
Palaeoreas   Bovidae
    lindermayeri Gentry, A. W. 1971A; Melentis,
        J. K. 1970A
Palaeorhinus   Phytosauridae Gregory, J. T. 1969B
Palaeorhynchidae   Perciformes–Scombroidei
    Palaeorhynchus
Palaeorhynchus   Palaeorhynchidae Jerzmańska, A.
        1968A
    altivelis Arambourg, C. 1966A
Palaeortyx   Cracidae–Gallinuloidinae
    depereti Ballmann, P. 1969A (in Phasianidae)
    intermedia Ballmann, P. 1969B (?, in
        Phasianidae)
    phasianoides Ballmann, P. 1969B
        (in Phasianidae)
        grivensis Ballmann, P. 1969A
        (in Phasianidae)
Palaeoryctidae see Deltatheridiidae
Palaeoryx   Bovidae Czyżewska, T. 1970A
    majori Melentis, J. K. 1970A; Melentis, J. K.,
        Schneider, H. 1966A
    pallasi Gentry, A. W. 1971A
    woodwardi Melentis, J. K. 1970A
Palaeosauriscidae [Palaeosauridae] Saurischia–
        Palaeopoda Colbert, E. H. 1970F
        (in Teratosauria)
    Ischisaurus, Staurikosaurus
Palaeosauropus   Ichnites
    antiquior Haubold, H. 1970A (?, subgen.
        Sauropus)
    brunensis Haubold, H. 1970A (subgen.
        Sauropus ?)
    primaevus [Sauropus] Haubold, H. 1970A
Palaeoscalopus   Talpidae Macdonald, J. R. 1970A
    pineridgensis Hutchison, J. H. 1972A (nomen
        nudum, see Quadrodens wilsoni);
        Macdonald, J. R. 1970A

Palaeoscaptor   Amphechinus
Palaeoscincus   Nodosauridae
    costatus Sahni, A. 1972A
Palaeosciurus   Sciuridae Hugueney, M. 1969A(?)
palaeosinensis (Martes, Martes pentelici, Panthera)
Palaeosinopa   Pantolestidae
    didelphoides Guthrie, D. A. 1971B
    lutreola Guthrie, D. A. 1971B
    veterrima Guthrie, D. A. 1971B (cf.)
Palaeosiren   Older Amphibia, incertae sedis
    beinerti Estes, R. 1970A (not organic)
Palaeosox see Palaeoesox
Palaeospheniscus   Spheniscidae [Paraspheniscus,
        Perispheniscus, Pseudospheniscus] Simpson,
        G. G. 1972B
Palaeospondylus   Placodermi incertae sedis
    gunni Lehman, J.-P. 1969A
palaeosumatrensis (Pongo pygmaeus)
Palaeosyops   Brontotheriidae Guthrie, D. A. 1971A
    fontinalis McGrew, P. O., Sullivan, R. 1970A
    major Friant, M. 1970B
Palaeotheriidae   Equoidea Franzen, J. L. 1968A
    Palaeotherium, Plagiolophus
    See also Equidae
Palaeotherium   Palaeotheriidae Hooker, J. J. 1972A
    castrense
        robiacense Franzen, J. L. 1968A
    crassum
        robustum Franzen, J. L. 1968A
    curtum
        frohnstettense Franzen, J. L. 1968A; Jehenne, Y.
            1969A
        villerealense Franzen, J. L. 1968A
    duvali
        priscum Franzen, J. L. 1968A
    magnum Bessonnat, G., Dughi, R., Sirugue, F.
        1969A (ichn.); Friant, M. 1970B
    medium
        suevicum Jehenne, Y. 1969A
    muehlbergi
        praecursum Franzen, J. L. 1968A
    pomeli Franzen, J. L. 1968A
    siderolithicum Sudre, J. 1969A
Palaeotinca   Cyprinidae Obrhelová, N. 1969A, 1970B
    egeriana Obrhelová, N. 1969A, 1970B
    obtruncata [Tinca] Obrhelová, N. 1970B(?)
Palaeotragus   Giraffidae Godina, A. Ia. 1971B,C
    asiaticus Godina, A. Ia. 1971A (subgen.
        Palaeotragus)
    berislavicus Korotkevich, E. L. 1970A (subgen.
        Achtiaria)
    coelophrys Churcher, C. S. 1970B
    decipiens Churcher, C. S. 1970B
    expectans Churcher, C. S. 1970B
    primaevus Churcher, C. S. 1970B, 1972A
    roueni Churcher, C. S. 1970B
    tungurensis Churcher, C. S. 1970B
Palaeotragus   Palaeotragus
Palatobaena   Baenidae–Palatobaeninae Gaffney, E. S.
        1972A
    bairdi Gaffney, E. S. 1972A
Palatobaeninae   Baenidae Gaffney, E. S. 1972A
Palealbula   Albulidae
    neocomiensis Weiler, W. 1969A (otol.)
    ventralis Weiler, W. 1971A (otol.)
Palelops   Elopidae Applegate, S. P. 1970A
    eutawensis Applegate, S. P. 1970A

Papio - cont.
  darti Maier, W. 1970B, 1972A [Simopithecus]
  jonesi Freedman, L., Stenhouse, N. S. 1972A
    [Parapapio]; Maier, W. 1970B [Parapapio]
  oswaldi Cooke, H. B. S., Coryndon, S. C. 1970A
    [Simopithecus]
  robinsoni Freedman, L., Brain, C. K. 1972A
  whitei Freedman, L., Stenhouse, N. S. 1972A
    [Parapapio]; Maier, W. 1970B [Parapapio]
Pappogeomys Geomyidae Alvarez, T. 1969A
Pappotheriidae Mammalia—Theria incertae sedis
    Pappotherium
Pappotherium Pappotheriidae Crompton, A. W. 1971A;
    Turnbull, W. D. 1971A
  pattersoni Slaughter, B. H. 1971A
papyraceus (Esox, Leuciscus)
Parabaropus Ichnites
  coloradensis [Megapezia] Haubold, H. 1970A
    (in Eryopoidea)
paraboliceps (Plagiorophus)
Parabos Bovidae Rădulescu, C., Kovács, A. 1968A;
    Samson, P., et al. 1971A
Paracamelus Camelidae Shotwell, J. A. 1970A
    [Megatylopus]
  alutensis Baĭgusheva, V. S. 1971A
  gigas Baĭgusheva, V. S. 1971A
  major Webb, S. D. 1969C [Megatylopus]
  See also Megatylopus
Paracanthopterygii Teleostei Rosen, D. E.,
    Patterson, C. 1969A (incl. series
    Polymixiomorpha, Salmopercomorpha)
Paraceratherium Rhinocerotidae Eroshkin, A. F.,
    Savinov, P. F. 1971A
Paraceratodus Ceratodontidae Beltan, L. 1968A
    (in Ceratodiformes—Ceratodidae)
Parachanos Chanidae
  aethiopicus Casier, E., Taverne, L. 1971A
Parachirotheriidae Ichnites Haubold, H. 1969B
    (in Saurischia indetermined, incl.
    Parachirotherium, Thecodontichnus,
    ?Agailopous)
Parachirotherium Ichnites Haubold, H. 1969B
    (in Parachirotheriidae)
paracnemis (Bufo)
Paracolobus Cercopithecidae Leakey, R. E. F.
    1969A (in Colobidae)
  chemeroni Leakey, R. E. F. 1969A
Paracoluber Colubridae Holman, J. A. 1970A
  storeri Holman, J. A. 1970A
Paraconger Congridae Nolf, D. 1970A (otol.)
  sauvagei Stinton, F. C., Nolf, D. 1969A (otol.)
Paracrax Cariamidae
  antiqua Cracraft, J. 1971A
    (in Bathornithidae)
  gigantea Cracraft, J. 1968B
    (in Bathornithidae)
  wetmorei Cracraft, J. 1968B, 1971A
    (in Bathornithidae)
Paracricetodontinae Cricetidae Mein, P.,
    Freudenthal, M. 1971A (incl.
    Paracricetodon)
Paracrocodylia Crocodylomorpha Walker, A. D.
    1970A (subord., incl. infraord.
    Pedeticosauria, Baurusuchia,
    Hallopoda)

Paracryptotis Soricidae Bachmayer, F., Wilson, R. W.
    1970A(?)
  gidleyi Choate, J. R. 1970A; [Blarina] Hibbard,
    C. W., Bjork, P. R. 1971A
  rex Choate, J. R. 1970A; Gureev, A. A. 1971A
Paracyclotosaurus Capitosauridae
  voltzii Gall, J.-C. 1971A [Odontosaurus]
Paracygnus ?Anatidae Short, L. L. 1969A
  plattensis Short, L. L. 1969A
Paradapedon see Parasuchus
Paradelphomys Echimyidae—Adelphomyinae
    Patterson, B., Pascual, R. 1968B
  fissus Patterson, B., Pascual, R. 1968B
Paraderma Parasaniwidae
  bogerti Sahni, A. 1972A
Paradesmatochoerus Desmatochoerus
Paradidelphys Didelphidae
  brachyodonta see Didelphis
  inexpectata Simpson, G. G. 1972A
Paradjidaumo Eomyidae
  trilophus Wood, A. E. 1969A (cf.)
Paradomnina Soricidae
  relictus Gureev, A. A. 1971A; Lindsay, E. H.
    1972B (cf.)
paradoxa (Psammolepis)
paradoxum (Amphistium)
paradoxus (Chroniosuchus)
Paraelephas see Parelephas
Paraelops Elopidae Silva Santos, R. 1971A
  cearensis Silva Santos, R. 1971A
Paraentelodon Entelodontidae
  intermedium Nikolov, Iv., Velichkov, V. 1969A
Paraethomys Muridae Petter, F. 1968A
  anomalus Jaeger, J.-J. 1971A
  filfilae Jaeger, J.-J. 1969A (aff.); Petter, F. 1968A
Paragalerhinus Gorgonopsidae—Gorgonopsinae
    Sigogneau, D. 1970A
  rubidgei [Galerhinus] Sigogneau, D. 1970A
Paragaleus Carcharhinidae
  pulchellus Cappetta, H. C. 1969B, 1970A;
    Telles Antunes, M., Jonet, S. 1970A
Paraglirulus Gliridae Engesser, B. 1972A
  lissiensis [Glirulus] Engesser, B. 1972A (cf.)
  werenfelsi Engesser, B. 1972A
Paraglis Gliridae Baudelot, S. 1970A
  astaracensis Baudelot, S. 1970A
Paragrus Gruidae
  prentici Cracraft, J. 1969A (in Geranoididae)
  shufeldti Cracraft, J. 1969A (in Geranoididae)
Parahippus Equidae Waldrop, J. 1969A
  cognatus Macdonald, J. R. 1970A (nr.)
  coloradensis
    praecurrens Macdonald, J. R. 1970A
  pristinus Macdonald, J. R. 1970A
  texanus Macdonald, J. R. 1970A
Parailurus Procyonidae
  anglicus Samson, P., et al. 1971A
Paralbula Albulidae Sahni, A. 1972A(?)
  casei Estes, R. 1969G (in Phyllodontidae)
  marylandica Estes, R. 1969B (in Phyllodontidae)
  salvani [Pseudoegertonia] Estes, R. 1969G
    (in Phyllodontidae)
  stromeri [Egertonia] Estes, R. 1969G
    (in Phyllodontidae)
Paralbulinae Phyllodontidae Estes, R. 1969G (incl.
    Paralbula, Pseudoegertonia, ?Eodiaphyodus)

Paratrisopterus - cont.
    caspius [Gadus] Fedotov, V. F. 1971B
    kiplingi [Gadus] Fedotov, V. F. 1971B
    kwitkae [Gadus] Fedotov, V. F. 1971B
    macropterygia [Morrhua] Fedotov, V. F. 1971B
Paratyto Phodilidae Brodkorb, P. 1969A
    arvernensis [Bubo] Brodkorb, P. 1969A
Paraulacodus Thryonomyidae
    indicus Black, C. C. 1972A
Paraustralopithecus Hominidae Vandermeersch, B.
        1970C
    aethiopicus Anfray, F. 1968A; Coppens, Y. 1970A
Parawalterosteus Pachyosteidae Stensiö, E. 1969A,B
parca (Ilchunaia)
pardina (Felis)
pardinensis (Acinonyx)
Pardocephalus see Arctops
Pardosuchus Alopecodontidae Boonstra, L. D. 1969A
pardus (Panthera)
Pareiasauridae Cotylosauria–Procolophonia
        Boonstra, L. D. 1969A
    Bradysaurus, Embrithosaurus, Hauboldisaurus,
        Pareiasaurus
Pareiasauridae Pareiasauridae
    pricei Findlay, G. H. 1970B [Nanoparia]
    serridens Findlay, G. H. 1970B
Parelephas see Mammuthus
Parendotherium Dryolestidae
    herrerei see P. herreroi
    herreroi [P. herrerei] Crusafont Pairó, M.,
        Adrover, R. 1965A, 1966A (corrected
        spelling)
Pareumys Cylindrodontidae Black, C. C. 1970B;
        Lindsay, E. 1969A
    guensburgi Black, C. C. 1970A
Parictis Canidae Clark, J., Guensburg, T. E. 1972A
        (n. subgen. Subparictis)
    dakotensis Clark, J., Guensburg, T. E. 1972A
        (subgen. Subparictis)
    gilpini Clark, J., Guensburg, T. E. 1972A
        (subgen. Subparictis)
    major Clark, J., Guensburg, T. E. 1972A
        (subgen. Subparictis)
    montanus Clark, J., Guensburg, T. E. 1972A
        (subgen. Subparictis)
    parvus Clark, J., Guensburg, T. E. 1972A
        (subgen. Campylocynodon)
    personi Clark, J., Guensburg, T. E. 1972A
        (subgen. Campylocynodon)
    primaevus Clark, J., Guensburg, T. E. 1972A
        (subgen. Parictis)
Parictis Parictis
Paridae Passeriformes
    Palaegithalus, Parus
parisiensis (Adapis, Choeropotamus, Laurillardia)
Parksosaurus Hypsilophodontidae Galton, P. M.
        1971A
Parmularius Bovidae
    altidens Cooke, H. B. S., Coryndon, S. C.
        1970A (cf.)
parodii (Argyrolagus)
Paroligobunis Mustelidae Stevens, M. R.,
        Stevens, J. B., Dawson, M. R. 1969A(?)
Paromomyidae see Phenacolemuridae
Paromomyini   Phenacolemuridae–
        Paromomyinae Szalay, F. S. 1969C
        (n. rank, in Paromomyidae, incl.
        Paromomys, Phenacolemur)

Paromomys Phenacolemuridae Szalay, F. S. 1969C
        (in Paromomyidae)
    depressidens Gazin, C. L. 1971A (nr., in
        Paromomyidae)
    maturus Szalay, F. S. 1968B
Paronychodon Coeluridae
    lacustris Sahni, A. 1972A (in Deinodontidae)
Parotosaurus Capitosauridae Schultze, H.-P. 1969B
        [Ptychosphenodon]; Schultze, H.-P. 1969B
        [Syphonodon]; Tverdokhlebov, V. P. 1970B
    lapparenti Lehman, J.-P. 1971A
    nasutus Lehman, J.-P. 1971A
    peabodyi see Wellesaurus
    pronus Howie, A. A. 1970A
    rajareddyi Chowdhury, T. R. 1970A
    semiclausus Lehman, J.-P. 1971A [Stenotosaurus];
        Ortlam, D. 1968A
    wadei Cosgriff, J. W. 1972A
Paroxyclaenidae Insectivora–Leptictoidea
    Kopidodon, Paroxyclaenus, Russelites, Spaniella,
        Vulpavoides
Paroxyclaeninae Arctocyonidae Tobien, H. 1969A
        (incl. Paroxyclaenus, Vulpavoides,
        Russelites, Kopidodon, Spaniella)
Paroxyclaenus Paroxyclaenidae Rich, T. H. V.
        1971A (cf.); Tobien, H. 1969A (in
        Condylarthra–Arctocyonidae)
parringtoni (Aelurognathus, Erythrotherium)
partium (Lyrurus)
Parus Paridae
    coeruleus Jánossy, D. 1972A (cf.)
    major Jánossy, D. 1972A (cf.)
parva (Necromanis)
parvidens (Cerdorhinus, Hybodus, Thelodus)
parviplicatus (Hypolagus)
parvula (Argentina)
parvulus (Elfomys, Protorhamphosus, Pseudaelurus,
        Pseudotheridomys, Uintasorex)
parvum (Chirotherium, Hipparion)
parvus (Bassariscus, Batrachichnus, Burramys,
        Captorhinikos, Diplocaulus, Duntroornis,
        Eozostrodon, Eutypomys, Gobibaatar,
        Leptotomus, Maraisaurus, Microparamys,
        Microsauropus, Mimomys intermedius,
        Parictis, Phascolomis, Pliogeomys,
        Protoreodon, Scylacognathus)
Parydrosorex Soricidae
    concisus see Petenyia
pasai (Dolomys bogdanovi)
Pasaichthys Monodactylidae Blot, J. 1969B
    pleuronectiformis Blot, J. 1969B
Paschatherium Hyopsodontidae
    dolloi Quinet, G. E. 1969B
    sjongersi Quinet, G. E. 1969B
Pascualgnathus Diademodontidae
    polanskii Bonaparte, J. F. 1972A
        (in Traversodontidae)
pascuali (Massetognathus, Sallamys, Thylatheridium)
Passeriformes Aves
passerinum (Glaucidium)
patachonica (Macrauchenia)
patagonica (Dinilysia)
Patene Borhyaenidae
    simpsoni Paula Couto, C. 1970A
Pateroperca Clupeidae Patterson, C. 1968B
        (in Aulolepididae)
Patriocetidae Cetacea–Mysticeti
    Ferecetotherium, Mirocetus, Patriocetus

Patriocetus Patriocetidae Hasegawa, Y., Hojo, Y.
 1965A
Patriofelis Oxyaenidae
 tigrinus Guthrie, D. A. 1971B
Patriomanis Manidae Emry, R. J. 1970A
 americanus Emry, R. J. 1970A
pattersoni (Chilotheridium, Groeberia,
 Nyanzachoerus, Pappotherium)
Pattersonichthys Aulolepidae Goody, P. C. 1969A
 delicatus Goody, P. C. 1969A (restor.)
paucai (Scopeloides)
paucidens (Glyptolepis)
Paucituberculata Mammalia—Marsupiata
 Turnbull, W. D. 1971A (order)
Paulchoffatia Paulchoffatiidae
 delgadoi Hahn, G. 1969A, 1971A
Paulchoffatiidae Multituberculata—Plagiaulacoidea
 Hahn, G. 1969A
 Bolodon, Kuehneodon, Paulchoffatia,
 Plioprion
Paulchoffatiinae Paulchoffatiidae Hahn, G. 1971A
 (incl. Paulchoffatia)
paulhiacensis (Heteroxerus)
pauloensis (Aequidens)
pavimentatum (Labrodon)
pavimentum (Labrodon)
pavlodarica (Crocidura)
pawneensis (Pancelosaurus)
peabodyi (Rhynchosauroides, Wellesaurus)
Pecoripeda Artiodactypedidae—Pecoripedinae
 amalphea Panin, N. 1964A, 1965A
 gazella Panin, N. 1964A, 1965A
pectinata (Mobula)
Pectinator Ctenodactylidae
 sivalensis see Sayimys
pectinoides (Lagodon)
pedemontanus (Porichthys)
Pedeticosauridae Crocodylomorpha—Paracrocodylia
 Walker, A. D. 1970A (incl. Hesperosuchus,
 Pedeticosaurus, Platyognathus,
 Saltoposuchus, Sphenosuchus)
Pedeticosaurus Sphenosuchidae Walker, A. D.
 1970A (in Pedeticosauridae)
Pediomyidae Marsupialia
 Aquiladelphis
 See also Didelphidae
Pediomys Didelphidae Lillegraven, J. A. 1972B
 (in Pediomyidae)
 clemensi Sahni, A. 1972A
 elegans Lillegraven, J. A. 1969B
 exiguus Fox, R. C. 1971B (in Pediomyidae)
 hatcheri Lillegraven, J. A. 1969B
 krejcii Lillegraven, J. A. 1969B
pedionomus (Pseudaelurus)
Pedomys Microtus
pedorhychus (Ellobius fuscocapillus)
Peisorex Soricidae
 pohaiensis Gureev, A. A. 1971A
Pekania Martes
pekinensis (Homo)
Pelagosaurus Teleosauridae
 typus Walker, A. D. 1972A
Pelanomodon Dicynodontidae Keyser, A. W. 1972A
 See also Rhachicephalus
Pelargorhynchus Dercetidae
 dercetiformis Goody, P. C. 1969B

Pelaspis Gabreyaspididae Noviťskaiá, L. I. 1971B
 teres Noviťskaiá, L. I. 1971B
Pelecanidae Pelecaniformes
 Protopelicanus
Pelecaniformes Aves
Pelecyphorus see Timanosteus
Pellegrinia Ctenodactylidae
 panormensis Thaler, L. 1972A
Pelobates Pelobatidae Vergnaud-Grazzini, C. 1970A
 cultripes Estes, R. 1970B
 fuscus Estes, R. 1970B; Iskakova, K. I. 1969A (cf.)
 syriacus Estes, R. 1970B
Pelobatidae Anura—Neobatrachia Sahni, A. 1972A;
 Špinar, Z. V., Boubelik, M.,
 Romanovský, A. 1971A
 Eopelobates, Macropelobates, Miopelobates,
 Pelobates, Scaphiopus
Pelobatinopsis see Palaeobatrachus
pelodes (Protodichobune)
Pelodytidae Anura—Neobatrachia
 Propelodytes
Pelomedusidae Chelonia—Pleurodira
 Bothremys, Carteremys, Eusarkia, Pelusios,
 Podocnemis, Shweboemys, Stereogenys,
 Taphrosphys
Pelomys Muridae
 europeus Bruijn, H., Dawson, M. R., Mein, P.
 1970A
Pelorocephalus Brachyopidae
 mendozensis Bonaparte, J. F. 1972A
 (in Chigutisauridae); Welles, S. P., Estes, R.
 1969A (in Stereospondyli incertae sedis)
Pelosaurus see Sclerocephalus
Peltosaurus Anguidae Macdonald, J. R. 1970A(?)
 abbottii Meszoely, C. A. M. 1970A
 granulosus Meszoely, C. A. M. 1970A
 piger Sahni, A. 1972A
Pelurgaspis Amphiaspididae
 macrorhyncha Noviťskaiá, L. I. 1971B
 (in Eglonaspididae)
Pelusios Pelomedusidae
 sinatus Broin, F. 1969A,B
pelvidens (Chriacus)
Pelycodus Adapidae Ginsburg, L., Lapierre, F.,
 Montenat, C. 1967A
Pelycosauria Reptilia—Synapsida
 Incl. subord. Ophiacodontia, Sphenacodontoidea,
 Edaphosauria
penai (Opsolagus)
penalvai (Microdon)
penelope (Anas)
Peneteius Teiidae Estes, R. 1969A
 aquilonius Estes, R. 1969A
penicillata (Bettongia)
peninsulae (Cephalaspis)
pennanti (Martes)
pennsylvanicus (Microtus)
Pentacodontidae Insectivora—Leptictoidea
 Aphronorus
pentadactyla (Notalacerta)
Pentaglis Gliridae
 meini Bruijn, H. 1967A
pentelici (Ctenocerus, Gomphotherium, Martes)
pentelicum (Ancylotherium)
Peraceras Rhinocerotidae Tanner, L. G. 1970A
Peramelidae Marsupialia—Peramelida Marshall, L. G.
 1972A

Peramelina   Mammalia–Marsupiata Turnbull, W. D.
   1971A (order)
Peramus   Amphitheriidae Crompton, A. W. 1971A;
   Turnbull, W. D. 1971A (in Eutheria–
   Tribosphena)
   tenuirostris Clemens, W. A., Mills, J. R. E.
   1971A (in Peramuridae)
Peratherium   Didelphidae Dehm, R. 1970A;
   Sudre, J. 1969B; Tobien, H. 1971A
   antiquum Crochet, J.-Y. 1969A; Koenigswald, W.
   1970B
   arvernense Koenigswald, W.   1970B
   blainvillei Koenigswald, W.   1970B
   chesteri Guthrie, D. A. 1971B (cf.)
   comstocki Guthrie, D. A. 1971B
   constans Quinet, G. E. 1969B
   cuvieri Crochet, J.-Y. 1969A
   frequens Crochet, J.-Y. 1969A; Koenigswald, W.
   1970B
      erkertshofense Koenigswald, W.   1970B
      frequens Koenigswald, W.   1970B
      gaimersheimense Koenigswald, W.   1970B
      wintershofense Koenigswald, W.   1970B
   gracile Koenigswald, W.   1970A
   laurillardi Crochet, J.-Y. 1969A
   marsupium McGrew, P. O., Sullivan, R. 1970A (cf.)
   spindleri Macdonald, J. R. 1970A
   valens Russell, L. S. 1972B
Perca   Percidae Brzobohatý, R. 1969A (?, otol.);
   Sychevskaĩa, E. K., Lebedev, V. D. 1971A
   alsheimensis Anďelković, J. 1970A
   fluviatilis Lebedev, V. D., Fedotov, V. F. 1969A
   uraschista Anďelković, J. 1970A
   See also Bilinia
Perchoerus   Tayassuidae
   decedens Macdonald, J. R. 1970A [Chaenohyus]
Percichthys   Serranidae
   antiquus Moncharmont Zei, M. 1970A
Percidae   Perciformes–Percoidei
   Acerina, Lucioperca, Perca, Percidarum
   See also Otolithus
Percidarum   Percidae see Otolithus
Perciformes   Teleostei
   Incl. subord. Percoidei, Mugiloidei, Labroidei,
      Trachinoidei, Notothenioidei, Blennioidei,
      Icosteoidei, Schindleroidei,
      Ammodytoidei, Callionymoidei, Gobioidei,
      Kurtoidei, Acanthuroidei, Scombroidei,
      Stromateoidei, Anabantoidei, Luciocephaloidei,
      Mastacembeloidei Svichenskaĩa, A. A. 1968A
Percomorpha   Acanthopterygii Rosen, D. E.,
   Patterson, C. 1969A (Series, incl. ord.
   Lampridiformes, Beryciformes, Perciformes
   and related groups)
Percopsidae see Aphredoderidae
Percrocuta   Hyaenidae
   tobieni Crusafont-Pairó, M., Aguirre, E. 1971B
percussor (Temnocyon)
perdix (Perdix)
Perdix   Phasianidae
   perdix Boecker, M., et al. 1972A; Jánossy, D.
   1972A (aff.)
peregrinus (Pseudocheirus)
peregusna (Vormela)
Pericentrophorus   Semionotidae Jörg, E. 1969A
   minimus Gall, J.-C. 1971A (aff.); Jörg, E.
   1969A, 1970A

Perichthyidae see Serranidae
Peridiomys   Heteromyidae
   borealis Storer, J. E. 1970A
Peridyromys   Gliridae Daxner-Höck, G. 1970A
   compositus Bachmayer, F., Wilson, R. W. 1970A
   hamadryas Telles Antunes, M., Mein, P. 1971A (cf.)
   murinus Bruijn, H. 1967A; Hugueney, M. 1968A,
   1969A
   occitanus Telles Antunes, M., Mein, P. 1971A
periprion (Sagenodus)
Perispheniscus see Palaeospheniscus
Perissodactyla   Mammalia
   Incl. superfam. Equoidea, Brontotherioidea,
      Chalicotherioidea, Tapiroidea,
      Rhinocerotoidea Radinsky, L. B. 1969A
      (evol.)
Perissognathus see Dinichthys
Peristedion   Triglidae
   acutum Gaemers, P. A. M. 1969A (otol.), 1971A
   (otol.)
Perleididae   Palaeonisciformes–Perleidoidei
   Colobodus, Dollopterus, Perleidus
Perleidus   Perleididae Beltan, L. 1968A
   permianum (Broomichnium)
   permicum (Prochirotherium)
   permira (Kushlukia)
Permocynodon   Procynosuchidae
   sushkini see Dvinia prima
Permotrituridae   Urodela–Palaeourodela Tatarinov,
   L. P. 1968B
   Permotriturus
Permotriturus   Permotrituridae Tatarinov, L. P. 1968B
   herrei Tatarinov, L. P. 1968B
Pernis   Accipitridae
   apivorus Ganĩa, I. M. 1969A; Jánossy, D. 1972A (cf.)
Perognathoides   Heteromyidae
   eurekensis Lindsay, E. H. 1972B
   halli Lindsay, E. H. 1972B
   kleinfelderi Storer, J. E. 1970A
Perognathus   Heteromyidae Akersten, W. A. 1972A;
   Forsten, A. 1970B
   cuyamensis Klingener, D. 1968A (cf.)
   furlongi Lindsay, E. H. 1972B
   hispidus Dalquest, W. W. 1967A; Schultz, G. E.
   1969A
   huastecensis Dalquest, W. W., Roth, E. 1970A
   magnus Zakrzewski, R. J. 1969A
   maldei Zakrzewski, R. J. 1969A
   minutus Lindsay, E. H. 1972B
   saskatchewanensis Storer, J. E. 1970A
Peromyscus   Cricetidae Hibbard, C. W. 1968A; King,
   J. A. (ed.) 1968A
   boylii Martin, L. D. 1968C (cf.)
   critinus Miller, W. E. 1971A (cf.)
   eremicus Martin, R. A. 1968C (cf.)
   floridanus Pinkham, C. F. A. 1971A
   gossypinus Martin, L. D. 1968C; Pinkham, C. F. A.
   1971A
   hagermanensis Zakrzewski, R. J. 1969A
   imperfectus see P. maniculatus
   kansasensis Hibbard, C. W. 1972A (cf., in Muridae–
   Cricetinae)
   leucopus Martin, R. A. 1968C
   maldonadoi Alvarez, T. 1969A
   maniculatus Martin, R. A. 1968C; [P. imperfectus]
   Miller, W. E. 1971A
   polionotus Pinkham, C. F. A. 1971A

Phenacolemur - cont.
  fremontensis *Gazin, C. L.* 1971A
    (in Paromomyidae)
  frugivorus Gazin, C. L. 1971A (cf., in
    Paromomyidae)
  jepseni Guthrie, D. A. 1971B
    (in Paromomyidae); Szalay, F. S. 1972B;
    Wilson, R. W., Szalay, F. S. 1972A
Phenacolemuridae [Paromomyidae] Primates—
    Plesiadapoidea Szalay, F. S. 1969C,
    1972C [Paromomyidae]
  Palaechthon, Palenochtha, Paromomys,
    Phenacolemur, Plesiolestes,
    Purgatorius, Torrejonia
Phenacomys Cricetidae
  intermedius Guilday, J. E., Parmalee, P. W.
    1972A
philippi (Pseudocricetodon)
philippovae (Liliaspis)
philisi (Cervus)
phillipsi (Rallus)
philoi (Palaeolagus)
Philomachus Scolopacidae
  pugnax Jánossy, D. 1972A (aff.)
    [Philomachos, aff.]
philomelos (Turdus)
philotau (Ekgmowechashala)
phiomense (Apidium)
Phiomia Gomphotheriidae
  wintoni Tobien, H. 1971C [Palaeomastodon,
    subgen. Phiomia]
Phlebolepilepididae Coelolepida [Thelodonti]—
    Phlebolepida
  Trimerolepis
Phlebolepis Thelodontidae
  elegans Ritchie, A. 1968B; Stensiö, E. 1968A
Phlegethontia Phlegethontiidae Berman, D. S.
    1970A(?)
Phlegethontiidae Aistopoda
  Phlegethontia
phlegon (Nannipus)
Phlyctaenaspidae Arthrodira—Arctolepida
  Actinolepis, Aethaspis, Aggeraspis, Ailuracantha,
    Anarthraspis, ? Antarctolepis, Arctaspis,
    Arctolepis, Bryantolepis, Diadsomaspis,
    Elegantaspis, Heightingtonaspis,
    Heterogaspis, Huginaspis, Kujdanowiaspis,
    Mediaspis, ? Murmur, Overtonaspis,
    Phlyctaenaspis, Prescottaspis, Prosphymaspis,
    ? Qataraspis, Simblaspis, Stuerzaspis,
    Svalbardaspis, Tiaraspis, Wheathillaspis
Phlyctaenaspis Phlyctaenaspidae Stensiö, E. 1969B,
    1971A (in Spinothoracidi—Dolichothoraci)
  acadica Pageau, Y. 1969B (in Dolichothoraci)
  atholi *Pageau, Y.* 1969B (in Dolichothoraci)
Phoca Phocidae
  hispida Harington, C. R., Sergeant, D. E. 1972A
    (subgen. Pusa)
Phocaena see Phocoena
Phocaenidae see Phocoenidae
Phocarctus (Phocarctos) see Otaria
Phocidae Carnivora—Pinnipedia
  Halichoerus, Mirounga, Phoca, Prionodelphis
  See also Monachinae
Phocoena Phocoenidae
  euxinica Macarovici, N., Zaharia, N. 1968B
    [Phocaena]

Phocoenidae [Phocaenidae] Cetacea—Odontoceti
    Barnes, L. G. 1971B
  Phocoena
Phocosaurus Tapinocephalidae Boonstra, L. D. 1969A
Phodilidae Strigiformes
  Paratyto
Phoenicopteridae Ardeiformes Harrison, C. J. O.
    1971A
  Elornis, Phoenicopterus, Plectropterus
Phoenicopterus Phoenicopteridae Harrison, C. J. O.
    1971A
  antiquorum Churcher, C. S. 1972C
Pholidophoridae Pholidophoriformes
  Pholidophorus
Pholidophoriformes Holostei Schaeffer, B. 1971C
Pholidophorus Pholidophoridae
  graciosus Ĩakovlev, V. N. 1968A [Baleiichthys]
Pholidopleuridae Palaeonisciformes—Pholidopleuroidei
  Australosomus
Pholidosauridae Crocodilia—Mesosuchia
  Teleorhinus
Pholidosteidae Arthrodira—Brachythoraci Stensiö, E.
    1969B, 1971A (in Spinothoracidi—
    Coccosteomorphi)
  Malerosteus, Pholidosteus, Tapinosteus
Pholidosteus Pholidosteidae Stensiö, E. 1969B, 1971A
Pholidota Mammalia
pholidotus (Thursius)
Phoxinus Cyprinidae Brzobohatý, R. 1969A(?);
    Sychevskaĩa, E. K., Lebedev, V. D. 1971A
Phrynosoma Iguanidae
  cornutum Holman, J. A. 1972A
Phrynosuchus Brachyopidae
  waitsi Welles, S. P., Estes, R. 1969A
    (in Stereospondyli incertae sedis)
Phthinosuchidae see Biarmosuchidae, Eotitanosuchidae
Phylactocephalus Enchodontidae
  microlepis [Halec] Goody, P. C. 1969B (in Halecidae,
    restor.)
Phyllodactylus Gekkonidae Estes, R. 1969J (cf.)
Phyllodontidae Elopiformes—Albuloidei Estes, R.
    1969G (incl. Phyllodontinae, Paralbulinae)
  See also Labridae, Albulidae
Phyllodus Labridae
  centralis *Casier, E.* 1967B (in Phyllodontidae)
  toliapicus Casier, E. 1967B (?, in Phyllodontidae);
    Estes, R. 1969G (in Phyllodontidae—
    Phyllodontinae)
Phyllolepida Placodermi Stensiö, E. 1969B, 1971B
    (in Spinothoracidi)
Phyllolepidae Phyllolepida
  Phyllolepis
Phyllolepis Phyllolepidae Stensiö, E. 1969B
    (in Phyllolepida)
Phyllostomatidae Chiroptera
  Mormoops
Phyllotillon Chalicotheriidae
  fraasi Nikolov, I. 1972A [Metaschizotherium]
  naricus Telles Antunes, M. 1966E
Physeteridae Cetacea—Odontoceti
  Scaldicetus
Physichthys see Macropetalichthys
Physodon Carcharhinidae Telles Antunes, M.,
    Jonet, S. 1970A
  fischeuri Cappetta, H. C. 1969B, 1970A
  secundus Casier, E. 1967B
Physodon Cetacea see Scaldicetus

Physonemus Edestidae Nassichuk, W. W. 1971A
striatus Murphy, J. L. 1971B (cf.)
Phytosauridae Thecodontia—Phytosauria
Westphal, F. 1970B
Angistorhinus, Mystriosuchus, Palaeorhinus,
Phytosaurus, Rutiodon
Phytosaurus Phytosauridae Gregory, J. T. 1969B
[Nicrosaurus]
kapffi Gregory, J. T., Westphal, F. 1969A
[Nicrosaurus]
Pica Corvidae
pica Ballmann, P., Adrover, R. 1970A;
Tate, J., Martin, L. D. 1968A
major *Jánossy, D.* 1972A (nov. subsp.)
pica (Pica)
picapicensis (Fulica)
Piceoerpeton Cryptobranchidae Estes, R. 1969F
(in Scapherpetontidae)
Picidae Piciformes
Campephilus, Dendrocopos, Picus
Piciformes Aves
Picrodontidae Insectivora—Dermoptera inc. sedis
Szalay, F. S. 1968B, 1969C, 1972C
(in Primates—Picrodontoidea)
Picrodus, Zanycteris
Picrodontoidea Primates *Szalay, F. S.* 1968B
(n. subord.)
Picrodus Picrodontidae
silberlingi Szalay, F. S. 1968B
picta (Chrysemys)
picteti (Haplomeryx, Maurimontia)
Picus Picidae
canus Jánossy, D. 1972A (cf.)
pidoplichkoi (Anourosoricodon)
pidoplickai (Geoemyda)
pieckoensis (Mayomyzon)
Piezodus Ochotonidae
branssatensis Tobien, H. 1970C
piger (Pancelosaurus, Peltosaurus)
pilaris (Turdus)
pilgrimi (Geoemyda, Rhizomyoides, Shweboemys)
pilosus (Sordes)
Pimephales Cyprinidae
promelas Smith, G. R., Lundberg, J. G. 1972A (cf.)
Pinacosaurus Nodosauridae Kielan-Jaworowska, Z.,
Kowalski, K. 1965A
grangeri [P. ninghsiensis, Syrmosaurus viminicaudus]
Maryańska, T. 1971A
ninghsiensis see P. grangeri
pinarhisarensis (Alosa)
pinckneyi (Neochoerus)
pinensis (Hesperhys, Promerycochoerus montanus)
pineoi (Megapezia)
pineridgensis (Palaeoscalopus)
pinjoricus (Rhizomyoides)
pinjorii (Procynocephalus)
Pinnipedia Carnivora Bartholomew, G. A. 1970A;
Erdbrink, D. P. 1972B [pinniped skull
and jaw]
pintoensis (Jaywilsonomys)
Pipidae Anura
Cordicephalus, Thoraciliacus
pipiens (Rana)
Pipistrellus Vespertilionidae
lasiopterus Jullien, R., Pillard, B. 1969B
[Nyctalus]
pirabensis (Sirenotherium)

Pisanosauridae Ornithischia—Ornithopoda
Pisanosaurus
See also Hypsilophodontidae
Pisanosaurus Pisanosauridae
mertii Bonaparte, J. F. 1972A
pisanus (Hoplostethus, Rhynchosauroides)
Pithecanthropus see Homo
Pitymys Cricetidae Altuna, J. 1970A; Jánossy, D.
1969B (in Arvicolidae)
arvalidens [P. arvaloides] Koenigswald, W. 1970A,
1972A
arvaloides Bartolomei, G., Pasa, A. 1970A
See also P. arvalidens
gregaloides Fejfar, O. 1969A
hintoni Fejfar, O. 1969A
melitensis Malec, F., Storch, G. 1970A
Pitymys Microtus
piveteaui (Ardea, Barbourofelis, Boreosomus,
Crocidosorex, Mustelictis, Saurichthys)
Piveteaunotus Parasemionotidae *Beltan, L.* 1968A
ifasiensis *Beltan, L.* 1968A
placidus (Calippus)
Placochelyanus Placochelyidae *Kuhn, O.* 1969D
malanchinii Kuhn, O. 1969D
Placochelyidae Placodontia
Placochelyanus, Psephosaurus
Placodermi Robertson, G. M. 1970A,B; Stensiö, E.
1969A,B [Placodermata, in
Elasmobranchiomorphi, incl. Holocephali,
Arthrodira]
Incertae sedis: Palaeospondylus
Placodontia Reptilia—Euryapsida Kuhn, O. 1969D
Placodontidae Placodontia
Placodus
Placodus Placodontidae Westphal, F., Westphal, I.
1967A
Plagiaulacidae Multituberculata—Plagiaulacoidea
Ctenacodon, Loxaulax, Plagiaulax, Psalodon
See also Paulchoffatiidae
Plagiaulacoidea Multituberculata, Hahn, G. 1969A
(sens. nov.)
Incertae sedis: Guimarotodon
Plagiaulax Plagiaulacidae
becklesii Hahn, G. 1969A, 1971A
dawsoni Hahn, G. 1969A(?), 1971A(?)
See also Bolodon
Plagiolophus Palaeotheriidae
cartailhaci Hooker, J. J. 1972A
fraasi Bergounioux, F. M., Crouzel, F. 1968B;
Brunet, M. 1970A
minor Bessonnat, G., Dughi, R., Sirugue, F. 1969A
(ichn.); Jehenne, Y. 1969A
Plagiorophus Brachyopidae
paraboliceps Welles, S. P., Estes, R. 1969A
(in Stereospondyli incertae sedis)
Plagiosauridae Temnospondyli—Plagiosauria
Lipatova, V. V., et al. 1972A
(nr. Plagiosuchus or Plagiosternum)
plainvillensis (Batrachichnus)
plana (Siberiaspis)
planatus (Gadus)
plancus (Deuterotetrapous)
planicanina (Archaeolambda)
planiceps (Broomisaurus, Rhinocephalus)
planifrons (Elephas, Entoptychus)
planimenta (Glossochelys)

Planiplastron   Testudinidae *Chkhikvadze, V. M.*
        1971C,E (in Platysternidae)
    tatarinovi *Chkhikvadze, V. M.* 1971C,E
planirostris (Mystriosuchus)
Planisorex   Soricidae *Hibbard, C. W.* 1972A
    dixonensis [Sorex] Hibbard, C. W. 1972A
planus (Eucastor)
Plastomenidae see Trionychidae
Plastomenus   Trionychidae
    mlynarskii *Chkhikvadze, V. M.* 1970B
        (in Plastomenidae)
Platacidae see Ephippidae
Platalea   Plataleidae
    leucorodia Churcher, C. S. 1972C
Plataleidae [Threskiornithidae] Ardeiformes
    Eudocimus, Platalea, Proplegadis
Platecarpus   Mosasauridae Russell, D. A. 1970B
    coryphaeus Thurmond, J. T. 1969B
    curtirostris Thurmond, J. T. 1969B (cf.)
    ptychodon Taverne, L. 1970A
    somenensis Thurmond, J. T. 1969B (cf.)
Platelephas
    platycephalus see Elephas hysudricus
platensis (Toxodon)
Plateosauria see Prosauropoda
Plateosauridae   Saurischia–Sauropodomorpha
    ?Herrerasaurus, Plateosaurus
    See also Palaeosauriscidae
Plateosaurus   Plateosauridae Bonaparte, J. F. 1972A;
        Lapparent, A. F. 1967A (reconstr.)
    polignensis Théobald, N., et al. s.d. (cf.)
Platinx   Chirocentridae
    cognitus *Danil'chenko, P. G.* 1968B
plattensis (Paracygnus)
Platybelodon   Gomphotheriidae Maglio, V. J. 1969A
    beliajevae *Alekseeva, L. I.* 1971A
Platycephalichthys   Rhizodontidae Schultze, H.-P.
        1969B
Platycephalidae   Scorpaeniformes–Platycephaloidei
    Platycephalus
Platycephalus   Platycephalidae
    aculeatus *Stinton, F. C., Nolf, D.* 1969A (otol.)
    indicus Aoki, N. 1968A (cf., otol.)
platyceps (Chanaria, Limnenetes, Mastodonsaurus)
Platychaerops   Plesiadapidae Gingerich, P. D. 1972A
Platydyptes   Spheniscidae
    amiesi Simpson, G. G. 1971C
    marplesi *Simpson, G. G.* 1971C(?)
    novaezealandiae Simpson, G. G. 1971C
platygnathus (Dinodontosaurus)
Platygonus   Tayassuidae Hibbard, C. W. 1972A;
        Shotwell, J. A. 1970A
    bicalcaratus Akersten, W. A. 1972A
    compressus Davis, L. C. 1969A; Guilday, J. E.,
        Hamilton, H. W., McCrady, A. D. 1971A;
        Lewis, G. E. 1970A; Ray, C. E., Denny,
        C. S., Rubin, M. 1970A; Schultz, G. E.
        1969A (cf.)
    alemanii Thenius, E. 1970C (cf.)
platyodus (Hipparion)
Platyognathus   Sphenosuchidae Walker, A. D. 1970A
        (in Pedeticosauridae)
Platyops   Archegosauridae Schultze, H.-P. 1969B
platyops (Potorous)
Platyosteus see Oxyosteus
platypternus (Xenacanthus)

Platypterygius   Stenopterygiidae McGowan, C. 1972B
platyrhina (Rubidgea)
platyrhinos (Heterodon)
platyrhynchos (Anas)
platyrhynchus (Palaeoloxodon antiquus)
Platyrrhini   Primates Hershkovitz, P. 1970B
Platysomidae   Palaeonisciformes–Platysomoidei
    Dorsolepis, Soetendalichthys
Platysternidae see Testudinidae
Plecotus   Vespertilionidae
    auritus Norberg, V. M. 1970A
        sacrimontis Koenigswald, W. 1972A (cf.)
    crassidens Malez, M. 1967C
Plectropoma
    uraschista see Bilinia
Plectropterus   Phoenicopteridae
    gambensis Churcher, C. S. 1972C
plenus (Allospalax)
Plesiadapidae   Primates–Plesiadapoidea Szalay, F. S.
        1969C, 1972C
    Platychaerops, Plesiadapis, Pronothodectes
Plesiadapis   Plesiadapidae Gazin, C. L. 1971A;
        Gingerich, P. D. 1971A (reconstr.)
    cookei Gingerich, P. D. 1972A
    tricuspidens Szalay, F. S. 1971A; Wilson, R. W.,
        Szalay, F. S. 1972A
Plesiarctomys   Paramyidae
    gervaisii Wood, A. E. 1970B
    hartenbergeri *Wood, A. E.* 1970B
    hurzeleri *Wood, A. E.* 1970B
    spectabilis Wood, A. E. 1970B
Plesictis   Procyonidae Macdonald, J. R. 1970A
        (in Mustelidae)
    lemanensis Beaumont, G. 1968D
Plesiobaena   Baenidae–Eubaeninae *Gaffney, E. S.*
        1972A
    antiqua [Baena] Gaffney, E. S. 1972A
    putorius *Gaffney, E. S.* 1972A
Plesiocathartes   Vulturidae
    europaeus Cracraft, J., Rich, P. V. 1972A
        (in Cathartidae)
Plesiodimylus   Dimylidae
    chantrei Engesser, B. 1972A
Plesiogale   Mustelidae
    angustidens Beaumont, G. 1968C
    angustifrons Beaumont, G. 1968C
    lemanensis Beaumont, G. 1968C
    robusta Beaumont, G. 1968C
Plesiogulo   Mustelidae
    brachygnathus Kurtén, B. 1970A
    crassa Kurtén, B. 1970A
    major Kurtén, B. 1970A
    marshalli Dalquest, W. W. 1969A
    minor Kurtén, B. 1970A
    montpessulanus Kurtén, B. 1970A
    praecocidens *Kurtén, B.* 1970A
Plesiolestes   Phenacolemuridae Szalay, F. S. 1969C
        (in Paromomyidae)
    problematicus Gazin, C. L. 1971A (cf., in
        Paromomyidae)
Plesiosauridae   Sauropterygia–Plesiosauria
    Microcleidus, Plesiosaurus
Plesiosaurus   Plesiosauridae Müller, H. 1960A;
        Sigov, A. P. 1969A; Wellnhofer, P. 1970B
    mauritanicus Taverne, L. 1970A

Plesiosminthus   Zapodidae Green, M. 1971A
    quartus *Shevyreva, N. S.* 1970A (subgen.
        Parasminthus)
    sabrae Sutton, J. F. 1972B (subgen.
        Schaubeumys)
    schaubi Hugueney, M. 1969A
Plesiosorex   Plesiosoricidae
    schaffneri *Engesser, B.* 1972A
        (in Metacodontidae)
Plesiosoricidae   Insectivora–Lipotyphla
    Plesiosorex, Saturninia
Plesippus   Equus
Plesispermophilus   Paramyidae
    angustidens Vianey-Liaud, M. 1969A
Plethodoidea   Elopiformes–Elopoidei *Applegate, S. P.*
        1970A (n. superfam., incl. Bananogmiidae,
        Plethodidae)
Plethodontidae   Urodela Brame, A. H., Murray, K. F.
        1968A
    Opisthotriton, Prodesmodon
Pleuracanthodii [Ichthyotomi] Chondrichthyes–
        Elasmobranchii
    Incertae sedis: Expleuracanthus
Pleuracanthus see Expleuracanthus
Pleuristion   Captorhinidae
    brachycoelous Olson, E. C. 1970A
Pleurocyon see Simidectes
Pleurolicus   Geomyidae
    clasoni see Sanctimus
    dakotensis Macdonald, J. R. 1970A
    leptophrys Macdonald, J. R. 1970A; McKenna, M. C.,
        Love, J. D. 1972A (cf.)
Pleuronectiformes   Teleostei
    Incl. subord. Psettodoidei, Pleuronectoidei
    Incertae sedis: Numidiopleura
pleuronectiformis (Pasaichthys)
Pleurosauridae   Rhynchocephalia Hughes, B. 1968A
Pleurosternidae   Chelonia–Amphichelydia
    Glyptops, Naomichelys
plicatile (Hipparion)
plicatulus (Glyptops)
plicatus (Nyanzachoerus)
pliciferus (Tetraclaenodon)
plieningeri (Chelonipus, Mystriosuchus)
Plinthicus see Aetobatus
Pliobatrachus see Bufo
pliocaenicus (Allophaiomys, Mimomys, Muscardinus)
pliocenica (Pliopetaurista)
pliocenicus (Blicca)
Plioceros   Sphenophalos
Pliocervini   Cervidae *Czyżewska, T.* 1968A (n. tribe
        for Pliocervinae; incl. Cervavitus, Pliocervus)
Pliocervus see Ctenocerus
Pliogeomys   Geomyidae
    parvus *Zakrzewski, R. J.* 1969A
Pliogulo see Cynogulo
Pliohippus [Astrohippus] Equidae Isphording, W. C.,
        Lamb, G. M. 1970A; Mount, J. D. 1970A;
        Waldrop, J. 1969A
    martini Webb, S. D. 1969C [Astrohippus, cf.]
    spectans Shotwell, J. A. 1970A
    supremus Webb, S. D. 1969C
    See also Astrohippus
Pliohyrax   Hyracidae
    graecus Melentis, J. K. 1966L, 1970A
        (in Procaviidae)

Pliolemmus   Cricetidae
    antiquus Hibbard, C. W. 1972A (in Muridae–
        Arvicolinae)
Pliometanastes   Megalonychidae Moore, W. 1972A
Pliomys   Cricetidae
    deeringensis *Guthrie, R. D., Matthews, J. V.* 1971A
    posterior *Jánossy, D.* 1969B (in Arvicolidae)
    See also Dolomys
Plionarctos   Ursus
Plionictis   Mustelidae
    ogygia Webb, S. D. 1969C [Martes, subgen.
        Plionictis]
    See also Martes
Pliopetaurista   Sciuridae *Kretzoi, M.* 1962D
    bressana *Mein, P.* 1970A
    dehneli [Pliosciuropterus] Mein, P. 1970A
    pliocenica [Sciuropterus] Kretzoi, M. 1962D;
        Mein, P. 1970A
Pliopetes   Sciuridae
    hungaricus Daxner-Höck, G. 1970A (cf.);
        Kretzoi, M. 1962D
Pliophenacomys   Cricetidae
    finneyi *Hibbard, C. W., Zakrzewski, R. J.* 1972A
    osborni *Martin, L. D.* 1972A
    primaevus Hibbard, C. W. 1972A (in Muridae–
        Arvicolinae)
Pliopithecus   Pongidae Morbeck, M. E. 1972A;
        Morbeck, M. E. 1972A [Limnopithecus];
        Simons, E. L., Pilbeam, D. R. 1972A;
        Simons, E. L., Pilbeam, D. R. 1972A
        [Limnopithecus]
Plioplatecarpus   Mosasauridae Quinet, G. E. 1968A,
        1970B
Pliopotamys   Cricetidae–Arvicolinae
    idahoensis Shotwell, J. A. 1970A
    meadensis Hibbard, C. W. 1972A (in Muridae–
        Arvicolinae); Martin, L. D. 1972A
    minor Zakrzewski, R. J. 1969A
Plioprion   Paulchoffatiidae
    minor Hahn, G. 1969A, 1971A
Pliopygerethmus   Dipodidae–Alactaginae *Topachevs'kyĭ,*
        V. O., Skoryk, O. F. 1971A
    brachydens *Topachevs'kyĭ, V. O., Skoryk, O. F.*
        1971A
Pliosauridae   Sauropterygia–Plesiosauria
    Liopleurodon, Pliosaurus
Pliosaurus   Pliosauridae Brunet, M. 1969A
    rossicus see Liopleurodon
Pliosciuropterus   Sciuridae Bachmayer, F., Wilson,
        R. W. 1970A; Daxner-Höck, G. 1970A
    dehneli see Pliopetaurista
Pliospalax   Spalacidae Kretzoi, M. 1970-71A
Pliotaxidea   Mustelidae
    nevadensis Dalquest, W. W. 1969A (cf.)
Plioviverrops   ? Viverridae
    guerini Crusafont Pairó, M., Petter, G. 1969A(?)
    orbignyi Beaumont, G. 1969B, 1970A
        (in Viverridae or Hyaenidae)
Ploceidae   Passeriformes–Passeres
    Carduelis, Coccothraustes, Loxia, Montifringilla,
        Pyrrhula
plocodus (Hipparion)
Plotopteridae   Pelecaniformes *Howard, H.* 1969A
    Plotopterum
Plotopterinae   Phalacrocoracidae Brodkorb, P. 1971A
    (n. rank for Plotopteridae)

Plotopterum Plotopteridae Howard, H. 1969A
 joaquinensis Howard, H. 1969A
Plourdosteus Coccosteidae Stensiö, E. 1969A,B
 livonicus Obrucheva, P. O. 1962C
 mironovi [Coccosteus] Obrucheva, P. O. 1962C
 panderi Obrucheva, O. P. 1962C(?)
 timanicus Obrucheva, O. P. 1962C
 trautscholdi Obrucheva, O. P. 1962C
poaphagus (Ogmodontomys, Ogmodontomys
      poaphagus)
Podicipedidae Podicipediformes
 Podiceps
Podicipediformes Aves
Podiceps Podicipedidae
 auritus Feduccia, J. A., Rich, P. V. 1972A
 griseigena Jánossy, D. 1972A (aff.)
Podocnemis Pelomedusidae
 alabamae see Bothremys barberi
 argentinensis Wood, R. C., Gamero, M. L. D.
      1971A (invalid)
 barberi see Bothremys
 bassleri Wood, R. C., Gamero, M. L. D. 1971A
 brasiliensis Wood, R. C., Gamero, M. L. D.
      1971A (invalid)
 carbajosai Jiménez Fuentes, E. 1971A
 elegans Wood, R. C., Gamero, M. L. D. 1971A
 geologorum Wood, R. C., Gamero, M. L. D.
      1971A (invalid)
 harrisi Wood, R. C., Gamero, M. L. D. 1971A
      (invalid)
 indica Wood, R. C. 1970A (in Pelomedusidae ?
      incertae sedis)
 venezuelensis Wood, R. C., Gamero, M. L. D.
      1971A
Podokesauridae Saurischia–Theropoda Steel, R.
      1970A
 Syntarsus
 See also Procompsognathidae
Podopterygidae Thecodontia–Pseudosuchia
      Sharov, A. G. 1971A
 Podopteryx
Podopteryx Podopterygidae Sharov, A. G. 1971A
 mirabilis Sharov, A. G. 1971A
Poebrotherium Camelidae Eklund, R. R. 1969A
poena (Chelydropsis)
poerthensis (Tetrapodichnus)
Pogonias Sciaenidae Harington, C. R. 1971C(?)
pohaiensis (Peisorex)
poirrieri (Rhizospalax)
polanskii (Pascualgnathus)
polignensis (Plateosaurus)
polionotus (Peromyscus)
polli (Neobythites)
polonica (Kowalskia)
polonicus (Mimomys, Muntiacus)
Polyacrodon Proterotheriidae
 ligatus see Polymorphis lechei
Polyacrodontidae see Hybodontidae
Polyacrodus Hybodontidae
 brabanticus Zhelezko, V. I., Glikman, L. S. 1971A
      (in Polyacrodontidae)
 illingworthi Zhelezko, V. I., Glikman, L. S.
      1971A (in Polyacrodontidae)
polydictios (Pseudoheterodontus)
Polydolopidae Marsupialia–Caenolestoidia
 Epidolops
polygyrus (Ptychodus)

Polymerolepididae Polymerolepidiformes Karatajūte-
      Talimaa, V. N. 1968B
 Polymerolepis
Polymerolepidiformes Heterostraci Karatajūte-Talimaa,
      V. N. 1968B
Polymerolepis Polymerolepididae Karatajūte-Talimaa,
      V. N. 1968B
 whitei Karatajūte-Talimaa, V. N. 1968B; Obruchev,
      D., Karatajūte-Talimaa, V. N. 1967A
polymicrodus (Bananogmius)
Polymixiidae Beryciformes–Polymixioidei
 Berycopsis, Homonotichthys, Omosoma,
      Pycnosterinx
Polymixiiformes [Polymixioidei] Paracanthopterygii–
      Polymixiomorpha Rosen, D. E.,
      Patterson, C. 1969A
Polymixioidei Beryciformes Rosen, D. E.,
      Patterson, C. 1969A [Polymixiiformes]
Polymixiomorpha Paracanthopterygii Rosen, D. E.,
      Patterson, C. 1969A (Series, incl. Ord.
      Polymixiiformes)
Polymorphis Proterotheriidae
 lechei [Polyacrodon ligatus] Rivas, O. E. O. 1969A
polyodon (Aelurosaurus, Allognathosuchus,
      Pristerognathus)
Polysphenodontidae Rhynchocephalia–
      Sphenodontoidea Kuhn, O. 1969D
Pomacentridae Perciformes–Percoidei
 Chromis
Pomatomidae [Scombropsidae] Perciformes–Percoidei
 Neoscombrops
 See also Carangidae
pomeli (Palaeotherium)
Pomolobus Clupeidae Jerzmańska, A. 1968A
 curtus Klebanova, N. I. 1971A
 facilis Ciobanu, M. 1969A; Klebanova, N. I. 1971A
pompeckji (Poraspis)
ponderosus (Pachydyptes)
Pongidae Primates–Catarrhini Brace, C. L., Nelson, H.,
      Korn, N. 1971A; Conroy, G. C., Fleagle,
      J. G. 1972A; Crusafont Pairó, M.,
      Hürzeler, J. 1969A; Petit-Maire-Heintz, N.,
      Dricot, J.-M. 1970A; Pilbeam, D. R. 1968C;
      Skaryd, S. M. 1971A,B (dentition)
 Aegyptopithecus, Aeolopithecus, ? Amphipithecus,
      Dryopithecus, Gigantopithecus,
      Hispanopithecus, Hylobates, Moeripithecus,
      Oligopithecus, Pliopithecus, Pongo,
      Propliopithecus, Sivapithecus, Symphalangus
Pongo Pongidae
 pygmaeus
  palaeosumatrensis Marcus, L. F. 1969A
pongoides (Homo)
pontica (Desmana, Macrocephalochelys)
pontifex (Cottus)
pontoborealis (Cervus)
Pontoceros Bovidae Vereshchagin, N. K., Alekseeva,
      L. I., David, A. I., Baĭgusheva, V. S. 1969A
 ambiguus Vereshchagin, N. K., Alekseeva, L. I.,
      David, A. I., Baĭgusheva, V. S. 1969A
Pontolias see Pontolis
Pontolis Otariidae
 magnus Shotwell, J. A. 1951A [Pontolias]
popoagicum (Lambdotherium)
populator (Smilodon)
Poracanthodes Ischnacanthidae
 porosus Gross, W. 1971A
 punctatus Gross, W. 1971A

Priacanthus   Priacanthidae
    croaticus Andelković, J. S. 1969A
pricei (Apodops, Dinogorgon, Lemurosaurus,
        Milleropsis, Pareiasaurus, Protocynodon,
        Staurikosaurus)
prima (Bothriolepis, Dvinia, Putoranaspis,
        Quadropedia, Squatina)
primaeva (Pteraspis)
primaevus (Amphisorex, Caranx, Megatylopus,
        Mesodma, Palaeosauropus, Palaeotragus,
        Parictis, Phenacodus, Pliophenacomys)
Primates   Mammalia
    Incl. subord. ? Plesiadapoidea, Lemuroidea,
        Tarsioidei, Platyrrhini, Catarrhini Ankel, F.
        1970A, 1972A; Cartmill, M. 1972A
        (origin); Charles-Dominique, P., Martin,
        R. D. 1970A; Chiarelli, B. (ed.) 1968C;
        Clark, W. E. LeGros 1971A, 1972A;
        Gregory, W. K. 1972A (evol.);
        Iurovskaia, V. Z. 1972A; Kretzoi, M.
        1969B,D; Manziĭ, S. F. 1968A (thoracic
        limbs); Noback, C. R., Montagna, W.
        (eds.) 1970A (brain); Piveteau, J. 1969D;
        Radinsky, L. 1972B (brain evol.);
        Sarich, V. M. 1970A; Sarich, V. M.,
        Wilson, A. C. 1967A (albumin evol.);
        Schultz, A. H. 1969A; Sicard, H. 1963A;
        Simons, E. L. 1969C, 1972A; Szalay, F. S.
        1971E (basicranium), 1972C (origin);
        Tattersall, I. 1970A; Tuttle, R. 1972A;
        Van Valen, L. 1969A (incl. subord.
        Prosimiae, Anthropoidea)
        Incertae sedis: Branisella
Primelephas   Elephantidae–Elephantinae
        Maglio, V. J. 1970B
    gomphotheroides Maglio, V. J. 1970B
    korotorensis [Stegodon] Maglio, V. J. 1970B
primigenia (Grus, Hystrix)
primigenium (Hipparion)
primigenius (Aeduella, Archaeolagus, Bos, Cervus
        elaphus, Ellobius, Hexanchus, Mammuthus,
        Simocyon)
primigenius-trogontherii (Mammuthus)
Primisardinella   Clupeidae Danil'chenko, P. G. 1968A
    genetrix Danil'chenko, P. G. 1968A
primitivus (Megalagus, Mesocricetus, Stegomastodon)
Primobucco   Bucconidae Brodkorb, P. 1970A
    mcgrewi Brodkorb, P. 1970A
primus (Agonus, Albertatherium, Blastomeryx,
        Collimys, Dvinosaurus, Leptarctus,
        Mimomys, Paramys anacingularis,
        Paranteosaurus, Peronedon)
Prionailurus   Felidae
    bengalensis
        koenigswaldi Hemmer, H. 1971D
Prionodelphis   Phocidae–Monachinae
    capensis Hendey, Q. B., Repenning, C. A. 1972A
Prionodon   Carcharhinidae
    egertoni Menesini, E. 1969A (in Galeidae)
Prionodon   Carcharhinus
Prionolepididae   Salmoniformes–? Cimolichthyoidei
        Goody, P. C. 1969B (incl. Prionolepis)
    See also Dercetidae
Prionolepis   Dercetidae
    cataphractus Goody, P. C. 1969B
        (in Prionolepididae, restor.)
    laniatus see Apateopholis

prior (Zenaidura)
prisca (Hyaena, Macracara, Seriola, Sphyrna)
priscinaria (Satherium)
Priscocamelus   Camelidae Stevens, M. S., Stevens, J. B.,
        Dawson, M. R. 1969A
    wilsoni Stevens, M. S., Stevens, J. B., Dawson, M. R.
        1969A
priscum (Cetotherium, Dacrytherium, Mixtotherium,
        Palaeotherium duvali, Synaptichnium)
priscus (Bison, Bison priscus, Carcharhinus, Cimexomys,
        Cuon, Cyprinus, Gliravus, Hadrodus,
        Prospalax, Scenopagus, Sus scrofa, Tapirus,
        Telmatornis)
priska (Sardina)
Pristerognathidae   Therapsida–Therocephalia
        Boonstra, L. D. 1969A
    Maraisaurus, Pristerognathus, Ptomalestes
Pristerognathus   Pristerognathidae Ricqlès, A. 1969A(?)
    polyodon Mendrez, C. 1972A
Pristichampsinae   Crocodylidae Kuhn, O. 1968C
        (incl. Pristichampsus, Weigeltisuchus)
Pristichampsus   Crocodylidae Berg, D. E. 1969A;
        Berg, D. E., Crusafont, M. 1970A
Pristidae   Batoidea–Pristoidea
    Ischirhiza, Onchopristis, Onchosaurus, Pristis,
        Schizorhiza, Sclerorhynchus
Pristigenys   Priacanthidae
    macropus Arambourg, C. 1966A (in Serranidae–
        Priacanthinae)
    spinosus Ciobanu, M. 1969A
pristinus (Brachypsalis, Cygnus, Parahippus,
        Rhynchobatus)
Pristiophoridae   Selachii–Squaloidea Telles Antunes, M.,
        Jonet, S. 1970A (in Pristiophoriformes)
Pristiophorus
Pristiophorus   Pristiophoridae
    suevicus Telles Antunes, M., Jonet, S. 1970A
Pristis   Pristidae
    aquitanicus Cappetta, H. C. 1969B, 1970A
    lanceolatus Jonet, S. 1968B
pristodontus (Squalicorax)
pritinus (Eumys)
Proagriocharis   Phasianidae–Meleagrinae Martin, L. D.,
        Tate, J. 1970A (in Meleagrididae)
    kimballensis Martin, L. D., Tate, J. 1970A
Proalactaga   Dipodidae–Allactaginae Savinov, P. F.
        1970A
    varians Savinov, P. F. 1970A
Proamphibos   Bovidae Groves, C. P. 1969A
Proamphiuma   Amphiumidae Estes, R. 1969B
    cretacea Estes, R. 1969B
proarchaicus (Archidiskodon meridionalis)
Probainognathus   Chiniquodontidae Bonaparte, J. F.
        1972A; Ricqlès, A. 1970A; Romer, A. S.
        1969G, 1970A
    jenseni Romer, A. S. 1970A
Probalearica   Gruidae
    moldavica Kurochkin, E. N., Ganiâ, I. M. 1972A
Probelesodon   Chiniquodontidae Romer, A. S. 1969A
    lewisi Bonaparte, J. F. 1972A; Romer, A. S. 1969A
probenoiti (Myctophum)
Probison   Bovidae–Bovinae Sahni, M. R., Khan, E.
        1968B
    dehmi Sahni, M. R., Khan, E. 1968B
Problastomeryx   Blastomeryx
problematicus (Dipoides, Eozostrodon, Megantereon,
        Plesiolestes)

Proheteromys - cont.
  ironcloudi *Macdonald, J. R.* 1970A
  matthewi Macdonald, J. R. 1970A
Prohylobates   Cercopithecidae
  tandyi [?Dryopithecus mogharensis] Simons, E. L.
      1969B
Prohypogeophis   Caeciliidae
  tunariensis Taylor, E. H. 1968A
Prolacertidae   Eosuchia–Prolacertiformes
  Macrocnemus
Prolacertipes   Ichnites *Dollé, P., Lapparent, A. F.,*
      Montenat, C. 1970A
  pruvosti *Dollé, P., Lapparent, A. F.,*
      Montenat, C. 1970A
Prolagurus   Cricetidae–Microtinae Zazhigin, V. S.
      1969B, 1970A
  See also Lagurus
Prolagus   Ochotonidae
  bilobus Berzi, A. 1970A
    See also P. sardus
  meyeri Berzi, A. 1970A
  oeningensis Bachmayer, F., Wilson, R. W. 1970A
      (cf.); Berzi, A. 1970A; Engesser, B. 1972A;
      Fondi, R. 1970A
  sardus Berzi, A. 1970A; Comaschi Caria, I. 1968A;
      Dawson, M. R. 1969A,B,C; [P. bilobus]
      Fondi, R. 1970A; Jaeger, J.-J. 1971A (cf.)
  savagei *Berzi, A.* 1970A
  vasconiensis Baudelot, S. 1969A (cf.); Baudelot, S.,
      Crouzot, F. 1969A (aff.); Berzi, A. 1970A;
      Janvier, Ph. 1971C (cf.); Tobien, H. 1970C
  zitteli Berzi, A. 1970A
Prolates   Serranidae
  dormaalensis *Casier, E.* 1967B(?)
Prolebias   Cyprinodontidae
  goreti Anđelković, J. 1970A
  napfi *Salis, K.* 1967A (otol.)
  weileri *Salis, K.* 1967A (otol.)
Prolicaphrium   Proterotheriidae
  spectabile Friant, M. 1967B
Prolimnocyon see Prototomus
Proluvarus   Luvaridae *Danil'chenko, P. G.* 1968B
  necopinatus *Danil'chenko, P. G.* 1968B
Promacrauchenia   Macraucheniidae
  antiqua Friant, M. 1967B
Promartes   Mustelidae
  gemmarosae Macdonald, J. R. 1970A
  lepidus Macdonald, J. R. 1970A
  olcotti Macdonald, J. R. 1970A
Promastodonsaurus   Capitosauridae
  bellmanni Bonaparte, J. F. 1972A
promelas (Pimephales)
Promerycochoerus   Merycoidodontidae
  barbouri Macdonald, J. R. 1970A
  carrikeri Macdonald, J. R. 1970A
  minor
    pygmyus Macdonald, J. R. 1970A
  montanus
    pinensis Macdonald, J. R. 1970A (subgen.
        Pseudopromerycochoerus)
prometheus (Australopithecus)
Promimomys   Cricetidae
  cor Kretzoi, M. 1962D
  insuliferus Michaux, J. 1971B
Promioclaenus   Hyopsodontidae
  acolytus Gazin, C. L. 1969A (cf.)
  lemuroides Gazin, C. L. 1969A (cf.)

Promylagaulus   Mylagaulidae
  riggsi Macdonald, J. R. 1970A; McKenna, M. C.,
      Love, J. D. 1972A
Pronothodectes   Plesiadapidae
  intermedius *Gazin, C. L.* 1971A
  matthewi Gazin, C. L. 1969A (cf.)
Pronotochoerus see Phacochoerus
pronus (Parotosaurus)
Pronycticebus   Adapidae
  gaudryi Szalay, F. S. 1971B
proosti (Scomberomorus)
Propachynolophus   Equidae Crusafont Pairó, M.,
      Remy, J. A. 1970A; Remy, J. A. 1972A
  gaudryi Ginsburg, L., Lapierre, F., Montenat, C.
      1967A (cf.)
  maldani Ginsburg, L., Lapierre, F., Montenat, C.
      1967A (cf.)
Propalaeocastor   Castoridae
  kumbulakensis *Lychev, G. F.* 1970A
Propalaeochoerus   Suidae
  gergovianus Schmidt-Kittler, N. 1971A
propalaeoryctes (Cimolestes)
Propalaeotherium   Equidae
  hassiacum Matthes, H. W. 1972A; Tobien, H.
      1969C
  messelense Tobien, H. 1969C
Propelanomodon   Dicynodontidae
  devillersi see P. tylorhinus
  tylorhinus [Dicynodon, P. devillersi] Keyser, A. W.
      1972A
Propelodytes   Pelodytidae
  wagneri Tobien, H. 1969C
Propenser   Acipenseridae–Propenserinae *Applegate,*
      S. P. 1970A
  hewletti *Applegate, S. P.* 1970A
Propenserinae   Acipenseridae *Applegate, S. P.* 1970A
Properca   Serranidae
  sabbai Anđelković, J. S. 1969A; Jerzmańska, A.
      1968A
Proplacerias   Kannemeyeriidae *Cruickshank, A. R. I.*
      1970A
  vanhoepeni [Kannemeyeria] Cruickshank, A. R. I.
      1970A
  See also Kannemeyeria
Proplegadis   Plataleidae *Harrison, C. J. O., Walker,*
      C. A. 1971A [in Ciconiiformes–
      Threskiornithidae]
  fisheri *Harrison, C. J. O., Walker, C. A.* 1971A
Propleopus   Macropodidae
  oscillans Bartholomai, A. 1972A
Propliomys   Cricetidae
  hungaricus Kretzoi, M. 1962D(?)
Propliopithecus   Pongidae Simons, E. L. 1968C
  haeckeli Simons, E. L., Pilbeam, D. R. 1972A
Propotto   Lorisidae
  leakeyi Walker, A. 1969A (in Chiroptera–
      Pteropidae)
Propteridium   Ophidiidae *Arambourg, C.* 1966A
      (in Brotulidae)
  douvillei [Urenchelys] Arambourg, C. 1966A
      (n. comb.); Haghipour, A., Brants, A. 1971A
      (in Brotulidae)
propterus (Pachythrissops)
propython (Clidastes)
proriger (Tylosaurus)
Prorosmarus   Odobenidae Kaiser, H. E. 1970A
prorsus (Triceratops)

Prorubidgea   Gorgonopsidae—Rubidgeinae
    alticeps [Lycaenops] Sigogneau, D. 1970A
      (n. comb.); [P. brinki] Sigogneau, D.
      1970A(?)
    brinki see Prorubidgea alticeps
    brodiei [Sycosaurus] Sigogneau, D. 1970A
      (n. comb.)
    maccabei Sigogneau, D. 1970A
    robusta Sigogneau, D. 1970A
Prosarctaspis   Gabreyaspididae *Novitskaîa, L. I.* 1968A
    taimyrica *Novitskaîa, L. I.* 1968A, 1971B
Prosauropoda   Saurischia—Sauropodomorpha
      Ellenberger, F., Ellenberger, P., Ginsburg, L.
      1970B [Plateosauria]
Proscalops   Talpidae
    evelynae Hutchison, J. H. 1972A; Macdonald, J. R.
      1970A
    secundus McKenna, M. C., Love, J. D. 1972A (cf.)
    terrenus Macdonald, J. R. 1970A [Arctoryctes]
Proscapanus   Talpidae
    sansaniensis Engesser, B. 1972A
Proscinetes see Microdon
Prosciurus   Paramyidae
    altidens *Russell, L. S.* 1972B
    arboraptus *Shevyreva, N. S.* 1971C
    dawsonae Macdonald, J. R. 1970A
      (in Ischyromyidae)
    major *Russell, L. S.* 1972B
    minor *Russell, L. S.* 1972B
    saskatchewanensis Russell, L. S. 1972B
    vetustus Russell, L. S. 1972B
Proserrivomer   Serrivomeridae *Arambourg, C.* 1966A
    mecquenemi *Arambourg, C.* 1966A; Haghipour, A.,
      Brants, A. 1971A
Prosimiae   Primates Van Valen, L. 1969A (incl.
      superfam. Microsyopoidea, Lemuroidea,
      Tarsioidea)
Prosimii   Primates Radinsky, L. B. 1970A
Prosiphneus   Cricetidae Sukhov, V. P. 1968A, 1970A
      (incl. Episiphneus, Mesosiphneus)
    praetingi [Mesosiphneus] Sukhov, V. P. 1970A
      (ex gr.)
    pseudoarmandi [Episiphneus] Sukhov, V. P. 1970A
    youngi-pseudarmandi Erbaeva, M. A. 1970A
      (ex gr.)
Prosiren   Sirenidae
    elinorae Estes, R. 1969I (in Prosirenidae)
Prosirenidae   Urodela *Estes, R.* 1969I (incl.
      Prosiren, Prodesmodon)
    ?Ramonellus
Prospalax   Spalacidae
    petteri *Bachmayer, F., Wilson, R. W.* 1970A
      (in ?Cricetidae)
    priscus Daxner-Höck, G. 1970A; Kowalski, K.
      1960C; Kretzoi, M. 1970-71A
      (in Anomalomyidae)
    rumanus see Pterospalax
Prosphymaspis   Phlyctaenaspididae Stensiö, E. 1969B,
      1971A (in Spinothoracidi—Dolichothoraci)
Prosthenops   Tayassuidae
    niobrarensis Webb, S. D. 1969C
Prostrepsiceros   Bovidae
    houtumschindleri Gentry, A. W. 1971A
    rotundicornis Gentry, A. W. 1971A
    woodwardi Melentis, J. K. 1970A
Prosybris   Tytonidae *Brodkorb, P.* 1969A
    antiqua [Strix] Brodkorb, P. 1969A

Prosynthetoceras   Protoceratidae
    francisi Patton, T. H. 1969B; Patton, T. H.,
      Taylor, B. E. 1971A (subgen.
      Prosynthetoceras)
    hessei Patton, T. H., Taylor, B. E. 1971A (subgen.
      Lambdoceras)
    siouxensis Patton, T. H., Taylor, B. E. 1971A
      (subgen. Lambdoceras)
    texanus Patton, T. H. 1969B; Patton, T. H.,
      Taylor, B. E. 1971A (subgen.
      Prosynthetoceras)
    trinitiensis *Patton, T. H., Taylor, B. E.* 1971A
      (subgen. Lambdoceras)
    See also Synthetoceras
Protacanthodes   Triacanthidae—Protacanthodinae
    omboni Tyler, J. C. 1968A
Protachyoryctes   Rhizomyidae
    tatroti Black, C. C. 1972A
Protadelomys   Pseudosciuridae
    alsaticus *Hartenberger, J.-L.* 1969A
    cartieri Hartenberger, J.-L. 1969A
    lugdunensis *Hartenberger, J.-L.* 1969A
protamphibius (Hippopotamus)
protapirinus (Homogalax)
Protapirus   Tapiridae
    gromovae Birîukov, M. D. 1962A
Protarctos   Ursidae
    boeckhi Samson, P., et al. 1971A
Protaspis   Protaspis
Protaspis   Pteraspididae Denison, R. H. 1970B (incl.
      subgen. Cosmaspis, Cyrtaspidichthys,
      Eucyclaspis, Europrotaspis, Gigantaspis,
      Protaspis)
    brevispina *Denison, R. H.* 1970B (subgen. Protaspis)
    bucheri Denison, R. H. 1970B (subgen. Protaspis)
    dorfi Denison, R. H. 1970B, 1971B (subgen.
      Protaspis)
    erroli Denison, R. H. 1970B (n. subgen.
      Eucyclaspis)
    mcgrewi *Denison, R. H.* 1970B, 1971B (subgen.
      Protaspis)
    ovata Denison, R. H. 1970B (subgen.
      Cyrtaspidichthys)
    sculpta Denison, R. H. 1970B (subgen.
      Cyrtaspidichthys)
    tenuistriatus Denison, R. H. 1970B (subgen.
      Protaspis)
    transversa *Denison, R. H.* 1970B (n. sp., n. subgen.
      Cosmaspis), 1971B (restor.)
Protemnodon   Macropodidae Plane, M. 1965B
    otibandus Plane, M. 1971A
Protenrec   Tenrecidae
    tricuspis Butler, P. M. 1969A
Protenrecinae   Tenrecidae *Butler, P. M.* 1969A
Proterochampsa   Proterochampsidae Romer, A. S.
      1971E
    barrionuevoi Bonaparte, J. F. 1972A
Proterochampsia   Thecodontia—Pseudosuchia
      Bonaparte, J. F. 1971A (n. infraord., incl.
      Cerritosauridae, Proterochampsidae)
Proterochampsidae   Crocodilia—Archaeosuchia
      Bonaparte, J. F. 1971A (in Pseudosuchia—
      Proterochampsia); Romer, A. S. 1971E,
      1972A (in Thecodontia—Proterosuchia,
      incl. Cerritosaurus)
    Chanaresuchus, Gualosuchus, Proterochampsa
    See also Erpetosuchidae

Proterogyrinidae   Anthracosauria–Embolomeri
     Romer, A. S. 1970B
Proterogyrinus
Proterogyrinus   Proterogyrinidae *Romer, A. S.* 1970B
     scheelei *Romer, A. S.* 1970B
Proterosuchia   Thecodontia Charig, A. J., Reig, O. A.
     1970A (classif.); Cruickshank, A. R. I.
     1972A (classif.); Reig, O. A. 1970A
Proterosuchidae   Thecodontia–Proterosuchia
     Cruickshank, A. R. I. 1972A (incl.
     Proterosuchus, Archosaurus)
     See also Chasmatosauridae
Proterosuchus   Chasmatosauridae [Chasmatosaurus,
     Elaphrosuchus] Cruickshank, A. R. I. 1972A
     vanhoepeni Cruickshank, A. R. I. 1972A;
     Thornley, A. L. 1970A
Proterotheriidae   Litopterna
     Brachytherium, Deuterotherium, Diadiaphorus,
     Heteroglyphis, Licaphrops, Polymorphis,
     Prolicaphrium, Proterotherium,
     Protheosodon, Thoatherium
Proterotherium   Proterotheriidae
     dichotomum Friant, M. 1967B
     simplicidens Friant, M. 1967B
proterva (Cynorca)
Protestudo   Testudinidae *Chkhikvadze, V. M.* 1970A
     alba *Chkhikvadze, V. M.* 1971D
     darewskii *Chkhikvadze, V. M.* 1971D
     illiberalis *Chkhikvadze, V. M.* 1971D
proteulophus (Mesohippus)
prothales (Coelostegus)
Protheosodon   Proterotheriidae Friant, M. 1967B
     (in Macraucheniidae)
Prothryptacodon   Arctocyonidae
     albertensis *Fox, R. C.* 1968C
Prothyracodon   Hyracodontidae Zhukov, Iū. V. 1970A
Protitanichthys   Coccosteidae Stensiö, E. 1969A,B;
     Stensiö, E. 1969B [Woodwardosteus, in
     Euarthrodira incertae sedis]
Protoadapis   Adapidae
     curvicuspidens Ginsburg, L., Lapierre, F.,
     Montenat, C. 1967A
Protobalistum   Trigonodontidae
     imperiale Tyler, J. C. 1968A (in Triacanthodidae–
     Spinacanthinae)
Protoceratidae   Artiodactyla–Traguloidea
     Prosynthetoceras, Syndyoceras, Synthetoceras
Protoceratops   Protoceratopsidae Bakker, R. T.
     1968A (restor.)
Protoceratopsidae   Ornithischia–Ceratopsia
     Leptoceratops, Protoceratops
Protocetidae   Cetacea–Archaeoceti
     Protocetus
Protocetus   Protocetidae
     sloani *Sahni, A., Mishra, V. P.* 1972A
Protocitta   Corvidae *Brodkorb, P.* 1972A
     ajax *Brodkorb, P.* 1972A
Protocynodon   Scaloposauridae
     pricei Mendrez, C. H. 1972D
     (in Procynosuchidae)
Protodichobune   Dichobunidae [Hexacodus]
     Van Valen, L. 1971C
     pelodes [P. uintensis] Van Valen, L. 1971C
     uintensis see P. pelodes
Protodidelphis   Didelphidae
     vanzolinii Paula Couto, C. 1970A

Protodus see Gomphonchus, Poracanthodes
Protogonia
     subquadrata see Tetraclaenodon puercensis
Protogonodon   Arctocyonidae
     kimbetovius West, R. M. 1971B
Protolabis   Camelidae Frick, C., Taylor, B. E. 1971A
     barstowensis *Lewis, G. E.* 1968A
     heterodontus Webb, S. D. 1969C
     notiochorinos *Patton, T. H.* 1969B
Protolophotus   Lophotidae
     elami Arambourg, C. 1966A [Protolophotes]
Protomeryx
     leonardi see Miotylopus gibbi
Protomomys   Omomyidae McKenna, M. C., et al.
     1969A (suppressed, = Teilhardina);
     Melville, R. V. 1971A (suppressed, =
     Teilhardina)
Protopelicanus   Pelecanidae
     cuvieri Brunet, J. 1970A
Protopelobates
     gracilis see Palaeobatrachus laubei
Protopteraspis see Pteraspis
Protoreodon   Agriochoeridae
     minimus [Agriochoerus] Wilson, J. A. 1971A
     parvus Wilson, J. A. 1971A
     petersoni Ferrusquía-Villafranca, I. 1969A;
     Wilson, J. A. 1971A
     pumilus Snyder, D. O. 1970A; Wilson, J. A. 1971A
Protorhamphosus   Macrorhamphosidae *Danil'chenko,
     P. G.* 1968B
     parvulus *Danil'chenko, P. G.* 1968B
Protorosauroidea   Araeoscelidia *Kuhn, O.* 1969D
     (n. subord., in Lepidosauria–Protorosauria,
     incl. Protorosauridae)
Protoryx   Bovidae
     carolinae Gentry, A. W. 1971A
     hentscheli Melentis, J. K. 1970A
Protosciurus   Sciuridae Macdonald, J. R. 1970A
Protoselene   Hyopsodontidae [Dracoclaenus]
     Van Valen, L. 1971C
Protospermophilus   Sciuridae Green, M. 1971A
     kelloggi Sutton, J. F. 1972B
Protosphyraena   Pachycormidae
     nitida Applegate, S. P. 1970A(?)
Protostrigidae   Strigiformes
     Eostrix
Protostrix   Protostrigidae see Eostrix
Protosuchidae   Crocodilia–Protosuchia
     Hemiprotosuchus, Orthosuchus, Protosuchus
Protosuchus   Protosuchidae Galton, P. M. 1971C;
     Walker, A. D. 1970A (in Stegomosuchidae)
     richardsoni Bonaparte, J. F. 1971B (reconstr.)
Prototheria   Mammalia Griffiths, M. 1968A; Hopson,
     J. A. 1970A (incl. infracl. Eotheria,
     Ornithodelphia, Allotheria)
Prototherium   Dugongidae
     veronense Bartolomei, G. 1969A
Prototomus   Hyaenodontidae
     antiquus Guthrie, D. A. 1971B [Prolimnocyon]
     multicuspis [P. vulpecula] Guthrie, D. A. 1971B
     palaeonictides Rich, T. H. V. 1971A (cf.)
     vulpecula see P. multicuspis
Protozapus   Zapodidae *Bachmayer, F., Wilson, R. W.*
     1970A
     intermedius *Bachmayer, F., Wilson, R. W.* 1970A

Protragelaphus Bovidae
  skouzesi Gentry, A. W. 1971A; Melentis, J. K.
      1970A
Protragocerus Bovidae
  labidotus *Gentry, A. W.* 1970A
Protriton Branchiosaurus
Protungulatum Arctocyonidae
  donnae Van Valen, L. 1969D
Proumbra Umbridae *Sychevskaia, E. K.* 1968A
  irtyshensis Nelson, G. J. 1972A [Umbra, subgen.
      Proumbra]; *Sychevskaia, E. K.* 1968A
proxima (Exellia)
Prunella Prunellidae
  collaris Jánossy, D. 1972A (aff.)
Prunellidae Passeriformes
  Prunella
pruvosti (Prolacertipes)
przewalskii (Equus)
Psalodon Plagiaulacidae Hahn, G. 1969A, 1971A
Psammodontidae Bradyodonti
  Psammodus
Psammodus Psammodontidae
  rugosus Patterson, C. 1968C
Psammolepis Drepanaspididae
  alata Liarskaia, L. A. 1971A
  paradoxa Liarskaia, L. A. 1971A; Ørvig, T. 1968B
  undulata Liarskaia, L. A. 1971A
Psammomys Cricetidae
  obesus Tchernov, E. 1968B (in Gerbillidae)
Psammornis Aepyornithidae Sauer, E. G. F. 1969A
      [? = Struthio in Struthionidae]
  rothschildi Tessier, F., Hebrard, L.,
      Lappartient, J.-R. 1971A (egg)
Psammosteidae see Drepanaspididae
Psenes Stromateidae
  macrolepis *Arambourg, C.* 1966A(?)
Psephaspis Drepanaspididae
  idahoensis *Denison, R. H.* 1968B, 1970B
      (in Pteraspididae)
  williamsi Denison, R. H. 1970B (in Pteraspididae)
Psephodus Cochliodontidae
  magnus Patterson, C. 1968C
Psephophorus Dermochelyidae
  rupeliensis Rothausen, K. 1970A
  scaldii Rothausen, K. 1970A
Psephosaurus Placochelyidae Haas, G. 1969A
Psettodes Psettodidae
  oedelemensis *Nolf, D.* 1970C (otol.)
Psettodidae Pleuronectiformes—Psettodoidei
  Psettodes
Psettopsis Monodactylidae *Blot, J.* 1969B
  subarcuatus Blot, J. 1969B
Pseudacris Hylidae
  clarki Chantell, C. J. 1971A (cf.)
Pseudadjidaumo Eomyidae *Lindsay, E. H.* 1972B
  stirtoni *Lindsay, E. H.* 1972B
pseudaeglefinus (Merlangius)
Pseudaelurus Felidae
  hibbardi *Dalquest, W. W.* 1969A
  intrepidus Forsten, A. 1970B
  lorteti Głazek, J., Oberc, J., Sulimski, A. 1971A;
      Telles Antunes, M. 1960C
  major Melentis, J. K. 1970A [Metailurus]
  parvulus Melentis, J. K. 1970A [Metailurus]
  pedionomus Webb, S. D. 1969C
  quadridentatus Głazek, J., Oberc, J., Sulimski, A.
      1971A (cf.)

Pseudamia see Pseudamiatus
Pseudamiatus Amiidae
  heintzi Vonderbank, K. 1970A [Pseudamia]
Pseudamphimeryx Amphimerycidae
  renevieri Sudre, J. 1969B (aff.)
  schlosseri Sudre, J. 1972A
pseudanaema (Issiodoromys)
Pseudaptenodytes Spheniscidae *Simpson, G. G.*
      1970C
  macraei *Simpson, G. G.* 1970C
  minor *Simpson, G. G.* 1970C(?)
Pseudarctos Canidae
  bavaricus Engesser, B. 1972A (aff., in Ursidae—
      Arctocyoninae)
Pseudemys Testudinidae Holman, J. A. 1972A
  See also Chrysemys
Pseudhesperosuchus Sphenosuchidae *Bonaparte, J. F.*
      1969B
  jachaleri *Bonaparte, J. F.* 1969B, 1971B, 1972A
Pseudhipparion Equidae
  gratum Webb, S. D. 1969C (n. comb.)
  retrusum Webb, S. D. 1969C
Pseudholocentrum Holocentridae *Arambourg, C.*
      1966A
  cristatum *Arambourg, C.* 1966A
Pseudictopidae Eutheria incertae sedis *Sulimski, A.*
      1968B; Szalay, F. S., McKenna, M. C. 1971A
      (in Anagalida)
  Pseudictops
Pseudictops Pseudictopidae
  arilophiodon see P. lophiodon
  lophiodon [P. arilophiodon] Sulimski, A. 1968B
Pseudoalactaga Dipodidae—Alactaginae
      Topachevs'kyĭ, V. O. 1971C
  minuta Topachevs'kyĭ, V. O. 1971C
pseudoarmandi (Prosiphneus)
Pseudoblastomeryx Blastomeryx
Pseudocheirus Phalangeridae
  marshalli *Turnbull, W. D., Lundelius, E. L.* 1970A
      (in Phascolarctidae)
  peregrinus Smith, M. J. 1971A (in Petauridae)
  stirtoni *Turnbull, W. D., Lundelius, E. L.* 1970A
      (in Phascolarctidae)
Pseudocorax Isuridae
  affinis Applegate, S. P. 1970A (in Anacoracidae)
Pseudocricetodon Cricetidae *Thaler, L.* 1969A;
      Vianey-Liaud, M. 1971A
  montalbanensis *Thaler, L.* 1969A; Vianey-Liaud, M.
      1969A, 1972B
  philippi *Hugueney, M.* 1971A
Pseudocylindrodon Cylindrodontidae Galbreath,
      E. C. 1969A; Wood, A. E. 1969A
  tobeyi *Black, C. C.* 1970B
Pseudodontornis Pseudodontornithidae
  stirtoni *Howard, H., Warter, S. L.* 1969A
Pseudodontornithidae Pelecaniformes
  Pseudodontornis
Pseudodryomys Gliridae
  fugax Hugueney, M. 1969A
  hamadryas Engesser, B. 1972A(?)
  ibericus Bruijn, H. 1967A
  ibericus-simplicidens Baudelot, S. 1969A
  robustus *Bruijn, H.* 1967A
  simplicidens Bruijn, H. 1967A; Telles Antunes, M.,
      Mein, P. 1971A

Pseudoegertonia Labridae
    granulosus [Eodiaphyodus] Estes, R. 1969G
        (?, in Phyllodontidae)
    salvani see Paralbula
    straeleni Estes, R. 1969G (in Phyllodontidae–
        Paralbulinae)
    See also Eodiaphyodus
Pseudogalerix Erinaceidae Friant, M. 1971C
Pseudoheterodontus Hybodontidae Zhelezko, V. I.,
        Glikman, L. S. 1971A
    polydictios Zhelezko, V. I., Glikman, L. S. 1971A
    rugosus Zhelezko, V. I., Glikman, L. S. 1971A
Pseudokoala Phascolarctidae Turnbull, W. D.,
        Lundelius, E. L. 1970A
    erlita Turnbull, W. D., Lundelius, E. L. 1970A
Pseudoloris Tarsiidae
    reguanti Tobien, H. 1971A (cf.)
Pseudoltinomys Theridomyidae–Issiodoromyinae
    gaillardi Ringeade, M. 1967B; Vianey-Liaud, M.
        1969A (aff.)
    nanus Thaler, L. 1969A
Pseudomeriones Cricetidae Birman, A. S., et al.
        1971A
Pseudomys Muridae
    oralis Schram, F. R., Turnbull, W. D. 1970A
Pseudopetalichthys Stensioellidae Stensiö, E. 1969B
        (in Stensioellidae–Pseudopetalichthyidae)
Pseudoplohophorus Glyptodontidae
    francisi Mones, A. 1970A
Pseudopriacanthidae Perciformes–Percoidei
    Pseudopriacanthus
Pseudopriacanthus Pseudopriacanthidae
    rutoti Stinton, F. C., Nolf, D. 1969A (otol.)
Pseudopromerycochoerus Promerycochoerus
Pseudoruscinomys Cricetodon Mein, P.,
        Freudenthal, M. 1971A (n. subgen.)
Pseudosciuridae Rodentia–Theridomyoidea
        Schmidt-Kittler, N. 1972A
    Protadelomys, Pseudosciurus, Sciuroides,
        Suevosciurus, Treposciurus
    See also Theridomyidae
Pseudosciurinae Theridomyidae Hartenberger,
        J.-L. 1971B (incl. Pseudosciurus,
        Suevosciurus)
Pseudosciurus Pseudosciuridae
    praecedens Schmidt-Kittler, N. 1971C
    suevicus Schmidt-Kittler, N. 1971C
Pseudospheniscus see Palaeospheniscus
Pseudosuchia Thecodontia Bonaparte, J. F. 1971A
        (incl. Ornithosuchia, Sphenosuchia,
        Proterochampsia); Krebs, B. 1969A
    Incertae sedis: Lagerpeton, Lagosuchus,
        Lewisuchus
pseudosuchoides (Chirotherium)
Pseudotheridomys Eomyidae Jánossy, D. 1969D
    baconicus Jámbor, A., Korpás, L., Kretzoi, M.,
        Pálfalvy, I., Rákosi, L. 1971A (n. sp.,
        n. subgen. Anomegodus)
    carpathicus Bruijn, H., Dawson, M. R., Mein, P.
        1970A
    parvulus Fahlbusch, V. 1968A, 1970A;
        Hugueney, M. 1969A (cf.)
    pusillus Fahlbusch, V. 1969B, 1970A
    schaubi Hugueney, M. 1969A (aff.)
Pseudotrimylus Soricidae–Soricinae Gureev, A. A.
        1971A
    roperi [Heterosorex] Gureev, A. A. 1971A

Pseudotsaganomys Cylindrodontidae
    mongolicus Shevyreva, N. S. 1971D
Psilichthys Birgeriidae
    selwyni Waldman, M. 1971C
        (in ?Coccolepididae)
Psittacosauridae Ornithischia–Ornithopoda
        Galton, P. M. 1972A (incl. Protiguanodon,
        Psittacosaurus, ?Stenopelix)
    Psittacosaurus
Psittacosaurus Psittacosauridae Kazarinov, V. P.
        1967A
Pteranodon Ornithocheiridae Bramwell, C. D. 1971B;
        Bramwell, C. D., Whitfield, G. R. 1970A
    bonneri Miller, H. W. 1972B (subgen. Nyctosaurus)
    eatoni [P. occidentalis] Miller, H. W. 1972B
        (n. subgen. Occidentalia)
    gracilis Miller, H. W. 1972B (subgen. Nyctosaurus)
    ingens Heptonstall, W. B. 1971C
        See also P. marshi
    longiceps Miller, H. W. 1972B (n. subgen.
        Longicepia), 1972C
    marshi [P. ingens] Miller, H. W. 1972B (subgen.
        Longicepia)
    occidentalis see P. eatoni
    sternbergi Miller, H. W. 1972B (n. subgen. Sternbergia)
    walkeri Miller, H. W. 1972B (subgen. Sternbergia)
Pteraspididae Heterostraci (in Pteraspidomorpha–
        Pteraspida, Stensiö) Balabai, P. P. 1959B;
        Denison, R. H. 1970B (incl. Pteraspidinae,
        Doryaspidinae)
    Doryaspis, Lampraspis, Oreaspis, Protaspis,
        Pteraspis
    See also Drepanaspididae
Pteraspidinae Pteraspididae Denison, R. H. 1970B
        (incl. Protopteraspis, Pteraspis, Althaspis,
        Rhinopteraspis, Protaspis, Oreaspis,
        Lampraspis, Psephaspis)
Pteraspidomorpha see Heterostraci
Pteraspis Pteraspididae Denison, R. H. 1970B
        [Protopteraspis, Althaspis, Rhinopteraspis];
        Dineley, D. L. 1971A [Protopteraspis,
        subgen. Simopteraspis]; Stensiö, E. 1968A
        [Zascinaspis]
    dixoni Denison, R. H. 1970B (in Pteraspididae
        incertae sedis)
    primaeva Stensiö, E. 1968A [Simopteraspis]
    rostrata Denison, R. H. 1971B (restor.)
    spatulirostris Stensiö, E. 1968A [Althaspis ?]
Pterichthyodes Astrolepidae Stensiö, E. 1969B
        (in Pterichthyodidae)
Pterodactylidae Pterosauria–Pterodactyloidea
    Belonochasma, Ctenochasma, Gnathosaurus,
        Pterodactylus, Pterodaustro
Pterodactyloidea Pterosauria Dehm, R. 1970B
Pterodactylus Pterodactylidae
    antiquus Wellnhofer, P. 1970A
    crassipes Ostrom, J. H. 1970A; Wellnhofer, P. 1970A
        (in Rhamphorhynchoidea)
    cristatus Wellnhofer, P. 1970A [Germanodactylus,
        in Germanodactylidae]
    elegans Wellnhofer, P. 1970A
    grandipelvis Wellnhofer, P. 1970A (in Pterodactyloidea
        incertae sedis)
    grandis Wellnhofer, P. 1970A (in Pterodactyloidea
        incertae sedis)
    kochi Wellnhofer, P. 1970A
    longicollum Wellnhofer, P. 1970A

Pterodactylus - cont.
  micronyx Wellnhofer, P. 1970A
  rhamphastinus Wellnhofer, P. 1970A
    [Germanodactylus, in Germanodactylidae]
  suevicus Wellnhofer, P. 1970A
Pterodaustriidae Pterosauria–Pterodactyloidea
    Bonaparte, J. F. 1971C (incl. Pterodaustro)
Pterodaustro Pterodactylidae Bonaparte, J. F. 1969F
  guinazui Bonaparte, J. F. 1969F, 1971C
    (in Pterodaustriidae)
Pterodon Hyaenodontidae Bessonnat, G., Dughi, R.,
    Sirugue, F. 1969A (ichn.)
  dasyuroides Jehenne, Y. 1969A
Pteromylaeus Myliobatidae Cappetta, H. C. 1969B,
    1970A
Pteronisculus Palaeoniscidae [Glaucolepis]
    Beltan, L. 1968A; Schaeffer, B. 1968C
  macropterus Beltan, L. 1968A (cf.)
Pteroplatea see Gymnura
Pteroplax Cricotidae Andrews, S. M. 1972A
    [Eogyrinus, in ?Rhizodontidae]
  attheyi Panchen, A. L. 1972A [Eogyrinus];
    Schultze, H.-P. 1969B [Eogyrinus]
Pteropodidae Chiroptera–Megachiroptera
    Archaeopteropus
Pterosauria Reptilia–Archosauria
  Incl. subord. Rhamphorhynchoidea,
    Pterodactyloidea Kuhn, O. 1970B
    (class; n. rank); Russell, D. A. 1972B
Pterospalax Anomalomyidae Kretzoi, M. 1970-71A
  rumanus [Prospalax] Kretzoi, M. 1970-71A
Pterothrissidarum Albulidae see Otolithus
Pterothrissus Albulidae Weiler, W. 1969A (otol.,
    in Clupeiformes–Pterothrissidae)
  angulatus Nolf, D. 1970A (otol.)
pteroticus (Acleistorhinus)
Ptilodontidae Multituberculata–Ptilodontoidea
    Lillegraven, J. A. 1969B
  Ptilodus
  See also Cimolodontidae
Ptilodus Ptilodontidae
  montanus Gazin, C. L. 1969A (cf.)
Ptomalestes Pristerognathidae
  avidus Mendrez, C. 1972A
ptychodon (Platecarpus)
Ptychodontidae Selachii–Hybodontoidea
    Ptychodus
Ptychodus Ptychodontidae
  mammillaris Shakh, L. N. 1968A (aff.)
  mortoni Applegate, S. P. 1970A
  polygyrus Applegate, S. P. 1970A
Ptychogaster Testudinidae Broin, P. de 1970A
Ptychosphenodon see Parotosaurus
Ptychotrygon Dasyatidae
  triangularis McNulty, C. L., Slaughter, B. H. 1970A
Ptyctodontida Placodermi Stensiö, E. 1969B, 1971B
    (in Spinothoracidi)
Ptyctodontidae Ptyctodontida
  Chelyophorus, Ctenurella, Desmoporella,
    Eczematolepis, Goniosteus, Paraptychodus,
    Ptyctodus, Rhamphodopsis, Rhynchodus
Ptyctodus Ptyctodontidae Stensiö, E. 1969B
  sibiricus Bel'skaîa, T. N. 1960A
puellaris (Gobius)
puercensis (Tetraclaenodon)
Puffinus Procellariidae
  tedfordi Howard, H. 1971C

Pugnax (Philomachus)
pulchellus (Eurypholis, Paragaleus)
pulchra (Boremys)
pulchriceps (Rhinochelys)
pulchrum (Myctophum)
pullus (Gobius)
Pulsatrix Strigidae
  arredondoi Brodkorb, P. 1968A
Pultiphagonides Bovidae
  africanus Cooke, H. B. S., Coryndon, S. C.
    1970A (cf.)
pumilus (Orohippus, Protoreodon)
punctatum (Diplovertebron, Tretosternon)
punctatus (Ictalurus, Poracanthodes)
pungens (Mixodectes)
punjabicus (Ramapithecus)
punjabiensis (Giraffokeryx, Rhizomyoides)
Purgatorius Phenacolemuridae Szalay, F. S. 1969C
    (in Paromomyidae)
purlensis (Dvinosaurus)
Pusa Phoca
pusilla (Ochotona)
pusillus (Buteo, Glirulus, Jordanomys, Mimomys,
    Pseudotheridomys, Rhynchosauroides)
pusio (Procoptodon)
pustulosa (Scotiophryne)
pustulosus (Spermatodus)
Putoranaspis Cyathaspididae
  dentata see Gerronaspis
  prima Novitskaîa, L. I. 1971B
    (in Amphataspididae)
Putorius Mustela
  See also Mustela
putorius (Mustela, Plesiobaena)
Pycnodontidae Pycnodontiformes Taverne, L. 1970A
  Coelodus, Gyrodus, Hadrodus, Microdon, Pycnodus
Pycnodontiformes Holostei Benedetto, J. L.,
    Sanchez, T. M. 1971A
Pycnodus Pycnodontidae
  praecursor Cappetta, H. C. 1972B (cf.)
  toliapicus Nolf, D. 1970C
Pycnosterinx Polymixiidae Patterson, C. 1968B
Pycnosteroides Pycnosteroididae
  levispinosus Patterson, C. 1968B
Pycnosteroididae Beryciformes–Dinopterygoidei
    Pycnosteroides
pygmaeus (Antiacodon, Choeromorus, Pongo, Sarcodon)
pygmyus (Promerycochoerus minor)
pyrenaicus (Allocricetus bursae, Mammut)
Pyrotheria Mammalia
Pyrrhocorax Corvidae Jánossy, D. 1972A
  alpinus Delpech, F. 1968A
  graculus Burchak-Abramovich, N. I. 1971A
Pyrrhula Ploceidae
  pyrrhula Jánossy, D. 1972A (cf., in Sturnidae)
pyrrhula (Pyrrhula)
Qataraspis Phlyctaenaspidae White, E. I. 1969A
  deprofundis White, E. I. 1969A
quadratum (Anthichnium)
quadratus (Aelurognathus)
quadricuneata (Rewana)
quadridentatus (Pseudaelurus)
quadrifidus (Dromillopus)
quadriplicatus (Neotoma)
Quadrodens Erinaceidae Macdonald, J. R. 1970A
  wilsoni [Palaeoscalopus pineridgensis] Hutchison,
    J. H. 1972A (in Talpidae); Macdonald, J. R.
    1970A

Quadropedia   Ichnites Haubold, H. 1970A (in Amphibia)
    levis [Cursipes] Haubold, H. 1970A
    prima Haubold, H. 1970A
quagga (Equus)
quartus (Plesiosminthus)
Quebecaspis   Arctolepida incertae sedis *Pageau, Y.*
        1969B (in Dolichothoraci)
    russelli *Pageau, Y.* 1969B
queenslandiae (Dinornis)
quenstedti (Teutomanis)
quercinus (Eliomys)
Quercygale   Viverridae
    angustidens Sudre, J. 1969B (in Miacidae)
quercyi (Eucricetodon, Melissiodon, Necromanis)
Quercyrallus   Rallidae
    ludianus Brunet, J. 1970A
querquedula (Anas)
quinni (Geomys)
quinquemolaris (Dinogorgon)
Quinquevertebron   Anura incertae sedis
    germanicum Špinar, Z. V. 1972B
quiricensis (Miopetaurista albanensis)
Qurliqnoria   Bovidae Gentry, A. W. 1968B
Rabidosaurus   Kannemeyeriidae *Kalandadze, N. N.*
        1970A
    cristatus *Kalandadze, N. N.* 1970A
radegondensis (Anchilophus)
radiata (Tyriolepis)
radobojanus (Capros, Mugil)
Radotina   Gemuendinidae Obruchev, D.,
        Karatajūte-Talimaa, V. N. 1967A;
        Stensiö, E. 1969B, 1971A
        (in Spinothoracidi—Radotinida)
Radotinida see Gemuendinidae
raeburni (Rhinoptera)
Raja   Rajidae Slaughter, B. H. 1972A
    duponti see Dasyatis
    gentili Cappetta, H. C. 1969B, 1970A
    louisi *Cappetta, H. C.* 1972B
    praeclavata *Jonet, S.* 1968B
rajareddyi (Parotosaurus)
Rajidae   Batoidea—Rajoidea
    Raja
Rallidae   Ralliformes Ballmann, P. 1969A
    Capellirallus, Coturnicops, Crex, Fulica,
        Gallinula, Gallirallus, Gypsornis,
        Laterallus, Ludiortyx, Palaeorallus,
        Porzana, Quercyrallus, Rallus,
        Telmatornis, ? Tertiariaporphyrula
    See also Ichnites
Ralliformes [Gruiformes] Aves Cracraft, J. 1968B
        [Gruiformes, incl. Cunampaiidae,
        Brontornithidae, Palaeociconiidae,
        Prophororhacidae, Phororhacidae,
        Psilopteridae, Bathornithidae, Cariamidae]
Rallus   Rallidae hodgeni see Capellirallus
    elegans-longirostris Feduccia, J. A. 1968 (group)
    lacustris Feduccia, J. A. 1968A
    phillipsi Feduccia, J. A. 1968A
    porzanoides Ballmann, P. 1969A (cf.)
    prenticei Feduccia, J. A. 1968A
    sumiderensis *Fischer, K., Stephan, B.* 1971B
Ramapithecus   Hominidae Chedd, G., Stubbs, P.
        1969A; Howell, F. C., Tattersall, I. M.
        1971A; Koenigswald, G. H. R. 1972B;
        Leakey, L. S. B. 1969B, 1970A; Pilbeam,
        D. R. 1967A, 1969A; Prasad, K. N. 1969A,D;
        Simons, E. L. 1971D,E; Simons, E. L.,
        Pilbeam, D. R. 1972A; Tattersall, I. 1969A,B
    brevirostris Lewis, G. E. 1971A; Prasad, K. N.
        1969B,C
    punjabicus Pilbeam, D. 1969B; Prasad, K. N.
        1969B,C; Simons, E. L. 1969A, (incl.
        Kenyapithecus wickeri), 1971C
    wickeri Andrews, P. 1971A
    See also Kenyapithecus
Ramoceros   Antilocapridae
    ramosus Patton, T. H. 1969B
Ramonellus   ? Prosirenidae Nevo, E., Estes, R. 1969A
    longispinus *Nevo, E., Estes, R.* 1969A
ramosus (Ramoceros)
ramsayi (Sceparnodon)
Rana   Ranidae Chantell, C. J. 1971A
    aurora Chantell, C. J. 1970A (cf.)
    catesbiana Holman, J. A. 1972A
    chensinensis Iskakova, K. I. 1969A (cf.)
    esculenta Vergnaud-Grazzini, C. 1970A (cf.)
    latastei Vergnaud-Grazzini, C. 1970A (cf.)
    luschitzana Špinar, Z. V. 1972B
    pipiens Chantell, C. J. 1970A (cf.); Holman, J. A.
        1969B, 1972A
    ridibunda Iskakova, K. I. 1969A (cf.)
    temporaria Iskakova, K. I. 1969A (cf.)
    terrestris Iskakova, K. I. 1969A (cf.)
Rangifer   Cervidae Bouchud, J. 1957B; Ficat, C.
        1963A (reindeer); Guthrie, R. D.,
        Matthews, J. V. 1971A; Mostecký, V. 1969A
    arcticus
        stadelmanni Kahlke, H.-D. 1969D
    tarandus Beden, M. 1970A; Bertouille, H.,
        Bouchud, J. 1969A; Boeuf, O. 1970A;
        Bonifay, M.-F. 1967A; Bouchud, J. 1968C;
        Churcher, C. S. 1968B; Delpech, F. 1968A;
        Delpech, F., et al. 1970A; Kuz'mina, I. E.
        1971A; Martin, R. 1968A; Schütt, G.
        1969C; Thenius, E. 1966G; Vozniachuk,
        L. N., et al. 1972A
Raniceps   Gadidae Weiler, W. 1969A (otol.)
    tuberculosus Anfossi, G., Mosna, S. 1969B (otol.)
Ranidae   Anura—Neobatrachia Seiffert, J. 1969B
    Asphaerion, Rana
Rapamys   Paramyidae
    wilsoni *Black, C. C.* 1971A (in Ischyromyidae—
        Paramyinae)
rapax (Aquila, Scapanorhynchus)
rapha (Procoptodon)
rarus (Siganopygaeus)
rastrosus (Smilodonichthys)
rata (Sardinella)
rateli (Diplocynodon)
rati (Rotodactylus)
ratticeps (Microtus)
Rattus   Muridae Schram, F. R., Turnbull, W. D. 1970A
    batei *Tchernov, E.* 1968B (subgen. Mastomys)
    colberti [Mastomys] Black, C. C. 1972A
    haasi *Tchernov, E.* 1968B
    nazarensis *Haas, G.* 1972A (subgen. ?Mastomys)
    norvegicus Chaline, J. 1969A
    rattus Tchernov, E. 1968B
rattus (Rattus)

Rhinoceros   Rhinocerotidae Pavia, G. 1970A
        (subgen. Dicerorhinus); Torres
        Perezhidalgo, T. 1971A
    etruscus see Dicerorhinus
    mauritanius see Ceratotherium simum
        mauritanicum
    mercki see Dicerorhinus
    simus see Ceratotherium simum mauritanicum
    sivalensis Saxena, M. N. 1968A [Rhinoceras]
    tichorhinus Beden, M. 1970A; Martin, R. 1968A;
        Popescu, A. 1964A
    latifrons Varlamov, 1959A
Rhinocerotidae   Perissodactyla–Rhinocerotoidea
        Heissig, K. 1972A; Klaits, B. G. 1972A
    Aceratherium, Aphelops, Begertherium,
        Brachypotherium, Ceratotherium,
        Chilotheridium, Chilotherium, Coelodonta,
        Diceratherium, Dicerorhinus, Diceros,
        Eggysodon, Elasmotherium, Eotrigonias,
        Epiaceratherium, Menoceras, Moschoedestes,
        Paraceratherium, Peraceras, Preaceratherium,
        Rhinoceros, Ronzotherium, Sinotherium,
        Subhyracodon, Teleoceras, Trigonias
Rhinochelys   Cheloniidae Collins, J. I. 1970A
        (in Protostegidae)
    cantabrigiensis Collins, J. I. 1970A
    elegans Collins, J. I. 1970A
    pulchriceps Collins, J. I. 1970A
Rhinochimaeridae   Chimaeriformes–Chimaeroidei
    Elasmodus
Rhinodicynodon   Shansiodontidae Kalandadze, N. N.
        1970A
    gracile Kalandadze, N. N. 1970A
Rhinodipterus   Dipteridae
    ulrichi Jarvik, E. 1968A
Rhinolophidae   Chiroptera
    Rhinolophus
Rhinolophus   Rhinolophidae
    blasii Heller, J. 1970A
    delphinensis Bachmayer, F., Wilson, R. W. 1970A
    euryale Heller, J. 1970A
    terrum
        equinum Heller, J. 1970A
    hipposideros Bouchud, J. 1961C; Heller, J. 1970A;
        Malec, F., Storch, G. 1970A
Rhinophrynidae   Anura
    Rhinophrynus
Rhinophrynus   Rhinophrynidae
    canadensis Holman, J. A. 1968B
    dorsalis Holman, J. A. 1969B
Rhinoplagusia   Cynoglossidae Cappetta, H. C. 1969B
        (otol.)
Rhinoptera   Rhinopteridae Menesini, E. 1969A
    raeburni Dachev, D. 1967A (in Myliobatidae)
    studeri Cappetta, H. C. 1969B, 1970A (cf.)
        (in Myliobatidae)
Rhinopteraspis see Pteraspis
Rhinopteridae   Batoidea–Myliobatoidea
    Rhinoptera
Rhinosteidae see Pachyosteidae
Rhinosteus   Pachyosteidae Stensiö, E. 1969A,B
        (in Rhinosteidae)
Rhinotitan   Brontotheriidae
    orientalis Bersenev, I. I., Ustinovskiĭ, Iu. B.,
        Bur'ianova, I. Z., Nevolina, S. I.,
        Medvedev, V. V. 1969A

Rhipaeosauridae   Cotylosauria–Pareiasauroidea
    Chudinoviella
Rhipaeosaurus
    talonophorus see Chudinoviella
Rhipidistia   Crossopterygii Andrews, S. M. 1972A;
        Schultze, H.-P. 1970D; Thomson, K. S.
        1968C (Order, incl. superfam.
        Holoptychoidea, Osteolepoidea,
        Rhizodontoidea)
Rhizodontida   Crossopterygii–Rhipidistia Andrews,
        S. M., Westoll, T. S. 1970B (n. order, incl.
        Rhizodontidae)
Rhizodontidae   Crossopterygii–Rhipidistia Andrews,
        S. M., Westoll, T. S. 1970B (in
        Rhizodontida); Thomson, K. S. 1968C
        (in Rhipidistia–Rhizodontoidea)
    Eusthenodon, Eusthenopteron, Litoptychus,
        Platycephalichthys, Rhizodopsis, Rhizodus,
        Sauripteris, Tristichopterus
Rhizodopsidae   Crossopterygii–Rhipidistia
        Thomson, K. S. 1968C (in Rhipidistia–
        Rhizodontoidea)
Rhizodopsis   Rhizodontidae Schultze, H.-P. 1969B
    sauroides Andrews, S. M., Westoll, T. S. 1970B
        (in Rhizodopsidae)
Rhizodus   Rhizodontidae Schultze, H.-P. 1969B
    hibberti Andrews, S. M., Westoll, T. S. 1970B
    ornatus Andrews, S. M., Westoll, T. S. 1970B
    sauroides Andrews, S. M., Westoll, T. S. 1970B
        [Strepsodus]; Schultze, H.-P. 1969B
        [Strepsodus]
    siberiacus Makarenko, G. F. 1971A
        [cf., Strepsodus]
Rhizomyidae   Rodentia–Spalacoidea
    Pararhizomys, Protachyoryctes, Rhizomyoides,
        Rhizomys, Tachyoryctoides
    See also Rhizospalacidae
Rhizomyoides   Rhizomyidae
    nagrii [Rhizomys] Black, C. C. 1972A
    pilgrimi [Rhizomys] Black, C. C. 1972A
    pinjoricus [Rhizomys] Black, C. C. 1972A
    punjabiensis [Rhizomys] Black, C. C. 1972A
    sivalensis Black, C. C. 1972A
Rhizomys   Rhizomyidae
    nagrii see Rhizomyoides
    pilgrimi see Rhizomyoides
    pinjoricus see Rhizomyoides
    punjabiensis see Rhizomyoides
Rhizospalacidae   Rodentia–Castoroidea
    Rhizospalax
Rhizospalax   Rhizospalacidae Kretzoi, M. 1970-71A
        (in Spalacidae)
    poirrieri Hugueney, M. 1969A
rhodanicum (Lophiobunodon)
rhodanicus (Eomys)
Rhodanomys   Eomyidae
    schlosseri Fahlbusch, V. 1968A (aff.), 1970A;
        Hugueney, M. 1969A
    transiens Hugueney, M. 1969A
rhodesiensis (Homo, Syntarsus)
Rhodeus see Rodeus
rhodius (Atlantoxerus)
Rhomaleosaurus see Thaumatosaurus
rhombea (Mene)
rhombica (Trigla)
rhombifera (Indaginilepis)

Ronzotherium - cont.
  filholi Bonis, L. 1969C; Brunet, M. 1970A
    elongatum *Heissig, K.* 1969A
    filholi Heissig, K. 1969A
    romani Heissig, K. 1969A
    kochi Heissig, K. 1969A
    velaunum Heissig, K. 1969A
roosevelti (Cervalces)
roperi (Pseudotrimylus)
roselli (Agerina)
rosmarus (Odobenus, Odobenus rosmarus)
rossiae (Myctophum)
rossicus (Liopleurodon)
rostae (Palaeobatrachus)
rostralis (Dercetis)
rostrata (Eglonaspis, Pteraspis)
rostriceps (Thoraciliacus)
rothi (Cynodontosuchus, Scalabrinitherium)
rothschildi (Psammornis)
Rotodactylidae Ichnites Haubold, H. 1969B,
    1971A (in Pseudosuchia, incl.
    Rotodactylus)
Rotodactylus Ichnites Haubold, H. 1969B,
    1971A (in Rotodactylidae)
    bradyi Haubold, H. 1971A
    cursorius Haubold, H. 1971A
    matthesi Haubold, H. 1971A
    mckeei Haubold, H. 1971A
    rati *Demathieu, G.* 1971A
rotundicornis (Helicotragus, Prostrepsiceros)
Rotundomys Cricetidae
    hartenbergeri Fejfar, O. 1970A
    sabadellensis Fejfar, O. 1970A
rotundus (Macrourus)
rouenii (Palaeotragus)
roulei (Boops)
roustami (Myroconger)
Rubidgea Gorgonopsidae—Rubidgeinae
    atrox Sigogneau, D. 1970A
    laticeps see Broomicephalus
    majora Sigogneau, D. 1970A
    platyrhina Sigogneau, D. 1970A
rubidgei (Broomisaurus, Cerdorhinus,
    Clelandina, Cyonosaurus, Dinogorgon,
    Leontocephalus, Milleretta,
    Paragalerhinus)
Rubidgeidae see Gorgonopsidae
Rubidgeinae Gorgonopsidae *Sigogneau, D.*
    1970A (incl. Sycosauridae and part of
    Arctognathoididae and Rubidgeidae of
    Romer)
Rubidgina Ictidorhinidae Sigogneau, D. 1970B
    angusticeps Sigogneau, D. 1970A
rubricati (Heteroxerus)
rudeli (Barbus)
Rueklinichnium Ichnites
    tridactylum Haubold, H. 1971A
rufa (Aplodontia)
rufifrons (Gazella)
rufocanus (Clethrionomys)
rufus (Canis, Felis)
rugosa (Dasyatis, Tsaotanemys)
rugosus (Psammodus, Pseudoheterodontus)
rumanus (Macrourus, Pterospalax)
Ruminantia Artiodactyla
  Incl. superfam. Cainotheroidea, Anoplotheroidea,
    Merycoidodontoidea, Cameloidea,

Ruminanatia - cont.
    Traguloidea, Cervoidea, Bovoidea
runtonensis (Cricetus, Sorex)
runtonensis-kennardi (Sorex)
rupeliensis (Lamna, Psephophorus)
Rupicapra Bovidae
    rupicapra Boecker, M., et al. 1972A; Bonifay, M.-F.
      1969A; Bouchud, J. 1968C; Delpech, F.
      1968A, 1969A; Martin, R. 1968A;
      Mostecký, V. 1969A; Schütt, G. 1969C
rupicapra (Rupicapra)
rurestris (Tomarctus)
Rusa Cervus
Ruscinomys Cricetidae Jaeger, J.-J. 1971A (cf.);
      Mein, P., Freudenthal, M. 1971A,B
    lasallei *Adrover, R.* 1969A
    schaubi Adrover, R. 1969B
rusconii (Venaticosuchus)
Rusconiodon Traversodontidae *Bonaparte, J. F.*
    1972A
    mignonei *Bonaparte, J. F.* 1972A
rusingae (Rhynchocyon)
rusingensis (Amphechinus)
Russelites Paroxyclaenidae Tobien, H. 1969A
    (in Condylarthra—Arctocyonidae)
Russellagus Ochotonidae *Storer, J. E.* 1970A
    vonhofi *Storer, J. E.* 1970A
russelli (Adjidaumo, Copemys, Dasyatis, Microparamys,
      Quebecaspis)
russula (Crocidura)
rustica (Hirundo)
rusticola (Scolopax)
rusticolus (Falco)
Rutilus Cyprinidae Brzobohatý, R. 1969A(?);
      Svychevskaîa, E. K., Lebedev, V. D. 1971A
Rutiodon Phytosauridae Gregory, J. T. 1969B
rutoti (Odontaspis, Pseudopriacanthus)
rzehaki Otolithus (inc. sed.)
saadii (Scomber)
sabadellensis (Cricetulodon, Rotundomys)
sabbai (Properca)
sabrae (Plesiosminthus)
Sachalinocetus Squalodontidae *Dubrovo, I. A.* 1971A
    cholmicus *Dubrovo, I. A.* 1971A; Siryk, I. M.,
      Dubrovo, I. A. 1970A
sacheti (Discosauriscus)
sackdilligensis (Glis)
sacrimontis (Plecotus auritus)
saevesoederberghi (Eusthenopteron)
saevus (Aelurodon, Enchodus)
Sagecephalus
    pachyrhynchus see Kannemeyeria simocephalus
Sagenodontidae Dipnoi
    Sagenodus
Sagenodus Sagenodontidae Berman, D. S. 1970A
    periprion Lund, R. 1970B (cf., in Ctenodontidae)
sagitta (Urosphenopsis)
Sagittariidae Accipitriformes—Accipitres
    Amphiserpentarius, Amynoptilon
sagorensis (Morone)
Saiga Bovidae Gentry, A. W. 1968B
    ricei Sher, A. V. 1968C
    tatarica Beden, M. 1970A; Kuz'mina, I. E. 1971A
saikanensis (Ergilemys insolitus)
Salamandra Salamandridae Vergnaud-Grazzini, C.
    1970A
Salamandridae Urodela Ozeti, N., Wake, D. B. 1969A
    Salamandra, Triturus

salamandroides (Anthichnium, Branchiosaurus)

Salamandromorpha   Amphibia *Kuhn, O.* 1970B
(n. subcl.)

salar (Salmo)

salebrosa (Kureykaspis)

Salichnium   Ichnites Haubold, H. 1970A
(in Microsauria)
adamsi [Ornithoides] Haubold, H. 1970A
becki *Haubold, H.* 1970A
heringi [Saurichnites] Haubold, H. 1970A

Salientia see Anura

Sallamys   Caviomorpha incertae sedis
Hoffstetter, R., Lavocat, R. 1970A
pascuali *Hoffstetter, R., Lavocat, R.* 1970A

salmanticensis (Stereogenys)

Salmo   Salmonidae
salar Delpech, F. 1968A

salmoneus (Allothrissops)

Salmonidae   Salmoniformes–Salmonoidei
Oncorhynchus, Salmo, Smilodonichthys,
Thymallus

Salmoniformes   Teleostei
Incl. subord. Salmonoidei, Argentinoidei,
Galaxioidei, Esocoidei, Stomiatoidei,
Alepocephaloidei, Bathylaconoidei,
Myctophoidei Goody, P. C. 1969B
(incl. n. subord. Ichthyotringoidei,
Cimolichthyoidei, Enchodontoidei,
Halecoidei)
Incertae sedis: Gaudryella, Humbertia

Salmopercomorpha   Paracanthopterygii
Rosen, D. E., Patterson, C. 1969A
(Series, incl. ord. Percopsiformes,
Gadiformes, Batrachoidiformes,
Lophiiformes, Gobiesociformes)

saltator (Allactaga)

Saltopoides   Ichnites Haubold, H. 1969B
(in Anchisauripodidae)

Saltoposuchus   Erpetosuchidae Walker, A. D. 1970A
(in Pedeticosauridae)

salvani (Paralbula)

Samotherium   Giraffidae Korotkevich, E. L. 1970A,
1972C
africanum *Churcher, C. S.* 1970B
irtyshense Godina, A. Ĩa. 1971A (nr.)

samsonowiczi (Erinaceus)

samueli (Dromiceiomimus)

sanctialbani (Tyto)

Sanctimus   Heteromyidae *Macdonald, J. R.* 1970A
clasoni [Pleurolicus] Macdonald, J. R. 1970A
(n. comb.)
stuartae *Macdonald, J. R.* 1970A
tiptoni *Macdonald, J. R.* 1970A

sandelensis (Gomphonchus)

sandersi (Sorex)

sanguineus (Harpagophagus)

Sangusaurus   Kannemeyeriidae *Cox, C. B.* 1969A
edentatus *Cox, C. B.* 1969A

Saniwa   Varanidae Schultze, H.-P. 1969B

sanjuanensis (Scaphonyx)

sanmeniensis (Equus)

sanpauloensis (Brazilosaurus)

sansaniense (Lantanotherium, Taucanamo)

sansaniensis (Dinosorex, Eomuscardinus, Eotragus,
Hemicyon, Heterosorex, Miopetaurista,
Proscapanus)

Sansanosmilus   Felidae–Machairodontinae
osborni see Barbourofelis
palmidens Schultz, C. B., Schultz, M. R.,
Martin, L. D. 1970A
whitfordi see Barbourofelis

santonjae (Eodiscoglossus)

Sapheosauroidea   Rhynchocephalia *Kuhn, O.* 1969D
(n. subord., incl. Sapheosauridae)

sapiens (Homo)

Sarcodon   Deltatheriidae Robinson, P. 1968C
(in Nyctitheriidae–Micropternodontinae)
pygmaeus [Opisthopsalis vetus] Szalay, F. S.,
McKenna, M. C. 1971A

sarcophagus (Albertosaurus)

Sarcoprion   Edestidae Bendix-Almgreen, S. E. 1968A

Sarcopterygii   Osteichthyes Thomson, K. S. 1969A,B;
Wahlert, G. 1968A

sarda (Sylvia)

Sardina   ?Clupeidae
priska *Danil'chenko, V. P.* 1969A

Sardinella   Clupeidae
beogradensis *Anđelković, J. C.* 1967A
perrara Iosifova, Ĩu. I., *Danil'chenko, P. G.* 1970A,B
rata Klebanova, N. I. 1971A

Sardinioides   Myctophidae Patterson, C. 1968B
minimus [Cassandra] Goody, P. C. 1969B
(in Sardinioididae)

Sardinioididae   Myctophiformes *Goody, P. C.* 1969B
See also Myctophidae

sardinites (Clupea)

Sardinius   Myctophidae
cordieri Goody, P. C. 1969B (restor.)

Sardinops see Sardina

sardous (Cynotherium)

sardus (Cuon, Prolagus)

Sargus   Sparidae Cappetta, H. C. 1969B [Diplodus]

sarmatica (Atherina)

sarmaticum (Chilotherium)

saskatchewanensis (Perognathus, Prosciurus)

Satapliasaurus   Ichnites
dsocenidzei Sarjeant, W. A. S. 1970A

satensis (Lagomeryx)

Satherium   Lutra

Satherium   Mustelidae
priscinaria Bjork, P. R. 1970A; Hibbard, C. W. 1972A

Saturninia   Plesiosoricidae Robinson, P. 1968C
(in Nyctitheriidae–Nyctitheriinae); Sudre, J.
1969B
gracilis Gureev, A. A. 1971A (in Soricidae–
Saturniinae); Tobien, H. 1971A (cf.)

Saturniinae   Soricidae *Gureev, A. A.* 1971A
(incl. Saturninia)

saulcetensis (Paratalpa micheli)

Sauravus   Keraterpetontidae Heyler, D. 1969A

Saurichnites   Ichnites see Anthichnium, Salichnium

Saurichthyidae   ?Acipenseriformes
Saurichthys

Saurichthys   Saurichthyidae Will, H.-J. 1969A
daubreei Gall, J.-C. 1971A
madagascariensis Beltan, L. 1968A
piveteaui *Beltan, L.* 1968A

Sauripteris   Rhizodontidae Schultze, H.-P. 1969B
taylori Andrews, S. M., Westoll, T. S. 1970B
[Sauripterus]; Thomson, K. S. 1968C

Saurischia   Reptilia–Archosauria
Incl. subord. Theropoda, Sauropodomorpha
Bonaparte, J. F. 1969D; Steel, R. 1970A

Saurocephalidae Osteoglossiformes–Ichthyodectoidei
    Bardack, D., Sprinkle, G. 1969A
        (in Ichthyodectiformes)
    Saurocephalus, Saurodon
Saurocephalus Saurocephalidae
    lanciformes Applegate, S. P. 1970A
        (in Saurodontidae); Bardack, D.,
        Sprinkle, G. 1969A
Saurodon Saurocephalidae
    leanus Applegate, S. P. 1970A (in Saurodontidae);
        Bardack, D., Sprinkle, G. 1969A
Saurodontidae see Saurocephalidae
sauroides (Rhizodopsis, Rhizodus)
Saurolophus Hadrosauridae
    angustirostris Gradziński, R. 1970A
Sauropelta Acanthopholidae Ostrom, J. H. 1970C
    edwardsi Ostrom, J. H. 1970C
Sauropodidae Ichnites Haubold, H. 1969B
        (in Saurischia–Coelurosauria, incl. Sauropus)
Sauropterygia Reptilia–Euryapsida
    Incl. subord. Nothosauria, Plesiosauria
Sauropus Ichnites Haubold, H. 1969B
        (in Sauropodidae)
    See also Baropezia, Palaeosauropus
Sauropus Palaeosauropus
Saurorhamphus Enchodontidae
    freyeri Goody, P. C. 1969B (in Eurypholidae)
Saurornis Eleutherornithidae Fischer, K.-H. 1967C
        (in Aves incerti ordinis)
    matthesi Brodkorb, P. 1971A; Fischer, K.-H.
        1967C
Saurornithoides Coeluridae
    mongoliensis Russell, D. A. 1969A
        (in Troodontidae)
Saurosuchus ?Erythrosuchidae
    galilei Bonaparte, J.-F. 1972A
        (in Rauisuchidae)
Saurothera Cuculidae
    merlini Fischer, K., Stephan, B. 1971B
saurus (Elops)
sauvagei (Paraconger)
savagei (Oligopithecus, Prolagus)
savini (Mimomys, Sorex, Ursus deningeri)
savornini (Chromis)
sawini (Lantanotherium)
sawrockensis (Ictalurus)
saxoniae (Anthracopus)
Sayimys Ctenodactylidae
    perplexus Black, C. C. 1972A
    sivalensis [Pectinator] Black, C. C. 1972A
Saykanomys Sciuravidae Shevyreva, N. S. 1972A
    chalchis Shevyreva, N. S. 1972A
scagliai (Aetosauroides, Argyrolagus)
Scalabrinitherium Macraucheniidae
    rothi Friant, M. 1967B
Scaldicetus Physeteridae [Hoplocetus, Physodon,
        Palaeodelphis] Menesini, E., Tavani, G.
        1968A
    grandis Menesini, E., Tavani, G. 1968A
scaldii (Psephophorus)
Scaloposauria Therapsida–Theriodontia
        Mendrez, C. H. 1972D (for Bauriamorpha)
Scaloposauridae Therapsida–Bauriamorpha
    Blattoidealestes, Icticephalus, Protocynodon,
        Zorillodontops
Scalopus Talpidae
    aquaticus Hibbard, C. W. 1972A

Scapanorhynchus Odontaspididae
    rapax Applegate, S. P. 1970A
    rhaphiodon Applegate, S. P. 1970A; Taverne, L.
        1970A
Scapanus Talpidae Hibbard, C. W., Bjork, P. R. 1971A
    latimanus Miller, W. E. 1971A
Scaphaspis see Lyktaspis
Scapherpeton Scapherpetontidae
    tectum Estes, R. 1969F; Sahni, A. 1972A
Scapherpetontidae Urodela
    Lisserpeton, Scapherpeton
    See also Cryptobranchidae
Scaphiopus Pelobatidae Holman, J. A. 1968B
    alexanderi Holman, J. A. 1970A (cf., subgen. Spea)
    bombifrons Chantell, C. J. 1971A (cf.); Holman,
        J. A. 1972A (cf.)
    hammondii Chantell, C. J. 1970A (cf.)
    holbrookii Chantell, C. J. 1971A (cf.)
    neuter Macdonald, J. R. 1970A
    skinneri Estes, R. 1970B
Scaphonyx Rhynchosauridae
    fischeri Barberena, M. C. 1971A; Bonaparte, J. F.
        1972A; Sill, W. D. 1971B
    sanjuanensis Bonaparte, J. F. 1972A
Scaptonyx Talpidae
    edwardsi Engesser, B. 1972A
Scardinius Cyprinidae Salis, K. 1967A; Sychevskaîa,
        E. K., Lebedev, V. D. 1971A
    erythrophthalmus Obrhelová, N. 1970A(?)
Scaridae Perciformes–Labroidei
    Scarus
Scarus Scaridae
    miocenicus Cappetta, H. C. 1969B
Scatophagidae Perciformes–Percoidei
    Scatophagus
Scatophagus Scatophagidae
    frontalis Blot, J. 1969B
Scaumenacia Phaneropleuridae
    curta Jarvik, E. 1968A
Scelidosauridae Ornithischia–Stegosauria
    Fabrosaurus, Scelidosaurus
    See also Fabrosauridae
Scelidosaurus Scelidosauridae Rixon, A. E. 1968A
Sceloporus Iguanidae Holman, J. A. 1970A, 1972A(?)
    variabilis Holman, J. A. 1969B (cf.)
Scenopagus Adapisoricidae
    priscus McGrew, P. O., Sullivan, R. 1970A
Sceparnodon Diprotodontidae
    ramsayi Ride, W. D. L. 1967A
    See also Phascolonus gigas
schafferi (Testudo)
schaffneri (Plesiosorex)
Schaubemys Plesiosminthus
schaubi (Democricetodon, Plesiosminthus,
        Pseudotheridomys, Ruscinomys)
scheelei (Proterogyrinus)
scheepersi (Clelandina)
schinzi (Halitherium)
Schizorhiza Pristidae
    stromeri Cappetta, H. C. 1972B
schlaikjeri (Heliscomys)
schlehenbergensis (Coelurosaurichnus)
schleiermacheri (Dicerorhinus)
schlosseri (Amphisepentarius, Gulo gulo,
        Metacordylodon, Oxyaenoides,
        Pseudamphimeryx, Rhodanomys, Tapirulus)
schmerlingi (Trogontherium)

Scorpaena   Scorpaenidae
    jeanneli Anđelković, J. S. 1969A
    minima Anđelković, J. S. 1969A
Scorpaenidae   Scorpaeniformes–Scorpaenoidei
    Scorpaena
Scorpaeniformes   Teleostei
    Incl. subord. Scorpaenoidei, Hexagrammoidei,
       Platycephaloidei, Hoplichthyoidei,
       Congiopodoidei, Cottoidei
Scotiophryne   Discoglossidae *Estes, R.* 1969C
    pustulosa *Estes, R.* 1969C
scotti (Cervalces, Equus)
scottianus (Microsyops)
scottii (Spurimus)
Scottimus   Cricetidae Macdonald, J. R. 1970A
    exiguus see Eumys
scrofa (Sus)
scropha (Sus)
sculpta (Griphognathus, Protaspis)
Scutemys   Testudinidae Chkhikvadze, V. M. 1971C
    (in Plesiochelyidae)
Scylacocephalidae see Gorgonopsidae–Gorgonopsinae
Scylacocephalus see Aelurosaurus
Scylacognathus   Gorgonopsidae–Gorgonopsinae
    Boonstra, L. D. 1969A (in Galesuchidae)
    grimbeeki [Cynarioides grimbeeki, Cynarioides
       laticeps] Sigogneau, D. 1970A (n. comb.)
    major see S. parvus
    parvus [S. major] Sigogneau, D. 1970A
    robustus [Cynariops] Sigogneau, D. 1970A
       (n. comb.)
Scylacops   Gorgonopsidae–Gorgonopsinae
    bigendens [Sycocephalus] Sigogneau, D. 1970A
       (n. comb.)
    capensis Sigogneau, D. 1970A
Scylacopsidae see Gorgonopsidae–Gorgonopsinae
Scylacosauridae   Therapsida–Therocephalia
    Scylacosuchus
Scylacosuchus   Scylacosauridae *Tatarinov, L. P.*
    1968C
    orenburgensis *Tatarinov, L. P.* 1968C
Scyliorhinidae   Selachii–Galeoidea Telles Antunes, M.,
    Jonet, S. 1970A [Scylliorhinidae, in
    Lamniformes–Scylliorhinoidei]
    Scyliorhinus
Scyliorhinus   Scyliorhinidae
    cabindensis Cappetta, H. C. 1972B (aff.)
    distans Cappetta, H. C. 1969B, 1970A;
       Telles Antunes, M., Jonet, S. 1970A
    fossilis Telles Antunes, M., Jonet, S. 1970A
    gilberti Casier, E. 1967B
    joleaudi *Cappetta, H. C.* 1969B, 1970A
    joneti *Cappetta, H. C.* 1969B, 1970A
    minutissimus Casier, E. 1967B
Scymnognathidae see Gorgonopsidae–Gorgonopsinae
Scymnognathus see Gorgonops, Aelurognathus,
    Lycaenops
Scymnorhinidae see Dalatiidae
Scymnorhinus see Broomisaurus
scythicus (Equus)
sebastopolitanum (Hipparion)
Sebecidae   Crocodilia–Sebecosuchia
    ?Ilchunaia, Sebecus
Sebecosuchia   Crocodilia
    Incertae sedis: Bergisuchus
Sebecus   Sebecidae
    icaeorhinus Gasparini, Z. B. 1972A

secans (Diacodexis)
sectator (Nimravus)
sectus (Gobius)
secundarium (Diplobune)
secundus (Paramys anacingularis, Physodon, Proscalops)
Sedenhorstia   Myctophidae
    dayi Goody, P. C. 1969A (in Sedenhorstiidae)
    orientalis *Goody, P. C.* 1969A (reconstr., in
       Sedenhorstiidae)
Sedenhorstiidae   Elopiformes–Elopoidei *Goody, P. C.*
    1969A (incl. Sedenhorstia)
seductus (Nanocynodon)
seekinsi (Hyracotherium)
segnis (Chamops)
sekwiae (Vernonaspis)
Selachii   Chondrichthyes–Elasmobranchii
    Incl. subord. Hybodontoidea, Heterodontoidei,
       Hexanchoidea, Galeoidea, Squaloidea
       Ortlam, D. 1967A (egg capsule, see
       Triasocapsula); Steininger, F. 1966A
selbyi (Spurimus)
Selenaletes   Helaletidae
    scopaeus Guthrie, D. A. 1971B
Selenichnidae   Ichnites Haubold, H. 1969B
    (in Saurischia–Coelurosauria, incl.
       selenichnus)
Selenichnus   Ichnites Haubold, H. 1969B
    (in Selenichnidae)
Selenosteidae   Arthrodira–Brachythoraci (incl.
    Leiosteidae of Stensiö)
    Gymnotrachelus, Paramylostoma, Selenosteus,
       Stenosteus
Selenosteus   Selenosteidae Stensiö, E. 1969A,B
    (in Pachyostei incertae sedis)
selwyni (Psilichthys)
Semibipedopus   Ichnites *Haubold, H.* 1971B
    meekerensis *Haubold, H.* 1971B
semiclausus (Parotosaurus)
Semigenetta   Viverridae
    mutata Engesser, B. 1972A
Semionotidae   Semionotiformes–Semionotoidei
    Archaeolepidotus, Lepidotes, Paralepidotus,
       Pericentrophorus
Semionotiformes   Holostei
    Incl. subord. Semionotoidei, Lepisosteoidei
semistriatus (Mesacanthus)
semseyi (Desmana)
sencta (Bathylagus)
sendaicus (Gomphotherium, Mizuhoptera)
senecta (Mesodma)
senectus (Eulamprogrammus)
senyureki (Hipparion)
septentrionalis (Litotaspis)
septimanus (Mimomys)
Sepulkomys   Cylindrodontidae *Shevyreva, N. S.* 1972A
    eboretus *Shevyreva, N. S.* 1972A
serbicus (Hypsodontůs)
serendipitus (Borealestes)
Serengetilagus   Leporidae Jaeger, J.-J. 1969A (cf.)
Seretolepis   Heterostraci incertae sedis
    elegans *Karatajüte-Talimaa, V. N.* 1968B;
       Obruchev, D., Karatajüte-Talimaa, V. N.
       1967A
Seriola   Carangidae
    prisca Blot, J. 1969B
serra (Hemipristis)
serralheiroi (Dasyatis)

Serranellus Serranus
Serranidae Perciformes—Percoidei
  Bilinia, Centropristis, Dapalis, Morone,
    Percichthys, Priacanthopsis, Prolates,
    Properca, Serranus
Serranus Serranidae Grechina, N. I. 1971B;
    Heinrich, W.-D. 1969B (otol.)
  budensis Bucur, I. 1971A; Jerzmańska, A. 1968A
  celebratus Danil'chenko, P. G. 1968B
  delicatulus Stinton, F. C., Nolf, D. 1969A
    (subgen. Serranellus, otol.)
  noetlingi Gaemers, P. A. M. 1969A (otol.),
    1971A (aff., otol.); Rado, G. 1965A,
    1969A (otol.)
  validus Anđelković, J. 1970A
serrata (Gnathorhiza)
serratidens (Aelurognathus)
Serratocentrus Holocentridae Gaudant, M. 1969A
  robustus Gaudant, M. 1969A
serrator (Mergus)
serratus (Acanthopleurus, Chaenobryttus,
    Eotrigonodon, Palaeogadus)
serridens (Pareiasaurus)
Serridentidae Proboscidea Alberdi, M. T.,
    Aguirre, E. 1970A
Serridentinus Gomphotheriidae
  gobiensis Dubrovo, I. A. 1970A; Kubiak, H. 1968A
  lusitanicus Alberdi, M. T., Aguirre, E. 1970A
Serrivomeridae Anguilliformes—Anguilloidei
  Proserrivomer
Serrodens Cyprinidae Salis, K. 1967A
serrulus (Kampholophos)
serum (Andegameryx)
serus (Hapalodectes)
Sespia Merycoidodontidae
  nitida Macdonald, J. R. 1970A
sessaoensis (Dasyatis)
sexlineatus (Cnemidophorus)
Seymouria Seymouriidae Schultze, H.-P. 1969B
  baylorensis Shishkin, M. A. 1968B
Seymouriamorpha [Batrachosauria]Anthracosauria
    Kuhn, O. 1972A; Tatarinov, L. P. 1972B
    [Batrachosauria, incl. subord. Seymourida,
    Lanthanosuchida, Chroniosuchida,
    Nycteroletorida]
  See also Ichnites
Seymourida Seymouriamorpha Tatarinov, L. P.
    1972B (? n. subord., in Batrachosauria,
    incl. Discosauriscidae, Kotlassiidae,
    Bystrowianidae, Seymouriidae)
Seymouriidae Anthracosauria—Seymouriamorpha
  Seymouria
Seymourioidea Seymouriamorpha Tatarinov, L. P.
    1972B (n. superfam., in Seymourida,
    incl. Seymouriidae)
Shansiodontidae Therapsida—Dicynodontia
  Rhinodicynodon
Sharemys see Clemmys
sharkovi (Microcetus)
sharpi (Allomys)
Shastasauridae Ichthyosauria
  Cymbospondylus, Himalayasaurus, Pessosaurus,
    Shastasaurus
Shastasaurus Shastasauridae
  nordensis Polubotko, I. V., Ochev, V. G. 1972A(?)
shastense (Nothrotheriops, Nothrotherium)

shawi (Meriones)
shermanensis (Vulpes)
shigensis (Elephas)
shikamai (Elaphurus)
Shikamainosorex see Anourosorex
shingi (Hopiichnus)
shirensis (Kennatherium)
shizukuishiensis (Diaphus)
shodoensis (Stegodon)
Shoshonius Omomyidae
  cooperi Guthrie, D. A. 1971B
shotgunensis (Elphidotarsius)
shufeldti (Paragrus)
shuleri (Tetrameryx)
Shweboemys Pelomedusidae
  gaffneyi Wood, R. C. 1970A
  pilgrimi Wood, R. C. 1970A
siberiacus (Rhizodus)
Siberiaspididae Heterostraci Novifskaîa, L. I. 1968A,
    1971B (in Amphiaspidiformes—
    Siberiaspidoidei, incl. Siberiaspis)
  Argyriaspis
  See also Olbiaspididae
Siberiaspis Olbiaspididae
  plana Novifskaîa, L. I. 1968A, 1971B
    (in Siberiaspididae); Stensiö, E. 1968A
sibericus (Lemmus)
sibirica (Marmota)
sibiricum (Elasmotherium)
sibiricus (Eutamias, Lagurus simplicidens, Parasagenodus,
    Ptyctodus)
Sicista Zapodidae Koenigswald, W. 1972A; Sukhov,
    V. P. 1970A
  bagajevi Savinov, P. F. 1970A (in Dipodidae—
    Zapodinae)
  betulina Chaline, J. 1968A (in Dipodidae)   •
  praeloriger Jánossy, D. 1969B
  subtilis-betulina Jánossy, D. 1969B (group)
sickenbergi (Panthera pardus)
sickleri (Chirotherium)
siderolithicum (Palaeotherium)
siderolithicus (Sciuroides)
siefkeri (Icarosaurus)
sigalovi (Discosauriscus)
Siganidae see Teuthidae
Siganopygaeus Teuthidae Danil'chenko, P. G. 1968B
    (in Siganidae)
  rarus Danil'chenko, P. G. 1968B
Sigmodon Cricetidae
  curtisi Cantwell, R. J. 1969A
  hudspethensis Akersten, W. A. 1972A
  medius Hibbard, C. W. 1972A (in Muridae—
    Cricetinae); Martin, R. A. 1970A
  minor Cantwell, R. J. 1969A,B; Martin, R. A. 1970A
sigmodon (Igdabatis)
sigmoides (Onychodus)
signata (Cephalaspis)
Sigurdia Thelodontidae Heintz, N. 1972A
  lata Heintz, N. 1972A
sihama (Sillago)
silberlingi (Picrodus)
silentiumis (Morosomys)
silesiacum (Aceratherium)
Sillaginidae Perciformes—Percoidei
  Sillago

Sillago   Sillaginidae
   sihama Aoki, N. 1968A (cf., otol.)
sillimani (Anchisauripus)
Silphedestidae   Therapsida—Cynodontia
         Mendrez, C. H. 1972D
Siluridae   Siluriformes
   Parasilurus, Silurus
Siluriformes   Teleostei
Silurus   Siluridae
   glanis Casier, E. 1957C
silvestris (Felis)
silvicola (Intasuchus)
Simamphicyon   Canidae Sudre, J. 1969B
         (in Ursidae)
   helveticus Sudre, J. 1969A,B
Simblaspis   Phlyctaenaspidae Stensiö, E. 1969B,
         1971A (in Spinothoracidi—Dolichothoraci)
Simidectes   Pantolestoidea incertae sedis
   magnus [Pleurocyon, Petersonella] Coombs,
         M. C. 1971A
   medius [Pleurocyon, Petersonella] Coombs, M. C.
         1971A
   merriami [Pleurocyon] Coombs, M. C. 1971A
similis (Cimolodon, Democricetodon, Lampropeltis,
         Sciaena)
Similisorex   Soricidae
   orlovi Gureev, A. A. 1971A
Simimys   Zapodidae Lindsay, E. 1969A
simionescui (Palaeogadus)
Simobison   Bison
simocephalus (Kannemeyeria)
Simocyon   Canidae
   primigenius Melentis, J. K. 1970A
Simoliophidae   Squamata—Lacertilia
   Mesophis, Pachyophis
simqnsi (Dormaalius)
Simopithecus see Papio
Simopteraspis see Pteraspis
simorrense (Hyotherium)
simorrensis (Conohyus)
simplex (Estramomys, Helodus, Urophycis)
simplicidens (Blarina, Equus, Lagurus, Lagurus
         simplicidens, Lutra, Nanomys,
         Palaeocastor, Proterotherium,
         Pseudodryomys)
simpsoni (Kuehneodon, Patene)
simum (Ceratotherium, Ceratotherium simum)
simus (Arctodus, Astronesthes, Cyclopidius)
Sinanthropus see Homo
sinatus (Pelusios)
sinensis (Nyctereutes, Tetralophodon)
singularis   Otolithus (Clupeidarum)
sinhaleyus (Dasyatis, Diodon, Labrodon,
         Myliobatis)
Sinoconodon   Triconodontidae Mills, J. R. E.
         1971A (in Sinoconodontidae)
   rigneyi Hopson, J. A., Crompton, A. W. 1969A
         (in Eozostrodontidae)
Sinoconodontidae   Mammalia—?Triconodonta
         Mills, J. R. E. 1971A (incl.
         ? 'Eozostrodon' problematicus,
         Sinoconodon)
   Megazostrodon
Sinokannemeyeria   Kannemeyeriidae Young, C. C.
         1957E

Sinolepis   Astrolepidae Stensiö, E. 1969B
         (in Antiarchi incertae sedis)
Sinomegacerus [Sinomegaceros] see Megaloceros
Sinotherium   Rhinocerotidae Beliaeva, E. I. 1971A
         (in Begertheriinae); Zhegallo, V. I.,
         Borisov, B. A. 1968A
siouxensis (Prosynthetoceras)
sipedon (Natrix)
Siphneus see Myospalax
Sirembo   Ophidiidae
   tumidus Nolf, D. 1970C (otol., in Brotulidae)
Sirenia   Mammalia Domning, D. P. 1972A; Reinhart,
         R. H. 1971A
Sirenidae   Urodela
   Habrosaurus, Prosiren
Sirenotherium   Trichechidae Paula Couto, C. 1967C
   pirabensis Paula Couto, C. 1967C
Sitta   Sittidae
   europaea Jánossy, D. 1972A (cf.)
Sittidae   Passeriformes
   Sitta
Sivacanthion   Hystricidae
   complicatus Black, C. C. 1972A
Sivachoerus see Nyanzachoerus
sivalensis (Caprolagus, Dryopithecus, Geoclemys, Hystrix,
         Kanisamys, Rhinoceros, Rhizomyoides,
         Sayimys)
Sivapithecus   Dryopithecus
Sivapithecus   Pongidae
   lewisi Pandey, J., Sastri, V. V. 1968A
   See also Dryopithecus
Sivatherium   Giraffidae Duisebaev, Zh. D.,
         Musakulova, L. T. 1968A
sjongersi (Paschatherium)
skinneri (Macrorhineura, Meliakrouniomys, Scaphiopus)
skouzesi (Protragelaphus)
Sloanbaatar   Eucosmodontidae Kielan-Jaworowska, Z.
         1970C
   mirabilis Kermack, K. A., Kielan-Jaworowska, Z.
         1971A; Kielan-Jaworowska, Z. 1970C, 1971A
sloani (Contogenys, Protocetus)
Smerdis see Dapalis
Smilesaurus see Arctops
Smilodectes   Adapidae
   gracilis McGrew, P. O., Sullivan, R. 1970A
         (in Notharctidae)
Smilodon   Felidae Mc Cain, P. 1971A; Oesch, R. D.
         1969B
   californicus Barthel, K. W. 1966A; Miller, G. J.
         1969A,B; Miller, W. E. 1971A (cf.)
   populator Moreira, L. E., Gomes de Melo, S. M.
         1971A
Smilodonichthys   Salmonidae Cavender, T. M.,
         Miller, R. R. 1972A
   rastrosus Cavender, T. M., Miller, R. R. 1972A
Sminthosinis   Mustelidae—Grisoninae Bjork, P. R.
         1970A
   bowleri Bjork, P. R. 1970A
sociale (Cynorca)
socialis (Galerix)
socoloviensis (Leuciscus)
Soederberghia   Phaneropleuridae
   groenlandica Schultze, H.-P. 1969A, 1970A
soemmeringi (Hyotherium)

Sparidae　Perciformes–Percoidei
  Boops, Dentex, Lagodon, Marsis, Oblata, Pagrus,
    Sargus, Sparidarum, Sparus, Spondyliosoma
  See also Otolithus
Sparidarum　Sparidae see Otolithus
Sparnacomys　Microparamys *Hartenberger, J.-L.*
  1971A (n. subgen.)
Sparus　Sparidae Cappetta, H. C. 1969B
  auratus Menesini, E. 1968A, 1969A
  brusinai Anđelković, J. S. 1969A
  cinctus Menesini, E. 1968A, 1969A
  doderleini [Otol. (Chrysophris)] Robba, E. 1970A
    (otol.)
  miolankae Deraniyagala, P. E. P. 1969B
    [Chrysophris, in Scaridae]
  neogenus Menesini, E. 1969A
Spatula　Anatidae
  clypeata Jánossy, D. 1972A (cf.)
spatulatus (Copodus, Merlangius)
spatulirostris (Pteraspis)
spatulus (Gigantocamelus)
Spea　Scaphiopus
speciosa (Corvina, Naomichelys)
speciosus (Scomberomorus)
spectabile (Prolicaphrium)
spectabilis (Gadus luscus, Plesiarctomys,
    Trisopterus luscus)
spectans (Pliohippus)
spelaea (Crocuta, Crocuta crocuta, Felis,
    Panthera, Panthera leo)
Spelaearctos see Ursus
spelaeus (Gulo gulo, Meles thorali, Strongyloceros,
    Ursus)
Speotyto　Strigidae
  cunicularia Feduccia, J. A., Rich, P. V. 1972A
    intermedia *Feduccia, J. A.* 1970A
Spermatodus　Coelacanthidae
  pustulosus Berman, D. S. 1970A
Spermophilinus　Sciuridae
  bredai Bachmayer, F., Wilson, R. W. 1970A (cf.);
    Bruijn, H., Meulenkamp, J. E. 1972A (cf.);
    Bruijn, H., Sondaar, P. Y., Zachariasse,
    W. J. 1971A
  bredai-turolensis Daxner-Höck, G. 1970A (form
    group)
  giganteus *Bruijn, H., Dawson, M. R., Mein, P.*
    1970A
Spermophilus　Sciuridae
  boothi *Hibbard, C. W.* 1972A (subgen.
    Otospermophilus)
  johnsoni *Hibbard, C. W.* 1972A (? subgen.)
  meltoni *Hibbard, C. W.* 1972A (? subgen.)
  See also Citellus
speyeri (Odontaspis)
sphaerodactylus (Rhynchosauroides)
Sphagesauridae　Crocodilia–Mesosuchia *Kuhn, O.*
  1968C (incl. Sphagesaurus)
  See also Notosuchidae
Sphagesaurus　Notosuchidae
  huenei Gasparini, Z. B. 1971A (not in
    Notosuchia); Kuhn, O. 1968C
    (in Sphagesauridae)
Sphenacodontidae　Pelycosauria–Sphenacodontoidea
  Ctenosauriscus, Dimetrodon, Haptodus,
    Macromerion

Spheniscidae　Sphenisciformes Simpson, G. G. 1970A,
  1972B
  Archaeospheniscus, Arthrodytes, Chubutodyptes,
    Duntroornis, Korora, Pachydyptes,
    Palaeeudyptes, Palaeospheniscus,
    Paraptenodytes, Platydyptes,
    Pseudaptenodytes, Spheniscus
Sphenisciformes　Aves Shtegman, B. K. 1970A
Spheniscus　Spheniscidae
  predemersus *Simpson, G. G.* 1971A
Sphenocephalidae　Beryciformes–Polymixioidei
  Sphenocephalus
Sphenocephalus　Sphenocephalidae
  brachypterygius *Rosen, D. E., Patterson, C.* 1969A
  fissicaudus Patterson, C. 1968B; Rosen, D. E.,
    Patterson, C. 1969A
Sphenodontidae　Rhynchocephalia Hughes, B. 1968A;
  Ostrom, J. H. 1962C
  Clevosaurus
Sphenophalos　Antilocapridae
  floblairi Webb, S. D. 1969C (subgen. Plioceros)
  nevadanus Shotwell, J. A. 1970A (cf.)
Sphenosuchia　Thecodontia–Pseudosuchia
  Bonaparte, J. F. 1971B (? n. infraord.)
Sphenosuchidae　? Crocodilia–Protosuchia Bonaparte,
  J. F. 1971B (in Pseudosuchia–Sphenosuchia
  incl. Sphenosuchus, Hesperosuchus,
    Pseudhesperosuchus)
  ? Pedeticosaurus, ? Platyognathus, Pseudhesperosuchus,
    Sphenosuchus
Sphenosuchus　Sphenosuchidae Walker, A. D. 1970A
  (in Pedeticosauridae), 1972A
Sphingopus　Ichnites Demathieu, G., Samana, J. C.
  1970A; Gand, G. 1971A
  ferox Demathieu, G. 1970B
Sphyraena　Sphyraenidae
  longimana *Arambourg, C.* 1966A
  olisiponensis Cappetta, H. C. 1969B
Sphyraenidae　Perciformes–Mugiloidei Arambourg, C.
  1966A (in Mugiliformes)
  Parasphyraena, Sphyraena
Sphyraenodus　Scombridae
  lerichei Nolf, D. 1970A
Sphyrna　Sphyrnidae
  arambourgi *Cappetta, H. C.* 1969B, 1970A
  prisca Menesini, E. 1969A [Cestracion]
  zygaena Telles Antunes, M., Jonet, S. 1970A
Sphyrnidae　Selachii–Galeoidea Telles Antunes, M.,
  Jonet, S. 1970A (in Lamniformes–
    Scylliorhinoidei)
  Sphyrna
spiegeli (Palaeochiropteryx)
spilosoma (Citellus)
spina (Bonapartia)
Spinacanthus　Trigonodontidae
  cuneiformis Tyler, J. C. 1968A (in Triacanthodidae–
    Spinacanthinae)
spindleri (Peratherium)
Spinemys　Geoemyda
spinosa (Clupea)
spinosus (Dinopteryx, Oligoplites, Pristigenys)
Spizaetus　Accipitridae
  tanneri *Martin, L. D.* 1971A
splendens (Listriodon)
splendida (Laurentaspis)

splendidum (Myctophum)
Spondyliosoma   Sparidae see Otolithus
Spondylosoma   Thecodontosauridae
  absconditum Bonaparte, J. F. 1972A;
    Colbert, E. H. 1970F
Sporadotragus [Microtragus] Bovidae *Kretzoi, M.*
    1968B (nov. nom.)
Spratticeps   Clupeiformes incertae sedis
    Patterson, C. 1970B
  gaultinus *Patterson, C.* 1970B
sprattiformis (Leptolepis)
Spurimus   Ischyromyidae—Prosciurinae
    Black, C. C. 1971A
  scottii *Black, C. C.* 1971A
  selbyi *Black, C. C.* 1971A
Squalicorax   Isuridae
  falcatus Applegate, S. P. 1970A
    (in Anacoracidae); Bilelo, M. A. M. 1969B
    (in Lamnidae); Taverne, L. 1970A
    [Anacorax, in Anacoracidae]
  kaupi Bilelo, M. A. M. 1969B (in Lamnidae);
    Taverne, L. 1970A [Anacorax, in
    Anacoracidae]
  pristodontus Applegate, S. P. 1970A
    (in Anacoracidae); Bilelo, M. A. M. 1969B
    (in Lamnidae)
  yangaensis Taverne, L. 1970A [Anacorax,
    in Anacoracidae]
Squalidae   Selachii—Squaloidea Telles Antunes, M.,
    Jonet, S. 1970A (in Squaliformes—
    Squaloidei)
  Deania, Squalus
Squalodon   Squalodontidae Whitmore, F. C. 1972A
  tiedemani Boreske, J. R., Goldberg, L.,
    Cameron, B. 1972A (cf.); Cameron, B.,
    Boreske, J. R. 1972A
Squalodontidae   Cetacea—Odontoceti Egorov, A. E.,
    Zarubin, S. I., Siryk, I. M. 1968A
  Austrosqualodon, Microcetus, Sachalinocetus,
    Squalodon
Squalodontoidea   Cetacea—Odontoceti Rothausen, K.
    1967A, 1970A
Squalus   Squalidae Hasegawa, Y., Ueno, T. 1967A
  almeidae *Telles Antunes, M., Jonet, S.* 1970A
  minor Casier, E. 1967B
  orpiensis Casier, E. 1967B
Squamata   Reptilia—Lepidosauria
  Incl. subord. Lacertilia, Ophidia Tarlo, L. B. H.
    1968A (incl. subord. Macronemia,
    Tanystrachelia, Askeptosauria,
    Eolacertilia, Trachelosauria)
  Incertae sedis: Tedorosaurus
squamifrons (Asineops)
Squatarola   Scolopacidae
  squatarola Jánossy, D. 1972A (aff., in
    Charadriidae)
squatarola (Squatarola)
Squatina   Squatinidae
  nigeriensis see Orectolobus
  prima Casier, E. 1967B
  subserrata Cappetta, H. C. 1969B, 1970A;
    Menesini, E. 1969A; Telles Antunes, M.,
    Jonet, S. 1970A
Squatinidae   Selachii—Squaloidea Telles Antunes, M.,
    Jonet, S. 1970A (in Squaliformes—
    Squatinoidei)
  Squatina

stadelmanni (Rangifer arcticus)
Stagodontidae see Didelphidae
Stagonolepidiidae see Aetosauridae
stahleckeri (Traversodon)
Stahleckeria   Stahleckeriidae
  potens Bonaparte, J. F. 1972A; Ricqlès, A. 1972B
    (in Kannemeyeridae—Stahleckeriinae)
Stahleckeriidae   Therapsida—Dicynodontia
  Chanaria, Dinodontosaurus, ? Elephantosaurus,
    Rechnisaurus, Stahleckeria, Wadiasaurus,
    Zambiasaurus
stamatini (Scophthalmus)
staringi Otolithus (Sciaenidarum)
Staurikosaurus   Palaeosauriscidae *Colbert, E. H.* 1970F
  pricei Bonaparte, J. F. 1972A; *Colbert, E. H.* 1970F
stavropolensis (Hipparion)
Stegoceras   Pachycephalosauridae Galton, P. M. 1970C
  validus Galton, P. M. 1971A; Sahni, A. 1972A(?)
Stegodibelodon   Elephantidae—Stegotetrabelodontinae
    Coppens, Y. 1972B
  schneideri *Coppens, Y.* 1972B
Stegodon   Elephantidae Maglio, V. J. 1970A (not in
    Elephantidae); Maglio, V. J., Hendey, Q. B.
    1970A (in Mammutidae); Nagasawa, J. 1968A
    [Parastegodon]; Prausnitz, M. W. 1969A
  fuchsi Cooke, H. B. S., Coryndon, S. C. 1970A
  hypsilophus Hooijer, D. A. 1970A
  insignis
    sugiyamai Chiji, M. 1971D
  kaisensis Cooke, H. B. S., Coryndon, S. C. 1970A
  korotorensis see Primelephas
  orientalis Chiji, M. 1971C
  shodoensis Otsuka, H. 1969A [Parastegodon]
    akashiensis Chiji, M. 1971D
  sompoensis Hooijer, D. A. 1970A
  szechuani Deraniyagala, P. E. P. 1965B (subgen.
    Sulcicephalus)
  timorensis Hooijer, D. A. 1969C, 1970A, 1972A,B;
    Sartono, S. 1969A
  trigonocephalus Hooijer, D. A. 1970A; Solheim, W. G.
    1969B
    florensis Hooijer, D. A. 1969C (cf.), 1972A,B
Stegolophodon   Elephantidae Fujii, S. 1970A; Maglio,
    V. J. 1970A (not in Elephantidae); Maglio,
    V. J., Hendey, Q. B. 1970A (in Mammutidae)
  tsudai Shikama, T., Yanagisawa, I. 1971A (cf.)
Stegomastodon   Gomphotheriidae
  mirificus Shotwell, J. A. 1970A
  primitivus Hibbard, C. W. 1972A
  waringi Lins Rolim, J. 1971A [Haplomastodon]
Stegomosuchidae   Crocodylomorpha—Crocodylia
    Walker, A. D. 1970A (incl. Erythrochampsa,
    Notochampsa, Orthosuchus, Protosuchus,
    Stegomosuchus)
    See also Erpetosuchidae, Notochampsidae,
      Protosuchidae
Stegomosuchus   Erpetosuchidae Walker, A. D. 1970A
    (in Stegomosuchidae)
Stegosauridae   Ornithischia—Stegosauria
  Echinodon
Stegotetrabelodon   Elephantidae
  orbus Coppens, Y. 1972B; *Maglio, V. J.* 1970B
    (in Stegotetrabelodontinae)
  syrticus Coppens, Y. 1972B; Maglio, V. J. 1970B
Stegotrachelidae   Palaeonisciformes—Palaeoniscoidei
  Kentuckia, Moythomasia, Oxypteriscus,
    Stegotrachelus

Stegotrachelus   Stegotrachelidae Kazanĭseva, A. A.
     1968A, 1971A
Stehlinella   Apatemyidae
     uintensis West, R. M. 1971A
stehlini (Chleuastochoerus, Cuon, Desmanella,
     Gazella, Romainvillia, Ursus)
stelleri (Hydrodamalis)
Stenailurus   Felidae–Metailurinae Crusafont-Pairó, M.,
     Aguirre, E. 1972A
     teilhardi Crusafont-Pairó, M., Aguirre, E. 1972A
Steneofiber   Castoridae
     castorinus Ginsburg, L. 1971A
          antiquus Ginsburg, L. 1971A
          castorinus Ginsburg, L. 1971A
     depereti Ginsburg, L. 1971A
          caliodorensis Ginsburg, L. 1971A
          carnutense Ginsburg, L. 1971A
          depereti Ginsburg, L. 1971A
     eseri Friant, M. 1965C
     jaegeri Friant, M. 1965C; Melentis, J. K. 1966Q,
          1967E
          See also Palaeomys
     minutus Engesser, B. 1972A
     viciacensis Lychev, G. F., Aubekerova, P. A.
          1971A (cf.)
     wenzensis see Boreofiber
Steneosaurus   Teleosauridae Dechaseaux, C. 1966A
     brevidens Cope, J. C. W. 1971A
     heberti Brunet, M. 1969A (cf.)
     obtusidens Maubeuge, P. L. 1968A
Stenichnus   Ichnites
     yakiensis Haubold, H. 1970A (in Microsauria)
Stenocranius   Microtus
stenodon (Aetobatus)
stenodonta (Monongahela)
stenodus (Allosorex)
Stenognathus see Heintzichthys
Stenomylus   Camelidae Stevens, M. S., Stevens, J. B.,
     Dawson, M. R. 1969A
stenonis (Equus)
Stenonychosaurus   Theropoda incertae sedis
     inequalis Russell, D. A. 1969A (in Troodontidae)
Stenonyx   Ichnites Haubold, H. 1969B
     (in Anchisauripodidae)
Stenopelix   Hypsilophodontidae
     valdensis Schmidt, H. 1969A
Stenopterygiidae   Ichthyosauria
     Leptopterygius, Platypterygius, Stenopterygius
Stenopterygius   Stenopterygiidae Schultze, H.-P.
     1969B
Stenosteus   Selenosteidae Stensiö, E. 1969A,B
     (in Pachyostei incertae sedis)
Stenotosauridae   Temnospondyli–Capitosauroidea
     Heyler, D. 1969B (incl. Stenotosaurus)
     See also Capitosauridae
Stenotosaurus   Capitosauridae
     lehmani Heyler, D. 1969B (in Stenotosauridae)
     semiclausus see Parotosaurus
stensioei (Micronothosaurus)
Stensioella   Stensioellidae Stensiö, E. 1969B
Stensioellida   Placodermi Stensiö, E. 1971B
Stensioellidae   Petalichthyida (in Stensioellida,
     incl. Stensioellidae, Pseudopetalichthyidae,
     ? Nessariostomidae of Stensiö)
     Nessariostoma, Paraplesiobatis,
          Pseudopetalichthys, Stensioella

stensioi (Birgeria)
stephani (Chondrostoma)
Stephanodus   Trigonodontidae
     lybicus Cappetta, H. C. 1972B
          (in Eotrigonodontidae)
Stereogenys   Pelomedusidae
     salmanticensis Jiménez Fuentes, E. 1968A, 1970A
Stereognathus   Tritylodontidae
     hebridicus Waldman, M., Savage, R. J. G. 1972A
Stereorachis   Eothyridae
     dominans Heyler, D. 1969A
Stereosternum see Mesosaurus
Sterna   Laridae
     hirundo Jánossy, D. 1972A (aff.)
sternbergi (Halisaurus, Pteranodon)
Sternbergia   Didelphidae Paula Couto, C. 1970A
     itaboraiensis Paula Couto, C. 1970A
Sternbergia   Pteranodon Miller, H. W. 1972B
     (n. subgen.)
Sternoptychidae   Salmoniformes–Stomiatoidei
     Argyropelecus
Stethacanthus   Chondrichthyes or Placodermi
     incertae sedis Hlavin, W. J. 1972A
stevensi (Tanupolama)
stewarti (Adjidaumo)
steytleri (Hipparion)
Stichocentrus   Holocentridae Patterson, C. 1968B
     elegans Gaudant, M. 1969A
Stichopteryx   Trachichthyidae Gaudant, M. 1969A
     lewisi [Hoplopteryx] Gaudant, M. 1969A
stillei (Okapia)
stintoni (Dactylopterus)
stipanicicorum (Gracilisuchus)
stirtoni (Allomys, Coendou, Dyseohyus, Martes,
     Paraleporillus, Pseudadjidaumo, Pseudocheirus,
     Pseudodontornis, Strobodon)
Stirtonia   Cebidae–Stirtoninae Hershkovitz, P. 1970B
     tatacoensis [Homunculus] Hershkovitz, P. 1970B
Stirtoninae   Cebidae Hershkovitz, P. 1970B
stolbovi (Panderichthys)
Stolephorus   Clupeidae
     lemoinei Anđelković, J. S. 1969A
stonehousensis (Cheiracanthoides)
stonei (Trematops)
storeri (Paracoluber)
stouti (Lynx, Phenacocoelus)
stovalli (Goniorhynchus)
straeleni (Pseudoegertonia)
Stratodus   Dercetidae
     apicalis Applegate, S. P. 1970A; Cappetta, H. C.
          1972B
strausi (Lepisosteus)
strenua (Tritemnodon)
Strenusaurus   Melanorosauridae Bonaparte, J. F. 1969B
     procerus Bonaparte, J. F. 1970A
strepera (Anas)
Strepsiceros   Bovidae
     maryanus Cooke, H. B. S., Coryndon, S. C. 1970A
          (cf.)
     nakuae Howell, F. C., Fichter, L. S., Eck, G. 1969A
          [Tragelaphus]
Strepsodus see Rhizodus
striata (Geoemyda, Moythomasia, Nostolepis,
     Striatolamia)
striatidens (Aelurosaurus)
Striatolamia   Odontaspididae

Striatolamia - cont.
  striata Casier, E. 1967B
  teretidens Dachev, D. 1967A
striatulus (Willomorichthys)
striatus (Apateodus, Bolosaurus, Physonemus)
Strictipes Ichnites see Limnopus
Strigidae Strigiformes
  Aegolius, Asio, Athene, Glaucidium, Nyctea,
    Otus, Pulsatrix, Speotyto, Strix, Surnia
Strigiformes Aves Sparks, J., Soper, T. 1970A
Strix Strigidae
  aluco Ballmann, P., Adrover, R. 1970A;
    Ganîa, I. M. 1969A
  brevis *Ballmann, P.* 1969B
  intermedia *Jánossy, D.* 1972A
  nebulosa Jánossy, D. 1972A (aff.)
  See also Prosybris, Tyto
Strobilodus see Caturus
Strobodon Canidae *Webb, S. D.* 1969C
  stirtoni *Webb, S. D.* 1969C
Stromateidae Perciformes—Stromateoidei
  ?Psenes
stromeri (Onchosaurus, Paralbula, Schizorhiza)
Stromeria Aepyornithidae
  fajumensis Sauer, E. G. F. 1969A
Stromeriella Mustelidae
  franconica Beaumont, G. 1968D
Strongyloceros Cervidae
  spelaeus Friant, M. 1971A
Strosipherus Eriptychiidae
  indentatus Karatajūte-Talimaa, V. N. 1970A
Struthio Struthionidae Rich, P. V. 1972A;
    Sauer, E. G. F. 1969A; Tessier, F.,
    Hebrard, L., Lappartient, J.-R. 1971A
    (egg)
  chersonensis Pidoplichko, I. G., Goldin, G. K.
    1964A
  orlovi *Kurochkin, E. N., Lungu, A. N.* 1970A,B
  transcaucasicus *Burchak-Abramovich, N. I.,*
    Vekua, A. K. 1971A
Struthiocephaloides Tapinocephalidae
  cavifrons Boonstra, L. D. 1969A
  duplessisi Boonstra, L. D. 1969A
Struthiocephalus Tapinocephalidae
  whaitsi Boonstra, L. D. 1968B, 1969A
Struthiomimus see Ornithomimus, Dromiceiomimus
Struthionidae Struthioniformes Sauer, E. G. F.
    1972A(?)
  Struthio
Struthioniformes Aves
Struthionops Tapinocephalidae
  intermedius Boonstra, L. D. 1969A
strymoniensis (Hipparion)
stuartae (Sanctimus)
studeri (Rhinoptera)
Stuerzaspis Phlyctaenaspidae Stensiö, E. 1969B,
    1971A (in Spinothoracidi—Dolichothoraci)
sturi (Ceratodus, Poraspis)
Sturnidae Passeriformes
  Laurillardia, Sturnus
  See also Fringillidae, Ploceidae
Sturnus Sturnidae
  vulgaris Jánossy, D. 1972A (cf.)
Stygimys Eucosmodontidae Lillegraven, J. A.
    1972B(?)

Stygiochelys Baenidae *Gaffney, E. S., Hiatt, R.* 1971A
  estesi Gaffney, E. S. 1972A (in Eubaeninae);
    Gaffney, E. S., Hiatt, R. 1971A
Stylemus see Stylemys
Stylemys Testudinidae
  nebrascensis Auffenberg, W. 1969A [Stylemus]
Stylinodon Stylinodontidae
  cylindrifer Guthrie, D. A. 1971B
Stylinodontidae Taeniodontia
  Stylinodon
Stylohipparion Hipparion
Styracocephalidae see Burnetiidae
Styracocephalus Burnetiidae Boonstra, L. D. 1969A
    (in Dinocephalia—Styracocephalidae)
Styracopteridae Palaeonisciformes—Palaeoniscoidei
  Benedenius, Styracopterus
  See also Canobiidae
Styracopterus Styracopteridae Kazantseva, A. A.
    1971A
suaveolens (Crocidura)
subaraneus (Sorex)
subarcuatus (Psettopsis)
subaureus (Acanthonemus)
subbuteo (Falco)
Subhyracodon Rhinocerotidae
  occidentalis Tanner, L. G. 1969A
submelba (Apus)
submersus (Zambiasaurus)
submilleri (Barbouromeryx)
subminutus (Sorex)
subnobilis (Dentex)
subovatus (Anaethalion, Thrissops)
Subparictis Parictis
subplanifrons (Elephas)
subregularis (Ogilbia)
subrubrum (Kinosternon)
subserrata (Squatina)
substriata (Odontaspis)
subterraneus (Microtus)
subtilis (Mookomys)
subtilis-betulina (Sicista)
subtriangularis (Lepidorhombus)
subtrigona (Asmithwoodwardia)
subtrigonus (Cyprinodon, Tricentes)
subulatus (Gnathosaurus)
subulensis (Attenosaurus)
sudamericanus (Ischignathus)
sudrei (Dasyatis)
suessoniensis (Lepisosteus)
suevica (Hystrix)
suevicum (Palaeotherium medium)
suevicus (Pristiophorus, Pseudosciurus, Pterodactylus)
Suevosciurus Pseudosciuridae
  ehingensis Schmidt-Kittler, N. 1971C
  fraasi Schmidt-Kittler, N. 1971C
  minimus [Sciuroides] Schmidt-Kittler, N. 1971C
sugiyamai (Stegodon insignis)
Suidae Artiodactyla—Suoidea Thenius, E.
    1970D
  Chleuastochoerus, Conohyus, Dicoryphochoerus,
    Hylochoerus, Hyotherium, Korynochoerus,
    Listriodon, Metridiochoerus, Nyanzachoerus,
    Omochoerus, Palaeochoerus, Phacochoerus,
    Potamochoerus, Propalaeochoerus, Sus
suillus (Cebochoerus)

Suina   Artiodactyla
  Incl. superfam. Entelodontoidea, Hippopotamoidea,
      Suoidea Golpe Posse, J. M. 1971C, 1972A
sulcata (Lamna)
sulcatus (Camelops)
Sulcicephalus   Stegodon
sulcidens (Carterodon, Echimys)
Suleobatrachus   Palaeobatrachus Špinar, Z. V.
      1972B (n. subgen.)
Sulidae   Pelecaniformes
  Morus
sullivani (Talpavus)
sumichrasti (Bassariscus)
sumiderensis (Rallus)
Suncus   Soricidae
  etruscus Gureev, A. A. 1971A
  infinitesimus Meester, J., Meyer, I. J. 1972A
  varilla Meester, J., Meyer, I. J. 1972A
Sundayichthys   Canobiidae Gardiner, B. G. 1969A
  elegantulus Gardiner, B. G. 1969A
sungi (Chinchenia)
Sunkahetanka   Canidae
  geringensis Macdonald, J. R. 1970A
  pahinsintewakpa Macdonald, J. R. 1970A
superbus (Lophosteus, Myliobatis)
superciliosus (Alopias)
supremus (Pliohippus)
Surnia   Strigidae
  capeki Jánossy, D. 1972A
Sus   Suidae Comaschi Caria, I. 1968A; Khatri, A. P.
      1966A; Quinn, J. H. 1970A
  antiquus Hünermann, K. A. 1968A
      [Microstonyx]; Schmidt-Kittler, N. 1971A
      [Microstonyx]; Thenius, E. 1970B, 1971A
      [Microstonyx]
  celebensis Hooijer, D. A. 1969A
  choeroides Hünermann, K. A. 1968A [Microstonyx]
  cristata Cooke, H. B. S., Coryndon, S. C. 1970A
  major Korotkevich, E. L. 1970A [aff., Microstonyx];
      Melentis, J. K. 1970A (subgen. Microstonyx);
      Thenius, E. 1971A [Microstonyx]
  minor Hünermann, K. A. 1971A; Samson, P., et al.
      1971A
  scrofa Beden, M. 1970A; Delpech, F. 1968A;
      Martin, R. 1968A; Melentis, J. K. 1966H;
      Mostecký, V. 1969A; Torres Perezhidalgo, T.
      1971A [S. scropha]
  priscus Hünermann, K. A. 1969B
  waylandi Cooke, H. B. S., Coryndon, S. C. 1970A
      (Sus sensu lato)
sushkini (Benthosuchus, Permocynodon)
sussenbornensis (Capreolus, Equus, Ovibos moschatus,
      Praedama, Ursus deningeri)
sussmilchi (Dipnorhynchus)
sutaiensis (Dmitrevichthys)
Svalbardaspis   Phlyctaenaspidae Stensiö, E. 1969B,
      1971A (in Spinothoracidi–Dolichothoraci)
svalis (Helicoprion)
svecica (Luscinia)
swanstoni (Hyla)
sweeti (Mesoreodon megalodon, Procastoroides)
swinnertoni (Otozoum)
Swinnertonichnus   Ichnites Sarjeant, W. A. S. 1967A
  mapperleyensis Sarjeant, W. A. S. 1967A
Sycocephalus see Scylacops
Sycosauridae see Gorgonopsidae–Rubidgeinae

Sycosaurus   Gorgonopsidae–Rubidgeinae
  brodiei see Prorubidgea
  kingoriensis [Lycaenops] Sigogneau, D. 1970A
      (?, n. comb.)
  laticeps Sigogneau, D. 1970A
  vanderhorsti [Leontosaurus] Sigogneau, D. 1970A
      (n. comb.)
sydenhami (Cephalaspis)
sydnensis (Baropezia)
sylvanus (Macaca)
sylvaticus (Apodemus)
sylvestris (Craseops, Hypolophus)
Sylvia   Sylviidae
  sarda Ballmann, P., Adrover, R. 1970A
Sylviidae   Passeriformes–Passeres
  Sylvia
Sylvilagus   Leporidae
  cunicularius Alvarez, T. 1969A
  floridanus Alvarez, T. 1969A; Campbell, K. E.
      1969A
Symbos   Bovidae Harington, C. R. 1968A; Ray, C. E.,
      Wills, D. L., Palmquist, J. C. 1968A
  cavifrons Khan, E. 1970A; Kraege, H. 1970A
symmetricus (Amblypterus)
Symmetrodonta   Mammalia Fox, R. C. 1972B
Symphalangus   Pongidae
  syndactylus Kitahara, J. 1971A
Symphodus   Labridae
  woodwardi Anđelković, J. S. 1969A [Bodianus]
synanthropus (Mus musculus)
Synapsida   Reptilia DeMar, R., Barghusen, H. R. 1972A
      (jaw evol.); Hopson, J. A. 1969A; Kemp, T. S.
      1969A (atlas-axis); Kuhn, O. 1970B (class)
Synaptichnium   Ichnites
  priscum Demathieu, G. 1970B
Synaptomys   Cricetidae
  anzaensis Zakrzewski, R. J. 1972A (n. subgen.
      Metaxomys, n. sp.)
  cooperi Schultz, G. E. 1969A
  landesi Zakrzewski, R. J. 1972A (n. subgen.
      Metaxomys)
  vetus Zakrzewski, R. J. 1972A (n. subgen.
      Metaxomys)
Synauchenia   Brachydeiridae Stensiö, E. 1969A,B
      (in Synaucheniidae)
Synaucheniidae see Brachydeiridae
Syncerus   Bovidae Cooke, H. B. S., Coryndon, S. C.
      1970A; Churcher, C. S. 1972C
syndactylus (Symphalangus)
Syndyoceras   Protoceratidae
  cooki Patton, T. H., Taylor, B. E. 1971A
Syndyodosuchus   Intasuchidae Schultze, H.-P. 1969B
      [Syndyosuchus]
  tetricus Shishkin, M. A. 1968B
Synechodontidae see Heterodontidae
Synechodus   Heterodontidae
  eocaenus Casier, E. 1967B (in Synechodontidae)
Syngnathidae   Gasterosteiformes–Syngnathoidei
  Hipposyngnathus, Nerophis, Syngnathus
Syngnathiformes   Teleostei
  See also Gasterosteiformes
Syngnathus   Syngnathidae
  incompletus Jerzmańska, A. 1968A
Synodontaspis   Odontaspis
Synodontidae see Mochokidae
Synodontis   Mochokidae Greenwood, P. H. 1968B

Tapirus - cont.
    priscus Combémorel, R., Guérin, C., Méon-Vilain, H.
        1970A
    terrestris Silva Santos, R. 1970A
Tapomys
    tapensis see Leptotomus
tarabukini (Anserobranta)
tarandus (Rangifer)
Tarbosaurus Tyrannosauridae Gradziński, R. 1970A
    bataar Russell, D. A. 1970C
tarda (Gabreyaspis)
Tardontia Aplodontidae
    occidentale Shotwell, J. A. 1970A (cf.)
Tareyaspis Gabreyaspididae Novitskaiâ, L. I. 1968A
    venusta Novitskaiâ, L. I. 1968A, 1971B
Tarsiidae Primates—Tarsioidei
    Microchoerus, Necrolemur, Pseudoloris
tatacoensis (Stirtonia)
tatalgolensis (Ictopidium)
tatalgolicus (Tachyoryctoides)
tatarica (Saiga)
tatarinovi (Planiplastron)
tatroti (Protachyoryctes)
tatsunokuchiensis (Mizuhoptera sendaicus)
taubachensis (Ursus arctos)
Taucanamo Tayassuidae
    sansaniense [Choerotherium] Pavlović, M. B. 1969A
    See also Choeromorus
Taurocephalus Tapinocephalidae
    lerouxi Boonstra, L. D. 1969A
taurus (Odontaspis)
taxandriae (Carcharhinus, Scoliodon)
Taxidea Mustelidae Akersten, W. A. 1972A;
        Bjork, P. R. 1970A; Khan, E. 1970A
    taxus Dalquest, W. W. 1967A; Hibbard, C. W.
        1972A (cf.)
taxoides (Aelurodon)
taxus (Taxidea)
Tayassu Tayassuidae Kaye, J. M. 1971A [peccary]
    tajacu Woodburne, M. O. 1969B [Dicotyles]
Tayassuidae Artiodactyla—Suoidea Webb, S. D. 1972B
    Choeromorus, Cynorca, Dyseohyus, Hesperhys,
        Perchoerus, Platygonus, Prosthennops,
        Taucanamo, Tayassu
taylori (Gyroptychius, Ophiomys, Sauripteris, Sorex,
    Spalacotherium, Tubulodon)
Tchadanthropus Hominidae
    uxoris Servant, M., Ergenzinger, P., Coppens, Y.
        1969A
tcherkesovae (Argyriaspis)
tchernychevi (Timanosteus)
tectum (Scapherpeton)
tedfordi (Puffinus)
Tedorosaurus Squamata incertae sedis Shikama, T.
        1967A
    asuwaensis Shikama, T. 1967A, 1969A
Teiidae Squamata—Lacertilia Estes, R. 1969A
    Chamops, Cnemidophorus, Leptochamops,
        Peneteius
teilhardi (Phenacodus, Stenailurus)
Teilhardidae Primates—Tarsiformes Quinet, G. E.
        1969B (incl. Teilhardina)
Teilhardina Omomyidae [Protomomys] McKenna,
    M. C., et al. 1969A
    belgica Melville, R. V. 1971A; Quinet, G. E.
        1966E, 1969B (in Teilhardidae)

Telanthropus Hominidae Gutgesell, V. J. 1970A;
        Mann, A. 1970A (Australopithecine);
        Montagu, A. 1969A; Wolpoff, M. H. 1968A
teleajensis (Centriscus)
Teleoceras Rhinocerotidae Brunet, J. 1969A;
        Forsten, A. 1970B; Shotwell, J. A. 1970A(?)
    fossiger Webb, S. D. 1969C
Teleolophus Deperetellidae
    beliajevi Kozhamkulova, B. S., Orlovskaiâ, E. R.
        1971A
Teleorhinus Pholidosauridae
    mesabiensis Erickson, B. R. 1969A
Teleosauridae Crocodilia—Mesosuchia
    Pelagosaurus, Steneosaurus
    See also Goniopholidae
Teleostei Osteichthyes—Actinopterygii Gosline, W. A.
        1971A; Nelson, G. J. 1969C
telleri (Gobius)
Telmatornithidae Charadriiformes Cracraft, J. 1972A
        (incl. Telmatornis)
Telmatornis Rallidae Cracraft, J. 1972A
        (in Telmatornithidae)
    affinis see T. priscus
    priscus [T. affinis] Cracraft, J. 1972A
    rex Cracraft, J. 1972A
telonensis (Ursus)
telonii (Heterocricetodon)
Temnocyon Canidae
    percussor Macdonald, J. R. 1970A
temnodon (Palaeolagus)
Temnospondyli Amphibia—Labyrinthodontia
    Incl. subord. Rhachitomi, Stereospondyli,
        Plagiosauria Schultze, H.-P. 1969B
    Incertae sedis: Rewana
temporaria (Rana)
tener (Biarmosuchus, Dictybolos, Dicynodon,
        Leptorophus)
Tenrecidae Insectivora—Tenrecoidea
    Erythrozootes, Protenrec
Tenrecoidea Insectivora—Zalambdodonta
tenue (Myctophum)
tenuiceps (Paratrachinotus)
tenuirostris (Aelurosaurus, Anoplosuchus, Lycaenops,
        Peramus)
tenuis (Aloposaurus, Batodon, Copemys, Gobius,
        Merlangius, Urophycis)
tenuisceps (Riojasuchus)
tenuistriatus (Protaspis)
Teracus Vulturidae
    littoralis Cracraft, J., Rich, P. V. 1972A (not in
        Cathartidae)
terakohensis (Actuariolum)
Teratornis Vulturidae
    incredibilis Howard, H. 1972A (cf.)
Teratosauria Saurischia—Palaeopoda Colbert, E. H.
        1970F (infraord., n. name for
        Palaeosauria, incl. Palaeosauriscidae,
        Teratosauridae)
Teratosauridae Saurischia—Palaeopoda see
        Plateosauridae
teres (Pelaspis)
teretidens (Striatolamia)
terminalis (Paramys anacingularis)
ternopolitana (Desmana moschata)
Terontosaurus Iguanodontidae Ostrom, J. H. 1970C
    tilletti Ostrom, J. H. 1970C

Thelodus - cont.
  schmidti Gross, W. 1968E; Halstead, L. B.,
    Turner, S. 1970A
Thenaropus   Ichnites see Limnopus
theniusi (Hipparion)
theobaldi (Hipparion)
Theosodon   Macraucheniidae Friant, M. 1967B
theotonicus (Chiniquodon)
Therapsida   Reptilia—Synapsida
  Incl. subord. Phthinosuchia, Theriodontia,
    Anomodontia Boonstra, L. D. 1971A;
    Crompton, A. W. 1972A (jaw
    articulation); Geist, V. 1972A (evol.);
    Kermack, K. A. 1972A (jaw joint,
    tooth differentiation); Kuhn, O. 1970C;
    Romer, A. S. 1969J
  Theria   Mammalia
  Incl. infraord. Trituberculata, Metatheria,
    Eutheria Crompton, A. W. 1970B
    (molar evol.); McKenna, M. C. 1969A;
    Ziegler, A. C. 1971A
  Incertae sedis: Kermackia, Potamotelses
Theridomyidae   Rodentia—Theridomyoidea
  Hartenberger, J.-L. 1971B (incl.
    Pseudosciurinae, Oltinomyinae,
    Sciuroidinae, Columbomyinae,
    Theridomyinae, Issiodoromyinae)
  Archaeomys, Ectropomys, Elfomys,
    Estellomys, Isoptychus, Issiodoromys,
    Pseudoltinomys, ? Sciuromys, Theridomys
  See also subfamilies
Theridomyinae   Theridomyidae Hartenberger, J.-L.
  1971B (incl. Theridomys, Taeniodus,
    Archaeomys, Blainvillimys)
Theridomyoidea   Rodentia
Theridomys   Theridomyidae—Theridomyinae
  crusafonti Thaler, L. 1969A
  helmeri Vianey-Liaud, M. 1972A (subgen.
    Blainvillimys)
  langei Vianey-Liaud, M. 1972A (subgen.
    Blainvillimys)
  varians Thaler, L. 1969A; Vianey-Liaud, M. 1969A
theriodis (Imperatoria)
Theriodontia   Therapsida Danilov, A. I.,
    Kalandadze, N. N. 1970A
Therizinosauridae   Carnosauria Rozhdestvenskii,
    A. K. 1970A,B
thermalis (Desmana)
Therocephalia   Therapsida—Theriodontia
theroni (Mentzichthys)
Theropithecus   Cercopithecidae Jolly, C. J.
    1970A,C,D
Theropoda   Saurischia Maleev, E. A. 1968A
    (classif.)
  Incertae sedis: Ammosaurus, Stenonychosaurus,
    Troodon
Theropsodon   Diademodontidae
  njalilus Ricqlès, A. 1969A(?)
Thescelosaurus   Hypsilophodontidae
  neglectus Sahni, A. 1972A (cf.)
Thescelus   Neurankylidae
  insiliens Gaffney, E. S. 1972A (in Baenidae)
thibetanus (Vulpes)
Thinocetus   Cetotheriidae Kellogg, R. 1969A
  arthritus Kellogg, R. 1969A
Thoatherium   Proterotheriidae Friant, M. 1967B

Tholodus see Omphalosaurus
tholodus (Dimylosorex)
Thomasinotus   Parasemionotidae
  divisus Beltan, L. 1968A
Thomomys   Geomyidae
  bottae Miller, W. E. 1971A
  gidleyi Zakrzewski, R. J. 1969A
  talpoides Schultz, G. E. 1969A (cf.)
  thompsoni (Domnina, Mesodma, Tomarctus)
Thoosuchus   Benthosuchidae
  jakovlevi [Trematosuchus] Ivakhnenko, M. F.
    1971A (n. comb.)
Thoraciliacus   Pipidae Nevo, E. 1968A
  rostriceps Nevo, E. 1968A
thorali (Meles)
thorslundi (Boreosaurus)
Threskiornithidae see Plataleidae
Thrinaxodon   Thrinaxodontidae Jenkins, F. A. 1971A;
    Ricqlès, A. 1969A
Thrinaxodontidae [Galesauridae] Therapsida—
    Cynodontia
  Galesaurus, Nanocynodon, Thrinaxodon
Thrissops   Chirocentridae
  formosus Nybelin, O. 1964A
  subovatus Nybelin, O. 1964A
  cirinensis Ny belin, O. 1964A
  See also Allothrissops
Thryonomyidae   Rodentia—Thryonomyoidea
  Paraulacodus
Thryonomyoidea   Rodentia
Thryptodontidae   Osteoglossiformes—Ichthyodectoidei
  Bananogmius
  See also Bananogmiidae
thuringiacum (Chirotherium)
thurmanni (Ischyodus)
Thursius   Osteolepidae
  pholidotus Andrews, S. M., Westoll, T. S. 1970B
  talsiensis Vorob'eva, E. I. 1971C
Thyestes   Cephalaspidae Gross, W. 1968E
Thylacinus   Dasyuridae
  cynocephalus Archer, M. 1971A
Thylacoleo   Thylacoleonidae Finch, E. 1971A
Thylacoleonidae   Marsupialia—Diprotodonta
  Thylacoleo
Thylacosmilus   Borhyaenidae
  atrox Schultz, C. B., Schultz, M. R., Martin, L. D.
    1970A
Thylatheridium   Didelphidae
  cristatum Simpson, G. G. 1972A
  pascuali Simpson, G. G. 1972A
Thylogale   Macropodidae Turnbull, W. D., Lundelius,
    E. L. 1970A
Thylophorops   Didelphidae
  chapalmalensis Simpson, G. G. 1972A
Thymallus   Salmonidae
  arcticus McAllister, D. E., Harington, C. R. 1969A
thyridata (Diomedea)
Thyrsitoides   Gempylidae
  zarathoustrae Arambourg, C. 1966A
Tiaraspis   Phlyctaenaspidae Stensiö, E. 1969B, 1971A
    (in Spinothoracidi—Dolichothoraci)
tibetensis (Himalayasaurus)
Ticholeptus   Merycoidodontidae Forsten, A. 1970B
    (cf.)
  rileyi Patton, T. H. 1969B
tichorhinus (Rhinoceros)

Tragocerus - cont.
  leskevitschi Korotkevich, E. L. 1970A (? aff.)
  See also Tragoceridus
Tragulidae   Artiodactyla–Traguloidea Musakulova,
    L. T. 1966A
  Dorcabune, Dorcatherium
transaltaiensis (Buginbaatar)
transbaicalicus (Allactaga saltator)
transcaucasica (Ochotonoides)
transcaucasicus (Struthio)
transiens (Archaeopteropus, Lagurus, Rhodanomys
    schlosseri)
transitorius (Entoptychus)
transitus Otolithus (Percidarum)
transvaalensis (Australopithecus, Mammuthus)
transversa (Protaspis)
trapezoidalis (Gobius)
Traquairaspididae   Heterostraci
  Traquairaspis
Traquairaspis   Traquairaspididae Obruchev, D.,
    Karatajūte-Talimaa, V. N. 1967A
trautscholdi (Plourdosteus)
travassosi (Monodelphopsis)
Traversodon   Traversodontidae
  major Bonaparte, J. F. 1972A(?);
    Ricqlès, A. 1969A(?)
  stahleckeri Bonaparte, J. F. 1972A;
    Ricqlès, A. 1969A
Traversodontidae   Therapsida–Cynodontia
  Andescynodon, ? Belesodon, Exaeretodon,
    Gomphodontosuchus, Ischignathus,
    Massetognathus, Megagomphodon,
    Proexaeretodon, Rusconiodon,
    Traversodon
  See also Chiniquodontidae, Diademodontidae
Tregosorex   Soricidae Hibbard, C. W.,
    Jammot, D. 1971A
  holmani Hibbard, C. W., Jammot, D. 1971A
Treleudytes see Paraptenodytes
Tremarctos   Ursidae
  floridanus Kurtén, B. 1968D
Tremataspidae   Osteostraci (in Oligobranchiata,
    Stensiö)
  Tremataspis
Tremataspis   Tremataspidae Gross, W. 1968E;
    Stensiö, E. 1968A
Trematops   Trematopsidae
  stonei Olson, E. C. 1970B
Trematopsidae   Temnospondyli–Eryopoidea
    Bolt, J. R. 1969A (in Dissorophoidea)
  Ecolsonia, Trematops
Trematosauridae   Temnospondyli–Trematosauroidea
  Aphaneramma, Lyrocephalus, Trematosaurus
Trematosauroidea   Temnospondyli–Rhachitomi
Trematosaurus   Trematosauridae Schultze, H.-P.
    1969B; Shishkin, M. A. 1968B;
    Tverdokhlebov, V. P. 1970B
Trematosteidae   Arthrodira–Brachythoraci (incl.
    Trematosteidae, Braunosteidae of Stensiö)
    Stensiö, E. 1969A,B (in Pachyosteomorphi–
    Pachyostei)
  Belosteus, Brachyosteus, Braunosteus, Cyrtosteus,
    Helmerosteus, Trematosteus
Trematosteus   Trematosteidae Stensiö, E. 1969A,B
Trematosuchus
  jakovlevi see Thoosuchus

Treposciurus   Pseudosciuridae Schmidt-Kittler, N.
    1970A
  intermedius Friant, M. 1965C [Sciuroides];
    [Sciuroides] Schmidt-Kittler, N. 1970A
    (n. comb.), 1971C
  mutabilis Schmidt-Kittler, N. 1970A, 1971C (aff.)
    helveticus Schmidt-Kittler, N. 1971C
    mutabilis Schmidt-Kittler, N. 1971C
Tretosternon   Dermatemydidae
  punctatum Borsuk-Białynicka, M., Młynarski, M.
    1968A (aff.)
Triacanthidae   Tetraodontiformes–Balistoidei
    Tyler, J. C. 1968A (in Plectognathi–
    Sclerodermi)
  Acanthopleurus, Cryptobalistes, Protacanthodes
Triacanthodidae see Trigonodontidae
Triacanthoidea   Plectognathi–Sclerodermi Tyler, J. C.
    1968A
triadicus (Onychopoides)
Triakis   Mustelidae [Triakidae]
  angustidens Cappetta, H. 1972A
triangularis (Gobius, Ptychotrygon)
triangulum (Mene)
triangulus (Glyptorhynchus, Isistius)
Triasocapsula   Selachii Ortlam, D. 1967A (egg capsule)
  becksmanni Ortlam, D. 1967A
Triassolestes   Procompsognathidae
  romeri Bonaparte, J. F. 1972A (in Triassolestidae);
    Colbert, E. H. 1970F (in Podokesauridae)
Triassolestidae   Thecodontia–Sphenosuchia
    Bonaparte, J. F. 1972A (incl. Triassolestes)
Tribosphena   Mammalia–Eutheria Turnbull, W. D.
    1971A (order, in cohort Tribosphenata,
    incl. Aegialodon, Peramus)
Tribosphenata   Mammalia–Eutheria Turnbull, W. D.
    1971A (cohort, incl. ord. Zalambdadonta,
    Tribosphena)
tricarinatus (lysorophus)
tricavus (Katoporus)
Tricentes   Arctocyonidae
  subtrigonus Gazin, C. L. 1969A (cf.)
Triceratops   Ceratopsidae
  prorsus Pinna, G. 1970A (reconstr.)
Trichechidae [Manatidae] Sirenia
  Sirenotherium
Trichiuridae   Perciformes–Scombroidei
  Eutrichiurides, Lepidopus, Trichiurus
Trichiurus   Trichiuridae
  gulincki Casier, E. 1967B
  miocenicus Cappetta, H. C. 1969B
Trichophanes   Aphredoderidae
  foliarum Rosen, D. E., Patterson, C. 1969A
Trichosurus   Phalangeridae Turnbull, W. D., Lundelius,
    E. L. 1970A
Triconodonta   Mammalia–subclass uncertain
Triconodontidae   Triconodonta Mills, J. R. E. 1971A
    (incl. Triconodontinae, Amphilestinae)
  Alticonodon, Astrocondon, Sinoconodon
  See also Sinoconodontidae
tricornatus (Synthetoceras)
tricuspidens (Plesiadapis, Spalacotherium)
tricuspis (Limnoecus, Protenrec)
Tricuspisaurus   Trilophosauridae Halstead, L. B.,
    Nicoll, P. G. 1971A
tridactylum (Ruecklinichnium)
tridecemlineatus (Citellus)

Trogontherium - cont.
  minus Radulesco, C., Samson, P. 1972A
  schmerlingi Jánossy, D. 1969B; [T. soergeli]
    Kretzoi, M. 1969A
  soergeli see T. schmerlingi
Trogosus Esthonychidae
  latidens McGrew, P. O., Sullivan, R. 1970A
trolli (Macrourus)
Troodon Theropoda incertae sedis
  formosus Sahni, A. 1972A (in Deinodontidae)
Troodontidae see Theropoda incertae sedis
Tropidosteus Groenlandaspididae Stensiö, E.
    1969B (in Euarthrodira incertae sedis)
Trucheosaurus Brachyopidae
  major Cosgriff, J. W. 1969A
truci (Eliomys)
truncatus (Batropetes, Chriacus)
Trygon see Dasyatis
Tsaganomys Cylindrodontidae
  altaicus Shevyreva, N. S. 1971D
Tsaotanemys Dermatemydidae
  rugosa Khosatzky, L. I., Młynarski, M.
    1971A (cf.)
Tschalimys Mylagaulidae Shevyreva, N. S. 1971B
  ckhikvadzei Shevyreva, N. S. 1971B
Tscherskia Cricetulus
Tseajaia Tseajaiidae
  campi Moss, J. L. 1971A, 1972A
Tseajaiidae Anthracosauria—Seymouriamorpha
  Tseajaia
tsudai (Stegolophodon)
Tubantia Trachichthyidae Patterson, C. 1968B
tuberculata (Lampraspis)
tuberculatum (Myctophum)
tuberculatus (Adroichthys, Neobythites, Raniceps)
tuberiferus (Aralosaurus)
tuberosa (Bauzaia)
Tubulidentata Mammalia
Tubulodon Orycteropodidae
  taylori Guthrie, D. A. 1971B (in Edentata
    incertae sedis)
tucki (Heterodontosaurus)
tuerkheimae (Apeomys)
tulotos (Nyanzachoerus)
tumididens (Ingentisorex)
tumidus (Sirembo, Stereosternum)
tunariensis (Prohypogeophis)
tungurensis (Amblycastor, Palaeotragus)
Tungurictis Hyaenidae Pavlović, M. B. 1969A
    (in Viverridae)
Tungussogyrinus Brachyopidae
  bergi Cosgriff, J. W. 1969A; Welles, S. P.,
    Estes, R. 1969A (in Stereospondyli
    incertae sedis)
Tupaiidae Insectivora—Leptictoidea Szalay, F. S.
    1969C
  ? Adapisoriculus
tupaiodon (Palaeochiropteryx)
Tupilakosaurus Brachyopidae
  heilmani Cosgriff, J. W. 1969A; Welles, S. P.,
    Estes, R. 1969A (in Stereospondyli
    incertae sedis)
  wetlugensis Cosgriff, J. W. 1969A
turanicus (Progrus)
Turdidae Passeriformes—Passeres
  Luscinia, Oenanthe, Turdus

Turdus Turdidae
  iliacus Ballmann, P., Adrover, R. 1970A
  merula Delpech, F. 1968A; Jánossy, D. 1972A (cf.)
  philomelos Jánossy, D. 1972A (aff.)
  pilaris Jánossy, D. 1972A (cf.)
  viscivorus Ballmann, P., Adrover, R. 1970A;
    Jánossy, D. 1972A (cf.)
turgaicus (Lophiomeryx)
Turgoniscus Palaeoniscidae Iakovlev, V. N. 1968A
  reissi Iakovlev, V. N. 1968A
turicensis (Mammut)
Turicius see Mammut
Turinia Osteostraci incertae sedis
  australiensis Gross, W. 1971C (in Thelodontidae)
  oervigi Karatajūte-Talimaa, V. N. 1968B (?, in
    Coelolepididae)
Turkanatherium see Aceratherium
turkanus (Homo palestinus)
Turkmene Turkmenidae Danil'chenko, P. G. 1968B
  finitimus Danil'chenko, P. G. 1968B
turkmenica (Scombrosarda)
turkmenicus (Palaeoloxodon)
Turkmenidae Lampridiformes Danil'chenko, P. G.
    1968B
  Danatinia, Turkmene
turoliensis (Valerymys)
turpior (Dicynodon, Dinodontosaurus)
Tutor Accipitridae—Buteoninae Kurochkin, E. N.
    1968C
  dementjevi Kurochkin, E. N. 1968C
  See also Venerator
tutus (Euoplocephalus)
Tuxeraspididae Heterostraci Novitskaia, L. I. 1968A,
    1971B (in Amphiaspidiformes—
    Siberiaspidoidei)
  Litotaspis, Tuxeraspis
Tuxeraspis Tuxeraspididae Novitskaia, L. I. 1971B
  varicostata Novitskaia, L. I. 1971B
Tylodus Agnatha incertae sedis
  deltoides Gross, W. 1971A
tylorhinus (Propelanomodon)
Tylosaurus Mosasauridae
  haumuriensis Welles, S. P., Gregg, D. R. 1971A
  proriger Thurmond, J. T. 1969B (cf.)
  zangerli Russell, D. A. 1970B
Typotheriidae [Mesotheriidae] Notoungulata—Typotheria
  Trachytherus
typus (Pelagosaurus)
Tyrannosauridae [Deinodontidae] Saurischia—Theropoda
    Russell, D. A. 1970C; Tabrum, A. R. 1970A
  Albertosaurus, Daspletosaurus, Gorgosaurus,
    Tarbosaurus, Tyrannosaurus
Tyrannosauropus Ichnites Haubold, H. 1971B
    (in Carnosauria)
  petersoni Haubold, H. 1971B
Tyrannosaurus Tyrannosauridae Newman, B. H. 1970A
  rex Russell, D. A. 1970C (cf.)
tyrannus (Martes flavigula)
Tyriaspis Dartmuthiidae
  whitei Heintz, A. 1969C
Tyriolepis ? Gemuendinidae Karatajūte-Talimaa, V. N.
    1968B
  radiata Karatajūte-Talimaa, V. N. 1968B;
    Obruchev, D., Karatajūte-Talimaa, V. N.
    1967A

Ursus - cont.
  prearctos Bonifay, M.-F. 1971A
  spelaeus Altuna, J. 1970A; Beaufort, F., Jullien, R.
    1968A; Bera, A. 1968A; Bonifay, M.-F.
    1967A, 1971A; Burchak-Abramovich, N. I.
    1960A [Spelaearctos]; [U. leodiensis,
    U. arctoideus, U. fornicatus magnus,
    U. f. minutus] Cordy, J.-M. 1972A; Delpech, F.
    1968A; Ehrenberg, K. 1967B; Ehrenberg, K.,
    et al. 1969A; Fedele, F. 1968A; Garevski, R.
    1969A; Koby, F.-E. 1960E, 1968A; Kurtén, B.
    1968D, 1969C, 1972B; Kuz'mina, I. E. 1971A;
    Lequatre, P. 1966A; Malez, M. 1956A;
    Martin, R. 1968A; Méroc, L. 1969A;
    Rakovec, I. 1967B; Schütt, G. 1969C;
    Steiner, U., Steiner, W. 1969A; Wójcik, M.
    1971A; Zapfe, H. 1966D
  stehlini Jánossy, D. 1969B
  telonensis Bonifay, M.-F. 1971A (subgen.
    Plionarctos)
  thibetanus Erdbrink, D. P. 1968A; Kurtén, B.
    1968D
  wenzensis Ryziewicz, Z. 1969B
Uruguaysuchidae Crocodilia–Mesosuchia Gasparini,
  Z. B. 1971A (in n. infraord. Notosuchia,
  incl. Araripesuchus, Uruguaysuchus)
Uruguaysuchus Notosuchidae Gasparini, Z. B. 1971A
  (in Uruguaysuchidae)
urvantzevi (Angaraspis)
Ustatochoerus Merycoidodontidae
  major Webb, S. D. 1969C (cf.)
  profectus Patton, T. H. 1969B; Webb, S. D. 1969C
utahensis (Lohsania)
uxoris (Tchadanthropus)
vaccinsulensis (Champsosaurus)
vafer (Leptocyon)
vagans (Macelognathus, Xestops)
vagrans (Sorex)
vagus (Limnopus, Pratilepus)
valdensis (Loxaulax, Stenopelix)
valenciennesi (Dipterus)
valens (Peratherium)
valentinensis (Bufo)
valeriani (Mimomys)
Valerymys Muridae Michaux, J. 1969B
  ellenbergi Michaux, J. 1969B
  turoliensis Michaux, J. 1969B
validus (Osteoborus, Serranus, Stegoceras,
  Uroconger)
vallesiensis (Progenetta montadai)
valletoni (Potamotherium)
vallicula (Dipoides)
vanalpheni (Archidiskodon)
vandebroecki (Dormaalius)
vanderbyli (Eoarctops)
vanderhorsti (Sycosaurus)
Vanellus Scolopacidae
  vanellus Jánossy, D. 1972A (cf., in
    Charadriidae)
vanellus (Vanellus)
vangionis (Arius)
vanhoepeni (Kannemeyeria, Proplacerias,
  Proterosuchus)
vanvaleni (Antiacodon)
vanzolinii (Protodidelphis)
Varanidae Squamata–Lacertilia
  Iberovaranus, Megalania, Saniwa, Varanus

Varanopsidae Pelycosauria–Sphenacodontoidea
  Milosaurus
Varanopus Ichnites
  curvidactylus Sarjeant, W. A. S. 1967A (aff.), 1971A
  didactylus see Moodieichnus
  langstoni Sarjeant, W. A. S. 1971A
Varanus Varanidae Schultze, H.-P. 1969B
  hofmanni Hoffstetter, R. 1968F (cf.)
Varhostichthys Cyprinidae Obrhelová, N. 1969A,
  1970B
  brevis [Leuciscus] Obrhelová, N. 1969A, 1970B
variabilis (Grallator, Sceloporus)
varians (Batrachopus, Cricetinus, Proalactaga,
  Theridomys)
Varicorhinus Cyprinidae
  nuntius Gabelaîa, Ts. D. 1970A
varicostata (Tuxeraspis)
varilla (Suncus)
vasacciense (Hyracotherium)
vasconiensis (Prolagus)
vaufrayi (Jansolfelis)
Vectisaurus Iguanodontidae Galton, P. M. 1971A
velaunum (Ronzotherium)
velifer (Exellia)
Veliferidae Lampridiformes–Veliferoidei
  ? Bathysoma
Velociraptor Coeluridae Colbert, E. H., Russell, D. A.
  1969A (in Dromaeosauridae)
velox (Matthewichnus, Notolagus, Vulpes)
Venaticosuchus Ornithosuchidae Bonaparte, J. F.
  1971B, 1972A
  rusconii Bonaparte, J. F. 1972A
Venatoripes Ichnites
  riojanus Bonaparte, J. F. 1965A (in Megatherioidea)
venenifer (Pharmacichthys)
Venerator [Tutor] Accipitridae Kurochkin, E. N.
  1969A,B
  dementjevi [Tutor] Kurochkin, E. N. 1969A,B
venezuelensis (Podocnemis)
venticolus (Notharctus)
ventralis (Palealbula)
ventriarmatum (Cephalerpeton)
venusta (Tareyaspis)
venustus (Cheiracanthoides, Gadus, Nothosaurus)
veredus (Bathornis)
verestchagini (Desmana)
Vernonaspis Cyathaspididae
  epitegosa Broad, D. S., Lenz, A. C. 1972A
  major Broad, D. S., Lenz, A. C. 1972A
  sekwiae Stensiö, E. 1968A
veronense (Prototherium)
verrucomalus (Merychyus)
Vertebratichnia Ichnites
verticornis (Megaloceros, Praemegaceros)
verus (Opsolagus, Trachinus)
Vespertilionidae Chiroptera Shotwell, J. A. 1970A
  (gen. and sp. indet.)
  Antrozous, Anzanycteris, Barbastella, Eptesicus,
    Miniopterus, Myotis, Pipistrellus, Plecotus
vespertinus (Falco)
vestenae (Ductor)
vestinus (Elephas meridionalis)
vestitum (Paraelops)
vestitus (Hybodus)
Vetagazella Gazella Dmitrieva, E. L. 1970A (n. subgen.)
veterior (Ischyromys)
veterrima (Palaeosinopa)

washingtonii (Mammuthus)
waterhousi (Palaeochoerus)
watermeyeri (Aelurosaurus)
watsoni (Arctops, Batrachosuchus, Morganucodon)
Watsonosteus Coccosteidae Stensiö, E. 1969A,B
Watsonulus Parasemionotidae
    eugnathoides Beltan, L. 1968A
. waylandi (Sus)
waynesburgensis (Limnopus)
wegneri (Glossotherium)
Weigeltisauridae ? Araeoscelidia Kuhn, O. 1969D
    (in Lepidosauria–Weigeltisauria)
weileri (Anchoa, Ceratoscopelus, Holocentrus,
    Prolebias, Trachichthodes, Umbra)
Wellesaurus Capitosauridae Lehman, J.-P. 1971A
    bussoni Lehman, J.-P. 1971A
    peabodyi [Parotosaurus]Lehman, J.-P. 1971A
wellsi (Gazella, Longirostromeryx)
wenzensis (Boreofiber, Martes, Procapreolus, Ursus)
werenfelsi (Paraglirulus)
westolli (Cephalaspis, Holonema)
wetherilli (Dilophosaurus)
Wetlugasaurus Capitosauridae Schultze, H.-P. 1969B
wetlugensis (Tupilakosaurus)
wetmorei (Paracrax)
whaitsi (Aelurosaurus, Gorgonops, Struthiocephalus)
Whaitsia Whaitsiidae Kemp, T. S. 1972A
Whaitsiidae Therapsida–Therocephalia Kemp, T. S.
    1972A,B
    Mirotenthes, Notosollasia, Whaitsia
whartoni (Ochotona)
Wheathillaspis Phlyctaenaspidae Stensiö, E. 1969B,
    1971A (in Spinothoracidi–
    ? Dolichothoraci)
wheelerensis (Entoptychus)
whitakeri (Apatemys)
whitei (Odontaspis, Papio, Polymerolepis, Sciurus,
    Tyriaspis)
Whiteia Coelacanthidae
    woodwardi Beltan, L. 1968A
Whiteichthys Canobiidae Kazanĉeva, A. A. 1971A
    (? in Styracopteridae)
whitfordi (Barbourofelis)
wichmannianus (Antarctosaurus)
wickeri (Kenyapithecus, Ramapithecus)
Wijdeaspis Macropetalichthyidae Patrulius, D.,
    Iordan, M. 1970A(?); Stensiö, E. 1969B
    [Wijelaspis]
Wijelaspis see Wijdeaspis
wildi (Eogliravus)
wildungensis (Chirodipterus)
wilferti (Neusibatrachus)
wilkinsoni (Blinasaurus)
Williamsaspidae Arthrodira–Arctolepida
    Williamsaspis
Williamsaspis Williamsaspidae Stensiö, E. 1969B,
    1971A (in Spinothoracidi–Dolichothoraci)
williamsi (Cercopithecoides, Dilophosauripus,
    Oreaspis, Psephaspis)
willistoni (Arctops, Erpetopus)
Willomorichthyidae Palaeonisciformes
    Gardiner, B. G. 1969A
    . Willomorichthys
Willomorichthys Willomorichthyidae
    Gardiner, B. G. 1969A
    striatulus Gardiner, B. G. 1969A

willsi (Heightingtonaspis)
wilmanae (Aelurosaurus)
wilsoni (Alphadon, Citellus, Eomacrones, Kannemeyeria,
    Meliakrouniomys, Microsyops, Priscocamelus,
    Quadrodens, Rapamys, Torrejonia)
wimani (Chilotherium, Eomellivora)
winkleri (Odontaspis)
winsnesi (Amaltheolepis)
wintershofense (Peratherium frequens)
wintershofensis (Otus)
wintoni (Phiomia)
woelferi (Progonomys)
wolfersheimensis (Blackia)
wombeyensis (Mastacomys)
wondrai (Chirotherium)
wongi (Myospalax aspalax)
woodhousi (Bufo)
woodi (Dikkomys, Eumys, Heliscomys, Lophiparamys,
    Palaechthon)
Woodomys Ctenodactylidae Shevyreva, N. S. 1971C
    chelkaris Shevyreva, N. S. 1971C
woodwardi (Coccolepis, Palaeoryx, Prostrepsiceros,
    Symphodus, Whiteia)
Woodwardosteus see Protitanichthys
woodworthi (Matthewichnus)
wortmani (Hyopsodus)
woschmidti (Eocyclotosaurus)
woutersi (Landenodon)
Wudinolepidae ? Antiarchi
    Wudinolepis
Wudinolepis Wudinolepidae Stensiö, E. 1969B
    (in Antiarchi incertae sedis)
wurmi (Panthera, Panthera spelaea)
wurnoensis (Myliobatis)
wusti (Mammuthus)
wyomingensis (Brachyhyops, Desmatochoerus, Ectocion,
    Mytonolagus, Oxydactylus, Paramys,
    Parasaniwa, Uranolophus)
Xantusiidae Squamata–Lacertilia
    Lepidophyma
Xenacanthidae Pleuracanthodii Zídek, J. 1965A,
    1967A
    ? Hypospondylus, Xenacanthus
Xenacanthus Xenacanthidae
    compressus Lund, R. 1970B [Orthacanthus]
    luedersensis Berman, D. S. 1970A
    platypternus Berman, D. S. 1970A
    texensis Berman, D. S. 1970A
    tocantinsensis Silva Santos, R., Sardenberg
        Salgado, M. 1970A
Xenarthra Edentata Hoffstetter, R. 1969A
Xenodelphis Didelphidae
    doelloi Paula Couto, C. 1970A
Xenorophus Agorophiidae Whitmore, F. C. 1972A
Xenosauridae Squamata–Lacertilia
    Exostinus
Xestops Anguidae
    vagans Meszoely, C. A. M. 1970A
xiehnensis (Lantianius)
Xiphactinus Ichthyodectidae Muralidhara, V. 1969B
    [Portheus]
    audax Applegate, S. P. 1970A
Xiphiidae Perciformes–Scombroidei
    Aglyptorhynchus, Coelorhynchus, Glyptorhynchus
Xiphodon Xiphodontidae
    castrense Sudre, J. 1969B